P9-DBS-166

The University of Chicago School Mathematics Project

Functions, Statistics, and Trigonometry

Second Edition

About the Cover The three curves shown on the cover represent the major themes of UCSMP *Functions, Statistics, and Trigonometry.* This text integrates algebraic and trigonometric functions with data analysis and probability explorations, using modeling throughout. More advanced statistical concepts and some discrete mathematics topics are also included.

Authors

Sharon L. Senk Steven S. Viktora Zalman Usiskin
Nils P. Ahbel Virginia Highstone David Witonsky
Rheta N. Rubenstein James E. Schultz Margaret Hackworth
John W. McConnell Dora Aksoy James Flanders Barry Kissane

Scott Foresman
Addison Wesley

Editorial Offices: Glenview, Illinois • Menlo Park, California
Sales Offices: Reading, Massachusetts • Duluth, Georgia • Glenview, Illinois
Carrollton, Texas • Menlo Park, California
http://www.sf.aw.com

ACKNOWLEDGMENTS

Authors

Sharon L. Senk
Professor of Mathematics,
Michigan State University, East Lansing, MI

John W. McConnell
Instructional Supervisor of Mathematics,
Glenbrook South High School, Glenview, IL

Steven S. Viktora
Chairman, Mathematics Department,
New Trier High School, Winnetka, IL

Zalman Usiskin
Professor of Education,
The University of Chicago

Nils P. Ahbel
Academic Technology Coordinator, Deerfield Academy, Deerfield, MA (Second Edition only)

Virginia Highstone
Mathematics Teacher, York High School,
Elmhurst, IL (Second Edition only)

David Witonsky
UCSMP (Second Edition only)

Rheta N. Rubenstein
Professor of Education
University of Windsor, Windsor, Ontario
(First Edition only)

James E. Schultz
Robert L. Morton Professor of Mathematics Education, Ohio University, Athens, OH
(First Edition only)

Margaret Hackworth—deceased
Former Mathematics Supervisor, Pinellas County Schools, Largo, FL (First Edition only)

Dora Aksoy
UCSMP (First Edition only)

James Flanders
UCSMP (First Edition only)

Barry Kissane
Senior Lecturer in Education,
Murdoch University, Perth, Western Australia
(First Edition only)

UCSMP Production and Evaluation

Series Editors: Zalman Usiskin,
Sharon L. Senk

Technical Coordinator: Susan Chang

Managing Editor: David Witonsky

Second Edition Teacher's Edition Editor:
Lianghuo Fan

Director of First Edition Studies:
Catherine Sarther (Mount Mary College, Milwaukee, WI)

We wish also to acknowledge the generous support of the **Amoco Foundation** and the **Carnegie Corporation of New York** for the development, testing, and distribution of the First Edition of these materials.

We wish to thank the many editors, production personnel, and design personnel at Scott Foresman Addison Wesley for their magnificent assistance.

Design Development

Steven Curtis Design, Inc.

ISBN: 0-673-45926-8

Printed in the United States of America

18 19—DOW—08

It is impossible for UCSMP to thank all the people who have helped create and test these books. We wish particularly to thank Carol Siegel, who heads our office staff; Alfred Estberg, David Snow, Chad Dau, Jeremy Hadix, Suzanne Levin, Ralph Schwartz, and Todd Clauer of our editorial staff; Christopher Naud, Peter Kim, Christopher Lee, Michael Campion, and Young Nam of our technical staff; and Kim Alkins, Marina Vasilyeva, Michelle Thatcher, Shaleane Gee, and Jennifer Moless of our clerical staff.

We wish to acknowledge and give thanks to the following teachers who taught preliminary versions of this text, participated in the field testing or formative evaluations, and contributed ideas to help to improve this text.

Todd Biederwolf
M. L. King High School
Detroit MI

Alan Bunner
The Culver Academies
Culver, IN

David Case
Woodward High School
Cincinnati, OH

Joseph Chamberlin
The Culver Academies
Culver, IN

Leslie Chew
Kenwood Academy
Chicago Public Schools

Raymond Heintz
Thornton Fractional High School North
Calumet City, IL

Sharon Llewellyn
Renaissance High School
Detroit, MI

Cheryl Murphy
Newark High School
Newark, Ohio

Gerald Pillsbury
Brentwood School
Los Angeles, CA

George Pryjma
Niles Township High School
Skokie, IL

Ray Thompson
Thornton Fractional High School South
Lansing, IL

David Williams
Southwestern High School
Detroit, MI

We also wish to express our thanks and appreciation to the many other schools and students who have used earlier versions of these materials. We particularly wish to thank the dozens of teachers who participated in a detailed survey for feedback on the first edition of this text and, in so doing, helped in the preparation of this second edition.

THE UNIVERSITY OF CHICAGO SCHOOL MATHEMATICS PROJECT

The University of Chicago School Mathematics Project is a long-term project designed to improve school mathematics in grades K-12. UCSMP began in 1983 with a 6-year grant from the Amoco Foundation. Additional funding has come from the National Science Foundation, the Ford Motor Company, the Carnegie Corporation of New York, the General Electric Foundation, GTE, Citicorp/Citibank, and the Exxon Education Foundation, and from royalties from the sales of UCSMP materials by Scott Foresman.

UCSMP is centered in the Departments of Education and Mathematics of the University of Chicago. The project has translated dozens of mathematics textbooks from other countries, held three international conferences, developed curricular materials for elementary and secondary schools, formulated models for teacher training and retraining, conducted a large number of large and small conferences, engaged in evaluations of many of its activities, and through its royalties has supported a wide variety of research projects in mathematics education at the University. UCSMP currently has the following components and directors:

Resources	Izaak Wirszup, Professor Emeritus of Mathematics
Elementary Materials	Max Bell, Professor Emeritus of Education
Secondary	Sharon L. Senk, Professor of Mathematics, Michigan State University Zalman Usiskin, Professor of Education
Evaluation Consultant	Larry Hedges, Professor of Education

From 1983 to 1987, the overall director of UCSMP was Paul Sally, Professor of Mathematics. Since 1987, the overall director has been Zalman Usiskin.

Functions, Statistics, and Trigonometry

The text *Functions, Statistics, and Trigonometry* has been developed by the Secondary Component of the project, and constitutes the core of the fifth year in a six-year mathematics curriculum devised by that component. The names of the six texts around which these years are built are:

Transition Mathematics
Algebra
Geometry
Advanced Algebra
Functions, Statistics, and Trigonometry
Precalculus and Discrete Mathematics

The content and questions of this book integrate functions, statistics, and trigonometry and apply the algebra and geometry students have studied in previous years. Sequences, counting problems, and other topics from discrete mathematics are also found, and this course contains many topics of traditional precalculus courses. In this way, *Functions, Statistics, and Trigonometry* provides an example of how a single mathematics course can involve all of the major areas of mathematics.

The first edition of *Functions, Statistics, and Trigonometry* included many features that have been retained in this edition. The value of some of these features has influenced other mathematics courses as well. As the content described in the preceding paragraph indicates, there is **wider scope**. These topics are not isolated as separate units of study or enrichment. They are employed to motivate, justify, extend, and otherwise enhance important concepts of functions, statistics, and trigonometry. A **real-world orientation** has guided both the selection of content and the approaches allowed the student in working out exercises and problems, because being able to do mathematics is of little use to an individual unless he or she can apply that content. We require **reading mathematics**, because students must read to understand mathematics in later courses and must learn to read technical matter in the world at large. The use of **up-to-date technology** is integrated throughout, with *automatic graphers* and *statistics utilities* assumed available at all times.

Four dimensions of understanding are emphasized: skill in carrying out various algorithms; developing and using mathematics properties and relationships; applying mathematics in realistic situations; and representing or picturing mathematical concepts. We call this the **SPUR** approach: **S**kills, **P**roperties, **U**ses, **R**epresentations.

The **book organization** is designed to maximize the acquisition of both skills and concepts. Ideas introduced in a lesson are reinforced through Review questions in the immediately succeeding lessons. This daily review feature allows students several nights to learn and practice important concepts and skills. Then, at the end of each chapter, a carefully focused Progress Self-Test and a Chapter Review, each keyed to objectives in all the dimensions of understanding, are used to solidify performance of skills and concepts from the chapter so that they may be applied later with confidence. Finally, to increase retention, important ideas are reviewed in later chapters.

There are **projects** at the end of each chapter because in the real world much of the mathematics done requires a longer period of time than is customarily available to students in daily assignments, and because teachers who have tried projects in the first edition of these materials have been enthusiastic about them.

The first edition of *Functions, Statistics, and Trigonometry* was published in 1992 and has been used in thousands of classes. Some of the teachers who used the first edition have made suggestions for improvements and there have been advances in technology and in thinking about how students learn. We have attempted to utilize these ideas in the development of the second edition. Every bit of text and every question has been examined, and many revisions have been made to improve the materials. We have moved many lessons and reorganized others. We have added many new applications and updated others.

Those familiar with the first edition will notice the following more significant changes. We assume familiarity with exponential functions as well as linear and quadratic functions because UCSMP students have studied these in two previous courses and because others, too, have strengthened their treatments of these functions in earlier courses. We have reordered the introductions to trigonometry and circular functions and moved them earlier because users felt these changes were very much needed. We also reworked the lessons on statistics in Chapter 10 because this was found to be the most demanding material in the book. In order not to lengthen the book, we eliminated those reading lessons at the end of some chapters that were found to be least interesting or useful by teachers.

There are also a number of features new to this edition, including the following: **In-class activities** have been incorporated between lessons to help students develop concepts before they read. **Activities** are also included within the lessons to help students understand as they read. There are many more questions requiring writing and a special writing font, because **writing** helps students clarify their own thinking, and writing is an important aspect of communicating mathematical ideas to others.

Comments about these materials are welcomed. Please address comments to:
UCSMP, The University of Chicago,
5835 S. Kimbark, Chicago, IL 60637.

CONTENTS

CHAPTER 8 486

SEQUENCES, SERIES, AND COMBINATIONS

CHAPTER 9 554

POLYNOMIAL FUNCTIONS

CHAPTER 10 626

BINOMIAL AND NORMAL DISTRIBUTIONS

CHAPTER 11 696

MATRICES AND TRIGONOMETRY

CHAPTER 12 752

QUADRATIC RELATIONS

CHAPTER 13 804

FURTHER WORK WITH TRIGONOMETRY

To the Student

GETTING STARTED

Welcome to Functions, Statistics, and Trigonometry.
We hope you enjoy this book—it was written for you.

Studying Mathematics

A goal of this book is to help you learn mathematics on your own, so that you will be able to deal with the mathematics you see in newspapers, magazines, on television, on any job, and in school. The authors, who are all experienced teachers, offer the following advice:

1 You can watch basketball hundreds of times on television. Still, to learn how to play basketball, you must have a ball in your hand and actually dribble, shoot, and pass it. Mathematics is no different. You cannot learn much mathematics just by watching other people do it. You must participate. You must think through and work problems. Some teachers have a slogan:

Mathematics is not a spectator sport.

2 You are expected to read each lesson. Sometimes you may do this as a class or in a small group; other times you will do the reading on your own. No matter how you do the reading, it is vital for you to understand what you have read. In *Functions, Statistics, and Trigonometry*, there are graphs and symbols that are necessary for this understanding. Here are some ways to improve your reading comprehension.

Read slowly and thoughtfully, paying attention to each word, graph, and symbol.

Look up the meaning of any word you do not understand.

Work examples yourself as you follow the steps in the text.

Reread sections that are unclear to you.

Discuss difficult ideas with a fellow student or your teacher.

3 Writing is a tool for communicating your solutions and thoughts to others and can help you understand mathematics, too. In *Functions, Statistics, and Trigonometry,* you will often be asked to justify your solution to a problem. Writing good explanations takes practice. You should use solutions to the examples in each lesson to guide your writing. What you might write is shown in a special font.

4 If you cannot answer a question immediately, don't give up! Read the lesson again. Read the question again. Look for examples. If you can, go away from the problem and come back to it a little later. Do not be afraid to ask questions in class and to talk to others when you do not understand something. School is designed so that you do not have to learn everything by yourself.

What are the purposes of this book?

Functions are correspondences or mappings that relate variables. For many people, functions are the most important content in all of high school mathematics. In your earlier work, you should have studied linear, quadratic, exponential, and logarithm functions, and perhaps also polynomial, trigonometric and circular functions. In this book, you will review and extend ideas about these functions. Many of the extensions are done with the aid of technology with graphics and statistical capabilities, for this technology has changed the ways in which people deal with these ideas.

The ability of computers to store and analyze information has made *statistics* an increasingly important subject to know. Statistics are used by people who work in government or journalism, who have to make decisions in business, who need to analyze or interpret the results of medical or psychological studies, or who wish simply to understand the world. The field of statistics is relatively new; even bar and circle graphs were unknown until about 200 years ago, and much of statistics has been developed in this century.

If you study further in any area in which mathematics is encountered, it is likely that you will need the mathematics presented in this book. A thorough knowledge of functions and trigonometry is needed for calculus, an area of mathematics that is fundamental in engineering and the physical sciences. Statistics is required for any who major in the social sciences or business. Even if you never take a course in mathematics itself in college, you are likely to encounter many of the ideas you see here in other courses and in your daily life.

Another purpose of this book is to review and bring together, in a cohesive way, what you have learned in previous courses. Functions, statistics, and trigonometry cover a wide range of topics. You may find topics close together in this book that you encountered in different chapters of books in previous years or that you studied even in different years. Mathematics is a unified discipline in the sense that what is learned in one area can be applied in all other areas, and we wish you to have that spirit of mathematics.

Equipment Needed for This Course

In addition to the lined and unlined notebook paper, pencils, and erasers you typically use when doing mathematics, you will need graph paper and a graphics calculator at all times. This calculator should have the capability to graph functions automatically and to calculate statistics, such as means and standard deviations. It helps if the calculator has the ability to create lists and graph them; to graph certain relations that are not functions, such as those whose graphs are circles; to graph in polar coordinates; to perform operations with matrices; and to generate random numbers. Many such calculators are available, and your teacher will tell you if one is preferred over others in your class. Many assignments will take you quite a bit longer to complete and some may even be inaccessible if you do not use this time-saving and accurate technology.

Getting Acquainted with *Functions, Statistics, and Trigonometry*

It is always helpful to spend some time getting acquainted with your textbook. The questions that follow are designed to help you become familiar with *Functions, Statistics, and Trigonometry.* The first set of questions is called Covering the Reading. You will find this type of question in every lesson in this book.

The second set of questions will help you become more familiar with special features of *Functions, Statistics, and Trigonometry.*

We hope you join the hundreds of thousands of students who have enjoyed this book. We wish you much success.

QUESTIONS

Covering the Reading

1. Name two purposes of this book.

2. What does it mean to say "mathematics is a unified discipline"?

3. What special features should you look for in a graphics calculator for this course?

4. How can the statement "Mathematics is not a spectator sport" be applied to the study of mathematics?

5. Name the way to improve reading comprehension given in this lesson that you think is the most helpful.

Knowing Your Textbook

In 6-14, answer the questions by looking at the Table of Contents, the lessons and chapters of the textbook, or material at the end of book.

6. Refer to the Table of Contents. What lesson is titled *Polar Coordinates*?

7. a. What are the four categories of questions at the end of each lesson?
b. What word is formed by the first letters of these categories?

8. Suppose you have just finished the questions in Lesson 9-7. On what page can you find answers to check your work? What answers are given?

9. In the vocabulary sections, why are some terms marked with an asterisk?

10. What is in the Glossary?

11. What should you do after taking a Progress Self-Test at the end of a chapter?

12. Answers to some questions are in this book. Where are they, and what answers are given?

13. Use the Index. In what lesson is *trigonometry* first mentioned? What is *trigonometry*?

14. This book has some Appendices. How many are there and what do they cover?

CHAPTER 1

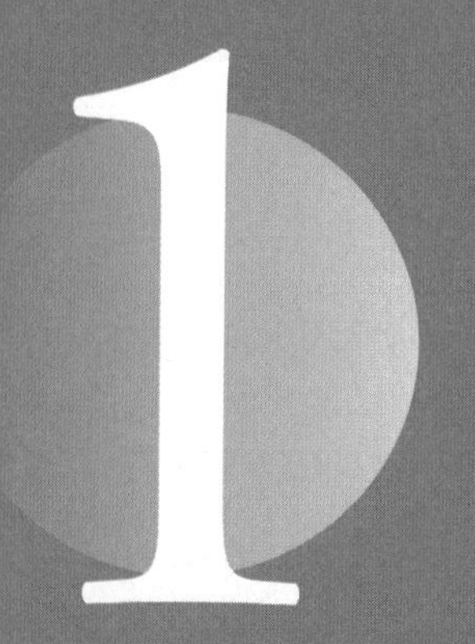

Exploring Data

Lethal Accidents, 1979–1992

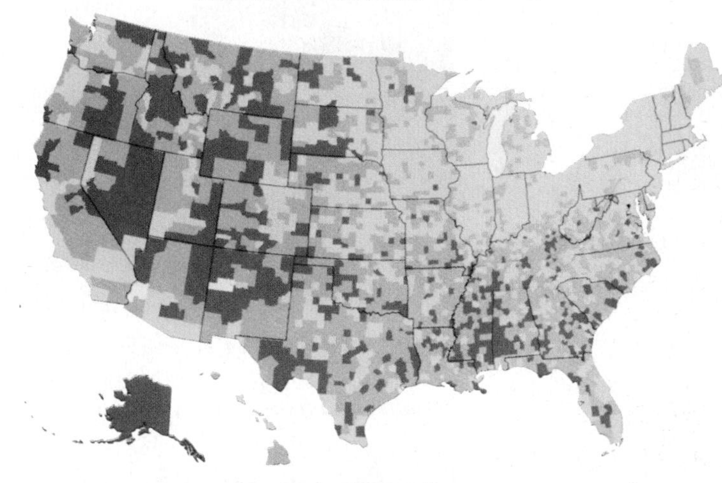

Age-adjusted rate per 100,000 people

☐ Under 45 accidents ☐ 45 to 64.9 ■ 65 or more

Source: Centers for Disease Control and Prevention; county data for Alaska not available

When a person is born, there is a birth certificate. Similarly, when a person dies, there is a death certificate. From studying death certificates, patterns of disease and causes of death can be detected and preventive measures taken.

The fifth largest cause of death in the United States is through accidents. In 1994, about 90,000 Americans died in accidents. Of these, 43,000 died from motor vehicle accidents, 13,300 from falls, 8,000 from poisons, 4,200 from fires, 4,000 from drownings, 3,000 from choking on foods or objects, 1,500 from firearms, and about 15,000 from other causes. Each of these deaths is particularly tragic because we think of accidental deaths as being preventable and because such deaths occur without warning.

A study of causes of accidental deaths from 1979 to 1992 was done by the Centers for Disease Control and Prevention. The study shows that the accident rate is now about half that in 1930, due to better safety procedures (such as seat belts and smoke detectors) and better medical procedures.

When the data are displayed by county, as shown above, there are definite patterns. People living in rural areas have more accidents than people living in cities or suburbs. The Northeast has the lowest accident rate, while many counties in the West have the highest accident rates.

LESSON

1-1

Tables and Graphs

Steel*ing* the show. *In 1995, the U.S. produced 104.9 million tons of raw steel. In the past 25 years, steel production has varied from 87.9 to 131.5 million tons; it is one variable which measures a nation's industrial economy.*

Statistics is the branch of mathematics dealing with the collection, organization, analysis, and interpretation of information, usually numerical information, called **data.** In statistics, a **variable** is a characteristic of a person or thing which can be classified, counted, ordered, or measured. For instance, some variables that describe a person are gender, religion, number of siblings, height, and family income. Some variables describing a country are population, area, major political parties, number of tons of steel produced, and infant-mortality rate.

The set of *all* individuals or objects you want to study is called the **population** for that study. If you cannot or do not collect data from the entire population, but study only a part of it, that part actually studied is called a **sample**. A sample is a subset of the population.

Sometimes, for reasons such as fairness or legal requirements, the entire population must be studied. For instance, to be fair, the president of a club might want to get opinions from every member of the club. Gathering facts or opinions through an interview or questionnaire is called a **survey**. The U.S. Constitution requires that every ten years a **census** be taken. The U.S. census is a survey of the entire population of the United States.

Other times, for reasons such as cost, safety, or preservation of a product, it is preferable to study a sample. For instance, it might be too expensive to ask all owners of a particular make of truck whether they are pleased with the product. So the manufacturer will study a sample of the owners. A grocer who wants to evaluate the taste of a new delivery of apples cannot taste every apple (the population), because doing so would destroy the product! So the grocer will taste one or two of the apples (the sample).

A sample of one to two milliliters of normal blood contains 5,000 to 10,000 white blood cells.

When samples are taken **randomly**, that is, in a way so that every member of the population has an equal chance of being chosen, data from the sample can be used to estimate information about the population. Later in this course you will study how to make predictions about populations from random samples. For now, you should be able to distinguish between populations and samples and identify the variables being studied.

Example 1

A medical laboratory technician counts the number of white blood cells in a drop of a patient's blood. Identify the variable, population, and sample.

Solution

The variable is the number of white blood cells. The population is all the patient's blood; and the sample is the drop of the patient's blood.

Note that in Example 1, if the population (the entire blood supply) had been studied, the patient would have died.

Reading a Table

To make sense of data, it helps to organize the data in a table or graph. The table below summarizes data collected in a study conducted by the U.S. Bureau of the Census. It relates to the following question: Does staying in school pay off by providing increased income for a family?

Before reading on, examine this table. Look at its title and the labels of its rows and columns. Try to determine the meaning of every number.

Income of Households. Percent distribution by income level and education of householder for 1993.

Highest level of education completed by householder	Number of households (1,000)	Percent distribution by income level							Estimated median income (dollars)
		Under $10,000	$10,000-$14,999	$15,000-$24,999	$25,000-$34,999	$35,000-$49,999	$50,000-$74,999	$75,000 and over	
Less than 9th grade	8,587	35.1	18.3	22.3	11.7	7.2	3.9	1.5	13,920
Some high school, but no diploma	9,712	28.2	14.5	20.9	15.8	11.6	6.5	2.5	17,966
High school graduate	29,420	13.6	10.2	19.3	17.3	18.0	14.9	6.7	28,700
Some college	22,327	8.7	7.1	16.2	16.0	20.0	20.4	11.8	36,398
Bachelor's degree or higher	21,795	3.7	3.4	8.5	10.2	16.9	25.0	32.3	56,116

Source: *Statistical Abstract of the United States 1995*

When reading a table, ask yourself questions such as the following.

1. What is being presented?
   To answer this question, first identify the variables. These are often named as labels of the rows and columns. In the table above, there are only two variables: the highest level of education completed by the householder, and the income of the household in 1993. The level of education of the householder is reported as one of five *categories*, described by the labels of the rows. For each level of education, income is reported two ways: as the percent of households in each of seven income intervals and as the median income of the level.

Next, examine the entries. Determine the type or the unit of each variable. If percents are given, identify what they are percents of.

2. Are the data trustworthy?
   Consider the data source, the accuracy of the data, and the time when the data were collected. Ideally, the data source should be given, allowing you to verify the data if you want, and it should be reputable. In the preceding table, the source is a reputable government agency, and the total number of households is a large percentage of all households in the United States.

   Data should be reported as accurately as possible. In this case, data are reported to the nearest dollar or tenth of a percent. This seems reasonable. Knowing when the data were collected helps you decide what conclusions to make. The data are from 1993, so due to inflation, the present median incomes may be somewhat higher than those reported.

3. What conclusions can you draw from the data?
   Although some conclusions can be read directly from data in a table, others can only be made after calculations using the data in a table, or after looking for patterns or trends in the data.

Example 2

Refer to the table on page 7. Assume the "householder" is the head of a household.

a. How many times as likely was a family to have an income of at least \$75,000 if the head of the household had graduated from college rather than not completed high school?

b. Describe how the median income of a family is related to the level of education of the head of the household.

Solution

a. We first need to know the percent of households headed by someone with no high school diploma with an income of at least \$75,000. *The number of thousands of households headed by someone with no high school diploma with an income of at least \$75,000 is 1.5% of 8,587 plus 2.5% of 9,712, or about 371. The total number of thousands of households of this type is 8,587 + 9,712, or 18,299. So about $\frac{371}{18299} \approx 2.0\%$ of households headed by someone with no high school diploma had incomes of at least \$75,000.*

The table shows that *32.3% of households headed by someone with a bachelor's degree had incomes of at least \$75,000. So a household headed by someone with a bachelor's degree was about 16 times as likely to have an income of at least \$75,000 as a household headed by someone with no high school diploma.*

b. Look at the relation between the data in the first and last columns. *As the number of years of education of the householder increases, median income of the household also increases.*

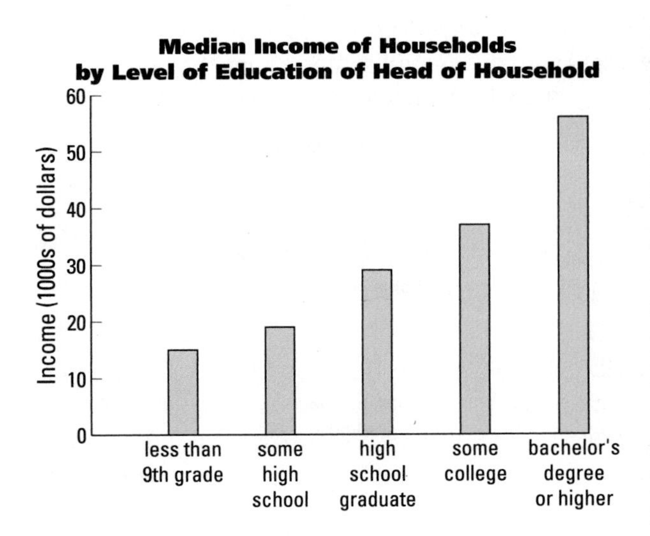

Bar Graphs

Conclusions can often be determined or supported by graphs. For instance, the *bar graph* at the left supports the conclusions in part **b** of Example 2.

Bar graphs are appropriate when one variable is a categorical variable, and the other is numerical. One axis labels the categories; the other is a scale, typically with counts or percents. A well-made bar graph has a descriptive title, identifies the variables being described, labels the numerical scale in equal intervals, uses bars of equal widths for each category, and provides a legend if data from more than one sample or population is shown.

Circle Graphs

Data consisting of a sum and its component parts can be displayed in a *circle graph*, which is sometimes called a *pie chart*. In the table on page 7, every householder must fall into one of the levels of education described. Thus, you can make a circle graph to show how incomes were distributed among the heads of the households in 1993.

To make a circle graph you must calculate the measure of a central angle corresponding to each component part of the sum. Recall that one revolution is 360°.

Example 3

Draw a circle graph showing the distribution of levels of education among householders in 1993.

Solution

First, calculate the total number of households sampled. This is done by adding the numbers in the second column.

$$8587 + 9712 + 29420 + 22327 + 21795 = 91841$$

In this survey there were about 91,841,000 households.

Second, calculate the measure of the central angle corresponding to each level of education. For instance, 8,587,000 of the 91,841,000 households were headed by someone with less than a 9th grade education. So this category should be represented by a sector of a circle with central angle of measure x, where

$$\frac{x}{360} = \frac{8587}{91{,}841}.$$

$$x \approx 34^\circ$$

The results for all levels of education are given (rounded to the nearest degree) in the table on page 10.

Third, draw a circle and sectors with the central angles having those measures. Label each sector with the level of education it represents.

Level of Education	Number (in 1000s)	Angle Measure (in degrees)
Less than 9th grade	8587	34
Some high school	9712	38
High school graduate	29,420	115
Some college	22,327	88
Bachelor's degree or higher	21,795	85

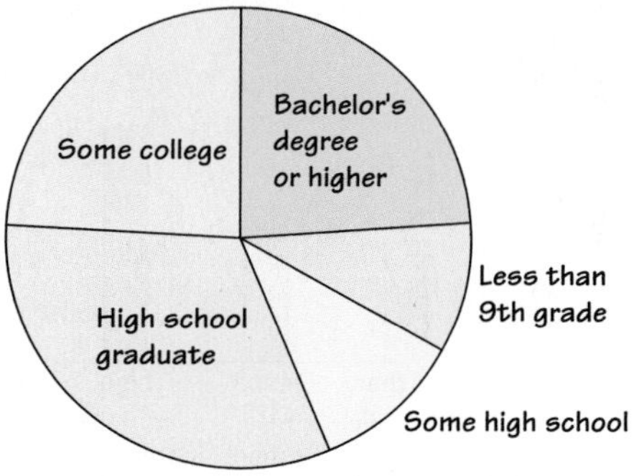

Often, circle graphs display percents next to the sectors. For instance, you might label the corresponding sector for the households that were headed by a college graduate with 24%, the percent nearest to $\frac{21,795}{91,841}$.

Notice that the circle graph gives a quick visual summary of the levels of education. Without looking at the numbers, you can see that about one-third of heads of households are high school graduates, and nearly one-half have attended college.

Circle graphs are seldom made by hand today. Virtually all spreadsheets can make them easily.

QUESTIONS

Covering the Reading

These questions check your understanding of the reading. If you cannot answer a question, you should go back to the reading to help you find an answer.

In 1–3, define each term.

1. variable **2.** population **3.** statistics

4. Give three examples of variables which were not mentioned in the lesson that might be studied for a person.

5. Give three characteristics of a situation which might cause a person to study a sample rather than a population.

In 6 and 7, identify: **a.** the population; **b.** the sample; and **c.** the variable of interest.

6. In order to learn the TV habits of all students in a certain high school, those students entering the north door of the school between 7:30 and 7:45 A.M. are asked which TV programs they watched last night.

7. A pastry inspector counts the number of raisins per cookie in 10 oatmeal-raisin cookies in a batch fresh out of the oven.

8. Refer to the study by the Centers for Disease Control and Prevention described on page 5.
   a. Describe the population. **b.** What variable was studied?

9. What is a *random sample*?

In 10–15, refer to the table on the distribution of households by income and level of education of the householder.

10. What percent of households in 1993 were headed by people who had some college, but not a bachelor's degree?

11. What percent of households headed by high school graduates (with no college) earned at least $25,000 annually?

12. **a.** How many households headed by someone who was not a high school graduate earned less than $15,000 in 1993?
    b. What percent of the total number of households is this?

13. Write a sentence or two describing how the income of households headed by someone with a bachelor's degree or higher compares to the income of households headed by someone with just a high school diploma.

14. Calculate the percent for each sector in the circle graph in Example 3.

15. Draw a circle graph showing the distribution of income of households headed by someone with less than a 9th grade education.

Applying the Mathematics

These questions extend the content of the lesson. You should take your time, study the examples and explanations, and try a variety of methods. Check your answers with the ones in the back of the book.

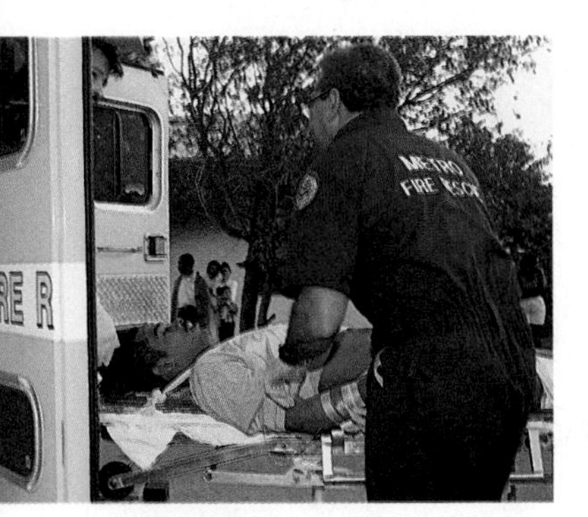

First Help. *More than a half-million paramedics in the U.S. have trained at least 1000 hours in areas such as transportation, anatomy and physiology, pharmacology, childbirth, cardiology, and rescue.*

In 16–19, the table below gives the numbers of deaths (in thousands) in the United States for ten principal types of accidents in the years 1970, 1980, and 1990. (Source: *Statistical Abstract of the United States 1995*)

	1970	1980	1990
Motor Vehicles	54.6	53.2	46.8
Falls	16.9	13.3	12.3
Drowning	6.4	6.0	4.0
Fires and Flames	6.7	5.8	4.2
Medical Procedures	3.6	2.4	2.7
Inhalation or Ingestion of Objects	2.8	3.2	3.3
Drugs and Medicines	2.5	2.5	4.5
Firearms	2.4	2.0	1.4
Water Transport	1.7	1.4	0.9
Air and Space Transport	1.6	1.5	0.9

16. How many people died in 1990 from motor vehicle accidents?

17. Over the three years shown, how many people died as a result of a firearm accident?

18. Ignoring the number of deaths from accidents not listed, what percent of accidental deaths in 1990 resulted from falls?

19. a. Describe the general trend in the numbers of accidental deaths from 1970 to 1990.
b. Which categories of accidents do not follow the trend in part **a**?

20. In the 1990 U.S. census, the final count was 248,709,873 people. The general population is estimated to have been undercounted by about 1.8%. That is, only 98.2% of the people were counted.
a. If this were the case, what was the actual 1990 population?
b. What are some factors which might cause the population to be undercounted?

Review

Each lesson in this book contains review questions to give you practice using ideas you have studied earlier. In this lesson all review questions are from previous courses.

21. *Skill sequence.* Solve each equation. *(Previous course)*
a. $7x = 140$ **b.** $.7x = 140$
c. $140x = 7$ **d.** $140x = .7$

22. *Multiple choice.* Which segment has the greatest slope? *(Previous course)*

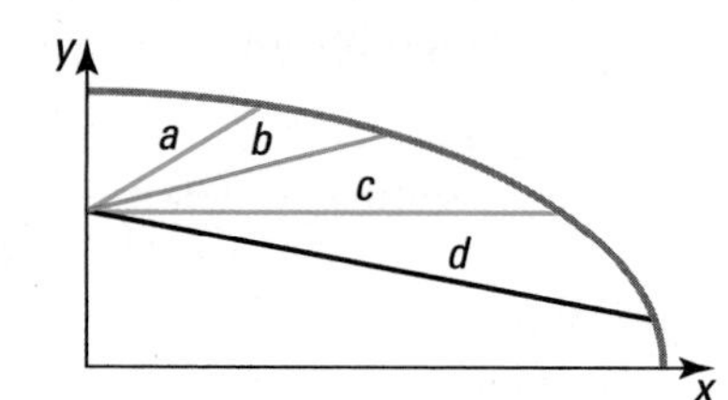

23. a. Find five pairs (x, y) such that $y = 3x - 4$.
b. Graph these ordered pairs. They should lie on a line.
c. What is the slope of this line?
d. What is its y-intercept? *(Previous course)*

24. Suppose $f(x) = x^2 - x - 12$. *(Previous course)*
a. Evaluate $f(8)$. **b.** Solve $f(x) = 8$.

Exploration

These questions ask you to explore ideas related to the lesson. Sometimes they require that you use reference books or other sources. Frequently, they have many possible answers.

25. Find an example of a bar graph or a circle graph in a newspaper, magazine, or other publication. What conclusion(s) can you draw from the graph? Do you think the graph is misleading in any way? Why or why not?

LESSON

1-2

Stemplots and Dotplots

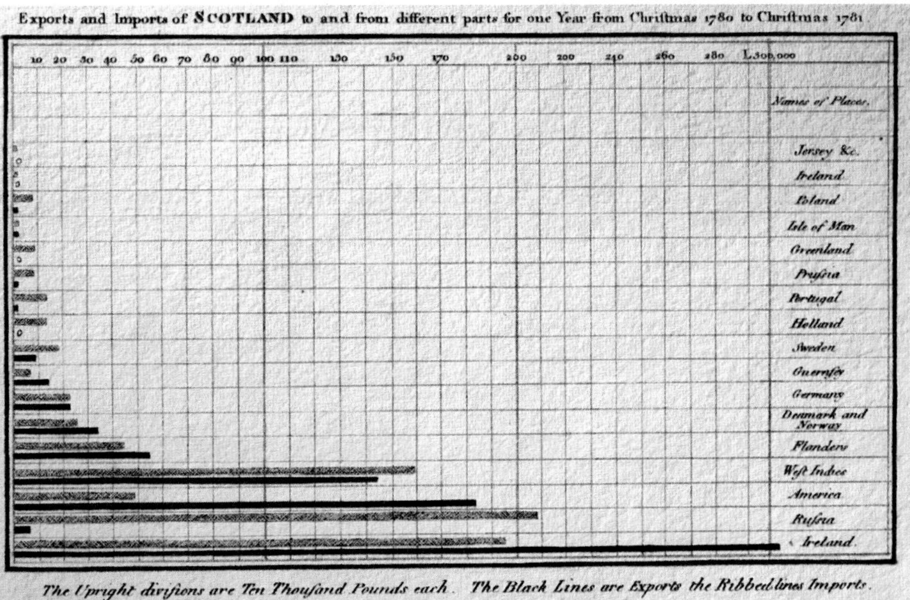

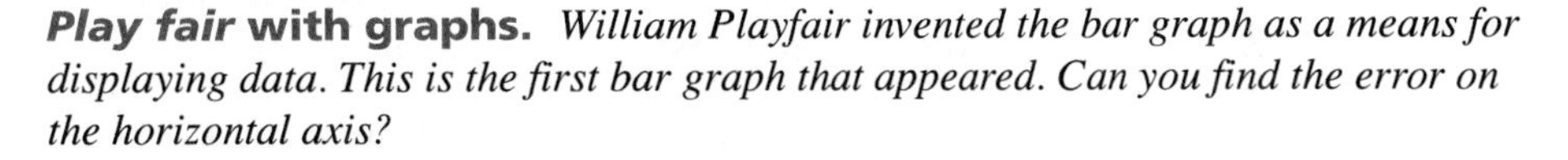

Play fair with graphs. *William Playfair invented the bar graph as a means for displaying data. This is the first bar graph that appeared. Can you find the error on the horizontal axis?*

Some methods of displaying data are quite old. Coordinate graphs, which you have studied for many years, were developed by the French mathematicians René Descartes and Pierre Fermat in the 16th century. The first bar graphs were published in 1786 by the Scottish economist William Playfair (1759–1823) in *The Commercial and Political Atlas*. Other methods are quite new. In the last half of the 20th century several new ways to represent data have been invented. For instance, in the 1960s Professor John Tukey of Princeton University invented the *stem-and-leaf diagram* or *stemplot*.

Stemplots

Consider the following 24 scores from a chemistry quiz.

75 34 80 95 62 75 98 93 84 87 94 85
70 39 84 78 98 78 90 68 75 82 76 85

It is difficult to see patterns when data are listed like this. A stemplot gives a quick way to picture the data set, or **distribution**, while including the actual numerical values.

Here is a way to make a stemplot.

1. Separate each piece of data into a **stem** (the first digit in this case) and a **leaf** (the second digit). In general, stems may have as many digits as needed, but each leaf should contain only a single digit.

2. List the stems vertically in increasing order from top to bottom, filling in missing integers. Draw a vertical line to the right of the stems. Add each leaf to the right of its stem.

Below, at the left, the test scores have been recorded in such a stemplot. Sometimes the leaves are arranged in increasing order from left to right, as shown below at the right.

24 scores from a test

stems	leaves
3	9 4
4	
5	
6	2 8
7	⑤ 8 0 8 ⑤ 6 ⑤
8	0 4 7 5 4 2 5
9	5 8 3 0 4 8

24 scores from a test (ordered)

stems	leaves
3	4 9
4	
5	
6	2 8
7	0 ⑤ ⑤ ⑤ 6 8 8
8	0 2 4 4 5 5 7
9	0 3 4 5 8 8

In these stemplots the stem indicates the tens digit of the score. Each leaf is the units digit of the score. For instance, the circled leaves represent scores of 75.

A stem-and-leaf diagram is something like a bar graph, because the stems are like categories and the length of the row of leaves represents the number of scores in that category. However, unlike a bar graph, the individual data values are not lost in a stemplot.

From a stemplot you can determine the **maximum** score, the highest value, and the **minimum** score, the lowest value. Then you can easily calculate the **range** of the data, that is, the difference between the highest and lowest scores. You can also tell if there are *clusters* or *gaps* in the data. All of this is easier to see in the stemplot at the right above.

Example 1

Refer to the chemistry scores above.

a. Identify the minimum and maximum scores.
b. Describe any clusters or gaps in the data.

Solution

a. The minimum score is 34, the maximum score is 98.
b. Most test scores cluster in the 70s, 80s, and 90s. There is a gap of about 30 points between the two lowest scores (34 and 39) and the next two lowest scores (62 and 68).

If some values in a data set are very different than all of the rest, they are called **outliers**. In the set of chemistry scores, the scores of 34 and 39 are outliers, but the highest scores are not outliers.

Back-to-back Stemplots

You can compare two related sets of data in a *back-to-back stemplot* as shown in Example 2. In a **back-to-back stemplot**, the stem is written in the center of the display, with one set of leaves to the right of the stem and another set of leaves to the left.

Example 2

The quiz grades in Tina Chare's two sections of geometry are shown below. To help compare the two data sets, the leaves for each stem are written in order from the center out.

a. Find the range of scores in each class.
b. How many students in each class took the quiz?
c. How many students scored in the 80s?
d. Which scores appear to be outliers?

1st Period		3rd Period
	3	2 9
0	4	
8 5 3	5	
9 6 5 2 0	6	8
5 5 2 0	7	0 5 8 8 8 9
5 2 1	8	0 2 4 5 5 5 6
	9	0 3 5 8
0 0 0	10	

Solution

a. In the 1st period class the highest score is 100, and the lowest is 40. So the range in the 1st period is $100 - 40 = 60$. In the 3rd period class the range is $98 - 32 = 66$.

b. Each leaf represents the score of a single student. So count the number of leaves on each side of the stem. There were 19 students in 1st period and 20 in 3rd period who took the quiz.

c. Count the number of leaves to the left and right of the stem representing 80. In the 1st period there are three scores in the 80s (81, 82, 85) and in the 3rd period there are seven (80, 82, 84, 86, and three scores of 85), for a total of 10 scores in the 80s.

d. The three scores of 100 in the 1st period and the two in the 30s (32 and 39) in 3rd period appear to be outliers because they seem quite different from others in the same class.

Dotplots

Recall that the **frequency** of an item or event is the number of times that item or event occurs. A **dotplot** (or **dot-frequency diagram**) is like a stemplot in that each data point is indicated separately. Typically, the number of dots corresponding to a particular item indicates the frequency of that item.

RHYMES WITH ORANGE

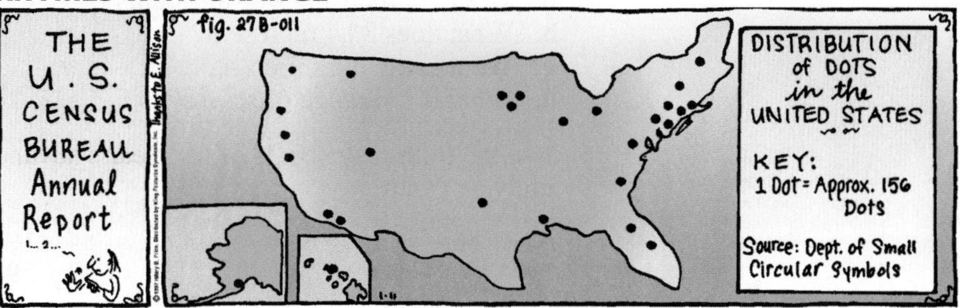

Example 3

The dotplot below shows the distribution of the number of siblings of the students in Mr. Maestro's homeroom.

a. How many students are in Mr. Maestro's homeroom?

b. How many students have no siblings?

c. What is the frequency of students having four siblings?

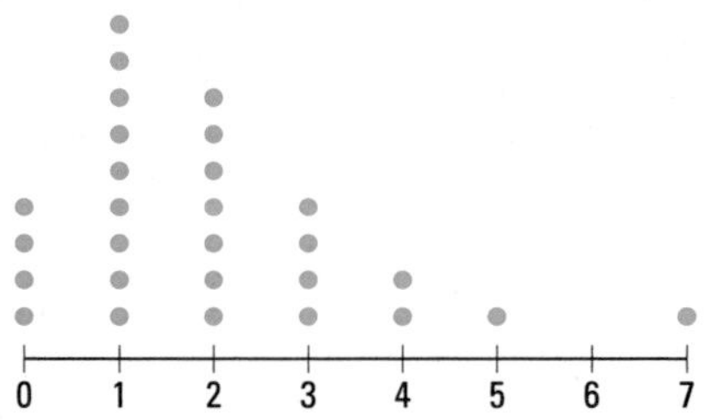

0 1 2 3 4 5 6 7
Number of Siblings

Solution

a. Each dot represents the data from one student. So count the number of dots. **There are 28 students in Mr. Maestro's homeroom.**

b. Count the number of dots above 0. **Four students have no siblings.**

c. Two students have four siblings each. **So the frequency of having four siblings is 2.**

Notice that dotplots, like stemplots, also allow you to see quickly any clusters, gaps, or trends in the data set.

QUESTIONS

Covering the Reading

1. About how many years ago were bar graphs invented, and by whom?

2. *True or false.* Stem-and-leaf diagrams were invented before the 20th century.

3. Consider a set of data. The smallest value is called the __a.__, and the largest is called the __b.__. The difference of the two is the __c.__.

4. Use the stemplot at the right below. The data represent quiz scores between 0 and 100.

a. What are the values of the stems?

b. What does 8 | 4 represent?

c. What is the minimum score?

d. What is the range of scores?

```
6 | 0 3
7 | 8 9
8 | 4 9
9 | 2 3 7 8
```

5. Use the following scores of last year's advanced algebra students on their midyear exam.

68	86	65	68	78	86	84	98	87	52	94	92
74	66	86	78	92	66	83	94	92	67	84	44

a. Make a stem-and-leaf diagram of the data.

b. Find the range of scores.

c. Describe any clusters or gaps in the data.

Maris		Ruth
8	0	
6 4 3	1	
8 6 3	2	2 5
9 3	3	4 5
	4	1 1 6 6 6 7 9
	5	4 4 9
1	6	0

In 6–9, consider the back-to-back stemplot at the left. The data represent the number of home runs per season hit by Babe Ruth and Roger Maris. Data for Ruth are for each year he played with the New York Yankees. Data for Maris are for the 10 years he played in the American League. Ruth held the record for number of home runs in a single season until 1961 when Maris hit more home runs than Ruth.

6. What does the entry 8 | 0 represent?

7. How many years did Ruth play for the Yankees?

8. What is the greatest number of home runs each player hit in a single season during his career?

9. Which number appears to be an outlier?

In 10–13, use the dotplot below of the distribution of heights (in inches) of some randomly chosen adults with the same occupation.

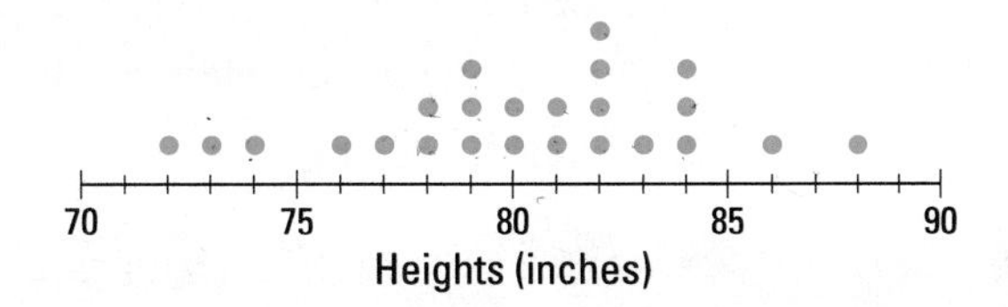

10. How many people are in this sample?

11. What is the maximum height?

12. Which height has the greatest frequency?

13. *Multiple choice.* Which is the most likely occupation of this group?
(a) ballerinas (b) basketball players
(c) circus performers (d) jockeys

5	2 3 6
6	4 5 6 9
7	1 2
8	
9	2
10	1 2
11	9
12	1 2
13	1 8
14	6
15	
16	
17	
18	
19	
20	
21	
22	
23	
24	
25	
26	
27	
28	
29	9
30	0

Applying the Mathematics

In 14–16, use the stem-and-leaf plot at the left for the Top Twenty Money-Making Movies for 1994. Each stem indicates 10 millions of dollars. For instance, 9 | 2 represents revenue of $92,000,000. (All values have been rounded to the nearest million.) (Source: *1996 Information Please Almanac*)

14. The largest revenue makers in 1994 were *The Lion King* (1) and *Forrest Gump* (2). About how much money did they earn that year?

15. The income of *The Lion King* was how many times as great as the income of *True Lies*, the third highest money maker?

16. How many movies had revenue from 100 to 150 million dollars?

In 17 and 18, use the following quiz scores of the students in a statistics class.

4	8	9	9	8	7	9	10	9	9	4	8	9
3	8	9	10	4	4	9	10	4	3	10	8	8

17. Which score occurs with the greatest frequency?

18. a. Make a dotplot of the distribution of scores.
b. Describe how the class performed. Mention any clusters or gaps in the data set.

Review

19. A medical researcher administers an experimental drug to 20 AIDS patients. The researcher then monitors the number of infections the patients contract. Identify the following for this study. *(Lesson 1-1)*
a. the sample **b.** the population **c.** the variable

In 20 and 21, refer to the graph on page 13, which was first published in 1786 by William Playfair. *(Lesson 1-1)*

20. Which four countries were major trading partners of Scotland in 1781?

21. *True or false.* In 1781, Scotland sold more to the United States of America than it bought from the United States.

22. Refer to the graph.

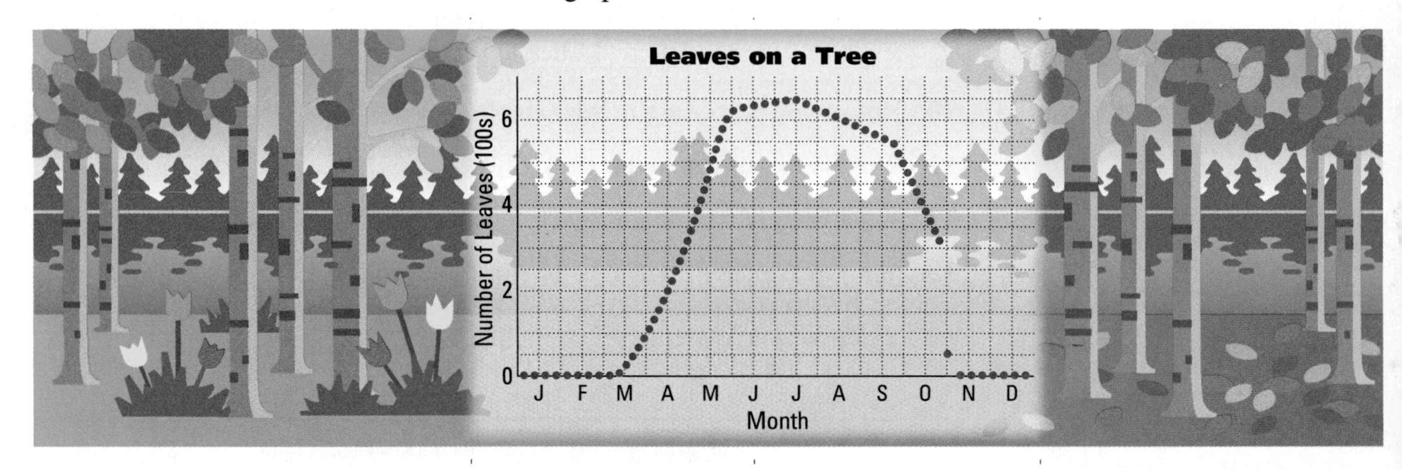

a. At what time was the number of leaves on the tree at its maximum, and what was that maximum?
b. Why is the graph made of points rather than a curve?
c. Describe what happened to the number of leaves as the months passed. *(Lesson 1-1, Previous course)*

23. *Skill sequence.* Solve each equation. *(Previous course)*
a. $\frac{x}{8} = 16$ **b.** $\frac{x^2}{8} = 16$ **c.** $\frac{x^2}{8} = 16 + x$

Exploration

24. Refer to the data about Babe Ruth and Roger Maris in Questions 6–9.
a. Which of the two baseball players do you think was a better home run hitter? Why?
b. Other than the number of home runs hit per year, what are some other variables you might consider to determine who was the greatest major league home run hitter of all time?

Introducing Lesson 1-3

Using a Statistics Utility to Enter and Analyze Data

In this activity, you will need a *statistics utility.*

A **statistics utility** is either a graphics calculator with statistics capability or statistics software for use on a computer. In this activity, we discuss what you need to know to use any statistics utility. Consult your calculator owner's manual or your statistics software documentation for specific information about your utility. Record how your technology works.

According to *The World Almanac and Book of Facts 1996*, the data presented on page 20 are the ages of Oscar-winning actresses and actors at the Award Ceremony and the films for which they won awards in the 25 years from 1971 to 1995. Examine the ages at which these people won their awards. Do there seem to be major differences in the ages of men versus the ages of women? Statistics can help in examining that question.

1 Entering and Editing Data.
a. Find out how to enter data with your statistics utility. If you are using a calculator, write the key sequence to open data storage. If you are using a computer, write the menu items.
b. Find out how your statistics utility clears data from storage. Write directions for clearing a column of data.
c. Enter the age data for Oscar-winning actors and actresses in two columns of your statistics utility. *Be sure to edit the data sets for accuracy before you proceed.*

2 Find out how to obtain one-variable statistics on your statistics utility.
a. What one-variable statistics does your utility give? Make a list of them using the symbols your package gives.
b. List the key sequence or menu items that will produce one-variable statistics.

3 Recall that the **mean** of a data set is its average; it is often given using the symbol $\bar{x}$ (read x-bar). The **median** of a data set is the middle number (or the average of the two middle numbers). The **mode** is the most-repeated number.
a. Give the mean and median for the ages of the Oscar-winning actresses.
b. Give the mean and median for the ages of the Oscar-winning actors.
c. Does your statistics utility give the mode? If yes, what is the mode of each data set?
d. What do *measures of center* such as the mean and the median tell you about the ages at which men and women win Oscars for Best Actor and Actress?

Year	Best Actress	Age	Movie	Best Actor	Age	Movie
1971	Jane Fonda	35	Klute	Gene Hackman	42	The French Connection
1972	Liza Minelli	27	Cabaret	Marlon Brando	48	The Godfather
1973	Glenda Jackson	37	A Touch of Class	Jack Lemmon	49	Save the Tiger
1974	Ellen Burstyn	42	Alice Doesn't Live Here Anymore	Art Carney	56	Harry and Tonto
1975	Louise Fletcher	41	One Flew Over the Cuckoo's Nest	Jack Nicholson	38	One Flew Over the Cuckoo's Nest
1976	Faye Dunaway	36	Network	Peter Finch	60	Network
1977	Diane Keaton	32	Annie Hall	Richard Dreyfuss	30	The Goodbye Girl
1978	Jane Fonda	41	Coming Home	Jon Voight	40	Coming Home
1979	Sally Field	33	Norma Rae	Dustin Hoffman	42	Kramer vs. Kramer
1980	Sissy Spacek	31	Coal Miner's Daughter	Robert De Niro	37	Raging Bull
1981	Katharine Hepburn	74	On Golden Pond	Henry Fonda	76	On Golden Pond
1982	Meryl Streep	33	Sophie's Choice	Ben Kingsley	39	Ghandi
1983	Shirley MacLaine	49	Terms of Endearment	Robert Duvall	53	Tender Mercies
1984	Sally Field	38	Places in the Heart	F. Murray Abraham	45	Amadeus
1985	Geraldine Page	61	The Trip to Bountiful	William Hurt	36	Kiss of the Spider Woman
1986	Marlee Matlin	21	Children of a Lesser God	Paul Newman	62	The Color of Money
1987	Cher	41	Moonstruck	Michael Douglas	43	Wall Street
1988	Jodie Foster	26	The Accused	Dustin Hoffman	51	Rain Man
1989	Jessica Tandy	80	Driving Miss Daisy	Daniel Day-Lewis	32	My Left Foot
1990	Kathy Bates	42	Misery	Jeremy Irons	42	Reversal of Fortune
1991	Jodie Foster	29	The Silence of the Lambs	Anthony Hopkins	54	The Silence of the Lambs
1992	Emma Thompson	33	Howards End	Al Pacino	52	Scent of a Woman
1993	Holly Hunter	36	The Piano	Tom Hanks	37	Philadelphia
1994	Jessica Lange	45	Blue Sky	Tom Hanks	38	Forrest Gump
1995	Susan Sarandon	49	Dead Man Walking	Nicolas Cage	32	Leaving Las Vegas

4 Does your statistics utility make stemplots or dotplots? If so, make one of these displays for the ages of Best Actress and another for the ages of Best Actor.

5 Look back at the calculations and displays you made. Do big gender differences exist in the ages at which men and women win Oscars? Justify your answer.

Save the data you have entered for the ages of Oscar winners for the In-class Activity on page 38.

LESSON

1-3

Measures of Center

Going to the dogs. *Two professional dog walkers on New York's Park Avenue lead a group from the same apartment complex for a daily city stroll. See Example 1.*

Summation Notation

Calculating a mean involves finding a sum, and sums are so basic to mathematics that a shorthand notation for representing numbers and sums is commonly used.

The scores of Ms. T. Chare's geometry students are shown again at the right. Let f_i (read f-sub-i) be the score of the ith student in the 1st period. Here the scores are ranked from lowest to highest, with f_1 being the lowest, f_2 the next lowest, and so on. In general data do not have to be in any special order.

1st period		3rd period
	3	2 9
0	4	
8 5 3	5	
9 6 5 2 0	6	8
5 5 2 0	7	0 5 8 8 8 9
5 2 1	8	0 2 4 5 5 5 6
	9	0 3 5 8
0 0 0	10	

The sum $f_1 + f_2 + f_3 + \ldots + f_{19}$ can be written $\sum_{i=1}^{19} f_i$, read, "The sum of the f-sub-i's as i goes from 1 to 19." The symbol Σ is the capital Greek letter **sigma**. It corresponds to the English letter S for sum. This notation is called **summation notation** or **sigma-notation** or **Σ-notation**.

The total number of points of the top five scorers in 1st period is the sum of the 15th to the 19th scores, $f_{15} + f_{16} + f_{17} + f_{18} + f_{19}$. That sum is

$$\sum_{i=15}^{19} f_i = 82 + 85 + 100 + 100 + 100 = 467.$$

In general, the expression $\sum_{i=a}^{b} x_i$ is read "the sum of the x-sub-i's as i goes from a to b." It represents the sum of the set of x-values from x_a to x_b. The number i is called an **index** because it indicates the position of a number in an ordered list.

Note that the mean score in the 1st period class is $\frac{f_1 + f_2 + f_3 + \ldots + f_{19}}{19}$,

which in Σ-notation is $\frac{\sum_{i=1}^{19} f_i}{19}$. We calculate this to be $\frac{1368}{19} = 72$.

Activity 1

Let g_i = score of the ith student in Ms. Chare's 3rd period class.

Calculate $\frac{\sum_{i=1}^{20} g_i}{20}$.

Summation notation provides a way to define the mean in symbols.

The Mean

Definition

Let $\{x_1, x_2, \ldots, x_n\}$ be a data set of n numbers. Then the **mean** $\overline{x}$ of the data set is $\overline{x} = \frac{\sum_{i=1}^{n} x_i}{n} = \frac{1}{n} \sum_{i=1}^{n} x_i$.

Example 1

An apartment building has 200 apartments. Let p_i = the number of pets in the ith apartment.

a. What does $\sum_{i=1}^{200} p_i$ represent?

b. Use Σ-notation to express the mean number of pets per apartment.

Solution

a. $\sum_{i=1}^{200} p_i = p_1 + p_2 + p_3 + \ldots + p_{200}$. This represents the total number of pets in the 200 apartments.

b. To find the mean, divide the total number of pets by the number of apartments.

$$\overline{p} = \frac{\sum_{i=1}^{200} p_i}{200} \text{ or } \frac{1}{200} \sum_{i=1}^{200} p_i$$

Most spreadsheets also have a notation for sums. For example, on some spreadsheets, the sum of the entries in cells F1, F2, F3, . . . , F19 is denoted SUM(F1:F19).

The Median

Recall that the *median* is the middle value of a set of data listed in increasing or decreasing order. When the data set has an even number of elements, the median is the average (mean) of the two middle values.

Example 2

Find the median score for each of T. Chare's classes.

Solution

There are 19 scores for 1st period, so the middle score is the 10th value as you count from either the maximum or minimum. **The median in 1st period is 70.** In 3rd period there are 20 scores. So the median is the average of the two middle (10th and 11th) scores.

$$\frac{80 + 82}{2} = \frac{162}{2} = 81$$

The median in 3rd period is 81.

We can conclude that both measures of center, the mean and the median, are higher for third period. This fact could be predicted from the shape of the data set. Scores in Period 3 are clustered in the 70s and 80s, while scores in Period 1 are clustered in the 60s. In Period 1 the mean is higher than the median because the scores at 100 exert a pull on the mean. In Period 3 the mean is lower than the median because the two scores in the 30s affect the mean.

The mean and median values of a data set are not always close together, as the next example shows.

Example 3

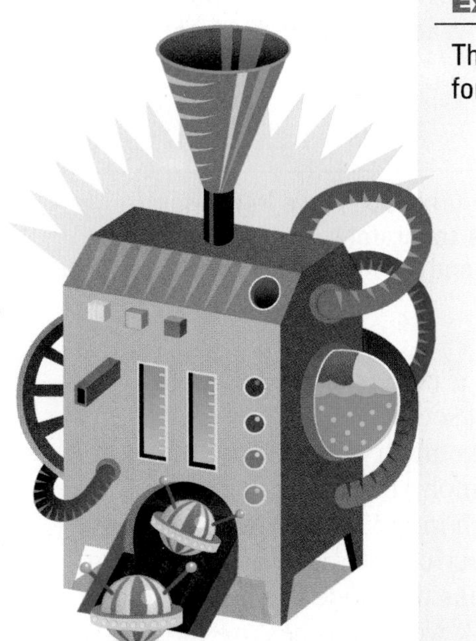

The Wacky Widget Company has 15 employees. The jobs and annual salary for each job are given below.

Job	Annual Salary
President	$250,000
Vice-President	100,000
Warehouse Supervisor	60,000
Sales Supervisor	60,000
Sales Representative NE	40,000
Sales Representative NW	40,000
Sales Representative SE	40,000
Sales Representative SW	40,000
Secretary to President	25,000
Secretary to Vice-President	20,000
Warehouse Worker	20,000
Warehouse Worker	20,000
Custodian	18,000
Custodian	16,000
Custodian	16,000

a. Rewrite the salary data in a table showing the frequency of each salary.
b. Find the mean salary.
c. Find the median salary.
d. Why do you suppose most employees were upset by a newspaper article reporting "Average Wacky Widget worker earns $51,000."

Solution

a. Make a table listing the salaries in rank order with the number of employees at that salary level.

Salary (in thousands of $)	Frequency
250	1
100	1
60	2
40	4
25	1
20	3
18	1
16	2

b. Calculate the mean (in thousands of dollars) by multiplying each salary by its frequency and dividing by the total number of salaries.

$$\frac{250 + 100 + 2(60) + 4(40) + 25 + 3(20) + 18 + 2(16)}{15} = 51$$

So the mean salary is $51,000.

c. The median in a set of 15 numbers is the 8th number.

The median salary is $40,000, the salary of a Sales Representative.

d. Even though the newspaper accurately reported the mean salary, 11 of the 15 employees earn far less than the mean. In this case, the typical salary at the Wacky Widget Company is better represented by the median.

Activity 2

a. Find out how to use a statistics utility to enter data using a frequency table rather than entering each data value separately.

b. Use the utility to check the answers for $\overline{x}$ and the median for salaries at the Wacky Widget Company.

The mean and median are called **measures of center** or **measures of central tendency**. A third measure of a data set is the *mode*, the most common item in that set. In Ms. T. Chare's geometry classes, the mode in 1st period is 100: it occurred three times. Among the 3rd period scores, there are two modes: 78 and 85. Even though in 3rd period the modes are fairly close to the mean and median, in 1st period the mode is an extreme value. For this reason, although in some books the mode is considered a measure of central tendency, and in this book we sometimes use the mode, we do not consider it a measure of the center of a data set.

Each of the mean, median, and mode has merits in different situations. A retailer stocking T-shirts likes to know the modal size. A teacher trying to see quickly how his or her class performed on an exam would look for the median score. A city council member budgeting the local income tax may want to know both the mean and median family income. Statisticians frequently use the mean because of its theoretical properties.

QUESTIONS

Covering the Reading

In 1–3, consider the following set of ages of students in a college seminar.

$$x_1 = 21, x_2 = 27, x_3 = 18, x_4 = 19, x_5 = 19, x_6 = 20, x_7 = 20$$

1. Calculate.

a. $\sum_{i=1}^{5} x_i$ **b.** $\sum_{i=3}^{6} x_i$

2. Write an expression using Σ-notation to represent the sum of the ages of the people in the seminar.

3. *Multiple choice.* Which of the following expresses the mean of the set?

(a) $\sum_{i=1}^{7} x_i$ (b) $\sum_{i=18}^{27} x_i$ (c) $\frac{1}{7} \sum_{i=1}^{7} x_i$ (d) $\frac{1}{7} \sum_{i=18}^{27} x_i$

4. Name two measures commonly used to describe the center of a data set.

5. What measure of center does $\bar{x}$ represent?

In 6–8, define each term.

6. mean **7.** median **8.** mode

9. Below are listed the 10 deadliest hurricanes to hit the U.S. since 1900.

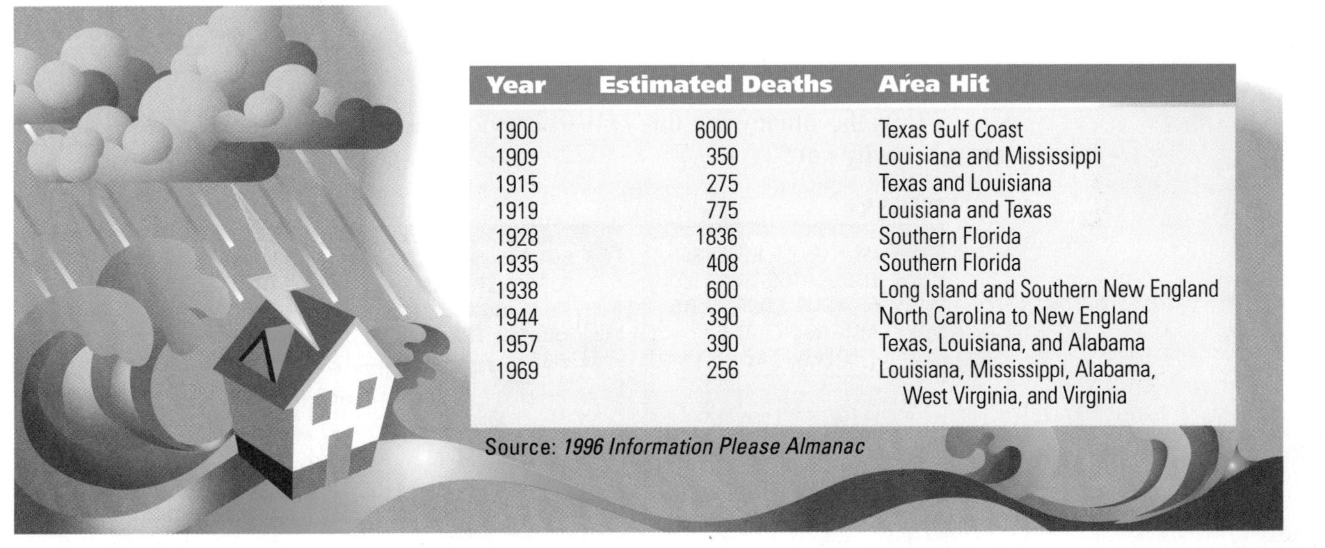

Year	Estimated Deaths	Area Hit
1900	6000	Texas Gulf Coast
1909	350	Louisiana and Mississippi
1915	275	Texas and Louisiana
1919	775	Louisiana and Texas
1928	1836	Southern Florida
1935	408	Southern Florida
1938	600	Long Island and Southern New England
1944	390	North Carolina to New England
1957	390	Texas, Louisiana, and Alabama
1969	256	Louisiana, Mississippi, Alabama, West Virginia, and Virginia

Source: *1996 Information Please Almanac*

a. Find the mean and median number of deaths caused by these hurricanes.

b. Which measure more accurately describes the death toll? Why?

In 10 and 11, *true or false.* If true, explain why. If false, give a counterexample.

10. The mean of a data set is always greater than its median.

11. The median of a data set is sometimes not a member of the set.

In 12 and 13, refer to Example 3.

12. In the computation of the mean, why is 60 multiplied by 2 and 40 multiplied by 4?

13. Consider the salaries of all employees except the president.
 a. Find the mean, median, and mode of the salaries.
 b. Compare your answers in part **a** to those in the solution to Example 3. By how much has each measure of center changed?
 c. In general, which is more affected by extreme values, the mean or the median?

Applying the Mathematics

14. A teacher has 15 algebra students in 2nd hour and 25 algebra students each in 3rd and 7th hour. The following are quiz results after all students have taken the quiz.

2nd hour	3rd hour	7th hour
$\overline{x} = 72$	$\overline{x} = 80$	$\overline{x} = 83$

What is the mean score for all three classes?

15. Consider the data on quiz scores for Ms. T. Chare's 3rd period class on page 21. A student missed the quiz because of a field trip. When that score was averaged in, the mean for this class fell to 76. What was that score?

16. Make up a data set consisting of five temperatures for which the mean is positive and the median is negative.

17. Is the situation in this Dilbert cartoon possible? If so, how? If not, why not?

DILBERT®

18. When data are non-numerical but can be ordered, such as letter grades, the mean cannot be calculated directly; but both the median and mode can be found. Last year in Mr. Flag's history course, the final grades were 8 A's, 6 B's, 3 C's, 3 D's, and 1 F.
 a. What was the modal grade?
 b. What was the median grade?
 c. Can you find a mean grade for the grades? If yes, devise a system that finds a mean grade. If not, explain why not.

In 19–21, refer to the table below. Let the index i be the number of the region, 1 to 6, and let e_i, x_i, m_i, and p_i represent the value of exports in 1993, exports in 1994, imports in 1993, and imports in 1994, respectively.

Exports from and Imports into the United States (in millions of dollars)

	Region	Exports		Imports	
i		e_i(1993)	x_i(1994)	m_i(1993)	p_i(1994)
1	Western Hemisphere	178,867.3	206,988.4	185,590.1	216,360.6
2	Western Europe	113,680.6	118,177.4	115,556.7	130,730.2
3	Eastern Europe (including former Soviet Republics)	10,080.0	8,862.6	5,619.9	9,679.5
4	Asia (Pacific Rim)	131,595.4	147,779.4	229,551.9	261,153.2
5	Asia (Near East and Central)	20,883.7	19,499.8	22,820.0	24,429.3
6	Other (Africa/Oceania)	9,984.0	11,318.9	21,520.8	20,902.9

Source: U.S. Department of Commerce

19. *Multiple choice.* Which expression represents the total value of exports from the United States in these six regions during 1993?

(a) $\sum_{i=1}^{6} e_i$ (b) $\sum_{i=1}^{6} x_i$ (c) $\sum_{i=1}^{6} m_i$ (d) $\sum_{i=1}^{6} p_i$

20. a. Write an expression using Σ-notation representing the total value of all imports from these regions in 1993.

b. Evaluate the expression in part **a**.

21. What quantity does $\sum_{i=1}^{6} p_i - \sum_{i=1}^{6} x_i$ represent?

Review

For 22 and 23, the dotplot below shows the number of pairs of jeans owned by students in the drama club. *(Lesson 1-2)*

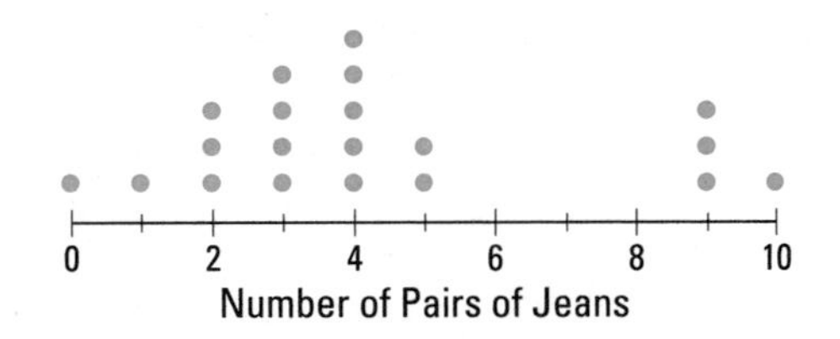

22. What is the maximum number of pairs of jeans owned by a student?

23. a. Which value has the greatest frequency?

b. Explain what the answer to part **a** means about jeans.

24. What might be misleading about the graph shown below? *(Lesson 1-1)*

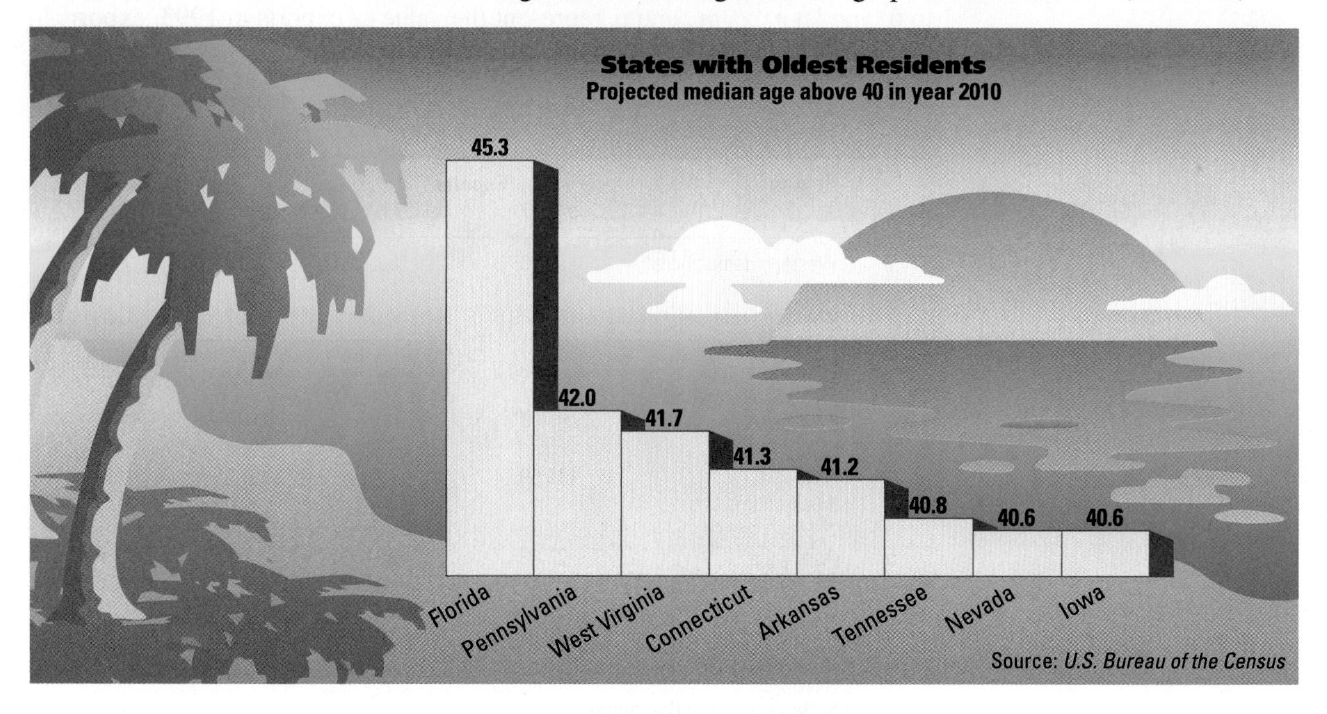

25. Complete the analogy. Set is to subset as population is to __?__.
(Lesson 1-1)

In 26 and 27, a line has slope 5 and contains the point (2, 3). *(Previous course)*

26. Name two other points on the line.

27. Find an equation for the line.

Exploration

28. a. Find a set of five numbers whose mean is 10, whose median is 15, and whose mode is 30.

b. Given that $x < y < z$, find a set of five numbers whose mean is x, whose median is y, and whose mode is z.

LESSON

1-4

Quartiles, Percentiles, and Box Plots

Basic Yearly Student Charges for Room, Board, and Tuition in Public Colleges by State, 1994–1995
U.S. Average $6,365

State	Charges ($)	State	Charges ($)
1. Oklahoma	4,205	26. Minnesota	6,182
2. Hawaii	4,734	27. Florida	6,192
3. North Carolina	4,858	28. Missouri	6,326
4. Arkansas	4,926	29. Colorado	6,523
5. Tennessee	5,130	30. South Carolina	6,758
6. Texas	5,175	31. Nevada	6,908
7. Nebraska	5,186	32. Indiana	6,921
8. Idaho	5,205	33. Oregon	6,929
9. Wyoming	5,237	34. Washington	7,070
10. Mississippi	5,248	35. Illinois	7,482
11. Louisiana	5,275	36. Ohio	7,733
12. South Dakota	5,319	37. Maine	7,794
13. Kentucky	5,324	38. California	7,922
14. Utah	5,349	39. Michigan	7,949
15. New Mexico	5,373	40. Virginia	7,951
16. Georgia	5,381	41. New York	7,952
17. Alabama	5,432	42. Delaware	8,131
18. Kansas	5,442	43. New Hampshire	8,145
19. North Dakota	5,513	44. Maryland	8,297
20. Wisconsin	5,615	45. Connecticut	8,505
21. Iowa	5,699	46. Massachusetts	8,536
22. Arizona	5,829	47. Pennsylvania	8,665
23. West Virginia	5,912	48. New Jersey	8,714
24. Montana	5,996	49. Rhode Island	9,080
25. Alaska	6,156	50. Vermont	10,401

Source: *1995 Digest of Education Statistics*

Questions that are simple to state often do not have simple answers. Consider the question, "How much does it cost to go to college?" Of course it depends on the college. And for many colleges it depends on the courses the student takes. A full answer would involve the costs of millions of students! The problem must be simplified and clarified. To create the table above, all public colleges were surveyed and asked to give the basic costs for room, board, and tuition for the students from their state. Then the mean of these costs was calculated for each state.

In the table, the data are rank-ordered in *ascending order,* that is, from lowest to highest cost. When data are not given in rank order, a statistics utility can be used to create the order. The rank order makes it easy to determine the median total cost. It is the mean of the 25th and 26th entries. So the median is

$$\frac{6156 + 6182}{2} = \$6169.$$

Because the measures of center do not indicate in any way how the costs vary from state to state, next we examine the *spread* of the data. One measure of *spread* is the range, which is $10401 − $4205, or $6196. The spread of a data set can also be identified by giving several single scores called *quartiles.*

Quartiles

Quartiles are so named because they are values which divide an ordered set into four subsets of approximately equal size. To calculate the quartile scores, first order the set and locate its median. The **second** (or **middle**) **quartile** is defined to be the median. The **first quartile** (or **lower quartile**) is the median of the numbers below the location of the median. The **third** (or **upper**) **quartile** is the median of the numbers above the median.

Arch Support. *Romanesque arches, like those at UCLA shown below, convey a sense of the classical origin of colleges.*

Example 1

For the set of costs at public colleges, find the following.

a. Q_1, the first (lower) quartile

b. Q_3, the third (upper) quartile

Solution

a. Q_1, the first quartile, is the median of numbers below the median. Because there are 50 states, there are 25 entries below the median. (They are in the left half of the preceding table.) The first quartile is the number in the 13th position, $5324.

b. Similarly, Q_3, the upper quartile, is the 13th value above the median. The total cost for the 38th state is $7922.

The difference $Q_3 - Q_1$ between the third quartile and the first quartile is called the **interquartile range**. It gives a measure of the spread around the center of the data. Specifically, it tells an interval in which you will find the middle 50% of the data. For the preceding data,

$$Q_3 - Q_1 = \$7922 - \$5324 = \$2598.$$

By picturing the 50 data points on a number line, you can see the quartiles. Because two of the quartiles are data points, there are 12 values before, between, and after the quartiles. The number line below shows cost in hundreds of dollars.

35 40 45 50 55 60 65 70 75 80 85 90 95 100

A —— B

The length of $\overline{AB}$ is the interquartile range.

C —— D

The length of $\overline{CD}$ is the range.

The quartiles, together with the minimum and maximum of the data set, provide a **five-number summary** of the data: min x = 4,205, Q_1 = 5,324, Med = 6,169, Q_3 = 7,922, max x = 10,401. Caution: There is another common use of the word quartile. The four intervals whose endpoints are the consecutive numbers in the five-number summary are sometimes themselves called quartiles. The two uses of the word are confusing, so we avoid this second use.

Percentiles

Each of the five numbers (the minimum, first quartile, median, third quartile, and maximum) is often associated with a *percentile*.

Definition

The *p*th **percentile** of a set of numbers is a value in the set such that *p* percent of the numbers are less than or equal to that value.

By definition, every value in a data set is less than or equal to the maximum, so the maximum value is the 100th percentile. The cost of college in Vermont is at the 100th percentile. The median is often called the 50th percentile, and the lower and upper quartiles are called the 25th and 75th percentiles, respectively. In practice, however, the quartiles may not correspond *exactly* to these percentiles.

For college costs by state, $\frac{1}{50} = 2\%$ of the numbers are at or below the minimum value, so the minimum value for the data is at the 2nd percentile.

Example 2

For the set of college costs, find the following.

a. the percentile rank of $5324, the first quartile

b. the college cost at the 85th percentile

Solution

a. There are 13 costs less than or equal to $5324.

$\frac{13}{50} = .26 = 26\%$. So $5324 is the 26th percentile.

b. 85% of 50 is $(.85)(50) = 42.5$.

There is no cost at the 42.5 position. Typically, when dealing with percentiles we round up to the next integer. So we take the 43rd highest cost. $8145, the cost in New Hampshire, is at the 85th percentile.

Box Plots

On page 30, the 50 data points and the five-number summary of the data were shown. A **box plot**, or a **box-and-whiskers plot**, is a visual representation of the five-number summary of a data set. Box plots were invented in the 1970s by John Tukey. A box plot is constructed as follows.

1. Draw a number line including the minimum and maximum data values.
2. Draw a rectangle with opposite sides at the lower and upper quartiles of the data. (Sometimes these segments are called "hinges.")
3. In the box, draw a segment parallel to the hinges at the median.
4. Draw segments from the midpoints of the hinges to the minimum and maximum values. (These segments are called "whiskers.")

Box plots convey a great amount of information. Below is a box plot for the data on the cost of college at public colleges.

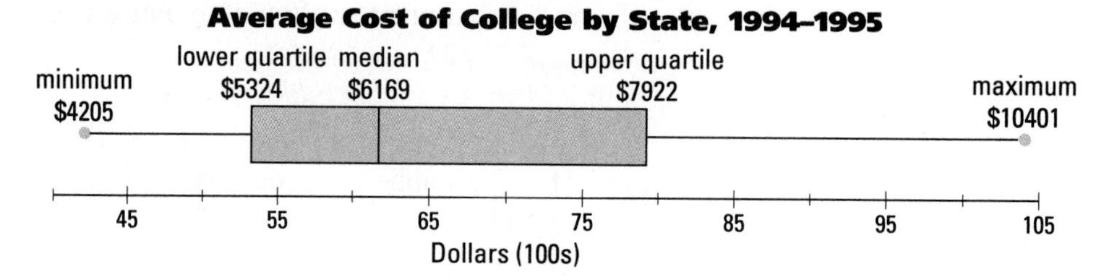

From this box plot, you can see that in about 75% of the states the average cost of college in 1994–95 was under $8000 annually. You can also see that there are as many states with costs within the small interval $5324 to $6169 as there are in the larger interval $6169 to $7922.

Box plots are often used to compare data sets. For instance, to investigate the question "In which part of the world—Africa or Latin America—are literacy rates generally higher?" you could make box plots of the literacy rates of the countries of these two regions. (Note that Latin America includes South America, Central America, and the Caribbean.)

Example 3

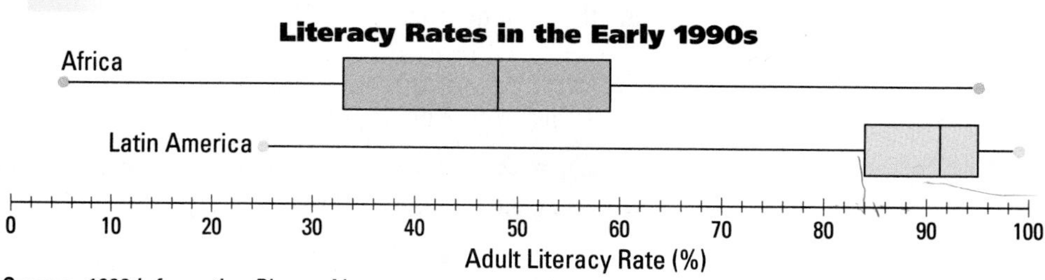

Source: *1996 Information Please Almanac*

Use the box plots above to answer the following.

a. Estimate the range of literacy rates in the two regions.

b. *True or false.* In Latin America there are more countries with literacy rates of 84% or less than there are with literacy rates of at least 91%. Justify your response.

c. Write a brief comparison of literacy rates in these two regions. Mention median and quartile values.

Solution

a. Recall that range = maximum − minimum.
For Africa, the range = 95 − 5 = 90;
for Latin America, the range = 99 − 25 = 74.
Thus, the literacy rates vary more in Africa than they do in Latin America.

b. False. In Latin America about 25% of the countries have literacy rates of 84% or less, whereas about 50% of the countries have literacy rates of at least 91%.

▶ **c.** Overall, the literacy rates are higher in Latin America than in Africa. The median literacy rates are about 91% in Latin America versus about 48% in Africa. In Latin America more than 75% of the countries have literacy rates of at least 84%, whereas in Africa about 75% of the countries have literacy rates under 59%.

Finding Outliers

Outliers can have a significant impact on statistics such as the mean. Also, outliers may be important because they represent special cases. For example, in Example 3 on page 23, the salary of the president probably should not be averaged with the salaries of other employees. Often, a specific standard is used to determine whether a value is an outlier. Here is an algorithm for one such criterion.

1. Find the value of $Q_3 - Q_1$, the interquartile range, or IQR.
2. Add $1.5 \times$ IQR to the 3rd quartile.
   Any number larger than $Q_3 + 1.5 \times IQR$ is an outlier.
3. Subtract $1.5 \times$ IQR from 1st quartile.
   Any number smaller than $Q_1 - 1.5 \times IQR$ is an outlier.

Example 4

Consider the college costs presented earlier. We know

min x = 4,205　　Q_1 = 5,324　　Med = 6,169
Q_3 = 7,922　　max x = 10,401

Use the $1.5 \times$ IQR criterion to determine if there are any outliers. If there are any, identify them.

Solution

IQR = $Q_3 - Q_1$ = 2598; so $1.5 \times$ IQR = 3897
The 3rd quartile is $7,922.

$$7922 + 3897 = 11,819$$

So any cost greater than $11,819 is an outlier.
Similarly, any cost $3897 lower than the 1st quartile is an outlier.

$$5,324 - 3,897 = 1,427$$

Thus, there are no outliers.

Some statistics utilities use the above procedure based on the interquartile range to determine outliers and then draw the whiskers to represent all values except the outliers. Sometimes a box plot is drawn with its whiskers ending at the $1.5 \times$ IQR level or at the 10th and 90th percentiles. Outliers are then indicated by dots.

QUESTIONS

Covering the Reading

1. The 25th percentile is often called the __?__ quartile.

2. What percentile corresponds to the third quartile?

3. What percentile corresponds to the maximum score?

4. Refer to the table on college costs on page 29. At what percentile is the cost of public colleges in your state?

5. **a.** What numbers are reported in a five-number summary?
   b. Which give(s) the center?
   c. Which give(s) information about the spread in the middle of the data set?
   d. Which determine the range?

6. Refer to the table below, which gives the mean length in days of a hospital stay by state in 1993. (Source: *The World Almanac of the U.S.A.*)

State	Mean Stay	State	Mean Stay	State	Mean Stay
MT	18.7	WY	7.5	AR	6.7
MI	13.2	RI	7.3	DE	6.7
ND	13.0	VT	7.3	GA	6.7
PA	13.0	CO	7.2	OK	6.7
SD	12.4	IL	7.2	SC	6.7
NJ	11.6	NC	7.2	ID	6.6
MA	10.7	OH	7.2	LA	6.5
MN	10.3	AL	7.1	NV	6.4
NY	10.2	WV	7.1	UT	6.3
NE	9.7	FL	7.0	TX	6.2
CT	8.6	MD	7.0	CA	6.1
HI	8.5	MS	7.0	AK	5.9
WI	8.2	VA	7.0	NM	5.9
ME	7.8	IN	6.8	AZ	5.8
IA	7.6	KY	6.8	OR	5.8
KS	7.6	NH	6.8	WA	5.8
MO	7.5	TN	6.8		

   a. Give the five-number summary for the data set.
   b. What is the number of days at the 34th percentile?
   c. What is the number of days at the 98th percentile?
   d. At what percentile is a stay of 7.8 days?
   e. At what percentile is a stay of 6.2 days?
   f. Make a box plot to display these data.
   g. Use the 1.5 × IQR criterion to show that there is an outlier.
   h. What factors do you think might cause states to differ on this variable by so much?

In 7–11, refer to the following box plot of student test scores on last year's advanced algebra mid-year exam.

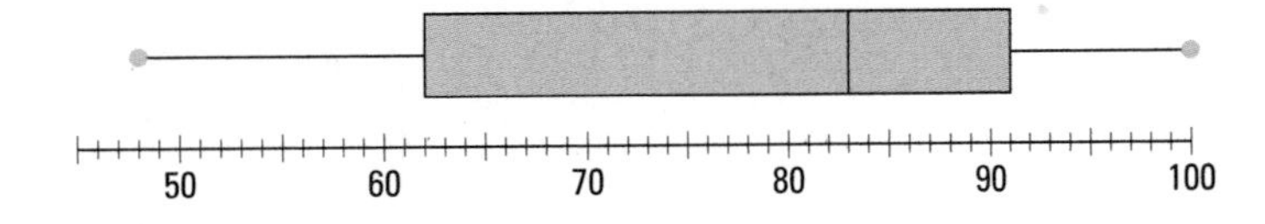

7. What is the median score?

8. What is the interquartile range?

9. What percent of the students scored between 62 and 91?

10. What is the interval of scores of students who ranked below the lower quartile?

11. Between which two quartiles is there the greatest spread?

In 12 and 13, use the five-number summaries below, which correspond to the box plot in Example 3.

Literacy Rate (%)

Region	min	Q_1	Median	Q_3	max
Africa	5	33	48	59	95
Latin America	25	84	91.3	95	99

Use the 1.5 × IQR criterion to determine if the following countries (and literacy rates) are outliers.

12. Rwanda (5%)

13. Haiti (25%)

Applying the Mathematics

In 14–16 use the box plots below of the lengths in meters of bridges in the United States and other countries in 1996. The 20 longest U.S. bridges are compared with the 20 longest bridges outside the U.S.
(Source: *1996 Information Please Almanac*)

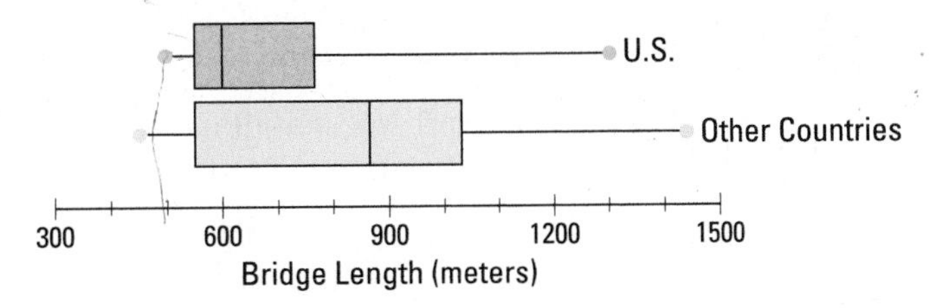

Verrazano Narrows Bridge, New York

14. Each of the ten longest bridges in the U.S. is longer than _?_ meters.

15. *True or false.* The shortest of the 40 bridges in the data set is in the U.S.

16. Write a paragraph comparing and contrasting the relative lengths of the 20 longest bridges in the U.S. and the 20 longest bridges outside the U.S.

17. Use the five-number summaries given below for the annual salaries in three divisions of a company. Data are in 1000s of dollars.

Division	min	Q_1	median	Q_3	max
A	18	28	34	40	57
B	23	35	43	48	59
C	19	24	27	30	43

a. Make three box plots to represent this information graphically. Use parallel number lines with the same scale.
b. *True or false.* Nearly all of the salaries in Division C are between the middle 50% of salaries in Division B.
c. Overall, which division has the lowest salaries? Justify your reasoning.

Review

18. A data set has 100 elements $a_1, a_2, \ldots, a_{100}$. Write an expression in Σ-notation to represent the mean of the set. *(Lesson 1-3)*

19. Suppose $x_1 = 2$, $x_2 = 7$, and $x_3 = 4$. Evaluate each expression. *(Lesson 1-3)*

a. $\sum_{i=1}^{3} x_i$ **b.** $\left(\sum_{i=1}^{3} x_i\right)^2$ **c.** $\sum_{i=1}^{3} x_i^2$

20. Here are the heights of four members of the Reach High basketball team.

Stretch: 5'10" Skyler: 6'2" Lanky: 6' Knees: 6'2"

They have a choice of adding Marvin (6'1") or Harry (7'1"). In parts **a–c**, calculate the mean and median for the heights of
a. the current team
b. the current team plus Marvin
c. the current team plus Harry
d. Which statistic in part **c** do you think better describes the team and why?
e. In general, which is less affected by extreme values, the mean or the median? *(Lesson 1-3)*

Stem	Leaf
0	3 8
1	7 9 8 1 0
2	3 8 0 6 0
3	4 7 1 3
4	5 5 2
5	0
6	5
7	6 2
8	
9	7
10	
11	3

21. At the left is a stemplot of the dollars spent by 25 shoppers at a grocery store. The stem is in $10 units. Find the median. *(Lessons 1-2, 1-3)*

22. The circle graph at the right shows eye colors of the students in T. Chare's 4th hour class. If 7 students have either green or hazel eyes, how many students are in the class? *(Lesson 1-1)*

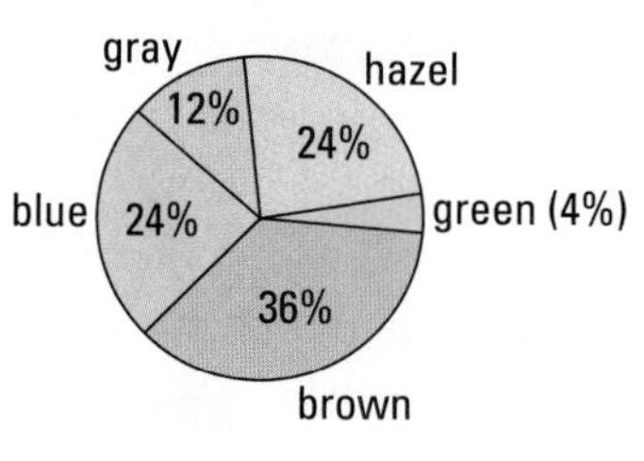

23. A line is graphed at the right.
a. Give its slope.
b. Give an equation for the line.
(Previous course)

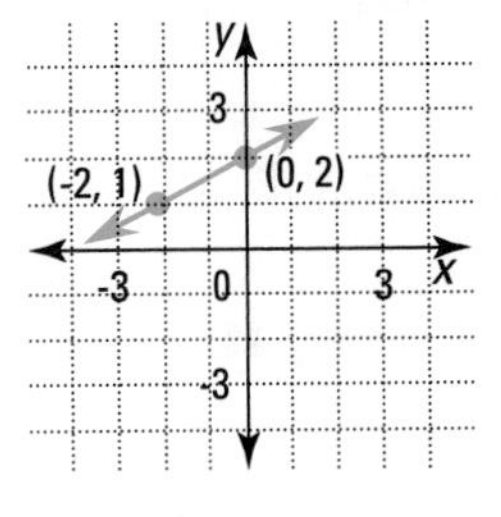

24. *Skill sequence.* Assume denominators do not equal zero. Simplify each expression. *(Previous course)*
a. $\frac{13x - x}{2x}$ **b.** $\frac{20x + 16x}{2x + 4x}$ **c.** $\frac{20x + 16}{2x + 4}$

Exploration

25. **a.** Collect the heights of a sample of 50 people in your school.
b. Make a box plot of the data.
c. Estimate any outliers visually from the box plot.
d. Identify outliers using the $1.5 \times$ IQR method.
e. Do you think your sample is representative of any larger population? Explain.

26. Find a report on test scores in your school that uses percentiles. Describe the way percentiles are calculated and what the percentiles tell about you and your classmates.

27. Some books and standardized tests use a different definition of percentile. They say that the pth percentile of a set of numbers is a value in the set such that p percent of the numbers are *less than* that value.
a. According to this definition, what percentile is the minimum value in a data set?
b. Can any value ever be at the 100th percentile?

Introducing Lesson 1-5

Displaying Data with a Statistics Utility

You will need a statistics utility for this activity.

1 Find out what data displays from this chapter can be produced by your statistics utility.

2 Consider the data on Oscar winners from page 20. If necessary, you should reenter the data into two separate columns or lists. If possible, use your statistics utility to draw box plots of the ages of Oscar-winning actors and actresses on parallel number lines with the same scale. Print a hard copy using your technology, or copy the display by hand. If possible, add a title to the box plot and label the number lines before printing. If not, add scales and labels after printing.

3 Produce a histogram of the ages of Oscar-winning actresses using your statistics utility. Most statistics utilities require the user to choose intervals for the horizontal and vertical axes. You should set the x-interval or scale at 10 to obtain a histogram by decade. Print or make a hard copy of the histogram.

4 Repeat the process in Step 3 for Oscar-winning actors. Do not change your intervals or scale. Again, print or make a hard copy of the histogram.

5 Using the data for ages of winning actors, make histograms with the x-scales of 5, 20, and 30. Which scale seems most appropriate for this data set? Why?

6 Compare the histograms of Steps 3–5 with the box plots of Step 2.

a. What are the advantages of each type of display?

b. What are the drawbacks?

c. Which type of display do you feel is more effective for comparing and contrasting these data sets? Give a reason for your answer.

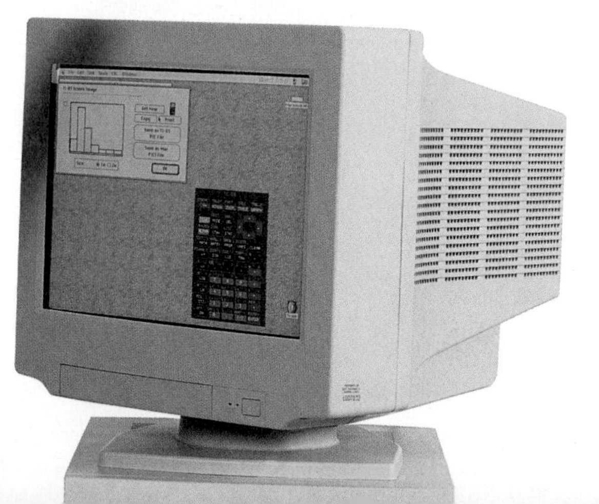

LESSON

1-5

Histograms

a. #2 pencil, b. calculator, c. brain. *These students are taking a practice version of TAAS (Texas Assessment of Academic Skills). The first standardized mathematics test was published in 1926 by Scott Foresman. Which of the preceding choices was required for that test?*

A *histogram* is a special type of bar graph. A good histogram breaks the range of values of a numerical variable into nonoverlapping intervals of equal width. **Frequency histograms** display the number of values that fall into each interval. **Relative frequency histograms** display the percent of values that fall into each interval.

The histograms below show the results of all students in one school on a final exam in geometry. The histogram at the left shows frequency; the one at right relative frequency. Here each interval includes its right endpoint but not its left. For instance, the left two intervals are $20 < x \leq 30$ and $30 < x \leq 40$.

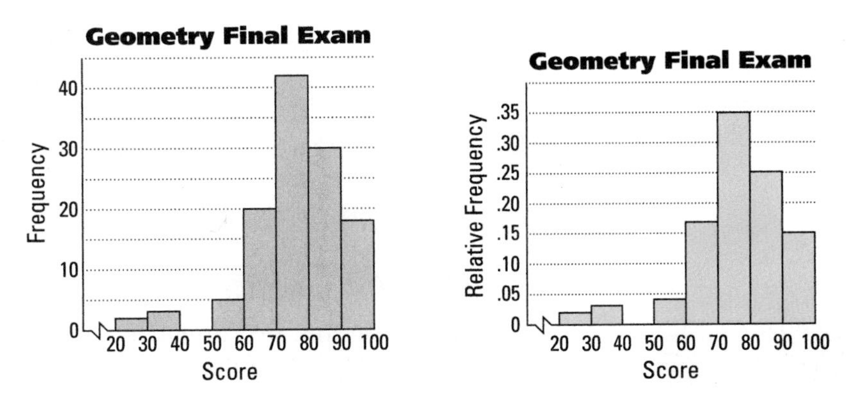

Example 1

Use the histogram at the left on page 39 for the following questions.

a. About how many students got scores between 60 and 70, including 70?
b. About how many students took the final exam?
c. In which 10-point interval does the median fall?

Solution

a. Read the height of the bar between 60 and 70. **Twenty students got scores in this interval.**

b. Add the heights of the bars in the histogram on the left. Note that for four of the intervals you must estimate the heights. Reading the intervals from left to right, an estimate is

$$2 + 3 + 0 + 5 + 20 + 42 + 30 + 18 = 120.$$

So about 120 students took the geometry exam.

c. When the 120 scores are rank-ordered, the median is between the 60th and 61st scores. From the estimates in part **b** we conclude that there are about 30 scores below 70, and about 42 between 70 and 80. So the 60th and 61st scores are between 70 and 80, and **so the median must be between 70 and 80.**

Different questions can be answered using a histogram showing relative frequencies.

Example 2

Use the histogram on the right on page 39.

a. About what percent of the students scored between 70 and 80?
b. About what percent of the students scored less than or equal to 50 on the exam?

Solution

a. .35 is 35%. **So about 35% of the students scored between 70 and 80.**

b. .02 +.03+ 0 =.05. **So about 5% of the students scored at or below 50.**

Activity

Use either histogram of geometry exam scores to write a brief paragraph (3–4 sentences) on the distribution of the scores. Be sure to indicate the presence of clusters and gaps and estimate any possible outliers.

Drawing a Histogram

To make a histogram, first organize the data into nonoverlapping intervals of equal width. Choosing the width of the interval is a matter of judgment. There is usually not a single best size. Generally, choosing 5 to 10 intervals is about right for a histogram. Too few intervals will lump all the data together; too many will result in only a few numbers in each one.

Second, count the number of observations per interval and record the results in a frequency table, that is, a table that gives the frequency or relative frequency for each of the intervals created.

Finally, draw the histogram. First, mark the endpoints of the intervals on a horizontal axis and a scale for the frequencies on a vertical axis. Then, draw a bar to represent the frequency in each interval. Unlike other bar graphs, histograms are drawn with no horizontal space between bars (unless an interval is empty, in which case its bar has height 0). This is because histograms often represent continuous variables.

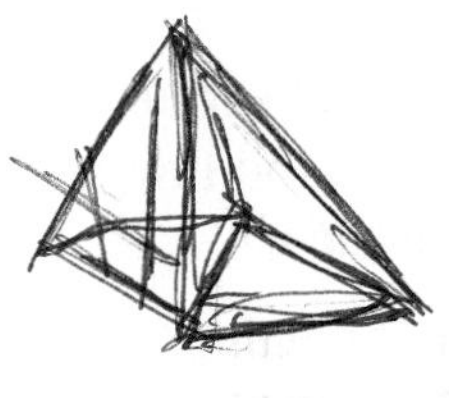

Example 3

Consider the data on public college costs on page 29. Display these data in a histogram.

Solution

1. Consider the range of the data to decide on an interval. The range is $10401 - 4205 = 6196 \approx 6000$. So intervals of size 1000 seem reasonable. Rather than start intervals at the minimum, we begin at the greatest multiple of 1000 less than the minimum. Thus, our first interval goes from 4000 to 5000, the second from 5000 to 6000. A refinement is needed, because 5000 would be in two intervals. So we make an arbitrary decision: the intervals are $4000 \le x < 5000$, $5000 \le x < 6000$, $6000 \le x < 7000$, and so on.
2. Next, make a frequency table. Begin with the intervals and count the occurrences for each interval.

Total Cost ($)	Frequency
$4000 \le x < 5000$	4
$5000 \le x < 6000$	20
$6000 \le x < 7000$	9
$7000 \le x < 8000$	8
$8000 \le x < 9000$	7
$9000 \le x < 10000$	1
$10000 \le x < 11000$	1

3. Draw and label the histogram. It is not necessary to indicate a break before 4000 on the horizontal axis.

Average Total Cost at Public Colleges by State, 1994–1995

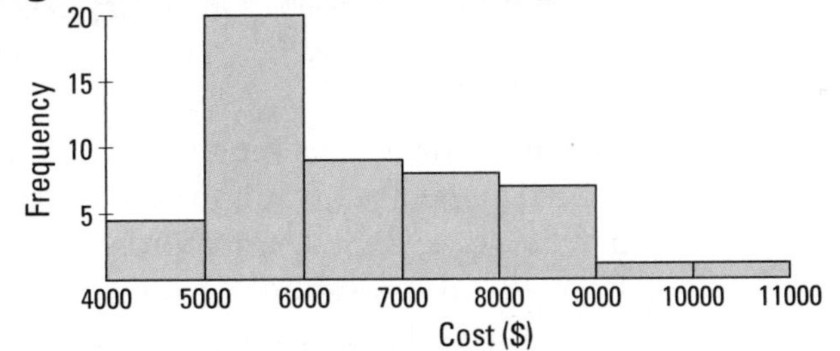

Analyzing a Histogram

A well-made histogram, like a box plot, gives information about the center and spread of the data. It shows where there are clusters of data and gaps in the data. From the histogram alone, it is clear that in most states the annual cost of public college is between $5000 and $6000, and that many states have average costs for public colleges between $6000 and $9000 per year. Some charge more than $10,000. The shape of a histogram often has a tail that extends farther to the right or left from its center. We then say that the histogram is *skewed* to the right or left. The histogram on page 41 is skewed to the right because of its rightward extending tail.

A poor choice of intervals—too large or too small—can make it difficult to interpret the data. For instance, the histogram below at the left has too few intervals to convey the college cost data effectively. The one on the right below has too many intervals.

In 1995, 14.2 million people were enrolled in colleges or universities in the U.S. That number is expected to grow to 15.5 million by the year 2000.

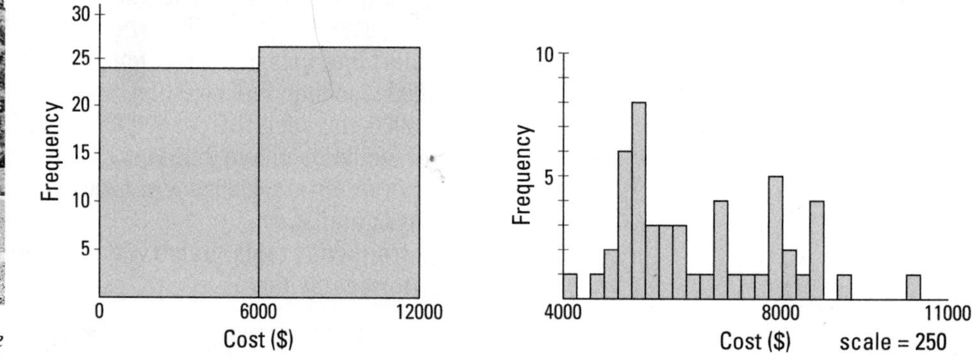

Histograms can be distorted if the intervals are not of equal width. Below at the left is a table whose data are in the histogram at the right. These data are rounded from U.S. Bureau of the Census estimates of the mid 1990s.

Age	Projection (1000s)
0–4	16,700
5–17	48,500
18–24	29,000
25–44	73,600
45–64	76,300
65+	37,100

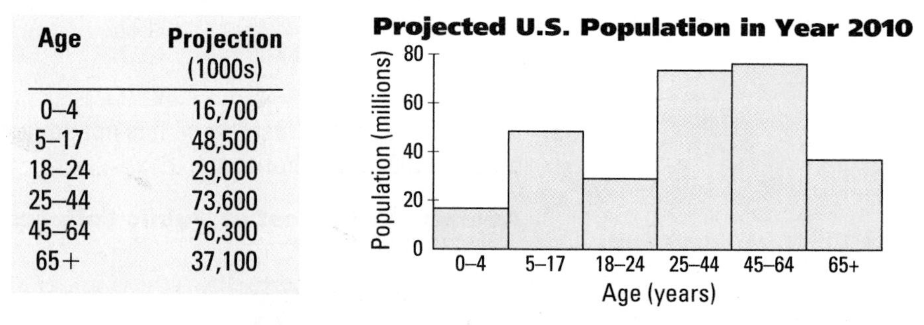

The histogram gives the impression that there are the fewest number of people at the ages from birth to 4, but the bar is shortest because only 5 years (0, 1, 2, 3, 4) are represented. That is also the reason the bar from 18–24 is so short. This histogram would be clearer if there were equal intervals, for example: 0–20, 21–40, 41–60, 61–80, 80+.

QUESTIONS

Covering the Reading

1. What is the difference between frequency and relative frequency?

In 2 and 3, use the histograms of geometry students on page 39.

2. What percent of students scored above 80?

3. In which interval is the 25th percentile?

In 4–8, use the frequency distribution below of the scores of students taking the SAT II Latin Subject Test of the College Entrance Examination Board in 1995.

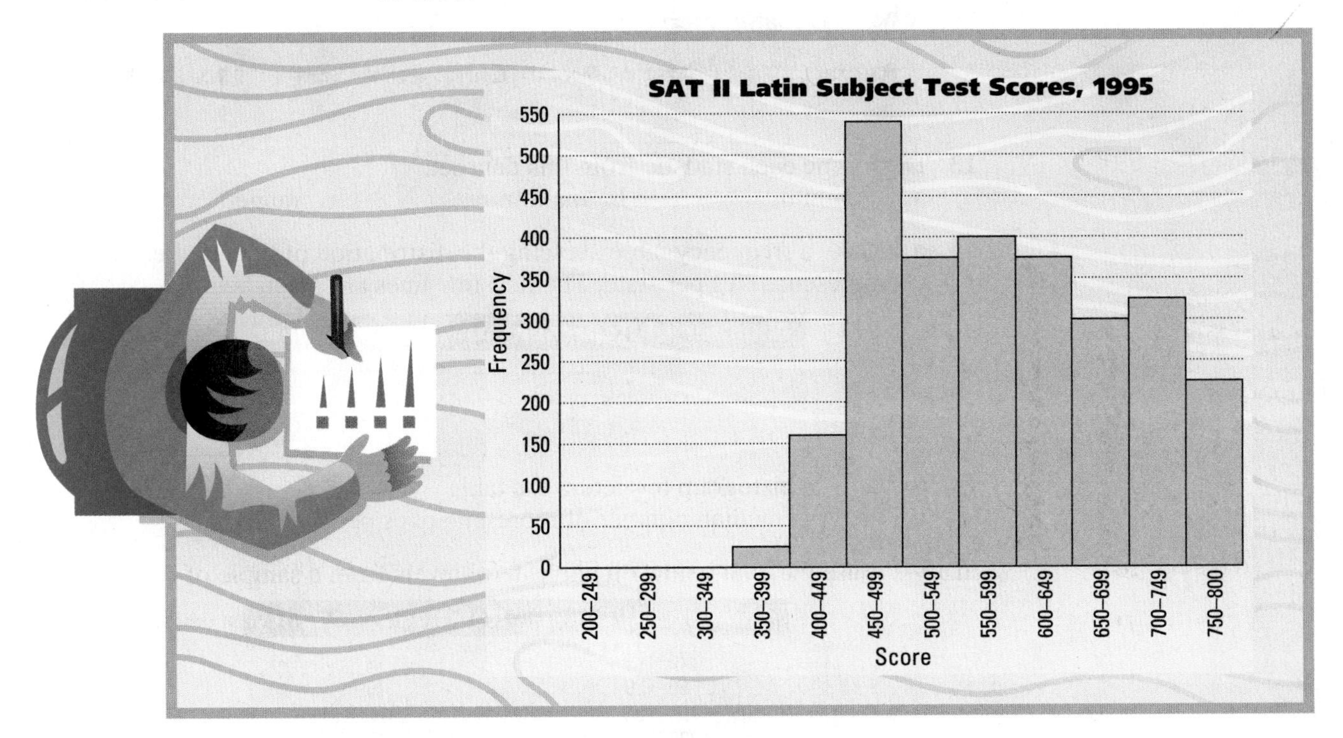

4. About how many students scored between 400 and 499?

5. What score interval was the mode?

6. To the nearest 10, about how many students took the Latin exam in 1995?

7. About what percent of the students scored 700 or better?

8. Estimate the median score.

In 9 and 10, consider the data on costs of attending college on page 29 and in Example 3 of this lesson.

9. a. Which interval has the highest frequency?
b. In which interval is the median? Justify your answer.

10. a. Make another histogram of the same data using intervals of size 500 beginning at 4000.
b. Mark the mean and median on the histogram.

In 11 and 12, use the population data on page 42.

11. About how many 23-year-olds are expected in the year 2010? What assumption did you make in arriving at your answer?

12. Which age group is expected to have the most people, 5–24, 25–44, 45–64, or 65–84?

Applying the Mathematics

In 13 and 14, use this information. The number of representatives each state has in the U.S. Congress depends on the population of the state. Below are the numbers of representatives from each state in the 107th Congress (1995–96).

7	1	6	4	52	6	6	1	23	11
2	2	20	10	5	4	6	7	2	8
10	16	8	5	9	1	3	2	2	13
3	31	12	1	19	6	5	21	2	6
1	9	30	3	1	11	9	3	9	1

13. Determine each statistic from this data set.
a. minimum **b.** maximum **c.** range

14. a. Make a frequency table showing the distribution of the number of representatives per state. The first few lines are given below.

Number of Representatives	Frequency
1 to 5	?
6 to 10	?
11 to 15	?

b. Draw a histogram to picture the table.
c. Find the median number of representatives per state.

In 15–17, use the data below on cholesterol levels from a sample of patients.

Cholesterol Level	Relative Frequency
170–179	.12
180–189	.16
190–199	.25
200–209	.15
210–219	.10
220–229	.07
230–239	.06
240–249	.05
250–259	.00
260–269	.04

15. A cholesterol level under 200 is generally desirable. What percent of this sample has a cholesterol level in the desirable range?

16. A cholesterol level from 200 to 239 is considered by some to put the patient at moderately high risk for heart attack. What percent of the patients are in this group?

17. a. Draw a histogram for these data.
b. In what direction is this data set skewed?

Review

18. Consider the data from Questions 13 and 14 on page 44.
a. Find the five-number summary for the data on number of U.S. representatives per state.
b. Draw a box plot of this data set. *(Lesson 1-4)*

19. For a data set with 25 elements, rank-ordered in descending order, which number in the data set is at the 12th percentile? *(Lesson 1-4)*

20. Let $p_1 = 2, p_2 = 3, p_3 = 5, p_4 = 7$, and $p_5 = 11$. Show that
$\sum_{i=1}^{5} (p_i^2) \neq \left(\sum_{i=1}^{5} p_i\right)^2$. *(Lesson 1-3)*

21. The mean height of the 25 students in Mr. Kolowski's 3rd grade class is 121 cm, and the mean height of the 20 students in Miss Jackson's 2nd grade class is 116 cm. Find the mean height of the combined group of 45 students. *(Lesson 1-3)*

22. In 1995, the National Association of Home Builders reported that the mean and median prices of new homes built in the United States were $158,700 and $133,900. Which is likely to be the mean and which the median price? Give a reason for your answer. *(Lesson 1-3)*

23. A statistics utility gives the following analysis of a data set.

$\Sigma x = 1362$	$\Sigma x^2 = 86924$	$Sx = 23.0237$	$\sigma x = 22.5586$	$n = 25$
$\min x = 12$	$Q_1 = 41$	$\text{Med} = 58$	$Q_3 = 59$	$\max x = 99$

a. Determine the range. **b.** Determine the mean. *(Lessons 1-2, 1-3)*

24. Give an equation of the line through (-1, -7) and (5, -8). *(Previous course)*

25. Match these graphs to their equations. Do not use a calculator.

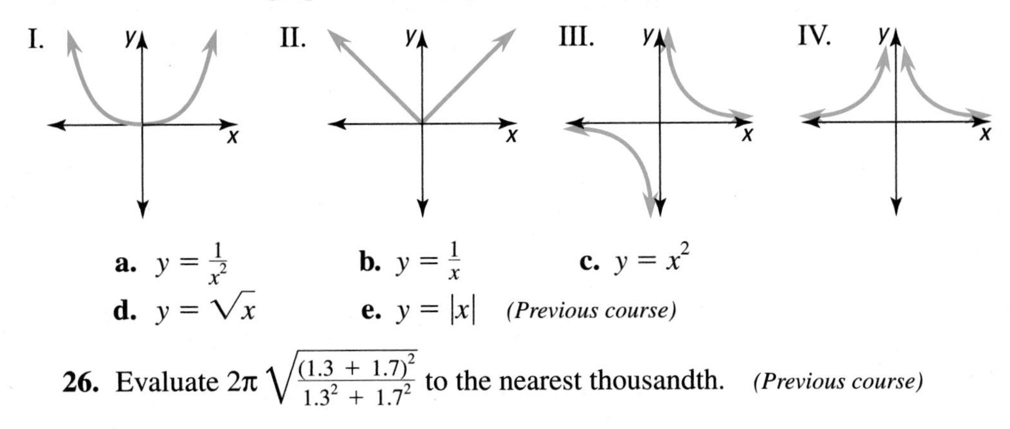

a. $y = \frac{1}{x^2}$ **b.** $y = \frac{1}{x}$ **c.** $y = x^2$
d. $y = \sqrt{x}$ **e.** $y = |x|$ *(Previous course)*

26. Evaluate $2\pi\sqrt{\frac{(1.3 + 1.7)^2}{1.3^2 + 1.7^2}}$ to the nearest thousandth. *(Previous course)*

Exploration

27. **a.** Locate a histogram from a publication.
b. Decide whether the histogram distorts or accurately represents the data.
c. Write a short paragraph summarizing what the histogram shows.

LESSON

1-6

Choosing a Good Display

What's in a name? *The name of this popular orchestra is related to the content in this lesson. A clue is on this page.*

William Playfair, who invented bar graphs, was also the first to display values of a numerical variable over time. Such data are called **time-series data** and often can be represented in a bar graph. However, drawing many bars can be tedious; and sometimes bar graphs can give false impressions.

Scatterplots and Line Graphs

With time-series data, there are two numerical variables, and it is natural to display them with *coordinate graphs*. If the points are plotted but not connected, the graph is called a **scatterplot**. If the data points are connected with line segments, the graph is called a **line graph**.

For example, consider the population of Boston for selected years from 1850 to 1990.

Year	1850	1900	1950	1960	1970	1980	1990
Population (in thousands)	140	561	801	697	641	563	574

These data are displayed here in a scatterplot, a line graph, and a bar graph.

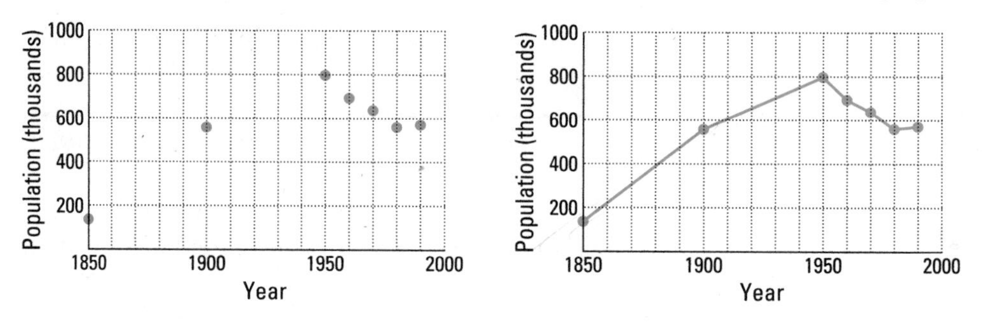

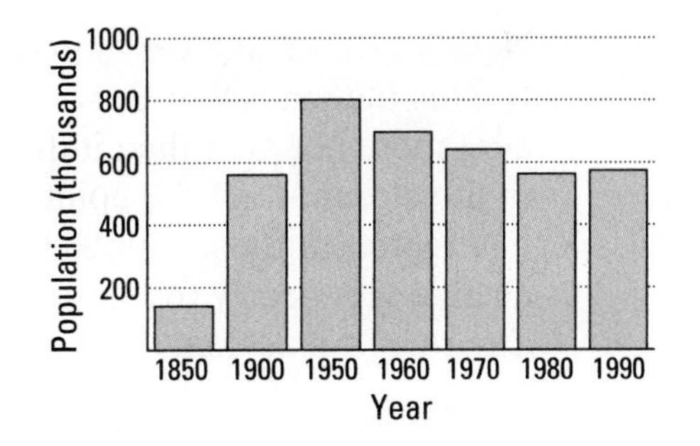

Read each graph from left to right. Notice that on each you can see that the population increased between 1850 and 1950, decreased between 1950 and 1980, and increased again between 1980 and 1990. But because the intervals on the bar graph do not represent equal intervals of time, you cannot get an accurate impression of how rapidly population changed in Boston. In contrast, on the coordinate graph both the horizontal and vertical axes are scaled evenly. Thus, on the line graph you can estimate the rate of change of population in any given interval more accurately than you can on the bar graph.

Recall that the **average rate of change** between two points is the **slope** of the segment joining them. If the points are (x_1, y_1) and (x_2, y_2), the slope m of the line through these points is given by

$$m = \frac{y_2 - y_1}{x_2 - x_1}.$$

Recall also that when a graph slants up as you read from left to right, its slope is positive; when a graph slants down as you read from left to right, its slope is negative; and when a graph is horizontal, its slope is 0. If a graph has positive slope on some interval, we say the graph is *increasing*; if a graph has negative slope on some interval, we say that the graph is *decreasing* on that interval.

Example 1

Calculate the average rate of change in the population of Boston in the following time intervals.

a. from 1900 to 1950 **b.** from 1980 to 1990

Solution

a. The endpoints of this interval are (1900, 561) and (1950, 801). The average rate of change of the population is

$$\frac{y_2 - y_1}{x_2 - x_1} = \frac{801 - 561}{1950 - 1900} = \frac{240}{50} = 4.8.$$

The unit for the numerator is thousands of people; for the denominator it is years. So between 1900 and 1950, the population increased about 4800 people per year.

b. Calculate the slope between (1980, 563) and (1990, 574).

$$\frac{574 - 563}{1990 - 1980} = \frac{11}{10} = 1.1$$

Between 1980 and 1990, the rate of change was about 1,100 people per year. The population increased by an average of 1,100 people per year.

Notice that the answer in part **a** is quite a bit larger than the answer in part **b**. This indicates that between 1900 and 1950, the population changed quite a bit more per year than it did between 1980 and 1990. However, because of the closeness of the points for 1980 and 1990 and the size of the dots that represent those points, the coordinate graph suggests that the rate of change was nearly the same. In this case, the bar graph gives a more accurate impression.

Types of Displays

The situation above shows that it is sometimes possible to display a data set in more than one way, and that sometimes one display may be easier to interpret or more accurate than another. Which display is appropriate depends on the type of data you have. *Circle graphs* should be used if you want to represent the relation between a whole set and its component parts. *Bar graphs* show the relative sizes of categories. *Box plots* display the distribution of values of a single numerical variable. Box plots are generally not used if there are fewer than 20 data points. *Histograms* display the frequency or relative frequency of intervals of values of a single numerical variable. Like box plots, histograms are generally not used with small data sets. *Stemplots* and *dotplots* are used to plot the frequency distribution of small data sets (generally not more than 20 or 30 values of a variable). *Scatterplots* and *line graphs* can only be used when there are *two* numerical variables.

Example 2

Below is a table of the number of women who participated in each varsity sport at Michigan State University in the 1994–1995 season.

Sport	Number of Varsity Athletes
Basketball	13
Cross Country	23
Field Hockey	21
Golf	14
Gymnastics	14
Soccer	27
Softball	18
Swimming	28
Tennis	8
Track (indoor)	42
Track (outdoor)	41
Volleyball	14

Which of the displays mentioned above could be used to represent these data?

Solution

There is only one numerical variable, so neither a scatterplot nor line graph can be used. Because there are only 12 data points, a box plot and a histogram should not be used either. All others are possible displays.

What Is an Effective Display?

To be effective, a display must satisfy several criteria. First, it must be technically accurate. That is, axes or scales should be labeled. Number lines and coordinate axes should have equal intervals. Second, a display should tell the story the author wants to convey. For instance, refer to the data in Example 2. Here are both a bar graph and circle graph displaying these data. Each is technically correct.

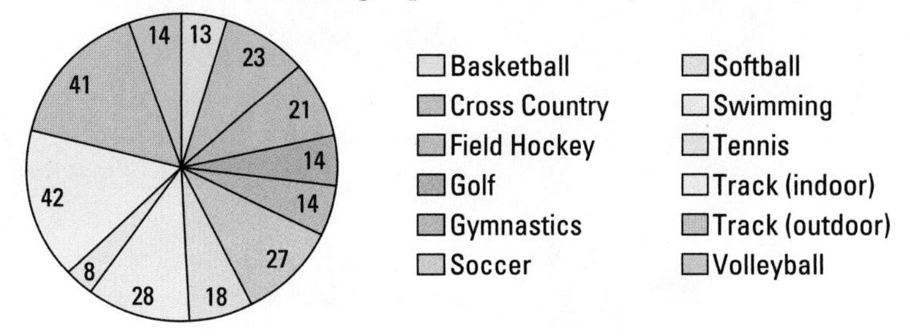

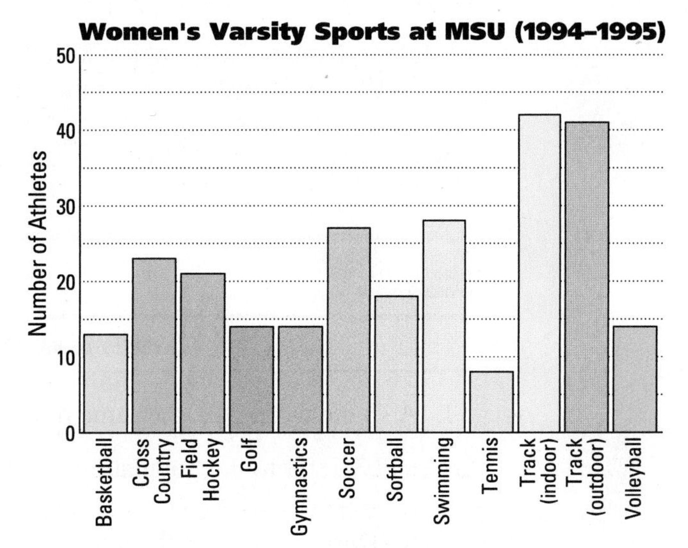

The circle graph is more effective in showing how many athletes are in each sport compared to all women's sports. From the bar graph it is easier to compare the number of women participating in each sport.

Using Displays to Compare Data Sets

Below is a table of the number of men participating in varsity sports at Michigan State University in the 1994–1995 school year. These data are displayed in the circle graph on page 50.

Sport	Number of Varsity Athletes	Sport	Number of Varsity Athletes	Sport	Number of Varsity Athletes
Baseball	33	Gymnastics	17	Swimming	25
Basketball	14	Golf	14	Tennis	13
Cross Country	24	Hockey	27	Track (Outdoor)	50
Fencing	10	Lacrosse	37	Track (Indoor)	48
Football	107	Soccer	26	Wrestling	27

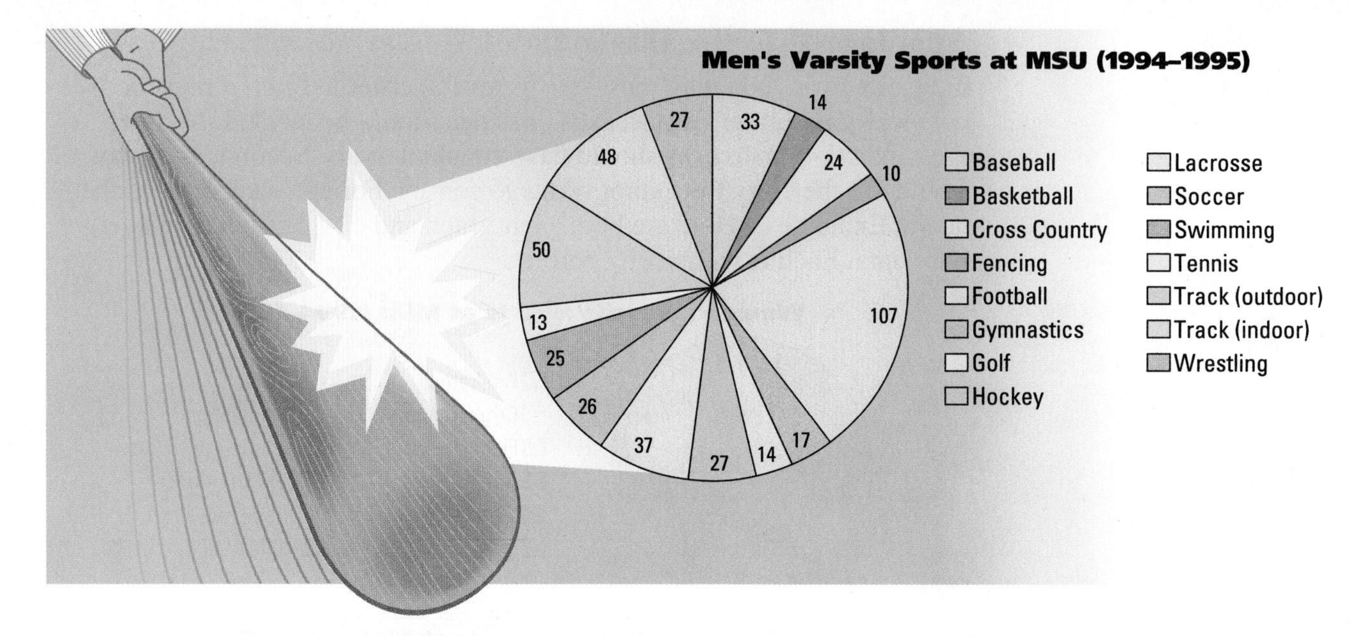

Different displays have their own advantages and disadvantages. The circle graphs do not compare the numbers of male and female athletes as well as they compare percents. In contrast, the tables compare numbers, not percents. You are asked to comment on bar graphs in the Questions.

QUESTIONS

Covering the Reading

1. A single word with the same meaning as *average rate of change* is __?__.

In 2 and 3, refer to the populations of Boston given in the lesson.

2. **a.** Find the average rate of change in population between 1850 and 1900.
b. During which of the intervals—1850 to 1900, 1900 to 1950, or 1980 to 1990—did the population of Boston increase most rapidly?

3. **a.** State one ten-year interval in which the average rate of change of population was negative.
b. Calculate that rate of change.

In 4–9, match each characteristic with one or more types of graphs.

4. Shows individual data points
5. May be used for one-variable data sets
6. Displays relation of parts to whole
7. Shows five-number summary
8. Displays distribution of data
9. Shows time-series data

a. Box plot
b. Stemplot
c. Scatterplot
d. Line graph
e. Histogram
f. Dotplot
g. Bar graph
h. Circle graph

10. The graph below shows the minimum wage in the United States when it changed from 1961 to 1997. (Source: Bureau of Labor Statistics)

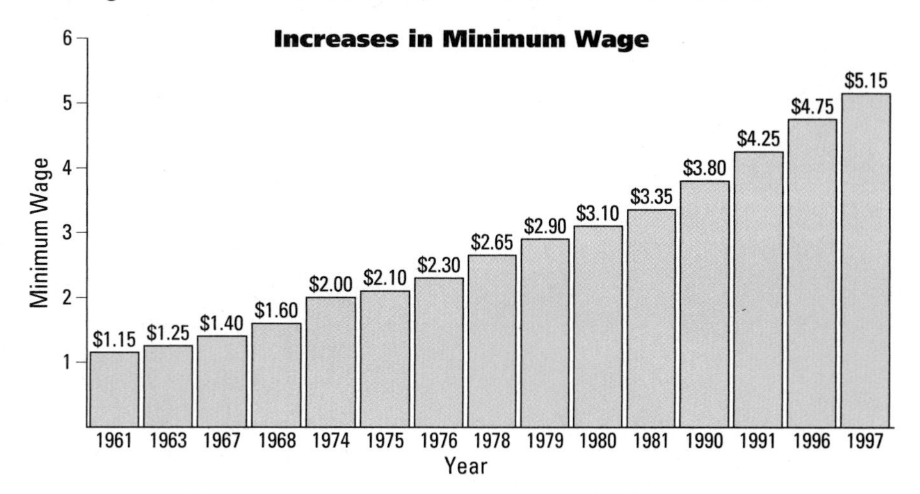

a. Use the data in the bar graph to draw a scatterplot.

b. What differences are seen in the scatterplot compared to the bar graph? Which gives a more accurate picture of the changes in the minimum wage over this time period?

11. a. Construct a bar graph of the number of men participating in various varsity sports at Michigan State University in the1994–1995 school year.

b. Explain whether the display in part **a** and the bar graph in the lesson effectively compare men's and women's participation in varsity sports at MSU in 1994–95.

Applying the Mathematics

12. A restaurant asked 100 customers to rate the quality of its food and the quality of its service on a scale from 1 to 5, with 5 being excellent and 1 being unsatisfactory. A frequency table for the ratings is shown below.

	1 Unsatisfactory	2 Fair	3 Satisfactory	4 Good	5 Excellent
Quality of Food	3	16	20	42	19
Quality of Service	10	24	31	30	5

a. Find the mean and median ratings for quality of food and for quality of service.

b. Display the results of the survey in a clear and convincing graph.

In 13 and 14, use the data below, indicating the number of motor vehicles registered per 1000 persons by state. Figures have been rounded to the nearest whole number.

WY	1187	ME	829	LA	738
SD	1121	MN	821	AZ	733
MT	1117	IN	818	CA	731
ND	1039	AK	818	TX	728
TN	975	GA	816	MD	718
IA	971	AL	811	NJ	718
ID	930	DE	795	UT	718
NE	892	CT	791	RI	695
NM	879	MI	782	KY	693
OR	865	MO	777	IL	691
OK	857	NC	772	PA	688
NH	853	KS	758	NV	678
CO	851	MS	758	HI	654
WA	839	WI	756	MA	638
OH	839	FL	741	AR	630
VT	839	WV	740	NY	600
VA	835	SC	739		

Source: *The World Almanac of the U.S.A.*

13. Make a relative frequency table and histogram for the data using ten equal intervals.

14. Make one other display—a box plot, stemplot, circle graph, or scatterplot—that you believe also effectively presents these data.

In 15 and 16, consider the table and graph below, showing expenditures for magazine advertising from 1990 to 1993. (Source: *Statistical Abstract of the United States 1995*)

Expenditures for Magazine Advertising (millions of dollars)

	1990	1991	1992	1993
A = Apparel, footwear, and accessories	428	419	496	511
C = Computers, office equipment	283	291	354	367
F = Food and food products	444	437	459	468

Expenditures for Magazine Advertising

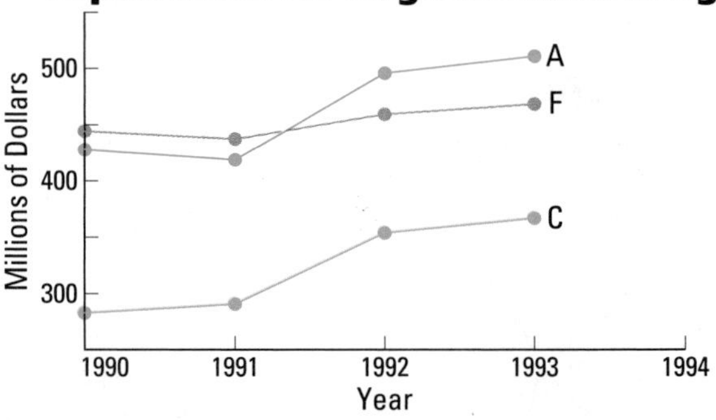

15. *Multiple choice.* During which of these intervals were the advertising expenditures for computers and office equipment decreasing?

(a) 1990–1991 (b) 1991–1992
(c) 1992–1993 (d) none of the above

16. a. Find the average rate of change of advertising expenditures for food and food products from 1990 to 1993.

b. Suppose that you expect expenditures for 1994 to 1996 to follow the same trend as from 1990 to 1993. Which category would you predict to have the greatest expenditures in 1996? Justify your answer.

Review

17. The frequency diagram below shows the responses of 100 people to the question "How many pairs of shoes do you own?" *(Lessons 1-3, 1-5)*

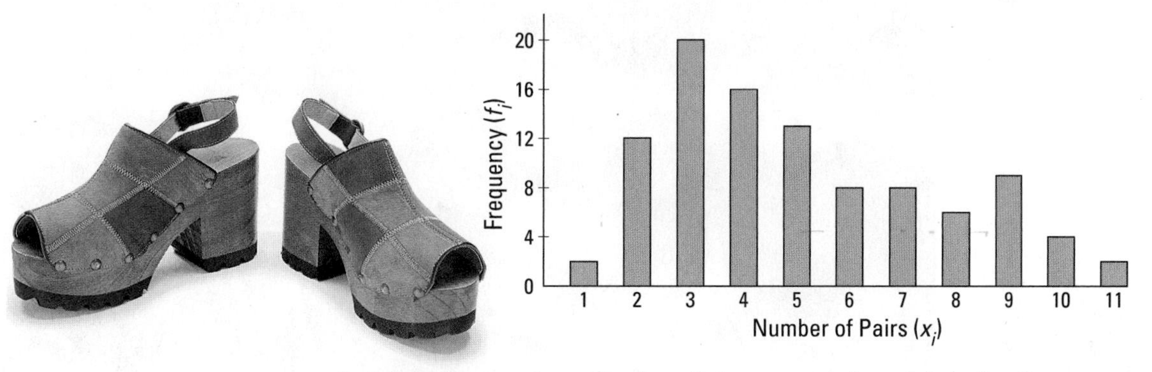

Let i = the number of pairs of shoes owned, and f_i = the frequency of that number.

a. What value of i is the mode?

b. Estimate f_5.

c. Evaluate $\sum_{i=1}^{11} f_i$.

d. What does the quantity $\dfrac{\sum_{i=1}^{11} (i f_i)}{\sum_{i=1}^{11} f_i}$ represent?

18. *Multiple choice.* Which expression equals the mean of n data values? *(Lesson 1-3)*

(a) $\frac{1}{x}\sum_{i=1}^{n} x_i$ (b) $\frac{1}{n}\sum_{i=1}^{n} x_{n-1}$ (c) $\frac{1}{n}\sum_{i=1}^{n} x_i$ (d) $\frac{1}{x_i}\sum_{i=1}^{n} n$

19. Suppose 10 students each toss a coin 40 times and record the number of heads which occurred. If the mean number of heads obtained per student is 18.2, find the total number of times the coins came up heads. *(Lesson 1-3)*

20. Consider the data set $\{c, -3c, 7c, 2c, 6c, -c\}$, for $c > 0$. Find each.

a. range **b.** median **c.** mean *(Lessons 1-2, 1-3)*

Exploration

21. Find a graph in a newspaper or magazine. Display the same data using a different kind of graph. Write a brief critique explaining the strengths and weaknesses of each graph.

LESSON

1-7

Variance and Standard Deviation

Participation in women's varsity sports sponsored by the NCAA rose from 92,778 in 1991 to 123,207 in 1996; that is an increase of 32.8% over five years.

Consider the dot frequency distributions below with the heights of the ten players on two women's college basketball teams.

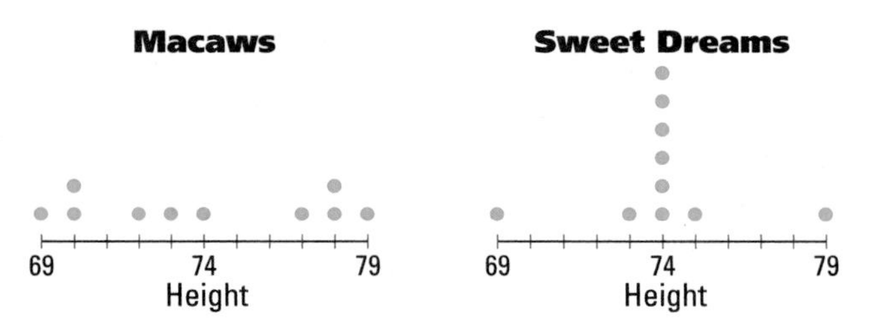

Each team has a mean height of 74". In this way the heights are quite similar. However, although the ranges are equal ($79 - 69 = 10$ in each case), the spread of the heights is different in each distribution. The heights of the Macaws seem more spread out than those of the Sweet Dreams.

The interquartile range, which uses the median as the measure of center, could be used as a measure of spread, but there are too few numbers to make percentiles reasonable. Two other measures of spread, which describe the spread of the scores in relation to the mean, are the *variance* and *standard deviation*.

Both the variance and standard deviation are calculated from the **deviation**, or difference of each data value from the mean. The variance is roughly the average of the squared deviations. The **standard deviation** is the square root of the variance. Because each of these measures is based on the mean, they are used only when it makes sense to calculate a mean.

Calculating the Variance and Standard Deviation

Here is an algorithm for calculating the variance and standard deviation for a data set with n numbers. Statistics utilities do all this automatically.

1. Calculate the mean of the data.
2. Find the deviation (difference) of each value from the mean.
3. Square each deviation and add the squares.
4. Divide the sum of squared deviations by $n - 1$. This is the variance.
5. Take the square root of the variance. This is the standard deviation.

Example 1

Find the variance and standard deviation for the heights of the Macaws.

Solution

To find the variance and standard deviation by hand it often helps to organize the work as follows.

1. Write the heights in a column. Find the mean by adding these numbers and dividing by 10.
2. In the second column record the result of subtracting the mean from each height. Some deviations are positive; others, negative or zero.
3. Square each deviation and record each result in the third column.
4. Add the squares of the deviations.
5. Divide the sum of the squared deviations by $n - 1$, in this case 9, to obtain the variance.
6. Find the square root of the variance to get the standard deviation.

Results of these steps are shown below.

	Height	Deviation	Square of deviation
	69	-5	25
	70	-4	16
	70	-4	16
	72	-2	4
	73	-1	1
	74	0	0
	77	3	9
	78	4	16
	78	4	16
	79	5	25
Total	740		128

The mean is $\frac{740}{10} = 74$ in., the variance is $\frac{128}{9} \approx 14.2$ in^2, and the standard deviation is $\sqrt{14.2} \approx 3.77$ in.

Notice that the unit for the variance is the square of the unit for the original variable, but the unit for standard deviation is the same as that of the original variable.

The variance and standard deviation can be described with Σ-notation. Recall that for a data set with numbers $\{x_1, x_2, x_3, \ldots, x_n\}$, the mean $\bar{x}$ is

$$\bar{x} = \frac{\sum_{i=1}^{n} x_i}{n}.$$

For the same set of data, each deviation from the mean can be written as $x_i - \bar{x}$, and the square of the deviation as $(x_i - \bar{x})^2$. Thus, the variance and standard deviation are defined as follows.

Definition

Let $\bar{x}$ be the mean of the set $\{x_1, x_2, \ldots, x_n\}$. Then the **variance** s^2 and **standard deviation** s are given by

$$s^2 = \frac{\sum_{i=1}^{n} (x_i - \bar{x})^2}{n - 1} \text{ and } s = \sqrt{\frac{\sum_{i=1}^{n} (x_i - \bar{x})^2}{n - 1}}.$$

Example 2

Use the definition above to calculate the variance s^2 and standard deviation s for the heights of the Sweet Dreams.

Solution

Follow the same steps used in Example 1. In the table below, column i labels the individual whose height is used. The symbols x_i, $x_i - \bar{x}$, and $(x_i - \bar{x})^2$ represent the height, deviation from the mean, and the square of the deviation, respectively.

i	x_i	$x_i - \bar{x}$	$(x_i - \bar{x})^2$
1	69	-5	25
2	73	-1	1
3	74	0	0
4	74	0	0
5	74	0	0
6	74	0	0
7	74	0	0
8	74	0	0
9	75	1	1
10	79	5	25

Total $\sum_{i=1}^{10} x_i = 740$ $\sum_{i=1}^{10} (x_i - \bar{x})^2 = 52$

Again the mean $\bar{x} = \frac{\sum_{i=1}^{10} x_i}{10} = \frac{740}{10} = 74$ inches.

The variance $s^2 = \frac{\sum_{i=1}^{n} (x_i - \bar{x})^2}{n - 1} = \frac{52}{10 - 1} = 5.\bar{7}$ square inches.

The standard deviation $s = \sqrt{\frac{\sum_{i=1}^{n} (x_i - \bar{x})^2}{n - 1}} = \sqrt{5.\bar{7}} \approx 2.40$ inches.

Notice that when deviations are squared, values of data farther from the mean contribute more to the variance than values close to the mean. For instance, a height of 79 contributes $(79 - 74)^2 = 5^2 = 25$ to the sum of squared deviations, but 75 contributes only $(75 - 74)^2 = 1^2 = 1$. Notice also that the heights of the Macaws differ more from the mean than the heights of the Sweet Dreams differ from the mean. As a result, the variance and standard deviation for the data about the Macaws are greater than the corresponding statistics about the Sweet Dreams. In general, groups with more data close to the mean have smaller standard deviations than groups with more data far from the mean.

Below are three relative frequency distributions of observations each with mean 15 but different standard deviations. Each bar represents the percent of observations falling within an interval containing its left endpoint. For example, in histogram C the tallest bar contains values x such that $2.5 \leq x < 7.5$. The three histograms illustrate the fact that the more the data vary from the mean, the larger the standard deviation.

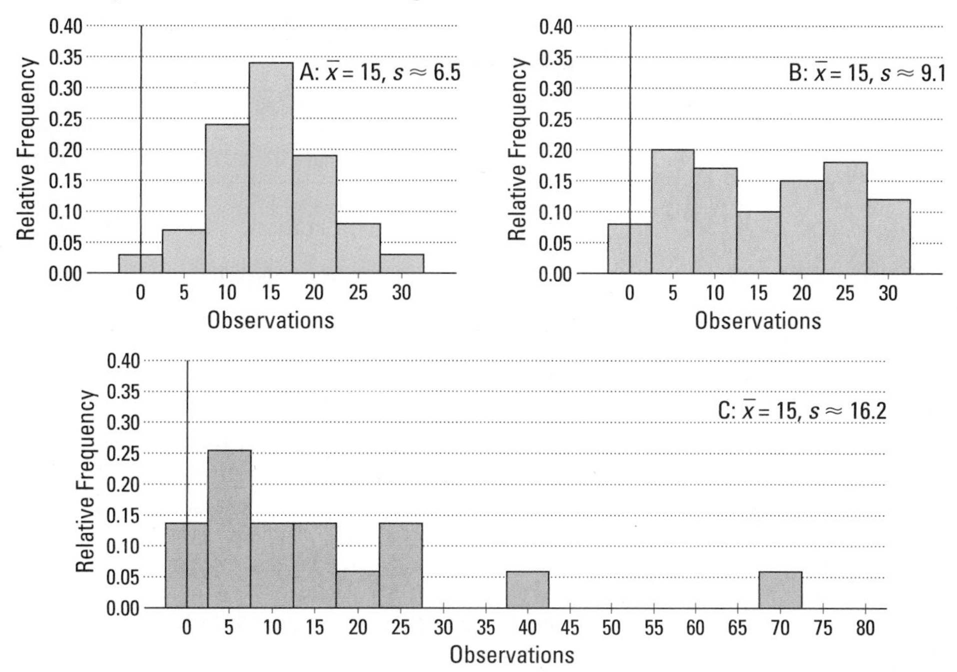

Other Formulas for Variance and Standard Deviation

In some books, $s^2 = \frac{\sum_{i=1}^{n} (x_i - \bar{x})^2}{n - 1}$ is called the *sample variance*, and the symbol σ^2 (σ is the lower-case Greek letter sigma) is used to represent the **population variance**, where $\sigma^2 = \frac{\sum_{i=1}^{n} (x_i - \bar{x})^2}{n}$. Note that the denominator in the population variance is n, rather than $n - 1$, so the population standard deviation (represented by the symbol σ) is found using this formula: $\sigma = \sqrt{\sigma^2} = \sqrt{\frac{\sum_{i=1}^{n} (x_i - \bar{x})^2}{n}}$.

Because of these different formulas, some statistics utilities have two sets of symbols: s^2 and s, and σ^2 and σ. Other calculators and programs use only one set of formulas for variance and standard deviation. Because we deal mostly with samples in this book, unless stated otherwise, we use the formulas for sample variance and standard deviation. That is, we use $n - 1$ in the denominator, not n.

Activity

Use your calculator or statistics software to find (to the nearest tenth) the standard deviation of the following data set.

90, 80, 75, 68, 100, 92, 85, 82

If more than one standard deviation is given, record all.

You should find that the mean is 84 and both the sample and population standard deviation are between 9 and 11.

QUESTIONS

Covering the Reading

1. State whether each statistic is a measure of center or a measure of spread.
a. mean
b. range
c. variance
d. interquartile range
e. standard deviation
f. median

2. *Multiple choice.* The standard deviation of a set of scores is
(a) the sum of the deviation scores.
(b) the difference between the highest and lowest scores.
(c) the score that occurs with the greatest frequency.
(d) the average spread of the scores with respect to the mean.
(e) none of (a)–(d)

3. Use the heights of the Macaws and Sweet Dreams shown on page 54.
a. Give the difference of the means.
b. Give the difference of the ranges.
c. Give the difference of the standard deviations.
d. Explain in your own words what the differences in means and standard deviations of the heights of the Macaws and Sweet Dreams tell you about the two data sets.

In 4 and 5, find the standard deviation of each data set.

4. 4, 7, 11, 13, 15

5. 18, 19, 20, 21, 22

6. The mean score of a group of high school students on the SAT (Scholastic Aptitude Test) Verbal Section is 453.
a. Jerry's score has a deviation of -23. What is his SAT Verbal score?
b. Sam's score has a squared deviation of 289. What is his SAT Verbal score?
c. Whose score would contribute more to the variance, Jerry's or Sam's?

7. Give the formula for the population variance σ^2 used in some statistics utilities.

8. Suppose two samples have the same mean, but different standard deviations s_1 and s_2, with $s_1 < s_2$. Which sample will show more variability?

9. Refer to the Activity on page 58. State the values your calculator gives for the following.
a. sample standard deviation
b. population standard deviation

Applying the Mathematics

10. Suppose you know the distance in miles each student in a class lives from school. For this data set, state the units for each statistic.
a. mean **b.** range
c. variance **d.** standard deviation

11. Perry found the variance of a data set to be ⁻27. Why must his answer be wrong?

12. **a.** Consider the weights in kilograms of a group of teenagers. If the standard deviation is 8.2 kg, what is the variance?
b. If the variance is 20 kg^2, what is the standard deviation?

13. Use the following hypothetical frequency distributions for ACT (American College Test) scores.

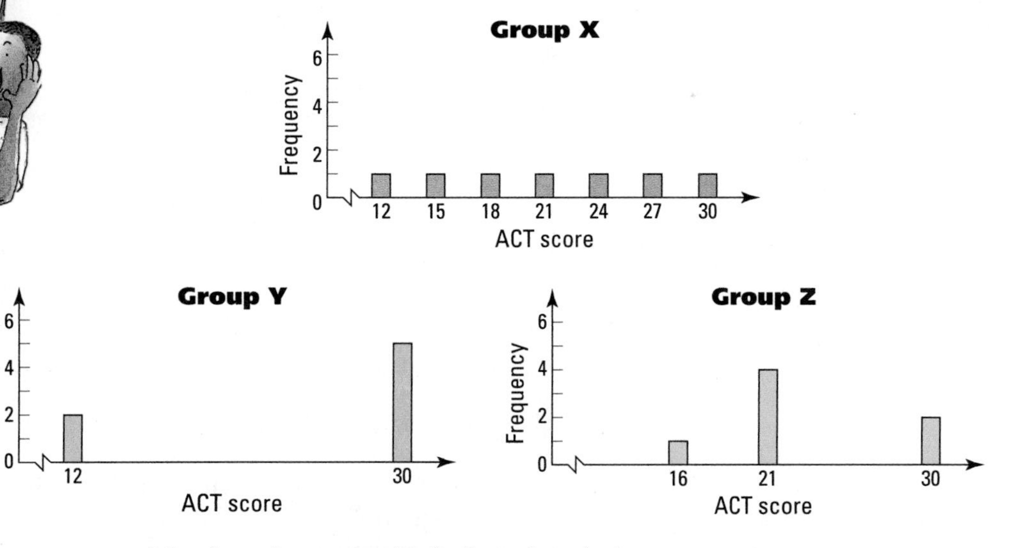

a. Match each group with its best description.
  i. consistently near the mean
  ii. very widely spread
  iii. evenly distributed.
b. Without calculating, tell which group's ACT scores have the greatest standard deviation and which have the smallest.
c. Verify your answer to part **b** with calculations.

14. In 1995, more than 1.1 million students in the United States took the SAT. On the mathematics section, $\bar{x} = 507$ and $s = 112$. Students receive scores rounded to the nearest 10. What is the interval of student scores that lie within one standard deviation of the mean?

15. a. Find the value of $\sqrt{\frac{500}{n}}$ and $\sqrt{\frac{500}{n-1}}$ for the following values of n.

i. 5 **ii.** 100 **iii.** 500

b. Make a conjecture about the values of the sample and population standard deviation formulas, as n gets larger.

In 16 and 17, use the following data for time in seconds for 20 sixth graders to run 400 meters.

Time (seconds) for 20 sixth graders to run 400 meters									
70	80	80	85	90	100	100	100	100	100
100	105	105	105	120	130	130	130	140	150

16. Find a group of five running times whose standard deviation is as small as possible.

17. Find a group of four running times whose standard deviation is larger than 25 seconds. Compute the standard deviation.

18. *Multiple choice.* A class of students is said to be *homogeneous* if the students in the class are very much alike on some measure. Here are four classes of students who were tested on a 20-point spelling test. Which class is the more homogeneous with respect to spelling?

a. $n = 20$ $\bar{x} = 15.3$ $s = 2.5$
b. $n = 25$ $\bar{x} = 12.1$ $s = 5.4$
c. $n = 18$ $\bar{x} = 11.3$ $s = 7.9$
d. $n = 30$ $\bar{x} = 10.4$ $s = 3.2$

Review

In 19 and 20, the percent of Advanced Placement Examinations in Mathematics or Computer Science taken by women is given below.

Year	1974	1979	1984	1989	1994
Percent Women	26	32	35	36	43

19. a. *Multiple choice.* Which of the following would be an appropriate graph for representing these data?
(i) box plot (ii) circle graph
(iii) histogram (iv) line graph

b. Draw such a graph, and describe trend(s) in the data. *(Lessons 1-1, 1-4, 1-5, 1-6)*

20. The total number of students taking AP Exams in Mathematics or Computer Science was about 89,000 in 1989 and about 121,000 in 1994.

a. What was the average annual increase in the number of women taking AP Exams in these areas during this period?

b. What was the average annual increase in the number of men taking these exams in this period? *(Previous course, Lesson 1-3)*

In 1893, when this photo was taken, most immigrants came by ships like the S.S. Pennland. Today, most immigrants arrive by land or air.

21. The histogram below shows how many states received the number of immigrants specified in each interval in the year 1994.

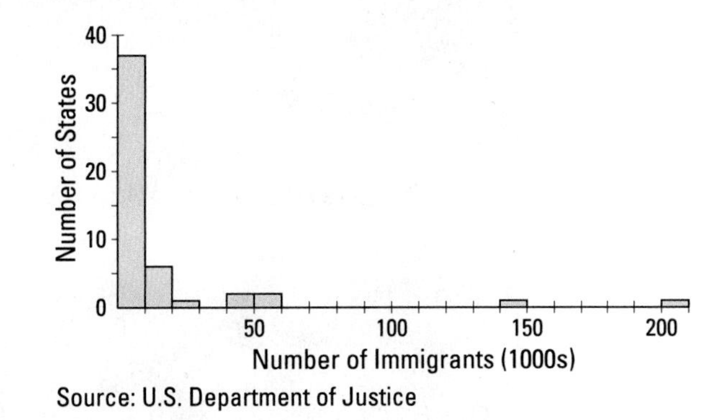

Write a short paragraph describing immigration to the 50 states in 1994. Include both specific information such as maximum, minimum, mean, or median values (when possible), and general trends such as clusters, skewness, or gaps. *(Lessons 1-2, 1-3, 1-5)*

22. Two data sets of heights of people each have minimum = 50", median = 67", and maximum = 80". One has IQR = 15"; the other has IQR = 10".

a. Draw box plots for each data set.

b. Which data set shows more variability? *(Lessons 1-3, 1-4)*

23. *Multiple choice.* $\sum_{i=1}^{n} x_i$ equals *(Lesson 1-3)*

(a) $\bar{x}$ (b) $\frac{\bar{x}}{n}$ (c) $\frac{n}{\bar{x}}$ (d) none of (a)–(c)

24. If the interval from a to b is split into n equal parts, the leftmost part is from a to $a + \frac{b-a}{n}$. Write the expression $a + \frac{b-a}{n}$ as a single fraction with denominator n. *(Previous course)*

25. Consider the graphs of $y = x^2$ and $y = |x|$.

a. Describe several ways the graphs are alike.

b. Describe several ways the graphs are different. *(Previous course)*

This stamp was issued by the Soviet Union to commemorate the 121st anniversary of the birth of P. L. Chebychev.

Exploration

26. The Russian mathematician P. L. Chebychev proved a remarkable theorem which implies that in any data set, if p is the fraction of the data that lies within k standard deviations to either side of the mean then $p \geq 1 - \frac{1}{k^2}$.

a. According to Chebychev what percent of a data set must lie within 2 standard deviations of the mean?

b. What percent must lie within 3 standard deviations?

c. Test Chebychev's theorem on a data set of your choice.

LESSON

1-8

Who Wrote The Federalist *Papers?*

We, the people. . . *Howard Chandler Christy's twenty-by-thirty-foot oil* Signing the Constitution *hangs in the Capitol. The Constitution was adopted September 1787, ratified June 1788, and in force March 1789.*

Once data are collected and organized they can be used to help answer many questions, sometimes in surprising ways. In fact, an analysis of frequency distributions helped decide the authorship of some famous documents in U.S. history, *The Federalist* papers.

The Federalist papers were written between 1787 and 1788 under the pen name "Publius" to persuade the citizens of the State of New York to ratify the Constitution. Of the 85 *Federalist* papers, 14 were known to be written by James Madison, 51 by Alexander Hamilton, and 5 by John Jay. Of the remaining 15, three were joint works, and 12 were called "disputed" because historians were unsure whether they were written by Hamilton or Madison. The dispute could not be settled by comparing the ideas in the papers, because at that time the philosophies of the men were similar.

In an attempt to identify which men had authored which of the disputed papers, in the 1960s two statisticians, Frederick Mosteller of Harvard University and David Wallace of The University of Chicago, used computers to count the occurrence of key words in documents whose authors were known. They first examined documents other than *The Federalist* papers known to have been authored by the two men: 48 papers written by Hamilton and 50 papers by Madison. Key words were chosen so that they did not reflect either author's writing style. The words were also chosen to be independent of the content of the paper being examined. For this particular study, the words chosen were 'by,' 'from,' and 'to.'

Then Mosteller and Wallace divided the counts of these key words by the number of words in the document. They reported each relative frequency as the rate per 1000. For example, if the key word 'by' occurred 32 times in a paper of 2075 words, the rate of occurrence was $32/2075 \approx 15.4/1000 =$ 15.4 occurrences per 1000 words.

The following table shows the results of their counts of the key words 'by,' 'from,' and 'to' in papers of known authorship. Take a few minutes to read the table before going on.

Frequency Distribution of Rate per Thousand Words of the Words 'by,' 'from,' and 'to' in 48 Hamilton and 50 Madison Papers

'by'			'from'			'to'		
Rate	H	M	Rate	H	M	Rate	H	M
1–3*	2		1–3*	3	3	23–26*		3
3–5	7		3–5	15	19	26–29	2	2
5–7	12	5	5–7	21	17	29–32	2	11
7–9	18	7	7–9	9	6	32–35	4	11
9–11	4	8	9–11		1	35–38	6	7
11–13	5	16	11–13		3	38–41	10	7
13–15		6	13–15		1	41–44	8	6
15–17		5				44–47	10	1
17–19		3				47–50	3	2
						50–53	1	
						53–56	1	
						56–59	1	
Totals	48	50	Totals	48	50	Totals	48	50

Source: Frederick Mosteller and David L. Wallace (1964), *Inference and Disputed Authorship: The Federalist,* Reading, MA: Addison-Wesley.
*Each interval excludes its upper endpoint. Thus a paper with a rate of exactly 3 per 1000 words would appear in the count for the 3–5 interval.

Notice that there are three pairs of frequency distributions within the table, one for each of the words 'by,' 'from,' and 'to.' Under each word there are three columns, one for the rate and one for each author (H for Hamilton and M for Madison). The asterisk (*) by the first rate for each word directs you to the footnote. The footnote explains that a rate of 1–3 means the rate was between 1 and 3 per thousand in this sense: If r is the rate per thousand, then $1 \le r < 3$.

The numbers under H and M are the frequencies among the papers of known authorship for that rate. For example, the 2 in the first H column means that two of Hamilton's papers used 'by' between 1 and 3 times per thousand. The last row shows the totals.

Overall, in the papers of known authorship the word 'by' is used much more frequently by Madison than it is by Hamilton. The rate of its occurrence seems to distinguish between the two authors. The word 'to' seems more used by Hamilton. In contrast, the use of the word 'from' does not distinguish one man's writing from the other.

Based on this information, Mosteller and Wallace compared the use of the word 'by' in the disputed *Federalist* papers to its use in the papers known to be authored by Hamilton and Madison. Below are relative frequency distributions comparing the use of the word 'by' in the Hamilton papers, the Madison papers, and the disputed papers.

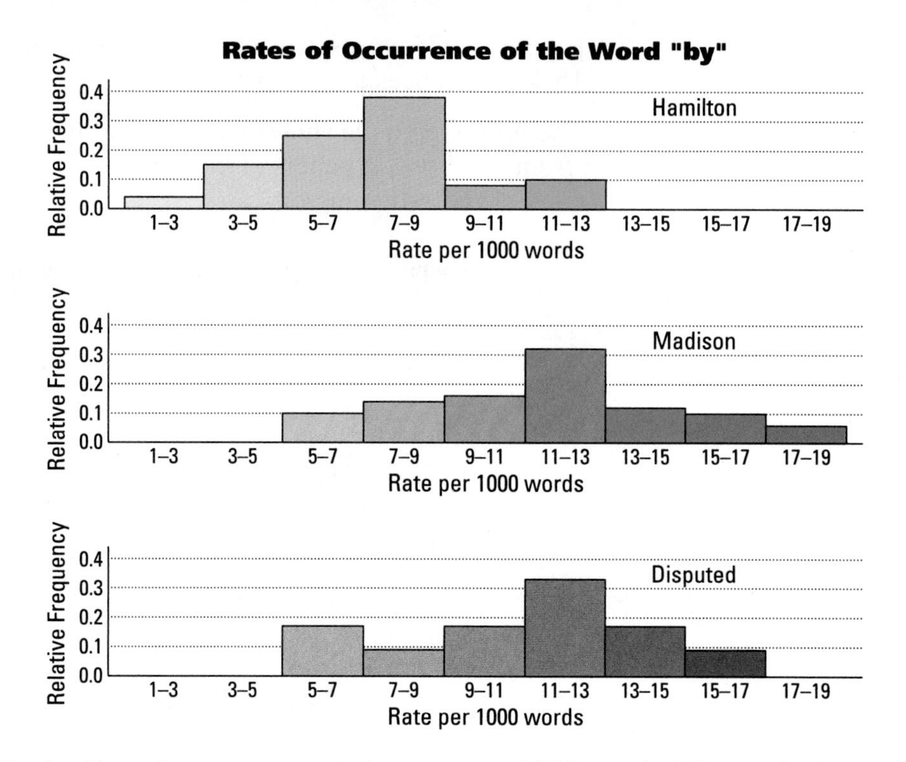

The horizontal axes represent the rates per 1000 words. The vertical axes represent the fraction of papers in each group with the given frequency. For instance, the tallest column on Madison's graph extends to about .32. This represents the 16 papers by Madison of the 50 studied which used 'by' between 11 and 13 times per thousand words.

The shape of the graph for the disputed papers is clearly more like the shape of Madison's than of Hamilton's. The median rate of occurrence of the word 'by' is 11–13 for Madison's and for the disputed papers, and the median rate is only 7–9 for Hamilton's papers. This evidence suggests that the disputed papers are Madison's. In fact, the full research study demonstrated that it is extremely likely that Madison authored 11 of the 12 disputed papers and probably the 12th as well.

Amuseing Role. *Clio, the Greek muse of history, is a subject in Jan Vermeer van Delft's painting,* The Allegory of Painting *(detail).*

Beware! Statistical reasoning is *inferential*, not deductive. That is, statistical research does not *prove* findings with certainty as in geometry or algebra. Instead, statistics gives evidence for what is very *likely*, and gives a measure for a level of confidence. For example, Mosteller and Wallace reported that for the *most* disputed paper, their evidence yields odds of 80 to 1 that the author was Madison. They called these odds strong but not overwhelming. The odds were much higher and considered to be overwhelming for the other 11 papers.

Applications of mathematics to history, such as this authorship dispute, are becoming more common. In fact, this new discipline has a name, *cliometrics*, in honor of the Greek muse of history, Clio.

QUESTIONS

Covering the Reading

Alexander Hamilton

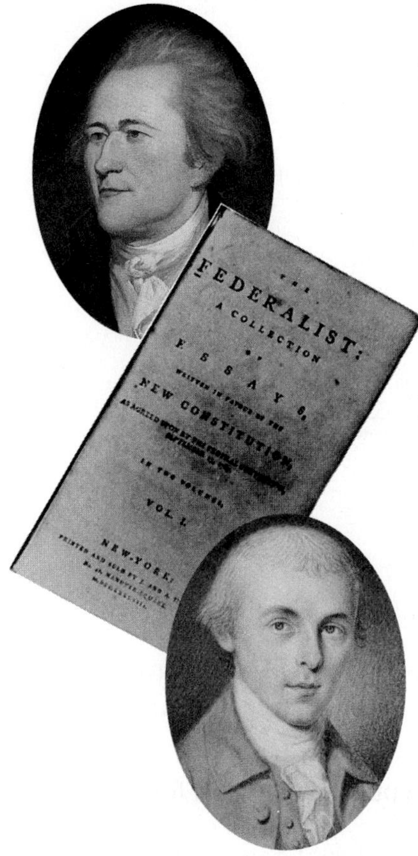

James Madison

1. Why were *The Federalist* papers written?

In 2–4, refer to the table on page 63.

2. In how many of Madison's papers was the word 'from' used at a rate between 3 and 5 words per 1000?

3. What does the 50 in the lower right corner represent?

4. *Multiple choice.* On the 'to' chart in the first column, a rate per thousand of 38–41 means the rate r is in which interval?
(a) $38 < r < 41$ (b) $38 < r \leq 41$
(c) $38 \leq r \leq 41$ (d) $38 \leq r < 41$

In 5 and 6, refer to the histograms on page 64.

5. In what percent of the disputed papers was 'by' used 5–7 times per thousand?

6. Would you expect more occurrences of the word 'by' in a 1000-word essay by Hamilton or by Madison? Why?

7. *Multiple choice.* Which best expresses one of the populations and sample sets used by Mosteller and Wallace?
(a) A sample of 48 papers by Hamilton was used to represent the population of all of Hamilton's writing.
(b) A sample of 50 papers by Madison was used to represent the population of disputed documents.
(c) A sample of 12 disputed papers was used to represent the population of all of Madison's writing.

8. *True or false.* Statistical reasoning proves its findings with absolute certainty.

9. What is the name of the discipline which applies mathematics to history?

Review

In this lesson there are no Applying the Mathematics questions. Instead, to help you prepare for the Chapter Test, there are more Review questions than in other lessons.

10. Imagine a shoe store with 20 salespersons. Suppose that on a particular day Mr. Webb sold 30 pairs of shoes and that this was the average number sold for all salespersons. Miss Feet sold 8 pairs less than the average and Ms. Slipper sold 40 pairs of shoes.
a. Which salesperson had sales which contribute the most to variance among salespersons?
b. Which salesperson had sales which contribute the least to variance among salespersons? *(Lesson 1-7)*

Porcineality. *Pigs are classified as growing pigs (40–125 lb) and finishing pigs (over 125 lb). The term "hog" generally describes an animal approaching market weight (about 230 lb).*

11. Suppose a data set consists of weights in pounds of hogs shown at a county fair. State the unit for each statistic. *(Lessons 1-2, 1-3, 1-7)*

a. mean **b.** range
c. variance **d.** standard deviation

12. Complete the analogy: Interquartile range is to median as standard deviation is to __?__. *(Lessons 1-3, 1-4, 1-7)*

13. **a.** Calculate the mean and standard deviation for the set 2, 2, 3, 4, 4, 5, 6, 6.
b. Make up another data set of eight numbers using only 2, 3, 4, 5, or 6 which has the same mean but a smaller standard deviation. *(Lessons 1-3, 1-7)*

In 14 and 15, use the table below with the average monthly high temperature (T) and average monthly precipitation (P) for Jakarta, Indonesia, and Sydney, Australia. (Source: *The Weather Handbook*)

		J	F	M	A	M	J	J	A	S	O	N	D
Jakarta	T (°F)	84	84	86	87	87	87	87	87	88	87	86	85
	P (in.)	12	12	8	6	5	4	3	2	3	4	6	8
Sydney	T (°F)	78	78	76	71	66	61	60	63	67	71	74	77
	P (in.)	4	4	5	5	5	5	5	3	3	3	3	3

14. **a.** Find the median, first, and third quartiles of the temperature data of each city.
b. Which city shows the least variability in temperature during the year?
c. Make two box plots using the same scale to illustrate the temperature data. *(Lessons 1-3, 1-4)*

15. **a.** Find the mean and standard deviation of the precipitation data for each city.
b. Which city shows the least variability in rainfall during the year?
c. Make two histograms using the same scale to illustrate the precipitation data. *(Lessons 1-3, 1-4, 1-5, 1-7)*

16. Examine these box plots of the ages at which people received Academy Awards ("Oscars") for best actor or actress between 1971 and 1995.

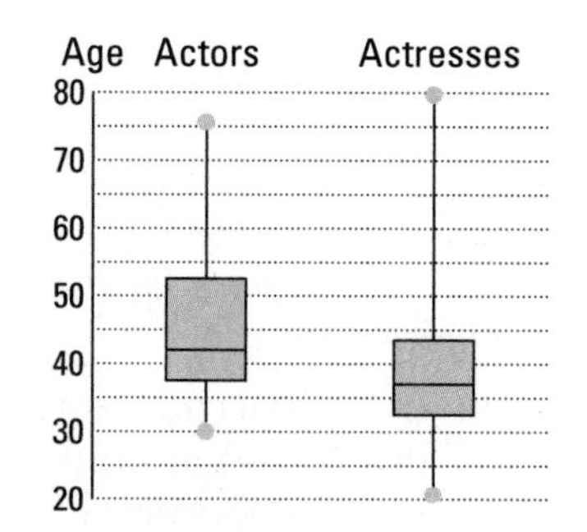

a. Estimate the median age of the men who won Oscars for Best Actor.
b. The youngest and oldest men to receive Oscars for Best Actor during this period were Richard Dreyfuss at age 30 and Henry Fonda at age 76. What is the range of ages for Best Actor?

c. The five-number summary for the data on actresses is: 21, 32.5, 37, 43.5, 80. The youngest and oldest actresses to receive Oscars in this period were Marlee Matlin in 1986 at age 21, and Jessica Tandy in 1989 at age 80. Which, if either of these, is an outlier using the $1.5 \times$ IQR method?

d. Do gender differences exist in the ages at which men and women win Oscars? Write a short paragraph using statistics to justify your answer. *(Lessons 1-2, 1-3, 1-4)*

17. Prove that $\frac{1}{8}\sum_{i=1}^{8} x_i = \sum_{i=1}^{8} \frac{x_i}{8}$. *(Lesson 1-3)*

18. Consider the line with equation $y + 5 = 2(x + 4)$. *(Previous course)*

a. Show that $y = 2x + 3$ is an equation for the same line.

b. What are the slope and y-intercept of the line?

c. Graph the line.

19. Find an equation of the line passing through (4, 0) and (-2, 12). *(Previous course)*

20. If the interval from x to y is split into n equal parts, there are $n - 1$ endpoints between x and y. *(Previous course)*

1st endpoint | 3rd endpoint

x | 2nd endpoint | n – 1st endpoint | y

a. Give the coordinates of the first, second, and third endpoints.

b. Write these coordinates as single fractions with denominator n.

Exploration

21. Refer to the data for Questions 14 and 15.

a. Make a scatterplot of month versus temperature in Sydney. Plot month on the horizontal axis. Repeat the months to show a two-year cycle.

b. Describe the pattern(s) you observe.

c. What physical factors account for these patterns?

d. Plot the temperatures for Jakarta on the same scatterplot.

e. What physical factor(s) account for the relatively constant temperature in Jakarta?

Sydney, Australia

Jakarta, Indonesia

PROJECTS

1

CHAPTER ONE

A project presents an opportunity for you to extend your knowledge of a topic related to the material of this chapter. You should allow more time for a project than you do for a typical homework question.

1 Graphing and Interpreting Statistical Data

Obtain a copy of either a recent edition of the *Statistical Abstract of the United States* or an almanac. Pick some data that you find interesting or surprising (or both) that are presented in a table. Design a poster, at least 22" × 28" in dimensions, that interprets the data in the table, including some displays to support your interpretation. Make sure that you choose a suitable headline for your poster that will attract people's attention.

2 Statistical Analysis of Texts

Obtain three samples of text; one of them from something you have written recently and two of them chosen from the list below.

- a book intended for beginning readers
- some pages from *The Complete Works of William Shakespeare*
- yesterday's newspaper
- the first chapter of *Functions, Statistics, and Trigonometry*
- another school textbook you are now using

Choose a common word, such as 'to,' 'by,' 'of,' or 'from,' and count the number of occurrences of the word in your three samples. Make a relative frequency graph of your results. Present your results in a display to highlight the similarities and differences between texts. Can you conclude whether your writing style is closer to one of these styles? Why or why not?

3 Local Land Use Survey

a. Contact your local planning commission (city, township, county, parish) for data about your area. Request resources to answer questions like those suggested below, or for some other questions on topics of interest to you.

  i. For each 100 (or 1000) acres devoted to residential development, how many acres must be set aside for recreational facilities, school sites, streets, utility easements, sidewalks, etc.?

  ii. How many parking spaces are required for an office building, an apartment complex, a shopping mall, or a school?

  iii. For the area you are investigating, what percent of space is allocated for residential, commercial, agricultural, industrial, educational, and transportation purposes?

b. Prepare several displays of the data you collect. Make the displays attractive so that people will want to read them.

c. What conclusions or recommendations can you make from your data or display?

4 Automobile Survey

What automobiles are most popular in your area?

a. Go to a large parking lot (near a shopping center, office building, or school) and classify at least 60 automobiles by the following criteria: style (van, truck, limousine, sports car, and so on), color, and manufacturer.

b. Report the results with at least three tables or displays.

c. Write a paragraph or two summarizing and interpreting your findings.

d. Describe the differences that might have resulted if you had collected your data at a different location (e.g., senior citizens center, executive office garage, used car lot) or at a different time (church lot on Sunday, movies on budget night).

5 Statistical Experiments

a. Perform one of the experiments listed below.

  i. Toss a group of ten pennies 100 times. Count the number of heads in each toss.

  ii. Toss six dice 100 times. Count the number of evens in each set.

  iii. Toss three dice 100 times. Count the number of times each sum appears.

b. Make at least three histograms using different-sized intervals on the horizontal axis (for example, by 1s, by 5s, by 10s). Describe the different impressions resulting from the various choices of intervals. Which histogram do you think is most effective? Why?

6 Class Survey

(This project is appropriate for a small group.) Compile a database of information about the members of your mathematics class.

a. Ask each person to complete an information sheet for the following data. Where appropriate, use metric measurements (that is, lengths in centimeters).

gender
age
height
grade in sc
eye color
number of siblings
circumference of wrist
circumference of neck
pulse rate
arm span (fingertip to fingertip)
hand span
foot length

b. Construct a computer or calculator file with the class database. The database will be used again in later chapters.

c. Choose at least three variables. Use a statistics utility to display and summarize the data. For each variable decide which type of display is most appropriate (box plot, stemplot, circle graph, bar graph, etc.). Whenever appropriate, calculate statistics such as mean, median, standard deviation, percentiles, and range.

d. Write a short paragraph describing a "typical" student in your class in terms of the variables you analyzed. For numerical variables, this will involve interpreting both the center and spread of the distributions.

e. Find a variable whose value differs quite a bit by gender. Find a variable whose value doesn't differ much by gender. Justify your conclusions with numerical measures or displays.

SUMMARY

Statistics is the branch of mathematics dealing with collecting, organizing, displaying, analyzing, and interpreting numerical information. Samples are frequently used to study the characteristics of large populations of interest. It is important that the samples are truly representative of the population they are chosen from, so that statistical findings can be generalized. Random selection is a common method used to avoid biases.

Data can be organized and displayed in several ways, including tables, graphs, and stem-and-leaf diagrams. Pie charts, bar graphs, line graphs, scatterplots, box plots, dotplots, and histograms are the kinds of graphs studied in this chapter.

Summary statistics help give a quick impression of a data set and allow for comparison of sets. Measures such as the mean, median (and sometimes the mode) indicate "centers" of the data. Measures of spread include the range, interquartile range, variance, and standard deviation. The five-number summary, which includes percentiles, is another way to summarize the center and spread in a data set. The symbol for summation, Σ (sigma), provides a short way to express formulas for several of these measures.

VOCABULARY

Below are the most important terms and phrases for this chapter. You should be able to give a general description and a specific example of each and a precise definition for those marked with an asterisk (*).

Lesson 1-1
statistics
*data, datum
variable
*population
*sample
survey, census
randomly
bar graph
circle graph
pie chart

Lesson 1-2
stem-and-leaf diagram
stemplot
distribution
stem, leaf
*maximum
*minimum
*range
cluster, gap
outlier
back-to-back stemplot
*frequency
dotplot, dot-frequency diagram

Lesson 1-3
statistics utility
measures of center
*mean, $\bar{x}$
*median
*mode
*Σ (sigma)
summation notation
sigma-notation
Σ-notation
index
measures of central tendency

Lesson 1-4
rank-ordered
ascending order
spread
quartile
first (lower) quartile
second (middle) quartile
third (upper) quartile
*interquartile range (IQR)
five-number summary
*percentile
box plot, box-and-whiskers plot

Lesson 1-5
histogram
frequency histogram
relative frequency histogram
skewed

Lesson 1-6
time-series data
coordinate graph
scatterplot
line graph
*average rate of change, slope
increasing, decreasing

Lesson 1-7
*variance
*standard deviation
deviation
sample standard deviation, s
sample variance, s^2
population standard deviation, σ
population variance, σ^2

PROGRESS SELF-TEST

Take this test as would take a test in class. You will need graph paper, a calculator, and a statistics utility. Then check the test yourself using the solutions at the back of the book.

In 1–3, refer to the following table from the *Statistical Abstract of the United States 1995*.

1. What information is conveyed by the number 10.2 in the first line of the table?
2. Between which two consecutive years in the table did the rate for divorced men remarrying decrease the most?
3. Describe one trend in the marriage rate for single women in the period 1970 to 1988.

Marriage Rates[1] of Men and Women by Previous Marital Status

Year	Women			Men		
	Single	Divorced	Widowed	Single	Divorced	Widowed
1970	93.4	123.3	10.2	80.4	204.5	40.6
1975	75.9	117.2	8.3	61.5	189.8	40.4
1980	66.0	91.3	6.7	54.7	142.1	32.2
1985	61.5	81.8	5.7	50.1	121.6	27.7
1986	59.7	79.5	5.5	49.1	117.8	26.8
1987	58.9	80.7	5.4	48.8	115.7	26.1
1988	58.4	78.6	5.3	48.3	109.7	25.1

[1]Rate per 1,000 population 15 years old and over in specified group.

4. Using the graph below, which shows the temperature (in degrees Celsius) of an apartment on a warm summer day, find the average rate of change of temperature between 6 A.M. and 4 P.M.

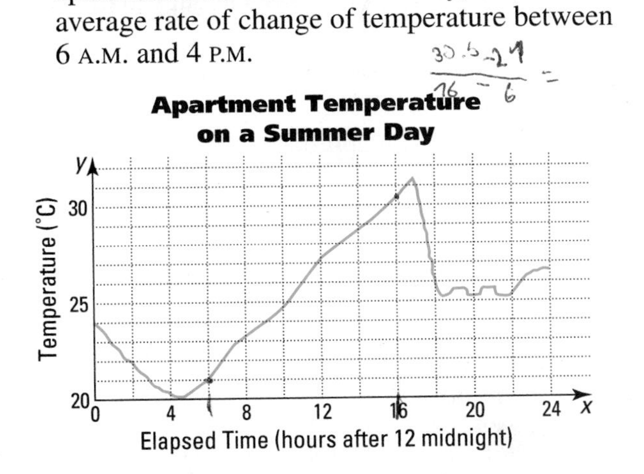

In 5–7, Jill tossed eight pennies a number of times and constructed the following frequency distribution of the number of heads observed each time.

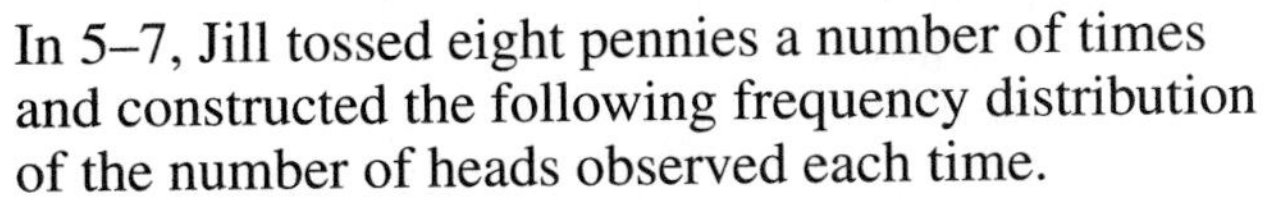

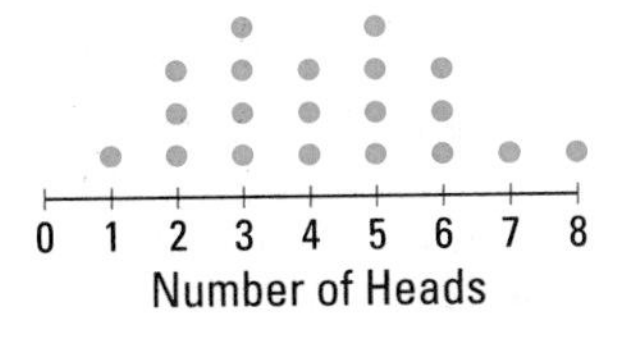

5. Find the median number of heads in the tosses.

6. In Jill's experiment, what percentile rank should be assigned to the event of getting three heads in a toss of eight coins?
7. Explain how to convert the graph to display a relative frequency distribution.
8. Each of the distributions below has the same mean. Which has the greater standard deviation? Justify your answer.

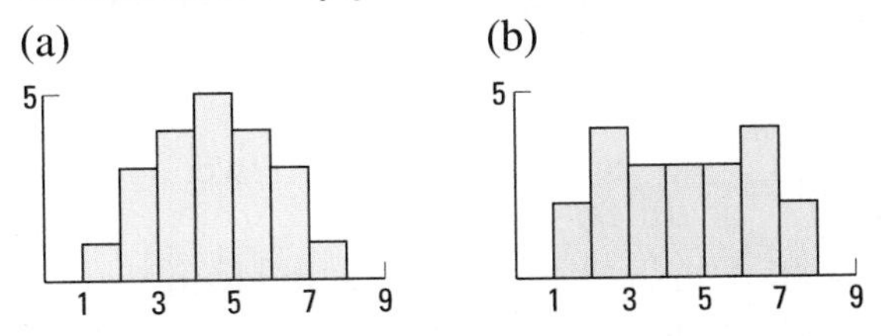

In 9–12, use the following box plots, which show the ages at inauguration of the first 42 presidents and the first 45 vice-presidents of the United States (through 1997).

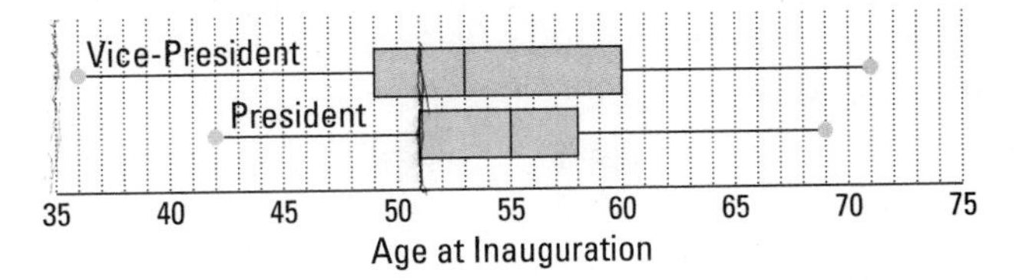

9. What was the range of ages for vice-presidents?

10. About what percent of the 42 presidents were 51 or older when they were inaugurated?

11. *Multiple choice.* The median inaugural age for presidents falls in which part of the distribution of vice-presidential ages?
    (a) below the first quartile
    (b) between the median and the 25th percentile
    (c) between the median and the 75th percentile
    (d) above the third quartile

12. Compare and contrast the ages at inauguration of the 42 presidents and the 45 vice-presidents.

13. Refer to the following table describing the estimated crude petroleum production in millions of 42-gallon barrels in 1994 by the members of the Organization of Petroleum Exporting Countries (OPEC). (Source: *1996 Information Please Almanac*)

Algeria	274
Ecuador	131
Gabon	111
Iran	1305
Iraq	183
Indonesia	480
Kuwait	730
Libya	503
Nigeria	718
Qatar	150
Saudi Arabia	2920
United Arab Emirates	814
Venezuela	885

a. Find the median, and the lower and upper quartiles.

b. Use the 1.5 × IQR test to identify any outliers.

c. Draw a box plot for data in the table.

In 14 and 15, to monitor office long-distance calls, Sheila checked her company's telephone account, which listed the length in minutes of each call. She let x_i stand for the length of the ith call. Here is the data for May 1.

$x_1 = 1$ $\quad x_2 = 1$ $\quad x_3 = 2$ $\quad x_4 = 1$
$x_5 = 12$ $\quad x_6 = 2$ $\quad x_7 = 1$ $\quad x_8 = 1$

14. Find $\sum_{i=1}^{8} x_i$.

15. a. Find the mean length of the calls May 1.
    b. Write an expression for $\overline{x}$ using Σ-notation.

16. a. Describe the difference between a sample and a population.
    b. Give an example to illustrate your definitions in part **a**.

17. Ian has scores of 88, 90, 85, 91, and 95 on five rounds of golf. What score will he need on the next round to have a mean score of 88?

Salaries for AA Technologies

2	6 5 8 5 8
3	4 1 2 1 9
4	8 8 5
5	0 5
6	
7	
8	5

In 18–20, examine the stemplot at the right showing salaries in a small company. The stems represent 10,000s of dollars. The leaves represent 1000s of dollars.

18. a. How many employees does AA Technologies have?
    b. Find the mean salary.
    c. Find the standard deviation of the data set.

19. *True or false.* If the data on salary were represented in a histogram, individual salary amounts would be lost.

20. Comment on any clusters and gaps in the distribution of salaries.

21. Use the data below giving the maximum depth of the world's 20 largest lakes in area.
    a. Is a circle graph appropriate for this data? Why or why not?
    b. Create a good display for this data set.

Lake	Depth (meters)
Caspian Sea	946
Lake Superior	406
Lake Victoria	82
Lake Huron	229
Lake Michigan	281
Aral Sea	55
Lake Tanganyika	1435
Lake Baikal	1741
Great Bear	82
Lake Nyasa	706
Great Slave Lake	614
Lake Chad	7
Lake Erie	64
Lake Winnipeg	62
Lake Ontario	237
Lake Balkhash	27
Lake Ladoga	225
Lake Onega	110
Lake Titicaca	370
Lake Nicaragua	70

Source: *1996 Information Please Almanac*

CHAPTER REVIEW

Questions on SPUR Objectives

SPUR stands for **S**kills, **P**roperties, **U**ses, and **R**epresentations. The Chapter Review questions are grouped according to the SPUR Objectives for this chapter.

SKILLS DEAL WITH THE PROCEDURES USED TO GET ANSWERS.

Objective A: *Calculate measures of center and spread for data sets.* *(Lessons 1-2, 1-3, 1-4, 1-7)*

In 1 and 2, use the data set below.

2, 4, 6, 7, 7, 8, 8, 9, 9, 10

1. a. Find the range. **b.** Find the median.

2. a. Find the mean. **b.** Find the variance.

c. Find the standard deviation.

In 3–6, use the test scores in the stemplot below. The stem represents tens.

Stem	Leaves
4	3 7
5	0 6
6	0 4 5
7	2 5
8	7 7 8
9	2 5
10	0

3. How many scores are given?

4. Calculate each statistic.

a. minimum **b.** maximum **c.** range

5. Which score is the mode?

6. Find each score.

a. median **b.** first quartile **c.** third quartile

7. A bowler has scores of

132, 181, 150, 97, and 165.

a. What is the mean score?

b. What score would the bowler need on the next game to bring his average up to 150?

8. In one geometry class with 20 students, the mean grade on an exam was 73; in another class with 25 students, the mean grade was 81. What is the combined mean of the two classes?

PROPERTIES DEAL WITH THE PRINCIPLES BEHIND THE MATHEMATICS.

Objective B: *Use Σ-notation to represent a sum, mean, variance, or standard deviation.* *(Lessons 1-3, 1-7)*

In 9–11, suppose g_i equals the number of points Vicki scored in the ith basketball game so far this season, and

$$g_1 = 14,\ g_2 = 12,\ g_3 = 18,\ g_4 = 14,\ g_5 = 18,\ g_6 = 19,\ g_7 = 27,\ g_8 = 16,\ g_9 = 12,\ g_{10} = 19,\ g_{11} = 26,\ g_{12} = 18.$$

9. Write an expression using Σ-notation which indicates the total number of points Vicki scored so far.

10. Evaluate each expression.

a. $\sum_{i=1}^{6} g_i$ **b.** $\sum_{i=9}^{12} g_i$

11. *Multiple choice.* Which expression represents the mean number of points Vicki scored per game?

(a) $\dfrac{\sum_{i=1}^{11} g_i}{11}$ (b) $\dfrac{\sum_{i=1}^{12} g_i}{12}$ (c) $\dfrac{\sum_{i=12}^{1} g_i}{12}$ (d) $\dfrac{\sum_{i=9}^{12} g_i^2}{12}$

12. *Multiple choice.* Which of the following is a correct formula for finding the standard deviation of a sample with the following data: $a_1, a_2, a_3, a_4, \ldots, a_{12}$?

(a) $\sqrt{\dfrac{\sum_{i=1}^{12} (a_i - a_{12})^2}{11}}$ (b) $\sqrt{\dfrac{\sum_{i=1}^{12} (a_i - \bar{a})^2}{11}}$

(c) $\sqrt{\dfrac{\sum_{i=1}^{12} a_i - \bar{a}^2}{11}}$ (d) $\sqrt{\dfrac{\sum_{i=1}^{12} a_i^2 - \bar{a}^2}{11}}$

Objective C: *Compare measures of center and compare measures of spread.* *(Lessons 1-3, 1-7)*

13. Which is generally affected more by extreme values in the data set—the mean or the median?

14. a. *True or false.* The mean and median of a data set can never be equal.

b. If true, explain why. If false, give a counterexample.

In 15 and 16, *multiple choice.*

15. The calculation of standard deviation uses which of the following?

(a) mean (b) median (c) mode (d) range

16. If the standard deviation of a set of n numbers is y, which of these is the variance of the set?

(a) $\sqrt{y}$ (b) y^2 (c) $\frac{y}{n-1}$ (d) $\frac{y}{n}$

USES DEAL WITH APPLICATIONS OF MATHEMATICS IN REAL SITUATIONS.

Objective D: *Use samples to make inferences about populations.* *(Lesson 1-1)*

In 17 and 18, identify **a.** the sample; **b.** the population; **c.** the variable being studied.

17. An independent polling agency calls 600 registered voters in Michigan asking them which candidate for U.S. Senate they favor.

18. A technician draws 10 cc of a patient's blood to be tested for cholesterol and for red blood cells.

19. Give two reasons for using a sample rather than a population.

20. The Mayor's office of a small city wants to estimate the teenage unemployment rate in the city. Criticize the given way of choosing a sample for this purpose.

a. going to the local arcade between 9 A.M. and 4 P.M. and interviewing teens

b. surveying people who look like teens at the city's shopping malls after 6 P.M.

Objective E: *Determine relationships and interpret data presented in a table.* *(Lesson 1-1)*

In 21–26, use the table below from the *Statistical Abstract of the United States 1995*, providing details of people moving households between 1992 and 1993.

Mobility Status of the Population, by Selected Characteristics: 1992–1993

Age and Region	Total (1,000)	Percent Distribution						
		Non movers	Movers (different house in United States)					Movers from Abroad
			Total	Same County	Different County			
					Total	Same State	Different State	
Total	250,210	83	16	11	6	3	3	1
1 to 4 years old	15,802	77	22	15	7	4	3	(Z)
5 to 9 years old	18,727	83	17	11	5	3	3	1
10 to 14 years old	18,427	86	13	9	4	2	2	1
15 to 19 years old	16,627	83	17	11	5	3	2	1
20 to 24 years old	17,802	64	35	22	13	7	6	1
25 to 29 years old	19,603	69	30	20	10	6	4	1
30 to 44 years old	62,603	83	17	11	6	3	3	1
45 to 64 years old	49,750	91	9	6	4	2	2	(Z)
65 to 74 years old	18,362	94	6	3	3	1	1	(Z)
75 to 84 years old	9,917	95	5	3	2	1	1	(Z)
85 years old and over	2,590	94	6	4	3	1	1	(Z)
Northeast	50,003	89	10	7	4	2	2	1
Midwest	60,031	84	16	10	6	3	3	(Z)
South	86,107	82	18	11	7	4	3	1
West	54,068	79	20	14	6	3	3	1

(Z) Less than 0.5 percent

21. **a.** Which numbers in the table total 250,210?

b. Give a reason why the sum of the numbers 50,003, 60,031, 86,107, and 54,068 in the first column is not 250,210.

22. Identify the variables for which data are provided in this table.

23. Explain the meaning of the number 7 in the column "Same State."

24. How many people 45-64 years old moved to a different county within their own state in 1992–1993?

25. How many people 20–24 years old moved to the United States in 1992–1993?

26. Which of the age groups shown was most mobile in the period shown?

Objective F: *Use statistics to describe data sets and to compare or contrast data sets.* *(Lessons 1-2, 1-3, 1-4, 1-7)*

27. Each of the members of a Girl Scout troop sold cookies as part of a fundraising effort. The number of boxes of cookies sold by each member is given below.

63	78	102	69	42	174	81
73	82	94	92	79	62	68
71	73	74	69	11	88	80
63	74	69	71	77	70	93
87	67	77	77	62	85	176

a. Find the mean, median, and standard deviation of these sales figures.

b. Which sales seem to be outliers to these data?

c. Remove the outliers and find the mean and standard deviation of the remaining sales figures.

d. Write several sentences describing the sales of this troop. Include notions of center and spread of the distribution. Comment on extreme cases.

28. Refer to the table below, which gives the median sales price of existing single family homes during 1994 for 13 large metropolitan statistical areas. Prices are in 1000s of dollars. (Source: National Association of Realtors)

Atlanta	93.6	New York	173.2
Chicago	144.1	Philadelphia	119.5
Cleveland	98.5	St. Louis	85.0
Dallas	95.0	San Francisco	255.6
Detroit	87.0	Seattle	155.9
Houston	80.5	Washington D.C.	157.9
Miami	103.2		

a. Compute the five-number summary for these data.

b. What conclusions can you make from these data regarding the price of housing in these metropolitan areas in the United States?

29. Use the data below of normal daily mean temperatures by month in Juneau, Alaska, and Minneapolis-St. Paul, Minnesota. Data have been rounded to the nearest degree Fahrenheit. (Source: U.S. National Oceanic and Atmospheric Administration)

Month	Juneau, AK	Minneapolis-St. Paul, MN
January	24	12
February	28	18
March	33	31
April	40	46
May	47	59
June	53	68
July	56	74
August	55	71
September	49	61
October	42	49
November	32	33
December	27	18

a. Which city has the higher summer temperatures?

b. Which has the lower winter temperatures?

c. On the average, which city has a higher average temperature? Use a measure of center to justify your answer.

d. On the average, which city shows greater variability in temperature? Use a measure of spread to justify your answer.

30. In a botany experiment, Lana recorded the number of days it took for each of ten plants to flower. She obtained the following data:

13, 15, 12, 10, 17, 18, 8, 10, 13, 14.

a. For these data, find the mean, variance, and standard deviation.

b. In an earlier experiment, Lana found that when fertilizer was applied, the number of days before plants flowered had mean 11 and standard deviation 1.5. What seems to be the effect of the fertilizer?

31. The back-to-back stemplot in the next column gives the scores of a sample of 25 male and 25 female high school students on a test.

a. Find the five-number summaries for each group.

CHAPTER ONE

b. Are there any outliers using the 1.5 × IQR criterion? If so, identify them.

c. Describe some similarities and differences between the two groups.

male		female
5 0	7	
8	8	
2 1	9	0
9 8 4	10	1 3 9 9
9 5 5 4 3	11	5 8
8 6	12	6 6 9
5 2	13	7 7 8
7 6 0	14	0 2 5 9 9
5 1	15	2 4 4
9	16	5 8
	17	8
8 0	18	
	19	
	20	0

REPRESENTATIONS DEAL WITH PICTURES, GRAPHS, OR OBJECTS THAT ILLUSTRATE CONCEPTS.

Objective G: *Read and interpret bar graphs, circle graphs, and coordinate graphs.*
(Lessons 1-1, 1-6)

32. Refer to the circle graph below, which shows who paid for the research and development done in the U.S. in 1994. If the total amount of research funded was about $172.55 billion, about how much was funded by each group? (Source: U.S. National Science Foundation)

a. the federal government

b. industry

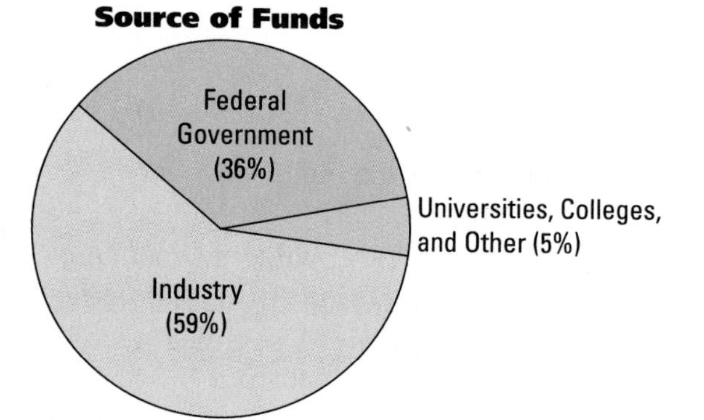

In 33 and 34, use the graph below showing the effect of Social Security benefits on poverty rates of the aged in the United States. (Source: Social Security Administration)

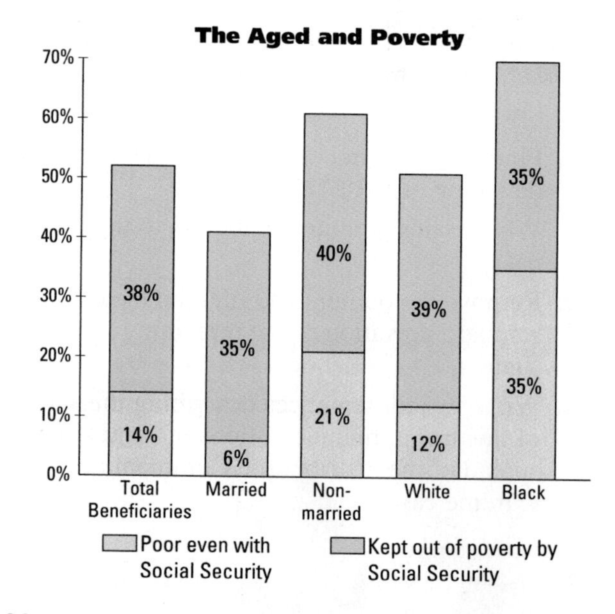

33. a. What percent of the aged were poor even with Social Security?

b. What additional percent would have been poor if it weren't for Social Security?

CHAPTER ONE

34. *Multiple choice.* Among which group of the aged did Social Security benefits keep the greatest percentage of people out of poverty?

(a) Married (b) Non-married
(c) White (d) Black

35. Use the graph below from *Drive Right* (eighth edition), by Johnson *et al.*,which was published in 1987 by Scott, Foresman and Company. The graph shows the blood alcohol concentration of a person attending a party.

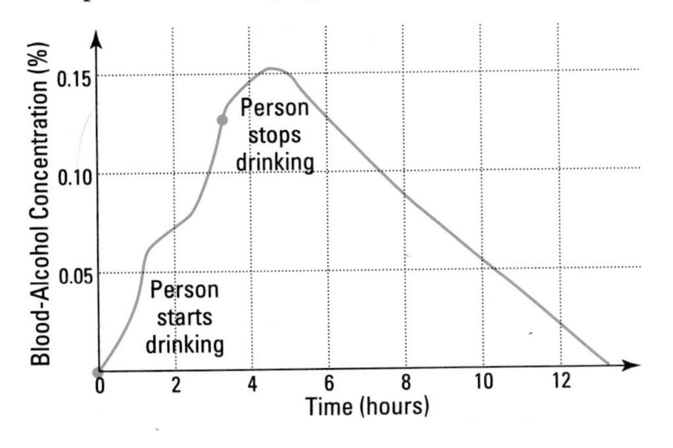

a. For how long after the person stopped drinking did the blood-alcohol content continue to rise?

b. The text says, "Alcohol is absorbed into the body very quickly, but it is very slow to leave." What feature of the graph is consistent with this statement?

c. The legal limit for blood-alcohol level in the U.S. is 0.10%. If the person started drinking at 9 P.M., during which hours was the person legally not permitted to drive?

d. To estimate a formula for blood-alcohol consumption, a police officer assumed the graph was linear between (5, 0.15) and (13, 0). Find the slope of the line joining those two points, and state the unit in which it is measured.

36. Use the graphs below, showing the percent distribution of household income for the census years 1980 and 1990.

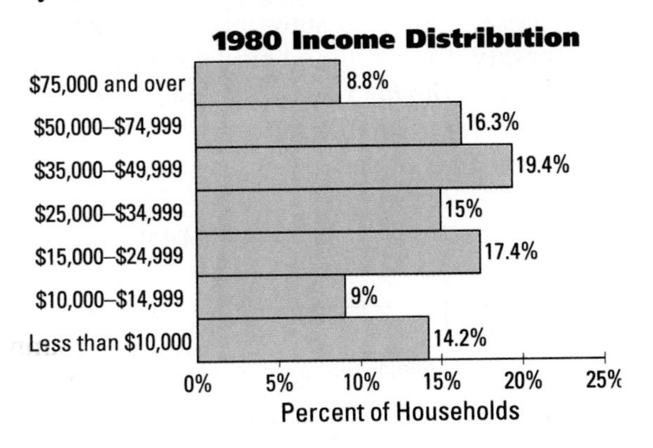

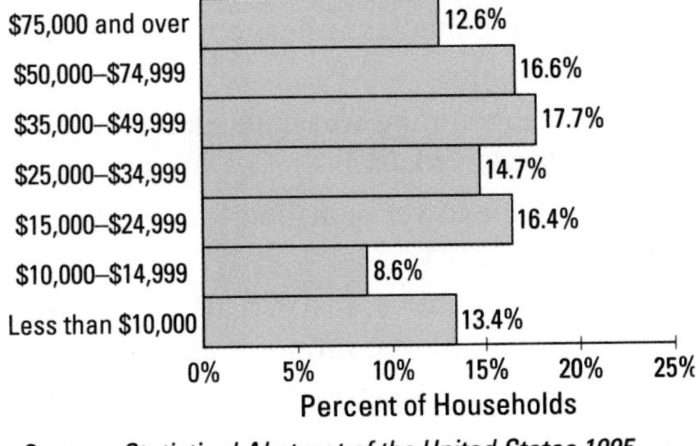

Source: *Statistical Abstract of the United States 1995*

a. What percent of households had an income below $10,000 in 1990?

b. In which level was there the greatest change in the percent of households from 1980 to 1990?

CHAPTER ONE

Objective H: *Read and interpret box plots.* *(Lesson 1-4)*

In 37–42, refer to the following box plots below, which represent the 1996 automobile mileage ratings for city driving, based on data collected in *Car and Driver Buying Guide.* The endpoints of each box plot represent the maximum and minimum values for each set of data.

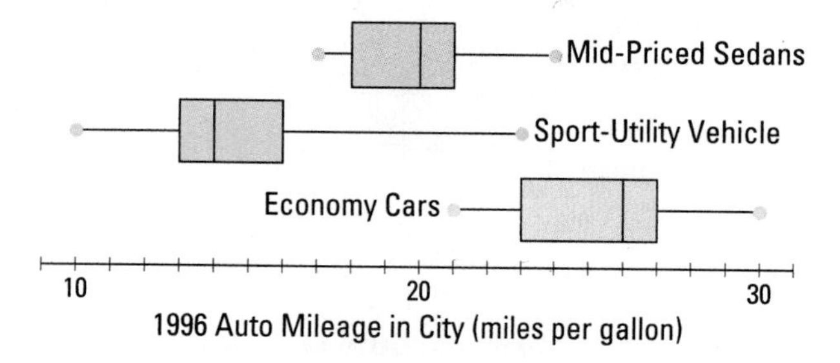

37. What was the median mileage rating for sport-utility vehicles?

38. What mileage rating was exceeded by only 25% of mid-priced sedans?

39. What was the lower quartile of mileage rating for economy cars?

40. From this set of data, in 1996 all mid-priced sedans had a mileage rating of at least __?__.

41. From this set of data, in 1996 the middle 50% of economy cars had mileage ratings between __?__ and __?__.

42. Should any of the endpoints of the box plots be considered outliers? Justify your answer.

Objective I: *Read and interpret dotplots and histograms.* *(Lessons 1-2, 1-5)*

43. Use the displays at the top of the next column, which show the Age Structure of the U.S. and Mexican populations from their 1990 censuses.

a. Describe the main difference between the populations of the U.S. and Mexico in the age interval 0–9.

b. What factors might account for such different shapes of the age structure of these two countries?

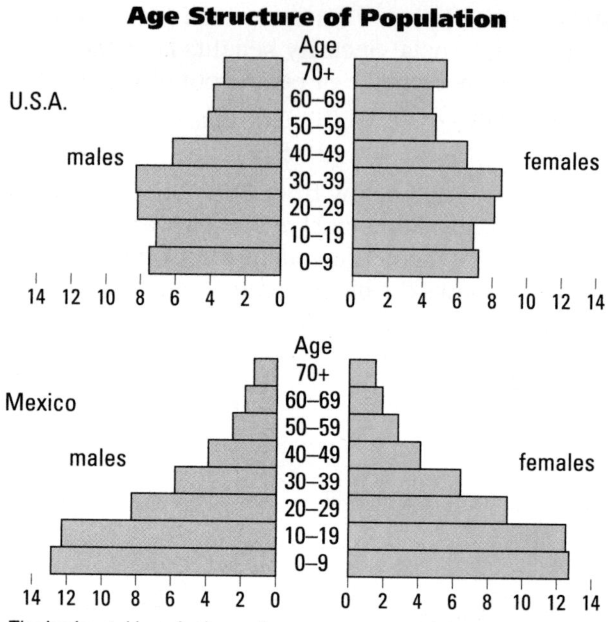

The horizontal bars in these diagrams represent the percentage of the male population and the percentage of the female population in the age group shown.

44. Ms. T. Chare made the following histogram of grades on her final examination in geometry. (Each bar includes the left endpoint. For instance, the lowest bar indicates the number of grades g where $30 \le g < 40$.)

a. How many students took the examination?

b. *True or false.* The median score is between 60 and 70 points.

c. About what percent of her students scored at least 80 points?

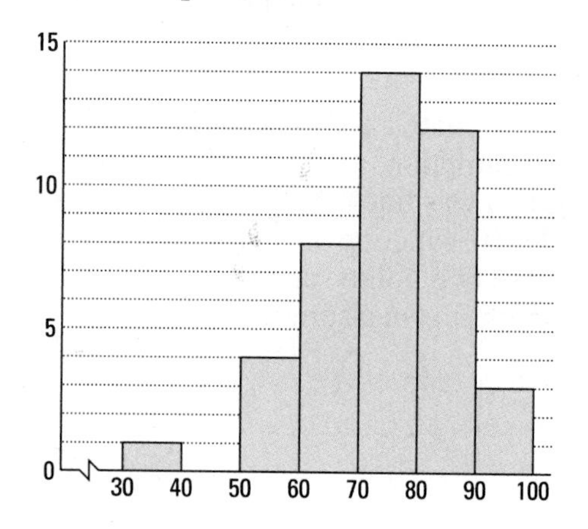

CHAPTER ONE

In 45–47, Zoe counted the number of students waiting in a line to be served at the school cafeteria at five-minute intervals over her lunch hour. Below is the frequency distribution of her results.

6 7 8 9 10 11
Number Waiting

45. How many students were in the longest line recorded?

46. Find each measure.

a. mode **b.** median **c.** range

47. What percent of the waiting lines was composed of nine or more students?

Objective J: *Draw graphs to display data.*

(Lessons 1-1, 1-2, 1-4, 1-5, 1-6)

48. Refer to the data on cookie sales given for Question 27.

a. Display these data in a histogram.

b. Describe any clusters or gaps in the data set.

49. Refer to the data on home sales in Question 28. Display the data in a boxplot or a histogram.

50. Refer to the monthly temperatures for Juneau and Minneapolis-St. Paul given for Question 29. Illustrate the data, and justify your responses to the questions by drawing either two boxplots or two histograms.

51. Refer to the test data in Question 31. Draw box plots to illustrate the two sets of scores.

In 52 and 53 draw a graph to display the data. The data are from the 970 students who enrolled at the University of Chicago as the class of 2000.

52. Of these, 41% came from the Midwest, 24% from Mid-Atlantic states, 7% from New England, 7% from the South, 4% from the Southwest, 12% from the West, and 5% from foreign countries.

53. Their combined SAT scores were as follows.

1500–1600	13%
1400–1499	29%
1300–1399	33%
1200–1299	17%
1100–1199	6%
1000–1099	2%
below 1000	0%

54. Consider the data on U.S. presidents and their children in the table below.

a. Display the data using an appropriate graph.

b. Explain your choice of graph in terms of the data set and its characteristics.

Presidents	Sons	Daughters
Washington	0	0
John Adams	3	2
Jefferson	1	5
Madison	0	0
Monroe	0	2
J. Q. Adams	3	1
Jackson	0	0
Van Buren	4	0
W. H. Harrison	6	4
Tyler	8	6
Polk	0	0
Taylor	1	5
Fillmore	1	1
Pierce	3	0
Buchanan	0	0
Lincoln	4	0
A. Johnson	3	2
Grant	3	1
Hayes	7	1
Garfield	5	2
Arthur	2	1
Cleveland	2	3
B. Harrison	1	2
McKinley	0	2
T. Roosevelt	4	2
Taft	2	1
Wilson	0	3
Harding	0	0
Coolidge	2	0
Hoover	2	0
F. D. Roosevelt	5	1
Truman	0	1
Eisenhower	2	0
Kennedy	2	1
L. B. Johnson	0	2
Nixon	0	2
Ford	3	1
Carter	3	1
Reagan	2	2
Bush	4	2
Clinton	0	1

Source: *1996 Information Please Almanac*

In 55–58, what type of graph(s) or display(s) could be used to display the given type of data?

55. quartiles

56. relative frequency data

57. time-series data

58. individual elements of a data set

CHAPTER

FUNCTIONS AND MODELS

United States National Debt							
End of Fiscal Year	1965	1970	1975	1980	1985	1990	1995
Amount (billions of $)	322	381	542	909	1,818	3,207	4,921

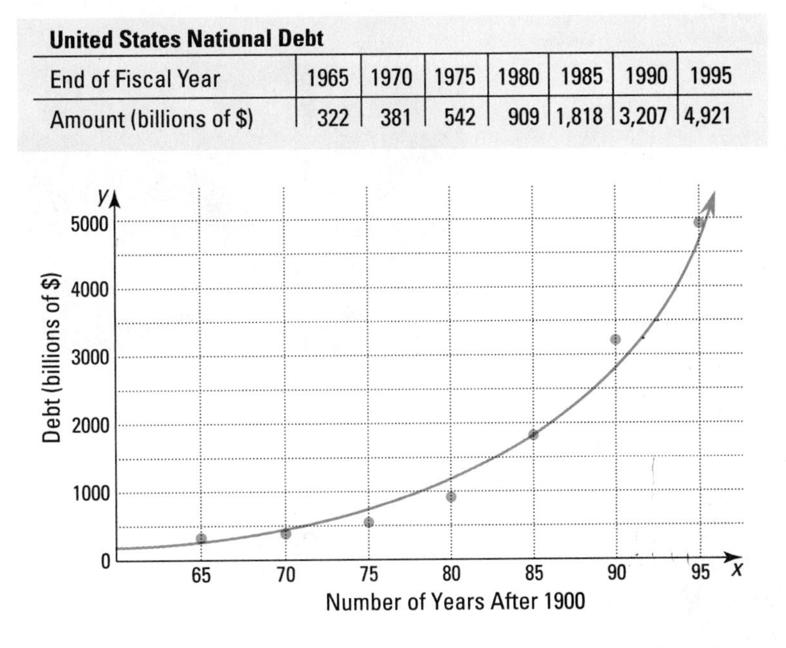

In Chapter 1, you learned to describe and display data involving a single variable, that is, **univariate** data. In this chapter, you will learn how to describe data involving relations between two variables, or **bivariate** data.

For example, data from the U.S. Office of Management and Budget show the United States national debt at the end of selected fiscal years. These data, pictured in the scatterplot, show that the national debt has been increasing dramatically since 1965.

To describe relations more fully, mathematicians seek models for data. A **mathematical model** is a mathematical description of a real situation, usually involving some simplification and assumptions concerning the situation. Such models not only describe relations between data, they also can be used to make estimates and predictions.

A function such as a linear, exponential, or quadratic function can be a good model. For instance, if x is the number of years after 1900 and y is the national debt in billions of dollars, then the national debt in the years from 1965 to 1995 can be modeled by the exponential function with equation $y = 0.443 \cdot 1.102^x$, which is graphed on the scatterplot above. Although the data points do not fall exactly on the graph of the exponential function, they are close. With such a model, you might estimate the national debt in 1992 or 1996, even though this information was not given.

LESSON

2-1

The Language of Functions

From 1995 to 1997, the national debt increased at an average rate of over $700 million per day; that is over $8000 per second. This clock was placed in front of the Capitol to increase citizen awareness.

The chapter opener lists seven ordered pairs of numbers. The first number is a year; the second is the U.S. national debt (in billions of $) at the end of that fiscal year. Any set of ordered pairs is a **relation**. In many contexts, the second number in each ordered pair depends in some way on the first number. For this reason, the first variable in a relation is called the **independent variable** and the second variable is called the **dependent variable**.

What Is a Function?

Two definitions of function are commonly used in mathematics. They are equivalent, but they stress different aspects of functions. One definition is as a special type of relation. This aspect is useful for graphing.

> **Definition**
> A **function** is a set of ordered pairs (x, y) in which each value of x is paired with exactly one value of y.

In the set of ordered pairs of a function, the set of first elements is the **domain** of the function. The set of second elements is the **range**. The domain consists of all allowable values of the independent variable; the range is the set of possible values for the dependent variable.

For the data in the chapter opener, we can say, "The U.S. national debt is a function of the year." The domain is the set of all years; the range is the set of all amounts (in dollars) of the national debt in those years.

The other definition of function stresses the independent-dependent variable idea.

Definition

A **function** is a correspondence between two sets A and B in which each element of A corresponds to exactly one element of B.

The domain is the set A; the range is the set of only those elements of B that correspond to elements in A.

For most functions studied in this course, A and B are sets of real numbers. Unless the domain of a function is explicitly stated, you may assume that it is the set of all real numbers for which the function is defined.

Example 1

A laundry service normally charges $1.00 per shirt for laundering. Customers get a $1.00 discount if they have 6 or more shirts laundered.

a. Which is true, "the cost C is a function of the number n of shirts" or "the number n of shirts is a function of the cost C"?

b. Identify the independent and dependent variables.

c. State the domain and range of the function.

Solution

a. Because there is exactly one cost C for a given number n of shirts, **the cost is a function of the number of shirts.** The cost of laundering either 5 shirts or 6 shirts is the same, so the number of shirts is not a function of the cost.

b. Because C depends on n, **n is the independent variable and C is the dependent variable.**

c. The domain is the set of all values for n. So **the domain is the set of nonnegative integers.** The range is the set of all possible values for C. Any whole-number cost is possible, so **the range is also the set of nonnegative integers.**

Representations of Functions

Functions can be represented in many ways; among the most frequently used are ordered pairs in tables or lists, rules expressed in words or symbols, and coordinate graphs. You should know how to recognize functions expressed in each of these forms and how to convert from one form to another.

Example 2

Consider again the cost C of laundering n shirts, as given in Example 1 above.

a. List the ordered pairs of the function for values of n from 1 to 9.

b. Graph the function.

Solution

a. Each ordered pair of this function is of the form (n, C) where n is number of shirts and C is cost. For 1 to 5 shirts the cost is $1 per shirt. So, for $1 \le n \le 5$, the ordered pairs of the function are

$$(1, 1) \qquad (2, 2) \qquad (3, 3) \qquad (4, 4) \qquad (5, 5).$$

▶

For more than 5 shirts, the cost is \$1 per shirt with a \$1 discount. So, for $n > 5$, the ordered pairs are

b. A graph is drawn below.

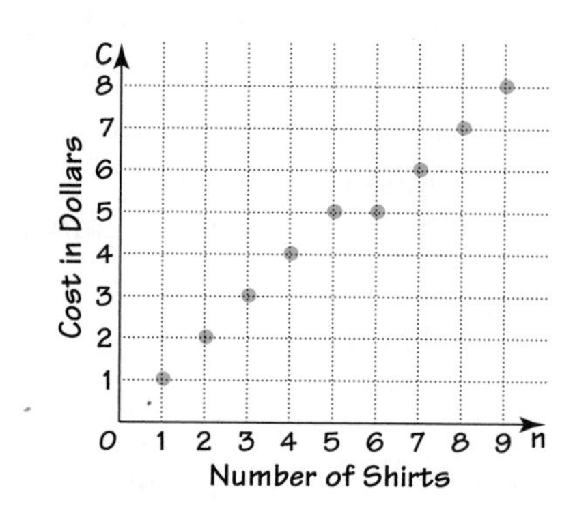

Example 3

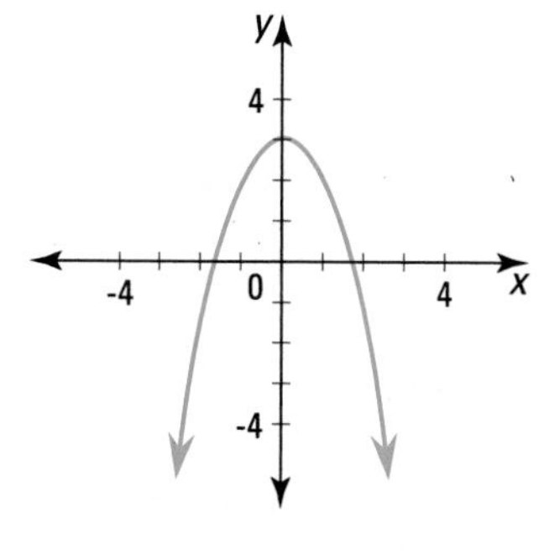

A rule for the function graphed at the left is $y = -x^2 + 3$. Find the range of the function.

Solution

The graph is a parabola, with maximum point (0, 3). From the graph, you can see that the values of the function are all real numbers less than or equal to 3. So **the range is $\{y: y \leq 3\}$.**

Check

Since $x^2 \geq 0$ for all real x, $-x^2 \leq 0$. So $-x^2 + 3 \leq 3$. This checks with the graph.

In a function, there is only one member of the range paired with each member of the domain. So if you draw any vertical line through the graph of a function, it will intersect the graph at no more than one point. This is often referred to as the **vertical line test** for determining whether a relation is a function. You can see how this works on the two graphs of relations shown below. Only the relation at the left is a function.

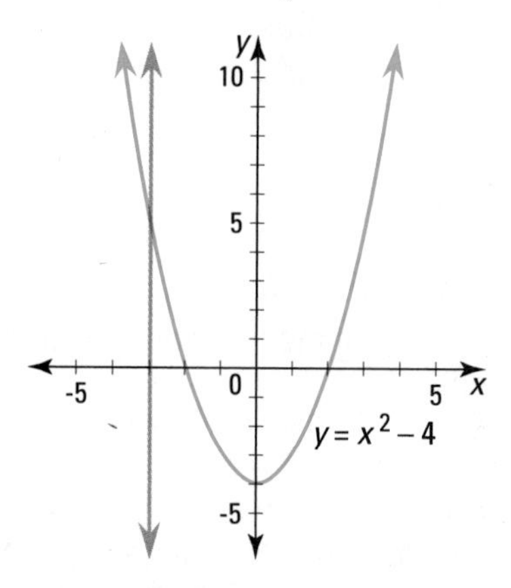

y is a function of *x*; any vertical line intersects the graph no more than once.

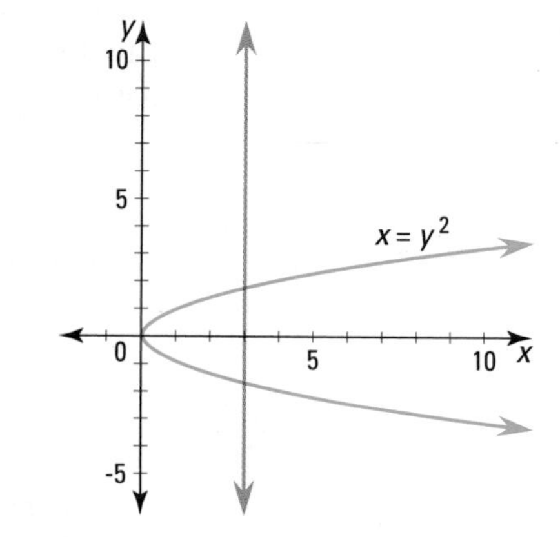

y is not a function of *x*; there is at least one vertical line that intersects the graph in two places.

Function Notation

Rules for functions are sometimes written using *function notation*. The symbol $f(x)$, which is read "f of x," was invented by the mathematician Leonhard Euler (pronounced "oiler") in the 18th century. It indicates the value of the dependent variable when the independent variable is x. The variable x is sometimes called the **argument** of the function. Euler's notation is particularly useful when evaluating two or more functions at specific values of the independent variable.

Example 4

Let $f(x) = 5 \cdot 2^x$.

a. Evaluate $f(4)$.

b. Does $f(3 + 4) = f(3) + f(4)$?

Solution

a. The rule for f says to "raise 2 to the x power and then multiply by 5."

So $f(4) = 5 \cdot 2^4 = 5 \cdot 16 = 80$.

b. $f(3 + 4) = f(7) = 5 \cdot 2^7 = 640$

$f(3) + f(4) = (5 \cdot 2^3) + (5 \cdot 2^4) = 40 + 80 = 120$

So, $f(3 + 4) \neq f(3) + f(4)$.

Example 4 illustrates that, in general, $f(a + b) \neq f(a) + f(b)$. That is, there is no general distributive property for functions over addition.

The three ways of looking at functions—as tables or lists, as graphs, or by their rules—highlight different aspects of functions. These three ways are united when we think of a function as a set of ordered pairs of the form $(x, f(x))$ which can be graphed in a coordinate plane.

QUESTIONS

Covering the Reading

In 1–3, give a definition.

1. function **2.** domain **3.** range

4. A photo lab usually charges \$1.30 per print to make a color print from a color transparency. During a special promotion, the charge is \$1.05 per print if 8 or more prints are made.

a. Which is true, "the cost C is a function of the number n of prints made" or "the number n of prints made is a function of the cost C"?

b. What is the cost of making 10 color prints from transparencies?

c. List all the ordered pairs (n, C) for $n \leq 12$.

d. Graph the relation in part **c** for $n \leq 12$.

e. What number of prints is a waste of money?

5. Consider the relationship $x = f(t)$. Identify the letter which represents each of the following.
   a. the function
   b. the dependent variable
   c. the independent variable

In 6–9, a set of ordered pairs is graphed. **a.** Tell whether the graph shows a relation. **b.** Tell whether the graph shows a function.

6. **7.** **8.** **9.**

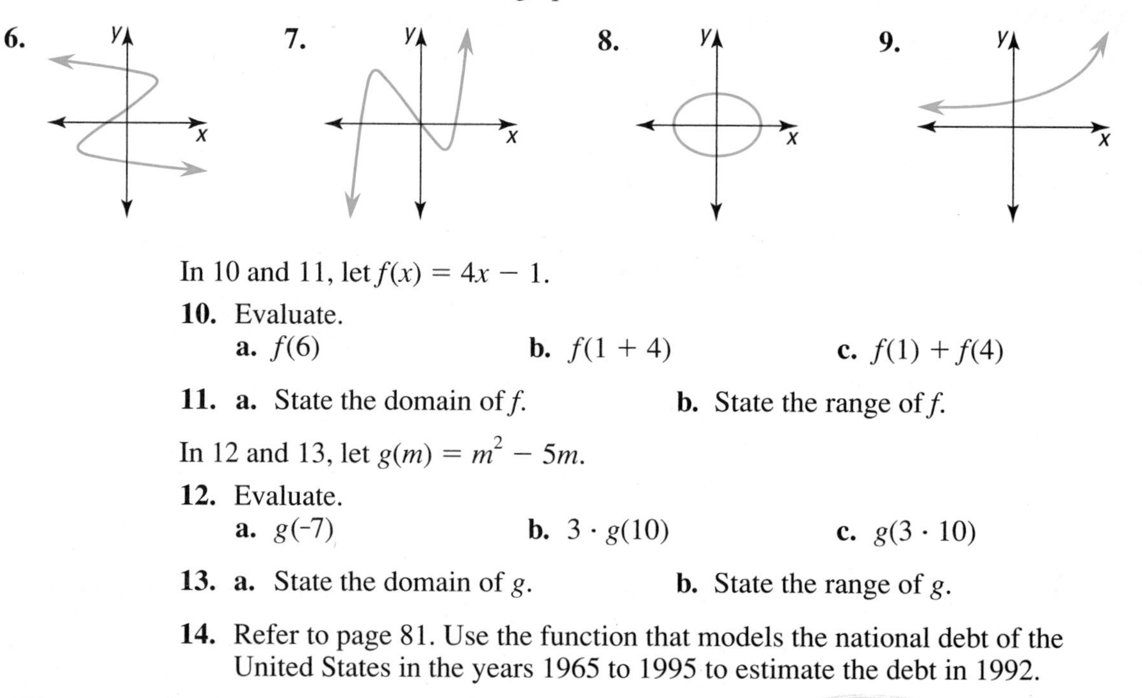

In 10 and 11, let $f(x) = 4x - 1$.

10. Evaluate.
   a. $f(6)$ **b.** $f(1 + 4)$ **c.** $f(1) + f(4)$

11. **a.** State the domain of f. **b.** State the range of f.

In 12 and 13, let $g(m) = m^2 - 5m$.

12. Evaluate.
   a. $g(-7)$ **b.** $3 \cdot g(10)$ **c.** $g(3 \cdot 10)$

13. **a.** State the domain of g. **b.** State the range of g.

14. Refer to page 81. Use the function that models the national debt of the United States in the years 1965 to 1995 to estimate the debt in 1992.

Applying the Mathematics

In 15–17, consider the relation defined by the sentence. **a.** Sketch a graph. **b.** Tell if the relation is a function. If so, give its domain and range.

15. $y = 2 \cdot 3^x$ **16.** $y = \sqrt{x}$ **17.** $y > x$

18. At a sale, all clothing prices are reduced by 20%.
   a. Write an equation for the sale price P of clothing originally marked at d dollars.
   b. Identify the domain and range of this function.
   c. List three ordered pairs in this function.
   d. Draw a graph of the function.

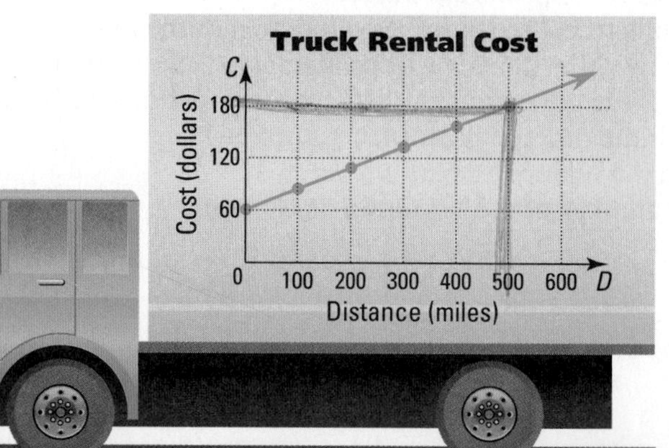

19. The graph at the left represents the cost of renting a truck for a day as a function of the number of miles driven.
   a. Write two ordered pairs which are part of this function.
   b. What is the range of the function?
   c. Find the slope of the line.
   d. What does the slope represent?

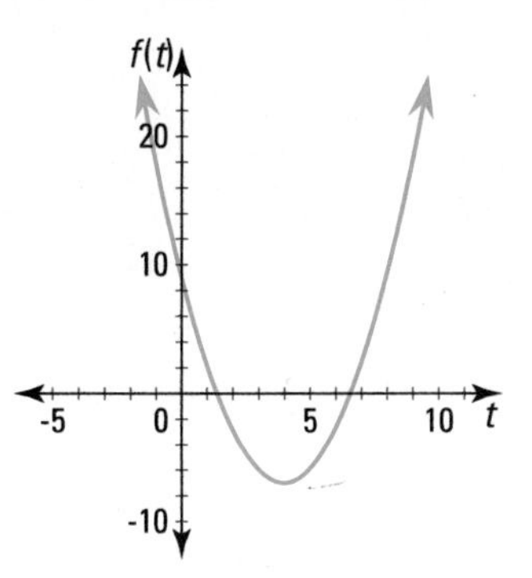

20. At the left is a graph of a function with the rule $f(t) = t^2 - 8t + 9$.
a. State the domain and range of f.
b. State two ordered pairs which are part of this function.

In 21 and 22, give an example of a function satisfying the given condition. In each case, give a domain and a rule.

21. The range is the set of all negative integers.

22. The range is the set of all nonnegative real numbers.

Review

In 23 and 24, suppose that a particular calculator is advertised at six different stores for the following prices (in dollars): 89.95, 88.95, 89.99, 87.99, 88.95, 89.99. *(Lessons 1-3, 1-7)*

23. Let C_i = the cost of this calculator in the ith store.
a. Evaluate $\frac{\sum_{i=1}^{6} C_i}{6}$.
b. Which statistical measure is represented by the quantity in part **a**?

24. **a.** Without calculating, tell whether the standard deviation of this data set will be less than 1 or greater than 10.
b. Calculate the standard deviation to verify your answer to part **a**.

25. Without graphing, tell whether the point (32, 98) is on the line with equation $y = 3x + 4$. Justify your answer. *(Previous course)*

26. **a.** State the slope-intercept form of the equation of a line.
b. State the point-slope form of the equation of a line.
c. Write an equation for the line which has slope -3 and passes through the point (2, 7). *(Previous course)*

27. *Skill sequence.* Match the equation to the shape of its graph. *(Previous course)*

a. $y = \frac{3}{x}$	**I.** parabola
b. $y = 3x$	**II.** hyperbola
c. $y = \frac{x}{3}$	**III.** line
d. $y = 3x^2$	

Exploration

28. Find out the size of the national debt for a date as close as possible to today's date. The chapter opener gives an equation to calculate the national debt as a function of the number of years since 1900. What does this equation predict for the debt on the date you have? Calculate the percent error of the prediction.

Introducing Lesson 2-2

Linear Regression

ACTIVITY

You will need a statistics utility to do this activity.

Recently, a consumer panel purchased 15 light-duty mountain bikes and evaluated their quality, based upon braking, handling, and off-road performance. Each bike was rated on a 0 to 100 scale. The price of each bike (in dollars) was also recorded. The data are listed in the table below.

Bike	Cost ($)	Rating	Bike	Cost ($)	Rating
Bianchi Timber Wolf	270	47	**Schwinn** Clear Creek	320	45
Diamond Back Outlook	225	31	**Schwinn** Sidewinder	260	45
Giant Rincon	300	49	**Specialized** Hardrock	270	44
Giant Yukon	370	49	**Specialized** Hardrock Sport	320	50
GT Outpost Trail	260	41	**Trek** 800 Sport	240	38
Mongoose Threshold	270	43	**Trek** 820	325	53
Raleigh M40GS	290	46	**Univega** Rover 303	250	42
Roadmaster Pro-Trac 3862WM	250	20			

Source: *Consumer Reports,* June 1995

1 Enter the "Cost" and "Rating" data in your statistics utility.

2 **a.** Draw a scatterplot of the data with "Cost" as the independent variable and "Rating" as the dependent variable.

b. What window did you use for the scatterplot?

c. Why did you choose this window?

3 **a.** In general, how does the rating appear to be related to the cost?

b. Identify any data points that appear to be outliers.

4 Your statistics utility has a feature called "linear regression" or "line of best fit." This is a feature that finds an equation of the line that best describes the linear trend in a data set.

a. Find out how to use the linear regression feature, and execute it for the bike rating data.

b. Write down exactly what is displayed on the screen.

c. Based on the results for the regression, write an equation which relates cost C to rating R.

5 If a new bike appears on the market costing $280, what rating does the regression equation predict?

LESSON

2-2

Linear Models and Correlation

Home-grown. *As the cost of living increases, some people resort to options such as gardening to stretch their food budget.*

Fitting a Line to Data

A **linear function** is a set of ordered pairs (x, y) which can be described by an equation of the form $y = mx + b$, where m and b are constants. Recall that the graph of every function of this form is a line with slope m and y-intercept b.

It is not uncommon for the points in the scatterplot of a data set to lie near a line. A linear model may be appropriate, even if the linear function does not contain all the data points. Most often, in fact, the best linear model does not contain any of the data points. Nonetheless, linear models can still be very useful in predicting values of either the dependent or independent variable.

The Consumer Price Index (CPI) is a measure of the cost of living in the United States. By definition, a change of $r\%$ in the CPI is supposed to represent a change of $r\%$ in the cost of living. For instance, as the CPI rises 3%, say from 100 to 103, the cost of living is then thought to have risen by 3%. The following table gives the Consumer Price Index for various years from 1980 to 1994.

Year	1980	1985	1988	1989	1990	1991	1992	1993	1994
CPI	82	108	118	124	131	136	140	145	148

Source: *Statistical Abstract of the United States 1995*

The graph on the right is a scatterplot of the data with a line which has been "fit to the data by eye." The independent variable is the number of years after 1900, and the dependent variable is the CPI.

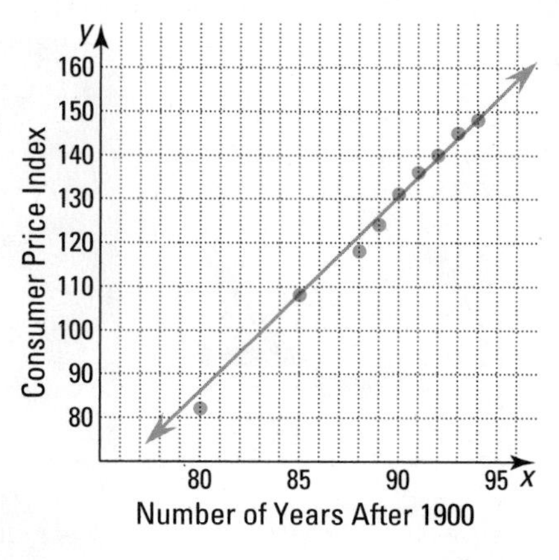

Example 1

a. Find a linear model for the relationship between years since 1900 and the CPI.
b. According to the model, estimate the CPI in 1981.

Solution

a. Find an equation for the line above. Notice that the line fit by eye passes through (85, 108) and (94, 148). Use (85, 108) and (94, 148) to find the slope *m*.

$$m = \frac{y_2 - y_1}{x_2 - x_1} = \frac{148 - 108}{94 - 85} = \frac{40}{9}$$

Substitute $m = \frac{40}{9}$ and (85, 108) into the point-slope equation of a line.

$$y - 108 = \frac{40}{9}(x - 85)$$

Solve for y.

$$y = 4.\overline{4}x - 269.\overline{7}$$

b. To predict the CPI for the year 1981, substitute $x = 81$ and solve for *y*.

$$y = 4.\overline{4}(81) - 269.\overline{7} = 90.\overline{2} \approx 90$$

According to the model, the CPI was about 90 in 1981.

In the In-class Activity preceding this lesson, you used a statistics utility to do a *linear regression*. Example 2 shows the steps in generating a linear model for the Consumer Price Index data with such a utility.

Example 2

a. Find a linear model using your statistics utility for the relationship between the number of years since 1900 and the CPI.
b. According to the linear regression model, what was the CPI in 1981?

Solution

a. Enter the data. Use the number of years after 1900 as *x* and the CPI as *y*. Use the linear regression feature to find an equation for *y* as a function of *x*.
The linear regression model is $y = 4.77x - 299.25$.

b. Substitute 81 for *x* and calculate *y*.

$$y = 4.77(81) - 299.25 = 87.12$$

According to the linear regression model, the CPI was about 87.

Correlation

For the CPI data, many of the data points lie close to a straight line. Overall, a line is a reasonably good model for these data. But how good is "reasonably good"?

To measure the strength of the linear relation between two variables, a measure called the **correlation coefficient** is used. The correlation coefficient is often denoted by the letter r. It was first defined by the English statistician Karl Pearson (1857–1936).

Suppose $(x_1, y_1), (x_2, y_2), \ldots, (x_n, y_n)$ are n observations of two variables x and y. Let $\bar{x}$ and s_x be the mean and standard deviation, respectively, of the n values of x. Similarly, let $\bar{y}$ and s_y be the mean and standard deviation of the n values of y. Then the correlation coefficient r between x and y is given by the following formula.

$$r = \frac{1}{n-1} \sum_{i=1}^{n} \left(\frac{x_i - \bar{x}}{s_x}\right)\left(\frac{y_i - \bar{y}}{s_y}\right)$$

Because the procedure for calculating the correlation coefficient is tedious, you are not expected to calculate r by hand. However, you should be able to interpret a value of r when a computer or calculator calculates it for you.

The correlation coefficient is always a number from -1 to 1. Some data sets and the corresponding values of r are shown in the scatterplots below.

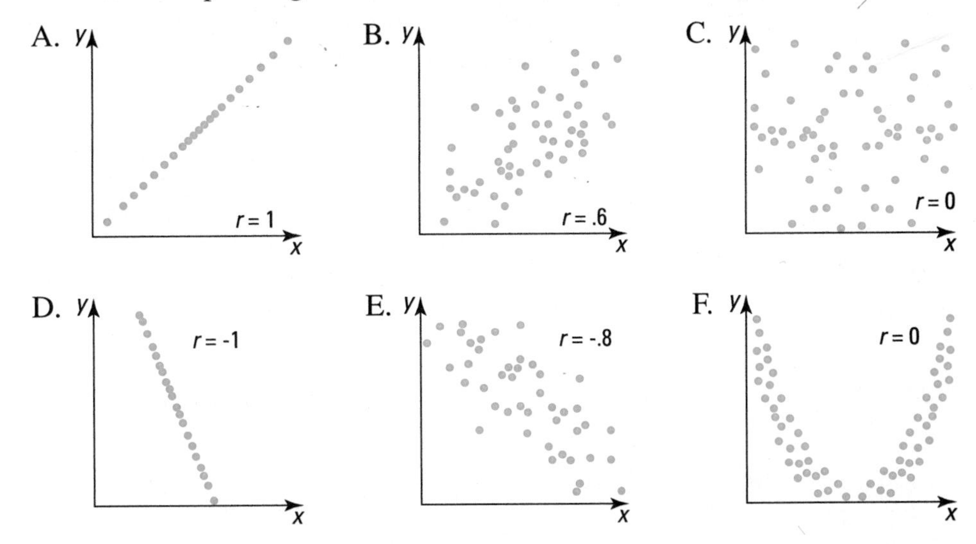

In general, the sign of r indicates the *direction* of the relation between the variables, and its magnitude indicates the *strength* of the relation. Positive values of r indicate a **positive relation** between the variables. That is, larger values of one variable are associated with larger values of the other. Negative values of r indicate a **negative relation** between the variables. That is, larger values of one variable are associated with smaller values of the other.

The extreme values of 1 and -1 indicate a perfect linear relation, as in scatterplots A and D. That is, all data points lie on a line. Thus, a situation in which $r = \pm 1$ is sometimes called a **perfect correlation**. A relation for which most of the data fall close to a line (scatterplot E) is called **strong**. A

weak relation is one for which, although a linear trend can be seen, many points are not very close to the line. A correlation close or equal to 0 (scatterplots C and F) indicates that the variables are not related by a linear model. Note, however, that as indicated in scatterplot F, if $r = 0$, the variables might be strongly related in some other way. The number line below summarizes these relations.

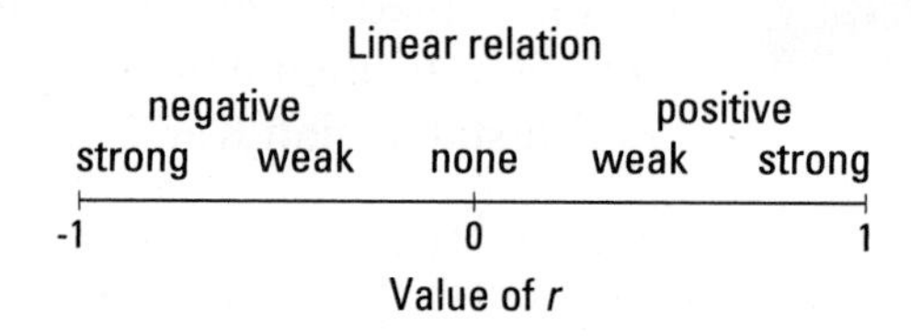

There are no strict rules about what correlations might be considered strong. Sometimes values of r with $|r| = 0.5$ are considered fairly strong, and at other times they might be considered moderate or weak.

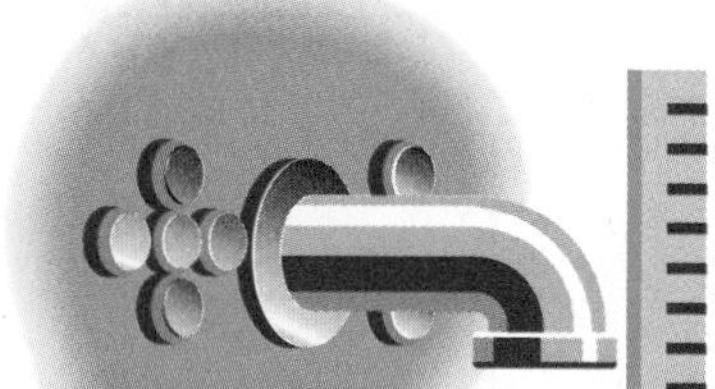

Some statistics utilities give values of r^2 rather than of r. This is because r^2 is used in advanced statistical techniques. You can calculate $|r|$ by taking the square root of r^2 and determine the sign by observing the direction of the relation in the scatterplot.

Example 3

A boy measured the depth of the water in a bathtub at one-minute intervals after the faucet was turned on. His data are below.

Time (minutes)	1	2	3	4	5	6	7	8	9	10	11	12	13	14	15	16	17	18
Depth (cm)	3	6	7	7	8	12	13	18	18	19	25	23	27	31	31	36	35	37

a. Use a statistics utility to draw a scatterplot of the data and a regression line.
b. Calculate the correlation coefficient *r*.
c. Describe the relationship between time and depth, and comment on the quality of the linear model.

Solution

a. Draw a scatterplot. Obtain a regression equation from a statistics package.

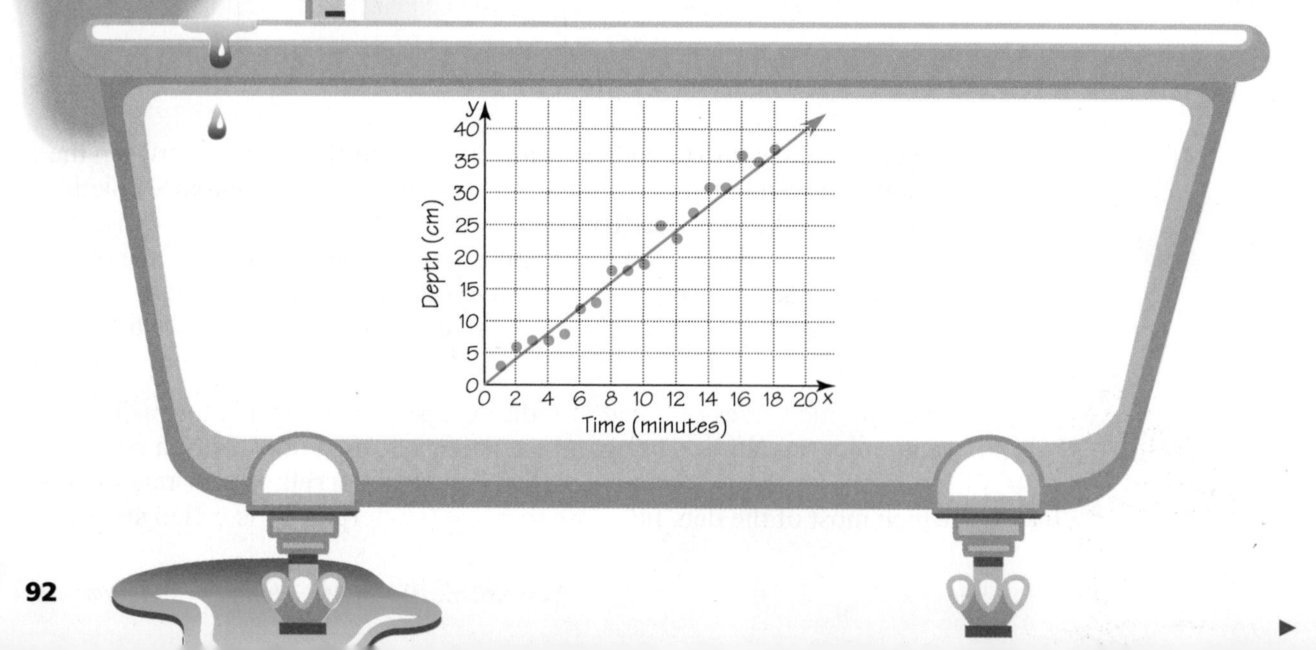

b. The statistics utility calculates a regression equation of $y = 2.103x - .2026$. Our statistics utility gives $r^2 = 0.982$. So $r = \pm\sqrt{0.982} \approx \pm 0.99$. Because the relation between the variables is positive (y increases as x increases), we conclude that $r = 0.99$.

c. A correlation of 0.99 indicates a very strong positive relation between the two variables. A line is a good model for these data, as is clear from the closeness of the points to the line of best fit. It seems likely that the water was running into the tub at a rather steady rate, that the bathtub had a fairly regular shape, and that the boy's measurements were reasonably careful.

A Caution about Correlation

It is important to note that while r provides a mathematical measure of *linearity*, it does not provide information about *cause and effect*. It is up to the people who analyze and interpret the data to determine why two variables might be related. For instance, there is a large positive correlation between shoe size and reading level of children. But this does not mean that learning to read better causes your feet to grow or that wearing bigger shoes improves your reading. The correlation is large because each variable is related to age. Older children generally have both larger feet and higher reading skills than younger children.

This idea can be summarized as *correlation does not mean causation.*

QUESTIONS

Covering the Reading

1. Define *linear function.*

2. Refer to the Consumer Price Index data.
  a. Find an equation of a line that passes through the points for 1980 and 1994.
  b. According to this model, estimate the CPI in 1981.

3. The regression line in Example 2 has equation $y = 4.77x - 299.25$.
  a. What is the slope of the line?
  b. Use this number in a sentence to explain the meaning of slope in the CPI situation.

In 4–6, *true or false.*

4. A correlation coefficient measures the strength of the linear relation between two variables.

5. If a linear model for a data set has positive slope, the correlation between the two variables is positive.

6. If the slope of the line of best fit to a data set is 2, the correlation coefficient is also 2.

In 7–11, match the scatterplot with the best description.
(a) strong negative correlation
(b) weak negative correlation
(c) strong positive correlation
(d) weak positive correlation
(e) correlation approximately zero

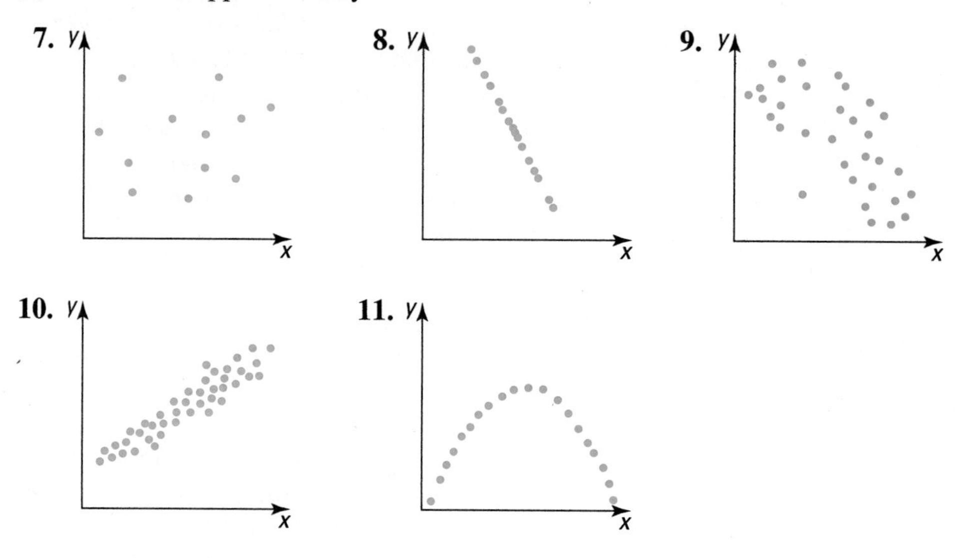

12. Draw a scatterplot for a data set showing perfect positive correlation.

13. Suppose $r^2 = 0.64$ for some data set. Find all possible values of r.

Applying the Mathematics

14. A scatterplot is shown at the right.

a. *Multiple choice.* What is the correlation between x and y?
(i) 1 (ii) 0 (iii) -1

b. Justify your answer to part **a**.

y
x

15. Use CPI data from this lesson. Let x = number of years after 1900 and y = the CPI.

a. Write the value of r given by your statistics utility.

b. Calculate $\overline{x}$ and s_x.

c. Calculate $\overline{y}$ and s_y.

d. Use the formula

$$r = \frac{1}{n-1}\sum_{i=1}^{9}\left(\frac{x_i - \overline{x}}{s_x}\right)\left(\frac{y_i - \overline{y}}{s_y}\right)$$

to write out the 9 terms that are added to find r. Calculate r to the nearest hundredth.

16. The following table lists estimates of life expectancy (span) for people of different ages in 1992.

Current Age	Expected Life Span	Current Age	Expected Life Span	Current Age	Expected Life Span
1	76.4	30	77.5	60	81.1
5	76.6	35	77.9	65	82.5
10	76.6	40	78.3	70	84.2
15	76.7	45	78.8	75	86.2
20	76.9	50	79.3	80	88.5
25	77.2	55	80.1	85	91.2

Source: *Statistical Abstract of the United States 1995*

Age span. *Human longevity has been largely determined by observations of past trends in mortality. It does not answer the question whether or not this 3-month-old baby girl will live as long as her 96-year-old great-grandmother.*

a. Make a scatterplot of the data. Use current age as the independent variable. (Hint: Scale the vertical axis from 72 to 92 with 1-yr units.)

b. Draw a line which seems to fit the data.

c. Using two points on the line in part **b**, find an equation for the line.

d. According to the equation in part **c**, what is a person's life expectancy at birth?

e. *Multiple choice.* What does the slope of your line represent?
 (i) expected months of life span gained per year of age
 (ii) expected months of life span lost per year of age
 (iii) expected years of life span gained per year of age
 (iv) expected years of life span lost per year of age

f. Calculate the life expectancy of a person age 15 according to your model. By how much does it differ from the corresponding value in the table?

17. The table below gives the percent of married women with children ages 6 to 17 in the labor force in the United States from 1950 to 1994.

Year	1950	1960	1970	1975	1980	1985	1990	1994
Percent in Labor Force	28.3	39.0	49.2	52.3	61.7	67.8	73.6	76.0

Source: *Statistical Abstract of the United States 1995*

a. Draw a scatterplot of these data with year on the horizontal axis. To simplify data entry, enter the number of years after 1900. For instance, enter 50 instead of 1950.

b. Use a statistics utility to find a linear model to fit the data. Graph the line on the scatterplot.

c. According to your answer in part **b**, about what percent of married women, with children ages 6 to 17, were in the labor force in the year 1982?

d. According to your answer in part **b**, in about what year will 85% of married women with children ages 6 to 17 be in the labor force?

e. What is the correlation coefficient for this data?

f. Write a sentence which explains the direction and strength of the correlation.

Review

18. Suppose $f(x) = -3x^2 + 5$. *(Lesson 2-1)*

a. Evaluate $f(-3)$.

b. Evaluate $2f(-1.5)$.

c. *True or false.* $f(1 + 6) = f(1) + f(6)$. Justify your answer.

19. The graph below is from *Weather on the Planets*, by George Ohring. It shows how temperature is a function of latitude on Earth and Mars when it is spring in one hemisphere on each planet. Let L be the latitude on each planet, $E(L)$ be the average temperature on the Earth, and $M(L)$ be the average temperature on Mars at latitude L.

Mars. *Wing-formed deposits such as sand dunes are common on the northern hemisphere of Mars, pictured here in a photograph taken from a Viking spacecraft. Mars, like Earth, has seasons, but it is much colder: the mean surface atmospheric temperature is -9.4°F.*

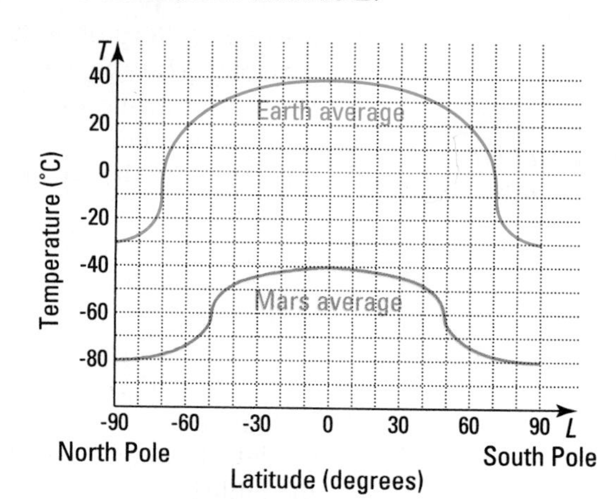

a. State whether L is the dependent or independent variable.

b. Estimate $E(60)$.

c. Estimate $E(0) - M(0)$, and state what quantity this expression represents.

d. What is the range of M? *(Lessons 1-2, 2-1)*

20. Let $f(x) = 9^x$.

a. Copy and complete the table below.

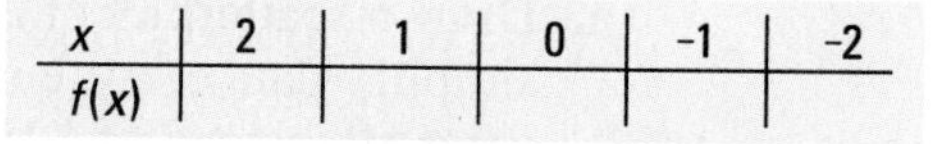

x	2	1	0	-1	-2
$f(x)$					

b. For what value of x does $f(x) = 3$?

c. If the domain of f is the set of real numbers, what is the range of f? *(Lesson 2-1, Previous course)*

Exploration

21. Find the height and weight of at least 5 people. How well do these two variables correlate for your sample?

LESSON

2-3

The Line of Best Fit

Plotting a path that fits. *The successful slalom skier's best path is a curve as close as possible to the turning points (gates) of the course—what might be called a curve of best fit.*

In the previous lesson, we found two linear models for the Consumer Price Index. The first was found by using two representative points, and the second by doing a linear regression. It turns out that the regression line is not only the better of the two models, it is in a particular way the best of all possible linear models. In fact, another name for the regression line is the *line of best fit*. In this lesson, we will explore exactly what is meant by "best" and why the regression line is the line of "best" fit.

A method for finding the line of best fit was published by the French mathematician Adrien Legendre in 1805. Using calculus, Legendre found formulas for the slope m and y-intercept b of the line of best fit for any set of data. The formulas are rather complicated, but they were developed from an analysis of simple concepts.

Data collected from sources such as experiments or surveys are called **observed values**. The points predicted by the linear model are called **predicted** or **expected values**. The line of best fit is found by minimizing the **errors** or **deviations** in the predictions, which are the differences between observed and predicted values of the dependent variable. More specifically, the **line of best fit** is the line with the smallest value for the sum of the squares of the errors. For this reason, the process of finding the line of best fit is sometimes called the **method of least squares**.

Method of Least Squares

To illustrate the meaning of the words "least squares," we look again at the Consumer Price Index data from Lesson 2-2. For that data set, number of years since 1900 is the x-value, the CPI for that year is the observed value, and the CPI according to the model is the predicted value.

Example 1

In 1991, the CPI was 136. Find the error in the values predicted by each of the following models.

a. $y = 4.44x - 269.78$, the model found by "eyeballing" the scatterplot and using two points to determine an equation of a line

b. $y = 4.77x - 299.25$, the model found by a statistics utility

Solution

You are given $x = 91$ and observed $y = 136$. You must first find the y-value predicted by each model.

a. For the two-point model, the predicted y-value is

$$y = 4.44(91) - 269.78 = 134.26.$$

So error = observed y − predicted y.
= 136 − 134.26
= 1.74

b. For the linear regression model, the predicted y-value is

$$y = 4.77(91) - 299.25 = 134.82.$$

So error = observed y − predicted y.
= 136 − 134.82
= 1.18

In the tables below, we calculate both the error and the square of the error for each data point, both for the two-point model and the linear regression model. Notice that the results from Example 1 appear in the sixth row of the table.

Two-point Model $y = 4.44x - 269.78$

x	Observed y	Predicted y	Error	Error^2
80	82	85.42	-3.42	11.70
85	108	107.62	0.38	0.14
88	118	120.94	-2.94	8.64
89	124	125.38	-1.38	1.90
90	131	129.82	1.18	1.39
91	136	134.26	1.74	3.03
92	140	138.70	1.30	1.69
93	145	143.14	1.86	3.46
94	148	147.58	0.42	0.18
Sum of the Squares				32.13

Linear Regression Model $y = 4.77x - 299.25$

x	Observed y	Predicted y	Error	Error^2
80	82	82.35	-0.35	0.12
85	108	106.20	1.80	3.24
88	118	120.51	-2.51	6.30
89	124	125.28	-1.28	1.64
90	131	130.05	0.95	0.90
91	136	134.82	1.18	1.39
92	140	139.59	0.41	0.17
93	145	144.36	0.64	0.41
94	148	149.13	-1.13	1.28
Sum of the Squares				15.45

Legendre defined the line of best fit to be the line with the smallest value for the sum of squares of the errors. In this example, the sum of squares of the errors for the two-point model is 32.13; it is 15.45 for the linear regression model. Not only does the linear regression have a smaller sum of squares than the two-point model, Legendre proved that the linear regression model has the *smallest* sum of squares of all linear models.

Activity

The linear regression model of x versus observed y of the following data set is $y = -x + 11.8$. Copy and complete the table.

x	Observed y	Predicted y	Error	Error²
2	10	9.8	0.2	0.04
4	7	7.8		
6	6			
8	5			1.44
10	1		-0.8	

What is the sum of the squares of the errors?

A scatterplot of the data from the Activity and the line $y = -x + 11.8$ from the regression model are graphed below. Each error is the directed length (positive or negative) of a vertical segment on the graph—above the regression line if positive, below if negative.

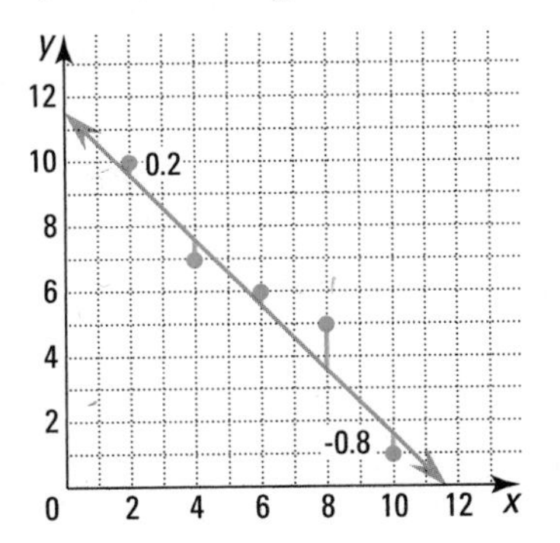

Although almost everyone today uses a statistics utility to find the line of best fit for a set of data, there is always one point on the line you can determine by hand without much trouble. That point is the **center of gravity** of the data. The coordinates of the center of gravity are the mean of the observed x-values and the mean of the observed y-values.

Example 2

There are several theories about relations between measurements of different parts of the human body (called *anthropometrics*). One theory states that there is a linear relation between the wrist circumference (C_w) and the neck circumference (C_n). To study this theory, the data on page 100 were gathered from seventeen persons.

C_w (cm)	C_n (cm)	C_w (cm)	C_n (cm)	C_w (cm)	C_n (cm)
14.4	31.0	16.2	32.2	17.1	36.6
14.8	33.5	16.2	35.5	17.2	38.5
15.0	33.0	16.2	35.8	17.6	39.8
15.4	35.2	16.3	36.4	17.8	38.3
15.7	34.2	16.7	37.3	17.9	37.1
16.1	33.7	16.9	35.3		

Notice that the wrist circumference of 16.2 cm is matched with three different neck circumferences (32.2, 35.5, and 35.8) in the data above. This leads to three y-coordinates corresponding to the same x-coordinate. Thus, the wrist vs. neck circumference data is not a function. However, we use a function, the line of best fit, to model it. The discrepancy is tolerable, and the equation of the line allows for predictions.

a. Use a statistics utility to find the line of best fit for predicting neck size y (in cm) from wrist size x (in cm).

b. What is the likely neck size of a person with wrist circumference 16 cm?

c. What is the likely neck size of a person with wrist circumference 19 cm?

Solution

a. Enter the data and follow the recommended procedure for the statistics package you use.

An equation for the line of best fit is $y = 1.92x + 4.23$.

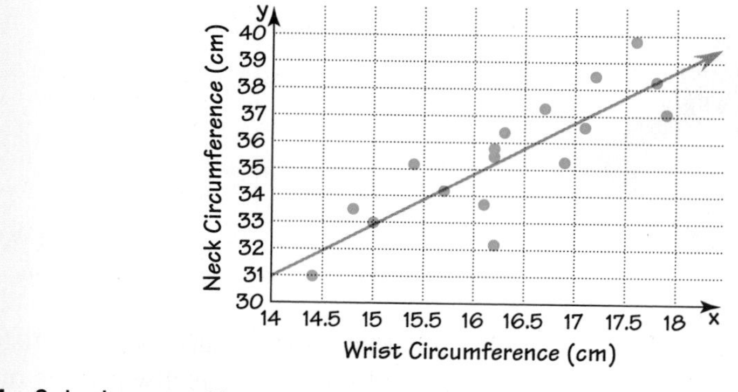

b. Substitute $x = 16$.

$y = 1.92(16) + 4.23 = 34.95$

A neck size of 35.0 cm is predicted.

c. Substitute $x = 19$.

$y = 1.92(19) + 4.23 = 40.71$

A neck size of 40.7 cm is predicted.

In the previous example, known wrist sizes range from 14.4 to 17.9 cm. In part **b**, calculating neck size for a 16 cm wrist size, the model was used to make a prediction between known values. Prediction like this is called **interpolation**. In part **c**, calculating neck size for a 19 cm wrist size, the model was used to make a prediction beyond known values. Prediction like this is called **extrapolation**. Extrapolation is usually more hazardous than interpolation, because it depends on an assumption that a relationship will continue past the known data.

QUESTIONS

Covering the Reading

1. For a data set, errors are the differences between **a.** values and **b.** values.

2. Does the sum of the squares of the errors mean (a) to sum the errors and then square or (b) to square the errors and then sum?

In 3 and 4, refer to your work on the Activity.

3. In the last row of the table, why is the error, -0.8, negative?

4. What is the sum of the squares of the errors?

In 5 and 6, refer to the CPI data.

5. What are the coordinates of the center of gravity?

6. Verify that this point is on the line of best fit.

7. Prediction between known values of a data set is called **a.** ; prediction beyond known values is called **b.** .

Applying the Mathematics

8. The following table lists again the estimates of life expectancy for people of different ages in 1992.

Current Age	Expected Life Span	Current Age	Expected Life Span	Current Age	Expected Life Span
1	76.4	30	77.5	60	81.1
5	76.6	35	77.9	65	82.5
10	76.6	40	78.3	70	84.2
15	76.7	45	78.8	75	86.2
20	76.9	50	79.3	80	88.5
25	77.2	55	80.1	85	91.2

Source: *Statistical Abstract of the United States 1995*

a. Make a scatterplot of the data. Use current age as the independent variable.
b. Find an equation of the line of best fit.
c. Calculate the life expectancy of a person age 15 according to your model. By how much does it differ from the corresponding value in the table?
d. Compare your answers to parts **b** and **c** to your answers to the corresponding part of Question 16 of Lesson 2-2. Which model in general produces the least amount of error?
e. What is the correlation coefficient for the model? What does it tell you about the relationship between age and expected life span?

9. The following table shows the winning jumps in the men's long jump event at the Olympic games.

Year	Gold Medalist	Jump
1896	Ellery Clark, United States	6.34 m
1900	Alvin Kraenzlein, United States	7.19 m
1904	Myer Prinstein, United States	7.34 m
1908	Francis Irons, United States	7.48 m
1912	Albert Gutterson, United States	7.60 m
1920	William Pettersson, Sweden	7.15 m
1924	DeHart Hubbard, United States	7.45 m
1928	Edward B. Hamm, United States	7.74 m
1932	Edward Gordon, United States	7.64 m
1936	Jesse Owens, United States	8.06 m
1948	Willie Steele, United States	7.82 m
1952	Jerome Biffle, United States	7.57 m
1956	Gregory Bell, United States	7.83 m
1960	Ralph Boston, United States	8.12 m
1964	Lynn Davies, Great Britain	8.07 m
1968	Robert Beamon, United States	8.90 m
1972	Randy Williams, United States	8.24 m
1976	Arnie Robinson, United States	8.35 m
1980	Lutz Dombrowski, East Germany	8.54 m
1984	Carl Lewis, United States	8.54 m
1988	Carl Lewis, United States	8.72 m
1992	Carl Lewis, United States	8.67 m

Source: *1996 Information Please Almanac*

Golden jump. *Carl Lewis won his fourth Olympic gold medal in the long jump in 1996 in Atlanta. He became the second athlete to win four consecutive gold medals in the same event.*

a. Make a scatterplot of these data.

b. Find the line of best fit predicting the winning jump for a given year.

c. What does the slope of the line tell you about the average rate of change in the length of the winning long jump?

d. Use the line of best fit to predict the winning jump for the Atlanta Olympics in 1996, and the error in the prediction (the actual jump by Carl Lewis was 8.50 m). Is this interpolation or extrapolation?

e. Calculate the center of gravity of the data, and verify that the regression line passes through this point.

f. Which data points seem to be outliers here? Why are they so far from the linear model?

10. The table below gives the percent of total plastic in the U.S. that was used and then recycled, for specified years from 1985 to 1994.

Year	1985	1989	1991	1993	1994
Percent	0.9	1.7	2.6	3.5	4.5

Source: *Statistical Abstract of the United States 1995*

a. Let x = number of years after 1900, and let y = percent. Calculate the line of best fit using a statistics utility.
b. What is the sum of squares of the errors?

11. Refer to the data on wrist and neck size in Example 2. Let x = neck circumference and y = wrist circumference.
a. Find the line of best fit for predicting wrist size from neck size.
b. What is the predicted wrist size of a person with a neck circumference of 37.5 cm?
c. What is the predicted wrist size of a person with a neck circumference of 17 in.?

Review

12. To develop a roll of film with up to 36 exposures, a photo lab charges \$2.49 per roll plus \$.30 per print. Let n = the number of prints developed and $f(n)$ = the cost of developing a roll of film with n prints.
a. Write a formula for $f(n)$.
b. What is the domain of f?
c. Find the cost of developing a roll of film and making 20 prints.
d. How many prints were made if the cost of developing and printing was \$12.09? *(Lesson 2-1)*

13. Suppose $Q(x) = \sqrt{x + 7}$.
a. Find $Q(2)$.
b. What is the domain of Q?
c. Give the range of Q. *(Lesson 2-1)*

14. Suppose $f(x) = x^2 - 8x - 9$. For what value(s) of x does $f(x) = 0$? *(Previous course, Lesson 2-1)*

In 15 and 16, an equation of a function $y = f(x)$ is given. **a.** Sketch a graph. **b.** Identify the domain and range of the function. *(Previous course, Lesson 2-1)*

15. $y = \frac{12}{x}$

16. $y = \frac{12}{x^2}$

In 17 and 18, solve. *(Previous course)*

17. $a^3 = 4^6$

18. $(-2)^n \cdot (-2)^5 = (-2)^{18}$

19. Without using a calculator, tell which expression is *not equal* to the others. *(Previous course)*
$\sqrt{100}$, $\sqrt[4]{10^4}$, $10000^{\frac{1}{4}}$, $(10^2)^{\frac{1}{2}}$, $(10^4)^{-4}$

20. The pie charts below display the responses of eighth- and twelfth-grade mathematics students to a statement about mathematics, as found in an international study.

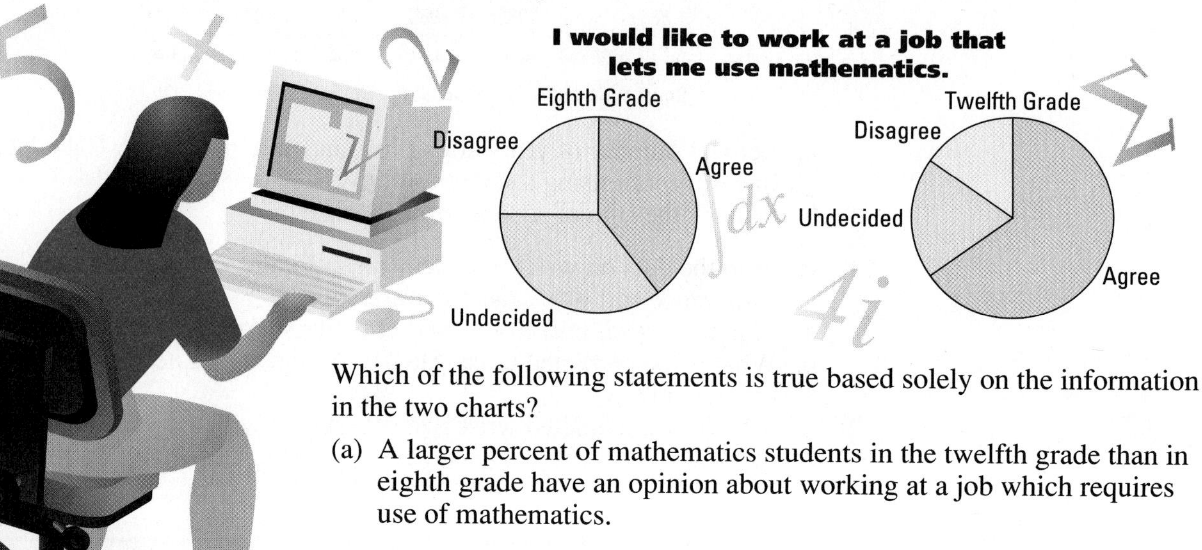

Which of the following statements is true based solely on the information in the two charts?

(a) A larger percent of mathematics students in the twelfth grade than in eighth grade have an opinion about working at a job which requires use of mathematics.

(b) About 40% of mathematics students in the eighth grade seem inclined to pursue a career in which they could use math.

(c) A larger proportion of mathematics students in the twelfth grade are looking for jobs. *(Lesson 1-1)*

Exploration

21. Legendre, who developed the method of least squares, was a mathematician of great breadth and originality. In addition to his work in calculus and statistics, he contributed to number theory and geometry. Find out more about his contributions to mathematics.

LESSON

2-4

Exponential Functions

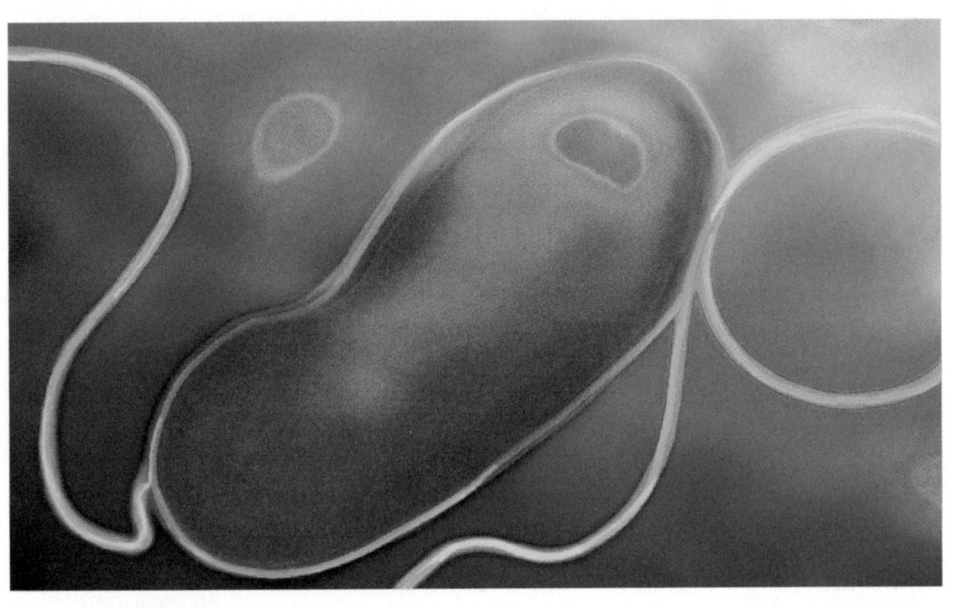

Tummy troubles. *The bacterium, Helicobacter pylori, is presently accepted as the cause of stomach and duodenal ulcers. If not treated with antibiotics, the organism will continue to reproduce exponentially.*

What Is an Exponential Function?

Consider a population of bacteria that doubles in number every hour. Suppose there are 10 bacteria initially. The table at the right shows the population P at the end of each of the first 4 hours.

Hours passed	Population
0	10
1	20
2	40
3	80
4	160

A graph of the data is at the left below. The population P is a function of the number of hours h. If N is that function, then $P = N(h) = 10 \cdot 2^h$ because h indicates the number of times the population has doubled.

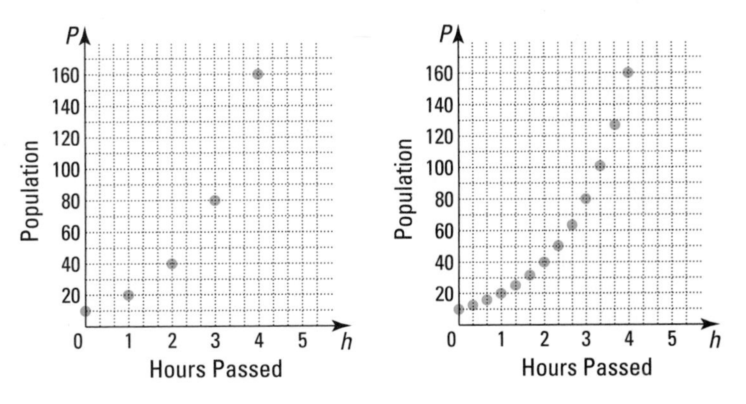

What can be said about the points between those shown on the left graph? Because time is a continuous variable, after half an hour you would expect there to be $N\left(\frac{1}{2}\right) = 10 \cdot 2^{1/2}$ bacteria. This is $10\sqrt{2} \approx 14.14$ bacteria, which should be truncated to 14 because it isn't meaningful to consider fractions of bacteria. Similarly, $N(h)$ can be calculated for other rational values of h to give a more complete graph, like the one at the right above.

If you think about $P = 10 \cdot 2^h$ out of the context of the bacteria situation, then h can be any positive real number. You can get a good approximation for powers with irrational exponents by using your calculator's powering key. To evaluate $2^{\sqrt{3}}$, use 2 as the base and $\sqrt{3}$ as the exponent. To the nearest thousandth, $2^{\sqrt{3}} \approx 3.322$. Check this on your calculator.

The function mapping h to P is an example of an *exponential function* with base 2.

Definition
An **exponential function with base b** is a function with a formula of the form:

$$f(x) = ab^x,$$

where $a \neq 0$, $b > 0$, and $b \neq 1$.

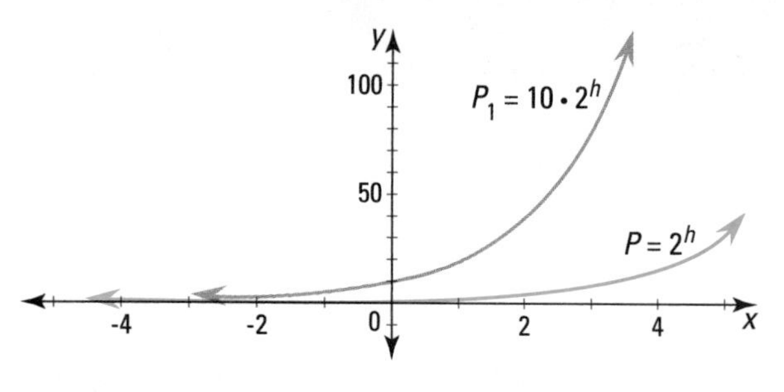

Exponential Growth

When an exponential function has base $b > 1$, and $a > 0$, as in the bacterial growth situation, the function is called an **exponential growth function**, and its graph is called an **exponential growth curve**. $P_1 = 10 \cdot 2^h$ is related to the parent exponential function whose equation is $P = 2^h$. These two functions are graphed to the left, with $P = 2^h$ in blue and $P_1 = 10 \cdot 2^h$ in orange.

Exponential functions occur naturally when a quantity changes by a constant factor during a given time period. Specifically, if a *growth rate* is a constant percent of the population, the relation between time and population can be described using an exponential function. In the bacteria growth situation above, the population doubles, or increases by 100 percent, every hour. That is why the base of the function is 2.

Whakairo. *The Maori recorded their history in woodcarvings called Whakairo. In 1997, the Maori comprised 9% of the population in New Zealand.*

Example 1

In 1993, the population of New Zealand was 3,424,000, with an average annual growth rate of 1.3%. Suppose that this growth rate were to continue.

a. Estimate the population of New Zealand in each of 1994, 1995, and 1996.

b. Express the population P as a function of n, the number of years after 1993.

c. Estimate New Zealand's population in the year 2010.

Solution

A growth rate of 1.3% annually means that each year the population is 1.013 times the previous year's population.

a. In 1994: $P = (3{,}424{,}000)(1.013) \approx 3{,}469{,}000$

In 1995: $P = (3{,}424{,}000)(1.013)^2 \approx 3{,}514{,}000$

In 1996: $P = (3{,}424{,}000)(1.013)^3 \approx 3{,}559{,}000$

b. Generalize the pattern in part **a**. In n years after 1993, the population will have increased by 1.3% n times. That is,

$$P = f(n) = (3{,}424{,}000)(1.013)^n$$

c. The year 2010 is 17 years after 1993, so $n = 17$ in the equation from part **b**.

$$P = f(17) = (3{,}424{,}000)(1.013)^{17} \approx 4{,}265{,}000$$

So, under the assumption that the growth rate remains at 1.3%, the population in the year 2010 will be about 4,265,000.

The exponential function in Example 1 arises from the assumption that the population growth rate is constant. In fact, there are many reasons why a growth rate may change: a trend toward smaller families, or changes in health care or nutrition resulting in a change in death rates. It is unwise to extrapolate growth rates beyond a few years. In fact, by 1996 the growth rate in New Zealand had decreased, and its population was about 3,548,000.

Another well-known example of exponential growth is the value of an investment after interest is compounded. Suppose you deposit P dollars in an account which pays an annual yield y (the growth rate), compounded yearly. If at the end of every year you leave the interest in the account, your balance is multiplied by $(1 + y)$ (the growth factor). After t years, your balance A is given by $A = P(1 + y)^t$. The function f with $A = f(y) = P(1 + y)^t$ is an exponential function with base $1 + y$.

Exponential Decay

The graph of the exponential equation $f(x) = ab^x$ with $a > 0$ and $0 < b < 1$ is closely related to the graph of the same equation with $b > 1$.

Example 2

Compare and contrast the graphs of $g(x) = 0.5^x$ and $f(x) = 2^x$. Describe such things as the domain and range of each function, their x- and y-intercepts, and how the two graphs are related.

Solution

Graph the two functions, and look for similarities and differences.

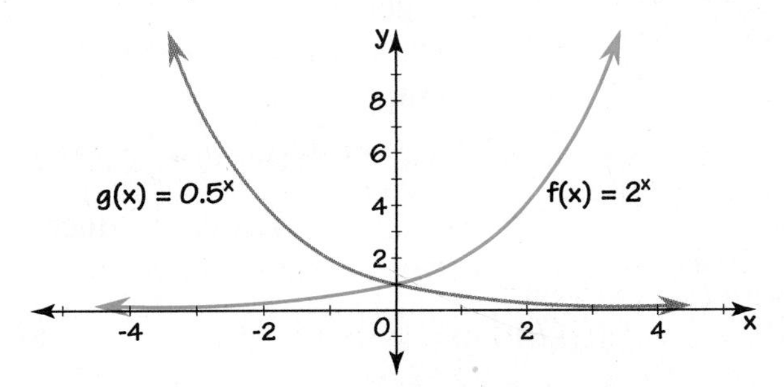

The expressions 2^x and 0.5^x are defined for all real numbers, so the domains of f and g are the set of real numbers. The range of each is then the set of positive reals. Each graph has y-intercept equal to 1; neither graph intersects the x-axis, because there is no real number x such that $2^x = 0$ or $0.5^x = 0$.

The graph of $g(x) = 0.5^x$ is a reflection image of $f(x) = 2^x$ over the y-axis. The reflection property in Example 2 is not so surprising when you recall two simple ideas.

(1) $0.5 = 2^{-1}$, so $0.5^x = (2^{-1})^x = 2^{-x}$. That is, $g(x) = f(-x)$.

(2) Reflection over the y-axis occurs when x is replaced by $-x$ in an equation.

If $a > 0$, graphs of exponential functions with base b, where $0 < b < 1$, are called **exponential decay curves**. The word "decay" comes from the fact that these exponential functions model situations—such as radioactive decay—in which a quantity is diminishing by a constant factor.

Properties of Exponential Functions

Based on the graphs on page 107 and your knowledge of powers, note the following properties of an exponential function with equation $y = f(x) = ab^x$.

(1) Its domain is the set of real numbers.

(2) Its range is the set of positive real numbers. That is, $f(x)$ is *strictly positive* because $ab^x > 0$ for all real x, when $a > 0$ and $b > 0$.

(3) Because the range is the set of positive real numbers, every positive real number can be expressed as a multiple of some power of b.

(4) Its graph contains the point $(0, a)$.

(5) Its graph does not intersect the x-axis.

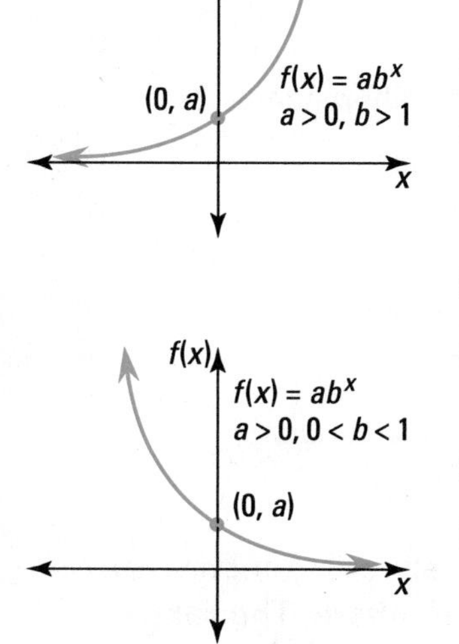

When $b > 1$ and exponential growth occurs,

(6) the function is **strictly increasing**, because as x-values increase, corresponding y-values increase;

(7) as x gets larger, $f(x)$ increases without bound;

(8) as x gets smaller, $f(x)$ decreases but is always positive and it approaches zero. We see that the graph has the x-axis as an **asymptote**.

In contrast, when $0 < b < 1$ and exponential decay occurs,

(6') the function is **strictly decreasing**, because as x-values increase, corresponding y-values decrease;

(7') as x gets smaller, $f(x)$ increases without bound;

(8') as x gets larger, $f(x)$ decreases but is always positive, and it approaches zero. So the x-axis is an asymptote of the exponential decay curve also.

Notice that properties (6) to (8) and (6') to (8') indicate that the end behavior of an exponential decay function is reversed from that of an exponential growth function.

QUESTIONS

Covering the Reading

1. In the bacteria population in the lesson, how many bacteria will there be after 3.5 hours?

2. Approximate $2^{\sqrt{5}}$ to the nearest hundredth.

3. Determine if the function with the given equation is an exponential function.

a. $k(m) = 4^m$ **b.** $s(t) = 6$

c. $j(z) = z^2$ **d.** $p(x) = 0.6^x$

In 4 and 5, an exponential equation is given. **a**. Estimate its solution by referring to a graph in this lesson. **b**. Solve using some other means.

4. $2^x = 20$

5. $10 \cdot 2^x = 60$

Not all of China is as crowded as this shopping district in Wuhan, China

6. The most populous country in the world is the People's Republic of China. In 1995 its population was estimated as 1,198,000,000; and the average annual growth rate was about 1.01%. Suppose this rate remains unchanged.

a. Estimate the population in 1996 and 1997.

b. Express the population P as a function of n, the number of years after 1995.

c. Use your answer to part **b** to predict the population of China in 2005.

d. Use your answer to part **b** to predict the population in 2995. Is this possible?

In 7 and 8, let $f(x) = 3^x$ and $g(x) = \left(\frac{1}{3}\right)^x$.

7. a. Graph the functions f and g on one set of axes scaled in 0.25 units for $-3 < x < 3$.

b. What transformation maps the graph of f onto the graph of g?

c. Rewrite the equation for g using a negative exponent and use this result to justify your response to part **b**.

8. Which function, f or g, represents exponential decay?

In 9 and 10, *true or false*.

9. All exponential functions contain the point (0, 1).

10. The graph of every function of the form $y = b^x$ where $b > 0$ and $b \neq 1$ is always above the x-axis.

11. If $a > 0$, state three ways in which exponential functions $y = ab^x$ with bases b in the interval $0 < b < 1$ differ from exponential functions with $b > 1$.

Applying the Mathematics

12. Consider $f(x) = 4^x$ and $g(x) = 5^x$.

a. Without graphing, which function has greater values when $x > 0$?

b. Without graphing, which function has greater values when $x < 0$?

c. Check your answers to parts **a** and **b** by graphing f and g on the same set of axes.

13. **a.** Graph $f(x) = 5^x$ and $g(x) = x^5$ on the same set of axes.

b. As x increases, between which two consecutive integers does $g(x)$ first exceed $f(x)$?

c. Estimate to the nearest tenth all values of x where $f(x) = g(x)$.

14. **a.** Graph $y = b^x$ for $b = 1$.

b. Can the graph in part **a** be called an exponential growth curve? Why or why not?

15. Phillip Theodore Rich deposits \$500 in an account paying 6.25% annual yield. If he leaves the account untouched, how much will the investment be worth after the given amount of time?

a. 3 years **b.** t years

16. A certain substance decays so that each year 90% of the previous year's material is still present.

a. How much of an initial 2 kilograms of material would remain after 1, 2, and 3 years?

b. After n years, how much of an initial 2 kilograms of material would remain?

c. *True or false.* After six years, more than half the material will have decayed.

Review

17. Which, interpolation or extrapolation, generally gives a more accurate prediction? *(Lesson 2-3)*

In 18–20 tell whether the relation graphed is a function. *(Lesson 2-1)*

18. **19.** **20.**

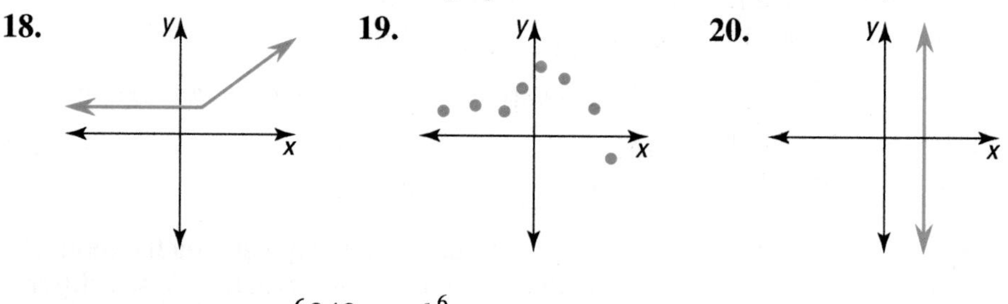

21. Solve the system $\begin{cases} 240 = ab^6 \\ 20 = ab^4 \end{cases}$. *(Previous course)*

22. Here are the world records (as of 1996) for the women's 4 × 100 m track relay, beginning in 1926. (Source: *International Amateur Athletic Federation*)

Year	Country	Time (seconds)
1926	Germany	50.4
1928	Germany	49.7
1932	Canada	48.4
1932	United States	46.9
1936	Germany	46.4
1952	Australia	46.1
1952	Germany	45.9
1953	USSR	45.6
1956	USSR	45.2
1956	Germany	45.1
1956	Australia	44.9
1956	Australia	44.5
1960	United States	44.4
1961	United States	44.3
1964	United States	43.9
1968	USSR	43.6
1968	United States	43.47
1968	United States	42.87
1972	West Germany	42.81
1973	East Germany	42.6
1974	East Germany	42.6
1974	East Germany	42.51
1976	East Germany	42.50
1978	East Germany	42.27
1979	East Germany	42.09
1980	East Germany	41.85
1980	East Germany	41.60
1983	East Germany	41.53
1985	East Germany	41.37

a. Enter the data into a statistics utility. Let the number of years after 1900 be the independent variable. Find the correlation between the number of years after 1900 and the record time.

b. What does the value of the correlation tell you about the relation between the two variables?

c. Find an equation for the line of best fit for predicting world records for this event.

d. Predict the year in which the 40-second barrier will be broken for the first time. *(Lessons 2-2, 2-3)*

Exploration

23. What factors other than a change in birth rate or death rate can affect the growth rate of a country?

LESSON

2-5

Exponential Models

How old are they? *Paleontologists excavating this site in South Dakota will rely on radiocarbon dating to determine the age of these skeletons of mammoths.*

Exponential models have the form $f(x) = ab^x$, where $a \neq 0$, $b > 0$, and $b \neq 1$. Since x frequently represents time and $f(0) = ab^0 = a$, a is called the **initial value** of the dependent variable. The number b, the base of the exponential function, is called the **growth factor**. When $a > 0$, if $b > 1$, the function models exponential growth, while if $0 < b < 1$, it models exponential decay. Exponential models are extremely important because they describe situations in many fields, such as biology, paleontology, sociology, physics, and economics, to name a few.

Comparing Linear and Exponential Models

To use a linear model $y = mx + b$ to make predictions for a particular situation, it is necessary to determine m and b. Similarly, to use an exponential model $y = ab^x$ to make predictions for a specific situation, we must determine a, the initial value, and b, the growth factor. As with the linear model, only two data points are needed to determine an exponential model.

There is an important difference between linear and exponential models. Linear functions are appropriate to model situations of constant increase or decrease, whereas exponential functions model situations that have a constant percentage change.

Finding an Exponential Model Using a System of Equations

Populations very often grow with a constant percentage increase, at least in the short run. Therefore, it is natural to fit an exponential model to population data.

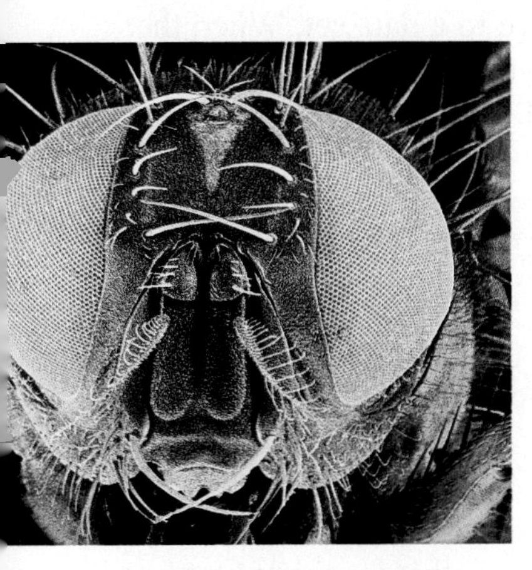

I only have eyes for you. *Each compound eye of this female housefly, Musca domestica, contains about 4000 separate image-forming elements called ommatidia.*

Example 1

In a laboratory experiment on the growth of insects, there were 74 insects three days after the beginning of the experiment and 108 after an additional two days. This information has been summarized in the table at the right.

Number of Days	Number of Insects
3	74
5	108

a. Find an exponential model for the data.
b. Find the initial number of insects.
c. Predict the number of insects 6.5 days after the beginning of the experiment.

Solution

a. An exponential model for the number of insects $f(t)$ after t days is $f(t) = a \cdot b^t$. You are given $f(3) = 74$ and $f(5) = 108$. Substitute these values into the equation to get a system.

$$74 = ab^3$$
$$108 = ab^5$$

Divide the second equation by the first: $\frac{108}{74} = b^2$ Because b must be positive in an exponential model, $b = \sqrt{\frac{108}{74}} \approx 1.208$. To find a, substitute this value of b into one of the equations involving a and b. Using the first equation,

$$74 \approx a(1.208)^3$$
$$a \approx \frac{74}{(1.208)^3} \approx 41.98.$$

So an exponential model is $f(t) = 41.98 \cdot 1.208^t$.

b. Initially, $t = 0$. Use the equation from part **a**.

$$f(0) = 41.98 \cdot (1.208)^0 = 41.98$$

About 42 insects were present initially.
So another reasonable exponential model is $f(t) = 42 \cdot (1.208)^t$.

c. Substitute $t = 6.5$.

$$f(6.5) = 42 \cdot (1.208)^{6.5} \approx 143.44.$$

So, about 143 insects were present 6.5 days after the experiment began.

Check

Draw a graph of the function $f(t) = 42 \cdot (1.208)^t$. The output from an automatic grapher is shown at the right.

This graph passes through the points (3, 74) and (5, 108). Use the trace key to verify the answers to parts **b** and **c**.

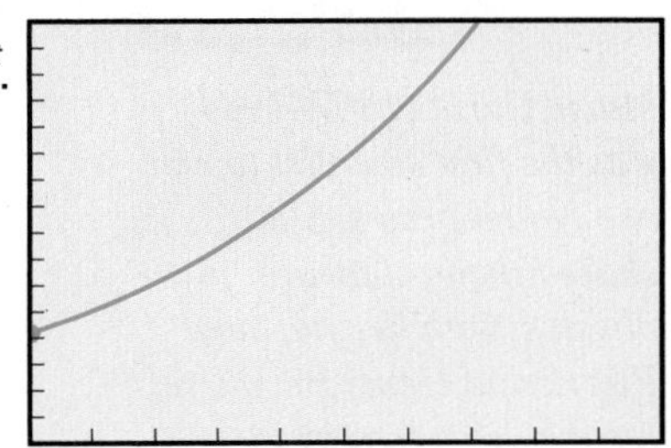

$0 \le x \le 10$, x-scale = 1
$0 \le y \le 160$, y-scale = 10

In the model $f(t) \approx 42(1.208)^t$, the growth factor 1.208 indicates that at the end of each day there are about 1.208 times as many insects as at the beginning of that day. An equivalent statement is that the growth rate is about 20.8% per day.

Exponential Regression

Many statistics utilities can fit an exponential curve to a data set. When the data set has just two points, as in Example 1, the statistics utility will give the same exponential model you can find by hand.

Activity

Enter the two columns from the table in Example 1 into your statistics package, letting the number of days be the independent (or x) variable and number of insects be the dependent (or y) variable. Calculate the exponential regression. Write an equation for the exponential model using all the digits your calculator provides.

Marie Curie (1867–1934) was the first scientist to win two Nobel prizes. She shared the first award, in physics, with her husband Pierre and Henri Becquerel for the discovery of radioactivity; the second prize, in chemistry, was for her work with radium.

Situations involving exponential growth or decay often contain information about the **doubling time** or the **half-life** of a quantity, that is, about how long it takes a quantity to double or to decay to half its original amount. If the initial condition is known, either the doubling time or half-life can be used to find other data points on the exponential curve.

Example 2

The half-life of a certain radioactive substance is 40 days. If 10 grams of the substance are present initially, how much of the substance will be present in 90 days?

Solution

Let $f(t)$ be the amount of the substance present t days after the radioactive decay starts. The function f is exponential, so a model for it has the form $f(t) = ab^t$. Make a table using the given information about the initial amount and the half-life.

Number of Half-Life Periods	0	1	2	3
t = Number of Days After Decay Starts	0	40	80	120
$f(t)$ = Amount Present (grams)	10	5	2.5	1.25

Enter the values of t and $f(t)$ into your statistics utility, and calculate an exponential regression. One statistics utility gives $y = 10 \cdot (0.98282059854525)^x$, so $f(t) = 10 \cdot (0.9828)^t$ is a reasonable exponential model for the data. Substituting $t = 90$, $f(90) = 10 \cdot (0.9828)^{90} \approx 2.1$. After 90 days, about 2.1 g of the radioactive substance would be left.

Check

Graph $y = 10 \cdot (0.9828)^x$. Are (40, 5), (80, 2.5), and (120, 1.25) on the curve? The check is left to you.

The data in Examples 1 and 2 were derived from models that describe situations that are exact or theoretical exponential models. When data points follow an approximately exponential pattern, a statistical utility will find a "best fitting" exponential curve using an algorithm similar to the one developed by Legendre for linear regression.

Example 3

The chapter opener included the following table on national debt.

Year	Amount (billions of $)
1965	322
1970	381
1975	542
1980	909
1985	1,818
1990	3,207
1995	4,921

a. Use your statistics utility to fit an exponential model of the form $f(x) = ab^x$ to the data. Make a scatterplot and superimpose the graph of the exponential model. Report the values of a and b in the exponential model to the nearest thousandth.

b. Write a paragraph about the national debt that explains the meaning of a and b.

Solution

a.

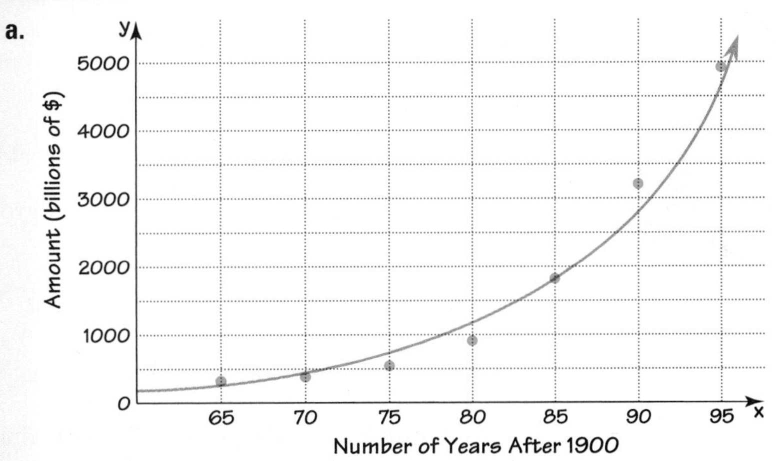

One statistics utility gives

$a = 0.4430181$ and $b = 1.102418973$.

Therefore,

$a \approx 0.443$, $b \approx 1.102$, and $f(x) \approx 0.443 \cdot 1.102^x$.

b. The initial value of the exponential model is 0.443, corresponding to \$.443 billion or \$443 million. According to the model, the national debt when $x = 0$, in 1900, is \$443 million. Because 1900 is beyond known values of the data, using the model to calculate the debt in 1900 is extrapolation. The growth factor of the model is 1.102. This means that during the years from 1965 through 1995, the national debt had a growth rate of about 10.2% per year.

QUESTIONS

Covering the Reading

In 1 and 2, consider the exponential model $f(x) = ab^x$.

1. *True or false.* The initial value of the model is $f(1)$.

2. For $a > 0$, if $0 < b < 1$, what type of exponential model is f?

3. For the exponential model $B = 37(1.32)^x$, find each.
   a. the initial value **b.** the growth factor

4. Refer to the Activity in the lesson. What equation does your statistics utility give for the exponential model for the data in Example 1?

5. Suppose an exponential model of the form $f(t) = ab^t$ contains the two points (3, 20) and (5, 40).
   a. Substitute the two points into the model to get a system of equations for a and b.
   b. Solve the system to yield an equation for the model.
   c. Use either a graph or exponential regression on your statistics utility to check your answer to part **b**.
   d. Give the initial value for the model.
   e. What is the growth factor for the model?

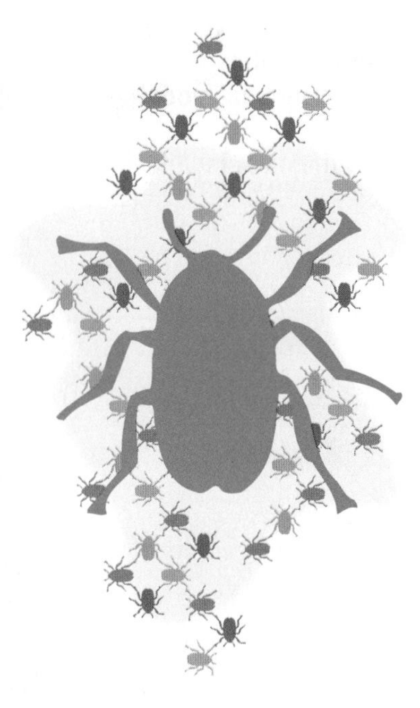

6. In a study of the change in an insect population, there were about 170 insects four weeks after the study began, and about 320 after two more weeks. Assume an exponential model of growth.
   a. Find an equation relating the population to the time in weeks.
   b. Estimate the initial number of insects.
   c. Predict the number of insects five weeks after the study began.

7. Use the following data from a bacterial growth experiment.

Hours passed (h)	0	1	2	3	4	5
Population (p)	200	600	1800	5400	16200	48600

   a. Every time one additional hour passes, what happens to the population?
   b. Give an exponential model for these data.
   c. Estimate the population size after 3 hours and 30 minutes have passed.

8. Radium has a half-life of 1620 years.
   a. Copy and complete this table.

Number of Half-Lives	0	1	2	3
t = Number of Years After Start	0	1620		
$f(t)$ = Amount of Radium Present (grams)	3			

   b. Suppose the initial mass of some radium was 3 grams. Give an exponential model for the amount of radium left from this mass as a function of time t.
   c. How much radium would you expect to find after 4000 years?

Applying the Mathematics

In 9 and 10, the half-life of the carbon isotope ^{14}C is about 5700 years.

9. About how many years does it take 1000 grams of this substance to decay to 500 grams?

10. About what percent of the original amount would you expect to find after 1000 years?

In 11 and 12, an exponential model for the population P (in millions) of Indonesia during the 1980s is given by $P = 148.7(1.021)^y$, where y stands for the number of years after 1980.

11. In that decade, what was the annual growth rate of Indonesia's population?

12. Use an automatic grapher to estimate when Indonesia's population reached 175 million.

13. A tour guide noticed that the larger the size of the group, the more time it took to assemble everyone for an event. The guide timed people and collected the following data.

Number of People	2	3	4	5	6	7	8	9	10
Minutes to Assemble	2	2.6	3.4	4.4	5.7	7.4	9.7	12.5	16.3

a. Make a scatterplot of the data.
b. Find the linear regression model. Write the equation and graph it.
c. Find the exponential regression model. Write the equation and graph it.
d. Which of the two models, linear or exponential, seems to fit the data better? Why?

Review

14. If the inflation rate was 7% when the cartoon below was published in 1977, what was the hourly wage rate then? *(Previous course, Lesson 2-4)*

In 15 and 16, consider the function $g: x \to 3(1.3)^x$. *(Lesson 2-4)*

15. **a.** Give the domain of g. **b.** Give the range of g.

16. State equations for any asymptotes to the graph of g.

17. Data were collected to decide whether people should be advised about possible dangers of taking a drug before driving a car. The data below show the reaction times t of a group of ten people administered various dosages d of the drug. Reaction time was measured as the average time for a person to respond to a red light over several trials.

Dosage d (mg)	Reaction Time t (sec)
85	0.5
89	0.6
90	0.2
95	1.2
95	1.6
103	0.6
107	1.0
110	1.8
111	1.0
115	1.5

a. Make a scatterplot of the data.
b. What is the correlation coefficient?
c. Find an equation for the line of best fit.
d. What is the error in the predicted reaction time for a dosage of 85 mg?
e. Write a sentence about the relationship between drug dosage and reaction time. *(Lessons 2-2, 2-3)*

In 18 and 19, a graph of a function is shown. **a.** Give the domain of the function. **b.** Estimate the range of each function. *(Lesson 2-1)*

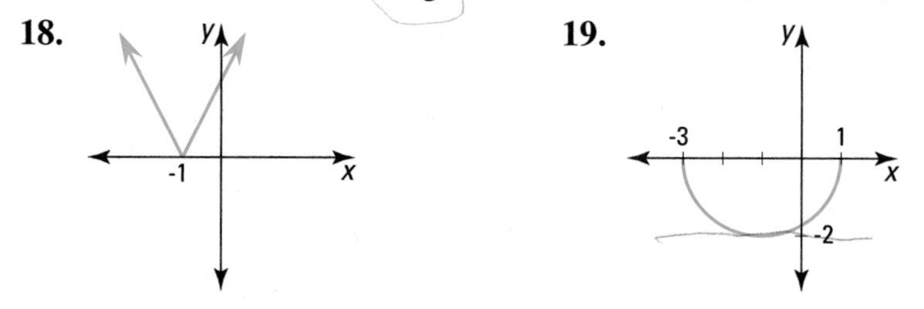

In 20 and 21, let $y = 2x^2 + 5x$. *(Previous course, Lesson 2-1)*

20. For what values of x does $y = 0$?

21. Is y a function of x? Why or why not?

Exploration

22. Carbon-14, or ^{14}C, as mentioned in Questions 9 and 10, has been used by archaeologists to date objects. Write about a place where this was done and the objects that were dated.

Introducing
Lesson 2-6

Using Quadratic Regression

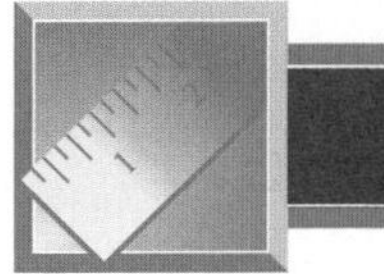

IN-CLASS ACTIVITY

A ball was thrown upward from an initial height of 15 m and the height of the ball was recorded every 0.5 seconds. The table shows the height h in meters t seconds after the ball was thrown.

t (sec)	0.0	0.5	1.0	1.5	2.0	2.5	3.0	3.5	4.0	4.5
h (m)	15	25.1	29.3	34.5	36.4	33.8	32.1	26	16.2	5.8

1 Enter the data into a statistics utility and make a scatterplot.

2 Explain why neither a linear nor an exponential model fits these data.

3 What type of curve do the points seem to lie on?

4 Find the feature called *quadratic regression* on the statistics utility and use it to find an equation to model this data set.

5 Plot the equation found in part **4** on the scatterplot. What does the quadratic regression seem to represent?

6 The *error* is the difference between observed and predicted values. Find the error in the quadratic regression model when $t = 2$.

7 Use the regression equation to find the time(s) when the ball was 27 m off the ground.

LESSON

2-6

Quadratic Models

What Is a Quadratic Function?

You have already studied linear functions, which model situations involving constant rate of change. You have also studied exponential functions, which model situations involving constant percentage change. In this lesson, we focus on **quadratic models**, that is, models based on quadratic functions. Recall that a quadratic function is of the form

$$f(x) = ax^2 + bx + c,$$

where $a \neq 0$. Recall also that graphs of quadratic functions are *parabolas*. If $a < 0$, the parabola has a *maximum point*; if $a > 0$, the parabola has a *minimum point*.

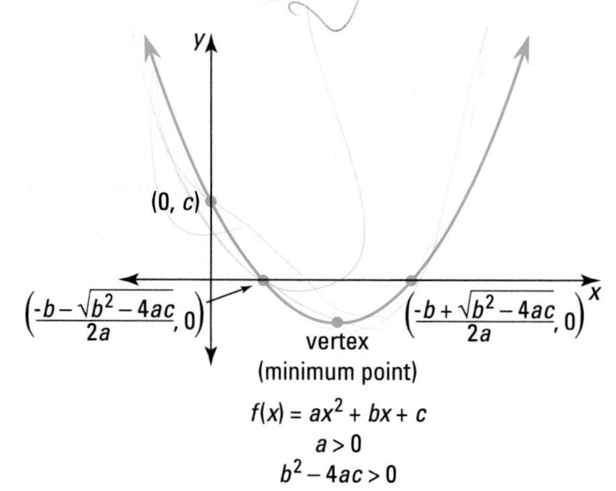

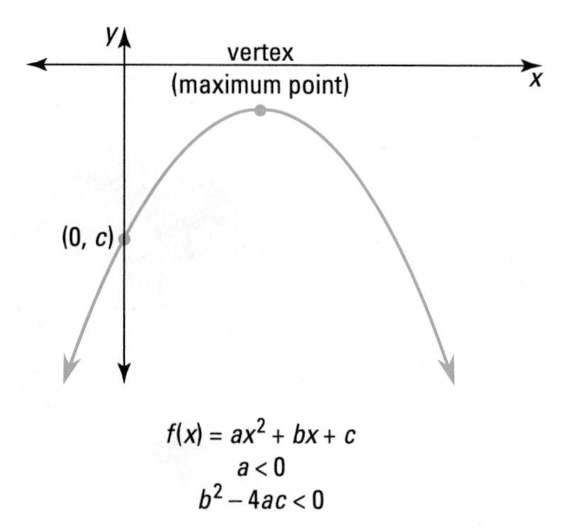

The domain of a quadratic function can be the set of all real numbers. Then, when $a < 0$, the range is the set of all real numbers less than or equal to the maximum value. When $a > 0$, the range is the set of all real numbers greater than or equal to the minimum value. The y-intercept is the y-coordinate of the point where $x = 0$.

$$f(0) = a \cdot 0^2 + b \cdot 0 + c = c$$

So c is the y-intercept. The x-intercepts are the x-coordinates of the points where $y = 0$. Remember that quadratic functions can have 0, 1, or 2 x-intercepts. The x-intercepts exist only when $b^2 - 4ac \geq 0$, and then can be found by solving the quadratic equation $ax^2 + bx + c = 0$. From the quadratic formula, the x-intercepts are

$$x = \frac{-b \pm \sqrt{b^2 - 4ac}}{2a}$$

The maximum or minimum point of any quadratic function occurs at the x-value that is the mean of the solutions to the equation $f(x) = 0$.

From one bounce to the next, the path of a ball is part of a parabola.

Example 1

Consider the function f with equation $f(x) = 2x^2 - 3x - 2$.

a. Find its x- and y-intercepts.

b. Tell whether the parabola has a maximum or minimum point and find its coordinates.

Solution

a. The y-intercept is -2, because $f(0) = 2(0)^2 - 3(0) - 2 = -2$.
To find the x-intercepts, let $f(x) = 0$ and solve for x.

$$2x^2 - 3x - 2 = 0$$

$$x = \frac{3 \pm \sqrt{(-3)^2 - 4(2)(-2)}}{2 \cdot 2}$$

$$= \frac{3 \pm \sqrt{25}}{4}$$

$$= 2 \text{ or } -\frac{1}{2}$$

The x-intercepts are 2 and $-\frac{1}{2}$.

b. Because the coefficient of x^2 is positive, the parabola has a minimum point. The x-coordinate of the minimum point occurs at the mean of the two x-intercepts.

$$\frac{2 + \left(-\frac{1}{2}\right)}{2} = \frac{3}{4}$$

$$f\left(\frac{3}{4}\right) = 2\left(\frac{3}{4}\right)^2 - 3\left(\frac{3}{4}\right) - 2 = \frac{-50}{16}$$

So the minimum point is $\left(\frac{3}{4}, -\frac{50}{16}\right)$, or (0.75, -3.125).

Check

Draw a graph. At the right is the output from an automatic grapher. Tracing along the curve shows that (0, -2), (-0.5, 0), and (2, 0) are on the curve. The minimum point seems to be (0.75, -3.125).

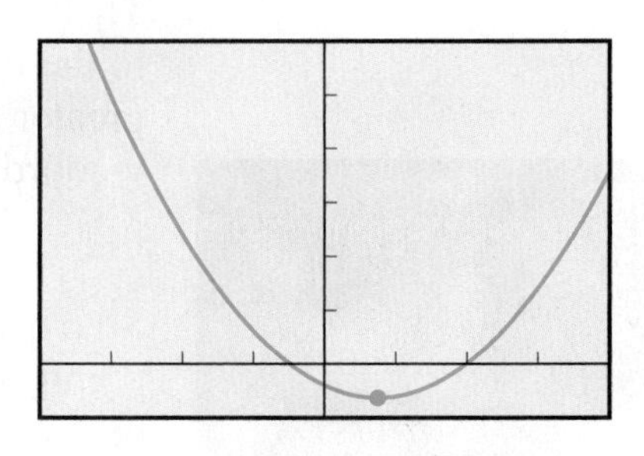

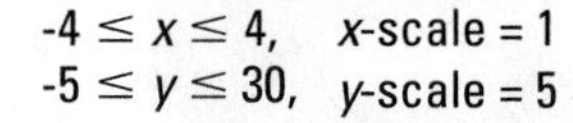
$-4 \le x \le 4$, x-scale = 1
$-5 \le y \le 30$, y-scale = 5

Using Known Quadratic Models

Some physical situations are modeled by quadratic functions. Among the most well-known is a famous function from physics. In the 17th century, Isaac Newton developed a theory that showed that the height h of an object at time t after it has been thrown upward with an initial velocity v_0 from an initial height h_0 satisfies the formula

$$h = -\frac{1}{2}gt^2 + v_0 t + h_0,$$

where g is the **acceleration due to gravity**. Recall that velocity is a rate of change of distance with respect to time; it is measured in units such as miles per hour or meters per second. Acceleration is the rate at which velocity changes, so it is measured in units such as miles per hour per hour or meters per second^2. Near the surface of the earth, g is approximately 32 ft/sec^2 or 9.8 m/sec^2. The equation you found for the data set in the In-class Activity should have a coefficient of t^2 approximately equal to $-\frac{1}{2}(9.8) = -4.9$.

Example 2

Suppose a ball is thrown upward from a height of 15 m with an initial velocity of 20 m/sec.

a. Find the relation between height h and time t after the ball is released.
b. How high is the ball after 3 seconds?

Solution

a. The conditions satisfy Newton's equation. Here $v_0 = 20 \frac{m}{sec}$, and $h_0 = 15$ m. Use the metric value $g = 9.8 \frac{m}{sec^2}$.

$$h = -\frac{1}{2}(9.8)t^2 + 20t + 15$$
$$h = -4.9t^2 + 20t + 15$$

b. We are given $t = 3$ and asked to find h.

$$h = f(3) = -4.9(3)^2 + 20 \cdot 3 + 15$$
$$= 30.9$$

After 3 seconds, the ball is 30.9 m high.

Finding a Quadratic Model

When data points appear to lie on a parabola, it is reasonable to look for an equation for that parabola. As with a linear or exponential model, there are two ways to fit a quadratic model to data. You can identify specific points on the quadratic model and set up a system of equations. For a quadratic model, the system must allow you to solve for the values of a, b, and c in the equation $y = ax^2 + bx + c$. Because there are three unknowns, you need three points to be able to find an equation of a parabola. This requires a bit of algebraic manipulation, but often it is not too tedious. This is done in Solution 1 to Example 3 below.

Alternately, you can use a statistics utility to do a *quadratic regression*. **Quadratic regression** is a technique, similar to Legendre's method of least squares, that finds an equation for the best-fitting parabola through a set of points.

An Exact Quadratic Model

Example 3

A store has a fall sale on air conditioners. The model on sale normally sells for \$350. On the first day of the sale, the store reduces the price by \$10. The second day they reduce the price by an additional \$20, the third day they reduce the price by an additional \$30, each day reducing the price by \$10 more than it had gone down the previous day. The store announces they will continue reducing the price until all air conditioners are gone, giving them away for free if any are left.

a. Copy and complete the table.

Day	0	1	2	3	4	5
Price (\$)	350	340	320			

b. Draw a scatterplot.

c. Find a quadratic model for the data.

Solution 1

a. On day 3, the price goes down \$30; on day 4, the price goes down \$40. So the table is

Day	0	1	2	3	4	5
Price (\$)	350	340	320	290	250	200

b. A scatterplot is drawn here.

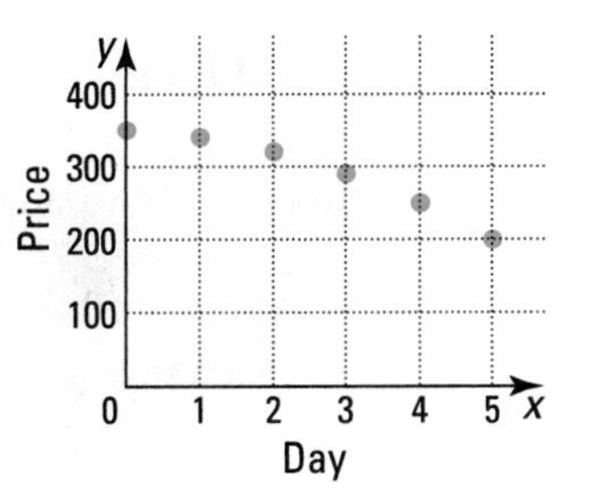

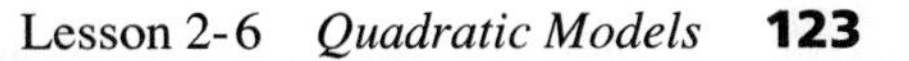

c. Choose three points on the parabola. (Using 3 points equally spaced on the x-axis simplifies the work.) We use (0, 350), (1, 340), and (2, 320). Substitute the coordinates into the equation $f(x) = ax^2 + bx + c$ to get a system of three equations, each with a, b, and c as unknowns.

$$f(x) = ax^2 + bx + c$$
$$f(0) = 350 = a \cdot 0^2 + b \cdot 0 + c$$
$$f(1) = 340 = a \cdot 1^2 + b \cdot 1 + c$$
$$f(2) = 320 = a \cdot 2^2 + b \cdot 2 + c$$

To solve the system $\begin{cases} 350 = c \\ 340 = a + b + c \\ 320 = 4a + 2b + c \end{cases}$

first substitute $c = 350$ into the other two equations, then subtract 350 from each side. This gives

$$\begin{cases} -10 = a + b \\ -30 = 4a + 2b. \end{cases}$$

Multiply the first equation by -4 and add the result to the second. This gives

$$10 = -2b, \text{ or } b = -5.$$

Substitute $b = -5$ into $-10 = a + b$ to get $a = -5$. So an equation to model this data set is

$$f(x) = -5x^2 - 5x + 350.$$

Solution 2

c. Enter the data into a statistics utility. Use the quadratic regression feature.

In Example 3, the model found by solving a system will be identical to the model formed by using the quadratic regression feature. That is, the predicted price and the actual price are *exactly* the same.

When data points all lie on a single parabola, the two solution strategies will yield an identical model. However, if the data points show a quadratic trend, but not an exact quadratic fit, then the two solution strategies may yield slightly different equations. In this case, most people prefer to use a statistics utility, because it gives the best-fitting parabola.

A Model for a Quadratic Trend

Consider the following data collected by a veterinarian working for a large pig cooperative who was interested in increasing the weight of its pigs. Twenty-four randomly selected pigs were each given a daily dosage (in pellets) of a food supplement. Groups of three pigs each received the same dosage, and their percent weight gain was averaged. The table below shows the average percent weight gain in one month for each group of three pigs in relation to the dosage.

Dosage (pellets)	0	1	2	3	4	5	6	7
Percent weight gain	10	13	21	24	22	20	16	13

A scatterplot of the data and the graph of the quadratic regression model $y = -1.0x^2 + 7.2x + 9.3$ are shown below. With the exception of the points (1, 13) and (3, 24), the data points lie fairly close to the parabola.

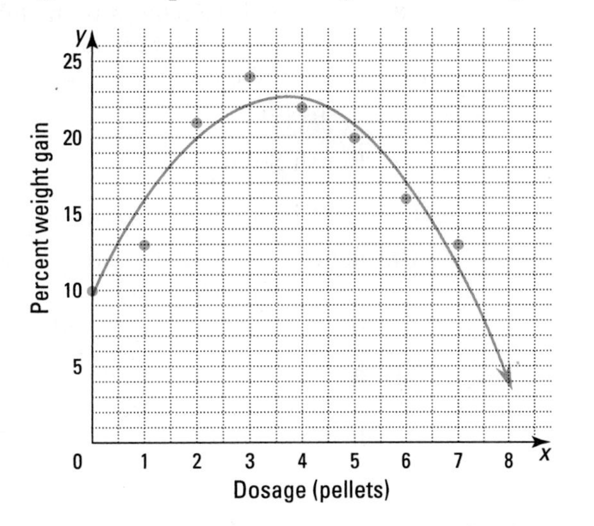

There is something quite different between this application and the previous two in the lesson. There is no theory that links dosage with percent weight gain. There is simply a rising and falling of percent weight gain as the dosage increases from 0 to 7. Models such as this one are called **impressionistic models** or **non-theory-based models** when no theory exists that explains why the model fits the data.

QUESTIONS

Covering the Reading

1. What is the general form of an equation of a quadratic function?

2. What are the solutions to $ax^2 + bx + c = 0$?

3. What is the range of the function $f(x) = 2x^2 - 3x - 2$ used in Example 1?

4. Consider the function $f(x) = 2x^2 - x - 4$.
- **a.** Give the y-intercept.
- **b.** Give the x-intercept(s).
- **c.** Sketch a graph for $-3 \le x \le 3$.
- **d.** Give the coordinates of the minimum point.

5. Graphs of which of the following have a maximum point?
- **a.** $y = 8x^2 - 3x - 7$
- **b.** $y = 2x + 4x^2$
- **c.** $y = 6 - 2x^2$
- **d.** $y = -x^2 + 5x + 177$

6. Suppose a ball is thrown upward at a velocity of 44 ft/sec from a cliff 200 feet above a dry riverbed.
- **a.** Write an equation for the height h (in feet above the riverbed) of the ball after t seconds.
- **b.** Predict the height of the ball after 3 seconds.
- **c.** At what time will the ball hit the riverbed?

In 7–9, refer to Example 3.

7. Using the quadratic model, verify that $f(4) = 250$.

8. **a.** Extend the pattern in the table to calculate the price of the air conditioner on days 6, 7, and 8.
b. Find the cost of the air conditioner on day 8 using the quadratic model.

9. Finish Solution 2.

In 10 and 11, refer to the data about weight gain in pigs on page 124.

10. **a.** Use the model to predict the percent weight gain in one month for pigs fed 4 pellets daily.
b. Is the prediction in part **a** extrapolation or is it interpolation?

11. **a.** Use the model to predict the percent weight gain in one month of pigs fed 10 pellets daily.
b. Explain why the prediction in part **a** may be unreasonable.

Applying the Mathematics

12. A piece of an artery or a vein is approximately the shape of a cylinder. The French physiologist and physician Jean Louis Poiseuille (1799–1869) discovered experimentally that the velocity v at which blood travels through arteries or veins is a function of the distance r of the blood from the axis of symmetry of the cylinder. Specifically, for a wide arterial capillary the following formula might apply:

$$v = 1.185 - (185 \cdot 10^4)r^2,$$

where r is measured in cm and v in cm/sec.
a. Find the velocity of blood traveling on the axis of symmetry of the capillary.
b. Find the velocity of blood traveling $6 \bullet 10^{-4}$ cm from the axis of symmetry.
c. According to this model, where in the capillary is the velocity of the blood 0?
d. For this application, what is the domain of the function?
e. Sketch a graph of this function.

13. Based on tests made by the Bureau of Public Roads, here are the distances (in feet) it takes to stop in minimum time under emergency conditions. Reaction time is considered to be 0.75 second.

Speed (mph)	10	20	30	40	50	60	70
Stopping Distance (ft)	19	42	73	116	173	248	343

a. Construct a scatterplot for these data.
b. Find a quadratic model for these data.
c. Copy the table and add two rows: one for the predicted stopping distance and one for the error (observed distance–predicted distance).

14. A pizza is sliced by a number of straight cuts as shown below. The table shows the greatest number of pieces $f(n)$ into which it can be sliced by n cuts.

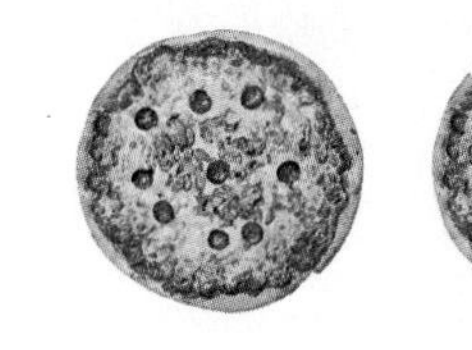
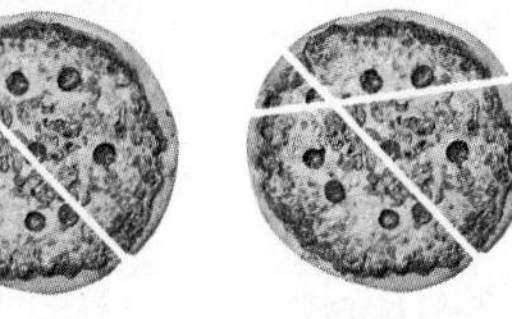
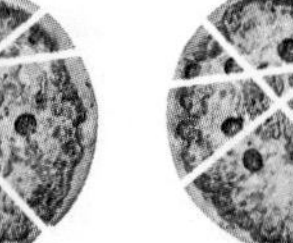

n	0	1	2	3	4
$f(n)$	1	2	4	7	11

a. Fit a quadratic model to these data.
b. Use your model to find the greatest number of pizza pieces produced by 5 straight cuts. Check your answer by drawing a diagram.

Review

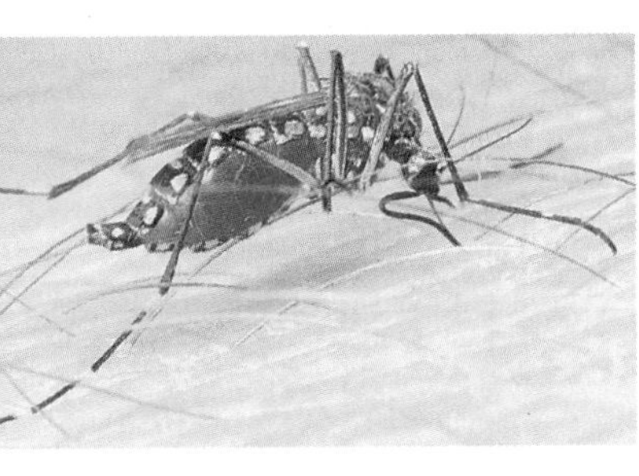
female yellow fever mosquito, Aedes aegypti

15. A mosquito population doubles every 15 days. If the population is initially 2000, what will it be t days later? *(Lesson 2-5)*

16. When a certain drug enters the blood stream, its potency decreases exponentially with a half-life of 6 hours. Suppose the initial amount of the drug present is A_0. How much of the drug will be present after each number of hours? *(Lesson 2-5)*
a. 6 **b.** 24 **c.** t

17. Find the value after 4 years of $1,500 invested at an annual yield of 5.75%. *(Lesson 2-4)*

18. *Multiple choice.* For which of the following scatterplots would a linear model be least suitable? *(Lessons 2-2, 2-3)*

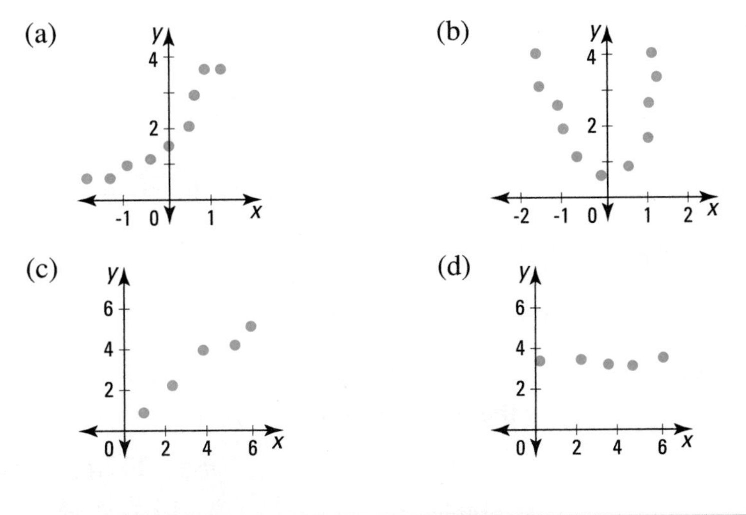

Exploration

19. What techniques do people use to measure the height or velocity of objects in air, such as the ball in Example 2?

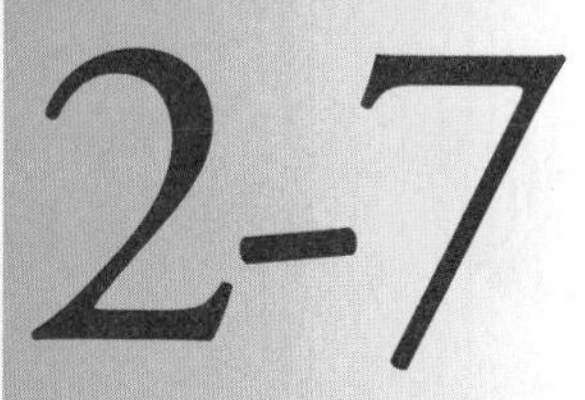

Step Functions

An Example of a Step Function

What function models the following situation?

> You have a dollars available to spend on cassettes, each of which costs \$8.99. How many cassettes n can you buy?

You know from your study of algebra that if you buy n cassettes, the cost is $8.99n$. From this you might conclude that $a = 8.99n$, so $n = \frac{a}{8.99}$. But this conclusion does not take into account the fact that n can only be a positive integer. For instance, if you have \$30 to spend, you cannot buy $\frac{30}{8.99} \approx 3.3$ cassettes. You can buy only 3.

The table below shows the number of cassettes you can buy for some integral multiples of \$5. These data are also shown in a scatterplot below.

Amount Available in Dollars (a)	5	10	15	20	25	30	35	40	45	50
Number of Cassettes (n)	0	1	1	2	2	3	3	4	5	5

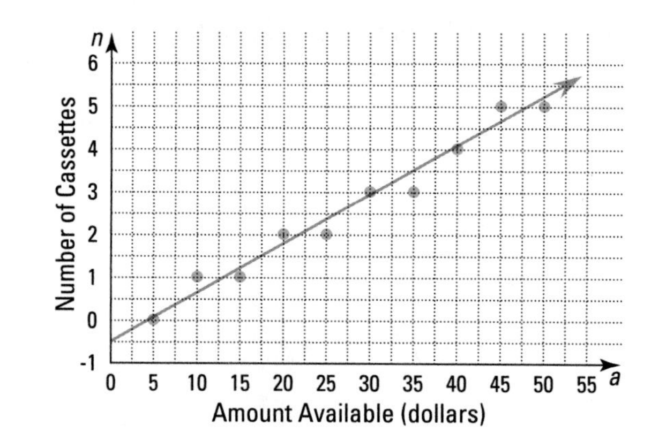

Clearly, these data show a linear trend. But neither the simple linear model you get from elementary algebra techniques,

$$n = \frac{a}{8.99},$$

nor the line of best fit obtained from a statistical utility and shown above,

$$n = .112a - .467,$$

is as precise as can be.

An exact model which describes the preceding situation can be found in the family of functions called *step functions*. **Step functions** are functions whose graphs look like steps.

The Greatest Integer Function

Many step functions are based on the *greatest integer function.*

Definition
The **greatest integer function** is the function f such that for every real number x, $f(x)$ is the greatest integer less than or equal to x.

The greatest integer function is also called the **rounding-down** or the **floor function**. The greatest integer less than or equal to x is often denoted by the symbol $\lfloor x \rfloor$. In some computer and calculator languages, $\lfloor x \rfloor$ is represented by INT(x). In some books, the symbol $[x]$ is used.

Example 1

Evaluate the following. **a.** $\lfloor -2.2 \rfloor$ **b.** $\left\lfloor \frac{29}{10} \right\rfloor$ **c.** INT (-1)

Solution

Each expression involves the greatest integer or rounding-down function.

a. The greatest integer less than or equal to -2.2 is -3. So, $\lfloor -2.2 \rfloor = -3$.

b. $\left\lfloor \frac{29}{10} \right\rfloor = 2$, because rounding down 2.9 gives 2.

c. No rounding is needed. INT (-1) = -1.

Example 2

a. Draw a graph of $f(x) = \lfloor x \rfloor$.

b. State the domain and range of f.

Solution

a. For any integer x, the greatest integer less than or equal to x is x. For any real number that is not an integer, we round down to find $\lfloor x \rfloor$. The graph is drawn at the right.

b. The domain is the set of all real numbers. The range is the set of integers.

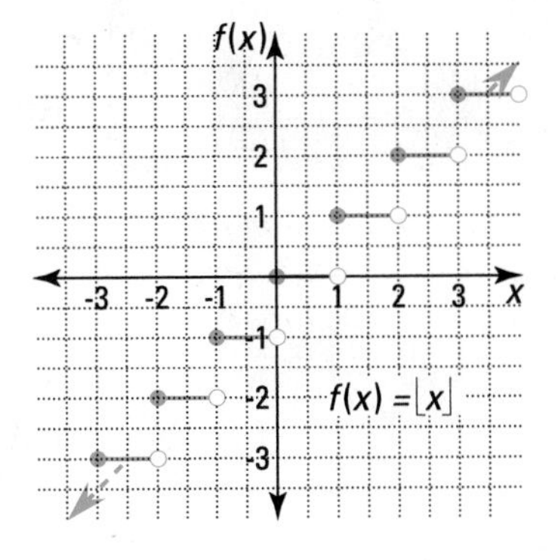

Note that the symbol •—o indicates that a segment includes a left endpoint, but not a right one. You should check the values for Example 1 by locating them on the graph in Example 2. They are (-2.2, -3), $\left(\frac{29}{10}, 2\right)$, and (-1, -1).

The greatest integer function is **discontinuous**, that is, its graph cannot be drawn without lifting your pencil off the paper. The values of x at which you lift your pencil are called **points of discontinuity**. In Example 2, each integer in the domain of f is a point of discontinuity. A function is **continuous** if its graph has no points of discontinuity.

Example 3

a. Find an exact formula for the number of cassettes n you can purchase at $8.99 each if you have a dollars.
b. Identify the points of discontinuity of this function.

Solution

a. The strategy used to find n is to divide the amount available by $8.99 and round down. Thus

$$n = \left\lfloor \frac{a}{8.99} \right\rfloor.$$

b. The function is discontinuous when $\frac{a}{8.99}$ is an integer. Thus the points of discontinuity occur when a is a multiple of 8.99, that is, when a = 8.99, 17.98, 26.97, ...

The Chateau Frontenac Hotel and Place Royale, Quebec City, Quebec

Cadillac production line, near Detroit, Michigan

The Rounding-Up Function

The function which pairs each number x with the smallest integer greater than or equal to x is called the **rounding-up** or **ceiling function**. The symbol $\lceil x \rceil$ is often used to denote the smallest integer greater than or equal to x. For instance, $\lceil 4.1 \rceil = 5$ and $\lceil 4.9 \rceil = 5$. The ceiling function often provides exact models for some situations which are approximately linear.

For example, with one long distance phone company, a call to Quebec City from Detroit on a Sunday in 1996 cost 28¢ per minute or fraction thereof, plus an 80¢ surcharge for using a calling card.

Let m = the number of minutes of the call, and c = the cost of the call. A linear model which approximates this situation is

$$c_1 = .80 + .28m.$$

But fractions of minutes need to be rounded up. So, an exact model for this situation is

$$c_2 = .80 + .28\lceil m \rceil.$$

Example 4

Calculate the cost of a call lasting 25 minutes 30 seconds to Quebec City from Detroit on a Sunday in 1996.

Solution

Convert 25 minutes 30 seconds to 25.5 minutes. Substitute $m = 25.5$ into the exact model.

$$\begin{aligned} c &= .80 + .28\lceil 25.5 \rceil \\ &= .80 + .28(26) \\ &= .80 + 7.28 \\ c &= 8.08 \end{aligned}$$

It cost $8.08 for the call.

Although the floor function $\lfloor x \rfloor$ is typically a built-in function with graphics calculators, the ceiling function $\lceil x \rceil$ is not. Fortunately, the ceiling function can be written in terms of the floor function as follows: $\lceil x \rceil = -\lfloor -x \rfloor$. This identity is helpful if you want to use technology to calculate values or to graph the ceiling function.

QUESTIONS

Covering the Reading

In 1–4, evaluate.

1. $\lfloor 3.9 \rfloor$ **2.** $\lfloor -3.9 \rfloor$ **3.** INT(7/8) **4.** $\lfloor 16 \rfloor$

5. For what values of x does $\lfloor x \rfloor = x$?

6. *Multiple choice.* Refer to the graph below of part of the greatest integer function. What part of the domain of the function does the graph represent?

(a) the set of numbers between 0 and 1
(b) the set of numbers between 0 and 1 including 0
(c) the set of numbers between 0 and 1 including 1
(d) the set of numbers from 0 to 1

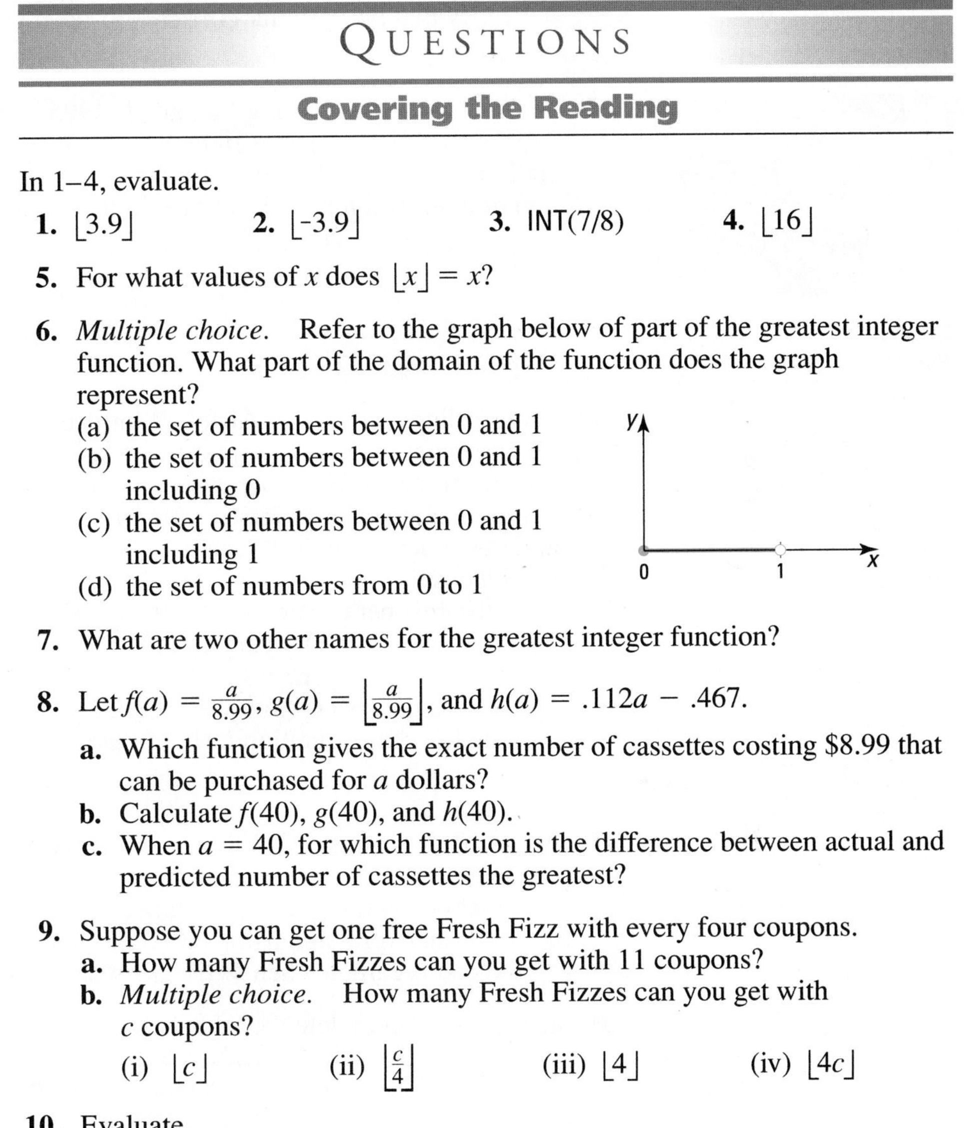

7. What are two other names for the greatest integer function?

8. Let $f(a) = \frac{a}{8.99}$, $g(a) = \left\lfloor \frac{a}{8.99} \right\rfloor$, and $h(a) = .112a - .467$.

a. Which function gives the exact number of cassettes costing \$8.99 that can be purchased for a dollars?
b. Calculate $f(40)$, $g(40)$, and $h(40)$.
c. When $a = 40$, for which function is the difference between actual and predicted number of cassettes the greatest?

9. Suppose you can get one free Fresh Fizz with every four coupons.

a. How many Fresh Fizzes can you get with 11 coupons?
b. *Multiple choice.* How many Fresh Fizzes can you get with c coupons?

(i) $\lfloor c \rfloor$ (ii) $\left\lfloor \frac{c}{4} \right\rfloor$ (iii) $\lfloor 4 \rfloor$ (iv) $\lfloor 4c \rfloor$

10. Evaluate.

a. $\lceil 3.9 \rceil$ **b.** $\lceil -3.9 \rceil$ **c.** $\left\lceil \frac{7}{8} \right\rceil$

In 11–12, f is the ceiling function.

11. State the domain and range of f.

12. a. Draw a graph of $y = f(x)$ for $-3 \le x \le 4$.
b. State three values of x at which f is discontinuous.

13. a. Draw a graph of $y = -\lfloor -x \rfloor$ for $-3 \le x \le 4$.
b. How is this graph related to the graph of either the ceiling or floor function?

Applying the Mathematics

14. A school bus holds 40 students. Suppose n students are going on a field trip.

a. Write a formula using the ceiling function for $f(n)$, the number of buses needed for the trip.

b. Verify that the formula $g(n) = -\left\lfloor \frac{-n}{40} \right\rfloor$ also gives the number of buses needed.

First class. *The U.S. Postal Service handles almost 50% of the world's postal traffic.*

15. *Multiple choice.* Starting January 1, 1995, the U.S. Post Office charged 32¢ for first class letters weighing up to one ounce and 23¢ for each additional ounce or fraction of an ounce. Which formula gives the cost $c(x)$ of mailing a letter of x ounces at these rates?

(a) $c(x) = 23 + 32\lceil 1 - x \rceil$

(b) $c(x) = 32 + 23\lceil x - 1 \rceil$

(c) $c(x) = 32 + 23\lceil 1 - x \rceil$

(d) $c(x) = 23 + 32\lceil x - 1 \rceil$

16. Some airlines provide an Airfone® service, for passengers to make telephone calls from the air. Here is a graph of the cost of making calls of various duration.

a. How much would a 10-minute phone call cost?

b. Is the cost per minute lower for several short calls or one longer call of the same total duration?

c. Express the cost C (in dollars) as a function of the duration L (in minutes) of the call.

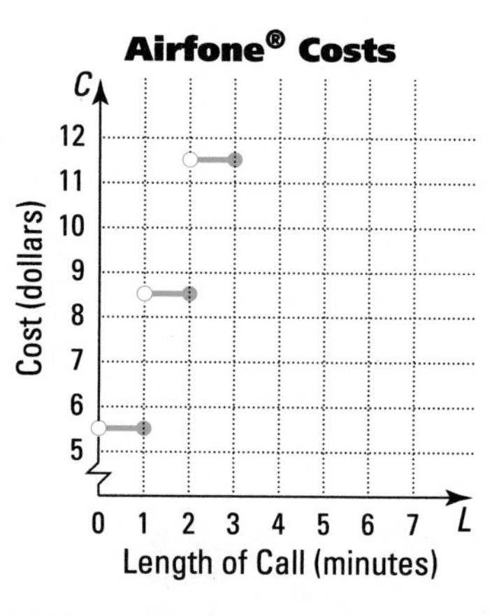

17. A salesperson earns a \$135 bonus for every \$1000 worth of merchandise sold.

a. What bonus is earned for selling \$2700 worth of merchandise?

b. Write an expression using either the floor or the ceiling function for the bonus earned when M dollars worth of merchandise is sold.

18. a. Copy and complete the table below.

X	X + 0.5	INT(X + 0.5)
12.4	12.9	12
12.7		
4.49		
5.50		

b. Describe the output of INT(X + 0.5) when any real number is input for X.

Review

19. To test the hypothesis that underinflated or overinflated tires can increase tire wear, new tires of the same type were tested for wear at different pressures. The results are shown in the table at the right.

x Pressure (psi)	y Miles (thousands)
29	25
30	30
31	33
32	35
33	36
34	35
35	32
36	27

a. Make a scatterplot of the data.
b. Fit a quadratic model to the data.
c. Based on these data, what advice would you give to an owner of this type of tire?
d. Without doing any calculations, to which of the following would you expect the correlation coefficient of the data set to be closest: -1, 0, or 1? Why?
e. Calculate the correlation coefficient. *(Lessons 2-2, 2-6)*

20. Suppose a function contains the two points (5, 50) and (7, 100).
a. Find an equation for the linear function containing these two points.
b. Find an equation for the exponential function containing these two points. *(Previous course, Lesson 2-5)*

21. *Multiple choice.* Which function f defined by the equation represents exponential decay? *(Lesson 2-4)*

(a) $f(x) = 5 \cdot 2^x$ (b) $f(x) = 5 \cdot 1^x$
(c) $f(x) = 5 \cdot 0^x$ (d) $f(x) = 5\left(\frac{1}{4}\right)^x$

22. **a.** Draw a scatterplot of a data set with 8 points that has a weak negative correlation.
b. Give a real world example of a situation that might have such a scatterplot. *(Lesson 2-2)*

Exploration

23. Find the current charges for postage for different classes of mail. Use a step function to model at least one set of postal rates different from the rates in this lesson.

LESSON

2-8

Choosing a Good Model

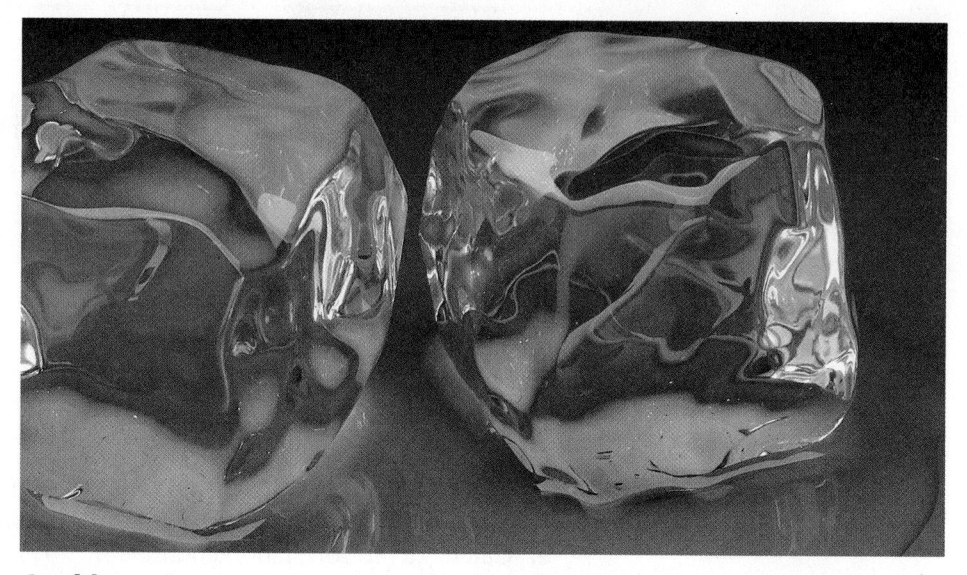

Cool ice. *How fast do ice cubes melt? Mathematical modeling can lend insight to this question.*

In this chapter you have learned how to fit linear, exponential, and quadratic models to data. One aspect of modeling, however, might still be unclear: *How do you know when you have found a good model?* This is a particularly important question when two different models appear to fit the data about equally well. One measure of how well the model fits the data is the correlation coefficient, but this applies only to linear models. There are measures of how well a nonlinear model fits data with a quadratic or an exponential trend, but they are not discussed in this course.

Another way to decide how well a model fits a data set is to examine the *errors*. "Error" is used here the same way it was used earlier, that is,

$$\text{error} = \text{observed } y - \text{predicted } y.$$

Residual is a synonym for error that is often used in statistics. A scatterplot of the residuals in relation to the values of the independent variable helps determine whether a proposed model is a good fit. If the model is a good fit, the residuals should tend to fall within a horizontal band centered around zero, as in the figure below on the left. If the residual plots show a systematic tendency to be positive at both ends (or negative at both ends), as in the figure in the center below, or to increase or decrease like a funnel, as in the figure on the right below, then a better model can probably be found, even though the correlation coefficient may be fairly high.

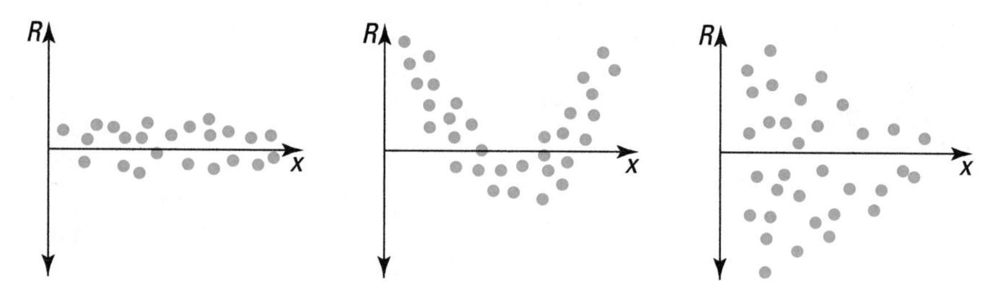

Analyzing Residuals

Water at room temperature, in this case 21.3°C, was poured into an ice cube tray, and the tray was put into the freezer. The temperature of the water was measured every five minutes. In the table and the scatterplot with regression line below, m is the number of minutes the water was in the freezer, and T is the temperature of the water in degrees Celsius.

m (minutes)	T (°C)
0	21.3
5	19.4
10	17.7
15	16.2
20	14.8
25	13.5
30	12.3

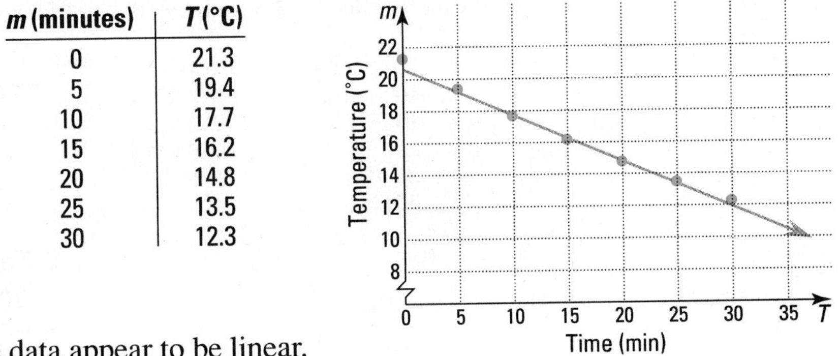

The data appear to be linear.

Activity 1

a. Enter these data into a statistics utility and calculate the correlation coefficient r.

b. Based on your value of r, does a linear model seem appropriate?

Example 1

a. Find an equation for the line of best fit for the above data on cooling.

b. Copy the table. Add columns for predicted temperature p and residual (error).

c. Plot m vs. the residuals R. Describe what you see.

d. Is the model (in part **a**) a good model? Explain why or why not.

Solution

a. The line of best fit has equation $y \approx -0.298x + 20.925$.

b.

Minutes (m)	Observed Temperature (T)	Predicted Temperature (P)	Residual ($T - p = R$)
0	21.3	20.93	0.38
5	19.4	19.44	-0.04
10	17.7	17.95	-0.25
15	16.2	16.46	-0.26
20	14.8	14.97	-0.17
25	13.5	13.48	0.02
30	12.3	11.99	0.31

c. As time passes from $m = 0$ to $m = 30$, the residuals are first positive, then negative, then positive again.

d. The residuals are positive at both ends, so there is probably a better model than the linear function.

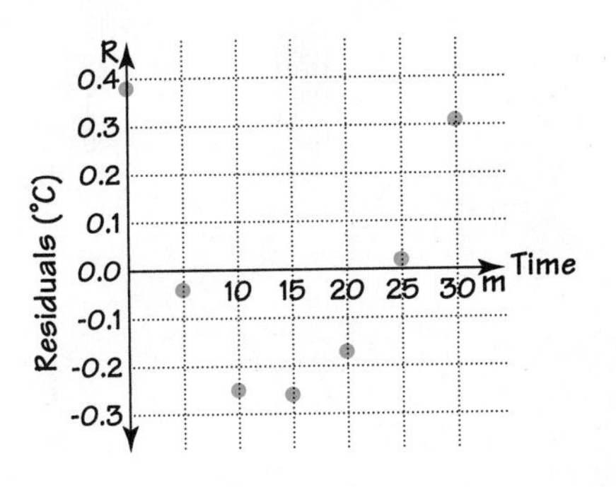

Example 2

Rework Example 1 using an exponential regression to model the data in part **a**.

Solution

a. The exponential regression model is $y \approx 21.27596 \cdot .98194^x$.

b.

Minutes (m)	Observed Temperature (T)	Predicted Temperature (P)	Residual ($T - p = R$)
0	21.3	21.28	0.02
5	19.4	19.42	-0.02
10	17.7	17.73	-0.03
15	16.2	16.19	0.01
20	14.8	14.78	0.02
25	13.5	13.49	0.01
30	12.3	12.32	-0.02

c.

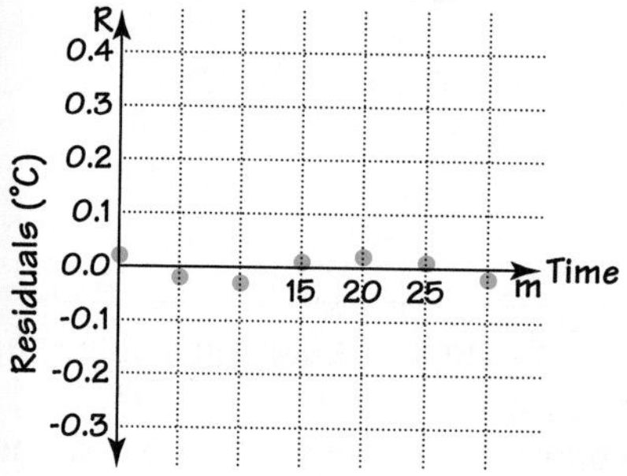

d. The exponential model is a good model because the residuals settle in a horizontal band centered around zero.

The exponential model is also a good model because it is a theory-based model. Physics theory tells us that objects cool exponentially with respect to time when the surrounding temperature is constant.

Unfortunately, sometimes theory-based models do not apply over the long term. Consider population growth. Very often populations grow at a relatively constant percentage increase, so it seems reasonable to fit an exponential regression model to population data.

United States Census data since 1790 are given in the table below. The scatterplot verifies that a linear model is not appropriate.

Year	Population (millions)
1790	4
1800	5
1810	7
1820	10
1830	13
1840	17
1850	23
1860	31
1870	40
1880	50
1890	63

Year	Population (millions)
1900	76
1910	92
1920	106
1930	123
1940	132
1950	151
1960	179
1970	203
1980	227
1990	249

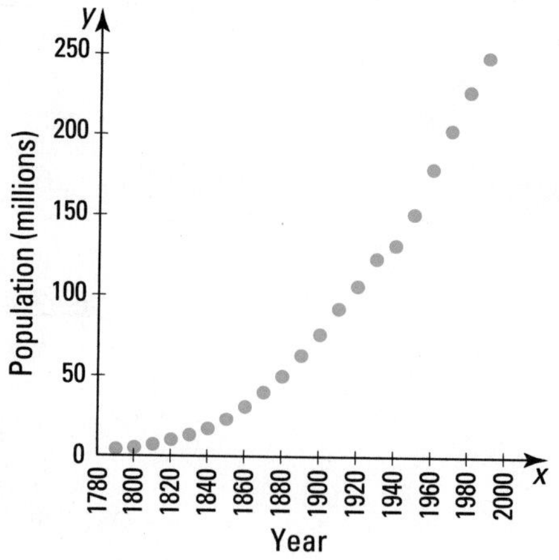

At the right, a graph of the exponential regression equation, $y = 3.868469 \cdot 10^{-16} \cdot 1.021026^x$, has been superimposed on the scatterplot. The exponential regression model follows the general shape of the data, but before 1940 most of the (observed) data points are above those predicted by the model and after 1940 they are below the predicted values.

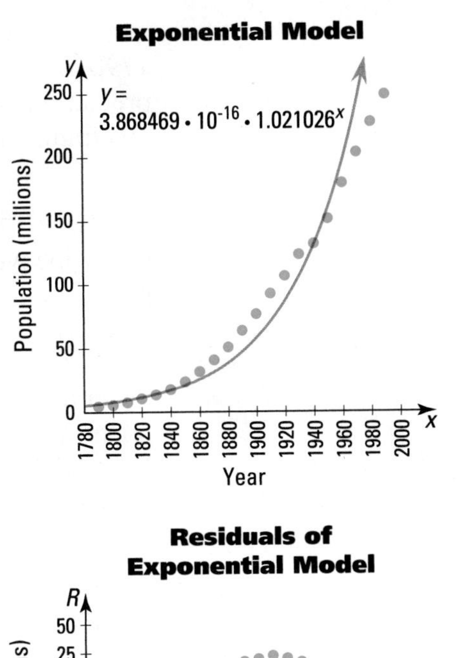

At the right is a graph of the residuals R of the exponential model. The increasing funnel effect makes it impossible to extrapolate from this model. The exponential model is not a good model for this data.

So we try a quadratic model. The graph of the quadratic regression model shown below is a much better fit than the exponential model. The residuals R cluster in a horizontal band centered around zero. The quadratic model is an impressionistic model because there is no theory that supports a quadratic relationship between year and population, but the quadratic model is a better model than the exponential model for the U.S. Census data.

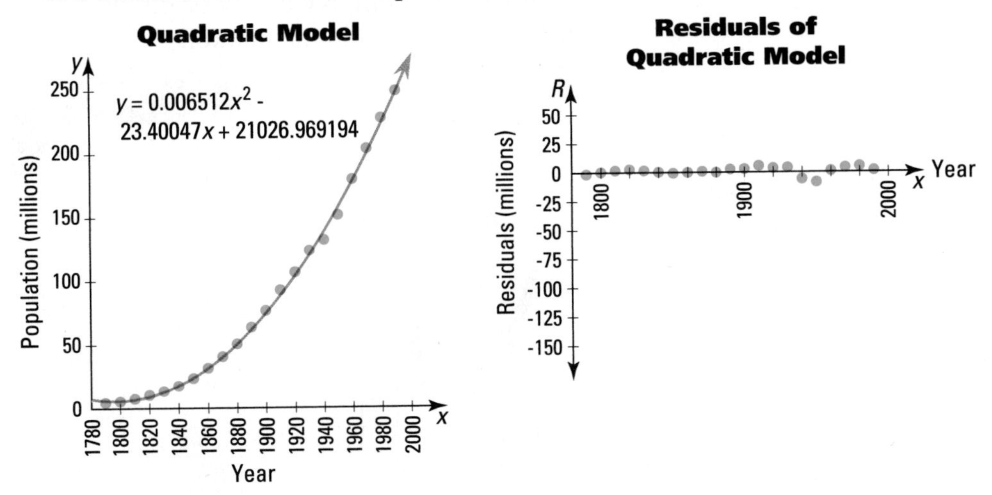

As mentioned earlier in the chapter, extrapolation is risky business. This is particularly true when there is no theory to support the model. The quadratic model was a very good model for the population of the U.S. from 1790 to 1990, but there is no assurance that the model will make accurate predictions for years outside the data set. An even better model than the quadratic model might be the union of several exponential models.

Sometimes There Is No Good Model

Everyone who invests in the stock market wants to buy stocks when their prices are low and sell when their prices are high. The difficulty is that when you buy today because you think the price is low, you have no guarantee that the price (and value) of the investment will not be even lower tomorrow. In the same way, you might sell today because you think prices are high, only to find out that the prices are even higher tomorrow. No model has been developed that can accurately predict changes in the stock market, but many people make a living by convincing others that they have such a model.

The following graph shows the Dow Jones industrial average for 1995 and the first half of 1996.

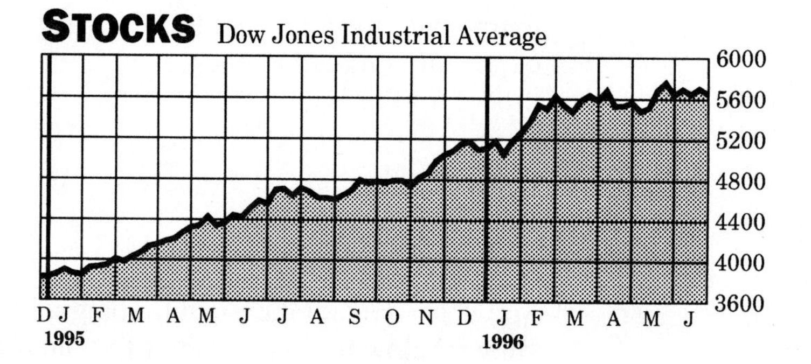

During that time, the overall trend might be described as linear, with stock prices increasing at the rate of about 100 points per month. However, the behavior for any given month, as you can see, does not appear to follow any pattern at all. From day to day or minute to minute it is even harder to predict the fluctuations in the market.

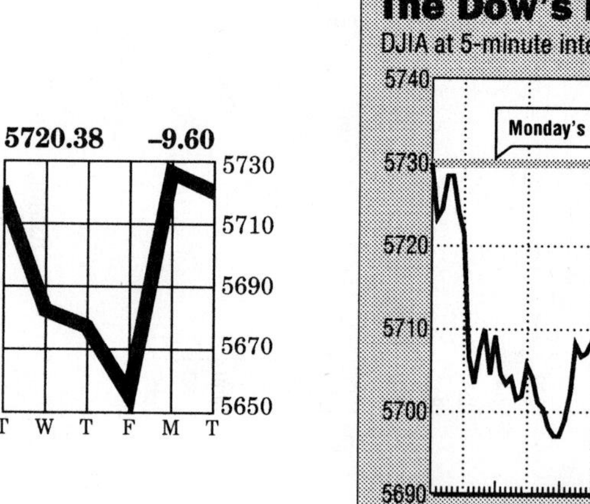

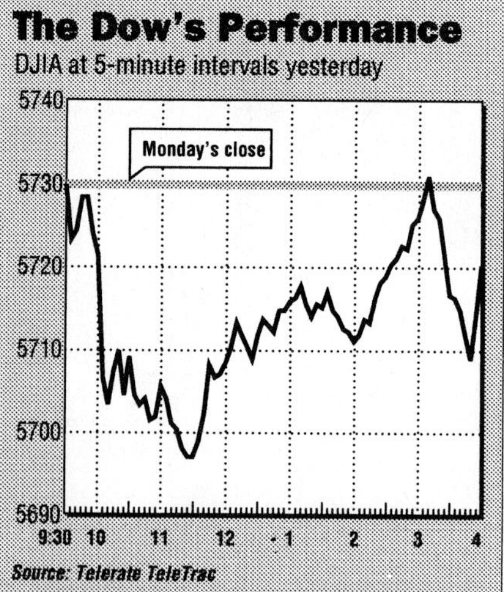

Because of the fluctuations in the stock market, many people use the "buy monthly and hold" strategy. Each month the investor buys a small amount of stock regardless of the price and keeps the stock as a long-term investment.

QUESTIONS

Covering the Reading

1. What is a *residual*?

2. What must be true when a residual is negative?

In 3 and 4, refer to the data on cooling water.

3. a. What is the correlation coefficient for the linear model?
b. Based on the correlation coefficient, is a linear model a model for the data? Why or why not?

4. Refer to Examples 1 and 2.
a. Based on the residuals, is a linear model a good model? Why or why not?
b. Why is the exponential model better than the linear model?

In 5–9, refer to the U.S. Census data in this lesson.

5. Why is it reasonable to expect that an exponential model fits population data?

6. a. Use the exponential regression equation to predict the 1990 population.
b. Use the value in part **a** to calculate the residual for the 1990 population.

7. a. Use the quadratic regression model to predict the 1990 population.
b. Calculate the residual for the 1990 population based on the result in part **a**.

8. *True or false.* A theory-based model always fits better than an impressionistic model.

9. a. Find an exponential regression model for the population data using only the years from 1790 to 1880.
b. Make a table with year, census population, predicted population, and residual.
c. Plot the residuals.
d. Is an exponential model appropriate for the 1790–1880 time period? Tell why or why not.

10. Why do you think no good model has been found for predicting the future prices of stocks?

Applying the Mathematics

11. A rock was thrown downward from a cliff 250 m off the ground. The height of the rock was measured at one-second intervals and is given in the table at the right.
    a. Find a good model for the data.
    b. Calculate and plot the residuals.
    c. Write a sentence or two explaining why your model is a good model.

Time (sec)	Height (m)
1	243
2	217
3	171
4	105
5	20

12. The population of Nevada from 1985 to 1994 is given in the table below.

Valley of Fire, Nevada

Year	1985	1987	1988	1989	1990	1991	1992	1993	1994
Population (thousands)	951	1023	1075	1137	1202	1285	1331	1382	1457

Source: U.S. Bureau of the Census

    a. Make a scatterplot of the data, plotting number of years after 1900 on the x-axis.
    b. Find a good model for the data. Justify why the model is good.
    c. Use your model to predict the population of Nevada in the year 2000.

13. Unemployment figures for the U.S. are given in the table below.

Year	1980	1985	1989	1990	1991	1992	1993	1994
Unemployed (thousands)	7637	8312	6528	6874	8426	9384	8734	7996

Source: U.S. Bureau of Labor Statistics

    a. Make a scatterplot of the data, plotting number of years after 1900 on the x-axis.
    b. Which, if any, of a linear, exponential, quadratic, or step function seems to model these data? Justify your answer.

Review

14. A taxi charges $2.50 for the first mile plus $.20 for each additional tenth of a mile or fraction thereof. Let $f(m)$ = the charge for a trip of m miles.
    a. Evaluate $f(5)$.
    b. Evaluate $f(4.7)$.
    c. Find a formula for $f(m)$ in terms of m. *(Lesson 2-7)*

15. a. Describe in words the function $f(x) = x - \lfloor x \rfloor$, for $x \geq 0$.
    b. Draw a graph of this function for $0 \leq x \leq 5$. *(Lesson 2-7)*

16. Solve a system to find a specific equation for the quadratic function $f: x \rightarrow ax^2 + bx + c$ containing the points (10, 25), (15, 40), and (20, 60). *(Lesson 2-6)*

Exploration

17. Cool a bowl of water in your freezer starting at room temperature. Record the temperature every five minutes. Find a good model to fit the data.

LESSON

2-9

The Men's Mile Record

The History of the World Record for the Men's Mile

Time	Athlete	Country	Year	Location
4:24.5	Walter Slade	England	1875	London, England
4:23.2	Walter George	England	1880	London, England
4:21.4	Walter George	England	1882	London, England
4:18.4	Walter George	England	1884	Birmingham, England
4:18.2	Fred Bacon	Scotland	1894	Edinburgh, Scotland
4:17.0	Fred Bacon	Scotland	1895	London, England
4:15.6	Thomas Conneff	United States	1895	Travers Island, New York
4:15.4	John Paul Jones	United States	1911	Cambridge, Massachusetts
4:14.4	John Paul Jones	United States	1913	Cambridge, Massachusetts
4:12.6	Norman Taber	United States	1915	Cambridge, Massachusetts
4:10.4	Paavo Nurmi	Finland	1923	Stockholm, Sweden
4:09.2	Jules Ladoumegue	France	1931	Paris, France
4:07.6	Jack Lovelock	New Zealand	1933	Princeton, New Jersey
4:06.8	Glenn Cunningham	United States	1934	Princeton, New Jersey
4:06.4	Sydney Wooderson	England	1937	London, England
4:06.2	Gunder Hägg	Sweden	1942	Göteborg, Sweden
4:06.2	Arne Andersson	Sweden	1942	Stockholm, Sweden
4:04.6	Gunder Hägg	Sweden	1942	Stockholm, Sweden
4:02.6	Arne Andersson	Sweden	1943	Göteborg, Sweden
4:01.6	Arne Andersson	Sweden	1944	Malmö, Sweden
4:01.4	Gunder Hägg	Sweden	1945	Malmö, Sweden
3:59.4	Roger Bannister	England	1954	Oxford, England
3:58.0	John Landy	Australia	1954	Turku, Finland
3:57.2	Derek Ibbotson	England	1957	London, England
3:54.5	Herb Elliott	Australia	1958	Dublin, Ireland
3:54.4	Peter Snell	New Zealand	1962	Wanganui, New Zealand
3:54.1	Peter Snell	New Zealand	1964	Auckland, New Zealand
3:53.6	Michel Jazy	France	1965	Rennes, France
3:51.3	Jim Ryun	United States	1966	Berkeley, California
3:51.1	Jim Ryun	United States	1967	Bakersfield, California
3:51.0	Filbert Bayi	Tanzania	1975	Kingston, Jamaica
3:49.4	John Walker	New Zealand	1975	Göteborg, Sweden
3:49.0	Sebastian Coe	England	1979	Oslo, Norway
3:48.8	Steve Ovett	England	1980	Oslo, Norway
3:48.53	Sebastian Coe	England	1981	Zurich, Switzerland
3:48.40	Steve Ovett	England	1981	Koblenz, West Germany
3:47.33	Sebastian Coe	England	1981	Brussels, Belgium
3:46.32	Steve Cram	England	1985	Oslo, Norway
3:44.39	Noureddine Morceli	Algeria	1993	Rieti, Italy

Source: *1996 Information Please Almanac*

In 1976, the International Athletic Federation announced that it would recognize track records only in meters—with one exception. The exception is the one-mile run. The mile run received this special treatment because it has long had a special mystique about it which has captured the interest even of those not normally interested in athletics.

Perhaps this was best illustrated in 1954 when the Englishman Roger Bannister became the first man in recorded history to run a mile in less than four minutes. This athletic feat was headline news around the world, with many commentators regarding the event as "breaking through a barrier." (A picture of Bannister as he crossed the finish line is shown at the left.) Bannister's run broke the nine-year-old record of the Swede

Gunder Hägg, and this long gap between records had encouraged many to think of a sub-four-minute mile as an impenetrable barrier, representing the limit of human potential. With hindsight, of course, we see that this is not the case, and that the barrier was both temporary and psychological.

The table on page 141 lists the world record holders for the men's one-mile run since 1875 and the year in which each record was set. The first entry in the table indicates that in 1875 Englishman Walter Slade ran the mile in 4 minutes, 24.5 seconds, a new world record time. This is written as 4:24.5. Nowadays, this time is often bettered by high school runners, and the women's world record is lower.

The current record (as of 1996) of 3:44.39, set in 1993 by an Algerian, Noureddine Morceli, indicates how much progress has been made over the intervening 110 years. In a present-day world-class field, Walter Slade, the record holder in 1875, would be beaten by well over an eighth of a mile! Has this progress been steady or erratic? Should we expect the record to continue to fall or have we now almost reached the "impenetrable barrier"? To answer such questions, a statistical analysis of the data is useful.

A scatterplot is a useful first step in modeling the men's mile record. Below, the data from the table and the line of best fit are graphed with the record (in seconds) on the vertical axis and the associated year on the horizontal axis.

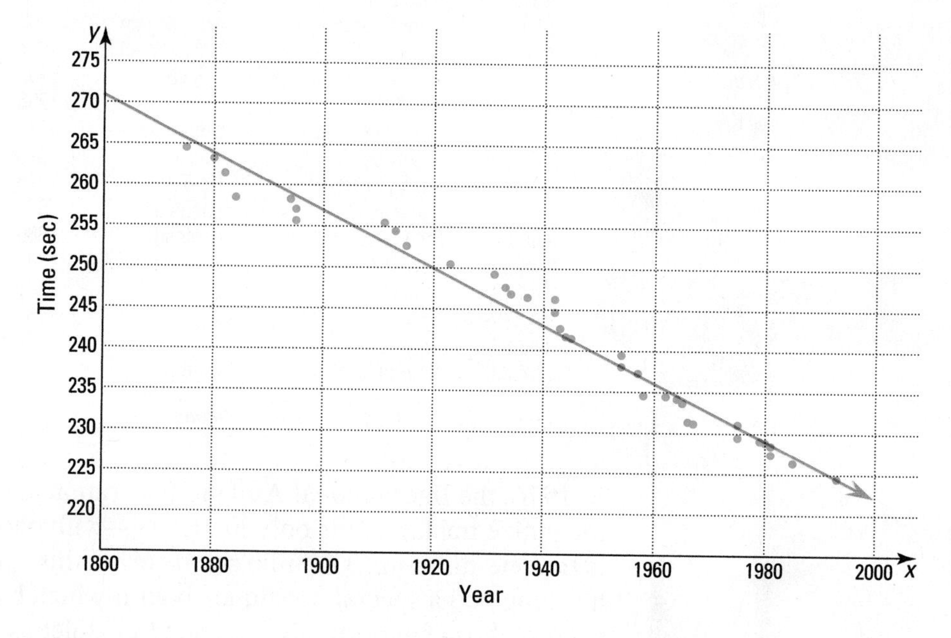

A Linear Model

The data seem to conform rather closely to a linear model. The line of best fit for predicting world record time y (in seconds) from the year x is

$$y = 914.784 - 0.346278x.$$

Because r^2 is about .975 and the slope of the regression line is negative, the correlation r between record time and year is about -0.99, indicating that a line is a remarkably good model for these data.

If the trend evident in the scatterplot continues, we might use the line of best fit to extrapolate from the data and to predict likely future changes in the world record. For example, to predict the men's mile record in the year 2000, substitute $x = 2000$ in the above equation:

$$y = 914.784 - 0.346(2000) \approx 222.80\,.$$

So in the year 2000, we anticipate a record time of 222.80 seconds, or 3 minutes 42.80 seconds. Such a time seems plausible.

The slope of the line of best fit tells how much improvement might be expected each year. The negative slope indicates that the world record is expected to get smaller each year, while the numerical size of the slope suggests that the record time should decrease by about 0.35 seconds each year.

Extrapolation into the far future, however, is a different matter. The line of best fit crosses the x-axis, suggesting that in the future a man will complete the one-mile run in no time at all, and shortly afterwards the record will be lowered to negative time! Consequently, a linear model is inappropriate to describe the trend over a very long time. A likely shape of the longer term trend for the mile record is shown here.

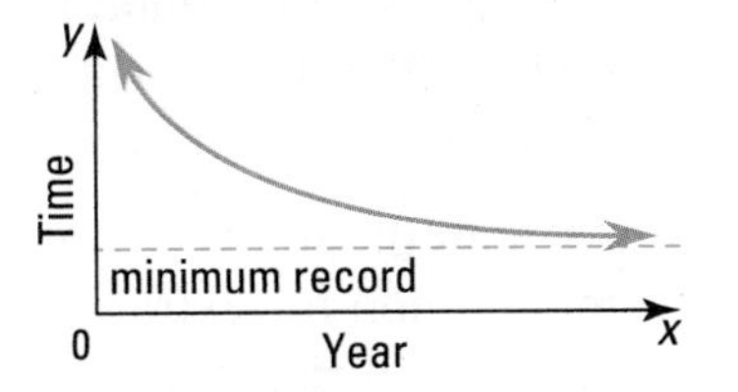

However, in the short term, a line is a good theoretical fit because we are seeing only part of this larger curve. A continually decreasing curve like this one will always appear approximately linear if you zoom in on it close enough.

The dotted line, a horizontal *asymptote* to the curve, represents a minimum time for running a mile that humans are unable to better. The minimum time is related to fundamental characteristics of human beings, such as lung capacity, the ability of the blood to use oxygen, and respiration rate. No one knows what that minimum is for the mile run.

One possible way of estimating this minimum for the mile is to extrapolate from a nonlinear model. For instance, assume that a quadratic model is a useful approximation to the mile record data.

Nonlinear Models

To estimate an equation for a quadratic model, it may be wise to use only more recent data, for instance, since 1930. Before that time, world records were measured with less sophisticated timing equipment, and thus might be less reliable. Recently, times have been measured to the hundredth of a second. Also, before 1930, it might be argued that athletes were more likely to be amateurs, whereas now the best athletes are almost full-time professionals trained by experts on exercise, diet, and biomechanics.

The scatterplot below shows a quadratic curve of good fit through the data beginning with the year 1930.

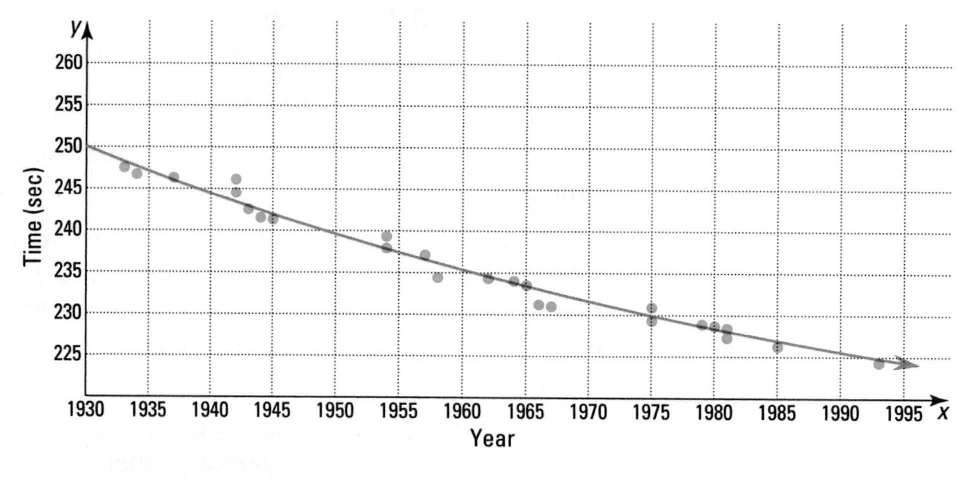

An equation of a quadratic model given by one statistics utility is

$$y = 0.00253169x^2 - 10.3377279x + 10771.6353.$$

Using an automatic grapher, this curve can be graphed and its relative minimum point found to be about (2041.7, 218.6). So, this quadratic model predicts that the world record for the men's one-mile run will not go below about 3 minutes 38.6 seconds, and that this will be reached around 2042.

As with the linear model, we know that the quadratic model cannot be relied upon for extrapolation too far beyond the data. Otherwise, the world record will rise after 2042! Also, the model depends critically on the data, and the choice of 1930 as a cut-off was essentially arbitrary.

An exponential model might be considered to model the data as well. An exponential regression of the data from 1930 on yields the function $y = 7230.61005 \cdot (.998255781)^x$. Substituting 2042 for x gives $y \approx 204.6$, indicating that the exponential model predicts the world record in 2042 to be about 3 minutes 24.6 seconds. This is about 14 seconds faster than the prediction from the quadratic model, which seems possible. The model, however, predicts that in the year 2400 the world record would be 109.4 seconds, which means athletes would be running at about 33 mph, more than twice as fast as today's pace. This does not seem reasonable.

Another Approach to Prediction

Another approach to the problem is to study the average speed of runners, rather than the time taken to run a certain distance. For example, as of 1996, the world record for the men's 800 meter run was 1:41.8, set by Sebastian Coe in 1981. Coe's average speed for this run was

$$800 \text{ m} \cdot \frac{1 \text{ km}}{1000 \text{ m}} \cdot \frac{3600 \text{ sec}}{1 \text{ hour}} \cdot \frac{1}{101.8 \text{ sec}} = 28.3 \text{ kph}.$$

Because there are 0.6214 miles in a kilometer, this speed is $28.3 \times 0.6214 \approx 17.6$ miles per hour. We might guess that the ultimate world record for the mile could not be run much faster than this speed (the best in 1996 for about half a mile), and compute the world record accordingly. Thus, if a person ran at a speed of 17.6 miles per hour for a whole mile, not merely for 800 m, the time would be $\frac{1}{17.6}$ hours, or about 3 minutes 25 seconds. This prediction is somewhat lower than the prediction from the quadratic model, but nearly identical to the exponential model.

Only time will tell whether such predictions as these are pessimistic, optimistic, or about right.

QUESTIONS

Covering the Reading

1. Convert Noureddine Morceli's 1993 world record of 3:44.39 into seconds.

2. Which world record for the mile stood for the longest period of time?

3. Suppose that Roger Bannister and Noureddine Morceli ran their world-record times for the mile run in the same race and that each ran at a constant speed. By how many yards would Morceli beat Bannister?

In 4–7, use the line of best fit for the men's mile record data.

4. Predict the mile record for each year.
a. 1960 **b.** 2020 **c.** 3000

5. Predict when the first $3\frac{1}{2}$-minute mile will be run by a man.

6. On average, how much has the world record decreased each year?

7. The equation of the regression line is given to considerable accuracy.
a. Use the equation with rounded coefficients, $y = 914.8 - 0.35x$, to predict the record for the years 1960, 2020, and 3000.
b. Compare your predictions to the answers you found for Question 4.
c. Which do you think is better to use, the equation given in the lesson or the equation given in part **a**, and why?

8. a. Use the quadratic and exponential models given in the lesson to predict the world record for the men's one-mile run in the year 2000.
b. By how much do these predictions differ from the record time predicted by the line of best fit?

In 9 and 10, use the fact that as of 1996 Sebastian Coe also holds the current world record for the 1000 m run. He set the record of 2:12.40 in 1981.

9. Convert this achievement into a speed expressed in each of the following units.
a. kilometers per hour **b.** miles per hour

10. If someone ran a mile at the same speed at which Coe ran his record-setting 1000 m, what would the time be?

Review

Year	Billions of Miles
1945	4
1950	10
1955	24
1960	39
1965	69
1970	132
1975	163
1980	255
1985	336
1987	405
1988	423
1989	433
1990	458
1991	448
1992	479
1993	489

In 11 and 12, use the data at the left from the Air Transport Association of America, showing the number of passenger miles for U.S. flights, both domestic and international, as a function of the year.

11. Let y = the year and $f(y)$ = the number of passenger miles.
   a. Evaluate $f(1980)$.
   b. Solve $f(y) = 132{,}000{,}000{,}000$.

12. a. Use your statistics utility to find a linear, exponential, and quadratic model to fit these data.
   b. Write a sentence for each model describing how well it fits the data.
   c. Rank the models from best fit to worst fit. Justify your response.
   (Lessons 2-1, 2-2, 2-3, 2-5, 2-6, 2-8)

In 13 and 14, a function is described. **a.** State its domain. **b.** Give its range.
(Lessons 2-1, 2-7)

13. $y = |x|$ **14.** $f(a) = \lfloor a \rfloor$

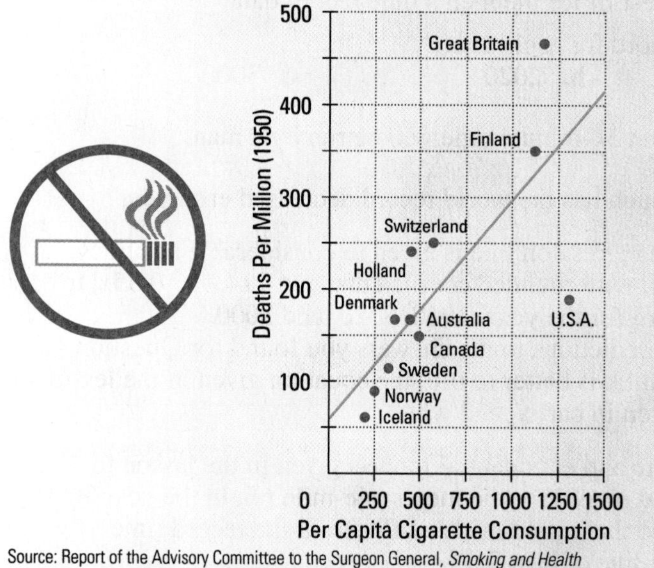

Source: Report of the Advisory Committee to the Surgeon General, *Smoking and Health* (Washington, D.C., 1964), p. 176; based on R. Doll, "Etiology of Lung Cancer," *Advances in Cancer Research*, 3 (1955), 1-50.

15. The graph at the left is from one of the earliest reports linking smoking to lung cancer. The line through the data is the line of best fit.
   a. Identify the independent and dependent variables.
   b. In which countries was the male death rate for lung cancer less than that predicted by the line of best fit?
   c. In which countries was the male death rate for lung cancer greater than that predicted by the line of best fit?
   d. In which country was the deviation of predicted death rate from observed death rate the greatest?
   e. Why do you think the authors chose to compare cigarette consumption and death rate 20 years apart, rather than in the same year?
   (Lessons 1-1, 2-1, 2-3)

In 16 and 17, identify the error made in the use of the correlation coefficient r.
(Lesson 2-2)

16. We found a high correlation ($r = 1.89$) between students' SAT scores and their grade-point-average.

17. The correlation between family income and amount spent by the family on vacations is $r = 0.68$ dollars.

In 18–21, match the scatterplot with the most likely correlation coefficient r.

(a) $r = -.85$ (b) $r = 0$ (c) $r = 0.75$ *(Lesson 2-2)*

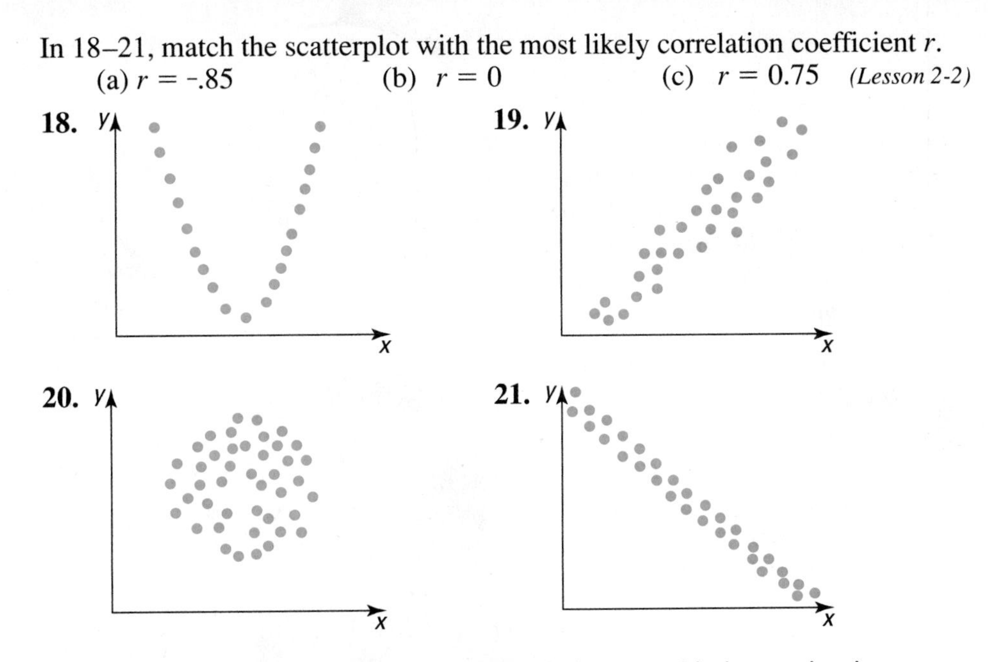

22. A manufacturer of copying machines is interested in improving its customer support services. As a result, a sample of 40 customers was surveyed to determine the amount of downtime (in hours) they had experienced in the previous month. The results are below.

2	6	5	6	11	19	28	4	37	0
14	5	3	8	2	1	12	7	21	0
4	0	5	7	10	9	12	8	18	9
24	16	7	1	54	9	8	14	39	40

a. Construct a box plot of these data.

b. How many customers are having excessive downtime using the $1.5 \times$ IQR criterion? *(Lesson 1-4)*

Exploration

23. Contact the athletic department of your school for school records in the boys' or girls' mile run. Plot the records over time. Do the data from your school show trends similar to the world records?

A project presents an opportunity for you to extend your knowledge of a topic related to the material of this chapter. You should allow more time for a project than you do for a typical homework question.

1 Body Data Revisited

Use the class database constructed as a project at the end of Chapter 1.

a. Some people claim that most people are squares. That is, their height and arm span are approximately equal.

i. If this conjecture were true, what would you expect a scatterplot of height vs. arm span to look like? Make a scatterplot, and find the line of best fit for your class data. Are most people in your class squares?

ii. Are there any outliers? If so, who are they? Remove these data from the set and obtain an equation for a new regression line.

b. Examine some other pairs of variables to find a pair with a high positive correlation.

i. Find an equation of the line of best fit for predicting one variable from the other.

ii. Reverse the order of the variables in part **i**. (i.e., make the former independent variable the new dependent variable). Find an equation of the line of best fit. Use your line of best fit to predict one variable from the other for some friends who are not in your class. How accurate is your model?

c. Which variables in your database, if any, show a negative correlation? Find an appropriate model for one such relation.

d. Write a brief report describing which variables seem most strongly related in your class.

2 The Women's Mile

How does the women's mile record compare to the men's?

a. Consult an almanac or other reference to obtain the world record times for the women's mile run. Enter the women's records into a statistical utility. Do these data show a linear trend? If so, find an equation for the line of best fit for the data.

b. Use the equation in part **a** and the equation of the regression line given in Lesson 2-9 to predict the year in which a woman will break the existing men's record in the mile run. Do you have confidence in this extrapolation? Why or why not?

c. What other model might be appropriate? Find such a model and use it to make the same prediction as in **a** and **b**.

d. Write a brief report comparing and contrasting the performance of males and females in the mile run.

3 Smoking Hazards

Much evidence has been gathered in recent years regarding the dangers of smoking.

a. Find data showing the relation between measures of smoking and measures of health. Some examples might be the percent of American adults who smoke in relation to year, the percent of teenagers who smoke in relation to year, or the per capita cigarette consumption in relation to lung cancer or throat cancer.

b. Display the data in tables and graphs.

c. Fit at least two mathematical models to your data and use them to make some predictions.

d. Use your models to support the argument that smoking is a health hazard.

e. What arguments might the tobacco industry present to counter your arguments in part **d**?

ALASKA

MAINE

MIAMI

4 Temperature vs. Latitude

Below are the latitude (in degrees North) and the average daily maximum temperature in April for various cities in North America.

Place	Latitude	Temperature (°F)
Acapulco, Mexico	16°51′	87
Bakersfield, CA	35°26′	73
Caribou, ME	46°52′	50
Charleston, SC	32°54′	74
Chicago, IL	41°59′	55
Dallas-Ft. Worth, TX	32°54′	75
Denver, CO	39°46′	54
Duluth, MN	46°50′	52
Great Falls, MT	47°29′	56
Juneau, AK	58°18′	39
Kansas City, MO	39°19′	59
Los Angeles, CA	33°56′	69
Mexico City, Mexico	19°25′	78
Miami, FL	25°49′	81
New Orleans, LA	29°59′	77
New York, NY	40°47′	60
Ottawa, Canada	45°26′	51
Phoenix, AZ	33°26′	83
Quebec, Canada	46°48′	45
Salt Lake City, UT	40°47′	58
San Francisco, CA	37°37′	65
Seattle, WA	47°27′	56
Vancouver, Canada	49°18′	58
Washington, DC	38°51′	64

a. Convert each latitude to decimal notation. For instance, 35°26' is read "35 degrees, 26 minutes." There are 60 minutes in a degree. So $35°26' = 35\frac{26}{60} \approx 35.42°$.

b. Use a statistics utility to draw a scatterplot with latitude on the x-axis, and average daily maximum temperature on the y-axis.

c. Find a linear model for these data.

d. Interpret the sign and magnitude of the slope of the regression line.

e. Over what domain do you expect the regression line to fit the data well?

f. Predict the average daily April maximum temperature for these cities:

Detroit, MI 42°22' N
Tampa, FL 27°49' N

g. The actual average daily high temperature in April is 47°F for Detroit and 72°F for Tampa. Find the percent error for each of your predicted values in part **f**.

h. Which cities appear to be outliers? Give plausible reasons why these cities might have a different relation between latitude and temperature than others.

i. Find the latitudes and average daily maximum temperatures in cities in other parts of the world, e.g., in Africa, Asia, or Europe. Explain any big differences between the regression lines you find for these areas and those found in part **c**.

SUMMARY

Any set of ordered pairs is a relation. Functions are particular kinds of relations—those for which each first element has exactly one second element. A function can also be viewed as a correspondence between two sets A and B, which relates each element of A to exactly one element of B.

In this chapter, sets of bivariate data are modeled by linear, quadratic, exponential, and step functions. Scatterplots can be used to represent the data and to determine the type of the relationship and the feasibility of a particular model. Some models are theory-based, others are impressionistic. When making predictions with any kind of mathematical model, interpolation is safer than extrapolation.

Linear functions model constant growth or decline. A linear model can be approximated by drawing a line close to all the data points. The line that minimizes the sum of the squared errors between observed and predicted values is called the line of best fit or the regression line. A statistics utility will generally give an equation for this line in slope-intercept form.

The strength of a linear relation between two variables is measured by the correlation coefficient, r. The sign of the correlation coefficient indicates the direction of the relation between the variables, and its magnitude indicates the extent of the linearity. An r with an absolute value close to 1 indicates a strong linear relation. An r-value close to zero indicates that the variables are not related linearly.

Exponential functions of base b, which are of the general form $y = ab^x$ with $a > 0$, $b > 0$, and $b \neq 1$, model exponential growth and decay. Exponential growth occurs when $b > 1$; exponential decay occurs when $b < 1$. Quadratic models of the form $y = ax^2 + bx + c$ are theory-based models for projectile motion. Most statistics utilities can find exponential and quadratic models of best fit.

Some data have y-values that are constant over an interval of x-values and then jump to another level. These can be modeled by step functions, such as the greatest integer function. Step functions have points of discontinuity.

Choosing a good model requires both an analysis of the data set and an understanding of how the data were obtained. Residuals, the differences between the observed values and the values predicted by the model, are used to judge the quality of a model. If the residuals are large or if there is a pattern to the residuals, the model is poor and another should be sought.

VOCABULARY

Below are the most important terms and phrases for this chapter. You should be able to give a general description and a specific example of each and a precise definition for those marked with an asterisk (*).

Lesson 2-1
univariate data, bivariate data
mathematical model
relation
*independent variable
*dependent variable
*function, *domain
*range, vertical line test
argument

Lesson 2-2
*linear function
linear regression
*correlation coefficient
positive relation, negative relation
perfect correlation
strong relation, weak relation

Lesson 2-3
observed, predicted/expected values
errors in prediction, deviations
*line of best fit
method of least squares
center of gravity
*interpolation, *extrapolation

Lesson 2-4
*exponential function, *base
exponential growth function
exponential growth curve
growth rate
exponential decay curve
strictly increasing/decreasing
asymptote

Lesson 2-5
*exponential model
initial value, *growth factor
doubling time, *half-life

Lesson 2-6
*quadratic model, parabola
maximum point, minimum point
acceleration due to gravity
quadratic regression
impressionistic model
non-theory-based model

Lesson 2-7
step function
*greatest integer function
rounding-down function
floor function
discontinuous
point of discontinuity
continuous
rounding-up function
ceiling function

Lesson 2-8
*residual

CHAPTER TWO

PROGRESS SELF-TEST

Take this test as you would take a test in class. You will need graph paper, a calculator, and a statistics utility. Then check the test yourself using the solutions at the back of the book.

In 1 and 2, a relation is described. **a.** State whether the relation is a function. If it is not, give a reason for your answer. **b.** If it is a function, determine the domain and the range of the function.

1.

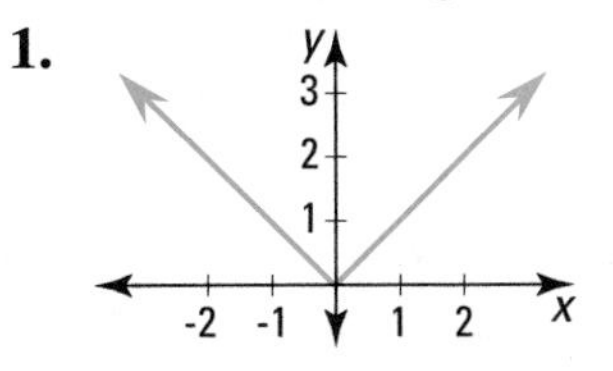

2. {(3, 4), (4, 9), (6, 12), (0, -1), (4, 7)}

In 3 and 4, let $k(x) = 2x^2 - 7$.

3. Evaluate $k(-3)$.

4. **a.** Graph $y = k(x)$.

b. Find the range of the function k.

5. Suppose $f(x) = \lceil x \rceil + 1$. Evaluate $f(6\pi)$.

6. *Multiple choice.* Which function models exponential decay?

(a) $a: x \to 5(.07)^x$ (b) $b: x \to 3 \cdot \left(\frac{5}{2}\right)^x$

(c) $c: x \to (.5) \cdot 2^x$ (d) $d: x \to 3 \cdot (1.25)^x$

7. Suppose a school bus holds 40 passengers.

a. How many of these buses are needed to transport 304 students?

b. Write a formula for the number n of buses needed to transport s students.

8. The table below lists the total funds available for arts programs through the National Endowment for the Arts for the years 1990–1994.

Year	1990	1991	1992	1993	1994
NEA Funding (millions of $)	170.8	166.5	163.0	159.7	158.1

a. Find the correlation coefficient.

b. What does the correlation coefficient tell you about the relationship between the year and funding for the arts?

c. Find an equation for the line of best fit. Let year be the independent variable.

d. What does the slope of the line of best fit tell you about funding for the arts?

9. Strontium-90 has a half-life of about 29 years. How much will be left of 10 grams of strontium-90 after 30 years?

10. The following table gives the number of World Wide Web sites during its first few years.

Month/Year	Number of Months Since January 1, 1993	Number of WWW Sites
6/93	6	130
12/93	12	623
6/94	18	2,738
12/94	24	10,022
6/95	30	23,500
1/96	37	100,000
6/96	42	230,000*
		*(estimated)

Source: http://www.mit.edu:8001/people/mkgray/net

a. Make a scatterplot of the data.

b. Find a good model.

c. Calculate the residuals for your model.

d. Justify that your model in part **b** is a good model based on the residuals.

11. The table below shows the height h in feet of a ball above ground level t seconds after being thrown off the top of a high building.

t	1	2	3	5	6
h	299	311	291	155	39

a. Fit a quadratic model to the data.

b. Is this a theory-based model or is it an impressionistic model? Explain.

c. From your model, what is the height of the ball 4 seconds after it was thrown?

d. Is the prediction made in part **c** an example of interpolation or of extrapolation?

e. To the nearest tenth of a second, when will the ball hit the ground?

12. For a data set, the line of best fit has equation $y = 3.7x - 14.1$, and $r^2 = 0.37$. What is the correlation between x and y?

CHAPTER REVIEW

Questions on SPUR Objectives

SPUR stands for **S**kills, **P**roperties, **U**ses, and **R**epresentations. The Chapter Review questions are grouped according to the SPUR Objectives for this chapter.

SKILLS DEAL WITH THE PROCEDURES USED TO GET ANSWERS.

Objective A: *Evaluate functions described with Euler's notation.* *(Lessons 2-1, 2-7)*

In 1 and 2, let $f(x) = 3^x$.

1. Evaluate.

a. $f(1)$ **b.** $f(-1)$

2. *True or false.* Justify your answer.

a. $f(2) + f(-2) = 0$ **b.** $f(2) \cdot f(3) = f(5)$

3. Let $g(x) = x^2 + 3$.

a. Evaluate $g(-1)$.

b. Does $g(4) - g(2) = g(2)$? Justify your answer.

4. *True or false.* Let $h(x) = |x - 5|$.

a. $h(3) = h(-3)$ **b.** $-h(3) = -h(7)$

5. Suppose $p(x) = \lfloor x \rfloor$. Evaluate.

a. $p(12.9)$ **b.** $p(-5)$ **c.** $p(\pi)$ **d.** $-p(-3.5)$

6. Find the value of each expression.

a. $\lceil -2.9 \rceil$ **b.** $\lceil \sqrt{75} \rceil$

PROPERTIES DEAL WITH THE PRINCIPLES BEHIND THE MATHEMATICS.

Objective B: *Identify the independent and dependent variables, domain, and range of a function.* *(Lessons 2-1, 2-4, 2-6, 2-7)*

In 7–12, a function is described. **a.** State its domain. **b.** Give its range.

7. $y = \lceil x \rceil$ **8.** $r(x) = 5(2^x)$

9. $j(x) = \frac{2}{-x}$ **10.** $f(t) = 2t^2 - 18$

11. $y = mx + b, m \neq 0$

12. $\{(-2, 2), (-1, 2), (0, 2), (2, 2), (5, 2)\}$

In 13 and 14, a function is described. **a.** Identify the independent variable. **b.** Identify the dependent variable.

13. $A = (1 + t)^2$ **14.** $y = f(x)$

In 15 and 16, identify the values at which the function with the given equation is not continuous.

15. $y = \lfloor x \rfloor$ **16.** $\left\lceil \frac{x}{4.4} \right\rceil$

Objective C: *Identify properties of regression lines and of the correlation coefficient.* *(Lessons 2-2, 2-3)*

17. Explain what is meant by a strong positive correlation.

In 18–21, r represents a correlation coefficient.

18. *Multiple choice.* Which of the following is indicated by an r value of 0.23?

(a) a strong positive relation

(b) a weak positive relation

(c) a weak negative relation

(d) a strong negative relation

19. What value of r indicates a perfect negative relation?

20. A statistics package gives values of r^2, where r is the correlation coefficient between two variables. If $r^2 = 0.54$, what are all possible values of r?

21. For a set of data, the line of best fit is given by $y = 6.2 - 1.7x$ and $r^2 = 0.80$. What is the correlation coefficient?

In 22–26, *true or false*.

22. If the sum of the errors calculated using a linear model for a given data set is zero, then the line of best fit goes through all the data points.

23. The correlation coefficient r is measured in the same unit as the slope of the regression line.

24. A residual is formed by subtracting predicted value from observed value.

25. The line of best fit is formed by minimizing the deviations between observed values and predicted values.

26. The line of best fit always contains the center of gravity of a data set.

Objective D: *Describe properties of quadratic and exponential functions.* (*Lessons 2-4, 2-6*)

In 27 and 28, consider the equation $f(t) = ab^t$ with $b > 0$ and $a > 0$.

27. a. Under what condition is f strictly increasing?

b. Under what condition is f strictly decreasing?

28. *True or false.* No exponential function has an x-intercept. Justify your answer.

29. Give the points of intersection of the graphs of $a(x) = 7^x$ and $b(x) = 9^x$.

30. Without graphing, decide which of the functions, $k(t) = 0.2(1.3)^t$ or $m(t) = 1.3(0.2)^t$, models exponential growth and which models exponential decay.

31. Without graphing, how can you tell whether the graph of $f(x) = ax^2 + bx + c$ has a maximum or minimum point?

32. Give the x-intercepts of the graph of $y = ax^2 + bx + c$, where $a \neq 0$, if $b^2 - 4ac > 0$.

USES DEAL WITH APPLICATIONS OF MATHEMATICS IN REAL SITUATIONS.

Objective E: *Find and interpret linear models.* (*Lessons 2-2, 2-3*)

33. The table contains data for total U.S. social welfare expenditures under public programs, 1970–1992.

a. Find the line of best fit for these data.

b. Plot the data and the model on the same graph.

c. Which data points appear to be outliers?

Number of Years After 1970	Total (billions of $)
0	146
10	493
15	732
19	957
20	1050
21	1161
22	1264

d. Use the model to predict the likely social welfare expense in 1996.

e. When would you expect social welfare expenditures to reach $1,525,000,000,000 annually?

f. Give a reason why this model should not be used to predict social welfare spending in the year 2010.

34. Use the table below listing the heights and shoe sizes for 13 men in an office. Shoe sizes are either whole numbers or half sizes.

a. Find an equation for the line of best fit for these data.

b. Use the line of best fit to predict the expected shoe size of a man 6'2" tall.

c. Over what domain would you expect this model to hold?

Height (in.)	Shoe size
70	10½
73	9½
68	7
69	10
72	10
68	9
74	12
71	12
69	9
66	8½
71	9
70	10
73	11½

CHAPTER TWO

35. An archaeologist counted the flintstones and charred bones at several sites, and obtained the following data.

Number of Flintstones	18	53	23	8	47	16	3	81	55	37
Number of Bones	2	4	2	0	6	0	1	9	5	4

a. Find the correlation between the number of flintstones and the number of bones.

b. Does it seem appropriate to use a linear function to model these data? Justify your answer.

c. The archaeologist claimed that the data prove that the flintstones were used to light fires that charred the bones. Do you think this claim is justified? Why or why not?

36. The table below contains average hourly earnings of production workers in the U.S. for the years 1990–1994.

Number of Years After 1990	0	1	2	3	4
Hourly Earnings	10.01	10.32	10.57	10.83	11.13
Predicted Values					
Deviation					
Deviation^2					

Source: *The World Almanac and Book of Facts 1996.*

The line of best fit for this data set is $y = .275x + 10$. Copy the table.

a. Find the predicted values for 1990–1994.

b. Find the deviation and squared deviation for each year.

c. What is the sum of the squared deviations? What conclusion can you draw about that number?

Objective F: *Find and interpret exponential models.* *(Lessons 2-4, 2-5)*

37. *Multiple choice.* The population of Myanmar (formerly Burma) was about 45 million in 1995 and was increasing at a rate of 1.9% per annum. Which of the following models the population P (in millions) of Myanmar y years after 1995?

(a) $P = 45 \cdot (1.019)^y$ (b) $P = 45 \cdot (0.019)^y$

(c) $P = (45 \cdot 1.019)^y$ (d) $P = 45.019^y$

38. The population of Tanzania in 1995 was about 28.5 million, with an annual growth rate of 3.0%.

a. Give a model for the population n years after 1995.

b. Predict the population in 2005.

c. Predict when the population will reach 30 million.

39. A certain radioactive substance has a half-life of 4 hours. Let A be the original amount of the substance and let L be the amount left after h hours.

a. Give an exponential model for L in terms of A and h.

b. What percent of the original amount of the substance will remain after 7 hours?

40. *True or false.* If the half-life of a substance is 3000 years, then after 1500 years, exactly half of the substance will remain.

41. A bacterial population was counted every day for a week with the following results.

Day (d)	1	2	3	4	5	6	7
Population (P)	5	14	24	50	90	186	404

a. Use a statistics utility to find an exponential model for P.

b. Make a scatterplot of the data and superimpose your model on it.

c. Comment on the quality of the model. Why is an exponential model appropriate in this situation?

d. Use your model to predict the population of bacteria on day 14.

e. Does your prediction seem reasonable? What conditions might alter the course of bacterial growth?

42. The population of Florida is given for various years from 1970–1994 in the table below.

a. Use a statistics utility to find an exponential model for the data.

b. Use the model to find the population in 1987. Is this interpolation or extrapolation?

c. The actual population (in thousands) in 1987 was 11,997. Give the error in your prediction.

Number of Years After 1970	Population (in thousands)
0	6791
10	9746
15	11351
20	12938
22	13510
24	13953

43. Copy the table below, which gives data on the speed of microprocessor chips in MIPS (millions of instructions per second) by year of introduction. The exponential regression equation for this data set is $y = .516(1.50)^x$.

a. Find the residuals for this model.

b. Based on the residuals, how good is this model?

Chip	Number of Years After 1980	MIPS	Residual
286	2	1	
386	5	5	
486	9	20	
Pentium	13	100	

Source: *Business Week,* March 29, 1993

Objective G: *Find and interpret quadratic models.* (*Lesson 2-6*)

44. A toy rocket launched off a cliff over the sea follows a quadratic model for height h feet above sea level as a function of time t seconds after launch: $h = 310 + 110t - 16t^2$.

a. Predict the height of the rocket 5 seconds after launch.

b. How long after launching will the rocket hit the sea?

c. *True or false.* This model is theory based.

45. The Illinois Department of Conservation has published information concerning the growth rate of largemouth bass. The average length of the fish is 9 inches at 2 years of age, 11.6 inches at 3 years, 17.4 inches at 6 years, and 20.7 inches at 10 years.

a. Construct a scatterplot of these data.

b. Give a reason for not expecting age and length to be linearly related.

c. Use a statistics utility to find a suitable quadratic model relating length to age.

d. Use your model from part **c** to predict the length of a largemouth bass that is 8 years old.

e. Use your model to give the likely age of a largemouth bass 13.5 inches long.

46. A *wind chill* number is an index of how cold it feels when the wind is blowing on a cold day. The following data give the wind chills for actual temperatures of 30° F at various wind speeds. Wind speeds greater than 45 mph have little additional chilling effect.

Wind Chill (°F)	27	16	9	4	1	-2	-4	-5	-6
Wind Speed (mph)	5	10	15	20	25	30	35	40	45

Source: National Weather Service, NOAA, U.S. Commerce Department

a. Identify the independent and dependent variables in this case.

b. Construct a scatterplot of these data.

c. Find a suitable quadratic model for the data.

Objective H: *Use step functions to model situations.* (*Lesson 2-7*)

47. A cereal manufacturer offers a free pound of bananas for every six coupons cut from their boxes of breakfast cereal. If each box has one coupon, write a formula for p, the number of pounds of bananas given away, as a function of b, the number of boxes of cereal.

48. A salesperson earns $167.50 commission for every $1000 worth of merchandise she sells. Write a formula for the amount of commission earned from selling k dollars worth of merchandise.

In 49 and 50, *multiple choice.*

49. Which of the following gives the century number c from the year y?

(a) $c = \lfloor \frac{y}{100} \rfloor$

(b) $c = \lfloor \frac{y}{100} \rfloor + 1$

(c) $c = \lfloor 100y \rfloor$

(d) $c = \lfloor \frac{y}{100} \rfloor + 100$

50. In 1996, the cost of phoning Los Angeles from Chicago between 8 am and 5 pm Monday through Friday using one phone company was 33¢ for the first minute and 28¢ for each extra minute or part thereof. Which of the following gives the cost d in dollars as a function of the time t in minutes?

(a) $d = 0.33 + 0.28\lfloor 1 - t \rfloor$

(b) $d = 0.33 - 0.28\lfloor 1 - t \rfloor$

(c) $d = 0.28 + 0.33\lfloor 1 - t \rfloor$

(d) $d = 0.28 - 0.33\lfloor 1 - t \rfloor$

REPRESENTATIONS DEAL WITH PICTURES, GRAPHS, OR OBJECTS THAT ILLUSTRATE CONCEPTS.

Objective I: *Graph linear, exponential, quadratic, and step functions.* *(Lessons 2-2, 2-4, 2-6, 2-7)*

In 51–54, sketch a graph of each function on the domain $-4 \leq x \leq 4$.

51. $f(x) = .5x + 3$

52. $y = 2^x$

53. $y = 2x^2 - 18x$

54. $y = \lfloor x \rfloor$

Objective J: *Interpret properties of relations from graphs.* *(Lessons 2-1, 2-4, 2-6, 2-7)*

In 55–58, state whether the graph represents a function.

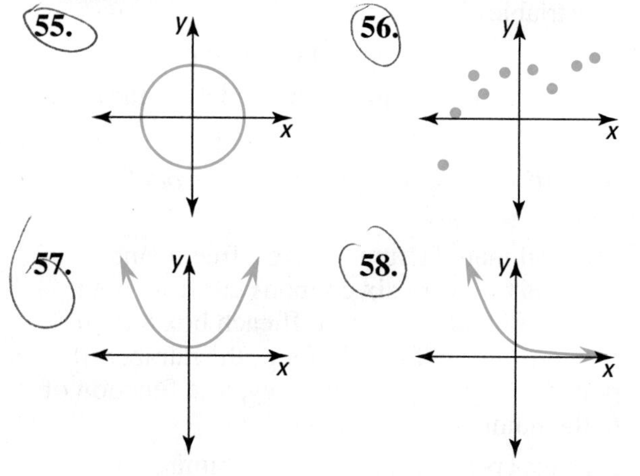

In 59–62, determine the domain and range of the relation.

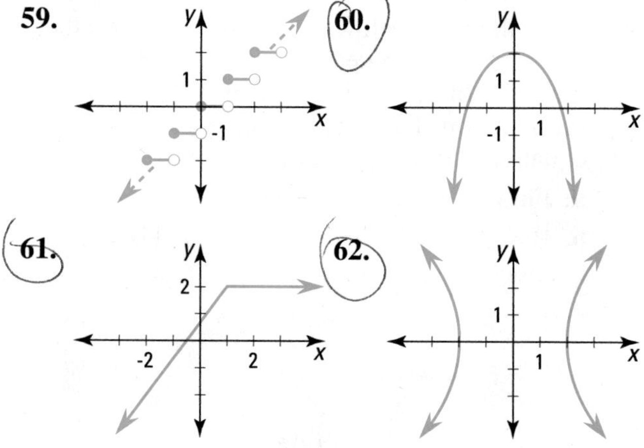

Objective K: *Use scatterplots to draw conclusions about models for data.* *(Lessons 2-2, 2-3, 2-5, 2-6, 2-8)*

In 63–66, a scatterplot is given. **a.** Determine whether a linear or a nonlinear model is more suitable. **b.** If a linear model is used, state whether the correlation coefficient is likely to be positive, negative, or approximately zero.

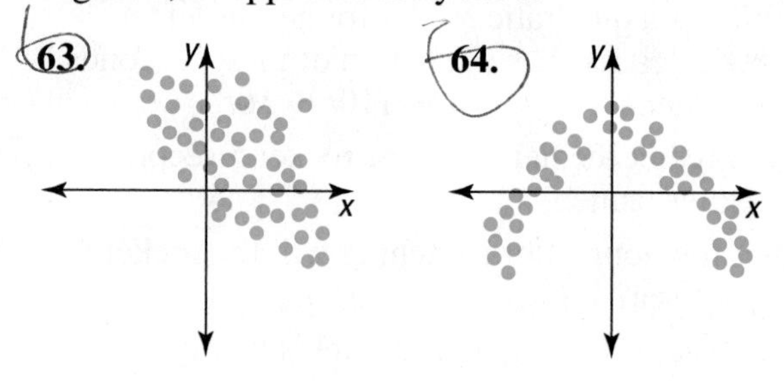

CHAPTER TWO

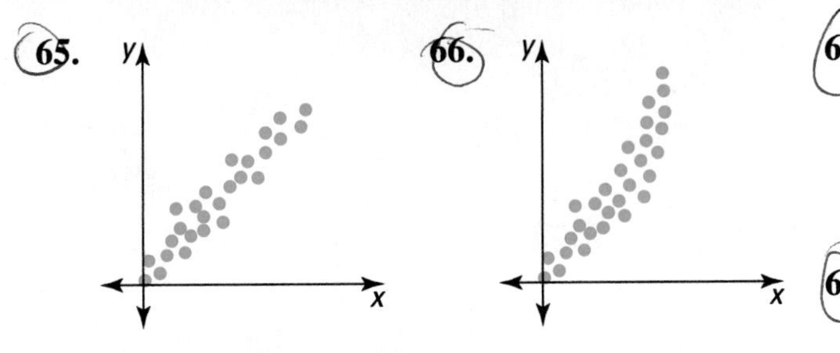

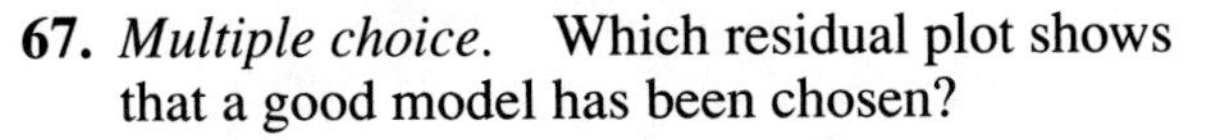

67. *Multiple choice.* Which residual plot shows that a good model has been chosen?

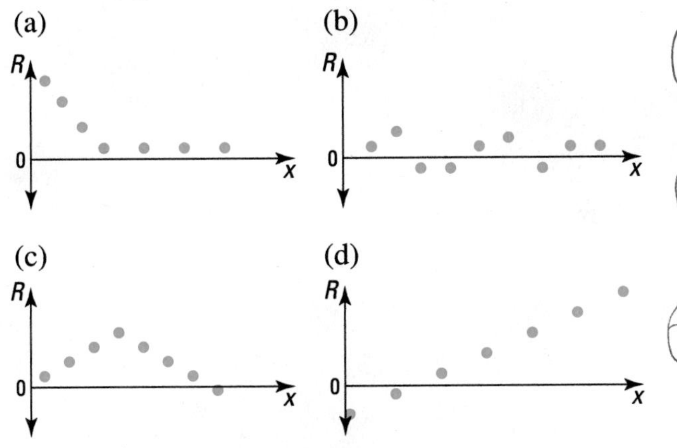

In 68–72, use the displays below showing both linear and quadratic models fitted to data relating the number of hours some students spent studying for a test and their marks on the test.

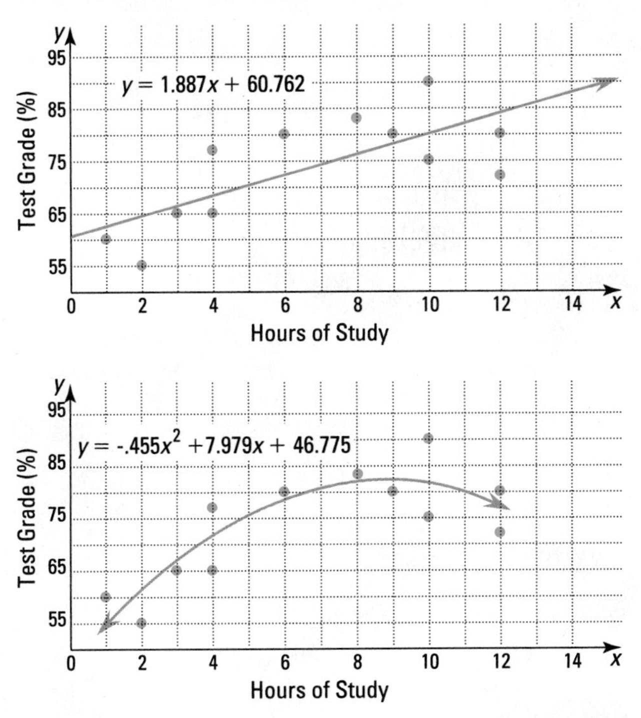

68. Consider the linear model and the student who studied six hours for the test.

a. What is the observed y-value?

b. What is the predicted y-value?

c. What is the error of prediction?

69. Consider the quadratic model and the student who studied six hours for the test.

a. What is the observed y-value?

b. What is the predicted y-value?

c. What is the error of prediction?

70. According to the quadratic model, what is the amount of time a student should study in order to achieve a maximum score? Explain why the existence of such a point might make sense.

71. One of the students who studied ten hours seems to be an outlier in both models. Which model comes closer to that student's actual performance?

72. The residuals for the linear and quadratic models are graphed below. What do these graphs tell you about the appropriateness of each model?

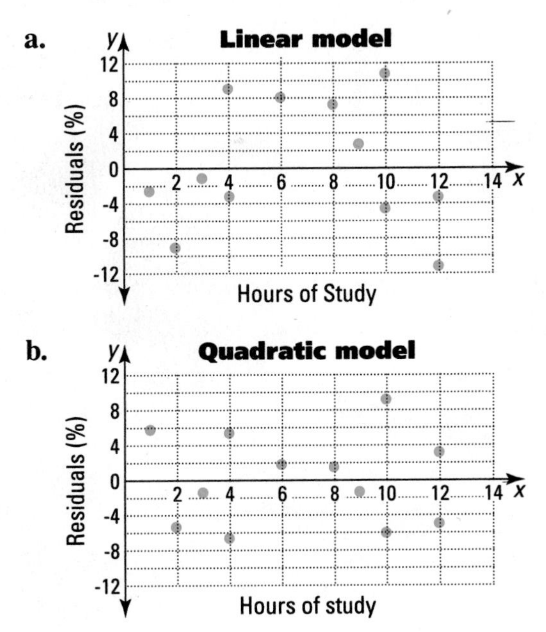

CHAPTER 3

Transformations of Graphs and Data

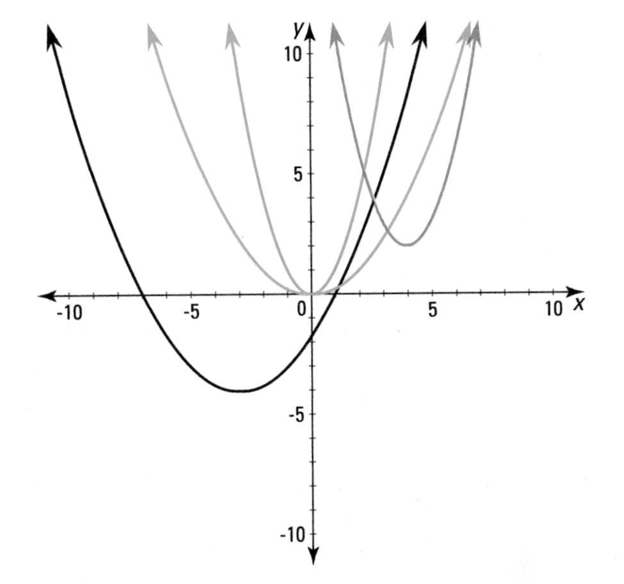

A **transformation** is a one-to-one correspondence between sets of points. Two important transformations are *translations* and *scale changes*. The picture above shows the images of the parabola with equation $y = x^2$ under various transformations, including a translation, a scale change, and a composite of a translation and a scale change.

Many transformations can be described by algebraic formulas. In this chapter you will study algebraic descriptions of translations and scale changes and their effects on functions and statistical measures.

LESSON

3-1

Changing Windows

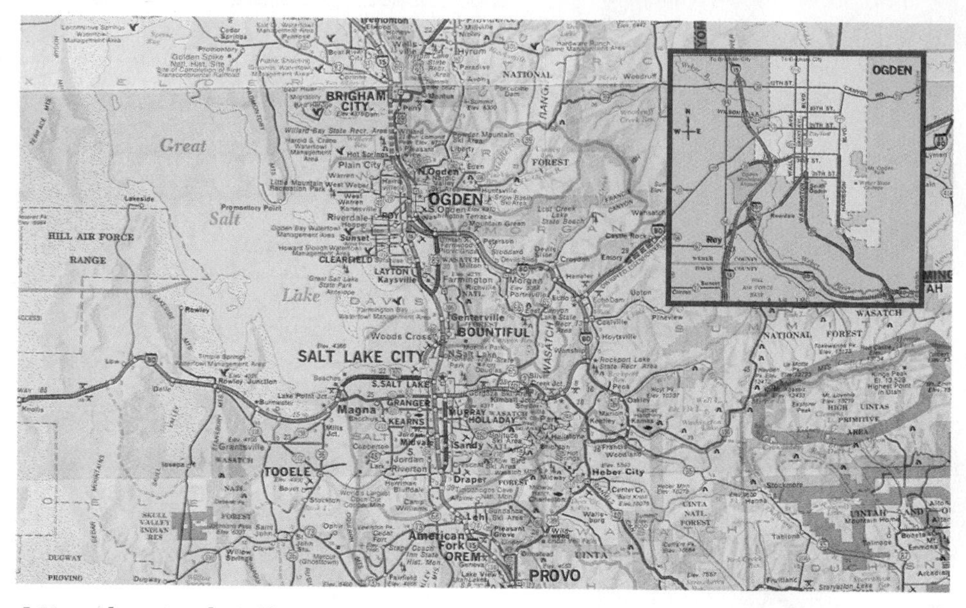

Attention to detail. *An inset, drawn on a larger scale, is often included to show a region in more detail. This allows a reader to see a point of interest both in isolation and in relation to the whole.*

Automatic Graphers

As you know, an **automatic grapher** is a calculator or computer software that draws the graph of a relation. On many automatic graphers, the relation to be graphed must be entered as a formula for y or $f(x)$ in terms of x. Thus,

$y = 7x$ and $f(x) = 3^x - 2$ can be entered directly,
but $x = 4y$ and $x + y = 10$ may not be accepted in that form.

Because automatic graphers differ, you should check with your teacher, your classmates, or the grapher's manual to learn how to use the particular grapher available to you.

What you see on a grapher depends entirely on its *window*. The **viewing window** or **viewing rectangle** is the subset of the coordinate plane that appears on the screen of an automatic grapher, and is described by a specific set of x- and y-values. For some graphers you must specify these values; others provide a **default window** if you do not.

Even a familiar graph may look quite different with different windows. For instance, on page 161 is the graph of $y = x^2$ as seen in four different windows. Each window is described by giving the interval of x-values $a \le x \le b$ and y-values $c \le y \le d$, and the scales that show the distance between tick marks.

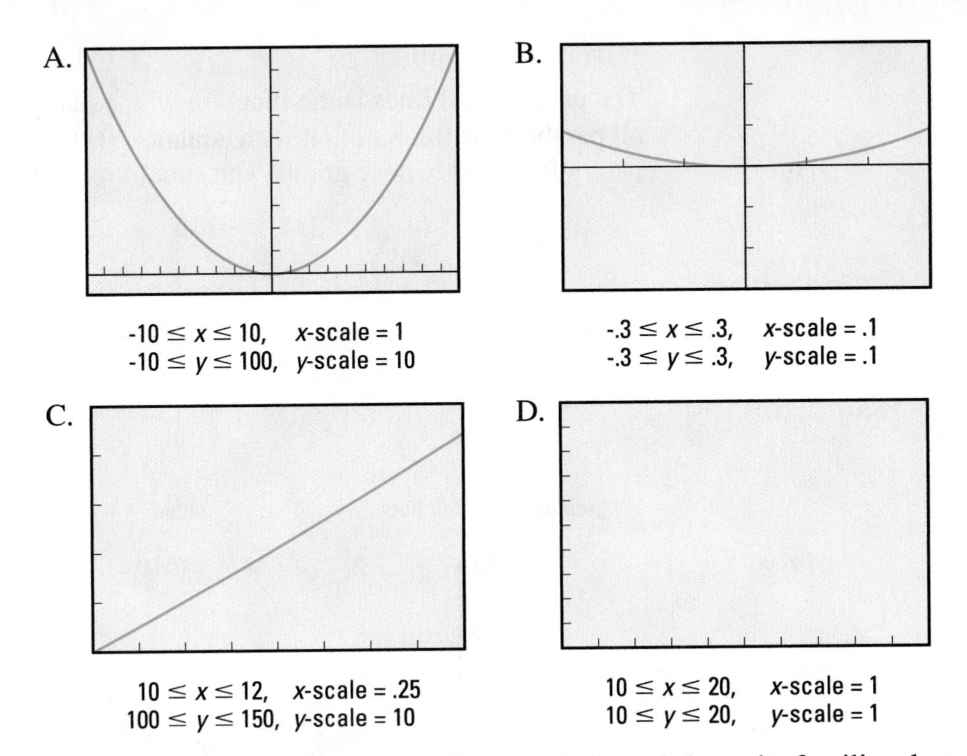

Window A contains the vertex of the parabola and shows its familiar shape. In window B, the graph has "zoomed in" on the vertex; less of the graph is shown and the characteristic shape is less obvious. Window C shows the result of "zooming in" on another part of the graph. Window D misses the graph entirely (not an uncommon event!). We prefer window A for an initial viewing window because it displays the key features of the graph, i.e., the vertex, the x-intercepts, and y-intercept.

You do not have to specify a viewing window in advance. If you can find part of a graph in a window, you can explore better windows either by moving the cursor along the graph until it goes off the screen or by zooming out or zooming in.

Activity

Give a viewing window for $F(x) = 12 + 4x - \frac{1}{2}x^2$ that shows all the key features of the parabola.

Predicting the shape of a graph from its equation and finding an equation for a relation given its graph are important mathematical skills. To develop these skills, you will find it helpful to look for "resemblances" among graphs of "families" of functions. Families of functions, like human families, have a *parent* from which other related functions are derived.

Parent Functions

The parent of all lines is the function with equation $f(x) = x$. The parent of all parabolas is the function with equation $f(x) = x^2$. Some other important parent functions whose graphs you should recognize are shown below.

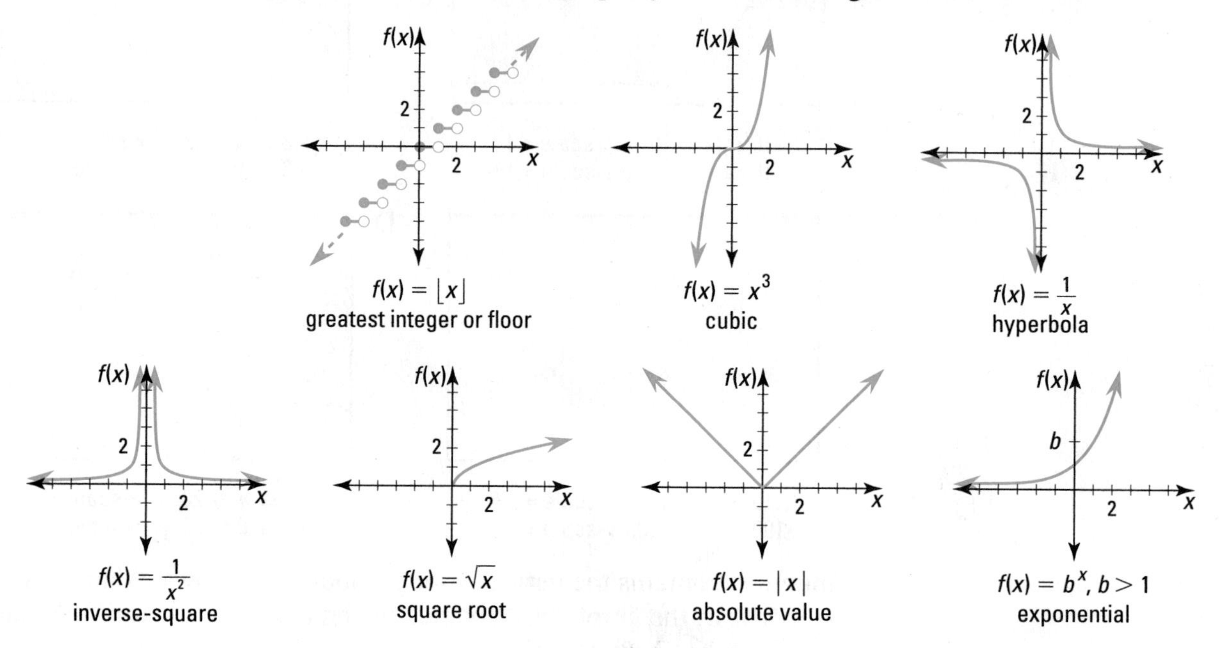

Graphs of other parent functions are given in Appendix A. Refer to the graphs above or Appendix A until you become familiar with their shapes.

Most automatic graphers can plot more than one graph in a single window. Some graphers use color or patterned lines to help distinguish graphs. On a screen that does not distinguish graphs, you need to depend on your knowledge of parent functions to distinguish them.

Example

a. Graph $f(x) = \sqrt{ax}$ when $a = \frac{1}{2}$, 1, 2, and 3.

b. What happens to the graph as a increases?

Solution

a. You are asked to graph $y = \sqrt{\frac{1}{2}x}$, $y = \sqrt{x}$, $y = \sqrt{2x}$, and $y = \sqrt{3x}$. Enter one equation at a time and do not clear the screen until all graphs have been drawn. For the default window $-10 \le x \le 10$, $-10 \le y \le 10$, our grapher produced the display shown at the right.

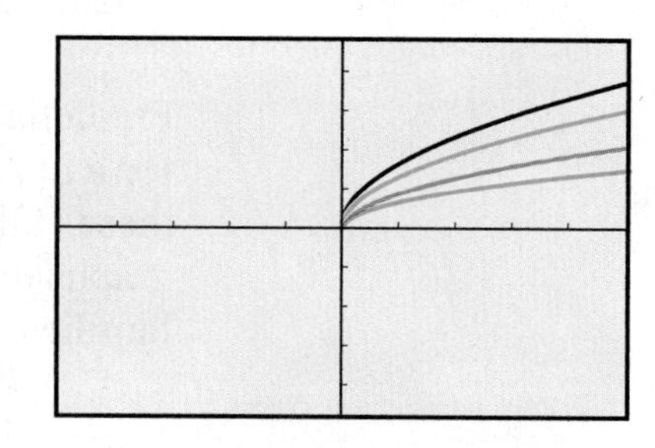

$-10 \le x \le 10$, x-scale = 2
$-10 \le y \le 10$, y-scale = 2

b. The graphs in part a are so close to each other that it is hard to answer part b. We could zoom in at the origin or change windows. For the window $-1 \le x \le 4$, $-1 \le y \le 4$, our grapher produced the following display.

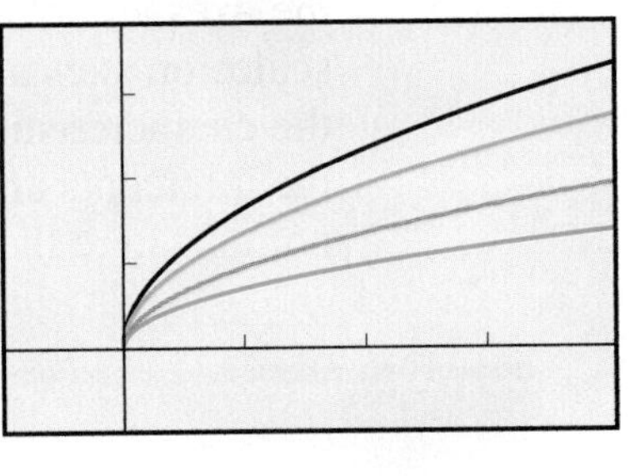

$-1 \le x \le 4$, x-scale = 1
$-1 \le y \le 4$, y-scale = 1

As the value of a increases, the graph is higher. For a given x-value, the function with the lowest y-value is $y = \sqrt{\frac{1}{2}x}$; the one with the greatest y-value is $y = \sqrt{3x}$.

Notice that, in general, none of the properties of a function change when you change the window.

Asymptotes and Points of Discontinuity

Recall that an **asymptote** is a line that the graph of a function $y = f(x)$ approaches as the variable x approaches some fixed value or as x increases or decreases without bound. **Points of discontinuity** arise when the graph of a function appears to "jump." Asymptotes and points of discontinuity are key features of graphs of some of the parent functions, and knowing when they occur can be helpful when graphing related functions. For example, because the graphs of $f(x) = \frac{1}{x}$ and $f(x) = \frac{1}{x^2}$ have both vertical and horizontal asymptotes, you should expect to find both horizontal and vertical asymptotes in graphs of functions related to them. As you have already seen in Lesson 2-7, the function $y = \lfloor x \rfloor$ has a point of discontinuity at each integer. Therefore, functions related to $y = \lfloor x \rfloor$ have an infinite number of evenly spaced points of discontinuity.

Natural discontinuity. *This Silurian red sandstone near Canberra, Australia, shows jumping fault lines. These jumps are points of discontinuity that indicate dramatic movement of the rock layers of Earth.*

It is important to note that some automatic graphers handle discontinuous graphs in a misleading manner. For example, some automatic graphers incorrectly draw vertical line segments at the points of discontinuity of the function $y = \lfloor x \rfloor$. Similarly, an extraneous vertical line may appear at the point of discontinuity $x = 0$ in the parent hyperbola and inverse-square functions. It is therefore very important to know the grapher's limitations and where a function's discontinuities occur when interpreting the graphs drawn on an automatic grapher.

Hard Copies of Graphs

If your grapher cannot produce a hard copy, you must read enough information from the screen to *sketch* by hand the graphs your grapher produces. A sketch generally should meet the following criteria:

> the axes are labeled,
> scales on axes are shown,
> the characteristic shape can be seen,
> the intercepts are shown, and
> points where the function is discontinuous are indicated.

QUESTIONS

Covering the Reading

1. Define *transformation*.

2. If your grapher has a default window, state its dimensions.

3. What viewing window did you use to see the key features of the parabola in the Activity?

4. Give an equation for the parent function of all parabolas.

5. Consider $f(x) = 3x^2$, $g(x) = 0.5x^2$, and $h(x) = -x^2$.
   a. Graph f, g, and h simultaneously on an automatic grapher.
   b. Graph $y = x^2$ on the same set of axes. Describe how each graph in part **a** is related to the graph of the parent function.

In 6 and 7, refer to the nine parent functions mentioned in this lesson.

6. Name all whose graphs pass through the origin.

7. Name all whose range is the set of all real numbers.

8. Let $f(x) = 5 \cdot 2^x$.
   a. Write an equation for p, the parent function of f.
   b. Give the equation for an asymptote of both p and f.

9. **a.** Describe two ways a function might be discontinuous.
   b. Give an example of a parent function to illustrate each type in part **a**.

In 10 and 11, two functions are given. **a.** Plot each pair of functions on the same set of axes. **b.** Sketch the graphs on paper or print a hard copy. **c.** Describe the relation between each pair of graphs.

10. $y = \sqrt{x}$, $y = \sqrt{x - 5}$

11. $y = |x|$, $y = |4x|$

Applying the Mathematics

12. **a.** Graph the function $f(x) = x^3 - x$ on the given windows.

i. $-1 \le x \le 1$, $-1 \le y \le 1$

ii. $-5 \le x \le 5$, $-5 \le y \le 5$

iii. $-10 \le x \le 10$, $-10 \le y \le 10$

iv. $-100 \le x \le 100$, $-100 \le y \le 100$

b. Which window provides the most useful graph? Why?

13. **a.** Graph $f(x) = \frac{1}{x}$, $g(x) = \frac{1}{x+6}$, and $h(x) = \frac{1}{x} + 10$ on the same axes.

b. At what value(s) of x is each of f, g, and h discontinuous?

c. Give an equation of the vertical asymptote of each curve.

d. How is each of g and h related to f?

14. **a.** Graph $f(x) = \frac{1}{x^2}$ and $g(x) = \frac{4}{x^2}$ on the same set of axes.

b. *True or false.* For all x, $f(x) < g(x)$.

c. Justify your response to part **b** both algebraically (by using the formulas) and geometrically (by using the graphs).

Review

Fish tales. *These salmon were caught near Sitka, Alaska.*

15. The number of fish caught by various competitors in a fishing contest are listed in the table below.

Number of fish	0	1	2	3	6	9
Number of competitors	4	7	13	8	2	1

a. How many competitors were there?

b. How many fish were caught?

c. Find the mean, median, and mode of the numbers of fish caught.

d. What is the standard deviation of the numbers of fish caught? *(Lessons 1-1, 1-3, 1-7)*

16. Use the following data about education in the United States. (Source: *Statistical Abstract of the United States 1995*)

Education	Unit	1970	1980	1985	1990	1993
School Enrollment:						
Total	Mil.	59.8	58.3	57.2	60.3	63.4
Elementary (grades K-8)	Mil.	36.6	31.6	31.2	34.0	35.7
Secondary (grades 9-12)	Mil.	14.6	14.6	13.8	12.5	13.2
Higher education	Mil.	8.6	12.1	12.2	13.8	14.6
School Expenditures:						
Total	\$Bil.[1]	242.7	285.7	313.6	403.0	437.9
Elementary and Secondary	\$Bil.[1]	153.1	178.0	189.2	242.9	262.5
Higher Education	\$Bil.[1]	89.6	107.8	124.4	160.1	175.4

[1]In 1990–91 dollars

a. Calculate the expenditures per student in 1970 and in 1993.

b. Did the average expenditure per student increase or decrease between these years? *(Lesson 1-3)*

17. **a.** Draw $\triangle ABC$ with $A = (3, 5)$, $B = (-4, -2)$, and $C = (2, -2)$.
b. Let $\triangle A'B'C'$ be the triangle determined by new points whose x-coordinates are 6 more than the corresponding coordinates in $\triangle ABC$.
c. How are $\triangle ABC$ and $\triangle A'B'C'$ related? *(Previous course)*

18. **a.** Draw a parallelogram $PQRS$ with $P = (0, 0)$, $Q = (0, -4)$, $R = (-3, -6)$, and $S = (-3, -2)$.
b. Draw $P'Q'R'S'$, its image under the transformation which maps (x, y) to $(x + 5, y - 2)$.
c. How are $PQRS$ and $P'Q'R'S'$ related? *(Previous course)*

19. *Skill sequence.* Find the missing expression. *(Previous course)*
a. $x^2 + 10x + \underline{\ ?\ } = (x + 5)^2$
b. $x^2 - \underline{\ ?\ } + 36 = (x - 6)^2$
c. $x^2 + 26x + 169 = (\underline{\ ?\ })^2$
d. $x^2 + 2ax + a^2 = (\underline{\ ?\ })^2$

20. Write without an exponent: $\frac{14.2 \cdot 10^5}{10^{-2}}$. *(Previous course)*

Exploration

21. **a.** Using only the parent functions $y = x^2$, $y = x^3$, $y = \sqrt{x}$, $y = |x|$, $y = \lfloor x \rfloor$, $y = \frac{1}{x^2}$, and $y = b^x$ $(b > 1)$ and the operation of addition, create some new functions. For instance, you might create $y = \sqrt{x} + |x|$.
b. What is the most interesting graph you can make from adding two of these parents? Why do you think it is interesting?

LESSON

3-2

The Graph-Translation Theorem

Color copies. *Color is the distinguishing feature of these houses in Svalbard, Norway, which are translation images of each other.*

The Translation Image of a Graph

Consider the graphs of the equations $y = |x|$ and $y = |x - 4|$. (The graph of $y = |x - 4|$ is shown in orange.)

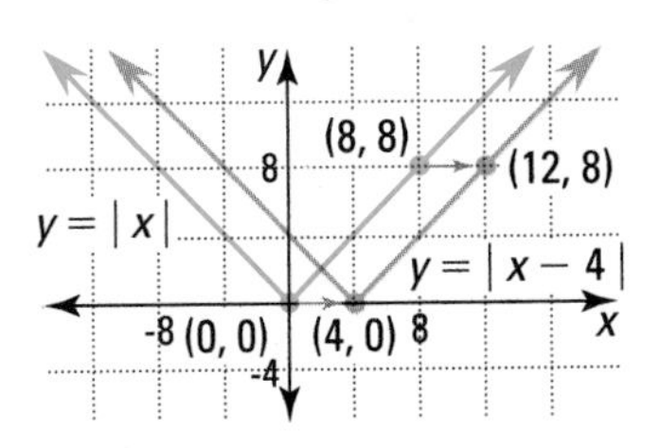

The graph of $y = |x - 4|$ is the **translation image** of the graph of $y = |x|$ under the *translation* 4 units to the right. In this situation, the graph of $y = |x|$ is called the **preimage**.

Translations are transformations. Specifically, the horizontal translation 4 units can be written as $(x, y) \to (x + 4, y)$, which is read "(x, y) is mapped onto $(x + 4, y)$." If T is such a translation, we can write $T(x, y) = (x + 4, y)$ or $T: (x, y) \to (x + 4, y)$. Similarly, the mapping that adds 3 to the y-coordinate of each point in a plane is a vertical translation. It can be written as $T(x, y) = (x, y + 3)$ or $T: (x, y) \to (x, y + 3)$. Below is the effect of this translation on the graph of $y = \sqrt{x}$.

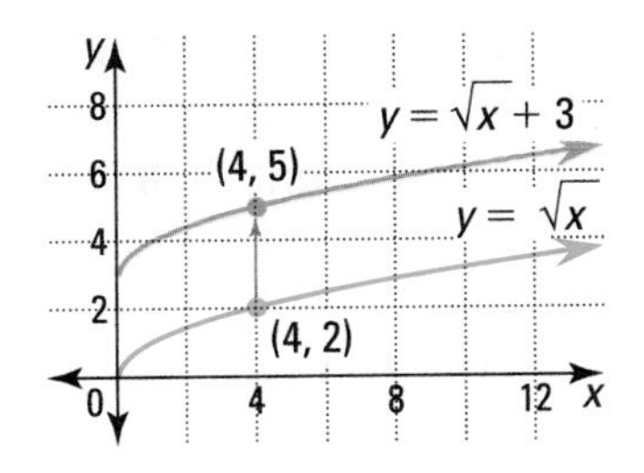

The general translation of the plane translates figures horizontally and vertically at the same time.

Definition

A **translation** in the plane is a transformation that maps each point (x, y) onto $(x + h, y + k)$.

The translation $T: (x, y) \rightarrow (x + h, y + k)$ moves points h units to the right and k units up. As is customary throughout mathematics, "left" is "negative right" and "down" is "negative up." For instance, if $T(x, y) = (x - 1, y + 6)$, then $T(4, 2) = (4 - 1, 2 + 6) = (3, 8)$. This transformation T translates the point (4, 2) one unit to the left and six units up.

Example 1

The graph of $y = x^2$ is shown below, together with its image under a translation T. The point (0, 0), which is the vertex of the graph $y = x^2$, maps onto the vertex (2, -5) on the image.

a. Find a rule for the translation T.

b. Find the image of (3, 9) under this translation.

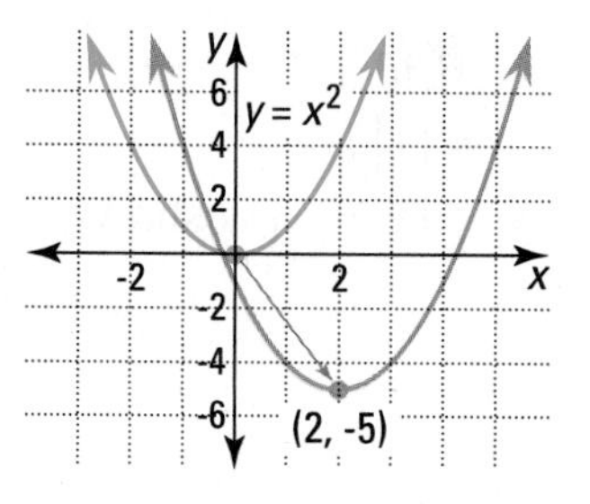

Solution

a. The second graph has been obtained from the graph of $y = x^2$ by a translation 2 units to the right and 5 units down. Thus, $T(x, y) = (x + 2, y - 5)$.

b. $T(3, 9) = (3 + 2, 9 - 5) = (5, 4)$.

The Graph-Translation Theorem

There is a direct relationship between replacing a variable expression in an equation and finding the image of a graph under a transformation.

Consider again the graphs of $y = |x|$ and $y = |x - 4|$, drawn at the right. As the arrow from the point (8, 8) to (12, 8) indicates, the graph of $y = |x - 4|$ can be obtained from the graph of $y = |x|$ by the translation 4 units to the right, or $(x, y) \rightarrow (x + 4, y)$. Note that adding 4 to each x-coordinate corresponds to replacing x by $x - 4$ in the equation of the preimage.

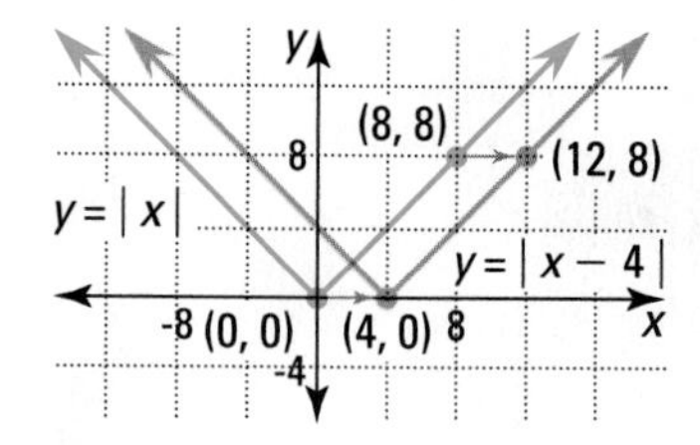

Similarly, graphs of the equations $y = x^2$ and $y = (x - 2)^2 - 5$ are drawn below. Notice that the graph of $y = (x - 2)^2 - 5$ is the image of the graph of $y = x^2$ under the translation that maps (x, y) to $(x + 2, y - 5)$. Because $y = (x - 2)^2 - 5$ is equivalent to $y + 5 = (x - 2)^2$, we can say that the translation $(x, y) \rightarrow (x + 2, y - 5)$ corresponds to replacing x by $x - 2$ and y by $y + 5$ in the equation of the preimage.

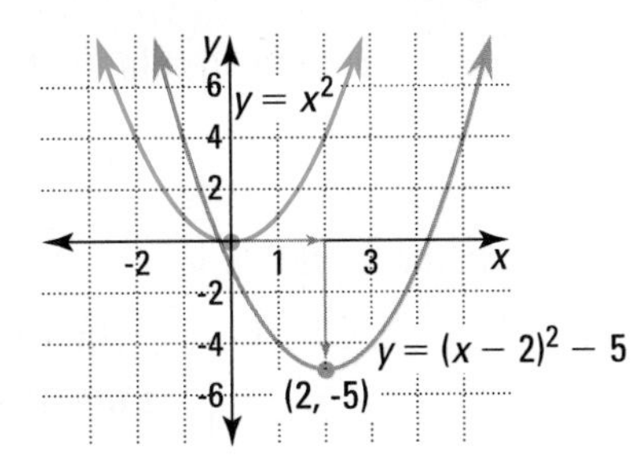

This leads to an important generalization, which can be proved.

The Graph-Translation Theorem
In a relation described by a sentence in x and y, the following two processes yield the same graph:

(1) replacing x by $x - h$ and y by $y - k$ in the sentence;

(2) applying the translation $(x, y) \rightarrow (x + h, y + k)$ to the graph of the original relation.

That is, under the translation $T(x, y) = (x + h, y + k)$, an equation of the image of $y = f(x)$ is $y - k = f(x - h)$.

The Graph-Translation Theorem can be applied to write an equation if a graph is given, and to sketch a graph if an equation is given.

Example 2

At the right are the graphs of the function $y = C(x) = x^3$ and its image $y = D(x)$ under the translation $(x, y) \rightarrow (x + 5, y - 4)$. Find an equation for the image.

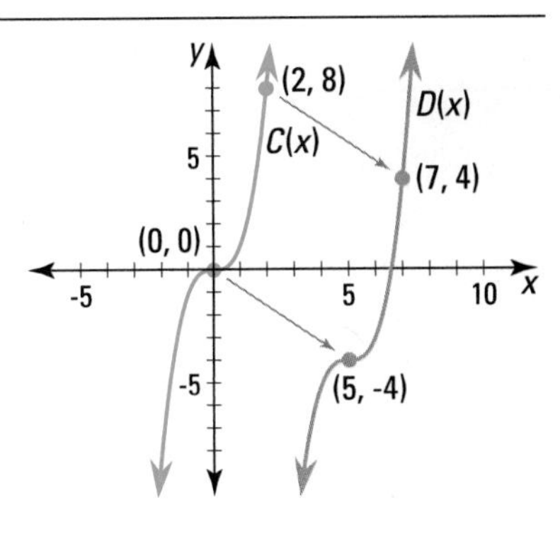

Solution

In $y = x^3$, the equation of the preimage, replace x by $x - 5$ and y by $y - -4 = y + 4$. Thus, an equation of the image is $y + 4 = (x - 5)^3$, or equivalently, $y = (x - 5)^3 - 4$.

Check

The points (0, 0) and (2, 8), which are on $y = x^3$, have the images (5, -4) and (7, 4), respectively, under this translation. Do these image points satisfy $y = (x - 5)^3 - 4$? $-4 = (5 - 5)^3 - 4$ and $4 = (7 - 5)^3 - 4$. Yes.

Example 3

Sketch a graph of $y = \frac{1}{(x+3)^2} + 2$.

Solution

First graph the parent function $y = \frac{1}{x^2}$. Then rewrite the sentence to see the replacements in relation to the function $y = \frac{1}{x^2}$.

$$y - 2 = \frac{1}{(x+3)^2} = \frac{1}{(x - -3)^2}$$

In the equation $y = \frac{1}{x^2}$, y has been replaced by $y - 2$ and x has been replaced by $x - -3$. Thus, by the Graph-Translation Theorem, the graph of $y - 2 = \frac{1}{(x - -3)^2}$ is the image of the graph of $y = \frac{1}{x^2}$ under the translation $T(x, y) = (x - 3, y + 2)$. Therefore, its graph is translated 3 units to the left and 2 units up from the graph of the parent inverse-square function. In particular, its asymptotes are $x = -3$ and $y = 2$. With this knowledge, its graph can be sketched. The graphs are drawn below.

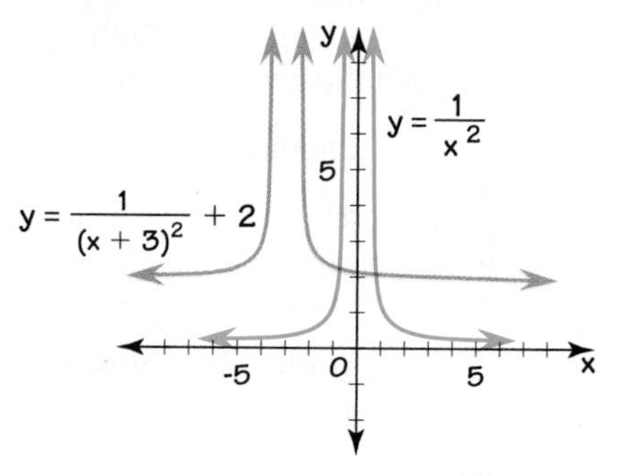

Check

Use an automatic grapher.

QUESTIONS

Covering the Reading

In 1–3, find the image of each point under the given translation.

1. (3, 5), down 6 units
2. (-4, -7), horizontal translation of 3 units
3. (r, s), horizontal a units and vertical b units

In 4 and 5, find the image of each point under T if $T(x, y) = (x - 2, y + 5)$.

4. (-2, 2)
5. (p, q)

6. *Multiple choice.* Which rule is for a translation T that has the effect of sliding a graph 6 units down and 7 units to the left?
   (a) $T(x, y) = (x - 6, y - 7)$
   (b) $T(x, y) = (x + 7, y + 6)$
   (c) $T(x, y) = (x - 7, y + 6)$
   (d) $T(x, y) = (x - 7, y - 6)$

7. Suppose $y = |x|$ and $T(x, y) = (x - 6, y + 5)$.
   a. Find the images of (-2, 2), (-1, 1), and (0, 0) under T.
   b. Verify that the three images under T satisfy $y - 5 = |x + 6|$.

8. The graph of $f(x) = \sqrt{x}$ is shown at the right, together with its image under a translation T. The image of (0, 0) on the graph is the point (-2, 1).
   a. Find a rule for the translation T.
   b. Find the image of (4, 2) under this translation.
   c. Find an equation for the image g.

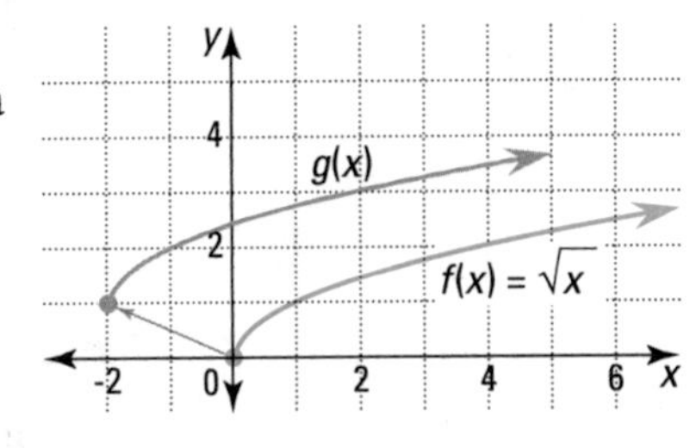

In 9 and 10, rules for two functions are given. **a.** State a rule for a translation that maps f to g. **b.** Graph f and g on the same set of axes.

9. $f(x) = \sqrt{x}$; $g(x) = \sqrt{x + 3}$

10. $f(x) = |x|$; $g(x) = |x - 1| - 2$

11. Use the Graph-Translation Theorem to find an equation of the image of $y = \frac{1}{x}$ under $T(x, y) \rightarrow (x - 3, y + 7)$.

In 12 and 13, the graph of the given function f is translated 5 units to the right and 3 units down. **a.** Find an equation of its image g. **b.** Sketch graphs of f and g on the same set of axes.

12. $f(x) = |x|$

13. $f(x) = x^2$

14. a. Without using an automatic grapher, sketch graphs of $y_1 = \frac{1}{x}$ and $y_2 = \frac{1}{x + 3} - 4$ on the same set of axes.
   b. Find equations for the asymptotes of y_2. How are they related to the asymptotes of y_1?

Applying the Mathematics

15. Find an equation for the translation image of $y = \frac{1}{x}$ pictured at the right.

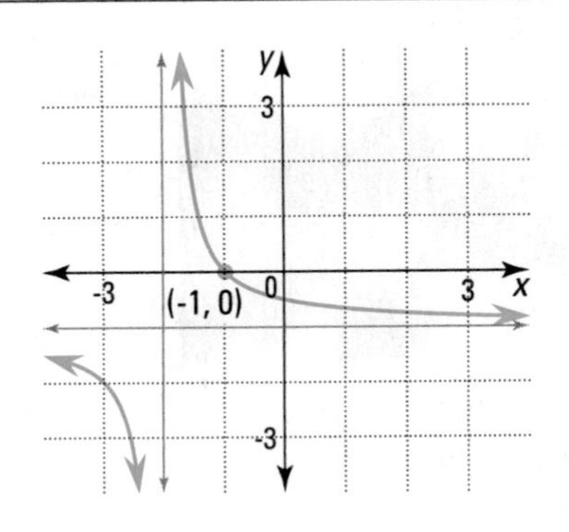

16. The equation $x^2 + y^2 = 16$ describes a circle of radius 4 with center at the origin. Describe the graph of the relation $(x + 7)^2 + (y - 6)^2 = 16$.

17. *Multiple choice.* A parabola has its vertex at (2, -3). Which of the following might be an equation for the parabola?
   (a) $f(x) = (x + 2)^2 + 3$
   (b) $f(x) = (x + 2)^2 - 3$
   (c) $f(x) = (x - 2)^2 - 3$
   (d) $f(x) = (x - 2)^2 + 3$

18. The formula $t = 260 - 0.4n$ approximately relates the number of years n after 1900 and the time t (in seconds) of the men's world record in the mile run. For instance, this formula estimates that the record in 1966 is $260 - 0.4(66) = 233.6 =$ 3 minutes, 53.6 seconds; the actual record is 3 minutes, 51.3 seconds. Convert the formula to one that maps the number y of the year to the time.

Review

19. **a.** Sketch graphs of the parent inverse-square curve and the parent hyperbola.
  b. Describe one way the curves are alike.
  c. Describe one way the curves are different. *(Previous course, Lesson 3-1)*

20. Consider the data set $\{x_1, x_2, x_3, \ldots, x_n\}$.
  a. Write an expression using Σ-notation for the mean $\bar{x}$ of the set.
  b. Write an expression using Σ-notation for the standard deviation s of the set. *(Lessons 1-3, 1-7)*

21. Solve for k: $\sum_{i=1}^{5} (x_i + 3) = k + \sum_{i=1}^{5} x_i$. *(Lesson 1-3)*

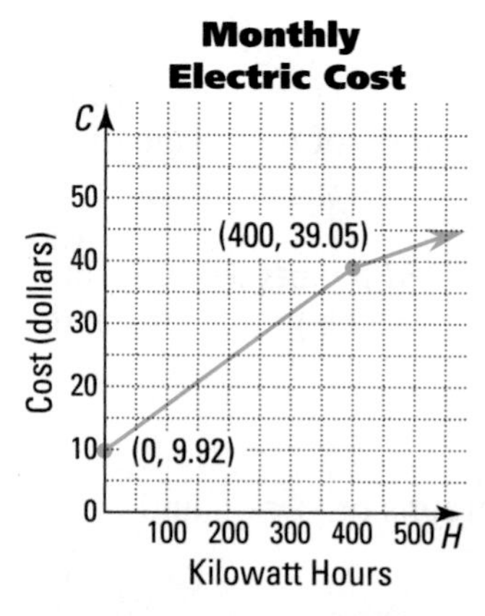

In 22–24, use the graph at the left, which shows residential electric rates in a big city. *(Previous course)*

22. What is the minimum monthly fee paid by a customer even if no electricity is used?

23. *Multiple choice.* Which is a unit for the slope between two points on this graph?
  (a) dollars
  (b) kilowatt hours
  (c) dollars per kilowatt hour
  (d) kilowatt hours per dollar

24. *True or false.* The cost per kilowatt hour declines after a customer uses 400 kilowatt hours.

ElectriCity. *The first practical incandescent lamp was invented in 1878. In 1880, Wabash, Indiana, was the first city to install electric streetlights.*

Exploration

25. **a.** Consider the linear equation $f(x) = 3x - 5$. Find an equation for the image of the graph of f under the following transformations.
    i. $T(x, y) = (x + 1, y + 3)$
    ii. $T(x, y) = (x + 2, y + 6)$
    iii. $T(x, y) = (x - 4, y - 12)$
    iv. $T(x, y) = (x + 1, y + 5)$
  b. Make a conjecture based on the results of part **a**.
  c. Prove your conjecture in part **b**.
  d. Generalize this problem to any line of the form $y = mx + b$.

LESSON

3-3

Translations of Data

Time translation. *In 1994, Tom Dolan set the world's record in the 400-meter Individual Medley with a time stated as "12.30." What does this mean?*

Translating Data

A data set can be transformed just as a set of points can. Consider the times of two American swimmers, Tom Dolan and Eric Namesnik, in the men's 400 meter individual medley event of the 1996 Olympic Games. Their winning times, which earned them gold and silver medals respectively, were 4 minutes, 14.90 seconds (written 4:14.90) and 4 minutes, 15.25 seconds (4:15.25). Swimmers and expert commentators commonly describe these times as "14.90" and "15.25," assuming that the listeners will know the meaning. The data have been transformed by subtracting 4 minutes. The same term is used as for geometric points; such a transformation is a *translation.*

A **translation** of a set of data $\{x_1, x_2, \dots, x_n\}$ is a transformation that maps each x_i to $x_i + h$, where h is some constant. If T is the translation, then this transformation can be described as

$$T: x \rightarrow x + h \text{ or } T(x) = x + h.$$

The number $x + h$ or the point it represents is the **translation image** of x. In the situation above, the transformation mapping each original swimming time x (in minutes) onto its image has the rule $T(x) = x - 4$.

As might be expected, translations have an effect on displays and on the measures of center and spread of data.

Effects of Translating Data

Example 1

Suppose that a restaurant employs 11 workers and that their daily earnings (in dollars) are:

60, 66, 67, 68, 70, 70, 72, 72, 72, 73, 80.

Suppose also that on a particular day the host of a large party held at the restaurant gives a $275 tip to be divided equally among the workers.

a. Find the total amount, including tip, received by each employee for that day.

b. Compare the distributions of employee pay with and without the tip amount.

c. Describe the effect of the tip on the median, mean, range, and standard deviation of the set of earnings.

Solution

a. Since each employee receives an extra $275/11, or $25, the translation applied here has the rule $x \rightarrow x + 25$. The earnings (in dollars) after the tip are

85, 91, 92, 93, 95, 95, 97, 97, 97, 98, 105.

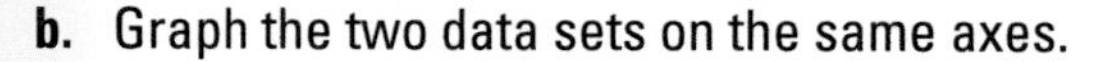

b. Graph the two data sets on the same axes.

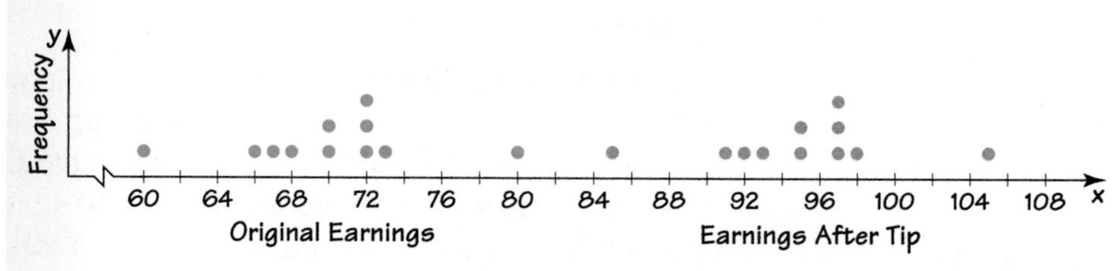

The distribution of the earnings after the tip is the image of the original frequency distribution after a translation 25 units to the right.

c. For the original data, the median is 70, the mean is 70, and the range is 80 − 60 = 20. For the transformed data, the median is 95, the mean is 95, and the range is 105 − 85 = 20. For both sets of data, the standard deviation is 5.

Thus, adding $25 to each individual's earnings increased the mean and median each by $25, but had no effect on the range or standard deviation.

Generalizations about Translating Data

You can generalize the results in Example 1 by examining what happens to the measures of center and spread of a data set $\{x_1, x_2, \ldots, x_n\}$ under a translation by h. Under such a translation, each value x_i is mapped to $x_i + h$. To find the mean of the image set, you must evaluate

$$\frac{\sum_{i=1}^{n} (x_i + h)}{n}.$$

By definition of Σ, this expression represents

$$\frac{\overbrace{(x_1 + h) + (x_2 + h) + (x_3 + h) + \ldots + (x_n + h)}^{n \text{ terms}}}{n}.$$

Using the associative and commutative properties of addition, rewrite the expression as

$$\frac{(x_1 + x_2 + x_3 + \ldots + x_n) + \overbrace{(h + h + h + \ldots + h)}^{n \text{ terms}}}{n}$$

$$= \frac{\left(\sum_{i=1}^{n} x_i\right) + nh}{n}$$

$$= \frac{\sum_{i=1}^{n} x_i}{n} + h = \overline{x} + h.$$

This proves that, under a translation by h, the mean of the image set of data is h units more than the mean of the original set of data. It also can be shown that after a translation of h units, the median and mode of the image set are also increased by h units.

Theorem
Adding h to each number in a data set adds h to each of the mean, median, and mode.

What happens to the measures of spread of a data set after a translation by h?

Activity

Refer to Example 1. Compute the deviations from the mean for the original set of data and for the image set. What do you notice?

The minimum m is mapped to $m + h$; and the maximum M is mapped to $M + h$. So the range of the translated data is

$$(M + h) - (m + h) = M - m,$$

which is the range of the original data.

Similarly, in the calculation of the variance and standard deviation, a translation by h maps each value x_i to $x_i + h$. By the theorem above, the mean $\overline{x}$ is mapped to $\overline{x} + h$. So, each new deviation equals $(x_i + h) - (\overline{x} + h) = x_i - \overline{x}$, which is the original deviation. Because each individual deviation stays the same under a translation, the variance and standard deviation also stay the same under a translation.

Theorem
Adding h to each number in a data set does not change the range, interquartile range, variance, or standard deviation of the data.

Because the measures of spread of a data set do not vary under a translation, they are said to be **invariant** under translation.

The preceding theorems can be used to simplify calculations of measures of center or spread.

Example 2

A swimmer recorded his last ten times for the 400 m individual medley in minutes and seconds:

4:21.81	4:20.36	4:22.06	4:22.16	4:21.77
4:21.62	4:20.97	4:20.80	4:20.50	4:20.38

Find the mean and standard deviation of these times.

Solution

To simplify calculations, **subtract 4 minutes 20 seconds from each time. That is, use the image times:**

1.81, 0.36, ..., 0.38.

For the translated data set, find the mean and standard deviation, either by hand or with a computer or calculator. **The mean is about 1.24 seconds, and the standard deviation about 0.71 second. So, by the theorem above, for the original data the mean is about 4:21.24, while the standard deviation is about 0.71 second.**

QUESTIONS

Covering the Reading

1. A transformation that maps a number x to $x + h$ is called a(n) __?__.

2. Suppose $T: x \rightarrow x - 4$, where x is a time in minutes. Evaluate each expression.
   a. $T(4.9)$ **b.** T(4 minutes, 38 seconds)

3. Refer to the data on earnings in Example 1. Suppose that, instead of a tip being added, $2 was deducted from each worker's earnings to pay for a staff holiday party. Give the following measures for the adjusted earnings.
   a. range **b.** mode **c.** median
   d. mean **e.** variance **f.** standard deviation

In 4 and 5, suppose $x_1 = -2$, $x_2 = 7$, $x_3 = 2.5$, $x_4 = 1.3$, and $x_5 = 9.2$. Evaluate the given expression.

4. $\sum_{i=1}^{5} (x_i + 8)$

5. $\sum_{i=1}^{5} x_i + 8$

6. What values did you get for the deviations you calculated in the Activity? What did you notice?

7. Name three statistical measures that are invariant under a translation.

8. On a set of test scores for a class of n students, the mean was $\bar{x}$ and the standard deviation was s. Later, every score was increased by b bonus points.

a. What is the mean of the image scores?

b. What is the standard deviation of the image scores?

Applying the Mathematics

9. Consider the two frequency distributions below.

Original Scores	6	10	12	16	22
Frequency	2	3	1	2	2

Transformed Scores	17	21	23	27	33
Frequency	2	3	1	2	2

a. Make a dot-frequency diagram showing the two sets of scores.

b. Identify the transformation used to get the transformed scores.

c. Find the range, mode, mean, and median for each set of scores.

10. Let $\{x_1, x_2, x_3, \ldots, x_n\}$ be a data set, and k a constant.

a. Prove that

$$\sum_{i=1}^{n} (x_i + k) = \sum_{i=1}^{n} x_i + nk.$$

b. Prove that $\sum_{i=1}^{n} (x_i - \bar{x}) = 0$, where $\bar{x}$ is the mean of the set. (Hint: Apply the result of part **a**.)

h	w
112	20
106	18
114	19
109	17
110	20
122	24
129	25
112	21
117	26
126	23
128	25
101	15

How does your kindergarden grow?
Most boys at age 6 and girls at age 5 have reached ⅔ of their adult height.

11. Consider the data at the left, which give the height h in cm and weight w in kg of the students in a kindergarten class.

a. Enter these data into a statistics utility. (You will use the data again in later lessons, so save the data file if you can.)

b. Find the mean and standard deviation of the heights and of the weights.

c. Draw a scatterplot with h on the horizontal axis.

d. Find the line of best fit for predicting w from h.

e. Reduce each height by 100 cm. (Your statistics utility may be able to do this for you.) Draw a new scatterplot. How is this scatterplot different from that in part **c**?

f. Without using a statistics utility, write an equation of the line of best fit for part **e**. Check using the statistics utility.

g. Reduce each height by 100 cm and each weight by 20 kg. Find the mean and standard deviation of the transformed variables.

h. Draw a scatterplot of the transformed variables. How is this scatterplot different from that in part **c**?

i. Without using a statistics utility, write an equation of the line of best fit for the data in part **g**. Check using the statistics utility.

12. Generalize the result of Question 11. If bivariate data are translated, which (if any) of the following are invariant?

(a) means of the two variables
(b) standard deviations of the two variables
(c) equation of the line of best fit
(d) slope of the line of best fit
(e) correlation between the two variables

Review

13. Consider the function with equation $y = \sqrt{x - 7} + 10$.

a. Sketch a graph of the function using paper and pencil.

b. Check your sketch with an automatic grapher.

c. State the transformation that maps the parent function $y = \sqrt{x}$ to the given function. *(Lesson 3-2)*

14. Suppose the translation $T: (x, y) \rightarrow (x + 6, y + 5)$ is applied to the graph of the function $y = \frac{1}{x^2}$.

a. Find an equation for the image.

b. Sketch graphs of the preimage and image. *(Lessons 3-1, 3-2)*

In 15 and 16, write an equation for the given graph. The parents are absolute value and cubic functions, respectively. *(Lesson 3-2)*

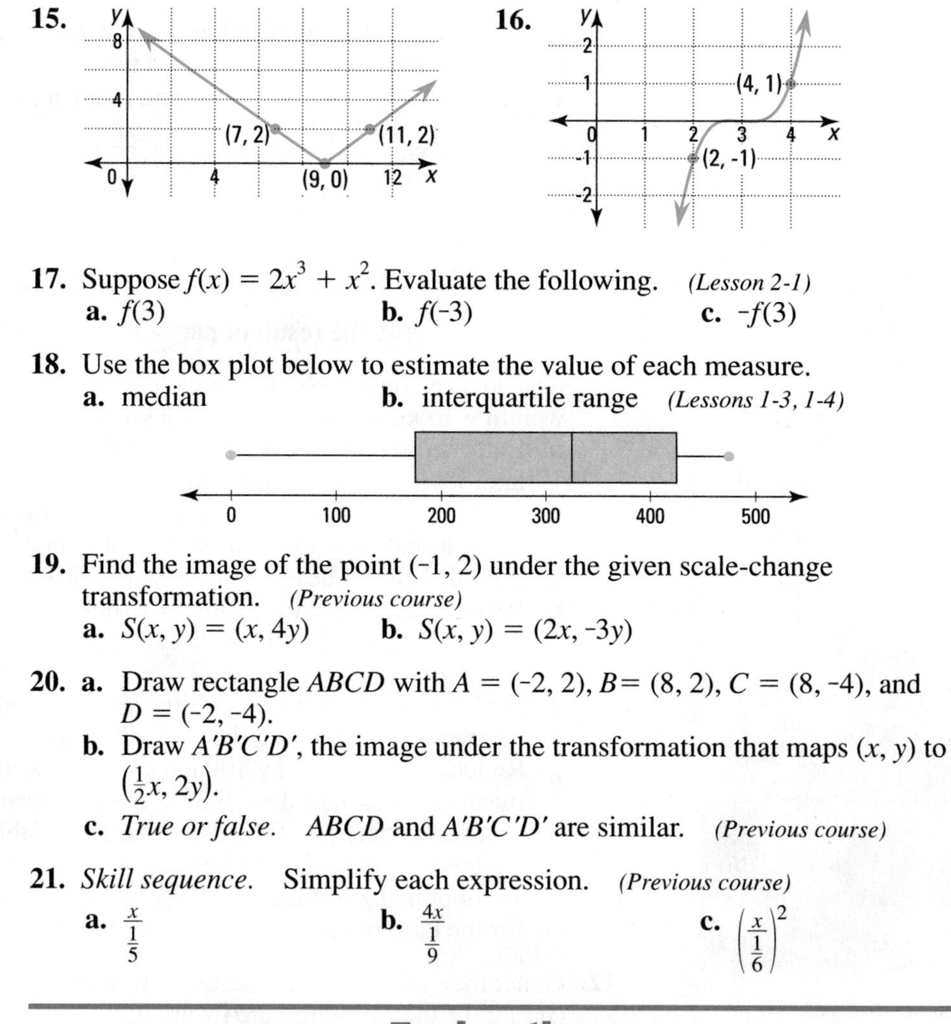

17. Suppose $f(x) = 2x^3 + x^2$. Evaluate the following. *(Lesson 2-1)*

a. $f(3)$ **b.** $f(-3)$ **c.** $-f(3)$

18. Use the box plot below to estimate the value of each measure.

a. median **b.** interquartile range *(Lessons 1-3, 1-4)*

19. Find the image of the point (-1, 2) under the given scale-change transformation. *(Previous course)*

a. $S(x, y) = (x, 4y)$ **b.** $S(x, y) = (2x, -3y)$

20. a. Draw rectangle $ABCD$ with $A = (-2, 2)$, $B = (8, 2)$, $C = (8, -4)$, and $D = (-2, -4)$.

b. Draw $A'B'C'D'$, the image under the transformation that maps (x, y) to $\left(\frac{1}{2}x, 2y\right)$.

c. *True or false.* $ABCD$ and $A'B'C'D'$ are similar. *(Previous course)*

21. *Skill sequence.* Simplify each expression. *(Previous course)*

a. $\frac{x}{\frac{1}{5}}$ **b.** $\frac{4x}{\frac{1}{9}}$ **c.** $\left(\frac{x}{\frac{1}{6}}\right)^2$

Exploration

22. Give an example of some situation other than athletic events where data are often translated, and explain why the translated data are used.

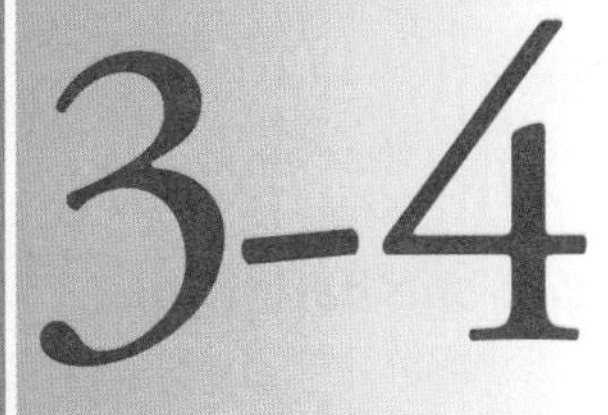

LESSON 3-4

Symmetries of Graphs

Recall from geometry that a figure is **reflection-symmetric** if and only if the figure can be mapped onto itself by a reflection over some line ℓ. The reflecting line ℓ is called the **axis** or **line of symmetry** of the figure. Similarly, a figure is **180°-rotation-symmetric** or has **symmetry to point *P*** or **point symmetry** if and only if the figure can be mapped onto itself under a rotation of 180° around P. The point P is called a **center of symmetry**. Because graphs are sets of points, these definitions apply to graphs. Any symmetry of a figure implies that one part of the figure is congruent to another part. So symmetry shortens the time needed to draw a graph and helps the study of it.

It is possible to *prove* that a graph possesses symmetry if you know an equation for the graph and if you know a formula for the image of every point under the symmetry transformation. At the right we graphed a point (x, y) and its images under reflections over the x-axis, y-axis, and line $x = y$, and its 180° rotation image about the origin.

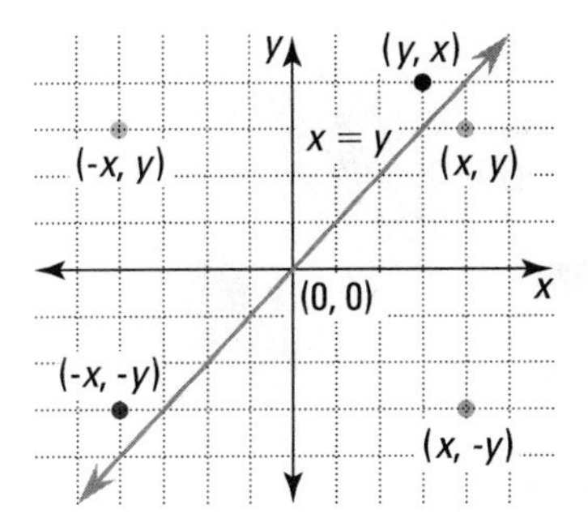

Symmetry with Respect to the *y*-axis

The graphs of $f(x) = |x|$ and $g(x) = \frac{1}{x^2}$ seem *symmetric with respect to the y-axis*. That is, it looks like they coincide with their reflection images over the y-axis.

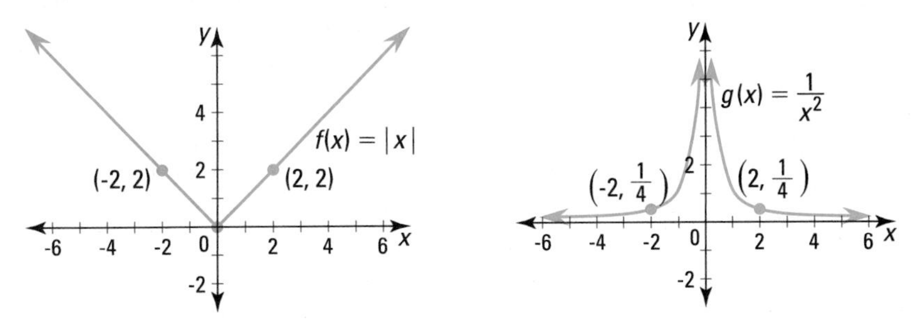

From the definition of reflection symmetry, a graph is symmetric with respect to the y-axis if for every point (x, y) on the graph, its reflection image over the y-axis, $(-x, y)$, is also on the graph.

Notice how this idea is used in Example 1.

Example 1

Prove that the graph of $y = |x|$ is symmetric to the y-axis.

Solution

To show that $f(x)$ is symmetric to the y-axis, we need to show that for all (x, y), if (x, y) is on the graph, so too is $(-x, y)$.

Suppose (x, y) is on the graph. Then $y = |x|$. From the definition of absolute value,

$$|-x| = |x|.$$

By substitution, $y = |-x|$. Consequently, $(-x, y)$ is on the graph.

Symmetry with Respect to the x-axis

If for each point (x, y) on a graph the point $(x, -y)$ is on the graph, the graph is **symmetric with respect to the x-axis**. For instance, if $x = y^2$, then $x = (-y)^2$ also. So, the graph of $x = y^2$ is symmetric to the x-axis. Note, however, that this graph does not represent y as a function of x.

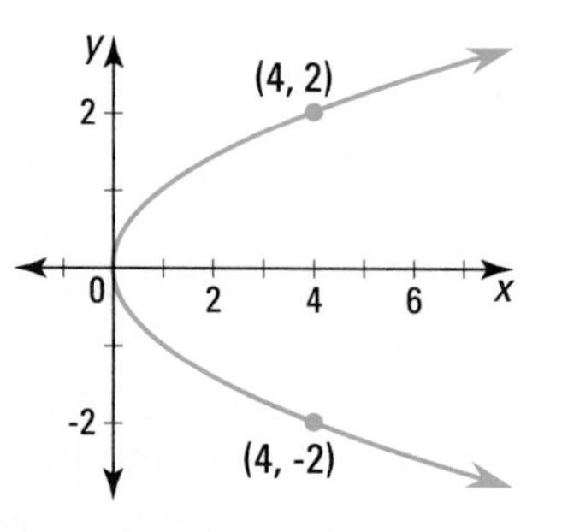

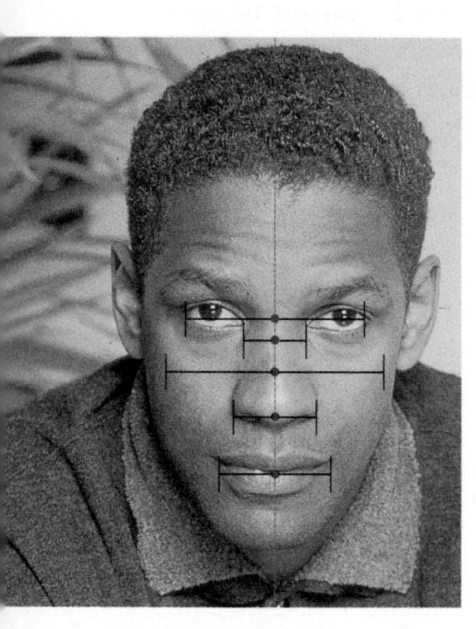

Human symmetry. *Some faces are more symmetric than others. Midpoints of line segments which connect corresponding points of actor Denzel Washington's face are nearly collinear, indicating that his face is almost perfectly symmetric.*

The reflection image of (x, y) over the x-axis is $(x, -y)$. So unless the graph of a function is a subset of the x-axis, it cannot be symmetric with respect to the x-axis. Otherwise, it would have two points with the same x-coordinate, which would violate the definition of function.

Symmetry with Respect to the Origin

When the point (x, y) is rotated 180° about the origin, its image is $(-x, -y)$. Consequently, a graph is **symmetric to the origin** if and only if for every (x, y) on the graph, $(-x, -y)$ is also on the graph. Consider the graphs of $y = x^3$ and $y = \frac{1}{x}$, shown below. These graphs are not symmetric with respect to the y-axis or the x-axis, but they are *symmetric to the origin.*

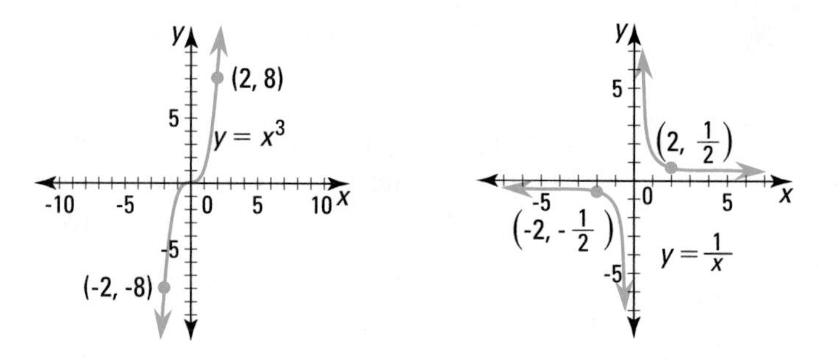

Example 2

Prove that the graph of $y = x^3$ is symmetric to the origin.

Solution

Suppose (x, y) is on the graph. Then $y = x^3$. We need to show that $(-x, -y)$ is on the graph; that is, that $(-y) = (-x)^3$. Since $y = x^3$, $-y = -x^3$. Now for all x, $(-x)^3 = -x^3$. Consequently, by the transitive property of equality, $-y = (-x)^3$. Thus, $(-x, -y)$ is on the graph of $y = x^3$.

Even and Odd Functions

A **power function** is a function f with an equation of the form $f(x) = x^n$, when n is a positive integer greater than or equal to 2. By the method of Example 1, the graphs of the power functions when n is even can all be proved to be symmetric to the y-axis. For this reason, any function whose graph is symmetric with respect to the y-axis is called an *even function*.

Definition
A function f is an **even function** if and only if for all values of x in its domain, $f(-x) = f(x)$.

Similarly, by the method of Example 2, the graphs of the power functions when n is odd can all be proved to be symmetric to the origin. For this reason, a function whose graph is symmetric to the origin is called an *odd function*.

Definition
A function f is an **odd function** if and only if for all values of x in its domain, $f(-x) = -f(x)$.

If you are not sure if a function is even, odd, or neither, then an automatic grapher may help you decide.

Example 3

Use an automatic grapher to see if the function $f(x) = x^3 - x$ appears to be odd, even, or neither. If it appears to be even or odd, prove it.

Solution

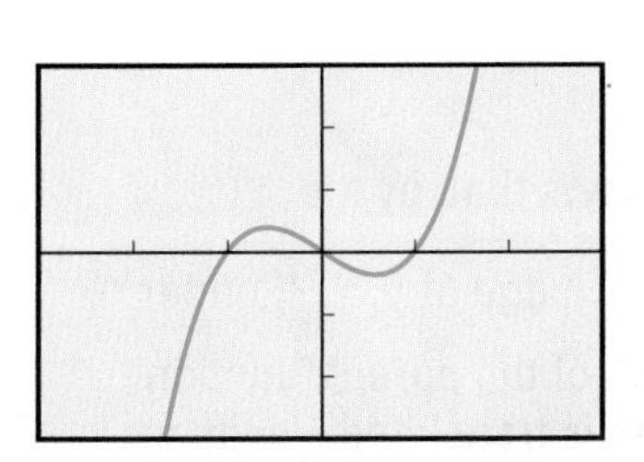

$-3 \le x \le 3$, x-scale = 1
$-3 \le y \le 3$, y-scale = 1

A graph of f is shown at the left. It appears to be symmetric to the origin, so f seems to be an odd function. To prove this, suppose (x, y) is on the graph. That is, $y = f(x) = x^3 - x$. Now consider $f(-x)$.

$$\begin{aligned} f(-x) &= (-x)^3 - (-x) \\ &= -x^3 + x \\ &= -(x^3 - x) \end{aligned}$$

Thus, $f(-x) = -f(x) = -y$. So $(-x, -y)$ is on the graph. This shows that f is an odd function.

Using the Graph-Translation Theorem to Find Symmetries

Reflection symmetry with respect to the x-axis or y-axis, and symmetry with respect to the origin, are special cases of more general symmetries.

Example 4

Consider the function $f(x) = (x + 3)^2 - 10$. Which, if either, of line symmetry or point symmetry does f have?

Solution

Let $y = f(x) = (x + 3)^2 - 10$. This equation is equivalent to $y + 10 = (x + 3)^2$, so its graph is the image of $y = x^2$ under the translation $(x, y) \rightarrow (x - 3, y - 10)$. The line of symmetry of $y = x^2$ is the y-axis. Its image under the translation is $x = -3$. Consequently, the graph of $f(x) = (x + 3)^2 - 10$ is reflection-symmetric to the line $x = -3$.

Check

Sketch a graph of the function.

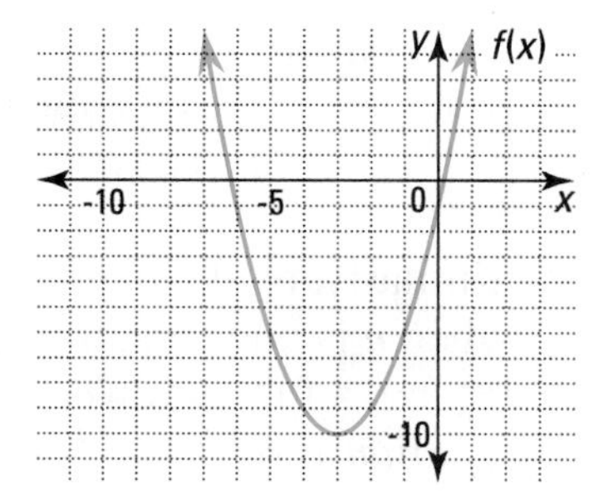

In general, if f is a function and each point (x, y) on its graph is mapped to $(x + h, y + k)$, then the graph of the image is congruent to the graph of the preimage, and all key points and lines are also mapped under this translation. Specifically, lines of symmetry map to lines of symmetry, maxima to maxima, minima to minima, vertices to vertices, symmetry points to symmetry points, and asymptotes to asymptotes.

Example 5

Consider the function F with $y = F(x) = \frac{1}{(x - 5)^2} - 4$.

a. Give equations for the asymptotes of its graph.

b. Describe any lines or points of symmetry.

Solution

a. Rewrite the equation as $y + 4 = \frac{1}{(x - 5)^2}$. This shows that, by the Graph-Translation Theorem, the graph of F is the image of $y = \frac{1}{x^2}$ under the translation $T(x, y) = (x + 5, y - 4)$. The graph of the parent function has asymptotes $x = 0$ and $y = 0$. Each asymptote is translated 5 units to the right and 4 units down. So, the asymptotes of F are $x = 5$ and $y = -4$.

b. Since the graph of $y = \frac{1}{x^2}$ is symmetric to the y-axis, **the graph of F is symmetric to the vertical line x = 5.** Indeed, this line is the translation image of $x = 0$ under $T: (x, y) \rightarrow (x + 5, y - 4)$.

Check

Sketch a graph of F.

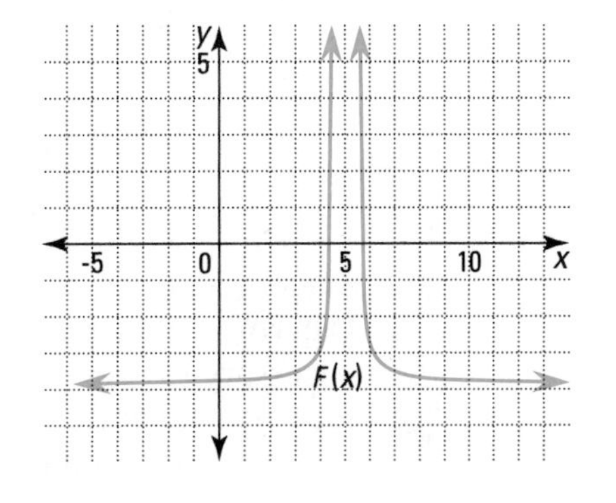

QUESTIONS

Covering the Reading

1. For each type of function in the left column, name two properties from the right column.

a. even function
b. odd function

I. The graph is symmetric to the origin.
II. If (x, y) is in the function, so is $(-x, y)$.
III. If (x, y) is in the function, so is $(-x, -y)$.
IV. The graph is symmetric with respect to the y-axis.

2. Consider the graphs of the functions used in Examples 1–5. Which have point symmetry?

In 3–5, suppose z is a relation which includes the point $(-3, 5)$. What other point must be included in the relation if z has the stated property?

3. z is odd.

4. z is even.

5. The graph of z is symmetric with respect to the x-axis.

6. Under what conditions, if any, does a function have a graph which is symmetric to the x-axis?

7. Prove that the function f defined by $f(x) = x^7$ is an odd function.

In 8 and 9, an equation of a function is given. **a.** Use a graph to tell if the function is odd, even, or neither. **b.** If the function appears to be either odd or even, prove it using the appropriate definition.

8. $f(x) = x$

9. $g(x) = x^3 - 5$

10. Tell whether the equation defines a power function.

a. $a(x) = 2$
b. $b(x) = x^2$
c. $c(x) = 2^x$
d. $d(x) = x^{11}$
e. $e(x) = x^{-1}$

11. Give a counterexample to prove that the function f with $f(t) = t^3 - 2$ is not an even function.

12. Consider the function $f: x \to \frac{1}{x+3} - 5$.
    a. Sketch a graph of $y = f(x)$.
    b. Give equations for the asymptotes of the graph.
    c. How are these asymptotes related to the asymptotes of the parent function?

Applying the Mathematics

In 13–15, a parent function and two related functions are given.

a. Sketch the functions.
b. Determine if each function is odd, even, or neither. (It is not necessary to prove them odd or even.)
c. Identify which function is the parent, and describe the relationship between the graph of the parent and the other graphs.
d. Give equations for all axes of symmetry for graphs having reflection symmetry; give coordinates for all centers of rotation for graphs having point symmetry.

13. $g(x) = x^3 + 2$; $h(x) = -x^3$; $j(x) = x^3$

14. $k(x) = |x|$; $m(x) = |x| - 2$; $n(x) = |x + 4| - 2$

15. $q(x) = \frac{1}{(x+5)^2}$; $r(x) = \frac{1}{x^2}$; $s(x) = \frac{1}{x^2} + 3$

16. Describe a function whose graph is symmetric to the x-axis.

Review

17. The results of a chapter test in a statistics class were $\bar{x} = 58$ and $s = 18$. The teacher decides to add 7 points to each student's score.
    a. John scored 63 on the test. What is his score after this transformation?
    b. What is the class mean after this transformation?
    c. What is the class standard deviation after this transformation?
    (Lesson 3-3)

18. The lower and upper quartiles of a set of 30 test scores are 62 and 87, respectively. What are the new values for the upper and lower quartiles if, because of a marking error, each score is increased by the following number of points?
    a. 3 points
    b. k points *(Lesson 3-3)*

In 19 and 20, if $x_1 = 3$, $x_2 = -8$, $x_3 = 9$, and $x_4 = -1$, evaluate the expression. *(Lesson 3-3)*

19. $\sum_{i=1}^{4} x_i + 3$

20. $\sum_{i=1}^{4} (x_i + 3)$

21. Suppose that under some translation T, the point (1, 3) is mapped to (7, 0).
    a. State a rule for $T(x, y)$.
    b. Find $T(12, 40)$. *(Lesson 3-2)*

22. Suppose the translation $T: (x, y) \rightarrow (x - 5, y + 2)$ is applied to the graph of the function $y = x^3$.

a. Find an equation for the image.

b. Are the graphs of the preimage and image congruent? Explain why or why not. *(Lessons 3-1, 3-2)*

In 23 and 24, refer to the graph below. *(Lessons 1-1, 1-2, 2-1)*

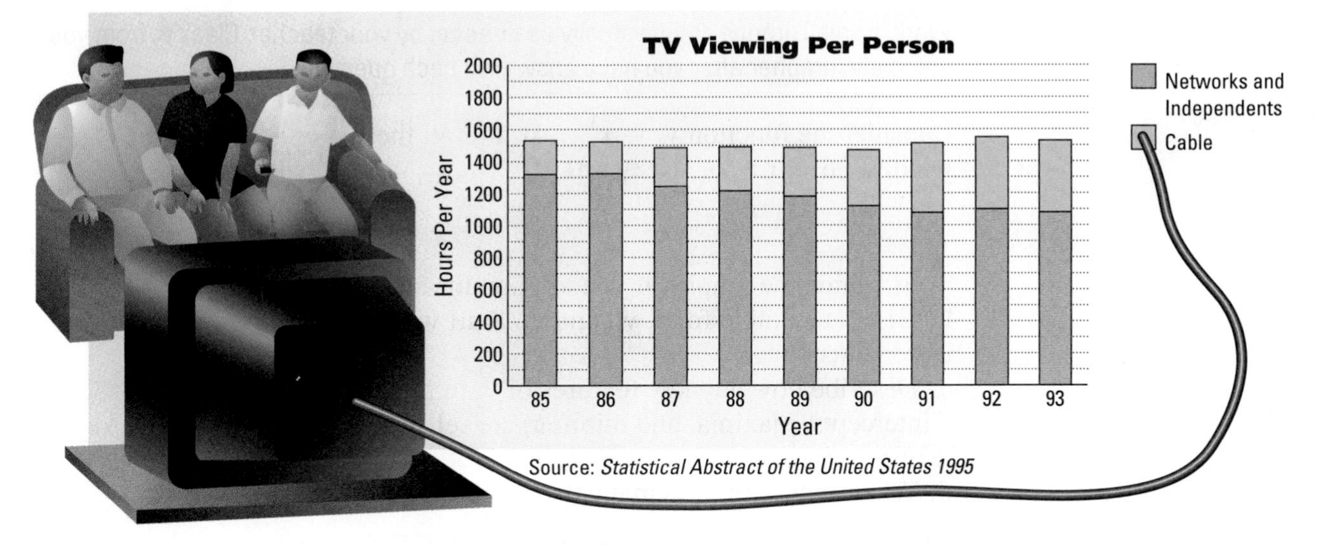

23. a. On the average, about how many more hours of cable television did TV viewers watch in 1993 than in 1985?

b. By about what percent did average cable television viewing increase from 1985 to 1993?

24. Suppose $T(y)$ represents the total number of hours of TV viewing per person in year y.

a. Estimate $T(1993) - T(1985)$.

b. What does the answer to part **a** represent?

25. Here is a formula relating women's shoe size S and foot length L in inches.

$$S = 3L - 21.25.$$

Change this formula so that it relates shoe size S and foot length L in feet. *(Previous course)*

26. *Skill sequence.* Simplify. *(Previous course)*

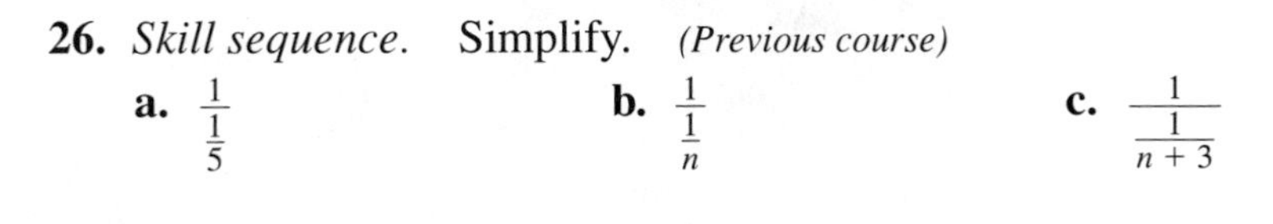

a. $\frac{1}{\frac{1}{5}}$ **b.** $\frac{1}{\frac{1}{n}}$ **c.** $\frac{1}{\frac{1}{n+3}}$

Exploration

27. a. Can the graph of a function be mapped onto itself by a rotation whose magnitude is not 180° or 360°? If so, give some examples. If not, explain why not.

b. Consider the question of part **a** for graphs of relations which are not functions.

Introducing Lesson 3-5

Functions and Scale Changes

Work in small groups or individually as directed by your teacher. Clear y_2 from your automatic grapher after you have answered each question.

Consider the function $y_1 = x^3 - 4x$. For all these questions, use the window $-6 \le x \le 6$, $-10 \le y \le 10$.

1 Let $\frac{y_2}{3} = x^3 - 4x$.

a. Draw the graphs of y_1 and y_2 on the same window.

b. Generate a table for x, y_1, and y_2. Start with $x = -3$ and increase x by increments of 1.

c. Describe how any key features of y_2 (e.g., values of x-intercepts, y-intercepts, maxima, and minima) are related to the corresponding key features of y_1.

d. What transformation maps the graph of y_1 onto the graph of y_2?

2 Let $5y_2 = x^3 - 4x$. Repeat parts **a–d** of Question 1.

3 Let $y_2 = \left(\frac{x}{2}\right)^3 - 4\left(\frac{x}{2}\right)$. Repeat parts **a–d** of Question 1.

4 Let $y_2 = (3x)^3 - 4(3x)$. Repeat parts **a–d** of Question 1.

5 Suppose that you began with the graph of an arbitrary equation $y = f(x)$. Conjecture about the effect on the graph of replacing y by $\frac{y}{b}$ and x by $\frac{x}{a}$ in the equation.

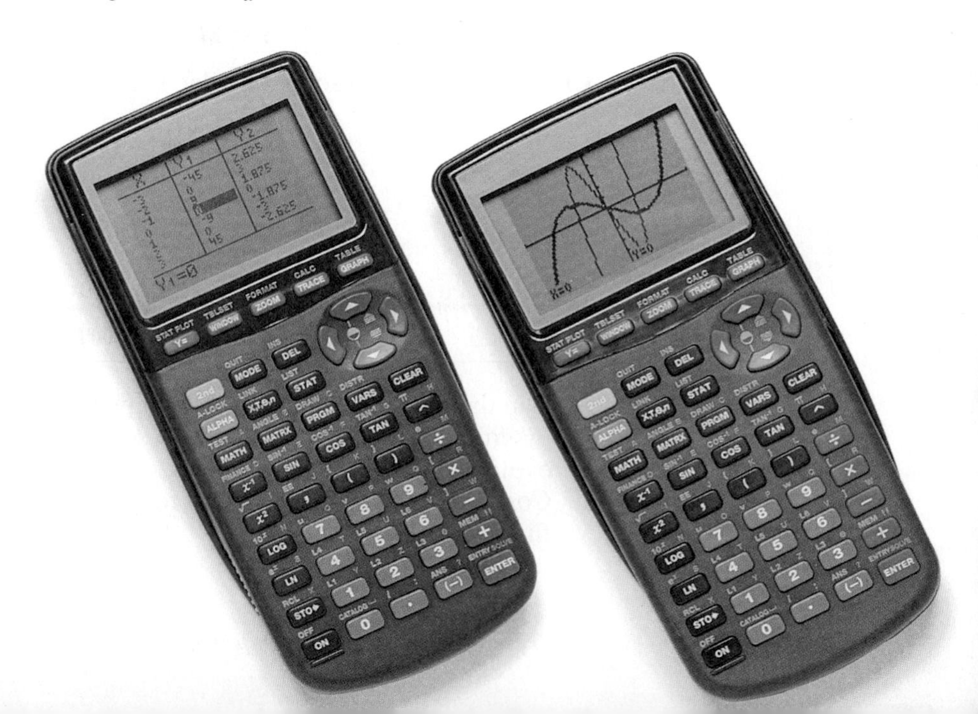

LESSON

3-5

The Graph Scale-Change Theorem

Small town. *The Madurodam in The Hague, Holland, shows buildings scaled down to 1/25 of their actual size. It demonstrates how Dutch cities have developed throughout the centuries.*

Vertical Scale Changes

Consider the function $y = x^3 - 4x$ that you graphed in the In-class Activity. When you replaced y by $\frac{y}{3}$, you obtained the function $\frac{y}{3} = x^3 - 4x$, or equivalently, $y = 3x^3 - 12x$. Call this new function g. Both f and g are graphed below.

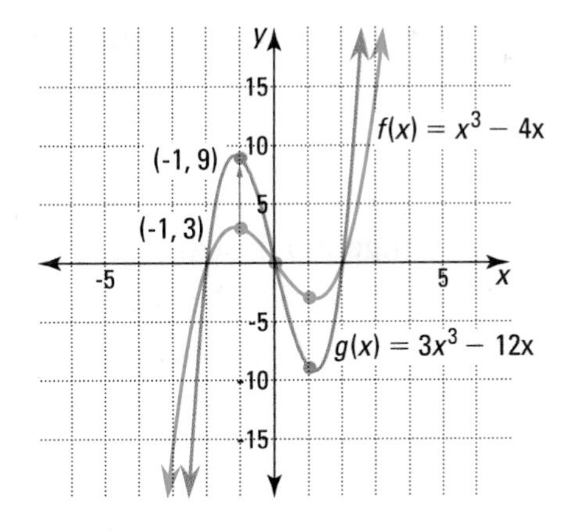

Notice the two graphs are *not* congruent. Each point (x, y) on f has been mapped to a point on g with the same x-coordinate, but with three times the y-coordinate. For instance, the y-value of the point $(-1, 9)$ on g is three times that of the y-value of the point on f with the same x-value. We say that g is the image of f under a *vertical scale change* or *vertical stretch* of magnitude 3. Each point on g is the image of a point on f under the mapping $(x, y) \rightarrow (x, 3y)$.

Horizontal Scale Changes

What happens if x is replaced by $\frac{x}{2}$? You might notice that the new x-values will be two times as large, so the graph will be stretched horizontally. Below are graphs of f and a new function h, where $h(x) = \left(\frac{x}{2}\right)^3 - 4\left(\frac{x}{2}\right)$. Notice that the point (-1, 3) on f is mapped onto (-2, 3) on h. Similarly, the x-intercepts of the image are also two times as far from the y-axis as are the x-intercepts of the preimage.

The graph of h is the image of the graph of f under a *horizontal scale change* or *horizontal stretch* of magnitude 2. That is, each point on h is the image of a point on f under the mapping $(x, y) \rightarrow (2x, y)$.

The Graph Scale-Change Theorem

In general, a **scale change** centered at the origin with **horizontal scale factor** $a \neq 0$ and **vertical scale factor** $b \neq 0$ is a transformation that maps (x, y) to (ax, by). The scale change S can be written

$$S: (x, y) \rightarrow (ax, by) \text{ or } S(x, y) = (ax, by).$$

If $a = 1$, the scale change is a vertical scale change. If $b = 1$, the scale change is a horizontal scale change. When $a = b$, the scale change is called a **size change**. Notice that in the preceding instances, replacing x by $\frac{x}{2}$ in an equation for a function results in the scale change $S: (x, y) \rightarrow (2x, y)$; and replacing y by $\frac{y}{3}$ leads to the scale change $S: (x, y) \rightarrow (x, 3y)$. These results generalize.

Graph Scale-Change Theorem

In a relation described by a sentence in x and y, the following two processes yield the same graph:

(1) replacing x by $\frac{x}{a}$ and y by $\frac{y}{b}$ in the sentence;

(2) applying the scale change $(x, y) \rightarrow (ax, by)$ to the graph of the original relation.

Under the scale change $S: (x, y) \rightarrow (ax, by)$, an equation for the image of $y = f(x)$ is $\frac{y}{b} = f\left(\frac{x}{a}\right)$. Notice that multiplication in the transformation corresponds to division in the equation of the image. This is analogous to the Graph-Translation Theorem in Lesson 3-2 for $y = f(x)$, where addition in the translation $(x, y) \rightarrow (x + h, y + k)$ corresponds to subtraction in the image equation $y - k = f(x - h)$.

Example 1

Sketch the graph of $y = \lfloor 0.5\,x \rfloor$.

Solution

The graph of $y = \lfloor 0.5x \rfloor$ is a scale-change image of the parent graph $y = \lfloor x \rfloor$, shown below at the left. To find the scale factors, rewrite the given equation $y = \lfloor 0.5x \rfloor$ as $y = \left\lfloor \frac{x}{2} \right\rfloor$. By the Graph Scale-Change Theorem, the result of replacing x by $\frac{x}{2}$ is the scale change that maps (x, y) to $(2x, y)$, so the parent graph is stretched horizontally by a factor of 2. The graph of $y = \left\lfloor \frac{x}{2} \right\rfloor$ is below at the right.

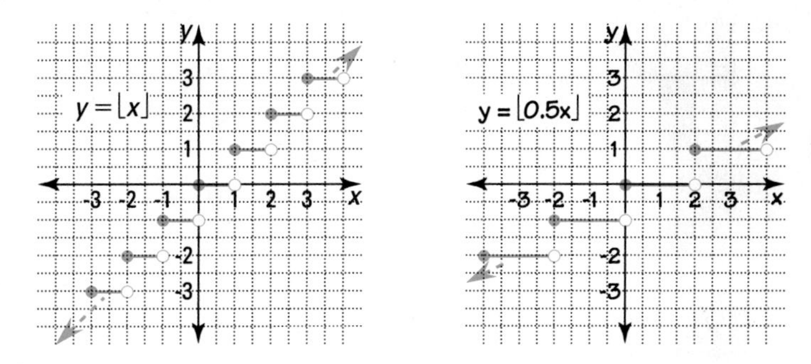

Check 1

Check that a point satisfying the given equation is on the graph. If $x = 3$, then

$$\begin{aligned} y &= \lfloor 0.5(3) \rfloor \\ &= \lfloor 1.5 \rfloor \\ &= 1. \end{aligned}$$

Is the point (3, 1) on the graph? Yes.

Check 2

Graph the function using an automatic grapher.

Example 2

The graph of $y = f(x)$ is drawn below. Draw the graph of $\frac{y}{3} = f(2x)$.

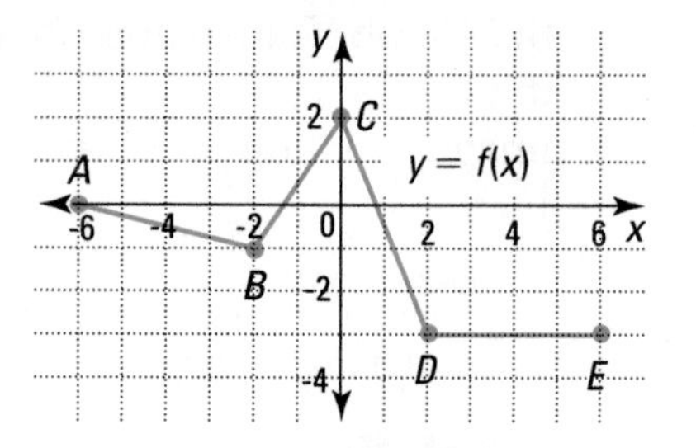

Solution

Rewrite $\frac{y}{3} = f(2x)$ as $\frac{y}{3} = f\left(\frac{x}{\frac{1}{2}}\right)$. By the Graph Scale-Change Theorem, replacing x by $\frac{x}{\frac{1}{2}}$ and y by $\frac{y}{3}$ is the same as applying the scale change $(x, y) \to \left(\frac{1}{2}x, 3y\right)$ to the graph of the function.

For instance, A = (-6, 0) → (-3, 0) = A'

and E = (6, -3) → (3, -9) = E'.

The graph of the image is shown below.

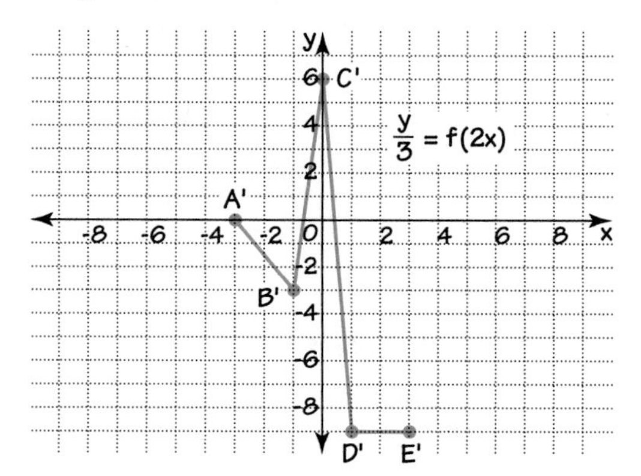

Thus, the parent function is shrunk horizontally by a factor of $\frac{1}{2}$ and stretched vertically by a factor of 3.

Negative Scale Factors

When a scale factor is -1, the graph is *reflected* over an axis. Specifically, consider the horizontal and vertical scale changes with scale factors equal to -1.

$$S_1: (x, y) \to (-x, y) \text{ and } S_2: (x, y) \to (x, -y)$$

In S_1, each x-value is replaced by its opposite, which produces a reflection over the y-axis. Similarly, in S_2, replacing y by $-y$ produces a reflection over the x-axis.

More generally, a scale factor of $-k$ produces the composite effect of a scale factor of k followed by a reflection over the appropriate axis.

Example 3

a. Sketch the image of the graph of $y = x^2$ under $S(x, y) = (x, -3y)$.
b. Give an equation for the image.

Solution

a. The graph of $y = x^2$ is shown below in blue. S is a vertical scale change by -3. The effect of the 3 is to stretch the graph vertically by a factor of 3. The effect of the negative sign is to reflect it over the x-axis. The resulting image is shown below in orange.

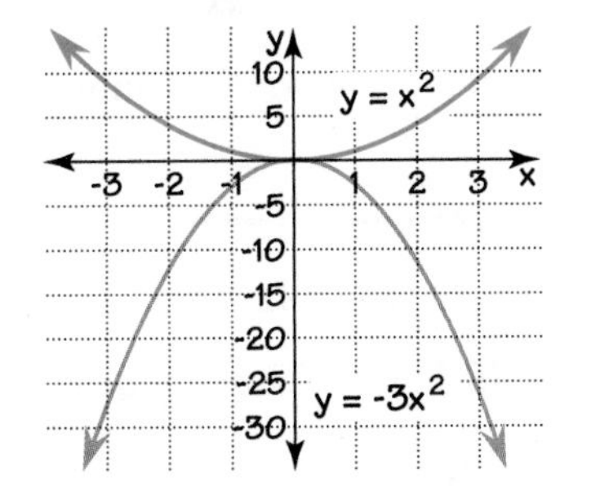

b. In the parent equation $y = x^2$, replace y by $\frac{y}{-3}$. An equation of the image is $\frac{y}{-3} = x^2$. Solving this equation for y, $y = -3x^2$.

QUESTIONS

Covering the Reading

1. *True or false.* Under a scale change, the graphs of the preimage and image are congruent.

2. Under a scale change with horizontal factor a and vertical factor b, the image of (x, y) is __?__.

3. Refer to the Graph Scale-Change Theorem.
   a. Why must there be the restrictions $a \neq 0$ and $b \neq 0$?
   b. If $a = b$, what special name is given to the transformation?

4. Suppose $y = f(x)$. If S maps each point (x, y) in the plane to $(3x, 4y)$, give an equation for the image of $y = f(x)$.

5. Sketch a graph of each function.
   a. $y = 3\lfloor x \rfloor$
   b. $y = \lfloor 3x \rfloor$

6. Refer to Example 2. Show that the image of the point $(-2, -1)$ on the graph of f is on the graph of the image.

7. Describe the effect of the scale change $S: (x, y) \rightarrow (-2x, 2y)$ on a graph.

8. Consider the parabola $y = x^2$. Let $S(x, y) = \left(\frac{x}{2}, 3y\right)$.
   a. Find images of $(-3, 9)$, $(0, 0)$, and $\left(\frac{1}{2}, \frac{1}{4}\right)$ under S.
   b. Show that the images in part **a** are on $\frac{y}{3} = (2x)^2$.

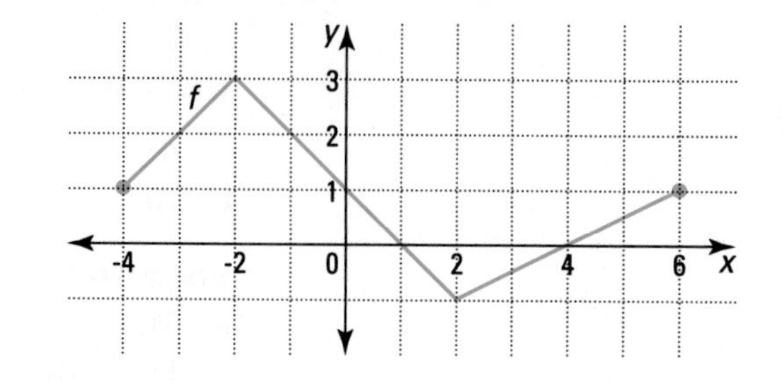

9. The graph of a function f is shown at the right.

a. Copy the graph of f, and graph its image f' under $S(x, y) = \left(3x, \frac{1}{2}y\right)$.

b. Find the intercepts of the image f'.

i. x-intercepts

ii. y-intercept

c. Find the coordinates where the y-value of the image of f reaches its

i. maximum. **ii.** minimum.

10. Give another name for the horizontal scale change of magnitude -1.

Applying the Mathematics

In 11 and 12, give a rule for a scale change that maps f to g.

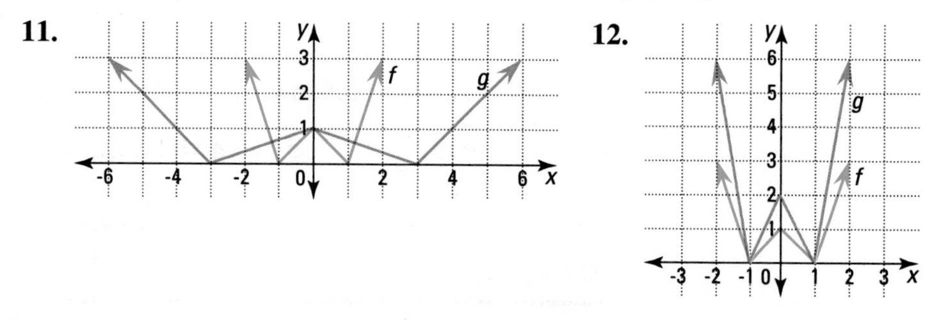

13. State whether the property is invariant under any scale change.

a. number of x-intercepts

b. values of x-intercepts

c. number of y-intercepts

d. values of y-intercepts

14. Scale changes of parabolas can be considered as horizontal scale changes, or vertical scale changes, or both. Refer to the graphs below.

a. Under what horizontal scale change is g the image of f?

b. Under what vertical scale change is g the image of f?

c. Under what size change is g the image of f?

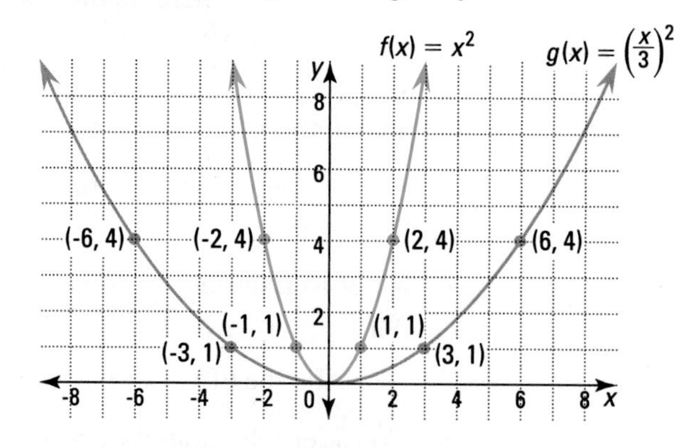

15. The formula $s = \sqrt{24d}$ can be used to estimate the pre-brake speed s in mph of a vehicle which skidded d feet on a dry concrete road before coming to a stop.
   a. This formula can be considered a vertical scale change of the function $s = \sqrt{d}$ by what factor?
   b. About how fast was a car going which skidded 27 ft before stopping?
   c. About how far would a car skid if its brakes locked at 55 mph?

Tuscan turns. *Whether wet or dry, curved roads, such as this one in Italy, require careful driving speeds to avoid skidding.*

16. A formula $S = 2\sqrt{5d}$, similar to the one in Question 15, is used to estimate the speed of a car based on skid marks on a wet concrete road. What scale change is used to obtain the formula for a wet surface from that for a dry surface?

Review

In 17 and 18, an equation for a function is given. **a.** Identify the function as odd, even, or neither. **b.** If the function is odd or even, prove it. *(Lesson 3-4)*

17. $f(x) = (x - 8)^3$

18. $g(x) = x^4 + 37$

19. If $f(x) = -g(x)$ for all x in the domains of f and g, how are the graphs of f and g related? *(Lesson 3-4)*

20. Consider the function $y = \frac{1}{x^2}$ and the translation $T(x, y) = (x - 3, y + 1)$.
   a. Sketch the image of f under this translation.
   b. Find the x-intercepts of the image.
   c. Find the y-intercept of the image.
   d. Find equations for any asymptotes of the image.
   e. Describe the symmetries of the graph of the image.
   (Lessons 3-1, 3-2, 3-4)

21. A geologist measured and recorded the weights of 120 mineral samples. The samples had a mean weight of 735.4 mg with a standard deviation of 6.2 mg. Later, the geologist discovered that the scale was incorrectly calibrated and the weights of all the samples were 2.6 mg too low.
   a. What is the mean of the corrected mineral sample weights?
   b. What is the standard deviation of the corrected mineral sample weights? *(Lesson 3-3)*

22. *Skill sequence.* Use the Power of a Product Property to rewrite the expression. *(Previous course)*
   a. $(5y)^3$
   b. $(xy)^3$
   c. $(xy)^p$

Exploration

23. Begin with a graph of a relation of your own choice. Replace x by y and replace y by $-x$, and graph the new relation. Repeat this with different relations until you can determine what transformation these substitutions cause.

LESSON

3-6

Scale Changes of Data

Scaled down. *People use scale models of dinosaurs because the size of the actual skeletons makes them too difficult to use.*

Scaling Data

Scale changes can also be applied to data sets. Consider, for example, the Consumer Price Index (CPI). To calculate the CPI, the cost of a specified set of goods is totaled. Suppose the total is $287.45 at a baseline time period (currently 1982–1984). This total is then *scaled down* to 100. That is, if the same set of goods costs $456.23 some years later, the CPI at that time is calculated from the proportion:

$$\frac{456.23}{287.45} = \frac{\text{CPI}}{100} \text{ or CPI} \approx 159.$$

Rescaling on a basis of 100 makes it easy to find the percent change of prices. In this case, there has been a 59% increase since the baseline time period.

A **scale change** of a set of data $\{x_1, x_2, \ldots, x_n\}$ is a transformation that maps each x_i to ax_i, where a is a nonzero constant. That is, S is a scale change if and only if

$$S: x \rightarrow ax, \text{ or } S(x) = ax.$$

The number a is called the **scale factor** of the scale change. The number ax, or the point it represents, is called the **scale image** of x. In the situation above, the 1982–1984 cost x of a set of goods is mapped to the later CPI value via the following scale change.

$$S: x \rightarrow 1.59x, \text{ or } S(x) \approx 1.59x.$$

When a scale change is applied to a data set, the process is usually called **scaling** or **rescaling**.

Scale changes, like translations of data, affect statistical measures derived from the data.

Effects of Scaling on Measures of Center and Spread

Example 1

Consider again the data from Lesson 3-3 for the daily earnings (in dollars) of the eleven employees:

60, 66, 67, 68, 70, 70, 72, 72, 72, 73, 80.

Suppose that each employee works 6 hours instead of the customary 8 hours.

a. Find the scaled daily earnings (in dollars).

b. Find the median, mean, range, and standard deviation of the original and scaled data.

Solution

a. Apply the transformation $x_i \to \frac{6}{8}x_i$ to each value. The scaled earnings in dollars are

45, 49.5, 50.25, 51, 52.5, 52.5, 54, 54, 54, 54.75, 60

b. In Example 1 of Lesson 3-3, these measures for the original data were calculated: median = 70, mean = 70, range = 20, and standard deviation = 5. For the scaled data, the median is 52.5, and the range is 60 − 45, or 15. The mean is 52.5 and the standard deviation is 3.75.

Notice that each of these measures is $\frac{6}{8}$, or $\frac{3}{4}$, of the corresponding measure in the original data.

Box plots of the original earnings and scaled earnings illustrate the effects of scaling on both measures of center and spread.

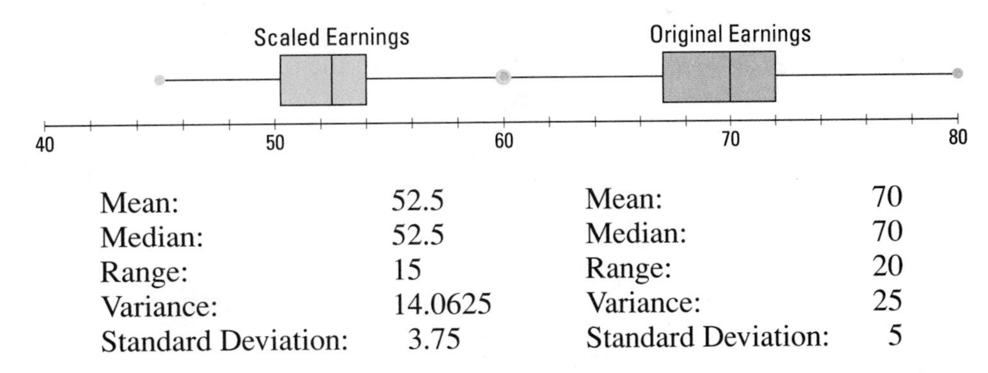

The mode of a data set is the point of maximum frequency. Under a scale change the frequency does not change, so the mode of the original data is mapped to the mode of the image data. For the data above, the image mode, 54, is $\frac{3}{4}$ of the original mode, 72.

To describe in general the effect of a scale change on statistical measures for a data set, represent the set as $\{x_1, x_2, x_3, \ldots, x_n\}$. Under a scale change that multiplies each value by a scale factor a, the image data set is

$$\{ax_1, ax_2, ax_3, \ldots, ax_n\}.$$

To find the mean $\bar{x}'$ of the image data, you need to evaluate $\dfrac{\sum_{i=1}^{n}(ax_i)}{n}$.

$$\begin{aligned}
\frac{\sum_{i=1}^{n}(ax_i)}{n} &= \frac{ax_1 + ax_2 + ax_3 + \ldots + ax_n}{n} && \text{Definition of } \Sigma \\
&= \frac{a(x_1 + x_2 + x_3 + \ldots + x_n)}{n} && \text{Distributive property} \\
&= a\left(\frac{\sum_{i=1}^{n} x_i}{n}\right) && \text{Definition of } \Sigma \\
&= a\bar{x} && \text{Definition of } \bar{x}
\end{aligned}$$

Thus, by definition of the mean, $\bar{x}' = a\bar{x}$, where $\bar{x}$ is the mean of the original data set.

This proves that, under a scale change, the mean of a set of data is mapped to the mean of the image set of data. A similar result holds for the median and mode.

Theorem

Multiplying each element of a data set by the factor *a* multiplies each of the mode, mean, and median by the factor *a*.

What happens to measures of spread, such as the range, variance, and standard deviation, when data are scaled?

Consider the data set $\{x_1, x_2, x_3, \ldots, x_n\}$ and its image under a scale change of magnitude a, $\{ax_1, ax_2, ax_3, \ldots, ax_n\}$. The mean of this data set is $a\bar{x}$, where $\bar{x}$ is the mean of the original data set. So the variance of the image data is given by

$$\begin{aligned}
\frac{\sum_{i=1}^{n}(ax_i - a\bar{x})^2}{n-1} &= \frac{\sum_{i=1}^{n}[a(x_i - \bar{x})]^2}{n-1} && \text{Distributive Property} \\
&= \frac{\sum_{i=1}^{n}[a^2(x_i - \bar{x})^2]}{n-1}. && \text{Power of a Product Property}
\end{aligned}$$

As in the derivation of the mean of the image data above, it can be shown that

$$\sum_{i=1}^{n}[a^2(x_i - \bar{x})^2] = a^2\sum_{i=1}^{n}(x_i - \bar{x})^2.$$

Hence, the variance of the image data is given by

$$\begin{aligned}
\frac{a^2\sum_{i=1}^{n}(x_i - \bar{x})^2}{n-1} &= a^2\left(\frac{\sum_{i=1}^{n}(x_i - \bar{x})^2}{n-1}\right) \\
&= a^2 s^2,
\end{aligned}$$

where s^2 represents the variance of the original data set. Thus, the variance of the image data is a^2 times the variance of the original data.

To get the standard deviation of the image data, take the square root of the variance. Thus, the standard deviation of the image data is $|a|s$, which is $|a|$ times the standard deviation of the original data set. It can also be proved that the range of the image data is $|a|$ times the range of the original data set.

Theorem
If each element of a data set is multiplied by a, then the variance is a^2 times the original variance, the standard deviation is $|a|$ times the original standard deviation, and the range is $|a|$ times the original range.

Example 2

Consider the data on daily earnings in Example 1. Find the mean, variance, and standard deviation of the earnings if each person works for three days.

Solution
For the data shown, the mean is 70, the variance is 25, and the standard deviation is 5. If each person works three days, this can be considered as scaling by the factor 3. Thus, the mean and standard deviation will triple and the variance will be multiplied by $3^2 = 9$. So, for the image data,

the mean is $3(70) = 210$,
the variance is $(3)^2(25) = 225$,
and the standard deviation is $3(5) = 15$.

Check

Calculate the three-day earnings, then calculate the statistics directly from them.

A common reason for rescaling data involves changes of units, as the next example shows.

Example 3

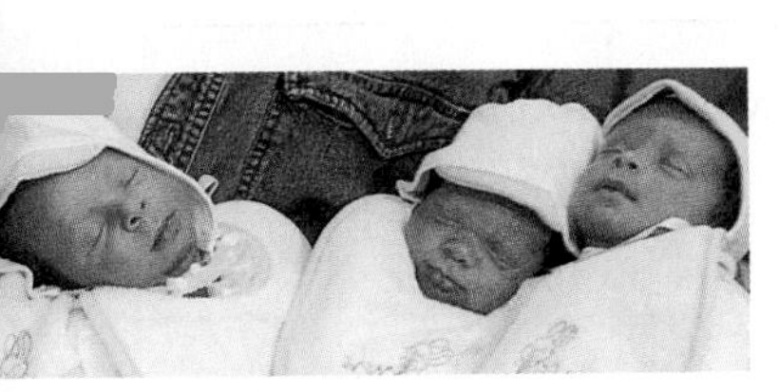

They ain't heavy, they're my brothers. *It is not unusual for children in a multiple birth to weigh less than two pounds each.*

In recent years, an obstetrician recorded the birth weights (in pounds) of the babies she delivered. She found that the distribution had a mean of 6.75 lb and a standard deviation of 1.14 lb. Find the mean and standard deviation of the distribution of birth weights in kilograms.

Solution
There are about 0.454 kg per pound. So, the data need to be scaled by the factor $a = 0.454$. Thus, the mean is

$$(0.454)(6.75) = 3.06 \text{ kg}$$

and the standard deviation is

$$(0.454)(1.14) = 0.52 \text{ kg}.$$

QUESTIONS

Covering the Reading

1. Define *scale change* of a set of data.

In 2 and 3, use the fact that in 1994 the CPI was 148.2.

2. On the average, what was the percentage increase of costs of goods from 1982–84 to 1994?

3. Approximately what would a set of items costing $577 in 1982–84 cost in 1994?

4. Refer to the original data on earnings of workers in Example 1. Consider their earnings if they are paid every five days.

a. For the five-day earnings calculate each statistic.

i. range　**ii.** mode　**iii.** median
iv. mean　**v.** variance　**vi.** standard deviation

b. Draw a box plot of the data set in part **a**.

5. Suppose $Y_1 = 6, Y_2 = 0, Y_3 = -4, Y_4 = 7, Y_5 = -6, Y_6 = 2$. Evaluate the given expression.

a. $\sum_{i=1}^{6} 10Y_i$　**b.** $\sum_{i=1}^{6} kY_i$　**c.** $\sum_{i=1}^{6} \left(\frac{Y_i}{m}\right)$

6. Let $\bar{x}$ = the mean and s = the standard deviation of scores on a test for a class of n students. Suppose everyone's score is multiplied by r. For the transformed scores find the following statistics.

a. the mean　**b.** the variance　**c.** standard deviation

7. As part of a study of the yield of orange trees, a biologist weighed a sample of sixty oranges, and found a mean weight of 0.32 pound and a range of 0.21 pound. Find the mean and range of the oranges in grams.

Applying the Mathematics

8. Let x_i be an individual student's score on a test worth M points. Write a rule which can be used by a teacher to convert each student's score to a percent.

9. Refer to the frequency distributions below.

Original Scores	6	10	12	16	22
Frequency	2	3	1	2	2

Scaled Scores	9	15	18	24	33
Frequency	2	3	1	2	2

a. Write a formula for the transformation used to get the scaled scores.

b. Find the range, mode, mean, and median for each set of scores.

c. Make two dot-frequency diagrams of the scores. Compare and contrast the distributions.

10. Let M represent the maximum value of a data set and let m represent the minimum value.
   a. Write an expression for the range of the data set.
   b. After a scale change with scale factor b, what are the maximum and minimum values of the image data set?
   c. Write and simplify an expression for the range of the image data.

11. Consider the following data, which give the height h in cm and weight w in kg of the students in a kindergarten class.

h	112	106	114	109	110	122	129	112	117	126	128	101
w	20	18	19	17	20	24	25	21	26	23	25	15

   a. Enter these data into a statistics utility. (You may have already done so for Question 11 of Lesson 3-3.) Draw a scatterplot with h on the horizontal axis.
   b. Find the line of best fit for predicting w from h.
   c. Use your statistics utility to convert the height to inches (1 in. = 2.54 cm). Draw a new scatterplot. How is the scatterplot different from that in part **a**?
   d. Without using your statistics utility, write an equation of the line of best fit for part **c**. Check using the statistics utility.
   e. Convert height to inches and kilograms to pounds (1 lb $\approx$ 0.454 kg). Draw a new scatterplot. How is the scatterplot different from that in part **a**?
   f. Without using a statistics utility, write an equation of the line of best fit for part **e**. Check using a statistics utility.

12. Generalize the result of Question 11. If bivariate data are rescaled, tell whether or not the following are invariant.
   a. means of the two variables
   b. variances of the two variables
   c. equation of the line of best fit
   d. slope of the line of best fit
   e. correlation between the two variables

Review

13. Consider the functions $f(x) = \lceil x \rceil$ and $g(x) = \lceil 3x \rceil$.
   a. Identify a scale change that maps f to g.
   b. Identify a scale change that maps g to f.
   c. Graph f and g on the same set of axes with different colors.
   (Lesson 3-5)

14. The graph of a certain hyperbola is a translation image of the graph of $y = \frac{1}{x}$ and has asymptotes $x = 1$ and $y = -7$. Give an equation for the image hyperbola. *(Lessons 3-1, 3-2)*

15. *Skill sequence.* Let $f(x) = x^2 + 7x$. Evaluate each expression. *(Lesson 2-1)*
   a. $2f(3)$ b. $f(6k)$ c. $f(a - 4)$

In 16–19, match each equation with its graph. *(Lessons 3-2, 3-5)*

16. $f(x) = |x + 3|$

17. $g(x) = |2x|$

18. $h(x) = \frac{1}{2}|x|$

19. $j(x) = |x - 3|$

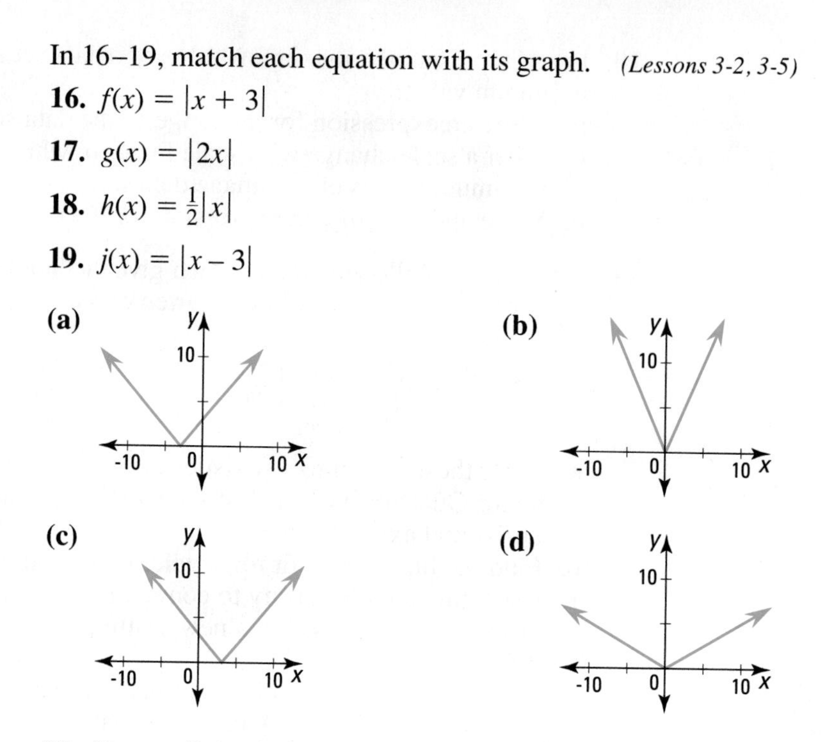

20. Name all the functions in Questions 16–19 that are even functions. *(Lesson 3-4)*

In 21 and 22, are the two triangles similar? Justify your answer. *(Previous course)*

21.

22.

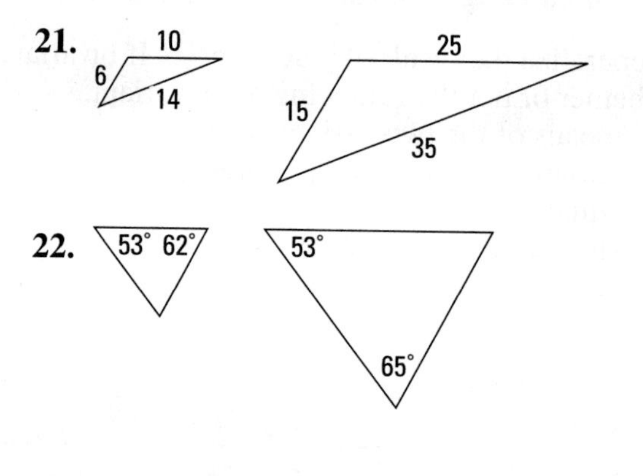

Exploration

23. What goods and services are used to calculate the Consumer Price Index? Why do you suppose these particular goods and services are used for the CPI?

LESSON

3-7

Composition of Functions

Composite Functions

Many people are interested in family trees, which show their ancestors and relatives. Here is part of John F. Kennedy, Jr.'s family tree. (For simplicity, "family" in this lesson refers to biological parents and children.) It shows that John Kennedy and Jacqueline Bouvier Kennedy are John, Jr.'s parents.

Functions can be used to describe the relationships between pairs of members of this tree. For example, suppose m is the "mother" function defined by

$$m(x) \text{ is the mother of } x,$$

and f is the "father" function defined by

$$f(x) \text{ is the father of } x.$$

Then m(John, Jr.) = Jacqueline, m(Jacqueline) = Janet Lee, f(John, Jr.) = John, and so on.

In studying family trees, as in studies of other functions, functions can be combined so that the value of one function becomes the argument of another. For example, if the mother function is first applied, followed by the father function, we have

$$m(\text{John, Jr.}) = \text{Jacqueline},$$
$$\text{and } f(\text{Jacqueline}) = \text{John Vernon}.$$

In words, the father of the mother of John, Jr. is John Vernon. This combination can be written

$$\begin{aligned} f(m(\text{John, Jr.})) &= f(\text{Jacqueline}) \\ &= \text{John Vernon}. \end{aligned}$$

We say that m and f have been *composed* to make a new function, which we might call the "maternal grandfather" function. We denote this function by the symbol $f \circ m$, the composite of f with m.

Definition

Suppose f and g are functions. The **composite** of g with f, written $\mathbf{g \circ f}$, is the function defined by

$$(g \circ f)(x) = g(f(x)).$$

The domain of $g \circ f$ is the set of values of x in the domain of f for which $f(x)$ is in the domain of g.

Using the composition notation,

$$\begin{aligned}(f \circ m)(\text{John, Jr.}) &= f(m(\text{John, Jr.}))\\ &= f(\text{Jacqueline})\\ &= \text{John Vernon.}\end{aligned}$$

Example 1

Consider John F. Kennedy, Jr.'s family tree. What biological relation does the composite function $m \circ f$ represent?

Solution

Use the definition. Note the order of the two functions. The composite $m \circ f$ is the function defined as $(m \circ f)(x)$, the mother of the father of x. This is the paternal grandmother function.

Check

Consider a specific case.

$$\begin{aligned}(m \circ f)(\text{John, Jr.}) &= m(f(\text{John, Jr.}))\\ &= m(\text{John})\\ &= \text{Rose}\end{aligned}$$

Rose is John, Jr.'s father's mother.

Notice that each of $f \circ m$ and $m \circ f$ is a function, because there is a single output associated with each input.

Composition of Functions Is Not Commutative

Also notice that, regarding the above example, the two functions $f \circ m$ and $m \circ f$ are *different* functions. The range of $f \circ m$ contains only men, while the range of $m \circ f$ contains only women. This illustrates that *composition of functions is not commutative*. The next two examples also illustrate this important fact.

Example 2

For $f(x) = x^2 + x$ and $g(x) = x - 5$, evaluate each.

a. $f(g(7))$ **b.** $g(f(7))$

Solution

a. To evaluate $f(g(7))$, first evaluate $g(7)$.

$$g(7) = 7 - 5 = 2$$

Then use this output as the input to f. So

$$\begin{aligned} f(g(7)) &= f(2) \\ &= 2^2 + 2 \\ &= 6. \end{aligned}$$

b.

$$\begin{aligned} g(f(7)) &= g(7^2 + 7) \\ &= g(56) \\ &= 56 - 5 \\ &= 51 \end{aligned}$$

To graph composites of functions, it is tedious to evaluate each point, as in Example 2. An alternative is to find a formula for the composite.

Example 3

Let $f(x) = x^2 + x$ and $g(x) = x - 5$.

a. Derive a formula for each of $f(g(x))$ and $g(f(x))$.

b. Verify that $f \circ g \neq g \circ f$ by graphing.

Solution

a. In $f(g(x))$, first substitute $x - 5$ for $g(x)$.

$$f(g(x)) = f(x - 5)$$

Now use $x - 5$ as the input to function f.

$$\begin{aligned} f(g(x)) &= (x - 5)^2 + (x - 5) \\ &= x^2 - 10x + 25 + (x - 5) \end{aligned}$$

So $$f(g(x)) = x^2 - 9x + 20.$$

Similarly, $$\begin{aligned} g(f(x)) &= g(x^2 + x) \\ &= (x^2 + x) - 5 \end{aligned}$$

So $$g(f(x)) = x^2 + x - 5.$$

b. The two functions, $f \circ g$ and $g \circ f$, are graphed at the right. Clearly, $f \circ g \neq g \circ f$, as the graph of each is a different parabola.

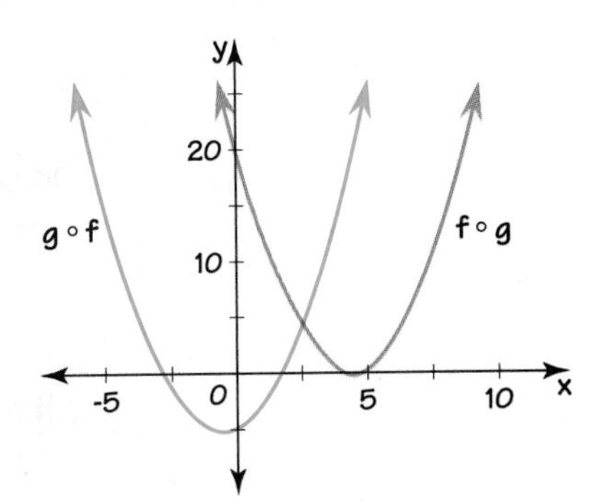

Check

Evaluate each function at $x = 7$ in order to compare the results with the results of Example 2. $f(g(7)) = 7^2 - 9 \cdot 7 + 20 = 6$; $g(f(7)) = 7^2 + 7 - 5 = 51$. The results agree with those in Example 2; $f(g(7)) \neq g(f(7))$.

Notice in Example 3 that although $f \circ g$ and $g \circ f$ are *not* the same function, there is at least one value of x at which they have the same y-values. This is the x-value at the point of intersection of the two parabolas.

Finding the Domain of a Composite of Two Functions

Example 4

Let $f(m) = \sqrt{m}$ and $g(m) = m^4$. Find the domain of $g \circ f$.

Solution 1

The domain of f is the set of all nonnegative real numbers. The values of f(m) will also be nonnegative real numbers. The domain of g is the set of all real numbers, so all values f(m) are in the domain of g. Thus, the domain of $g \circ f$ is the set of nonnegative real numbers, or the set of real numbers m with $m \geq 0$.

Solution 2

Find a formula for $g \circ f$ and analyze the domain.

$$(g \circ f)(m) = g(f(m)) = g(\sqrt{m}) = (\sqrt{m})^4$$

$\sqrt{m}$ is undefined in the real number system unless $m \geq 0$.
So, $(g \circ f)(m) = m^2$ and $m \geq 0$.

Check

Use an automatic grapher to graph $g(f(x)) = (\sqrt{x})^4$. You should get one branch of the parabola $y = x^2$, as shown at the right.

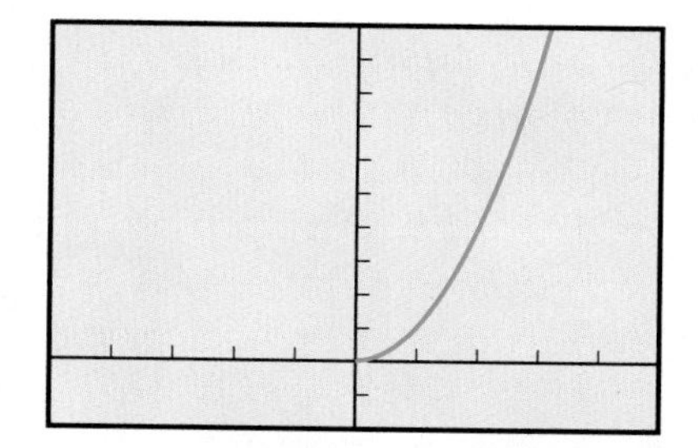

$-5 \leq x \leq 5$, x-scale = 1
$-2 \leq y \leq 10$, y-scale = 1

The domain of a composite function is not necessarily the domain of either of its component functions, as Example 5 illustrates.

Example 5

If F and G are functions defined on the real numbers, $F(n) = 13 - n$ and $G(n) = \frac{2}{n + 1}$, find the domain of $G \circ F$.

Solution 1

The domain of F is the set of reals. The domain of $G \circ F$ is the set of all n in the domain of F for which F(n) is in the domain of G. Because G is not defined when the denominator n + 1 equals 0, the domain of G cannot contain -1. So the domain of $G \circ F$ excludes the point(s) for which F(n) = -1. This is where 13 – n = -1, that is, where n = 14. So the domain of $G \circ F$ is the set of reals except 14.

Solution 2

Find a formula for $G \circ F$ and analyze its domain.

$$\begin{aligned}(G \circ F)(n) &= G(13 - n)\\ &= \frac{2}{13 - n + 1}\\ &= \frac{2}{14 - n}\end{aligned}$$

This function is defined for all reals except when the denominator is 0. The domain of $G \circ F$ is the reals except n = 14.

Check

Draw a graph of $y = G \circ F$. You will see that $x = 14$ is a vertical asymptote of $y = \frac{2}{14 - x}$.

QUESTIONS

Covering the Reading

In 1 and 2, consider John F. Kennedy, Jr.'s family tree.

1. What biological relation does the composite $m \circ m$ represent?

2. In 1996 John, Jr. married Carolyn Bessette. Suppose they have a child x.
   a. Evaluate $(m \circ f)(x)$.
   b. Explain why $(f \circ m)(x) \neq (m \circ f)(x)$.

In 3 and 4 refer to the functions f and g of Example 2.

3. Verify that $f(g(0)) \neq g(f(0))$.

4. *True or false.*
   a. $f(g(6)) = g(f(6))$
   b. $f(g(2.5)) = g(f(2.5))$

In 5 and 6, let $m(x) = x + 8$ and $n(x) = \frac{4}{x}$.

5. a. Evaluate $m(n(-11))$.
   b. Find a formula for $(m \circ n)(x)$.
   c. State the domain of $m \circ n$.

6. a. Evaluate $n(m(-11))$.
   b. Find a formula for $(n \circ m)(x)$.
   c. State the domain of $n \circ m$.

7. *True or false.* Composition of functions is commutative.

In 8 and 9, consider $g(t) = t^2$ and $h(t) = 2t + 1$.

8. Evaluate.
   a. $g(h(-2))$
   b. $h(g(-2))$

9. a. Find a formula for each of $(g \circ h)(t)$ and $(h \circ g)(t)$.
   b. Show that $g \circ h \neq h \circ g$ by graphing both functions on the same set of axes.

Applying the Mathematics

In 10–12, consider the sets A, B, and C below.

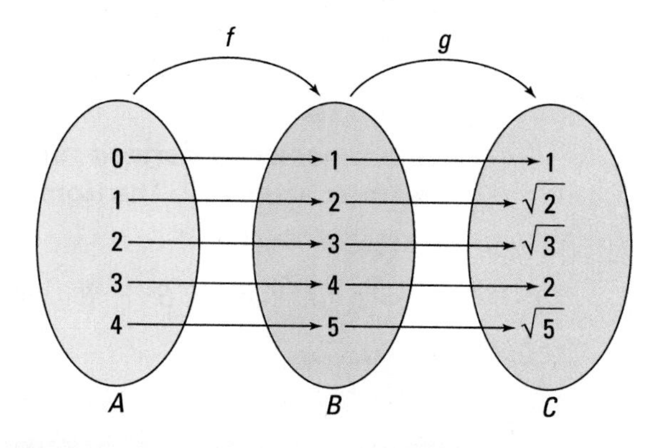

10. Evaluate $g(f(3))$.

11. The composite $g \circ f$ maps 4 to what number?

12. Assume the rules defining the mappings above are $f(x) = x + 1$ and $g(x) = \sqrt{x}$.
    a. Write a formula for $g(f(x))$.
    b. If the domain of f is extended to the set of all reals, what is the domain of $g \circ f$?

In 13–15, consider a discount function $D(x) = 0.9x$ and a rebate function $R(x) = x - 100$.

13. Explain why it is appropriate to call D a discount function and R a rebate function.

14. a. A stereo system normally sells for $1200. Evaluate $D(R(1200))$ and $R(D(1200))$.
    b. Refer to your answer to part **a**. If you are buying a stereo for $1200, is it better to apply the discount after the rebate or before the rebate?

15. Find rules for $D \circ R(x)$ and for $R \circ D(x)$. Prove that in general $D \circ R \neq R \circ D$.

16. Consider the functions $k(x) = 2x - 7$, $m(x) = 5x + 12$, and $n(x) = 8 - x$.
    a. Find $k \circ m$ and $m \circ k$.
    b. Find $m \circ n$ and $n \circ m$.
    c. Prove that the composite of any two linear functions is a linear function. (Hint: Let $f(x) = ax + b$ and $g(x) = cx + d$.)

17. Is the composite of any two quadratic functions always a quadratic function? Justify your answer.

Review

In 18 and 19, suppose a scientist has collected some data with mean 3.92 and variance 1.69. What will be the effect of the transformation on the mean and standard deviation of the data? *(Lessons 3-3, 3-6)*

18. Subtract 8 from each data value.

19. Triple each data value.

20. The graph of $y = f(x)$ is shown below. Draw the graph of $\frac{y}{-2} = f(-3x)$. *(Lesson 3-5)*

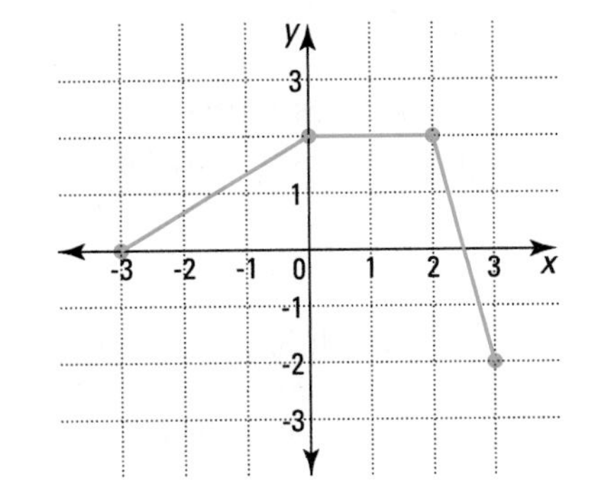

Playing tag with a bumblebee. *To collect data for pollination research, this bumblebee was tagged with a small radar antenna.*

In 21 and 22, find an equation for the image of the graph of $f(x) = x^2$ under the indicated transformation. *(Lessons 3-2, 3-5)*

21. $(x, y) \rightarrow \left(\frac{x}{3}, -y\right)$

22. $(x, y) \rightarrow (x + r, y - s)$

23. a. Graph $x = |y|$.
b. Tell whether the graph in part **a** represents a function. *(Lesson 2-1)*

In 24 and 25, consider the relation $R = \{(-4, 0), (-5, 1), (-3, 1), (-6, 4), (-2, 4)\}$. *(Lesson 2-1)*

24. a. State its domain.
b. State its range.

25. Is R a function? How do you know?

26. *Skill sequence.* Solve for y. *(Previous course)*
a. $xy = 12$
b. $xy = 10 + x$
c. $x = \frac{4}{y}$
d. $x + 2 = \frac{1}{y}$

27. a. Draw $\triangle ABC$ with $A = (2, 7)$, $B = (2, 4)$, and $C = (-2, 4)$.
b. Let r be the transformation that maps each point (x, y) to (y, x).
c. Draw $\triangle A'B'C' = r(\triangle ABC)$.
d. What transformation is r? *(Previous course)*

Exploration

28. Find a function f such that $f(f(x)) = x$ for all x in its domain.

LESSON

3-8

Inverse Functions

Suppose you purchase n boxes of cereal at \$3.50 each. Then the total cost C is given by $C = 3.50n$, and C is a function of n. It is natural to want to write n as a function of C. Here it is easy: $n = \frac{C}{3.50}$. The two functions that arise in this situation are called inverse functions.

Finding the Inverse of a Function

Recall that by definition a function is a set of ordered pairs in which each first element is paired with exactly one second element. If you switch coordinates in the pairs, the resulting set of ordered pairs is called the **inverse of the function.**

Example 1

Let $f = \{(-3, 9), (-2, 4), (-1, 1), (0, 0), (1, 1), (2, 4), (3, 9)\}$.

a. Find the inverse of f.

b. Is the inverse a function?

Solution

a. Let g be the inverse of f. The ordered pairs in g are found by switching the x- and y-coordinates of each pair in f.

$g = \{(9, -3), (4, -2), (1, -1), (0, 0), (1, 1), (4, 2), (9, 3)\}$

b. The inverse is not a function because there are some ordered pairs for which the same first element is paired with different second elements. For example, $(9, -3)$ and $(9, 3)$ are both in g.

If the original function is described by an equation, then switching the variables in the equation gives an equation for the inverse.

Example 2

a. Give an equation for the inverse of the function $y = x^2$.

b. Sketch a graph of $y = x^2$ and its inverse on the same set of axes.

c. Is the inverse a function?

Solution

a. To form the inverse, switch x and y. The inverse of $y = x^2$ is $x = y^2$.

b. The graphs are drawn at the right. The graph of $y = x^2$ is blue; the graph of its inverse is orange.

c. The graph of the inverse fails the vertical line test, so $x = y^2$ is not an equation for y as a function of x.

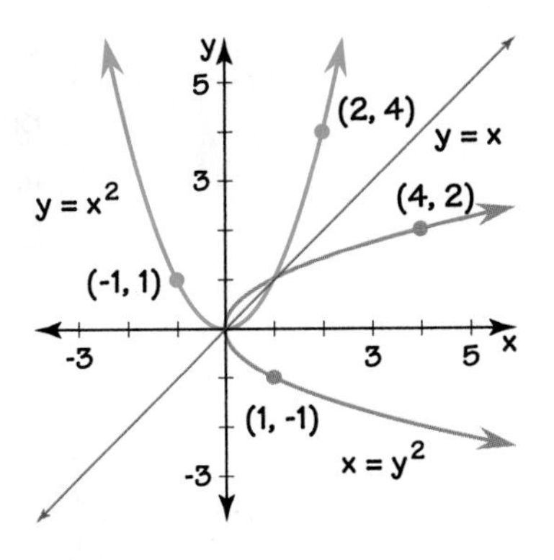

Note that in Example 2, the graphs of $y = x^2$ and $x = y^2$ are reflection images of each other over the line $y = x$. This is due to the fact that the mapping $(x, y) \rightarrow (y, x)$ is a reflection over the line $y = x$. Thus, the graphs of any function and its inverse are reflection images of each other over the line $y = x$.

Suppose a vertical line intersects the graph of the inverse of a function in more than one point, as in Example 2. That line is the reflection image over the line $y = x$ of a horizontal line that intersects the original function in more than one point. This leads to a way to look at the graph of a function and to determine quickly whether its inverse is a function or not.

Theorem (Horizontal-Line Test for Inverses)
The inverse of a function *f* is itself a function if and only if no horizontal line intersects the graph of *f* in more than one point.

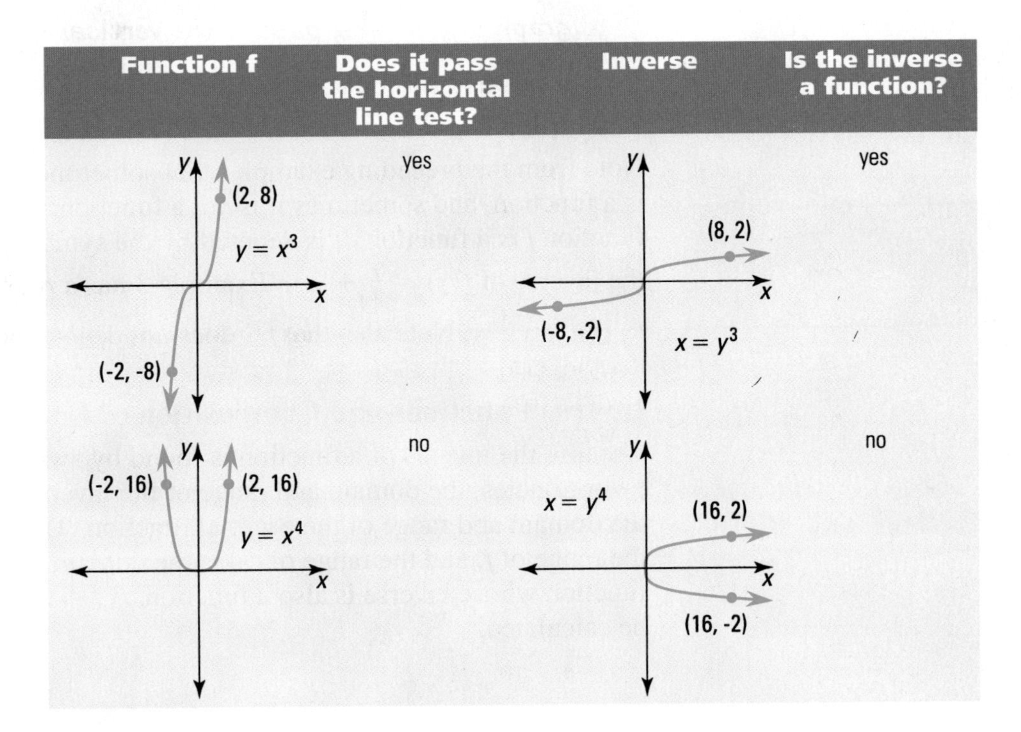

Function f	Does it pass the horizontal line test?	Inverse	Is the inverse a function?
$y = x^3$; (2, 8); (-2, -8)	yes	$x = y^3$; (8, 2); (-8, -2)	yes
$y = x^4$; (-2, 16); (2, 16)	no	$x = y^4$; (16, 2); (16, -2)	no

Example 3

Consider the function f with $f(x) = \frac{1}{x} + 2$.

a. Give an equation for its inverse.

b. Graph $f(x) = \frac{1}{x} + 2$ and its inverse on the same set of axes.

c. Is the inverse a function?

Solution

a. Let $y = f(x) = \frac{1}{x} + 2$. To form the inverse of $y = \frac{1}{x} + 2$, switch x and y. So an equation of the inverse is

$$x = \frac{1}{y} + 2.$$

Solve for y.

$$x - 2 = \frac{1}{y}$$

$$y = \frac{1}{x - 2}$$

b. The graphs of $y = \frac{1}{x} + 2$ and of $y = \frac{1}{x - 2}$ are shown at the right. To check that they are inverses, we also graphed $y = x$. Note that each branch of the inverse is the image of one of the branches of the original hyperbola under a reflection over $y = x$. Both curves are translation images of the graph of $y = \frac{1}{x}$.

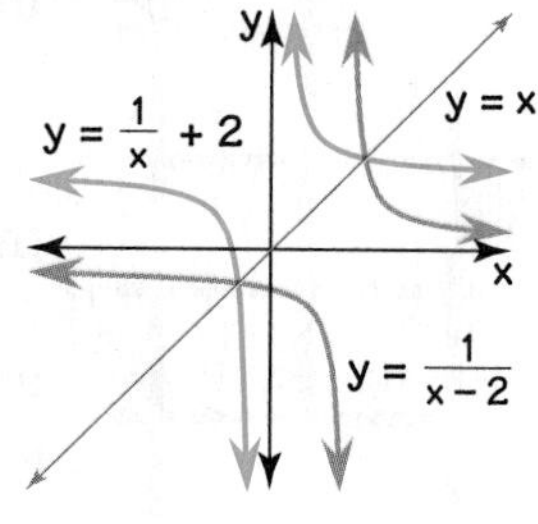

c. The graph of $f(x) = \frac{1}{x} + 2$ passes the horizontal line test (the graph of $y = \frac{1}{x - 2}$ passes the vertical line test), and so the inverse is a function.

Note from the preceding examples that sometimes the inverse of a function is a function, and sometimes it is not a function. When the inverse of a function f *is* a function, it is denoted by the symbol f^{-1}, read "f inverse." So the inverse of $f(x) = \frac{1}{x} + 2$ in Example 3 has a rule that can be written $f^{-1}(x) = \frac{1}{x - 2}$. Note also that f^{-1} does not denote the reciprocal of f.

Inverse Functions and Composition of Functions

Because the inverse of a function is found by switching the x- and y-coordinates, the domain and range of the inverse are found by switching the domain and range of the original function. Thus, the domain of f^{-1} is the range of f, and the range of f^{-1} is the domain of f. Hence, if f is a function whose inverse is also a function, $f(f^{-1}(x))$ and $f^{-1}(f(x))$ can always be calculated.

Note that for the function in Example 3,

$$f(f^{-1}(3)) = f\left(\frac{1}{3-2}\right) = f(1) = 1 + 2 = 3.$$

Also $f^{-1}(f(3)) = f^{-1}\left(\frac{1}{3} + 2\right) = f^{-1}\left(\frac{7}{3}\right) = \frac{1}{\frac{7}{3} - 2} = \frac{1}{\frac{1}{3}} = 3$. As shown in Example 4, for these functions, $f \circ f^{-1}(x) = f^{-1} \circ f(x) = x$ for all values of x for which the compositions are defined. This is why f^{-1} is called the inverse of f; f^{-1} undoes the effect of f.

Example 4

Verify that if $f(x) = \frac{1}{x} + 2$ and $f^{-1}(x) = \frac{1}{x-2}$, then $f(f^{-1}(x)) = x$ for all $x \neq 2$ and $f^{-1}(f(x)) = x$ for all $x \neq 0$.

Solution

First find $f(f^{-1}(x))$:

$$\begin{aligned} f(f^{-1}(x)) &= f\left(\frac{1}{x-2}\right) \text{ for } x \neq 2 \\ &= \frac{1}{\frac{1}{x-2}} + 2 \\ &= x - 2 + 2 \\ &= x. \end{aligned}$$

Now find $f^{-1}(f(x))$:

$$\begin{aligned} f^{-1}(f(x)) &= f^{-1}\left(\frac{1}{x} + 2\right) \text{ for } x \neq 0 \\ &= \frac{1}{\left(\frac{1}{x} + 2\right) - 2} \\ &= \frac{1}{\frac{1}{x}} \\ &= x. \end{aligned}$$

Thus, $f(f^{-1}(x)) = f^{-1}(f(x)) = x$ for all x except when $x = 0$ or $x = 2$.

This characteristic property of the composition of inverses is an instance of the following theorem.

Inverse Function Theorem

Any two functions f and g are inverse functions if and only if $f(g(x)) = x$ for all x in the domain of g, and $g(f(x)) = x$ for all x in the domain of f.

When f and g are inverse functions, then $f = g^{-1}$ and $g = f^{-1}$. The theorem states that two functions are **inverses** of each other if and only if $f \circ g$ and $g \circ f$ are the function I with $I(x) = x$, a function which is called the **identity function**. The Inverse Function Theorem enables you to test if two functions are inverse functions even if you have not derived one from the other.

Example 5

a. Use the Inverse Function Theorem to show that f and g, with $f(x) = 3x + 4$ and $g(x) = \frac{1}{3}x - 4$, are *not* inverses.

b. Verify your result in part **a** by examining the graphs of f and g.

Solution

a. You must show that at least one of $f(g(x)) = x$ or $g(f(x)) = x$ fails to hold.

First,
$$\begin{aligned} f(g(x)) &= f\left(\tfrac{1}{3}x - 4\right) \\ &= 3\left(\tfrac{1}{3}x - 4\right) + 4 \\ &= x - 12 + 4 \\ &= x - 8. \end{aligned}$$

No further work is necessary. Because $(f \circ g)(x) \neq x$, the functions are not inverses.

b. The graphs of f and g are shown at the right. Note that they are not reflection images of each other over $y = x$.

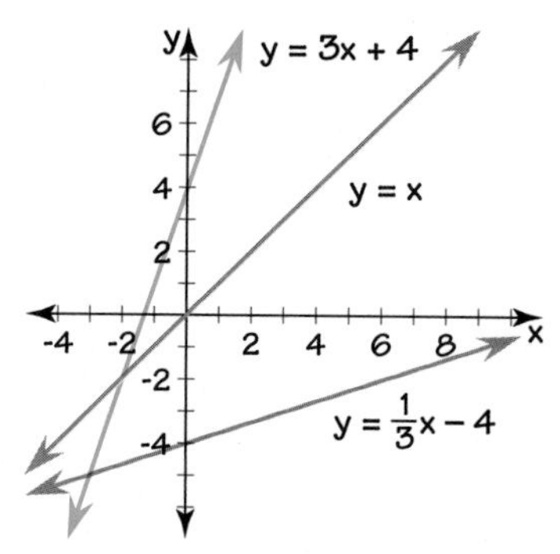

QUESTIONS

Covering the Reading

1. Define *inverse of a function.*

2. Let $f = \{(5, 4), (6, 6), (7, 8), (8, 10)\}$.
  a. Find g, the inverse of f.
  b. Graph f and g on the same set of axes.
  c. What transformation relates the graphs of f and g?

3. a. Suppose $f(x) = -x^2$. Graph f and its inverse on the same set of axes.
  b. Explain why the inverse of f is not a function.

4. Give an example different from those in the lesson of a function whose inverse is *not* a function.

In 5–7, give an equation for the inverse of the function with the given equation. Solve your equation for y. Is the inverse a function?

5. $y = 3x + 6$ **6.** $y = x^3$ **7.** $y = \sqrt{x}$

8. Suppose the inverse of a function h is a function. If $h(-2) = 4$, what is $h^{-1}(4)$?

In 9 and 10, a rule for a function f is given. Is the inverse of f a function?

9. $f(x) = |x|$

10. $f(x) = x$

In 11 and 12, two functions are given. **a.** Determine if the functions are inverses by determining $g \circ f$ and $f \circ g$. **b.** Check your conclusion by graphing the functions.

11. $f(x) = x + 7$; $g(x) = x - 7$

12. $f(x) = \frac{2}{x} - 5$; $g(x) = \frac{2}{x + 5}$

Applying the Mathematics

13. At one point in the summer of 1996, one U.S. dollar was worth 7.63 Mexican pesos. Let $M(x)$ be the amount in pesos of an item priced at x U.S. dollars and $U(x)$ be the amount in dollars of an item priced at x Mexican pesos. (Note: M gives Mexican values; U gives U.S. values.)
a. Write expressions for $M(x)$ and $U(x)$.
b. What was the U.S. price of an item which cost 20,000 pesos?
c. Are M and U inverses of each other? Justify your answer.

14. The rule for converting from degrees Fahrenheit to degrees Celsius is "subtract 32, then multiply by $\frac{5}{9}$."
a. Determine the rule for converting Celsius to Fahrenheit.
b. Do the two rules represent inverse functions? Why or why not?

"Let's go over to Celsius' place. I hear it's only 36° over there."

In 15 and 16, a graph is given.
a. Sketch the graph of the inverse of the function.
b. State whether or not the inverse is a function.

15.

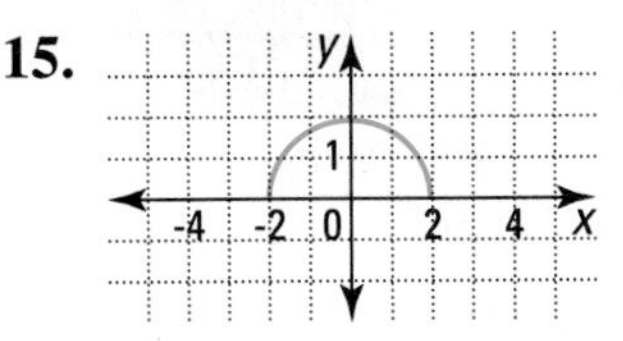

16.

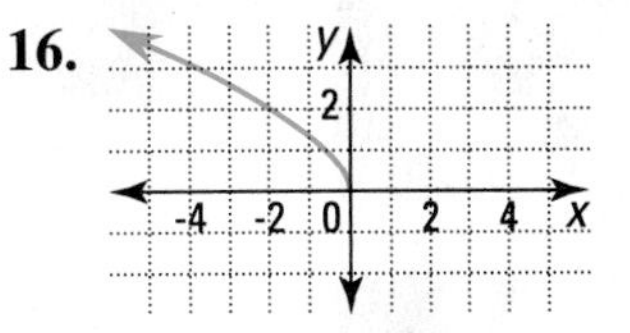

17. A function is **one-to-one** if no two domain values correspond to the same range value.
a. Explain why $f: x \rightarrow \lfloor x \rfloor$ is not a one-to-one function.
b. Give an example of a one-to-one function whose domain is the set of all real numbers.

18. If h is the function defined by $h(p) = \frac{1}{p}$, show that $h(p) = h^{-1}(p)$ for all $p \neq 0$.

19. **a.** Let $f(x) = mx + b$, where $m \neq 0$. Find a formula for $f^{-1}(x)$.
b. *True or false.* The inverse of every linear function is a linear function. If false, give a counterexample.

Review

20. A clock maker makes pendulums for grandfather clocks from a mass of metal. The clock maker finds that the length L of the pendulum (in centimeters) is a linear function of the mass of metal m (in grams):

$$L = f(m) = \frac{m}{10} - 30.$$

The time t (in seconds) for the pendulum to swing across and back once is a function of L:

$$t = g(L) = 2\pi\sqrt{\frac{L}{980}}.$$

a. Evaluate $g(f(950))$.
b. Give the time a pendulum made from 950 grams of metal will take to swing across and back once.
c. Find $(g \circ f)(m)$.
d. Give the domain of $g \circ f$.
e. What relationship is expressed by $g \circ f$? *(Lesson 3-7)*

21. Sergio is a Mexican citizen who wants to attend a university in the U.S. While completing a scholarship form from the Mexican government, he took the itemized costs (e.g., tuition, room, board, books) from the university's catalog and multiplied each by 7.59, the cost of one U.S. dollar in pesos. What kind of a transformation did he apply to the data? *(Lesson 3-6)*

22. Consider the transformation $T(x, y) = (3x, y - 2)$.
a. Describe the effects of T on the graph of a function.
b. Graph the image of $y = \frac{1}{3}x + 2$ under T. *(Lessons 3-2, 3-5)*

23. **a.** Prove that the function p defined by $p(x) = 5 - |x|$ is an even function.
b. What types of symmetry does the graph of $y = p(x)$ have? *(Lesson 3-4)*

24.

Number of black elected officials (total of local, state, and federal levels)

year	1970	1980	1985	1990	1991	1992	1993
total	1469	4890	6016	7335	7445	7517	7984

Source: *Statistical Abstract of the United States 1995*

a. Graph the data in the table above.
b. Find the line of best fit for these data.
c. Use the linear model to predict the number of black elected officials in the year 2000.
d. What factors might influence the accuracy of your prediction? *(Lesson 2–3)*

Barbara Jordan (1936–1996), Texas state Senator, U.S. Congresswoman, and distinguished orator

25. Rewrite $x_1y_1 + x_2y_2 + x_3y_3 + \ldots + x_ny_n$ using sigma (Σ) notation. *(Lesson 1–3)*

Exploration

26. Find two functions f and g such that for all x, $f(g(x)) = x$ but there exists a value of x such that $g(f(x)) \neq x$.

LESSON

3-9

z-Scores

Lining up for better wages. *In March 1997 in New York City, 4000 people lined up to apply for 700 jobs at a renovated hotel. Some were unemployed; some hoped for a better paying job.*

What Is a z-Score?

Sometimes a person wants to know how his or her score or salary compares to a group as a whole. One way to do this is to compute percentile scores; another way is to analyze how many standard deviations the score or salary is above or below the mean.

Consider again the daily earnings (in dollars) of eleven employees.

60, 66, 67, 68, 70, 70, 72, 72, 72, 73, 80

In Lesson 3-3, we found that the mean of the data is 70 and the standard deviation is 5. Thus, the \$80 wage is two standard deviations above the mean, and the \$60 wage is two standard deviations below the mean. In general, the transformation that maps each wage x to the score $\frac{x - 70}{5}$ tells you how many standard deviations that wage is above or below the mean.

In the table below, row L_1 is the original data set, L_2 is the image of L_1 under the translation $T(x) = x - 70$, and L_3 is the image of L_2 under the scale change $S(x) = \frac{x}{5}$.

L_1	60	66	67	68	70	70	72	72	72	73	80
L_2	-10	-4	-3	-2	0	0	2	2	2	3	10
L_3	-2	-0.8	-0.6	-0.4	0	0	0.4	0.4	0.4	0.6	2

The transformation of the original data set to that in L_3 is the result of the composite

$$S \circ T(x) = S(T(x)) = S(x - 70) = \frac{x - 70}{5}$$

applied to each element x. Each value of the image variable is called the **z-score** for the value x. For example, -2 is the z-score for 60; this means that 60 is two standard deviations below the mean. In the same way, .6 is the z-score for 73; 73 is .6 standard deviation above the mean.

The preceding discussion can be generalized in the following definition.

Definition
Suppose a data set has mean $\bar{x}$ and standard deviation s. The ***z*-score** for a member x of this data set is

$$z = \frac{x - \bar{x}}{s}.$$

A positive z-score tells how far the score is above the mean in terms of the standard deviation. A negative z-score tells how many standard deviations below the mean the score is.

Example 1

Stacey scored 82 on a mathematics quiz on which the mean was 64 and the standard deviation was 12. Find her z-score and tell how far her score was from the mean.

Solution

Her z-score is

$$z = \frac{82 - 64}{12} = 1.5.$$

So her score was 1.5 standard deviations above the mean.

Sometimes the original data are called **raw data** or **raw scores**, and the results of the transformation are called **standardized data** or **standardized scores**. Thus in Example 1, a raw score of 82 corresponds to a standardized score of 1.5.

Properties of z-Scores

What happens to the mean and standard deviation of a data set if each score is converted to a z-score? Refer again to the employee's earnings given at the start of this lesson, and shown in row L_1 of the table on page 215. Because adding (or subtracting) the number h from every number in a data set adds (or subtracts) h from the mean, the mean of the data set in L_2 is $70 - 70 = 0$. Under a translation of a data set, the standard deviation is invariant. Thus, the standard deviation of the data set in L_2 is still 5. Because the scale change $S(x) = ax$ multiplies the mean by a and the standard deviation by $|a|$, the mean of the data set in L_3 is $\frac{1}{5} \cdot 0 = 0$ and the standard deviation is $\frac{1}{5} \cdot 5 = 1$.

In general, the z-transformation z is the composite of the translation $T\colon x \to x - \bar{x}$ and the scale change $S\colon x \to \frac{x}{s}$. That is, $z(x) = (S \circ T)(x) = S(T(x)) = S(x - \bar{x}) = \frac{x - \bar{x}}{s}$. The translation is applied first; it maps the mean to $\bar{x} - \bar{x} = 0$ but does not change the standard deviation s. The scale change maps the mean of 0 to $\frac{0}{s} = 0$ and the standard deviation to $\frac{s}{s} = 1$. This proves the following theorem.

Theorem
If a data set has mean $\overline{x}$ and standard deviation s, the mean of its z-scores will be 0, and the standard deviation of its z-scores will be 1.

Using z-Scores to Make Comparisons

Standardized scores, or z-scores, make it easier to compare different sets of numbers, as Example 2 shows.

Example 2

Nolan scored 76 on an English test on which the mean was 70 and the standard deviation was 12. He scored 66 on a geography test on which the mean was 62 and the standard deviation was 4. Use z-scores to determine on which test he performed better compared to his classmates.

Solution

Compute his z-scores:

$$\text{English: } \frac{76 - 70}{12} = .5$$

$$\text{Geography: } \frac{66 - 62}{4} = 1$$

Because his z-score on the geography test is higher, Nolan performed better on that test compared to his classmates.

In Example 2 you should notice that Nolan scores above the mean on both tests, but the z-scores provided more information. The z-scores are sensitive to the fact that the scores on the English test are spread out more than those on the geography test.

QUESTIONS

Covering the Reading

In 1–3, refer to the data sets in L_2 and L_3 at the start of the lesson.

1. By computing directly, find the mean and standard deviation of each data set.

2. What does the z-score of 2 mean?

3. Which salary is 0.4 standard deviation below the mean?

In 4 and 5, find the z-score for a test score of 82 for each situation.

4. mean = 90; standard deviation = 6.4

5. mean = 65; standard deviation = 8.7

6. Explain what a negative z-score means.

7. What is a standardized score?

8. A data set has a mean of 9 and a standard deviation of 3.4. How can the data set be transformed so the mean is 0 and the standard deviation is 1?

9. Refer to Example 2. Virginia scored 52 on the English test and 48 on the geography test. Use z-scores to determine on which test she did better compared to her classmates.

10. In 1996, the mean (and standard deviation) on the Scholastic Aptitude Test were 505 (110) for the Verbal test and 508 (112) for the Quantitative test. Libby scored 570 on the SAT Verbal test and 610 on the SAT Quantitative. Use z-scores to find out on which section of the test she did better compared to others who took the test.

Applying the Mathematics

In 11 and 12, consider a population of men with mean weight of 180 pounds and standard deviation of 15 pounds and a population of women with mean weight of 135 pounds and standard deviation of 12 pounds.

11. Who is heavier, relative to his or her population: a man who weighs 192 lb or a woman who weighs 144 lb?

12. Suppose a woman in her population weighs 100 lb. What would be the equivalent weight of a man in his population?

In 13 and 14, an achievement test has a mean of 500 and a standard deviation of 100. Find the raw score corresponding to the given z-score.

13. $z = 1.8$

14. $z = -0.6$

15. Considering the data sets in L_1 and L_3 at the start of the lesson, use the translation $T(x) = x - \bar{x}$ and the scale change $S(x) = \frac{x}{s}$.

a. Find $(T \circ S)(x)$.

b. Apply $T \circ S$ to the data set in L_1. What are the mean and standard deviation of this new data set?

c. Are these the same mean and standard deviation as for the data set in L_3? Explain why or why not.

In 16–19, use the table below with the test scores of students on two tests.

	Physics	Mathematics
Fern	82	80
Rick	68	68
	Mean: 58	Mean: 74
	Standard Deviation: 6.9	Standard Deviation: 10.7

16. How many standard deviations above the mean is Fern's score on the physics test?

17. On which test did Rick do better compared to others who took the test?

18. Sue had a 58 on the physics test. She scored equally well (in terms of z-score) on the mathematics test. What was her raw score on the mathematics test?

19. Angela had the same raw score on each test, and she performed equally well on them. What raw score did she get?

Review

20. If $f(x) = 3x - 5$, find $f^{-1}(x)$. *(Lesson 3-8)*

21. *True or false.* Let $f(x) = x^3$ and $g(x) = x^{-3}$. *(Lessons 3-7, 3-8)*
a. For all $x \neq 0$, $f(g(x)) = g(f(x))$. **b.** f and g are inverses of each other.

22. Explain why the inverse of a one-to-one function is a function. *(Lesson 3–8)*

In 23 and 24, *true or false.* *(Lessons 3-4, 3-8)*

23. The inverse of an even function is a function.

24. The inverse of an odd function is a function.

25. Consider a 10% discount function $D(x) = 0.90x$ and a 5% total-with-tax function $T(x) = 1.05x$. *(Lesson 3-7)*
a. If you buy an item with a list price of x dollars, what will it cost you after this discount and tax?
b. From the customer's point of view, which is better to compute first, the discount or the tax? Justify your answer.

26. If $f: x \rightarrow ax$, $g: x \rightarrow x - h$, and $p: x \rightarrow x^2$, composing the functions in which order yields the function $t: x \rightarrow a(x - h)^2$? *(Lesson 3-7)*

27. *Multiple choice.* A transformed set of data has a variance twice that of the original set. How were the data transformed? *(Lesson 3-6)*
(a) translated by 2 (b) multiplied by $\sqrt{2}$
(c) multiplied by 2 (d) multiplied by 4

28. *Multiple choice.* The graph of which relation has rotation symmetry? *(Lesson 3-4)*
(a) $y = |x|$ (b) $y = x^2$ (c) $y = x^3$ (d) $y = \frac{1}{x^2}$

29. In the U.S., rainfall is measured in inches. In most other countries it is measured in millimeters. (There are exactly 25.4 mm in an inch.) Change the following data for mean monthly rainfall (in inches) for a year in Kansas City, Missouri, to millimeters to conform to the rest of a meteorological handbook. *(Lesson 3-6)*
a. mean: 3.135 in. **b.** range: 3.95 in. **c.** variance: 2.188 in^2

Exploration

30. Find the mean and standard deviation for a national or state test you took recently. Determine your z-score on this test and tell what your z-score indicates about your performance on this test.

A project presents an opportunity for you to extend your knowledge of a topic related to the material of this chapter. You should allow more time for a project than you do for a typical homework question.

1 Investigating Parabolas

In this project, you should use an automatic grapher to explore the location of the vertices of parabolas of the form $y = ax^2 + bx + c$ when a and c are constant and b varies.

a. Draw a parabola for $y = x^2 + 8x + 5$. Draw five more parabolas with the same values of a and c, but different values of b.

b. What point do all the graphs have in common? Justify your answer.

c. Find the vertex of each of the parabolas you drew. On what type of curve does each of the vertices lie? (Hint: The x-value of the vertex is $-\frac{b}{2a}$.)

d. Draw 5 to 10 more parabolas with the same values of a and c as in part **a**. Does your conjecture in part **c** still hold? Can you justify your conclusion? Write an equation of this curve.

e. Repeat parts **a–d** using parabolas in which a is a constant different from 1. Write an equation of the curve.

f. Write an equation for the curves you obtained in terms of a, b, and c.

g. Write a report summarizing your findings.

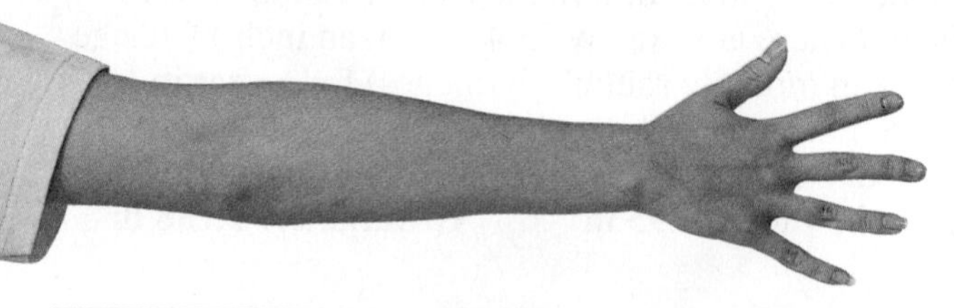

2 Body Data Revisited

Use the class database constructed as a project at the end of Chapter 1. Consider the variables which involve units, for example, height, arm span, circumference of wrist, etc.

a. Convert these measurements to other units (for example, if the data were originally in centimeters, change to inches). Do not erase the original data. Rather, apply transformations to create new data sets.

b. Compare the descriptive statistics of the transformed data with those of the original data to confirm the results of Lessons 3-3 and 3-6.

c. Examine some relations between pairs of original variables (e.g., between arm span and foot length) and between their images under these transformations. What statistics are invariant under these transformations?

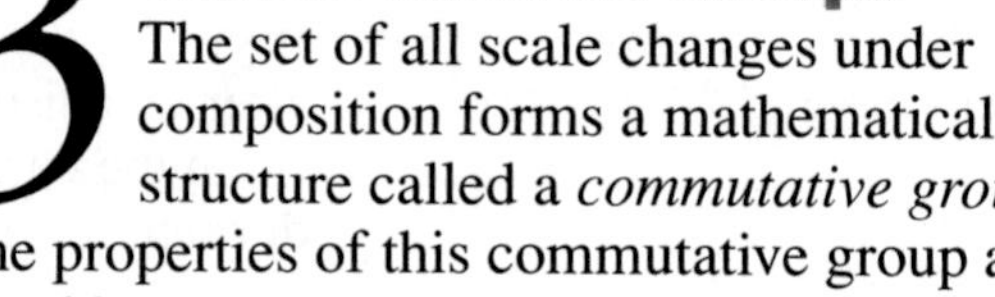

3 Transformation Groups

The set of all scale changes under composition forms a mathematical structure called a *commutative group*. The properties of this commutative group are listed here.

i. Closure: If S_1 and S_2 are scale changes, then so is $S_2 \circ S_1$.

ii. Commutativity: $S_1 \circ S_2 = S_2 \circ S_1$.

iii. Associativity: $(S_3 \circ S_2) \circ S_1 = S_3 \circ (S_2 \circ S_1)$.

iv. Identity: There is a scale change I such that
$$S \circ I = I \circ S = S.$$

v. Inverses: For every scale change S there is an inverse scale change S^{-1} such that
$$S \circ S^{-1} = S^{-1} \circ S = I.$$

Each of these properties can be proven. For instance, for property **ii**, let $S_1(x, y) = (ax, by)$ and $S_2(x, y) = (cx, dy)$. Then

$$(S_2 \circ S_1)(x) = S_2[S_1(x, y)]$$
$$= S_2(ax, by) = (cax, dby)$$
$$(S_1 \circ S_2)(x) = S_1[S_2(x, y)]$$
$$= S_1(cx, dy) = (acx, bdy)$$

Because multiplication of real numbers is commutative, $ac = ca$ and $bd = db$. So $S_1 \circ S_2 = S_2 \circ S_1$.

a. Prove the remaining properties for scale changes.

b. Does the set of all translations form a commutative group under composition?

4 Similarity Transformations

Informally, two figures are similar if they have the same shape but not necessarily the same size. More formally, recall the general definition of *similarity* from geometry: two figures are similar if and only if one is the image of the other under a composite of reflections, rotations, translations, and size changes. So, figures related by a size change are similar. Also, figures related by a size change followed by a reflection, rotation, or translation are similar.

a. A square has corners with coordinates $A = (0, 0)$, $B = (6, 0)$, $C = (6, 6)$, and $D = (0, 6)$. Find its image under the size change $S: (x, y) \to (5x, 5y)$.

b. The graph of $x^2 + y^2 = 36$ is a circle centered at the origin with radius 6. Find an equation of its image under the size change $S: (x, y) \to (4x, 4y)$.

c. The unit circle centered at the origin can be written as $x^2 + y^2 = 1$. Using size changes and translations, prove that all circles are similar.

d. Consider the parabola $y = x^2$. Find an equation of its image under $S: (x, y) \to (3x, 3y)$. What can you conclude about the image and preimage?

e. Find an equation for the image of $y = x^2$ under $S: (x, y) \to (ax, ay)$.

f. *True or false.* All graphs of $y = ax^2 + bx + c$ are similar. Explain your reasoning.

5 Sports Handicaps

To enable a wide variety of players to play against one another, in golf and bowling players are given handicaps which are taken from or added to their scores.

a. Obtain the full set of raw scores for a golfer or bowler for a season. Also, determine the handicap for this person.

b. Calculate the descriptive statistics you studied in Chapter 1 for this set.

c. Apply the handicap of this person to these scores and calculate the same descriptive statistics for the image set.

d. Show how the results that you found in parts **b** and **c** agree with theorems mentioned in this chapter.

e. Discuss whether you think the handicap was too small, just about right, or too large. In your discussion, you might wish to consider the following questions: Would this handicap enable the person to compete with a professional? With a good high school athlete? What handicap do you think you would need?

SUMMARY

Equations and graphs of functions and data can be transformed in similar ways. Two such transformations—translations and scale changes—are studied in this chapter. When translated or scaled, graphs of functions resemble the graphs of parent functions. Translations slide graphs, and scale changes stretch or shrink them horizontally or vertically. So some features of graphs can be predicted if just the equation is given, and equations can be written if just the graph is given. Some symmetries of graphs of functions can also be predicted from their equations. Odd functions have 180° rotation symmetry around the origin; even functions have reflection symmetry over the y-axis.

Under a translation of magnitude h, measures of center for a data set are translated by h, while measures of spread are unaffected. In contrast, when data are scaled by a factor a, measures of center are scaled by a, and measures of spread are scaled by $|a|$.

An automatic grapher is a valuable tool for getting accurate graphs of functions quickly. By viewing more than one function on the same window, you can see the effects of various transformations on parent functions or other functions.

Composites of functions are performed by letting one function, say g, operate on the outputs of another, f, which are in g's domain. The composite of g with f is denoted by $g \circ f$, which is defined by $(g \circ f)(x) = g(f(x))$. In general, composition is not commutative.

The inverse of a function f can be obtained by switching x's and y's in the defining equation or switching x- and y-coordinates in the set of ordered pairs. When the resulting relation is a function, it is denoted by f^{-1}. The graphs of a function and its inverse are reflection images of each other with respect to the line $y = x$. Another characteristic property of inverse functions is that the composite of a function f and its inverse f^{-1} is the identity function I. That is, for all x in the domain of the composite, $f(f^{-1}(x)) = f^{-1}(f(x)) = I(x) = x$.

A z-score is the result of a composite of a specific translation ($T(x) = x - \bar{x}$) and scale change ($S(x) = \frac{x}{s}$) of data. If $\bar{x}$ is the mean and s is the standard deviation of a data set, then the z-score, $z = \frac{x - \bar{x}}{s}$, corresponding to the raw score x, tells how many standard deviations x is above or below the mean. A data set transformed in this way has mean 0 and standard deviation 1. Using z-scores makes it possible to compare scores from different data sets.

VOCABULARY

Below are the most important terms and phrases for this chapter. You should be able to give a general description and a specific example of each and a precise definition for those marked with an asterisk (*).

Lesson 3-1
*transformation
automatic grapher
viewing window
viewing rectangle
default window
parent function
asymptote
points of discontinuity

Lesson 3-2
translation image
preimage
*translation (of a graph)
Graph-Translation Theorem

Lesson 3-3
*translation (of data)
translation image (of a data value)
invariant

Lesson 3-4
reflection-symmetric
axis (of a figure)
axis of symmetry
*line of symmetry
180°-rotation-symmetric
symmetry to point P
point symmetry
*center of symmetry
*symmetric with respect to the y-axis
*symmetric with respect to the x-axis
*symmetric to the origin
power function
*even function
*odd function

Lesson 3-5
vertical scale change, stretch
horizontal scale change, stretch
*scale change (of a graph)
horizontal scale factor
vertical scale factor
size change
Graph Scale-Change Theorem

Lesson 3-6
*scale change (of data)
scale factor
scale image
scaling, rescaling

Lesson 3-7
composite
*composition (of functions)

Lesson 3-8
*inverse of a function
*Horizontal Line Test
inverse function f^{-1}
Inverse Function Theorem
*identity function
*one-to-one function

Lesson 3-9
*z-score
raw data, raw score
standardized data, standardized scores

CHAPTER THREE

PROGRESS SELF-TEST

Take this test as you would take a test in class. You will need an automatic grapher. Then check your work with the solutions at the back of the book.

In 1 and 2, the translation $T: (x, y) \rightarrow (x - 1, y + 5)$ is applied to the function $y = 3x^2$.

1. Write an equation of the image.

2. What are the coordinates of the vertex of the image?

3. Consider the graph at the right. Sketch a graph of its image under the transformation $S: (x, y) \rightarrow (-x, 2y)$.

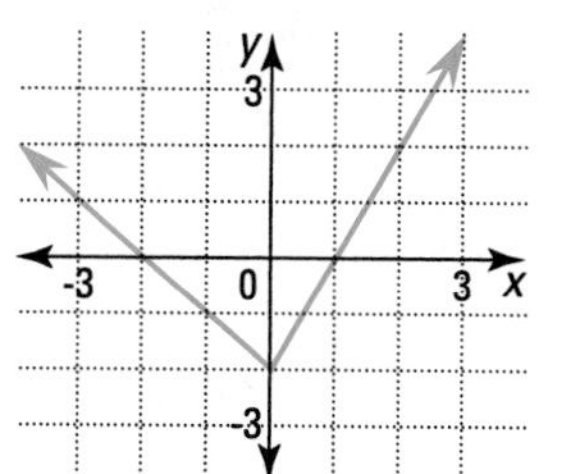

4. Give an example of a parent function which has a vertical asymptote at $x = 0$.

In 5 and 6, consider the following situation. To make the calculations easier, an entomologist subtracted 20 g from the mass of each of 170 beetle specimens she had collected. She found the following statistics for the masses of her specimens after this transformation:

mean: 7.9 g
median: 7.4 g
maximum: 11.8 g
minimum: 3.4 g
standard deviation: 1.3 g

5. For the actual beetle masses, give each statistic.
a. median **b.** range **c.** variance

6. To compare her results with those of other entomologists, she converted some statistics to ounces (1 g ≈ 0.0353 oz). Give the mean and standard deviation of her transformed sample masses in ounces.

In 7–9, let $a(x) = 18 - 3x$ and $b(x) = 4x^2$.

7. Evaluate $(b \circ a)(2)$

8. Find $a(b(x))$.

9. Give the domain of $a \circ b$.

In 10–12, let $f(x) = \frac{2}{x - 3}$.

10. Find an equation for the inverse of f.

11. Graph f and its inverse. Sketch or print a hard copy of the graphs.

12. Is the inverse of f a function? If the inverse is a function, prove it. If it is not, explain why not.

13. A data set has a mean of 12 and a standard deviation of 5. What transformation should be applied so that the image set has a mean of 0 and a standard deviation of 1?

In 14 and 15, consider the function f with $f(x) = 3x^2 - 2$.

14. Explain why the inverse of f is not a function.

15. Prove that f is an even function.

In 16 and 17, consider the graph of the function g below, which is the image of $y = |x|$ under a scale change.

16. Find an equation for g.

17. Describe any symmetries of g.

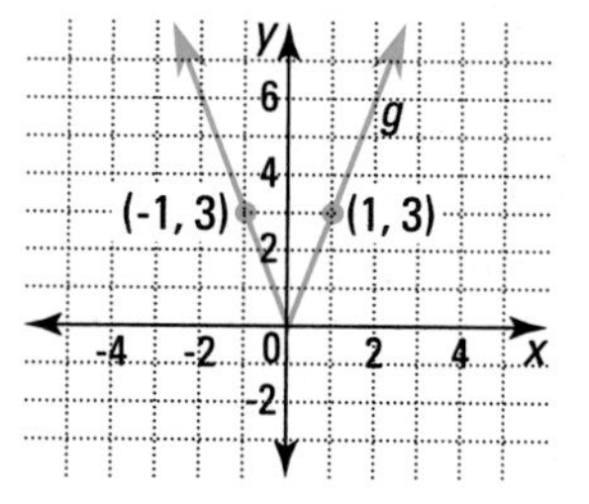

In 18 and 19, *true or false*.

18. If each element of a data set is multiplied by k, then the variance of the new data set is k times the variance of the original data set.

19. Consider two functions f and g. If f is the image of g under a translation, then the graph of f is congruent to the graph of g.

20. Jadranka, a recent arrival from Bosnia, scored 72 on a biology test on which the mean was 60 and the standard deviation was 8. She scored 59 on a psychology test on which the mean was 50 and the standard deviation was 4. On which test did she do better compared to other students? Explain your reasoning.

CHAPTER REVIEW

Questions on SPUR Objectives

SPUR stands for **S**kills, **P**roperties, **U**ses, and **R**epresentations. The Chapter Review questions are grouped according to the SPUR Objectives for this chapter.

SKILLS DEAL WITH THE PROCEDURES USED TO GET ANSWERS.

Objective A: *Find formulas and values of composites of functions.* *(Lesson 3-7)*

In 1 and 2, let $f(t) = 6t - 2$ and $g(t) = t - t^2$.

1. Evaluate each composite.

a. $f(g(-1))$ **b.** $g(f(-1))$

2. Find a formula for each composite.

a. $f(g(t))$ **b.** $g(f(t))$

In 3 and 4, consider the function f mapping A to B, and g mapping B to C.

3. Evaluate $g(f(4))$.

4. Evaluate $(g \circ f)(2)$

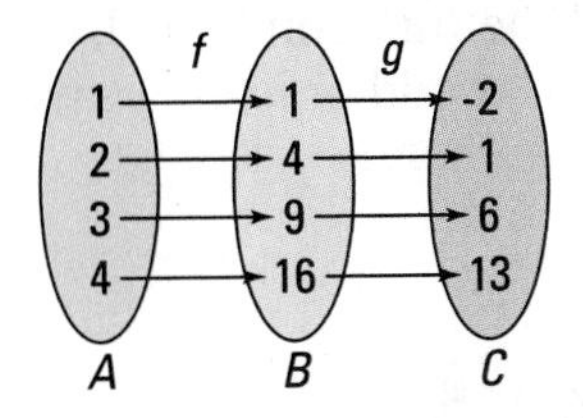

In 5 and 6, let $m(x) = \frac{3}{x}$ and $n(x) = x + 5$.

5. Evaluate each composite.

a. $(m \circ n)(-6)$ **b.** $(n \circ m)(-6)$

6. Find a formula for each function.

a. $m \circ n$ **b.** $n \circ m$

Objective B: *Find inverses of functions.* *(Lesson 3-8)*

In 7–10, a function is described. **a.** Find the inverse using a set of ordered pairs or an equation. **b.** State whether the inverse is a function.

7. $y = 2x + 7$

8. $f(x) = |x|$

9. $g(x) = \frac{2}{x + 1}$

10. $\{(3, 7), (4, 8), (5, 9), (6, 10), (7, 11)\}$

PROPERTIES DEAL WITH THE PRINCIPLES BEHIND THE MATHEMATICS.

Objective C: *Use the Graph-Translation Theorem or the Graph Scale-Change Theorem to find transformation images.* *(Lessons 3-2, 3-5)*

In 11 and 12, *multiple choice.*

11. Which translation has the effect on a graph of moving each point 3 units down and 8 units to the right?

(a) $T(x, y) = (x - 3, y + 8)$

(b) $T(x, y) = (x + 8, y - 3)$

(c) $T(x, y) = (x - 8, y + 3)$

(d) $T(x, y) = (x - 8, y - 3)$

12. Which scale change has the effect on a graph of stretching horizontally by a factor of 12 and shrinking vertically by a factor of 5?

(a) $S(x, y) = (12x, 5y)$

(b) $S(x, y) = \left(\frac{x}{12}, 5y\right)$

(c) $S(x, y) = \left(12x, \frac{y}{5}\right)$

(d) $S(x, y) = \left(\frac{x}{12}, \frac{y}{5}\right)$

In 13 and 14, find an equation for the image of $y = x^2$ under the transformation.

13. $T: (x, y) \rightarrow (x + 7, y - 3)$

14. $S: (x, y) \rightarrow \left(2x, \frac{y}{3}\right)$

In 15 and 16, suppose $f(x) = |x|$. Find an equation for the image of f under the transformation.

15. $S(x, y) = \left(\frac{x}{4}, 5y\right)$

16. $T(x, y) = (x + 1, y)$

17. What transformation maps the graph of $y = \sqrt{x}$ onto the graph of $y = \sqrt{10x}$?

18. What transformation maps the graph of $y = 5^x$ onto the graph of $y = 5^x + 9$?

Objective D: *Describe the effects of translations or scale changes on functions and their graphs.* *(Lessons 3-2, 3-5)*

19. In an equation for a function or relation, if x is replaced by $x - h$ and y is replaced by $y - k$, how is the graph of the image related to the graph of the preimage?

20. In an equation for a function or relation, if x is replaced by $\frac{x}{a}$ and y by $\frac{y}{b}$, how is the graph of the resulting equation related to the graph of the original?

In 21 and 22, *true or false.*

21. Under a translation, asymptotes are mapped to asymptotes.

22. Under a scale change $(x, y) \rightarrow (ax, by)$, y-intercepts of a graph are mapped to y-intercepts.

23. Under which transformation—translation or scale change—is the number of x-intercepts of a graph invariant?

24. Give a rule for a scale change that has the effect of reflecting a graph over the y-axis.

Objective E: *Describe the effects of translations or scale changes on measures of center or spread.* *(Lessons 3-3, 3-6)*

In 25 and 26, suppose 10 is added to each element in a data set. Describe the effect of this transformation on each measure.

25. mean

26. standard deviation

In 27 and 28, if each element in a data set is multiplied by k, how is the following measure affected?

27. median

28. variance

In 29 and 30, what is the effect of the transformation on the standard deviation of a set of data?

29. subtracting 11 from each element

30. dividing each element by 2

Objective F: *Describe the symmetries of graphs.* *(Lesson 3-4)*

In 31–33, *true or false.*

31. If a function can be mapped onto itself under a rotation of 180° around the origin, then it is an odd function.

32. If a function is symmetric to the line $x = 10$, then it is an even function.

33. It is possible for an even function to be one-to-one.

In 34–37, a function is described by its rule.
a. Determine if the function is odd, even, or neither.
b. If the function is odd or even, prove it. If it is neither, give a counterexample.

34. $f(x) = 8x^3$

35. $s(t) = 5t^2 - t^4$

36. $g(m) = |3m - 4|$

37. $f(x) = |x| - 3$

Objective G: *Identify properties of composites and inverses.* *(Lessons 3-7, 3-8)*

38. If $f(x) = \sqrt{x}$ and $g(x) = x + 10$, what is the domain of $f(g(x))$?

39. If two relations are inverses of each other, what transformation maps one to the other?

40. *True or false.* If f and g are inverse functions, then for all x in the domain of f, $f \circ g(x) = x$.

In 41 and 42, multiple choice.

41. If (p, q) is a point on the graph of a relation, what point must be on the graph of its inverse?

(a) $(-p, q)$ (b) $(p, -q)$
(c) $(-p, -q)$ (d) (q, p)

42. Which condition is sufficient for concluding that f and g are inverses of each other?
   (a) $f(g(x)) = g(f(x))$ for all x in the domains of f and g.
   (b) $f(g(x)) = x$ for all x in the domain of g and $g(f(x)) = x$ for all x in the domain of f.
   (c) f is always positive and g is always negative.
   (d) f and g each pass the vertical line test.

Objective H: *Identify properties of z-scores.* *(Lesson 3-9)*

In 43 and 44, a z-score is given. Explain what it means in terms of the mean and standard deviation of the original data set.

43. $z = -1.6$ **44.** $z = 0.5$

In 45 and 46, a new data set is formed by taking the z-scores of some raw data.

45. What is the mean of the image data set?

46. What is the standard deviation of the image data set?

USES DEAL WITH APPLICATIONS OF MATHEMATICS IN REAL SITUATIONS.

Objective I: *Use translations, scale changes, or z-scores to analyze data.* *(Lessons 3-3, 3-6, 3-9)*

47. Use a translation to mentally calculate the average of these bowling scores: 102, 112, 110, 106, 115.

48. a. Identify the transformation used below to scale the scores.

Raw Scores	Scaled Scores	Frequency
3	15	1
4	20	3
5	25	2
7	35	7
8	40	2

b. Find the mode, mean, and median of the raw data.

c. Find the mode, mean, and median of the scaled scores.

d. What property of data transformations is shown in parts **b** and **c**?

49. A swimmer training for the World Championships recorded the following times for the 800-meter freestyle event (in minutes: seconds).

8:28.71	8:31.06	8:30.14
8:31.02	8:29.91	8:27.88
8:28.13	8:29.37	8:30.00
8:28.65	8:29.50	8:31.36

Use a translation to find the mean and standard deviation of her times. Explain why the translation you used is appropriate.

50. For a sample of a certain butterfly species, a scientist found a mean length of 1.76 inches with a range of 3.02 inches and a standard deviation of 0.53 inches. If the data are converted to millimeters, give the following statistics of the resulting data.

a. mean **b.** range **c.** variance

51. Kim scored 85 on a Latin test on which the mean was 80 and the standard deviation was 4.2. Her score on a history test was 62. On the history test the mean was 55 and the standard deviation was 5.1. On which test did she do better compared to her classmates?

52. A population of dogs has a mean weight of 26 pounds and a standard deviation of 3.6 pounds. A population of cats has a mean weight of 10.5 pounds and a standard deviation of 1.9 pounds. Which animal is heavier relative to its population, a dog which weighs 24 pounds or a cat which weighs 19 pounds?

domestic Bengal cats

CHAPTER THREE

REPRESENTATIONS DEAL WITH PICTURES, GRAPHS, OR OBJECTS THAT ILLUSTRATE CONCEPTS.

Objective J: *Recognize and graph parent functions.* *(Lesson 3-1)*

In 53–58, match each graph with its equation.

53. $y = \frac{1}{x}$ **54.** $y = x$ **55.** $y = |x|$

56. $y = \lfloor x \rfloor$ **57.** $y = x^3$ **58.** $y = \sqrt{x}$

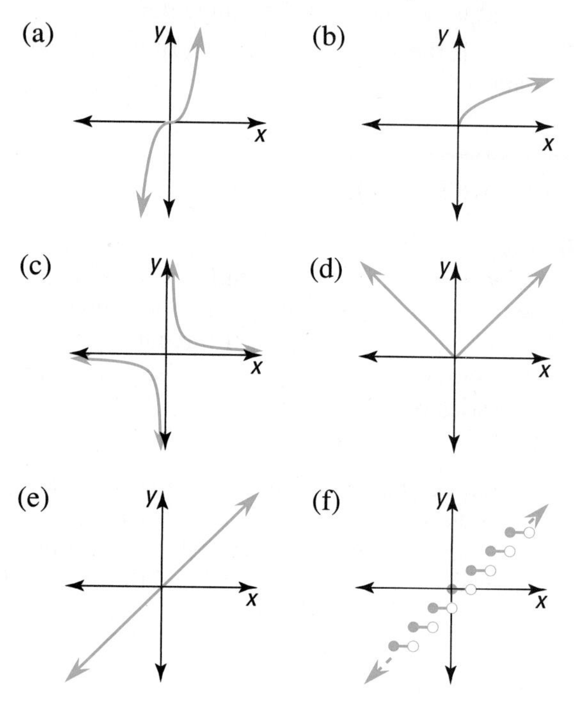

Objective K: *Apply the Graph-Translation Theorem or the Graph Scale-Change Theorem to make or identify graphs.* *(Lessons 3-2, 3-5)*

59. Sketch the graphs of $y = |x - 7| + 10$ and its parent function on the same set of axes.

60. Let $k(x) = 5 + \frac{1}{x + 6}$.

a. Sketch a graph of k.

b. Give the equations of the asymptotes.

c. Give the coordinates of the intercepts.

d. Identify the transformation that maps the parent function to $y = k(x)$.

61. a. Sketch a graph of $y = 3\lfloor 0.4x \rfloor$.

b. Name three x-values at which the function is discontinuous.

62. a. Graph $f(x) = x^3$ and $g(x) = 2x^3$ on the same set of axes.

b. *True or false.* g is the image of f under the transformation S: $(x, y) \rightarrow (2x, y)$.

63. The graph of $y = f(x)$ is drawn below. Draw the graph of $y = -2f(3x)$.

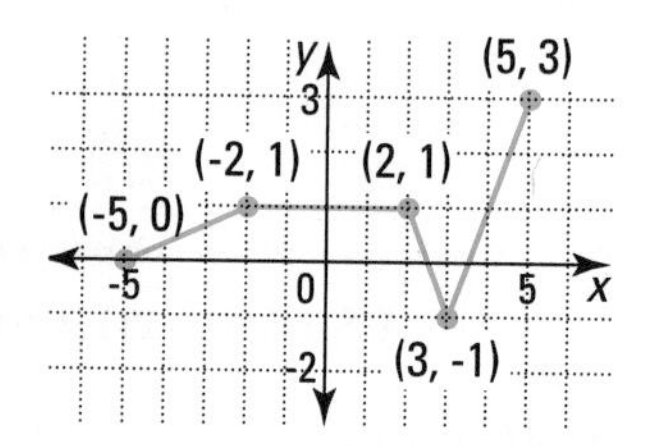

64. What transformation maps the graph of f onto that of g?

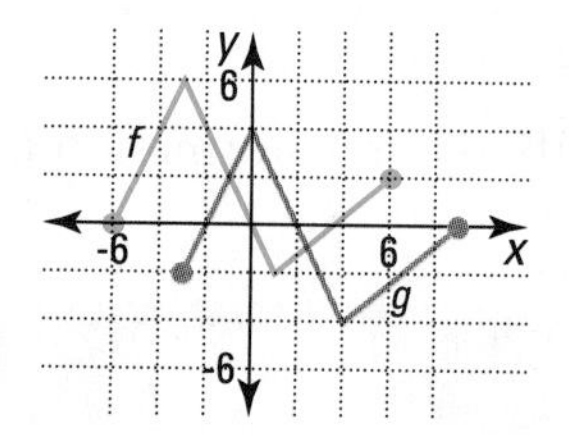

In 65–68, the graph is a translation or scale change image of the given parent function. Write an equation for the graph.

65. parent: $y = x^2$ **66.** parent: $y = |x|$

67. parent: $y = \sqrt{x}$ **68.** parent: $y = \frac{1}{x^2}$

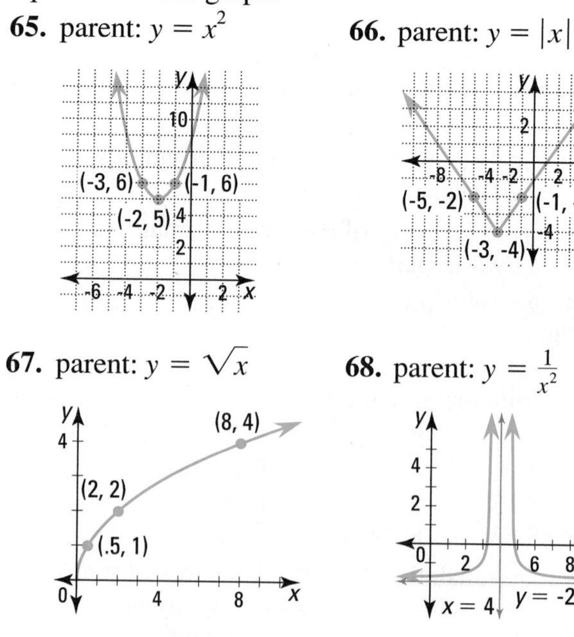

CHAPTER THREE

Objective L: *From a graph of a function, determine its symmetries or whether its inverse is a function.* *(Lessons 3-4, 3-8)*

In 69–72, classify the graphed function as odd, even, or neither.

69. **70.** **71.** **72.**

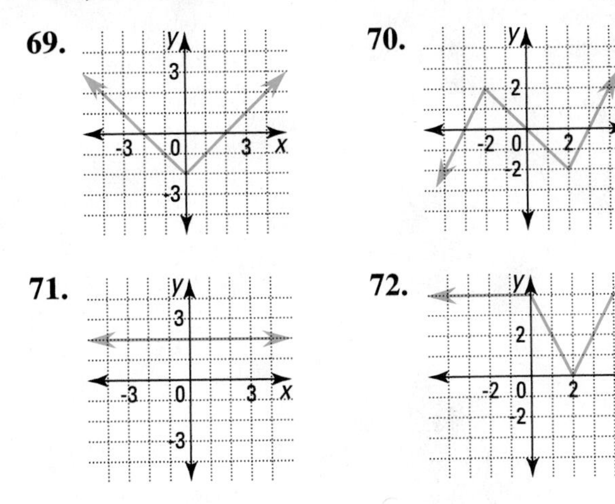

In 73–75, determine whether the graphed function has an inverse which is a function. Give a reason for your answer.

73. **74.**

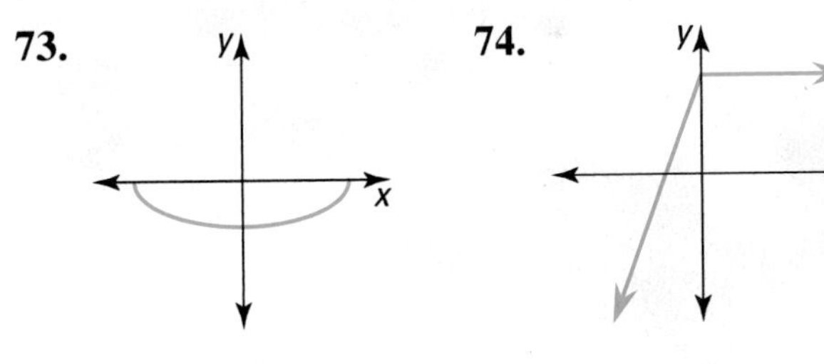

75.

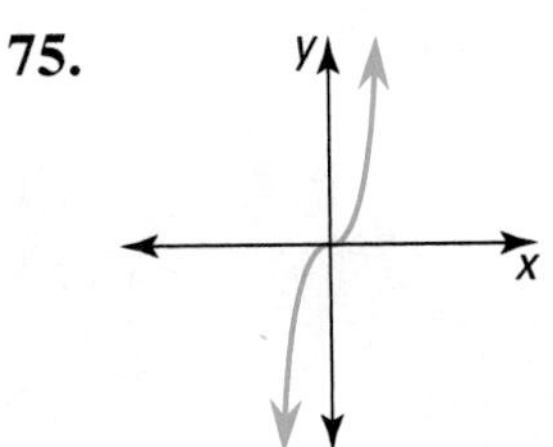

Objective M: *Graph inverses of functions.*

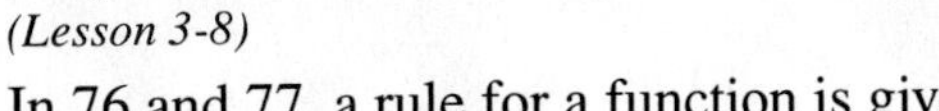

(Lesson 3-8)

In 76 and 77, a rule for a function is given. **a.** Find an equation for the inverse. **b.** Graph the function and its inverse. **c.** Determine if the inverse is a function.

76. $h(x) = \frac{3}{x}$

77. $y = x^2$

In 78 and 79, two graphs f and g are drawn. Tell whether or not f and g are inverses of each other.

78.

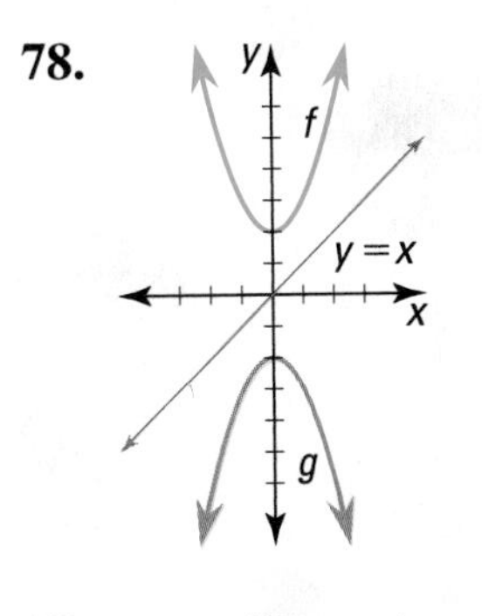

79.

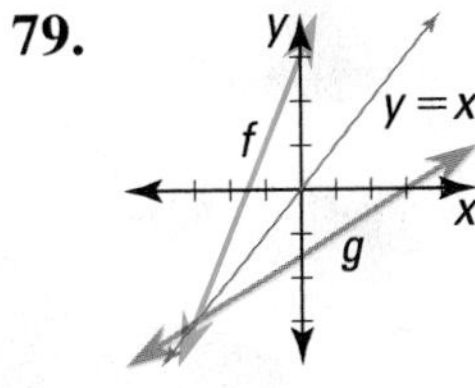

CHAPTER 4

Circular Functions

Sound is produced by fluctuations in the pressure of the air. Different kinds of fluctuations cause us to hear different kinds of sounds. Variations in air pressure can be picked up by a microphone and can be pictured by an *oscilloscope* as a graph of air pressure versus time.

Below are graphs of different sounds produced. From such graphs you can see why sound is said to travel in waves.

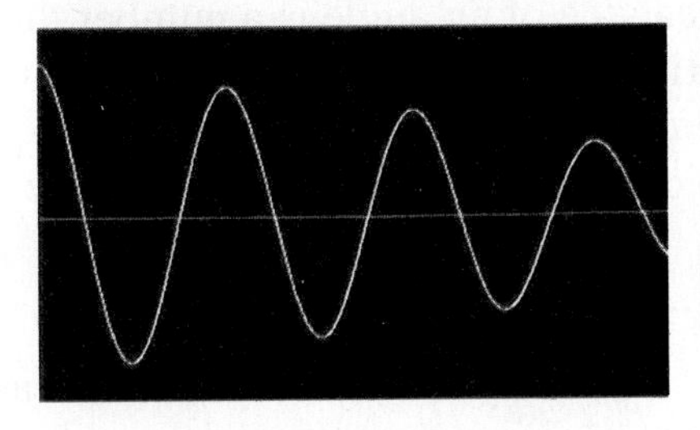

Sound wave of a pure tone decreasing in amplitude

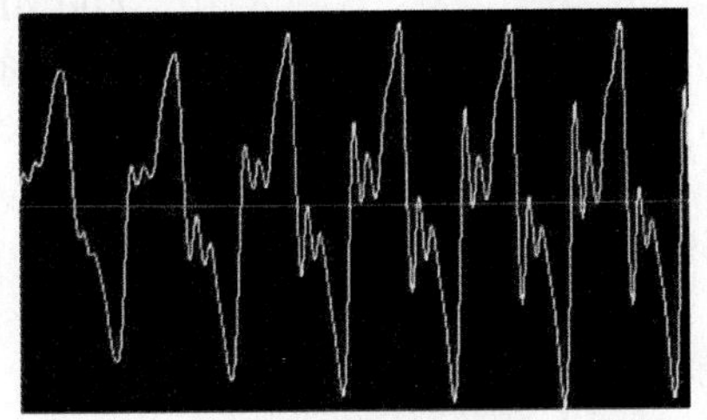

Sound wave of a single tone produced by a clarinet

A pure tone is a tone in which air pressure varies *sinusoidally* with time, that is, as a **sine wave** which is the graph of the *sine function*. Pure tones seldom occur in nature. They can be produced, however, by certain tuning forks and electronic music synthesizers. Mathematically and physiologically, pure tones or sine waves are the foundation of all musical sound.

The sine function, and the related functions called the cosine and tangent functions, are examples of *circular functions*. In this chapter, you will study some of the properties of these functions, and you will study effects of transformations on the graphs of the parent circular functions. You will also learn how graphs of the circular functions are used to model sound, electricity, and other periodic phenomena.

LESSON

4-1

Measures of Angles and Rotations

Recall that an **angle** is the union of two rays (its **sides**) with the same endpoint (its **vertex**).

An angle can be thought of as being generated by rotating a ray either counterclockwise or clockwise around its endpoint from one position to another. For instance, in $\angle AQB$ at the right, you can think of $\overrightarrow{QB}$ as the image of $\overrightarrow{QA}$ under a counterclockwise rotation with center Q.

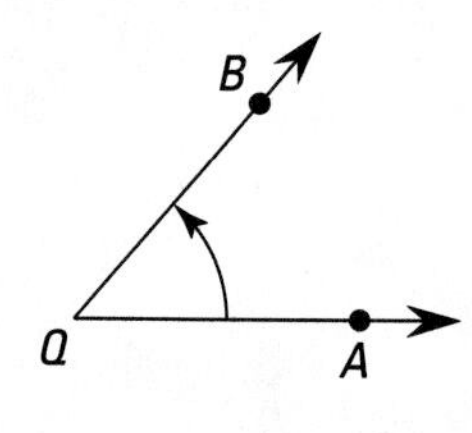

The **measure** of an angle is a number that represents the size and direction of rotation used to generate the angle. In trigonometry, angles generated by counterclockwise rotations are measured with positive numbers. Those generated by clockwise rotations are measured with negative numbers.

Degrees and Revolutions

In other courses you have learned to measure angles in degrees. For instance, angle AQB above has measure 50°. If $\overrightarrow{QA}$ is considered the initial side, and $\overrightarrow{QB}$ is its image under a counterclockwise rotation, then $m\angle AQB = 50°$. If $\overrightarrow{QB}$ were rotated clockwise 50° around Q, its image would be $\overrightarrow{QA}$, and the rotation would have magnitude -50°.

Another unit for measuring rotations is the **revolution**, related to degrees by the conversion formula: 1 revolution counterclockwise = 360°. Some examples of revolutions and their equivalent degree measures are shown below.

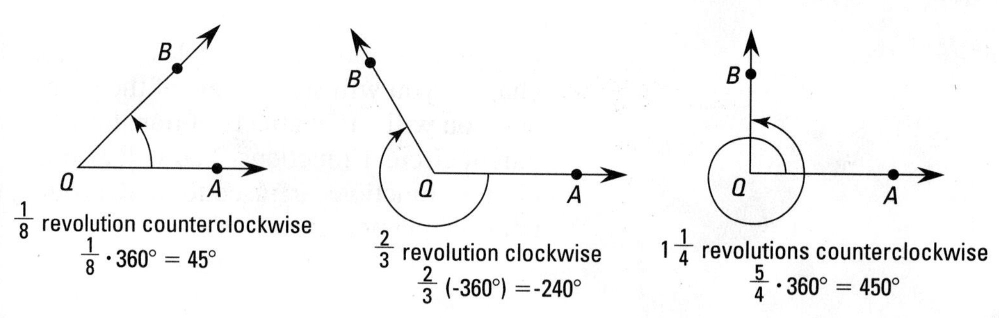

Notice that the same rotation can have many different magnitudes. For instance, a rotation of $\frac{1}{6}$ revolution counterclockwise also has magnitude $1\frac{1}{6}$ revolutions counterclockwise or $\frac{5}{6}$ revolution clockwise. In degrees, that rotation has magnitude 60°, 420°, or -300°. Adding 1 revolution or 360° to the magnitude of a rotation does not change the rotation.

Activity

a. Draw an angle representing a rotation of $\frac{3}{8}$ revolution counterclockwise.
b. Give three degree measures of this rotation.

Radian Measure

The *radian* is another important unit for measuring angles or rotations. Radians have been in use for only about 100 years, but they are important in the study of calculus and other advanced mathematics. Radian measure is based on the following idea.

Consider $\angle AOP$, a central angle in circle O with radius 1, as pictured below at the left. Recall from geometry that an arc of a circle has both a measure and a length. Its measure depends on the measure of its central angle, but its length is a fraction of the circumference of the circle. The **radian measure** of $\angle AOP$ is defined as the length of $\overset{\frown}{AP}$. That is, the radian measure is based on how far A travels along the unit circle.

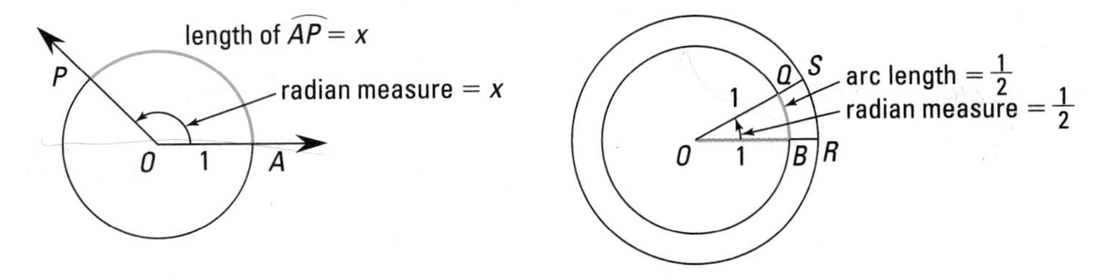

For example, an angle whose measure is $\frac{1}{2}$ radian cuts off an arc on a unit circle of length $\frac{1}{2}$. At the right above, $m\angle ROS = m\angle BOQ = \frac{1}{2}$ radian. If $\overset{\frown}{BQ}$ were cut from the circle and laid out along $\overline{OB}$, its length would be half that of $\overline{OB}$. You can think of B as having traveled $\frac{1}{2}$ unit to reach Q.

Radians, Degrees, and Revolutions

Radians are also used to measure the magnitude of a rotation. For instance, in the figure at the left above, if $\overrightarrow{OA}$ were physically rotated through one complete revolution, or 360°, point A would have traveled over an arc of length 2π, the circumference of the circle. Consequently, a rotation of 360° is considered a rotation of 2π radians. Similarly, a rotation of one-half revolution is a rotation of π radians, and a rotation of one-quarter revolution is a rotation of $\frac{2\pi}{4} = \frac{\pi}{2}$ radians.

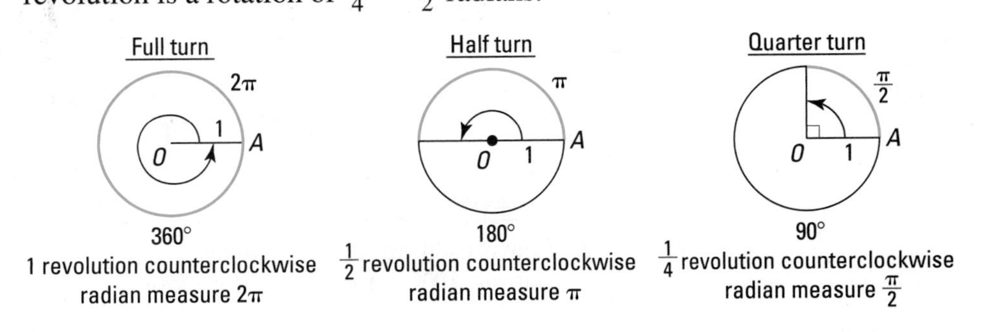

The spokes at the top of this carousel are equally spaced. Since there are 24 of them, one pair of consecutive spokes determines an arc of 15° or $\frac{\pi}{12}$ radians.

Example 1

a. Draw a circle and rays showing a rotation of $\frac{7\pi}{6}$ radians.
b. Give two other radian measures of the same rotation.

Solution

a. $\frac{7\pi}{6} = 1\frac{1}{6}\pi$. So the desired rotation is $\frac{\pi}{6}$ units more than π. $\frac{\pi}{6}$ results from dividing a semicircle into sixths. A correct figure is shown below at the left.

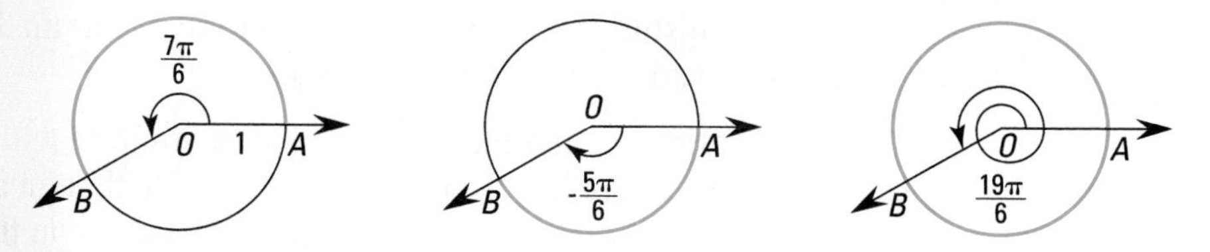

b. The rotation might be considered as clockwise. Subtract 2π from the magnitude. $\frac{7\pi}{6} - 2\pi = -\frac{5\pi}{6}$. **A rotation of magnitude $-\frac{5\pi}{6}$ radians is the same rotation.** The rotation could also be considered as larger than one revolution, in which case 2π can be added to the magnitude: $2\pi + \frac{7\pi}{6} = \frac{19\pi}{6}$.

Notice that a rotation is unchanged if 2π radians are added to or subtracted from the magnitude.

Using the conversion formula

$$360° = 1 \text{ revolution} = 2\pi \text{ radians},$$

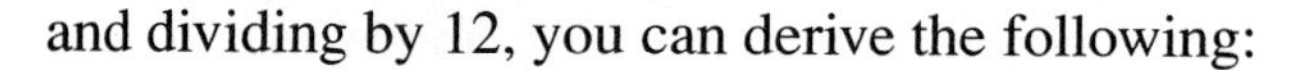

and dividing by 12, you can derive the following:

$$30° = \frac{1}{12} \text{ revolution counterclockwise}$$
$$= \frac{2\pi}{12} = \frac{\pi}{6} \text{ radians.}$$

30°

$\frac{\pi}{6}$ radians

The following table lists a set of equivalent measures that result directly from the basic relationship.

Degrees	0°	30°	45°	60°	90°	120°	135°	150°	180°	360°
Radians	0	$\frac{\pi}{6}$	$\frac{\pi}{4}$	$\frac{\pi}{3}$	$\frac{\pi}{2}$	$\frac{2\pi}{3}$	$\frac{3\pi}{4}$	$\frac{5\pi}{6}$	π	2π
Revolutions	0	$\frac{1}{12}$	$\frac{1}{8}$	$\frac{1}{6}$	$\frac{1}{4}$	$\frac{1}{3}$	$\frac{3}{8}$	$\frac{5}{12}$	$\frac{1}{2}$	1

From the conversion formula, you can derive conversion factors useful for converting any measure from one unit to another. The most common conversions are between degrees and radians.

$$1 = \frac{360°}{2\pi \text{ radians}} = \frac{180°}{\pi \text{ radians}} \text{ or } 1 = \frac{\pi \text{ radians}}{180°}$$

Example 2

a. Convert 100° to radians exactly.
b. Convert 100° to radians approximately.

Solution

a. $100° = 100° \cdot \frac{\pi \text{ radians}}{180°} = \frac{100}{180}\pi = \frac{5}{9}\pi$ radians

b. Use a calculator to get a decimal approximation for $\frac{5\pi}{9}$.

$$\frac{5\pi}{9} \approx 1.7453$$

So 100° is about 1.75 radians.

Most calculators allow you to specify whether angles are measured in degrees or radians (sometimes by using a key marked DRG). Some even allow you to make conversions between radians and degrees. Check your calculator to see what it does and how to use it.

Example 3

Convert 1 radian to degrees.

Solution

Use the conversion factor $\frac{180°}{\pi \text{ radians}}$.

So
$$1 \text{ radian} = 1 \cancel{\text{radian}} \cdot \frac{180°}{\pi \cancel{\text{radians}}} = \frac{180°}{\pi} \approx 57.3°.$$

Check

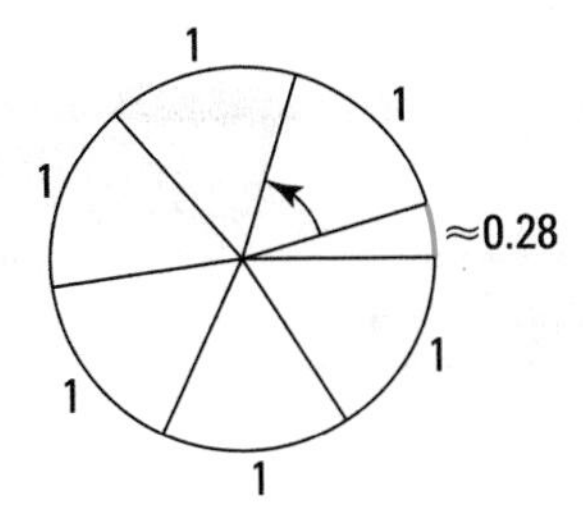

The circumference of a unit circle is $2\pi \approx 6.28$. So there are about $6\frac{1}{4}$ radians in one revolution. So one radian is slightly less than $\frac{1}{6}$ revolution. But $\frac{1}{6}$ revolution $= 60°$. So one radian should be slightly less than 60°. It checks.

The check for Example 3 suggests that you can approximate the equivalence between radians and revolutions without using a conversion formula. Many people remember that $\frac{1}{2}$ revolution is slightly more than 3 radians or that 1 radian is about $\frac{1}{6}$ of a revolution.

Example 4

How many revolutions equal 10 radians?

Solution

Use a proportion.
$$\frac{1 \text{ revolution}}{2\pi \text{ radians}} = \frac{x \text{ revolutions}}{10 \text{ radians}}$$
$$2\pi x = 10$$
$$x = \frac{10}{2\pi} \approx 1.59$$
$$10 \text{ radians} \approx 1.59 \text{ revolutions}$$

Check

1 revolution $= 2\pi$ radians ≈ 6.28 radians. So 10 radians is slightly more than $1\frac{1}{2}$ revolutions. It checks.

Example 5

Convert $-\frac{\pi}{18}$ radians to revolutions.

Solution 1

Use a conversion factor.

$$-\frac{\pi}{18} \text{ radian} \cdot \frac{1 \text{ revolution}}{2\pi \text{ radians}} = -\frac{1}{36}$$

$$-\frac{\pi}{18} \text{ radian} = \frac{1}{36} \text{ revolution clockwise}$$

Solution 2

Use a proportion.

$$\frac{1 \text{ revolution}}{2\pi \text{ radians}} = \frac{x \text{ revolution}}{-\frac{\pi}{18} \text{ radian}}$$

$$2\pi x = -\frac{\pi}{18}$$

$$x = -\frac{\pi}{18} \cdot \frac{1}{2\pi} = -\frac{1}{36}$$

So $-\frac{\pi}{18}$ radian $= \frac{1}{36}$ revolution clockwise.

Long winded. *The Chesterton Windmill in Warwickshire, England, was built in 1632 and was last used in 1910. The rate of revolution of the sails of a windmill is dependent upon the speed of the wind.*

Caution: It is customary to omit the word "radians" when giving the radian measure of an angle. For example, we may write "$\frac{\pi}{6}$" instead of "$\frac{\pi}{6}$ radians." For this reason, in this course you should always indicate a degree measure with the ° symbol.

QUESTIONS

Covering the Reading

1. What is a pure tone?

In 2 and 3, convert to degrees.

2. $\frac{1}{3}$ revolution counterclockwise

3. $\frac{3}{4}$ revolution clockwise

4. What answers did you get to the Activity in the lesson?

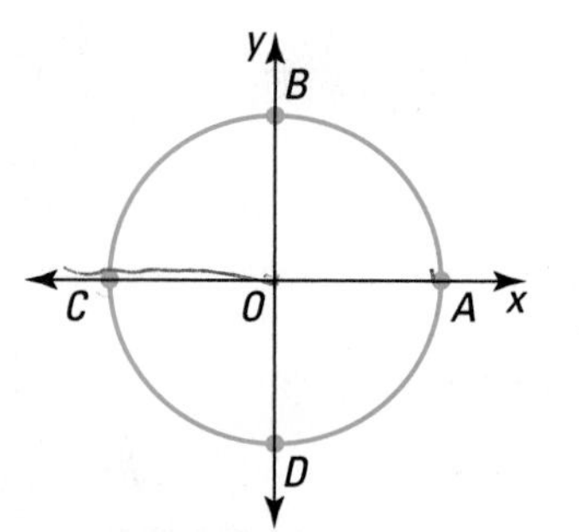

5. At the left is a graph of a circle with radius 1.
   a. Give the length of $\overset{\frown}{AC}$.
   b. What is the smallest positive magnitude in radians of the rotation that maps $\overrightarrow{OA}$ to $\overrightarrow{OC}$?

In 6 and 7, convert to radians.

6. $\frac{2}{3}$ revolution counterclockwise

7. $\frac{3}{5}$ revolution clockwise

In 8 and 9, draw a circle with radius 1. **a.** On this circle, mark an arc with the given length. **b.** Give the measure in degrees of the central angle determining this arc.

8. $\frac{\pi}{3}$

9. 1

10. Draw a unit circle. On this circle mark an arc with the given radian measure.

a. $\frac{3\pi}{2}$

b. 3

In 11 and 12, a measure is given. **a.** Convert the measure to revolutions. **b.** Convert the measure to degrees. Give your answers correct to three decimal places.

11. -4.2 radians

12. -4.2π radians

In 13 and 14, convert to radians exactly without using a calculator.

13. 225°

14. -40°

15. **a.** Draw an angle representing a rotation with measure $-\frac{7\pi}{12}$ radians.

b. Give two other radian measures of the same rotation.

Applying the Mathematics

16. Order from smallest to largest: 1 revolution, 1 degree, 1 radian.

17. An angle whose measure is $\frac{\pi}{2}$ is about __?__ times as large as an angle whose measure is $\frac{\pi}{2}°$.

18. Consider the following statement:

Two magnitudes of the same rotation are opposites.

a. Find a case in which it is false.

b. In what circumstances is it true?

19. A compact disc rotates at varying speeds so that the laser beam can read data at a constant rate. When the beam is reading the inner track, the disc rotates at 500 revolutions per second (rps). When the beam is reading the outer track, the disk rotates at 200 rps.

a. At its highest speed, through how many radians will a point on the inner track of the CD move in 2.5 seconds?

b. At its slowest speed, through how many radians will a point on the outer track of the CD move in 2.5 seconds?

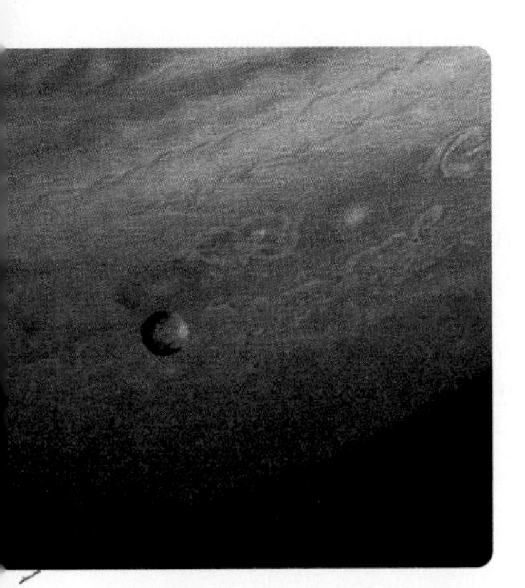

Jupiter and its moon Io. *At its equator, the radius of Jupiter is about 71,500 km. Its moon Io, with an equatorial radius of about 1800 km, has active volcanoes.*

In 20 and 21, use the fact that the planet Jupiter rotates on its axis at a rate of approximately 0.6334 radians per hour.

20. Is this faster or slower than Earth's rate of rotation?

21. What is the approximate length of the Jovian day (the time it takes Jupiter to make a complete rotation)?

22. A *grad* (or *gradient*) is another unit of angle measure, often used by engineers. There are 400 grads in a circle. One grad is equivalent to how many radians?

Review

23. The graph of a transformation image of $y = |x|$ is drawn at the right. Give an equation for the graph. *(Lesson 3-5)*

24. *Multiple choice.* Which value of r indicates the strongest linear relationship between two variables?
(a) 0.90 (b) 0.50
(c) -0.09 (d) -0.95 *(Lesson 2-2)*

25. The following instructions are taken from a spaghetti packet. Explain what is wrong with the instructions (assuming all portions are equal). *(Previous course)*

A perfect portion measures up every time!

Here's how it works:

1. GRASP a handful of spaghetti.

2. PLACE it on **END** on one of the portion circles on the box. (For instance, when the circle of spaghetti matches the 2-portion circle, you know it's the right amount to cook for two people.

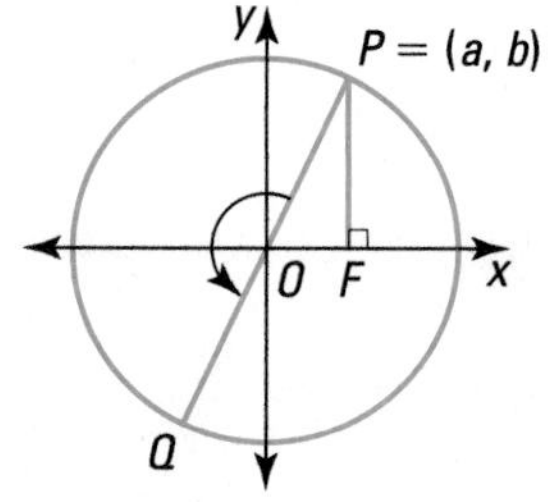

In 26–29, use the circle at the right. $P = (a, b)$, and Q is the image of P under a 180° rotation around O. Express each of the following in terms of a and b. *(Previous course)*

26. OF

27. OP

28. x-coordinate of Q

29. y-coordinate of Q

30. The point (1, 0) is rotated 270° around the origin. What is its image? *(Previous course)*

31. Consider a right isosceles triangle. *(Previous course)*
a. If the legs have length s, how long is the hypotenuse?
b. If the hypotenuse has length h, how long are the legs?

Exploration

32. The term "radian" is derived from "radius" or "ray." Find several other words with the same derivation and relate them to the idea of a ray.

LESSON

4-2

Lengths of Arcs and Areas of Sectors

Wheel mathematics. *Women's cycling events at the 1996 Olympics included a 3000-meter, a 24-kilometer, and a 104.4-kilometer race. See Question 13.*

You have studied angles and rotations for years and never used radians. You may be wondering why radians are used and if they are ever needed. One advantage of radians over degrees is that certain formulas are simpler when written with radians.

Arc Length

Example 1 considers a problem from geometry, done with degrees.

Example 1

Find the length of an arc of a 75° central angle in a circle of radius 6 ft.

Solution

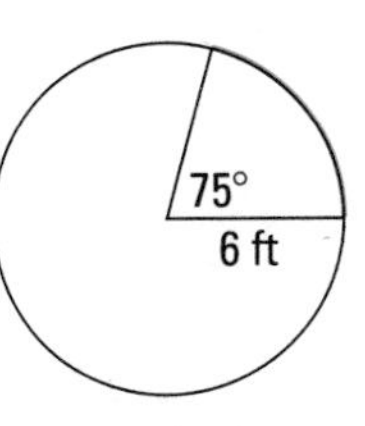

The 75° central angle determines an arc whose length is $\frac{75}{360}$ of the circumference of the circle. The circumference has length $2\pi r$, or $2\pi \cdot 6$ ft. So, the length of the arc is

$$\frac{75}{360} \cdot 2\pi \cdot 6 \text{ ft},$$

which simplifies to $\frac{5}{2}\pi$ ft exactly, or 7.85 ft approximately.

The Greek letter θ (theta) is frequently used to refer to an angle or its measure. In general, the length s of an arc of a central angle of θ° in a circle of radius r is given by the formula $s = \frac{\theta°}{360°} \cdot 2\pi r$. But notice how much simpler the formula is if the central angle is measured in radians.

Circular Arc Length Formula
If s is the length of the arc of a central angle of θ radians in a circle of radius r, then

$$s = r\theta.$$

Proof

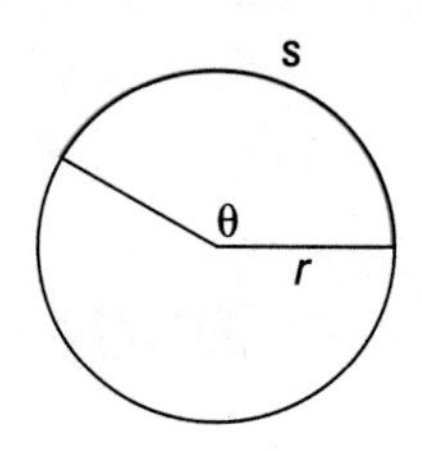

The central angle is $\frac{\theta}{2\pi}$ of a revolution. So the length of the arc is $\frac{\theta}{2\pi}$ of the circumference.
The circumference of the circle is $2\pi r$.
Thus, $\quad s = \frac{\theta}{2\pi} \cdot 2\pi r.$
So $\quad s = r\theta.$

Had the measure of the central angle in Example 1 been given as $\frac{5}{12}\pi$ radians instead of 75°, the Circular Arc Length Formula would give the arc length immediately as $6 \cdot \frac{5}{12}\pi$, or $\frac{5}{2}\pi$, which equals the result in Example 1.

Areas of Sectors

Radians also simplify some area formulas. Recall that a **disk** is the union of a circle and its interior. A **sector of a circle** is that part of a disk that is on or in the interior of a central angle. The sector at the right below is formed by a central angle of measure θ.

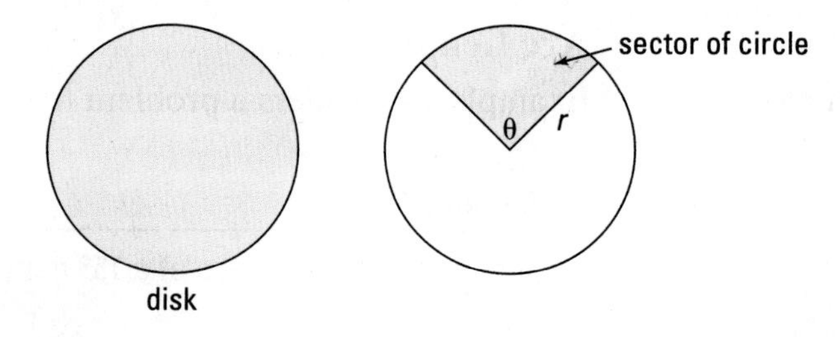

The area of a sector is $\frac{\theta°}{360°}$ of the area of a circle.

$$A = \frac{\theta°}{360°}\pi r^2$$

This formula is of the form $A = kr^2$, where $k = \frac{\theta°\pi}{360°}$. In radians, the form of the formula is the same but the value of k is simpler.

Circular Sector Area Formula
If A is the area of the sector formed by a central angle of θ radians in a circle of radius r, then

$$A = \frac{1}{2}\theta r^2.$$

Proof

The proof is very similar to the previous proof. The area A of the sector is $\frac{\theta}{2\pi}$ of the area of the circle. The area of the circle is πr^2.

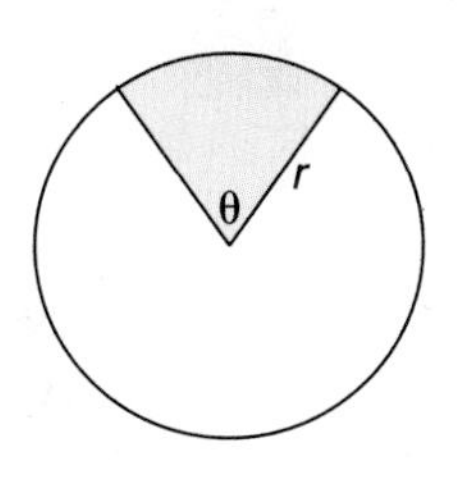

Thus, $$A = \frac{\theta}{2\pi} \cdot \pi r^2$$
$$A = \frac{1}{2}\theta r^2.$$

Example 2

Find the area of the sector of a circle of radius 5 cm if the central angle of the sector is $\frac{2\pi}{3}$.

Solution

Since the angle is given in radians, use the formula with $r = 5$, $\theta = \frac{2\pi}{3}$.

$$A = \frac{1}{2}\theta r^2 = \frac{1}{2} \cdot \frac{2\pi}{3} \cdot 5^2 = \frac{25\pi}{3} \text{cm}^2$$

Check

Convert $\frac{2\pi}{3}$ to degrees. $\frac{2\pi}{3} = \frac{2}{3} \cdot 180° = 120°$. The area of the sector is $\frac{120}{360}$ or $\frac{1}{3}$ of the area of the circle. The area of the circle is $\pi r^2 = 25\pi$ cm^2. So it checks.

Caution: It is essential that the central angle be in radians in order to apply the Circular Sector Area Formula.

Example 3

Each circle in this Nevada valley is the result of irrigation by one rotating sprinkler arm.

A water irrigation arm 500 m long rotates around a pivot P once every day. How much area is irrigated every hour?

Solution 1

In a day the irrigation arm covers πr^2 square meters, where $r = 500$. In an hour it covers $\frac{1}{24}$ of that.

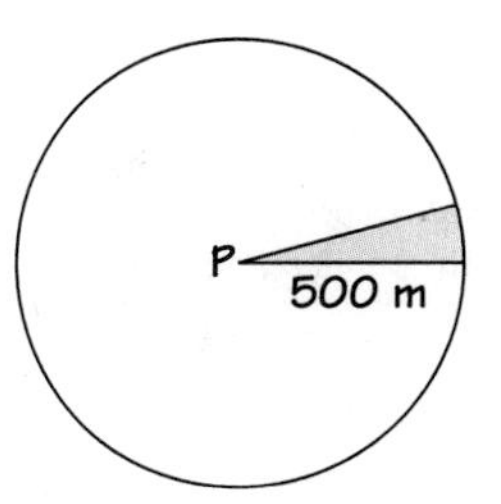

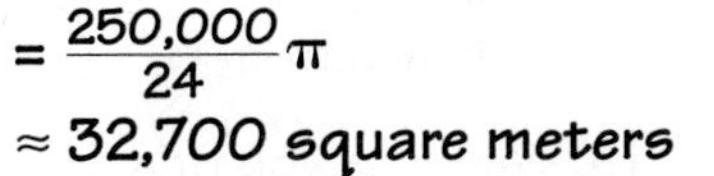

$$\frac{1}{24} \cdot \pi \cdot 500^2 = \frac{250{,}000}{24}\pi$$
$$\approx 32{,}700 \text{ square meters}$$

Solution 2

Use the Circular Sector Area Formula. In a day the arm rotates 1 revolution, or 2π radians. So in an hour it rotates $\frac{2\pi}{24}$ radian.

Thus, $A = \frac{1}{2}\theta r^2 = \frac{1}{2} \cdot \frac{2\pi}{24} \cdot 500^2 = \frac{250{,}000}{24}\pi$ square meters.

QUESTIONS

Covering the Reading

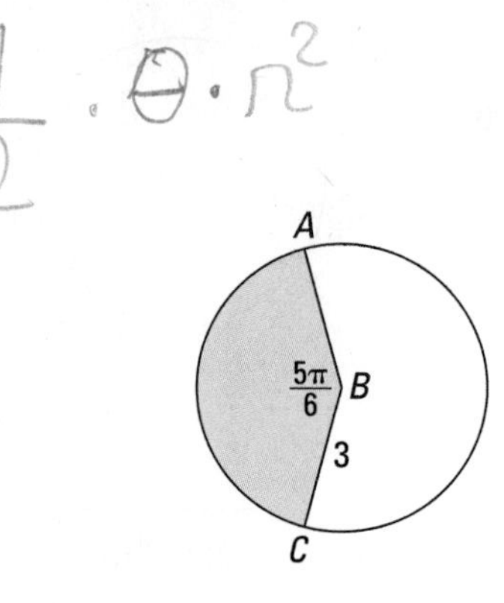

In 1 and 2, use circle B at the left, in which $m\angle ABC = \frac{5\pi}{6}$ radians.

1. Compute the area of sector ABC.

2. Compute the length of $\widehat{AC}$.

In 3 and 4, consider a circle with radius 8 cm and a central angle of $\frac{3\pi}{4}$.

3. Find the length of the arc cut off by this angle.

4. Find the area of the sector determined by this angle.

In 5 and 6, repeat Questions 3 and 4 if the central angle has measure 48°.

7. Refer to Example 1. Find the area of the sector exactly.

8. The Circular Sector Area Formula is of the form $A = kr^2$. When the central angle of the sector has measure θ radians, what is the value of k?

9. Refer to Example 2. Find the length of the arc of the sector to the nearest tenth of a millimeter.

10. Refer to Example 3. To the nearest centimeter, how far does the tip of the arm travel in one minute?

Applying the Mathematics

11. The windshield wiper at the back of a hatchback has an 18" blade mounted on a 10" arm, as shown at the left. If the wiper turns through an angle of 124°, what area is swept clean?

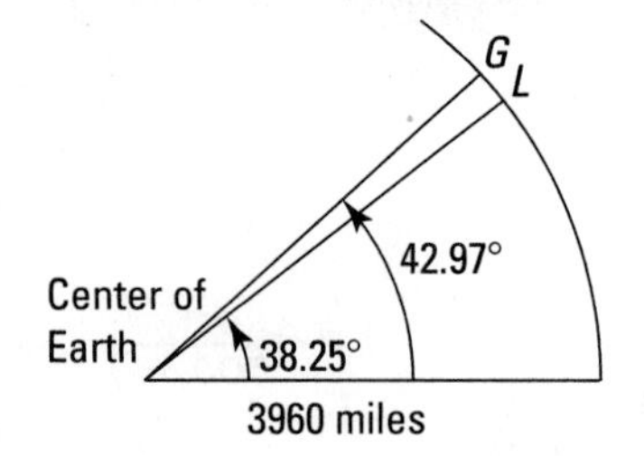

12. The diagram at the left shows a cross section of Earth. G represents Grand Rapids, MI (longitude 85.67 degrees W and latitude 42.97 degrees N) and L represents Louisville, KY (85.77 degrees W, 38.25 degrees N). Because their longitudes are close, assume that Grand Rapids is directly north of Louisville. If the radius of Earth is about 3,960 miles, estimate the air distance from Grand Rapids to Louisville.

13. Suppose you ride a bike with wheels 22" in diameter so that the wheels rotate 150 revolutions per minute.

a. Find the number of inches traveled during each revolution.

b. How many inches are traveled each minute?

c. Use your answer from part **b** to find the speed, in miles per hour, that you are traveling. (Hint: Write the units in each step as you multiply by appropriate conversion factors. Cancel units until mph remains.)

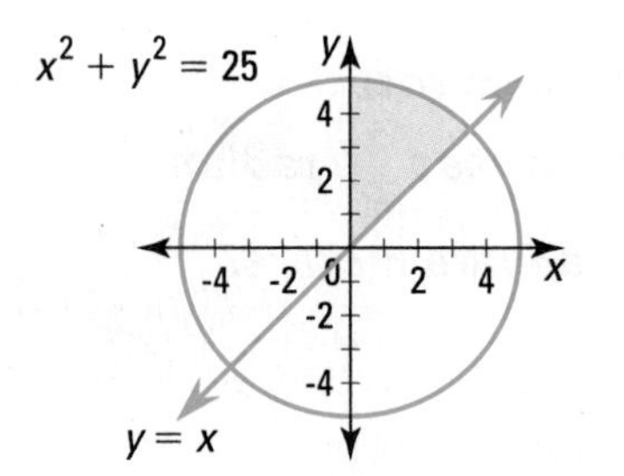

14. If a sector in a circle with a central angle of $\frac{\pi}{6}$ has an area of 3π square meters, what is the radius of the circle?

15. At the left, the circle $x^2 + y^2 = 25$ and the line $y = x$ are graphed. Find the area of the shaded sector.

Review

16. How many radians equal $5\frac{1}{2}$ revolutions?

a. Give an exact answer.

b. Answer to the nearest hundredth. *(Lesson 4-1)*

17. Let A' be the image of $A = (1, 0)$ under a rotation of $-\frac{\pi}{3}$ with center (0, 0). Give two other magnitudes of the rotation with center (0, 0) such that the image of A is A'. *(Lesson 4-1)*

18. Convert $\frac{3\pi}{4}$ radians to degrees. *(Lesson 4-1)*

19. Convert 10° to radians. *(Lesson 4-1)*

20. a. Through how many radians does the minute hand of a clock move in 20 days?

b. Through how many radians does the hour hand of a clock move in 20 days? *(Lesson 4-1)*

21. After noticing some initial symptoms of a flu, Chris took his temperature at various times. He recorded the following data.

hours elapsed	0	5	7.5	16	20.5
temperature (°F)	98.8	101.4	102.7	103	101.7

a. Give a quadratic model that best fits these data.

b. Use the model to estimate the highest temperature of Chris's fever.

c. According to this model, after approximately how many hours will his temperature be back to normal (98.6° F)? *(Lesson 2-6)*

22. The following table gives the number (in thousands) of workers in the U.S. by age group in 1994.

age (years)	16–24	25–34	35–44	45–54	55–64	over 65
number (thousands)	21,612	34,353	35,226	24,318	11,713	3,834

Source: *Statistical Abstract of the United States 1996*

a. What percentage of the labor force is under 55 years of age?

b. Draw a relative frequency histogram for these data.

c. Give the interval which contains the median age. *(Lesson 1-5)*

23. Consider the formula $A = \frac{1}{2}\theta r^2$ from this lesson.

a. Choose the correct word from the choices given. A varies _?_ (directly, inversely) as θ and _?_ (directly, inversely) as _?_ (half, the square) of r.

b. If the radius r is multiplied by t, what happens to the area A? *(Previous course)*

Exploration

24. The German astronomer Johannes Kepler (1571–1630) formulated three laws of planetary motion. Find out what these laws were and how they used elliptical arcs and/or sectors.

Introducing Lesson 4-3

Introducing Sines, Cosines, and Tangents

Work on this activity with a partner. Have a good quality compass, a protractor, graph paper, and calculator.

1 Draw a set of coordinate axes on graph paper. Let each square on your grid represent 0.1 unit. With the origin as center draw a circle of radius 1. Label the figure as at the right.

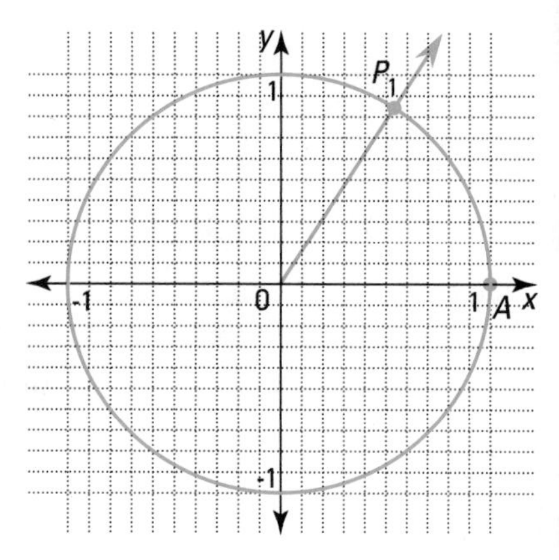

2 **a.** Use a protractor to mark the image of $A = (1, 0)$ under a rotation of 1 radian. Label this point P_1.
b. Use the grid to estimate the x-coordinate and y-coordinate of P_1, and the slope of $\overline{OP_1}$.
c. Set your calculator to radian mode. Use your calculator to find cos 1, sin 1, and tan 1.
d. Set your calculator to degree mode. Use your calculator to find cos 57.3°, sin 57.3°, and tan 57.3°.

3 **a.** Use a protractor to mark the image of $A = (1, 0)$ under a rotation of 2 radians. Label this point P_2.
b. Use the grid to estimate the x- and y-coordinates of P_2, and the slope of $\overline{OP_2}$.
c. With your calculator in radian mode, find cos 2, sin 2, and tan 2.
d. With your calculator in degree mode, find cos 114.6°, sin 114.6°, and tan 114.6°.

4 Look back at your work for Questions 2 and 3.
a. What relation(s) do you see between the coordinates of the image of (1, 0) under a rotation of magnitude θ and the values of $\cos\theta$, $\sin\theta$, and $\tan\theta$?
b. How is $\tan\theta$ related to $\cos\theta$ and $\sin\theta$?

5 **a.** Use your calculator to find a value of n, where n is a whole number of radians, such that $\cos n > 0$ and $\sin n < 0$.
b. Draw the point P_n on your unit circle that is the image of (1, 0) under your rotation of n radians.
c. From your drawing estimate the slope of $\overline{OP_n}$. Explain how to use one of $\cos n$, $\sin n$, or $\tan n$ to check your estimate.

LESSON

4-3

Sines, Cosines, and Tangents

Definitions of the Sine, Cosine, and Tangent

The **unit circle** is the circle with center at the origin and radius 1. The circle in the In-class Activity on page 244 is a unit circle.

Consider the rotation of magnitude θ with center at the origin. We call this R_θ. Regardless of the value of θ, P, the image of (1, 0) under R_θ, is on the unit circle. We associate two numbers with each value of θ: the **cosine** of θ (abbreviated cos θ) is the x-coordinate of P; the **sine** of θ (abbreviated sin θ) is the y-coordinate of P.

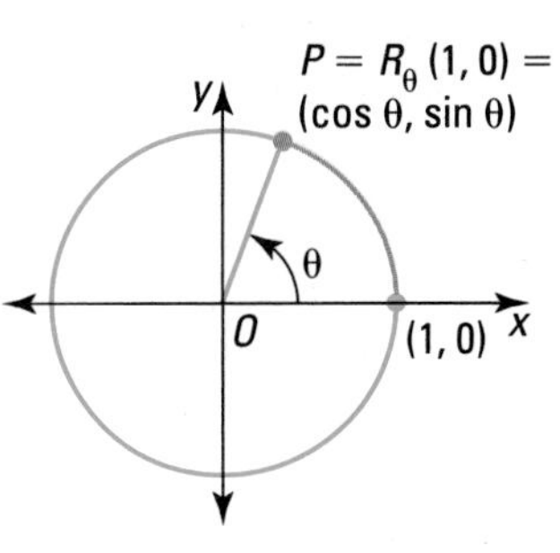

Definition
For all real numbers θ, $(\cos \theta, \sin \theta)$ is the image of the point (1, 0) under a rotation of magnitude θ about the origin. That is, $(\cos \theta, \sin \theta) = R_\theta(1, 0)$.

To find values of cosines and sines when θ is a multiple of $\frac{\pi}{2}$ or 90°, you can use the above definitions and mentally rotate (1, 0) the appropriate amount.

Example 1

a. Evaluate $\cos \pi$. **b.** Evaluate $\sin \pi$.

Solution

Because no degree sign is given, π is in radians. Think of $R_\pi(1, 0)$, the image of (1, 0) under a rotation of π. R_π maps (1, 0) onto (-1, 0). By definition, $(\cos \pi, \sin \pi) = (-1, 0)$. *So* **a.** $\cos \pi = -1$ *and* **b.** $\sin \pi = 0$.

Check

Use a calculator in radian mode.

Cosines and sines of other multiples of $\frac{\pi}{2}$ radians are shown on the unit circle below.

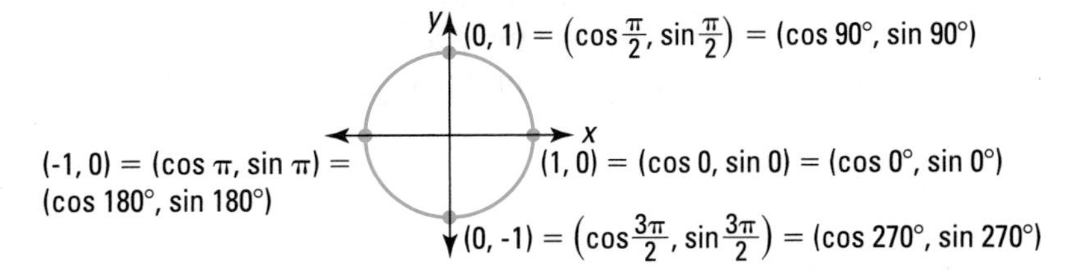

The **tangent** of θ (abbreviated tan θ) is defined in terms of the sine and cosine functions. It equals the ratio of sine θ to cosine θ.

Definition
For all real numbers θ, provided $\cos\theta \neq 0$,

$$\tan\theta = \frac{\sin\theta}{\cos\theta}.$$

When cos θ *does* equal zero, which occurs at any odd multiple of $\frac{\pi}{2}$, then tan θ is *undefined*.

Example 2

a. Evaluate tan π.
b. Evaluate tan (-270°).

Solution

a. From Example 1, $\cos\pi = -1$ and $\sin\pi = 0$. So

$$\tan\pi = \frac{\sin\pi}{\cos\pi} = \frac{0}{-1} = 0.$$

b. The image of (1, 0) under a rotation of -270° is (0, 1).
So $\cos(-270°) = 0$ and $\sin(-270°) = 1$.

$$\tan(-270°) = \frac{\sin(-270°)}{\cos(-270°)} = \frac{1}{0}$$

tan (-270°) is undefined.

You can find approximations to other values of sin θ, cos θ, or tan θ using a calculator.

Example 3

The point (1, 0) is rotated $\frac{13\pi}{15}$ about the origin. Find the coordinates of its image correct to three decimal places.

Solution

By definition, $R_{13\pi/15}(1, 0) = \left(\cos\frac{13\pi}{15}, \sin\frac{13\pi}{15}\right)$. Set your calculator to radian mode and calculate. $\cos\frac{13\pi}{15} \approx -.9135$ and $\sin\frac{13\pi}{15} \approx .4067$. So the image of (1, 0) under a rotation of $\frac{13\pi}{15}$ is approximately (-.914, .407).

Check

Draw a picture. The image lies in the second quadrant, closer to the *x*-axis than the *y*-axis. So the calculations seem correct.

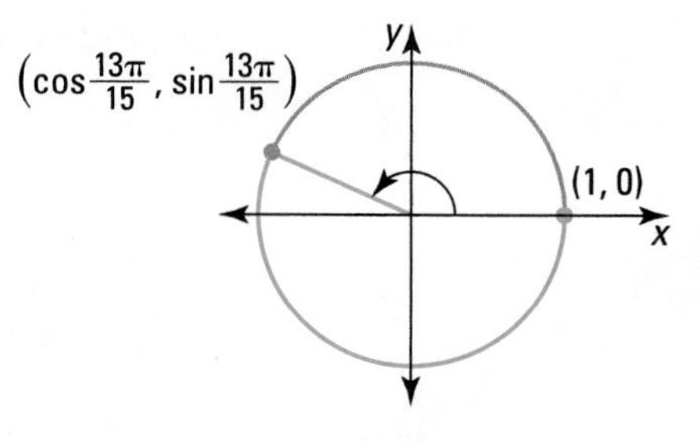

For a given value of θ, you can determine whether sin θ, cos θ, and tan θ are positive or negative without using a calculator by using coordinate geometry and the unit circle. The cosine is positive when $R_\theta(1, 0)$ is in the first or fourth quadrant. The sine is positive when the image is in the first or second quadrant. The tangent is positive when the sine and cosine have the same sign, negative when they have opposite signs. The following table summarizes this information for values of θ between 0 and 2π.

(−, +) y (+, +)
P
θ
x
(−, −) (+, −)

$P = (\cos\theta, \sin\theta) = R_\theta(1, 0)$

θ	quadrant of $R_\theta(1, 0)$	cos θ	sin θ	tan θ
$0 < \theta < \frac{\pi}{2}$	first	+	+	+
$\frac{\pi}{2} < \theta < \pi$	second	−	+	−
$\pi < \theta < \frac{3\pi}{2}$	third	−	−	+
$\frac{3\pi}{2} < \theta < 2\pi$	fourth	+	−	−

Example 4

Give the sign of the following. Do not use a calculator.

a. cos (-7) **b.** sin (-7) **c.** tan (-7)

Solution

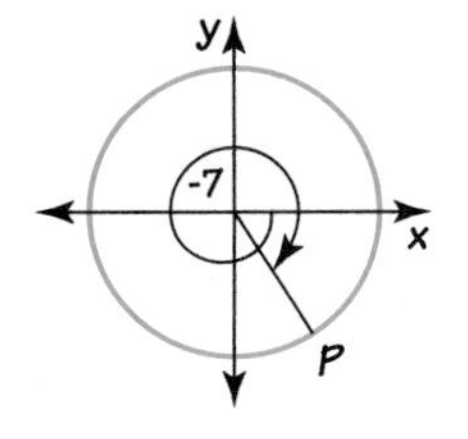

-7 radians is the magnitude of a clockwise rotation slightly more than 1 revolution. The terminal side of the angle is in the fourth quadrant. So **a. cos (-7) is positive, b. sin (-7) is negative, c. tan (-7) is negative.**

Check

Use a calculator.

The applications of sines, cosines, and tangents are many and diverse. One application is to locate points in the plane and calculate certain distances.

Example 5

Suppose you are sitting in a Ferris wheel that has 12 spokes from which hang its seats. If the radius of the Ferris wheel is 17 feet, how high is the seat off the ground as you travel around the wheel?

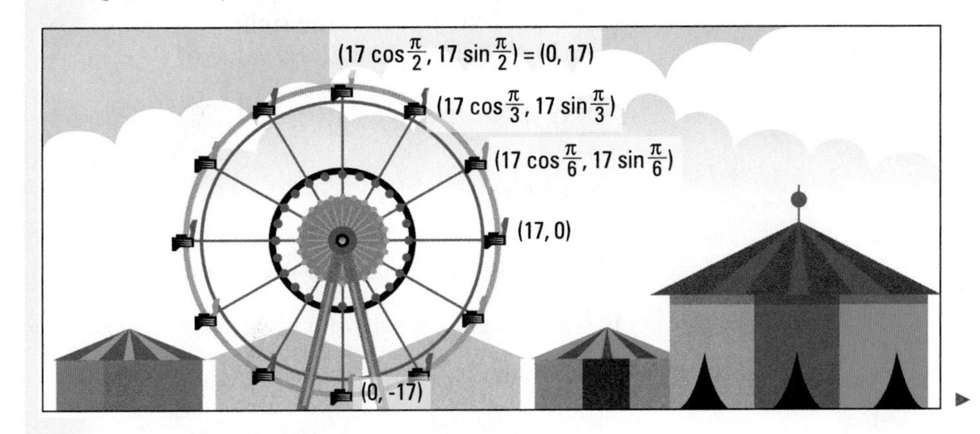

Solution

We need to make some assumptions. Assume that the seat's lowest point is at ground level. Also assume the seat is the same distance directly below the end of the spoke the entire way around. So you and the seat travel in a circle tangent to the ground in a plane perpendicular to the ground.

The key to answering the question is to realize that the height of the seat is determined by the angle of the spoke from the horizontal. To see this, imagine the Ferris wheel on a coordinate system whose origin is the center of the wheel. Think of the unit circle as having radius 17 feet. By the definition of the sine, when the spoke has turned θ counterclockwise from the horizontal, the height of the end of the *spoke above the center of the wheel* is $17 \sin \theta$.

Add the radius 17 to get the height of the *seat above the ground.* Thus, in general, a seat that has been turned an angle θ counterclockwise from the horizontal is at a height

$$17 + 17 \sin \theta$$

above the ground. Thus, when one seat is at the bottom, going counterclockwise from the right-most seat, the 12 seats on the Ferris wheel are at heights

$$17 + 17 \sin 0 = 17 \text{ feet}$$
$$17 + 17 \sin \tfrac{\pi}{6} = 25.5 \text{ feet}$$
$$17 + 17 \sin \tfrac{\pi}{3} \approx 31.7 \text{ feet}$$
$$17 + 17 \sin \tfrac{\pi}{2} = 34 \text{ feet}$$
$$17 + 17 \sin \tfrac{2\pi}{3} \approx 31.7 \text{ feet, and so on.}$$

QUESTIONS

Covering the Reading

1. Suppose the point $A = (1, 0)$ is rotated a magnitude θ around the point $O = (0, 0)$.
a. $\cos \theta$ is the __?__ of $R_\theta(A)$. **b.** $\sin \theta$ is the __?__ of $R_\theta(A)$.

In 2–4, use the figure at the right. Which point is $R_\theta(1, 0)$ for the given value of θ?

2. $\frac{9\pi}{2}$ **3.** -13π **4.** $-810°$

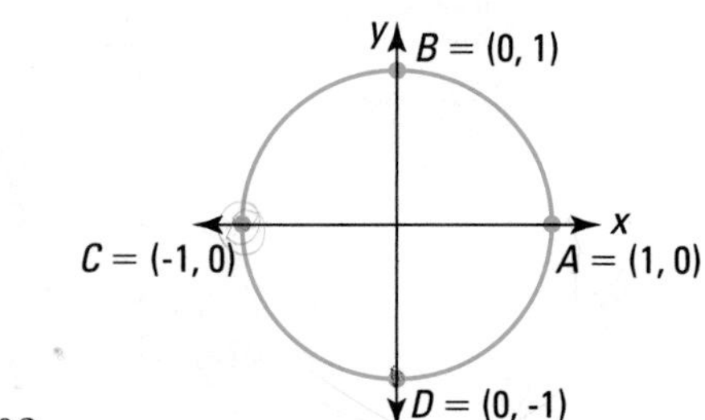

5. How is $\tan \theta$ related to $\cos \theta$ and $\sin \theta$?

In 6 and 7, give exact values.

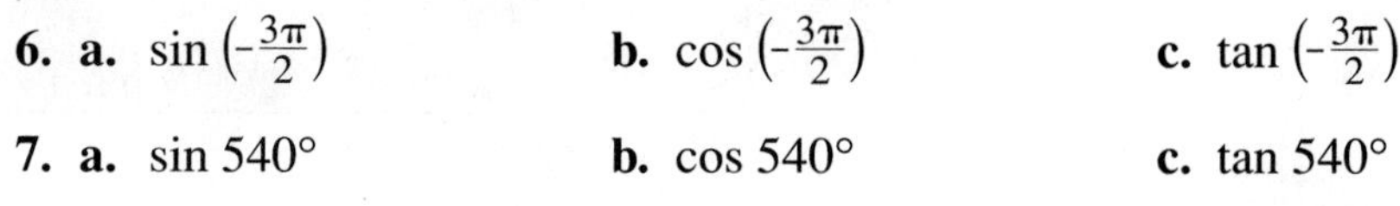

6. a. $\sin\left(-\frac{3\pi}{2}\right)$ **b.** $\cos\left(-\frac{3\pi}{2}\right)$ **c.** $\tan\left(-\frac{3\pi}{2}\right)$

7. a. $\sin 540°$ **b.** $\cos 540°$ **c.** $\tan 540°$

8. Give two values of θ, in radians, for which tan θ is undefined.

In 9 and 10, find the image of (1, 0) under the given rotation about the origin.

9. 200°

10. $\frac{8\pi}{5}$

In 11 and 12, **a.** use a calculator to approximate the value to three decimal places. **b.** Use a picture to explain how you could have found the sign of the value without using a calculator.

11. sin (-10°)

12. tan (-10°)

In 13 and 14, let $P = R_\theta(1, 0)$.

13. If P is in the second quadrant, state the sign of the following.
a. cos θ
b. sin θ
c. tan θ

14. If sin θ < 0 and cos θ < 0, in what quadrant is P?

In 15–17, refer to Example 5.

15. How high is the seat above the ground when it is at the top of the Ferris wheel?

16. How high is the seat above the ground when it has been rotated $\frac{4\pi}{3}$ from the horizontal?

17. Suppose the seat next to you is at ground level. How high are you off the ground?

Applying the Mathematics

18. Find three values of θ in radians for which cos θ = -1.

19. For what values of θ between 0 and 2π is sin θ positive?

20. As θ increases from 0 to $\frac{\pi}{2}$, tell whether $y = \cos \theta$ increases or decreases.

21. Draw a unit circle on graph paper. Use the graph paper to approximate sin (-49°) and cos (-49°) to the nearest tenth. Use these values to approximate tan (-49°). Check your work with a calculator.

22. The name "tangent" is derived from the use of the word "tangent" in geometry. Here is how. At the right, line ℓ is tangent to the unit circle at $A = (1, 0)$. P is the image of A under a rotation of magnitude θ with center O, and $\overrightarrow{OP}$ intersects ℓ at Q.

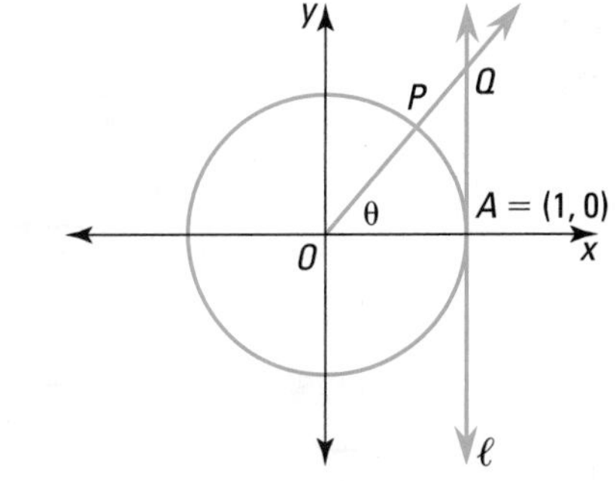

a. When $0 < \theta < \frac{\pi}{2}$, prove that $QA = \tan \theta$.

b. Draw a diagram similar to the one in part **a** for the case of $\frac{\pi}{2} < \theta < \pi$. Explain how to find tan θ from your diagram.

Review

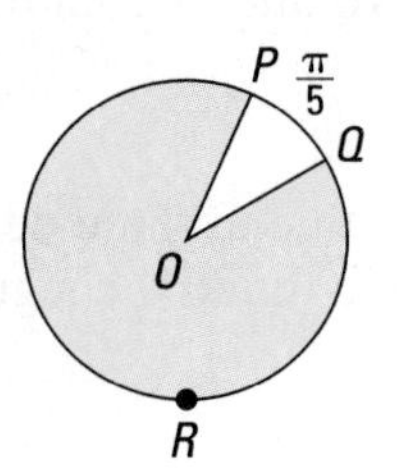

23. Suppose an arc $\overparen{PQ}$ of a unit circle with center O has length $\frac{\pi}{5}$ as shown at the left.

a. Give the radian measure of ∠POQ.

b. Give the degree measure of ∠POQ.

c. Give the length of major arc $\overparen{PRQ}$.

d. Give the area of the sector of $\overparen{PRQ}$. *(Lesson 4-2)*

24. A cylinder is pictured at the right.

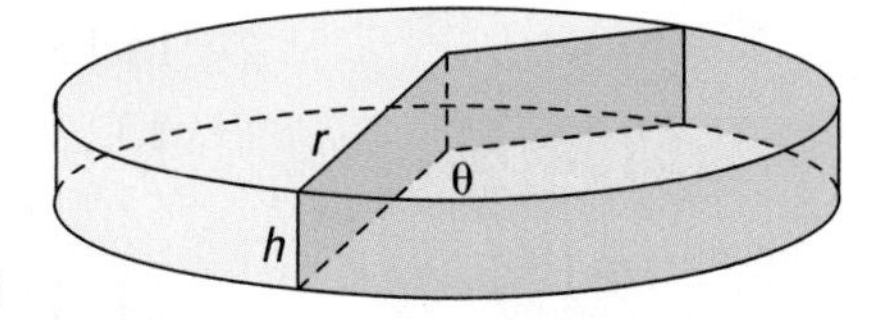

a. What is its volume?

b. What is the volume of the shaded region of the cylinder with central angle θ? *(Previous course, Lesson 4-2)*

In 25 and 26, fill in the blank with a radian measure. *(Previous course, Lesson 4-1)*

25. The sum of the measures of the angles of a triangle is __?__.

26. If two angles are complementary and one has measure θ, the other has measure __?__.

27. A frozen 6" diameter personal cheese pizza box lists its total calories as 590. About how many calories are in a single bite of 2 square inches? *(Previous course)*

28. Suppose $\triangle ABC$ is equilateral with $AB = BC = AC = x$, and that $\overline{AD}$ is the altitude to $\overline{CB}$. Find each measure. *(Previous course)*

a. $m\angle DAB$ **b.** BD **c.** AD

In 29–31, suppose (a, b) is a point in the first quadrant. Give the coordinates of its image after each transformation. *(Previous course)*

29. reflection over the y-axis

30. reflection over the x-axis

31. rotation of 180° around (0, 0)

32. *Skill sequence.* Simplify in your head. *(Previous course)*

a. $\dfrac{\frac{1}{4}}{\frac{5}{4}}$ **b.** $\dfrac{\frac{\sqrt{3}}{4}}{\frac{5}{4}}$ **c.** $\dfrac{\frac{1}{8}}{\frac{\sqrt{3}}{8}}$

Exploration

33. $\sin .25 = .2474\ldots$, so to the nearest hundredth, $\sin .25 = .25$. Describe all values of θ between 0 and $\frac{\pi}{2}$ such that when $\sin\theta$ is rounded to the nearest hundredth, $\sin\theta = \theta$.

LESSON

4-4

Basic Identities Involving Sines, Cosines, and Tangents

In this detail from School of Athens, a fresco by Raphael on a wall in the Vatican Palace, Pythagoras is shown teaching some of his students.

The Pythagorean Identity

An **identity** is an equation that is true for all values of the variables for which the expressions are defined. All the theorems in this lesson are identities. The first identity we derive in this lesson comes directly from the equation $x^2 + y^2 = 1$ for the unit circle. Because, for every θ, the point $(\cos \theta, \sin \theta)$ is on the unit circle, the coordinates must satisfy the equation of the circle. Thus, every number θ satisfies the equation $(\cos \theta)^2 + (\sin \theta)^2 = 1$. This argument proves a theorem called the *Pythagorean Identity*.

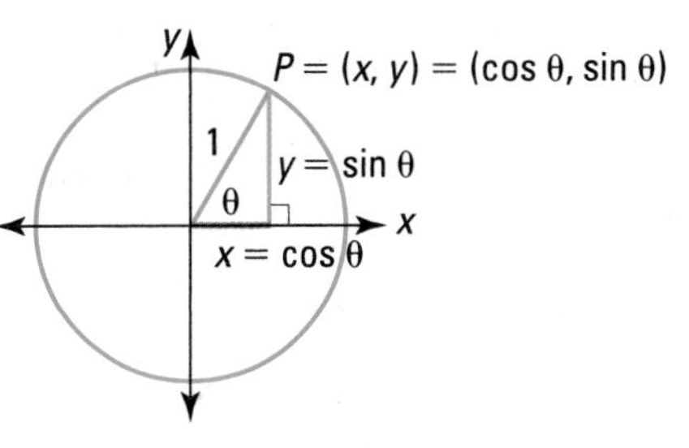

It is customary to write $\cos^2 \theta$ and $\sin^2 \theta$ for $(\cos \theta)^2$ and $(\sin \theta)^2$, respectively. Notice that we do not ever write $\cos \theta^2$ for $(\cos \theta)^2$.

Pythagorean Identity
For every θ, $\cos^2 \theta + \sin^2 \theta = 1$.

The name of the above identity comes from the Pythagorean Theorem, because in the first quadrant, as shown above, $\cos \theta$ and $\sin \theta$ are the sides of a right triangle with hypotenuse 1. Among other things, the Pythagorean Identity enables you to obtain either $\cos \theta$ or $\sin \theta$ if you know the other.

Example 1

If $\cos \theta = \frac{3}{5}$, find $\sin \theta$.

Solution

Substitute into the Pythagorean Identity.

$$\left(\frac{3}{5}\right)^2 + \sin^2 \theta = 1$$

$$\frac{9}{25} + \sin^2 \theta = 1$$

$$\sin^2 \theta = \frac{16}{25}$$

$$\sin \theta = \pm\frac{4}{5}$$

There are two possible values of $\sin \theta$, $\frac{4}{5}$ or $-\frac{4}{5}$.

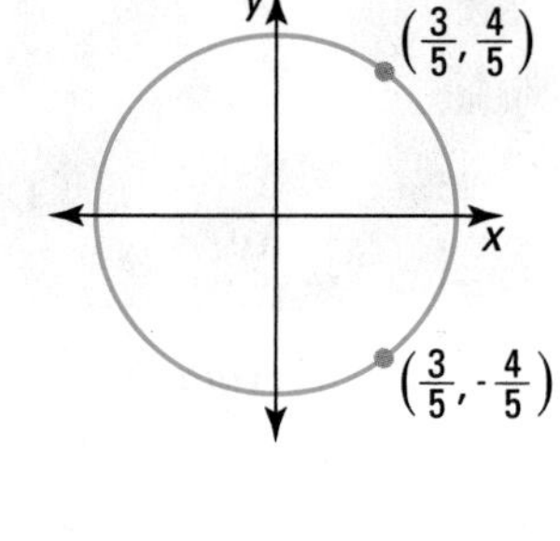

Check

Refer to the unit circle. There are two points whose x-coordinate ($\cos \theta$) is $\frac{3}{5}$. One is in the first quadrant, in which case the y-coordinate ($\sin \theta$) is $\frac{4}{5}$. The other is in the fourth quadrant, where $\sin \theta$ is $-\frac{4}{5}$.

Properties of Opposites

Many other properties of sines and cosines follow rather quickly from their definitions.

Activity 1

Use your calculator to find the following values.

a. $\sin \frac{\pi}{6}$ **b.** $\sin \left(-\frac{\pi}{6}\right)$ **c.** $\sin 2.8$ **d.** $\sin (-2.8)$

e. $\cos \frac{3\pi}{4}$ **f.** $\cos \left(-\frac{3\pi}{4}\right)$ **g.** $\cos 72°$ **h.** $\cos (-72°)$

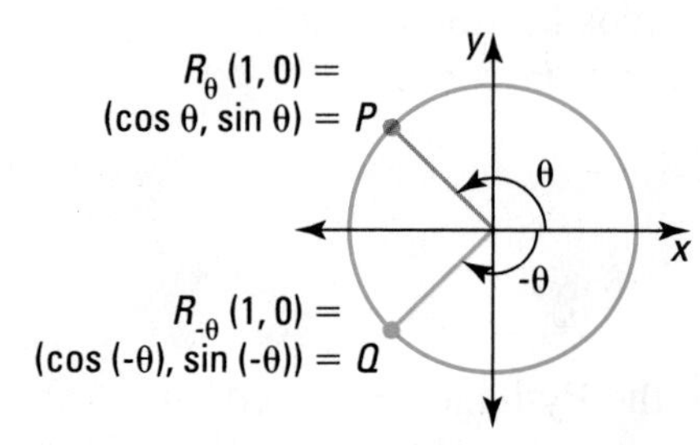

Notice that the sine and cosine of opposites act differently. You can use the definitions and your knowledge of transformations to explain why.

Let $P = R_\theta(1, 0)$. Let $Q = R_{-\theta}(1, 0)$. Notice that P and Q are reflection images of each other over the x-axis. Thus, their x-coordinates (cosines) are equal, but their y-coordinates (sines) are opposites. It follows that the ratios of the y-coordinate to the x-coordinate (tangents) are opposites. This argument proves the following.

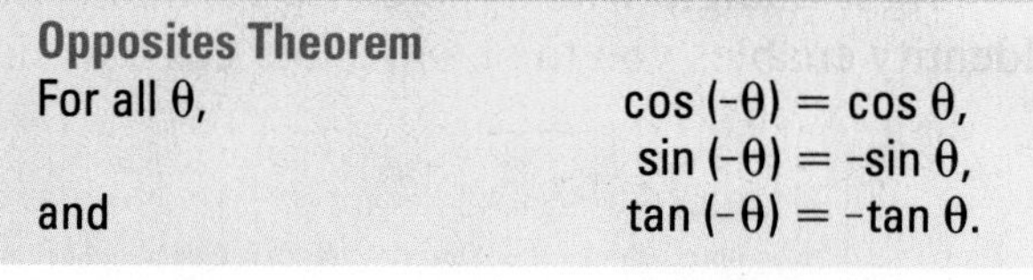

Opposites Theorem

For all θ,
$$\cos (-\theta) = \cos \theta,$$
$$\sin (-\theta) = -\sin \theta,$$
and
$$\tan (-\theta) = -\tan \theta.$$

Properties of Supplements

In radians, if an angle has measure θ, then its supplement has measure $\pi - \theta$. A second property relates the sines, cosines, or tangents of θ and $\pi - \theta$. For this property, it is understood that radian measure is being used.

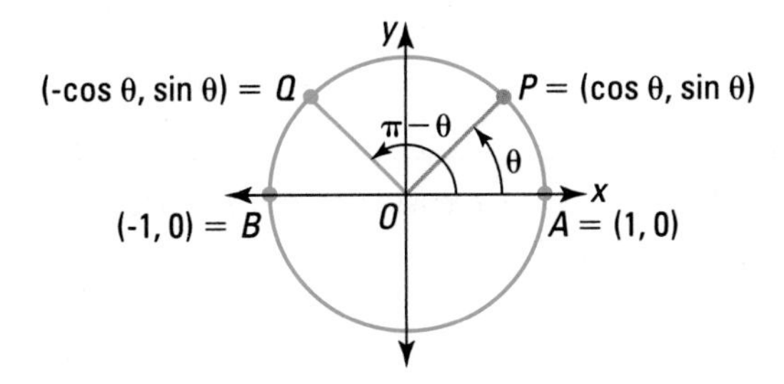

Let $P = (\cos \theta, \sin \theta)$. Let Q be the reflection image of P over the y-axis, as in the diagram at the left. Because the reflection image of (x, y) over the y-axis is $(-x, y)$, Q has coordinates $(-\cos \theta, \sin \theta)$. Recall from geometry that reflections preserve angle measure, so

$$m\angle QOB = m\angle POA = \theta.$$

Also, since $\angle AOB$ is a straight angle, in radians

$$m\angle AOB = \pi.$$

Thus,
$$m\angle AOQ = m\angle AOB - m\angle QOB = \pi - \theta.$$

So, by the definitions of cosine and sine, Q also has coordinates $(\cos(\pi - \theta), \sin(\pi - \theta))$.

Thus, $$(\cos(\pi - \theta), \sin(\pi - \theta)) = (-\cos \theta, \sin \theta).$$

Therefore, $$\cos(\pi - \theta) = -\cos \theta,$$

and $$\sin(\pi - \theta) = \sin \theta.$$

Dividing the last equation by the previous gives

$$\tan(\pi - \theta) = -\tan \theta.$$

This completes the proof of the following theorem.

Supplements Theorem
For all θ, measured in radians,

$$\sin(\pi - \theta) = \sin \theta,$$
$$\cos(\pi - \theta) = -\cos \theta,$$
and $$\tan(\pi - \theta) = -\tan \theta.$$

If θ is measured in degrees, then the Supplements Theorem is:
For all θ,

$$\sin(180° - \theta) = \sin \theta,$$
$$\cos(180° - \theta) = -\cos \theta,$$
and $$\tan(180° - \theta) = -\tan \theta.$$

Example 2

Suppose $\sin \theta = 0.15$. Evaluate without using a calculator.

a. $\sin(-\theta)$ **b.** $\sin(\pi - \theta)$

Solution

a. By the Opposites Theorem, $\sin(-\theta) = -\sin \theta = -0.15$.

b. By the Supplements Theorem, $\sin(\pi - \theta) = \sin \theta = 0.15$.

Properties of Complements

If an angle has radian measure θ, then its complement has measure $\frac{\pi}{2} - \theta$. As with the supplements, the sines, cosines, and tangents of θ and $\frac{\pi}{2} - \theta$ are also related.

Activity 2

Pick any real number x. Evaluate $\sin\left(\frac{\pi}{2} - x\right)$ and $\cos x$. Make a conjecture. Test your conjecture with two other values of x.

To examine this relationship for values of θ between 0 and $\frac{\pi}{2}$, consider the unit circle at the right. Let $P = R_\theta(1, 0)$. Then $P = (\cos\theta, \sin\theta)$. Now let Q be the reflection image of P over the line $y = x$. Since $r_{y=x}(x, y) = (y, x)$, $Q = (\sin\theta, \cos\theta)$. Now use the magnitude of the rotation mapping A onto Q. Since $m\angle QOA = \frac{\pi}{2} - \theta$, $Q = \left(\cos\left(\frac{\pi}{2} - \theta\right), \sin\left(\frac{\pi}{2} - \theta\right)\right)$. Equating the two known ordered pairs for Q, $\cos\theta = \sin\left(\frac{\pi}{2} - \theta\right)$ and $\sin\theta = \cos\left(\frac{\pi}{2} - \theta\right)$.

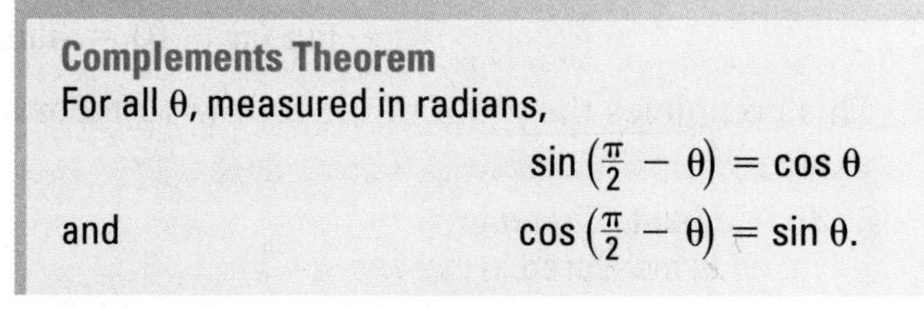
Complements Theorem
For all θ, measured in radians,
$$\sin\left(\frac{\pi}{2} - \theta\right) = \cos\theta$$
and
$$\cos\left(\frac{\pi}{2} - \theta\right) = \sin\theta.$$

Activity 3

Rewrite the Complements Theorem for θ measured in degrees.

Example 3

Given $\cos\theta = k$. Find the following.

a. $\cos(\pi - \theta)$ **b.** $\sin\left(\frac{\pi}{2} - \theta\right)$

Solution

a. Use the Supplements Theorem: $\cos(\pi - \theta) = -\cos\theta = -k$.

b. Use the Complements Theorem: $\sin\left(\frac{\pi}{2} - \theta\right) = \cos\theta = k$.

Sines, Cosines, and Tangents of $\theta + \pi$

The final type of identity in this lesson has to do with adding π to the argument θ of a circular function. Geometrically, this is akin to going halfway around the unit circle.

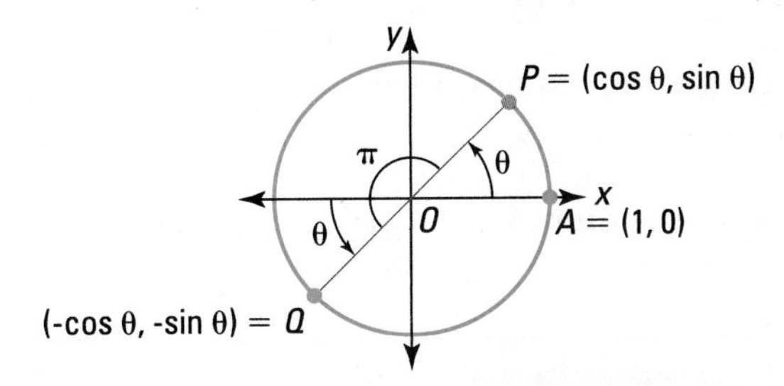

Let $A = (1, 0)$. Again, let $P = R_\theta(1, 0) = (\cos\theta, \sin\theta)$. Now let Q be the image of P under R_π. Because R_π maps (a, b) to $(-a, -b)$, Q has coordinates $(-\cos\theta, -\sin\theta)$. But Q is also the image of A under a rotation of $\pi + \theta$. So Q also has coordinates $(\cos(\pi + \theta), \sin(\pi + \theta))$. Equating the two ordered pairs for Q proves the first two parts of the following theorem.

Half-Turn Theorem
For all θ, measured in radians,

$$\cos(\pi + \theta) = -\cos\theta,$$
$$\sin(\pi + \theta) = -\sin\theta,$$
and
$$\tan(\pi + \theta) = \tan\theta.$$

The third equation follows by dividing the second equation by the first.

In using these identities, it is not enough to memorize the theorems' statements. You should also be able to use the unit circle to do a visual check of your answers, or to derive a property if you forget one.

QUESTIONS

Covering the Reading

1. *True or false.* For all θ, $\cos^2\theta + \sin^2\theta = 1$.

2. **a.** If $\cos\theta = \frac{24}{25}$, what are two possible values of $\sin\theta$?
   b. Draw a picture to justify your answers to part **a**.

3. Write your answers to Activity 1.

4. **a.** *True or false.* $\cos 4 = \cos(-4)$.
   b. Use both a unit circle and a calculator to justify your answer to part **a**.

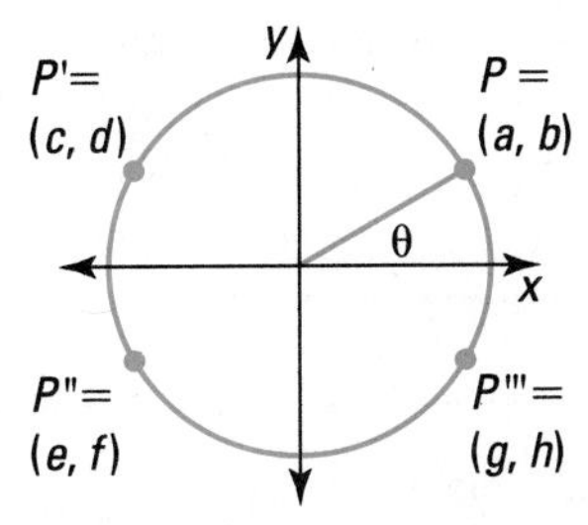

In 5–7, refer to the figure at the left. $P = R_\theta(1, 0)$, $P' = r_{y\text{-axis}}(P)$, $P'' = R_\pi(P)$, and $P''' = r_{x\text{-axis}}(P)$. Identify the coordinates equal to each expression.

5. $\cos(\pi - \theta)$

6. $\sin(\pi + \theta)$

7. Write an expression for $\tan(-\theta)$.

8. Show your work for Activity 2.

In 9 and 10, θ is measured in degrees and $\sin\theta = .4$. Evaluate without using a calculator.

9. $\sin(-\theta)$

10. $\sin(180° - \theta)$

11. Show the answer to Activity 3.

In 12 and 13, θ is measured in radians and $\cos\theta = .2$. Evaluate without using a calculator.

12. $\cos(\pi + \theta)$

13. $\sin\left(\frac{\pi}{2} - \theta\right)$

In 14 and 15, $\tan\theta = k$ and θ is measured in radians. Evaluate.

14. $\tan(-\theta)$

15. $\tan(\pi - \theta)$

16. Write the version of the Half-Turn Theorem for θ measured in degrees.

Applying the Mathematics

In 17 and 18, *true or false.* If true, state the theorem that supports your answer. If false, use the unit circle to show that it is false.

17. $\sin\left(\frac{-2\pi}{3}\right) = \sin\left(\frac{2\pi}{3}\right)$

18. $\cos\left(\frac{\pi}{6}\right) = \cos\left(\frac{5\pi}{6}\right)$

19. Give a counterexample to prove that $\sin(\pi - \theta) = \sin\pi - \sin\theta$ is *not* an identity.

20. Given that $\sin\left(\frac{\pi}{10}\right) = \frac{\sqrt{5} - 1}{4}$, find each value.

a. $\sin\left(\frac{9\pi}{10}\right)$ **b.** $\sin\left(-\frac{\pi}{10}\right)$ **c.** $\sin\left(\frac{11\pi}{10}\right)$ **d.** $\cos\left(\frac{4\pi}{10}\right)$

21. Prove: For all θ, $\cos\theta + \cos(\pi - \theta) = 0$.

Review

In 22–24, without using a calculator, give exact values for the following.

22. $\sin\frac{\pi}{2}$

23. $\cos 5\pi$

24. $\tan\left(\frac{\pi}{2} + \frac{\pi}{2}\right)$ *(Lesson 4-3)*

25. Refer back to the Ferris wheel in Lesson 4-3. How high is your seat off the ground if you are 2 seats away from a seat being loaded? *(Lesson 4-3)*

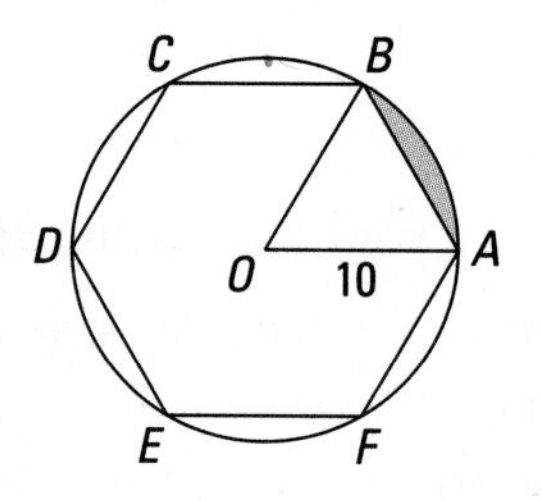

26. At the left *ABCDEF* is a regular hexagon inscribed in a circle with radius 10. What is the area of the shaded region shown? *(Lesson 4-2)*

27. Change 135° to radians. *(Lesson 4-1)*

28. Find an equation for the image of the graph of $y = x^2$ under the scale change $(x, y) \rightarrow \left(\frac{1}{2}x, 5y\right)$ *(Lesson 3-5)*

Exploration

29. Use a calculator to explore whether the statement $\frac{\sin^2\theta}{1 + \cos\theta} = 1 - \cos\theta$ is an identity. Justify your answer, either by providing a counterexample or by using properties of sines and cosines to prove the statement.

LESSON

4-5

Exact Values of Sines, Cosines, and Tangents

Exact science. *Triangles are part of the architecture of the Holocaust Museum, Washington, D.C. Architects use trigonometry in designing buildings.*

For most values of θ, the values of sine, cosine, and tangent are not known exactly, but must be approximated. However, you already know exact values of the sine, cosine, and tangent of multiples of π, and of the sine and cosine of multiples of $\frac{\pi}{2}$. By applying algebra and geometry, you can also obtain exact values of $\cos\theta$, $\sin\theta$, and $\tan\theta$ when $\theta = \frac{\pi}{6} = 30°$, or $\theta = \frac{\pi}{4} = 45°$, or $\theta = \frac{\pi}{3} = 60°$, and multiples of these values.

Exact Values of Sines, Cosines, and Tangents for $\theta = \frac{\pi}{4} = 45°$

To find $\cos\frac{\pi}{4}$ and $\sin\frac{\pi}{4}$, draw a right triangle such as $\triangle OPF$. With central angle $\theta = \frac{\pi}{4} = 45°$, $\triangle OPF$ has two $45°$ angles, and its hypotenuse $OP = 1$. Recall from geometry that in a $45°$-$45°$-$90°$ triangle, the length of the hypotenuse is $\sqrt{2}$ times the length of each leg. Hence, $OF = FP = \frac{1}{\sqrt{2}} = \frac{\sqrt{2}}{2}$.

$P = (a, b) = \left(\cos\frac{\pi}{4}, \sin\frac{\pi}{4}\right)$

So $\qquad P = \left(\frac{\sqrt{2}}{2}, \frac{\sqrt{2}}{2}\right).$

Therefore, $\qquad \cos\frac{\pi}{4} = \frac{\sqrt{2}}{2}$ and $\sin\frac{\pi}{4} = \frac{\sqrt{2}}{2}.$

By definition, $\tan\theta = \frac{\sin\theta}{\cos\theta}$.

So $$\tan\frac{\pi}{4} = \frac{\sin\frac{\pi}{4}}{\cos\frac{\pi}{4}} = \frac{\frac{\sqrt{2}}{2}}{\frac{\sqrt{2}}{2}} = 1.$$

Exact Values of Sines, Cosines, and Tangents for $\theta = \frac{\pi}{6}$ or $\theta = \frac{\pi}{3}$

Again, geometry can be used. Consider central $\angle AOP$ on the unit circle, with $m\angle AOP = 30°$. Draw PF perpendicular to the x-axis. Recall that in a 30°-60°-90° right triangle the length of the leg opposite the 30° angle is $\frac{1}{2}$ the length of the hypotenuse; so $PF = \frac{1}{2}$. OF is the leg opposite the 60° angle. So $OF = PF \cdot \sqrt{3} = \frac{1}{2}\sqrt{3} = \frac{\sqrt{3}}{2}$. Since $\cos\frac{\pi}{6} = OF$ and $\sin\frac{\pi}{6} = PF$, $\cos\frac{\pi}{6} = \frac{\sqrt{3}}{2}$ and $\sin\frac{\pi}{6} = \frac{1}{2}$.

Activity 1

Use the figure at the right to explain why $\cos\frac{\pi}{3} = \frac{1}{2}$ and $\sin\frac{\pi}{3} = \frac{\sqrt{3}}{2}$.

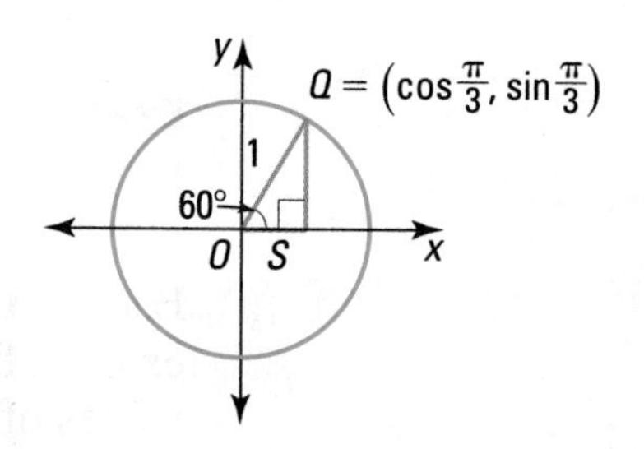

Example 1

Find exact values of $\tan\frac{\pi}{6}$ and $\tan\frac{\pi}{3}$.

Solution

Begin with the definition of the tangent.

$$\tan\frac{\pi}{6} = \frac{\sin\frac{\pi}{6}}{\cos\frac{\pi}{6}} = \frac{\frac{1}{2}}{\frac{\sqrt{3}}{2}} = \frac{1}{2} \cdot \frac{2}{\sqrt{3}} = \frac{1}{\sqrt{3}} \cdot \frac{\sqrt{3}}{\sqrt{3}} = \frac{\sqrt{3}}{3}$$

$$\tan\frac{\pi}{3} = \frac{\sin\frac{\pi}{3}}{\cos\frac{\pi}{3}} = \frac{\frac{\sqrt{3}}{2}}{\frac{1}{2}} = \sqrt{3}$$

You should memorize the exact values of $\cos\theta$, $\sin\theta$, and $\tan\theta$ for $\theta = \frac{\pi}{6}, \frac{\pi}{4}$, and $\frac{\pi}{3}$, as you will very likely see them on tests and in future mathematics courses.

Exact Values for Multiples of $\frac{\pi}{6}$, $\frac{\pi}{4}$, and $\frac{\pi}{3}$

Using the definitions and properties of sines, cosines, and tangents and your knowledge of transformations, you can find exact values of sines, cosines, and tangents for all integer multiples of $\frac{\pi}{6}$, $\frac{\pi}{4}$, and $\frac{\pi}{3}$.

Example 2

Find exact values of $\cos\frac{2\pi}{3}$, $\sin\frac{2\pi}{3}$, and $\tan\frac{2\pi}{3}$.

Solution

Use a unit circle and locate P', the image of (1, 0) under a rotation of $\frac{2\pi}{3}$. Because $\frac{2\pi}{3} = \pi - \frac{\pi}{3}$, $P' = \left(\cos\frac{2\pi}{3}, \sin\frac{2\pi}{3}\right)$ is also the image of $P = \left(\cos\frac{\pi}{3}, \sin\frac{\pi}{3}\right)$ under a reflection over the y-axis.

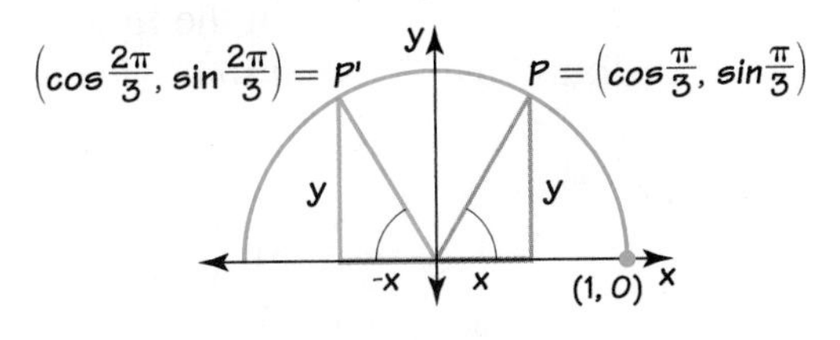

By the Supplements Theorem, the x-coordinates of P and P' are opposites and the y-coordinates are equal. So,

$$\cos\frac{2\pi}{3} = \cos\left(\pi - \frac{\pi}{3}\right) = -\cos\frac{\pi}{3} = -\frac{1}{2}$$

and

$$\sin\frac{2\pi}{3} = \sin\left(\pi - \frac{\pi}{3}\right) = \sin\frac{\pi}{3} = \frac{\sqrt{3}}{2}.$$

Thus,

$$\tan\frac{2\pi}{3} = \frac{\sin\frac{2\pi}{3}}{\cos\frac{2\pi}{3}} = \frac{\frac{\sqrt{3}}{2}}{-\frac{1}{2}} = -\sqrt{3}$$

Check

Use a calculator set to radian mode.
$\cos\frac{2\pi}{3} = -0.5$, $\sin\frac{2\pi}{3} \approx 0.866 \approx \frac{\sqrt{3}}{2}$, and $\tan\frac{2\pi}{3} \approx -1.732 \approx -\sqrt{3}$.

Example 3

Find exact values of $\sin\left(\frac{-11\pi}{4}\right)$, $\cos\left(\frac{-11\pi}{4}\right)$, and $\tan\left(\frac{-11\pi}{4}\right)$.

Solution

First relate $-\frac{11\pi}{4}$ to one of the key rotations of $\frac{\pi}{6}$, $\frac{\pi}{4}$, or $\frac{\pi}{3}$. A rotation of $\theta = -\frac{11\pi}{4}$ equals $-2\frac{3}{4}\pi$ radians. This is equivalent to a rotation of $\frac{-3\pi}{4}$, which is equivalent to a rotation of $\frac{5\pi}{4}$. But $\frac{5\pi}{4} = \pi + \frac{\pi}{4}$. So $\frac{5\pi}{4}$ is a rotation of $\pi + \frac{\pi}{4}$ about the origin.

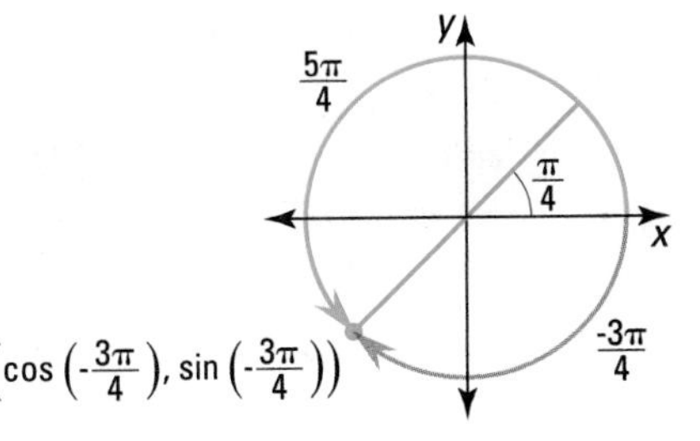

Now use the values of the sines, cosines, and tangents for $\theta = \frac{\pi}{4}$ and the Half-Turn Theorem. So $\sin\left(\frac{-11\pi}{4}\right) = \sin\left(\pi + \frac{\pi}{4}\right) = -\sin\frac{\pi}{4} = -\frac{\sqrt{2}}{2}$; $\cos\left(\frac{-11\pi}{4}\right) = \cos\left(\pi + \frac{\pi}{4}\right) = -\cos\frac{\pi}{4} = -\frac{\sqrt{2}}{2}$, and $\tan\left(\frac{-11\pi}{4}\right) = 1$.

The thought processes for Example 3 take time to write down. With practice, you will become adept at relating negative rotations to positive rotations and positive rotations of any magnitude to a rotation between 0 and $\frac{\pi}{2}$, for which the exact values of sine, cosine, and tangent are known.

On the unit circle below are the images of (1, 0) under all rotations of integral multiples of $\frac{\pi}{6}$ or $\frac{\pi}{4}$. You should be able to calculate exact values of sines, cosines, and tangents for all values of θ pictured by relating them to one of the points in the first quadrant or on the axes. The tangent values are found using the ratio of sine to cosine.

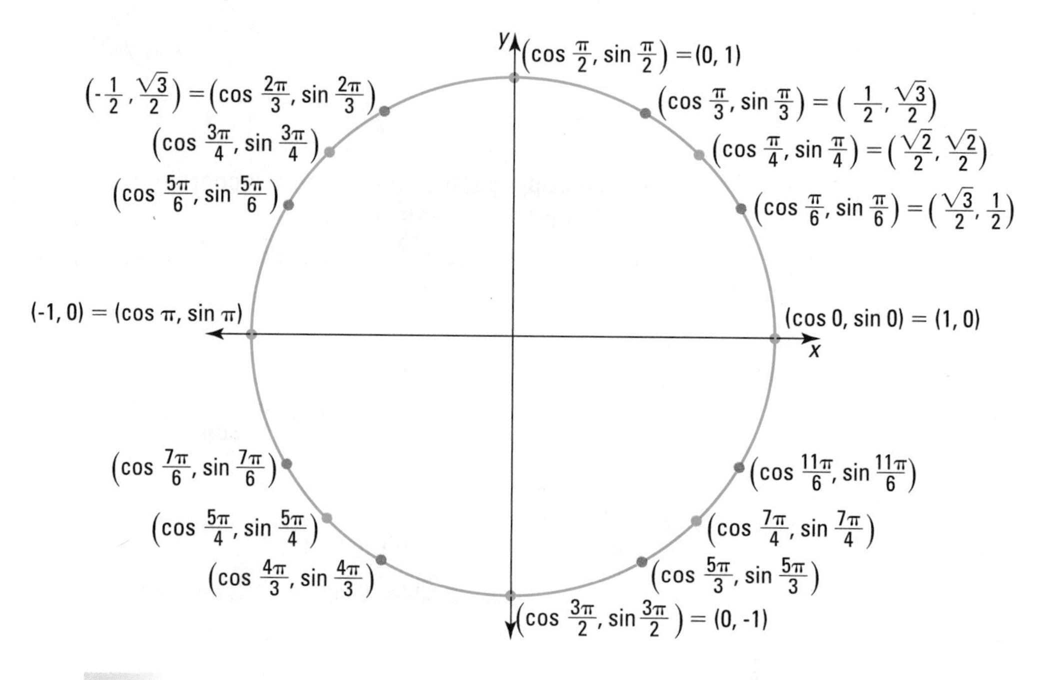

Activity 2

Copy the unit circle and the exact values of (cos θ, sin θ) given above. Use your knowledge of reflections and symmetries to complete the exact values for multiples of $\frac{\pi}{6}$, $\frac{\pi}{3}$, and $\frac{\pi}{4}$ in Quadrants II, III, and IV.

QUESTIONS

Covering the Reading

In 1–3, refer to the unit circle at the right in which m∠POA = 30°, m∠QOA = 45°, and m∠ROA = 60°. Name the segment whose length equals the following.

1. $\cos\frac{\pi}{6}$ **2.** $\sin\frac{\pi}{4}$ **3.** $\sin\frac{\pi}{3}$

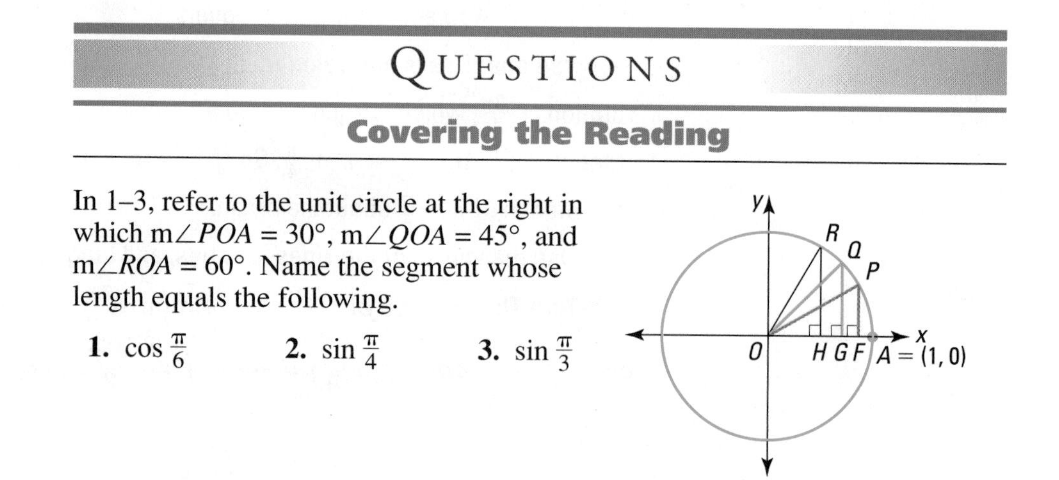

4. Write your solution to Activity 1.

5. Write your solution to Activity 2.

In 6–10, give the exact values.

6. a. $\sin\left(\frac{3\pi}{4}\right)$ **b.** $\cos\left(\frac{3\pi}{4}\right)$ **c.** $\tan\left(\frac{3\pi}{4}\right)$

7. a. $\sin\left(\frac{11\pi}{6}\right)$ **b.** $\cos\left(\frac{11\pi}{6}\right)$ **c.** $\tan\left(\frac{11\pi}{6}\right)$

8. $\sin 210°$ **9.** $\cos 300°$ **10.** $\tan(-405°)$

Applying the Mathematics

11. Find two values of θ between $-\frac{\pi}{2}$ and $\frac{\pi}{2}$ for which $\cos\theta = \frac{1}{2}$.

12. Suppose $\sin\theta = -\frac{1}{2}$.
a. Give two values of θ between 0 and 2π which make the equation true.
b. Give a value of θ between 10π and 12π which makes the equation true.
c. Give a negative value of θ which makes the equation true.

13. a. Find four values of θ between -2π and 2π such that $\cos\theta = \sin\theta$.
b. What is the value of $\tan\theta$ for each value of θ in part **a**?

14. *True or false.* If $\tan\theta = \pm1$, then $\theta = \frac{n\pi}{4}$ and n is an odd integer. Justify your answer.

15. The regular heptagon *ABCDEFG* pictured at the right is inscribed in the unit circle.
a. Give the exact coordinates of point *B*.
b. Estimate *AB* to the nearest thousandth.

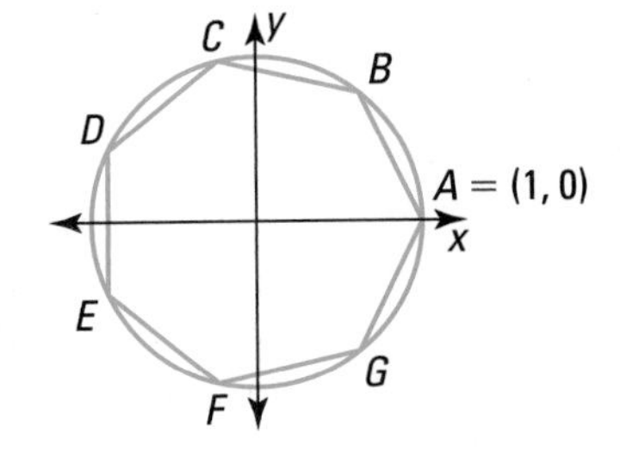

Review

16. Without using a calculator, given that $\sin 12° \approx .2079$, estimate each value. *(Lesson 4-4)*
a. $\sin(-12°)$ **b.** $\sin 168°$ **c.** $\sin 192°$ **d.** $\cos 78°$

17. *True or false.* For all θ, $\cos(\pi - \theta) + \cos(\pi + \theta) = \cos 2\pi$. Justify your answer. *(Lesson 4-4)*

18. Without using a calculator, give the exact value for $\cos\left(-\frac{\pi}{2}\right)$. *(Lessons 4-3, 4-4)*

19. a. Prove that $\cos\theta \cdot \tan\theta = \sin\theta$ for all $\cos\theta \neq 0$.
b. Why is it impossible to have $\cos\theta = 0$ in part **a**? *(Lesson 4-3)*

20. **a.** Change 4.1 revolutions to radians.
b. Change 4.1 revolutions to degrees. *(Lesson 4-1)*

21. The pedals of an exercise bicycle revolve at a constant 45 revolutions per minute.
a. Through how many radians do they move in one minute?
b. Through how many radians do they move in one second? *(Lesson 4-1)*

22. Give equations for all asymptotes of the graph of $y = \frac{1}{x - 5}$. *(Lesson 3-2)*

23. Find the x-intercept(s) of the graph of the equation $y = |x + 2|$. *(Previous course)*

24. The measure of the supplement of an angle is six times the measure of the angle's complement. Find the measure of each. *(Previous course)*
a. the angle **b.** its complement **c.** its supplement

Exploration

25. Use a calculator to investigate whether the statement $\frac{\sin x + \cos x \tan x}{\tan x} = 2 \cos x$ is an identity. Try to justify your answer, either by providing a counterexample or by using the definitions and properties of sines, cosines, and tangents to show the statement is true.

Introducing
Lesson 4-6

Graphing Circular Functions

You will need a calculator and graph paper for this activity.

The table below contains some exact values of cos θ. It also shows decimal equivalents of those values.

θ	0	$\frac{\pi}{6} \approx .524$	$\frac{\pi}{4} \approx .785$	$\frac{\pi}{3} \approx 1.047$	$\frac{\pi}{2} \approx 1.571$
cos θ*	1	$\frac{\sqrt{3}}{2}$	$\frac{\sqrt{2}}{2}$	$\frac{1}{2}$	0
cos θ**	1	0.866	0.707	0.5	0

θ	$\frac{2\pi}{3} \approx 2.094$	$\frac{3\pi}{4} \approx 2.356$	$\frac{5\pi}{6} \approx 2.618$	$\pi \approx 3.142$
cos θ*	$-\frac{1}{2}$	$-\frac{\sqrt{2}}{2}$	$-\frac{\sqrt{3}}{2}$	-1
cos θ**	-0.5	-0.707	-0.866	-1

θ	$\frac{7\pi}{6} \approx$ ___	$\frac{5\pi}{4} \approx$ ___	$\frac{4\pi}{3} \approx$ ___	$\frac{3\pi}{2} \approx$ ___
cos θ*				
cos θ**				

θ	$\frac{5\pi}{3} \approx$ ___	$\frac{7\pi}{4} \approx$ ___	$\frac{11\pi}{6} \approx$ ___	$2\pi \approx$ ___
cos θ*				
cos θ**				

* exact values
**some entries are approximations

1 Copy the table and fill in values for the multiples of $\frac{\pi}{6}$, $\frac{\pi}{4}$, and $\frac{\pi}{3}$ between π and 2π.

2 Complete the table above, showing exact and approximate values of $y = \cos \theta$.

3 Below is a graph of the points in the first part of the table. Copy this graph, and on it plot the points you found in Steps 1 and 2. Identify the coordinates of all zeros, maxima and minima.

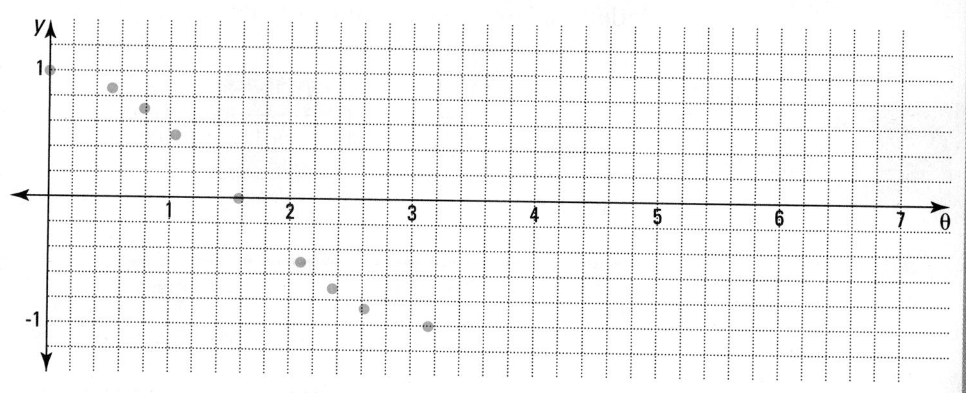

4 Draw a smooth curve through these points. Pick a value of θ such that $\frac{\pi}{3} < \theta < \frac{\pi}{2}$. Use a calculator to find $\cos \theta$, and add this point to your graph. Does this point lie on your curve?

5 Use an automatic grapher to plot $y = \cos x$ for $-2\pi \leq x \leq 2\pi$. (Remember to use radian mode.) Describe some symmetries of the graph.

6 Predict what the complete graph of $y = \cos x$ looks like. Check your prediction by changing the viewing window or by tracing along the graph you made in Step 5.

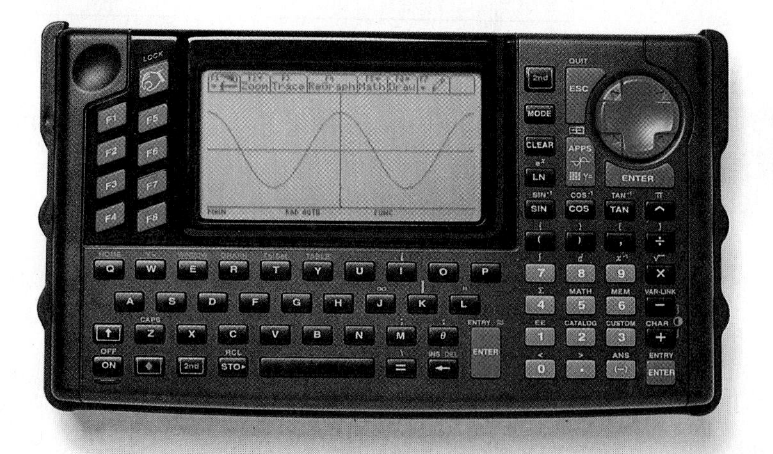

LESSON

4-6

The Sine, Cosine, and Tangent Functions

The Sine Function

The function that maps each real number θ to the y-coordinate of the image of $(1, 0)$ under a rotation of θ is called the **sine function**. The domain of the sine function is the set of all possible values of θ, the set of all real numbers. The range of the function is the set of all possible values of $\sin \theta$, that is, the set of y-coordinates on the unit circle, $\{y: -1 \le y \le 1\}$.

From the unit circle, you can tell that the sine function is positive when $0 < \theta < \pi$ and negative when $\pi < \theta < 2\pi$. The maximum value is 1, when $\theta = \frac{\pi}{2}$, and the minimum is -1, when $\theta = \frac{3\pi}{2}$.

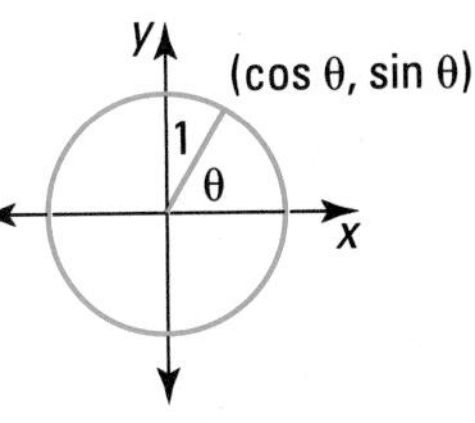

The table below contains the exact values and decimal approximations of $f(\theta) = \sin \theta$, for all multiples of $\frac{\pi}{6}$ or $\frac{\pi}{4}$ from 0 to 2π.

θ	0	$\frac{\pi}{6}$	$\frac{\pi}{4}$	$\frac{\pi}{3}$	$\frac{\pi}{2}$	$\frac{2\pi}{3}$	$\frac{3\pi}{4}$	$\frac{5\pi}{6}$	π
$\sin \theta$*	0	$\frac{1}{2}$	$\frac{\sqrt{2}}{2}$	$\frac{\sqrt{3}}{2}$	1	$\frac{\sqrt{3}}{2}$	$\frac{\sqrt{2}}{2}$	$\frac{1}{2}$	0
$\sin \theta$**	0	0.5	0.707	0.866	1	0.866	0.707	0.5	0

θ	$\frac{7\pi}{6}$	$\frac{5\pi}{4}$	$\frac{4\pi}{3}$	$\frac{3\pi}{2}$	$\frac{5\pi}{3}$	$\frac{7\pi}{4}$	$\frac{11\pi}{6}$	2π
$\sin \theta$*	$-\frac{1}{2}$	$-\frac{\sqrt{2}}{2}$	$-\frac{\sqrt{3}}{2}$	-1	$-\frac{\sqrt{3}}{2}$	$-\frac{\sqrt{2}}{2}$	$-\frac{1}{2}$	0
$\sin \theta$**	-0.5	-0.707	-0.866	-1	0.866	-0.707	-0.5	0

* exact values **some entries are approximations

The graph of the sine function, for $0 \le \theta \le 2\pi$, is shown here. To make it easier to locate zeros, maxima, and minima, the scale on the horizontal axis is in multiples of $\frac{\pi}{2}$.

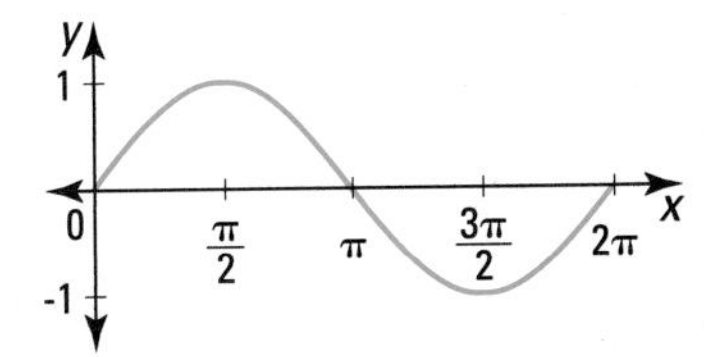

This is one *cycle* of the graph of the sine function. Because the image of $(1, 0)$ under a rotation of θ repeats itself every 2π radians, the y-coordinates in the ordered pairs of the function $f(\theta) = \sin \theta$ repeat every 2π. Thus, the table and graph above can be easily extended both to the right and left without calculating any new sine values. The graph of the entire sine function has infinitely many cycles. A graph showing three complete cycles of the function $f(\theta) = \sin \theta$ appears on page 266.

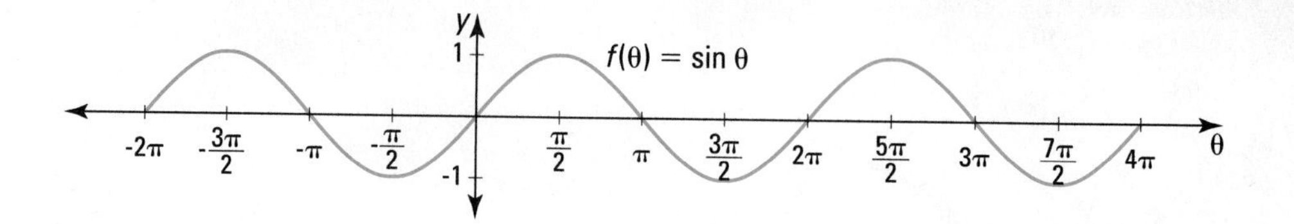

Notice from the graph that the sine function's y-intercept is 0. The sine function's x-intercepts (zeros) are $\ldots, -2\pi, -\pi, 0, \pi, 2\pi, 3\pi, 4\pi, \ldots$, that is, the integral multiples of π.

Recall the Opposites Theorem, namely that $\sin(-\theta) = -\sin \theta$ for all θ. Also notice that the graph of the sine function is 180° rotation-symmetric to the origin. Thus, the sine function is an odd function.

The Cosine Function

The function g that maps each real number θ to the x-coordinate of the image of (1, 0) under a rotation of θ is called the cosine function. The cosine function has many characteristics like those of the sine function. In the preceding In-class Activity you graphed the cosine function. You should have found a graph like the one below.

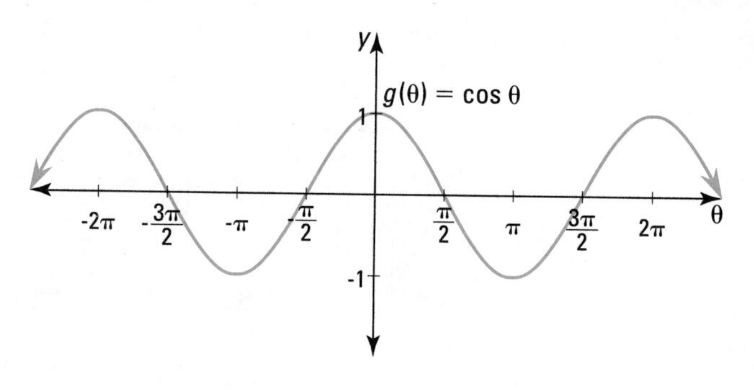

Example 1

Consider the cosine function $g(\theta) = \cos \theta$.

a. Give the domain and range of g.

b. What are the maximum and minimum values of g?

c. Identify the y-intercept and zeros of g.

Solution

a. Because θ can be any real number, **the domain of the cosine function is the set of all real numbers.** On the unit circle, it is clear that the cosine function takes all values between -1 and 1. So, **the range is $\{y: -1 \le y \le 1\}$.**

b. **The maximum value is 1 and the minimum value is -1.**

c. **The y-intercept of the cosine function is 1. The zeros are $\ldots, \frac{-5\pi}{2}, \frac{-3\pi}{2}, \frac{-\pi}{2}, \frac{\pi}{2}, \frac{3\pi}{2}, \frac{5\pi}{2}, \ldots$, that is, the odd multiples of $\frac{\pi}{2}$.**

The graph of the cosine function is congruent to that of the sine function. In fact, it can be shown that the graph of $g(\theta) = \cos \theta$ is a translation image of the graph of $f(\theta) = \sin \theta$.

Also notice that the cosine function is symmetric with respect to the y-axis. Thus, the cosine function is an even function. Again, this is because of the Opposites Theorem, namely, that $\cos(-\theta) = \cos(\theta)$ for all θ.

The Graph of the Tangent Function

The correspondence $\theta \rightarrow \tan\theta$, when θ is a real number, defines the **tangent function**. From the definition $\tan\theta = \frac{\sin\theta}{\cos\theta}$, values for the tangent function can be generated. The graph of $h(\theta) = \tan\theta$ for $-\frac{3\pi}{2} \leq \theta \leq \frac{5\pi}{2}$ is drawn below.

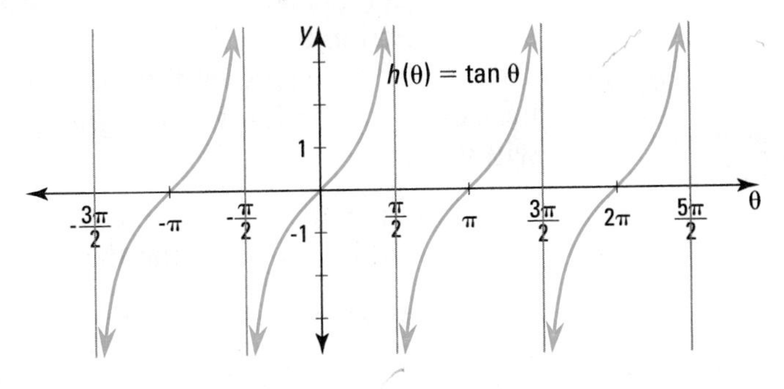

Example 2

Consider $h(\theta) = \tan\theta$.

a. Give the domain and range of h.

b. Identify the y-intercept and zeros of h.

c. Tell whether h is an odd function, an even function, or neither. Justify your answer.

Solution

a. The tangent function has points of discontinuity where $\cos\theta = 0$. Notice also that when $\cos\theta$ is close to 0, $\sin\theta$ is close either to 1 or -1 and $\tan\theta$ becomes large in magnitude. So the lines with equations $\theta = \frac{\pi}{2} + n\pi$, where n is an integer, are vertical asymptotes of the graph of the tangent function. Therefore, the domain of the tangent function is the set of all real numbers except odd multiples of $\frac{\pi}{2}$; that is, all θ such that $\theta \neq \frac{\pi}{2} + n\pi$ for all integers n. Notice that the tangent function has no minimum or maximum values. Therefore, its range is the set of all real numbers.

b. The y-intercept of the tangent function is 0. The tangent function has zeros at every multiple of π, that is, at ..., -2π, $-\pi$, 0, π, 2π, ..., or, in short, at $n\pi$ for all integers n.

c. The tangent function appears to be 180° rotation symmetric to the origin, and, from the Opposites Theorem, $\tan(-\theta) = -\tan\theta$ for all θ. Thus the tangent function is an odd function.

Because their definitions are based on a circle, the sine, cosine, and tangent functions are called **circular functions**.

Periodic Functions

The circular functions are examples of periodic functions. Values of periodic functions repeat at regular intervals.

> **Definition**
> A function f is **periodic** if and only if there is a smallest positive real number p such that $f(x + p) = f(x)$ for all x. Then p is the **period** of the function.

The period of the sine function is 2π, because 2π is the smallest positive number such that $\sin(x + 2\pi) = \sin x$ for all x. Similarly, the period of the cosine function is 2π. In contrast, the period of the tangent function is π. The graph of the tangent function can be mapped onto itself under a horizontal translation with magnitude π, and no smaller magnitude will work.

The periodic nature of the sine, cosine, and tangent functions is summarized in the following theorem.

> **Periodicity Theorem**
> For all θ, and for every integer n:
> $$\sin(\theta + 2\pi n) = \sin\theta,$$
> $$\cos(\theta + 2\pi n) = \cos\theta,$$
> and
> $$\tan(\theta + \pi n) = \tan\theta.$$

The Periodicity Theorem provides one way to find more than one solution to a trigonometric equation.

Example 3

Given that $\cos 2.300 \approx -0.666$. Find three other values of θ with $\cos\theta \approx -0.666$.

Solution 1

The cosine function has a period of 2π, so some other solutions can be found by adding or subtracting multiples of $2\pi \approx 6.283$ to 2.300. For instance,

$$2.300 + 2\pi \approx 8.583,$$
$$2.300 + 4\pi \approx 14.866,$$
$$2.300 - 2\pi \approx -3.983.$$

Check 1

Evaluate cos 8.583, cos 14.866, and cos (-3.983) with a calculator. In each case, the value is about -0.666.

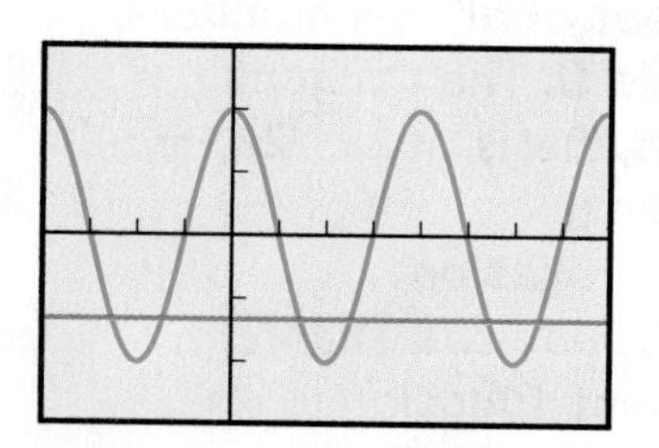

$-2\pi \le x \le 4\pi$, x-scale $= \frac{\pi}{2}$
$-1.5 \le y \le 1.5$, y-scale $= 0.5$

Check 2

Use an automatic grapher, as shown at the left. Trace along the cosine curve to find x-values when $y \approx -0.666$. You will see that some x-values are approximately 8.6, 14.9, and -4.

QUESTIONS

Covering the Reading

1. Consider the sine function, $f(\theta) = \sin \theta$.
   a. Identify the domain and the range of this function.
   b. Find five values of θ such that $f(\theta) = 0$.
   c. Find the period of f.
   d. Identify two non-overlapping intervals on which the function is positive.

2. a. Sketch a graph of $y = \cos \theta$ for $-2\pi \le \theta \le 4\pi$.
   b. How many cycles of the cosine curve appear in the graph in part **a**?
   c. Find five values of θ such that $\cos \theta = 0$.
   d. Give two non-overlapping intervals on which the cosine function is negative.

3. The table below contains some exact values of $\tan \theta$. It also shows decimal equivalents of those values.

θ	0	$\frac{\pi}{6} \approx .524$	$\frac{\pi}{4} \approx .785$	$\frac{\pi}{3} \approx 1.047$	$\frac{\pi}{2} \approx 1.571$
$\tan \theta$*	0	$\frac{\sqrt{3}}{3}$	1	$\sqrt{3}$	undefined
$\tan \theta$**	0	0.577	1	1.732	undefined

θ	$\frac{2\pi}{3} \approx 2.094$	$\frac{3\pi}{4} \approx 2.356$	$\frac{5\pi}{6} \approx 2.618$	$\pi \approx 3.142$
$\tan \theta$*	$-\sqrt{3}$	-1	$-\frac{\sqrt{3}}{3}$	0
$\tan \theta$**	-1.732	-1	-0.577	0

θ	$\frac{7\pi}{6} \approx$ ___	$\frac{5\pi}{4} \approx$ ___	$\frac{4\pi}{3} \approx$ ___	$\frac{3\pi}{2} \approx$ ___
$\tan \theta$*				
$\tan \theta$**				

θ	$\frac{5\pi}{3} \approx$ ___	$\frac{7\pi}{4} \approx$ ___	$\frac{11\pi}{6} \approx$ ___	$2\pi \approx$ ___
$\tan \theta$*				
$\tan \theta$**				

* exact values
**some entries are approximations

   a. Copy the table above and fill in values of $\tan \theta$ for all multiples of $\frac{\pi}{6}$, $\frac{\pi}{4}$, and $\frac{\pi}{3}$ between π and 2π.
   b. Pick a value of θ such that $\frac{\pi}{3} < \theta < \frac{\pi}{2}$, and use your calculator to find $\tan \theta$.

c. Pick a value of θ such that $\frac{\pi}{2} < \theta < \frac{2\pi}{3}$, and use your calculator to find tan θ.

d. A graph of the values of the tangent function given in the first part of the table on page 269 is shown below. Copy this graph, and add the points you found in parts **a**, **b**, and **c** to the graph. Identify the coordinates of all zeros.

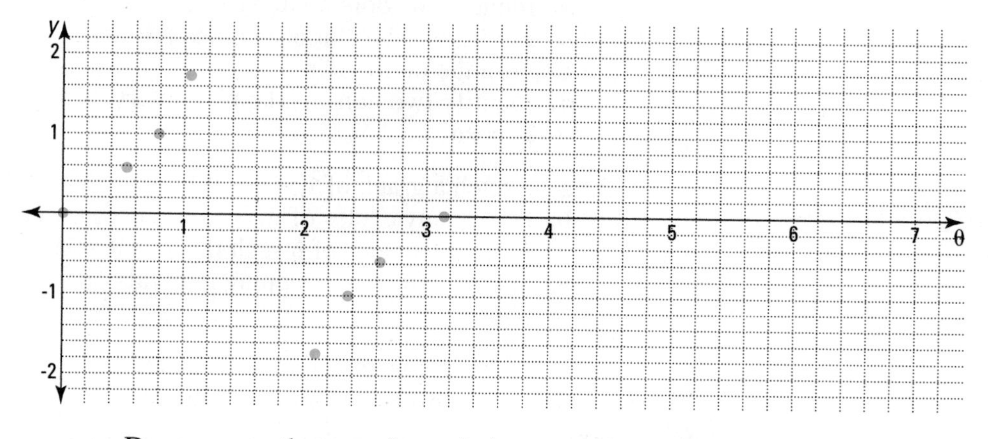

e. Draw a smooth curve through these points, to show the graph of $y = \tan x$ for all x, $0 \le x \le 2\pi$, where tan x is defined.

In 4–6, name all functions (among the sine, cosine, and tangent) for which the property is true.

4. The domain is the set of all real numbers.

5. The range is the set of all real numbers.

6. The graph is symmetric with respect to the y-axis.

7. a. One solution to the equation $\sin \theta = 0.85$ is $\theta \approx 1.016$. Find three other solutions to this equation.

b. Show your solutions on a sketch of the sine curve.

Applying the Mathematics

8. Use the graph of $y = f(\theta)$ at the right. Suppose f is known to be either the cosine function or the sine function.

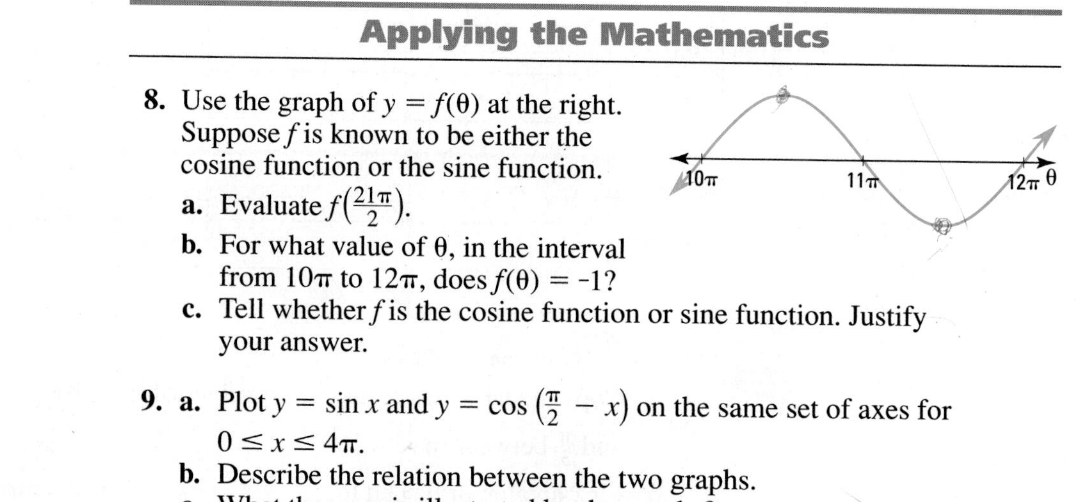

a. Evaluate $f\left(\frac{21\pi}{2}\right)$.

b. For what value of θ, in the interval from 10π to 12π, does $f(\theta) = -1$?

c. Tell whether f is the cosine function or sine function. Justify your answer.

9. a. Plot $y = \sin x$ and $y = \cos\left(\frac{\pi}{2} - x\right)$ on the same set of axes for $0 \le x \le 4\pi$.

b. Describe the relation between the two graphs.

c. What theorem is illustrated by the graphs?

10. Describe the translation with the smallest positive magnitude that maps the graph of $g(x) = \sin x$ onto that of $y = \cos x$.

11. Is the function $f(x) = \lfloor x \rfloor$ periodic? Justify your answer.

12. The graph at the right shows normal blood pressure as a function of time. The changes in pressure from systolic to diastolic create the pulse. For this function, determine each.
   a. the range
   b. the maximum and minimum values
   c. the period

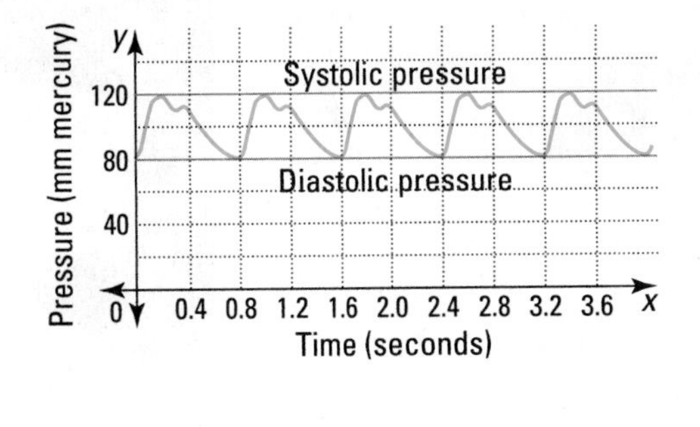

Review

In 13 and 14, A is a point on a circle with center O at the origin. Find the exact coordinates of A for the given value of θ. *(Lesson 4-5)*

13. 14.

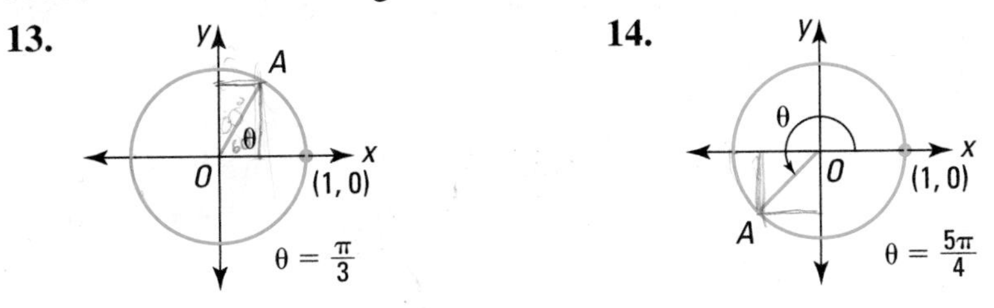

A blast from the past. In the 1950s and 1960s, 45 RPM recordings were used for popular music.

15. The measure of an angle is k degrees. Convert this to radians. *(Lesson 4-1)*

16. An old 45 RPM record revolves through 45 revolutions in a minute. How many radians is this per second? *(Lesson 4-1)*

17. Give an equation for the image of the graph of $y = 2\sqrt{x} - 3$ under the scale change $S(x, y) = (8x, 8y)$. *(Lesson 3-5)*

18. At a certain video store, a regular, one-day video rental costs \$2.75 and customers receive 1 free rental with every 11 regular rentals. *(Lesson 2-7)*
   a. Write an equation for $F(n)$, the number of free videos after n rentals.
   b. Write an equation for $C(n)$, the cost of n rentals.

19. The students in a geometry class measured their heights h in centimeters and recorded the following five-number summary of their data.

   $\bar{h} = 165$ min $h = 137$ $Q_1 = 154$
   med $= 168$ $Q_3 = 174$ max $h = 188$

   Are there any outliers in the data set? Explain your answer. *(Lesson 1-4)*

Exploration

20. At what angle to the x-axis does the graph of $y = \sin x$ pass through $(0, 0)$? Give numerical and visual evidence supporting your answer.

LESSON

4-7

Scale-Change Images of Circular Functions

Musical images. *A computer can use both pure tones and combinations of tones to synthesize music. A light pen can be used to edit this music on screen.*

Sine Waves

You are probably aware that a pure tone, such as that produced by a tuning fork, travels in a *sine wave*. A **sine wave** is the image of the graph of the sine or cosine function under a composite of translations and scale changes. The pitch of the tone is related to the period of the wave; the longer the period, the lower the pitch. The intensity of the tone is related to the **amplitude** of the wave, half the distance between its maximum and minimum values.

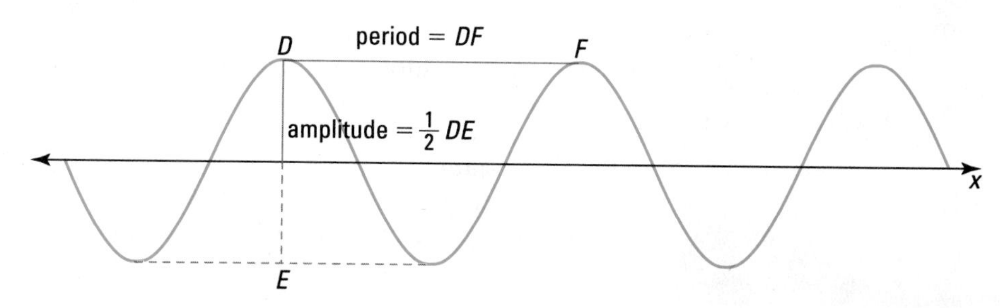

Thus, stretching a sine wave horizontally or vertically pictures changes in a tone's pitch and intensity. These stretches can be accomplished by applying the Graph Scale-Change Theorem.

Example 1

Consider the function with equation $y = 5 \cos\left(\frac{x}{2}\right)$.

a. Explain how this function is related to its parent function $y = \cos x$.

b. Identify its amplitude and its period.

c. Check your answers to parts **a** and **b** using an automatic grapher. ▶

Solution

a. Divide each side of the given equation by 5. This rewrites the function rule in a form that can be analyzed using the Graph Scale-Change Theorem.

$$\frac{y}{5} = \cos\left(\frac{x}{2}\right)$$

In the equation $y = \cos x$ of the parent function, y has been replaced by $\frac{y}{5}$. Thus, the graph of the parent function is stretched by a factor of 5 in the vertical direction. In the equation $y = \cos x$, x has been replaced by $\frac{x}{2}$, indicating a horizontal stretch factor of 2.

b. The vertical stretch means that the maximum and minimum values of the parent graph are multiplied by 5. Hence, the given function has amplitude $\frac{1}{2}(5 - -5) = 5$. The horizontal stretch means that the period 2π of the parent graph is also stretched by a factor of 2. So the function $y = 5\cos\left(\frac{x}{2}\right)$ has a period of $2 \cdot 2\pi = 4\pi$.

c. Graphs of $y = \cos x$ (in blue) and $y = 5\cos\left(\frac{x}{2}\right)$ (in orange) are shown below. You can see that the amplitude and period found above are correct.

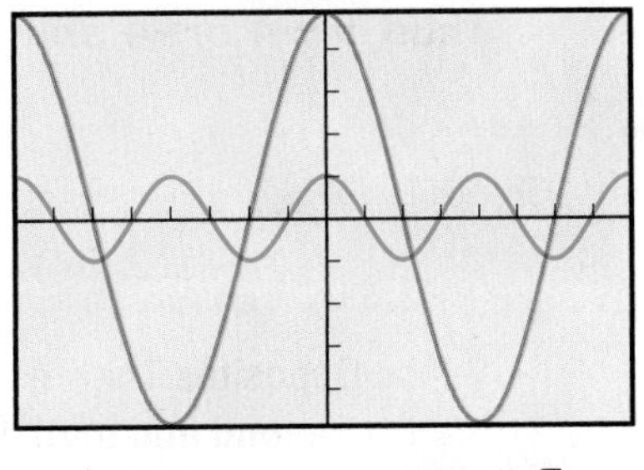

$-4\pi \le x \le 4\pi$, x-scale $= \frac{\pi}{2}$
$-5 \le y \le 5$, y-scale $= 1$

If the functions $y = \cos x$ and $y = 5\cos\left(\frac{x}{2}\right)$ in Example 1 represent sound waves, the sound of $y = 5\cos\left(\frac{x}{2}\right)$ is 5 times as loud as the sound of $y = \cos x$. The sound represented by $y = 5\cos\left(\frac{x}{2}\right)$ has a lower pitch than the one represented by $y = \cos x$.

In general, from the Graph Scale-Change Theorem, the functions defined by

$$y = b\sin\left(\frac{x}{a}\right) \text{ and } y = b\cos\left(\frac{x}{a}\right),$$

where $a \neq 0$ and $b \neq 0$, are images of the parent functions

$$y = \sin x \text{ and } y = \cos x$$

under the scale change that maps (x, y) to (ax, by). The following theorem indicates the relationship of the constants to the properties of sine waves.

Theorem

The functions defined by $y = b \sin\left(\frac{x}{a}\right)$ and $y = b \cos\left(\frac{x}{a}\right)$ have amplitude $= |b|$ and period $= 2\pi\,|a|$.

Example 2

The graph below shows an image of $y = \sin x$ under a scale change. Find an equation for f.

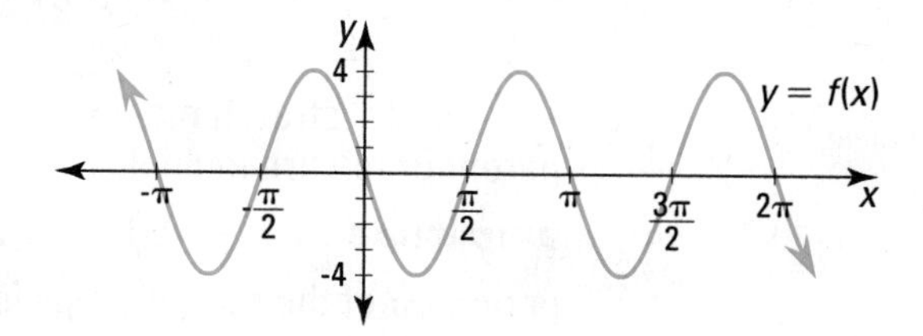

Solution

An equation for f is of the form $y = b \sin\left(\frac{x}{a}\right)$. From the graph, the amplitude is 4 and the period is π. So $|b| = 4$ and $2\pi\,|a| = \pi$. Thus, $b = 4$ or -4 and $a = \frac{1}{2}$ or $-\frac{1}{2}$. Consider the four possibilities.

$$y = 4 \sin(2x)$$
$$y = 4 \sin(-2x)$$
$$y = -4 \sin(2x)$$
$$y = -4 \sin(-2x)$$

By the Opposites Theorem, the first and fourth equations are equivalent, as are the second and third. Substituting a few specific points shows that either $y = 4 \sin(-2x)$ or $y = -4 \sin(2x)$ could be an equation for the given function, but that $y = 4 \sin(2x)$ and $y = -4 \sin(-2x)$ are not.

Check

Graph the equations. Below are graphs produced by an automatic grapher.

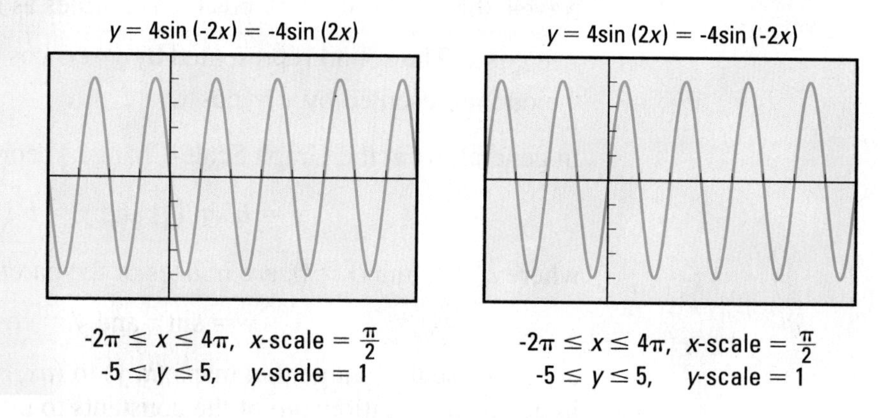

The Frequency of a Sine Wave

Note that the graph of $y = \cos x$ in Example 1 completes two cycles for every one completed by $y = 5\cos\left(\frac{x}{2}\right)$. We say that $y = \cos x$ has twice the *frequency* of $y = 5\cos\left(\frac{x}{2}\right)$.

In general, the **frequency** of a periodic function is the reciprocal of the period, and represents the number of cycles the curve completes per unit of the independent variable. Thus, the frequency of the function $y = \cos x$ is $\frac{1}{2\pi}$; and the frequency of the function $y = 5\cos\left(\frac{x}{2}\right)$ is $\frac{1}{4\pi}$. When a sine wave represents sound, doubling the frequency results in a pitch one octave higher. So the graph of $y = \cos x$ represents a sound with pitch one octave higher than the pitch of $y = 5\cos\left(\frac{x}{2}\right)$.

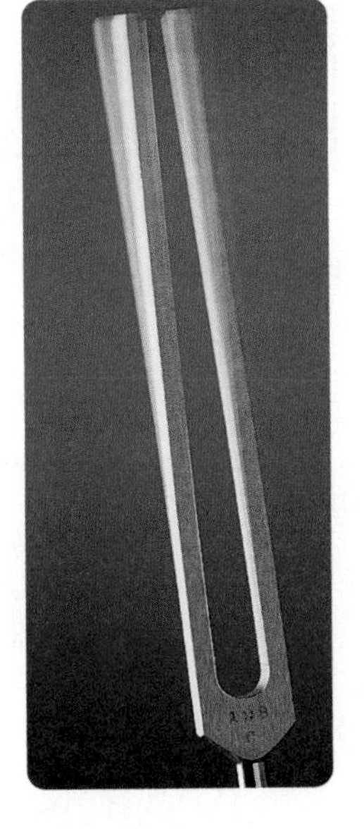

Example 3

Suppose a tuning fork vibrates with a frequency of 440 cycles per second. If the vibration displaces air molecules by a maximum of 0.3 mm, give a possible equation for the sound wave that is produced.

Solution

The equation has the form $y = b\sin\left(\frac{x}{a}\right)$, where x is the number of seconds after the tuning fork is struck. Since the amplitude is 0.3, $b = 0.3$. The period of the graph is $2\pi|a|$. Since the frequency is the reciprocal of the period,

$$440 = \frac{1}{2\pi|a|}.$$

$$\text{So, } |a| = \frac{1}{880\pi}.$$

We take a to be positive, so an equation is

$$y = 0.3\sin\left(\frac{x}{\frac{1}{880\pi}}\right) = 0.3\sin(880\pi x).$$

QUESTIONS

Covering the Reading

1. Consider the function $y = \frac{1}{2}\cos x$.
   a. *True or false.* The graph of this function is a sine wave.
   b. What is its period?
   c. What is its amplitude?
   d. Sketch graphs of $y = \frac{1}{2}\cos x$ and $y = \cos x$ on the same set of axes for $-\pi \le x \le 2\pi$.
   e. Describe how the two graphs in part **d** are related.

In 2–4, an equation for a function is given. **a.** Find its amplitude. **b.** Find its period.

2. $y = 3\sin x$

3. $y = \sin 3x$

4. $y = 4\sin\left(\frac{x}{3}\right)$

5. *Multiple choice.* Which equation could yield the graph at the right?

(a) $y = 5 \sin 2x$ (b) $y = 5 \cos 2x$

(c) $y = 5 \sin \frac{x}{2}$ (d) $y = 5 \cos \left(\frac{x}{2}\right)$

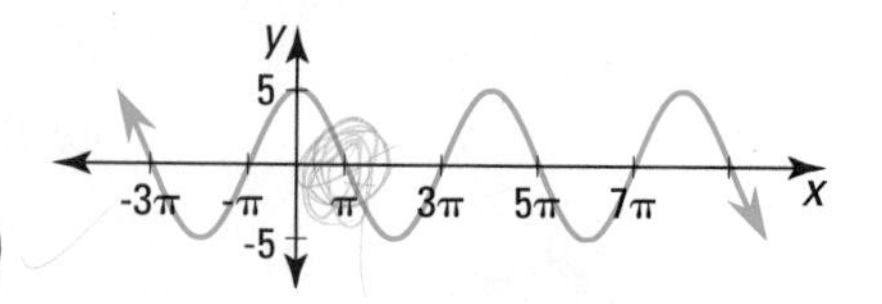

6. a. Find an equation of the image of the function $y = \sin x$ under the transformation $(x, y) \rightarrow (4x, y)$.

b. Graph the parent and the image on the same set of axes.

c. Find the amplitude of the image.

d. Find the period of the image.

7. a. Give the period and amplitude of $y = \frac{1}{3} \sin 5x$.

b. Check using an automatic grapher.

8. The graph at the right is an image of $y = \sin x$ under a scale change. Find an equation for this curve.

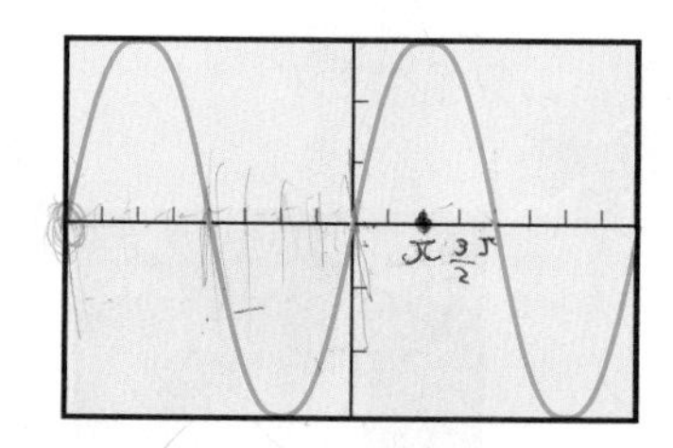

$-4\pi \leq x \leq 4\pi$, x-scale $= \frac{\pi}{2}$
$-3 \leq y \leq 3$, y-scale $= 1$

9. Refer to the graph sketched below.

a. Identify the amplitude.

b. Give the period. Give the frequency.

c. If this graph represents a sound wave, then it is __i.__ times as loud and has __ii.__ times the frequency of the parent sound wave.

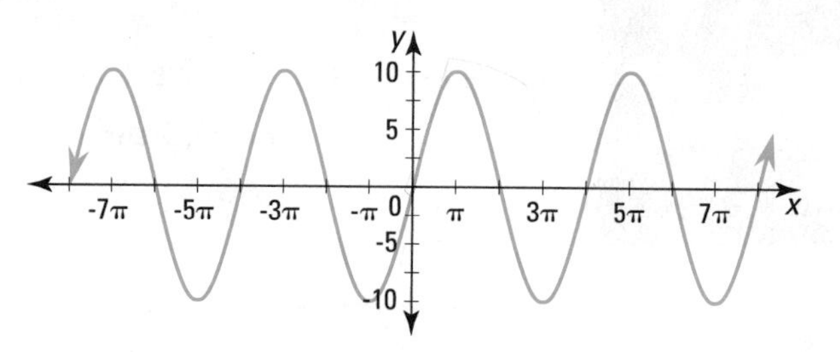

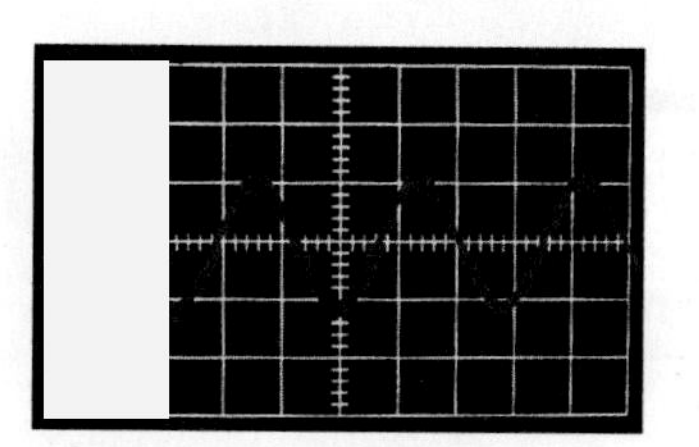

Good vibes. *A tuning fork's vibration of 440 cycles per second caused compression and rarefaction of air molecules which generated the sound waves traced by this oscilloscope.*

10. Suppose one tone has a frequency of 440 cycles per second, and another tone has a frequency of 880 cycles per second.

a. Which has the higher pitch?

b. How much higher is that pitch?

11. Consider a tuning fork vibrating at 512 cycles per second and displacing air molecules by a maximum of 0.14 mm. Give a possible equation for the sound wave that is produced.

12. *Multiple choice.* A sound wave whose parent graph is $y = \sin x$ has five times the frequency and is four times as loud as the parent. What is a possible equation for this sound wave?

(a) $y = 5 \sin 4x$ (b) $y = 4 \sin 5x$

(c) $y = 4 \sin \frac{1}{5}x$ (d) $y = \frac{1}{4} \sin \frac{1}{5}x$

Applying the Mathematics

13. Sketch one complete cycle of $8y = \cos \frac{x}{12}$, and label the zeros of the function.

14. Residential electricity is called AC for "alternating current," because the direction of current flow alternates through a circuit. The current (measured in amperes) is a sine function of time. The graph at the right models an AC situation.

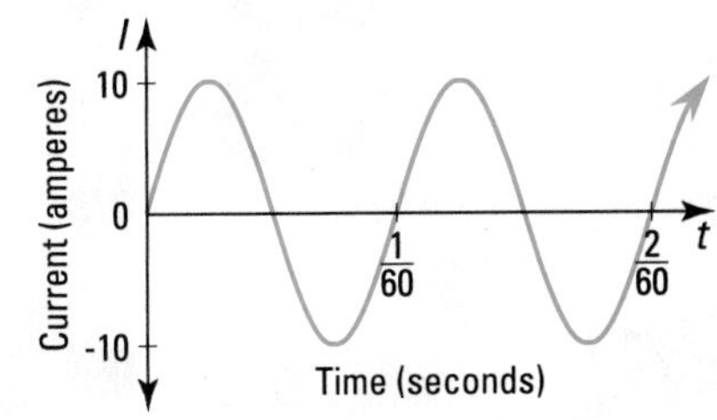

a. Write an equation for current I as a function of time t.

b. Find the current produced at 0.04 seconds.

15. Consider the function $g: x \rightarrow \sin\left(-\frac{x}{3}\right)$.

a. Use the Opposites Theorem to rewrite the function without a negative argument.

b. Give the period and the amplitude of g.

c. Sketch a graph of g on the domain $-3\pi \leq x \leq 6\pi$.

16. Which two of the functions f, g, and h, defined by $f(x) = \tan x$, $g(x) = \tan 2x$, and $h(x) = 2 \tan x$, have the same period?

Review

17. Given that $\tan 0.464 \approx 0.5$, find three other values of θ with $\tan \theta \approx 0.5$. *(Lesson 4-6)*

18. Find the exact value of $\tan(-120°)$. *(Lesson 4-5)*

19. a. Graph $y = \cos x$ and $y = \cos(\pi - x)$ on the same set of axes.

b. Describe the relation between the graphs.

c. What theorem is illustrated by parts **a** and **b**? *(Lesson 4-4)*

In 20 and 21, given $\cos \theta = c$, evaluate each of the following. *(Lessons 4-4, 4-6)*

20. $\cos(2\pi + \theta)$

21. $\cos\left(\frac{\pi}{2} - \theta\right)$

22. State the Graph-Translation Theorem. *(Lesson 3-2)*

23. a. Graph $f(x) = |x|$ and its image under the transformation $T: (x, y) \rightarrow (x + 4, y - 7)$.

b. Find an equation for the image. *(Lesson 3-2)*

24. *Skill sequence.* Rewrite each of the following in the form $a(x - h)$.

a. $2x - 4$ **b.** $4x - 2\pi$ **c.** $3x + \pi$ *(Previous course)*

Exploration

25. Other than pitch and loudness, what other characteristics do sounds have?

LESSON

4-8

Translation Images of Circular Functions

Shifty work. *Astronomers at observatories, such as Mount Palomar pictured here, can determine the distance of a star from Earth by analyzing the phase shift of the spectrum of light emitted by the star.*

Phase Shifts

From the applications of circular functions to sound and electricity, horizontal translations of them have acquired a special name—*phase shift*. In general, the **phase shift** is the least positive or the greatest negative magnitude of a horizontal translation that maps the graph of $\frac{y}{b} = \cos\frac{x}{a}$ or $\frac{y}{b} = \sin\frac{x}{a}$ onto the given wave.

Example 1

Consider the function $P(x) = \sin\left(x + \frac{2\pi}{3}\right)$. Identify the phase shift.

Solution

Rewrite the equation $P(x) = \sin\left(x - -\frac{2\pi}{3}\right)$. The graph of P is the image of $y = \sin x$ under a horizontal translation of $-\frac{2\pi}{3}$ units. Thus the phase shift is $-\frac{2\pi}{3}$.

Check

Graph $P(x) = \sin\left(x + \frac{2\pi}{3}\right)$, and compare it to $f(x) = \sin x$. At the right is the output from an automatic grapher.

Notice that the graph of P (in orange) is the image of f (in blue) under a translation of $\frac{2\pi}{3} \approx 2.09$ units to the left.

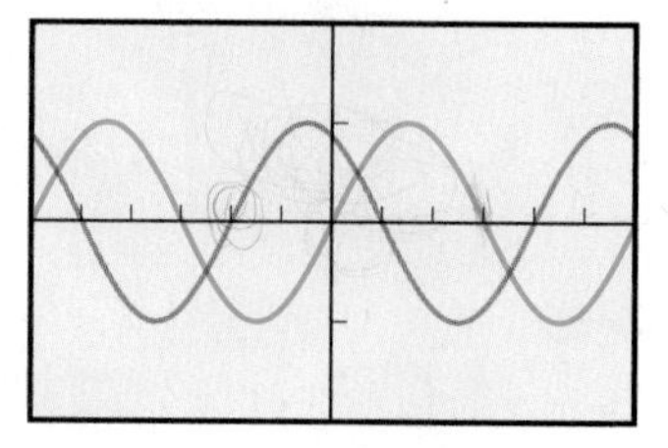

$-2\pi \le x \le 2\pi$, x-scale $= \frac{\pi}{3}$
$-2 \le y \le 2$, y-scale $= 1$

Vertical Translations

The vertical translation in Example 2 is reminiscent of the Ferris wheel in Lesson 4-3.

Example 2

Consider the function f, where $f(x) = \sin x$.

a. Find its image g under the translation $(x, y) \rightarrow (x, y + 2)$, and sketch a graph of $y = g(x)$.

b. Find the amplitude and period of g.

Solution

a. **According to the Graph-Translation Theorem, an equation for the image is $y - 2 = \sin x$ or $y = \sin x + 2$.** This results in a vertical shift two units up from the parent function. The graphs of f (in blue) and its image g (in orange) are below.

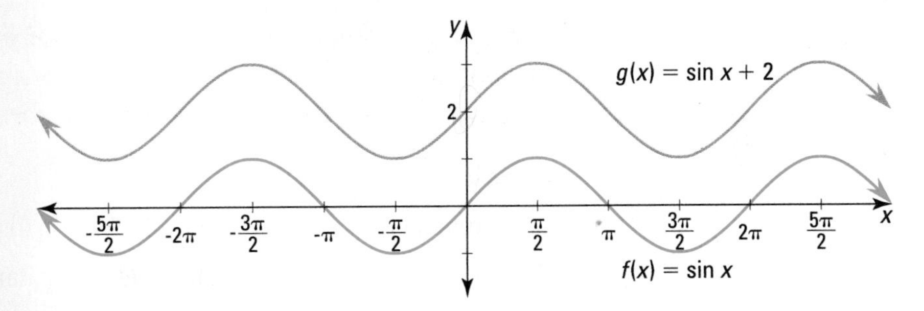

b. The maximum and minimum values of the sine function are 1 and -1, respectively. So the maximum and minimum values of $y = \sin x + 2$ are 3 and 1, respectively. Thus, **the amplitude of $y = \sin x + 2$ is $\frac{1}{2}(3 - 1) = \frac{1}{2} \cdot 2 = 1$,** the same as the amplitude of the parent sine function. Similarly, **the period of $y = \sin x + 2$ equals 2π,** the same as the period of the parent sine function.

In general, if two curves are translation images of each other, then they are congruent. Thus, translation of a sine wave preserves both its amplitude and its period.

From an analysis of a graph showing a translation image of any of the parent circular functions, you can determine an equation for a translation image.

Example 3

The graph below represents a translation image of $y = \tan x$. Find an equation for the function.

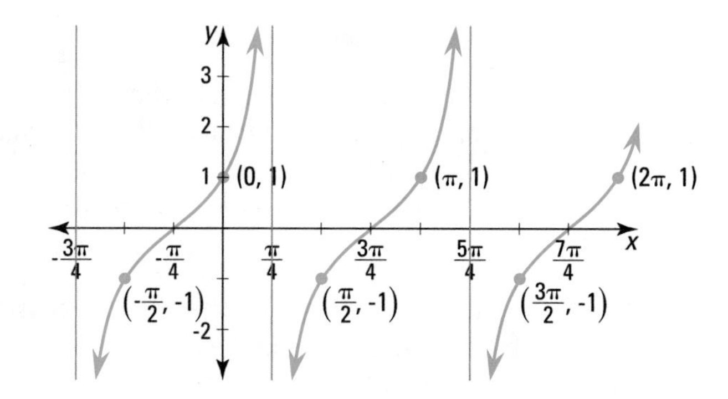

Solution

The graph is the image of the graph of $y = \tan x$ under a translation of $\frac{\pi}{4}$ to the left. By the Graph-Translation Theorem, an equation for the graph is $y = \tan\left(x - -\frac{\pi}{4}\right)$, or $y = \tan\left(x + \frac{\pi}{4}\right)$.

Check

Substitute some points on the graph. Try $\left(\frac{3\pi}{4}, 0\right)$.

Does $0 = \tan\left(\frac{3\pi}{4} + \frac{\pi}{4}\right)$? $0 = \tan \pi$. Yes. At $\frac{\pi}{4}$, $\tan\left(\frac{\pi}{4} + \frac{\pi}{4}\right) = \tan\frac{\pi}{2}$, which is undefined. The equation $y = \tan\left(x + \frac{\pi}{4}\right)$ checks.

As with other functions, translations may involve both vertical and horizontal translations.

Activity

Consider the function defined by $y = \cos(x - \pi) + 1$.

a. Graph the function using an automatic grapher and the window $-2\pi \le x \le 2\pi$, $-3 \le y \le 3$.

b. Use the graph to find the coordinates of all points where this function attains its maximum value.

c. Use the Graph-Translation Theorem to explain how you could have found these points without graphing the function.

Hoover Dam and Powerplant on the Arizona-Nevada border

Inductance and Sine Waves

People who work with electricity, such as electrical engineers and electricians, use phase shifts. In an alternating current circuit, for example, two waves—the voltage and the current flow—are involved. If these waves coincide, then they are said to be *in phase*. If the current flow lags behind the voltage, then the circuit is *out-of-phase* and an *inductance* is created. Inductance helps to keep current flow stable.

Example 4

Maximum inductance in an alternating current occurs when the current flow lags behind the voltage by $\frac{\pi}{2}$. Assume that the two waves have the same amplitude and period, and that the voltage is modeled by the equation $y = \sin x$. In a situation of maximum inductance, find an equation for the current, and sketch the two sine waves.

Solution

Maximum inductance in an alternating current occurs when the current has phase shift of $\frac{\pi}{2}$. So an equation for the current is $y = \sin\left(x - \frac{\pi}{2}\right)$.
Both waves are graphed below.

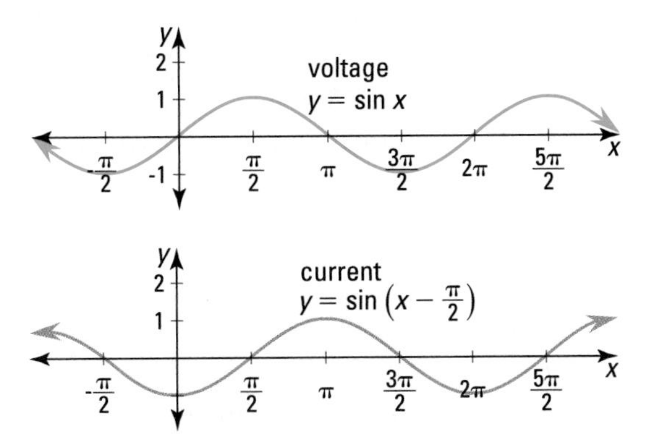

Because the goal in Example 4 was simply to illustrate maximum inductance, any sine wave could have been used. Below are graphs of $y = \cos x$ and $y = \cos\left(x - \frac{\pi}{2}\right)$, which also are out of phase by $\frac{\pi}{2}$, the voltage wave leading the current wave.

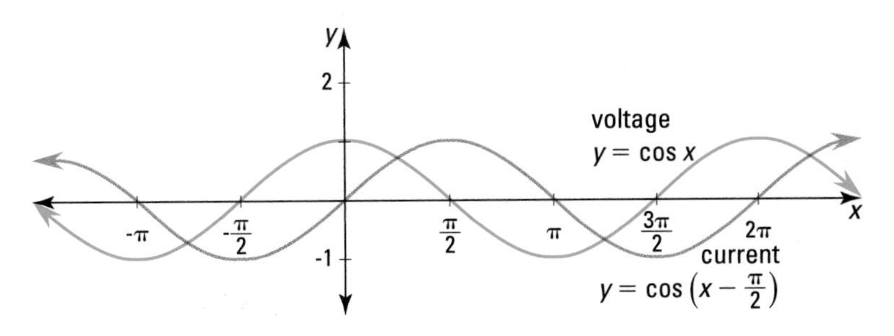

A Theorem Suggested by Translation Images

Examine all four graphs above carefully. Notice that the graph of $y = \cos\left(x - \frac{\pi}{2}\right)$ seems to coincide with the graph of $y = \sin x$. This suggests an identity similar to the Complements Theorem.

Theorem
For all real numbers x, $\cos\left(x - \frac{\pi}{2}\right) = \sin x$.

Proof

$\cos\left(x - \frac{\pi}{2}\right) = \cos\left(-\left(x - \frac{\pi}{2}\right)\right)$ Opposites Theorem

$= \cos\left(\frac{\pi}{2} - x\right)$ Distributive and Commutative Properties

$= \sin x$ Complements Theorem

Many other properties can be found by translating sine waves using an automatic grapher, including some not covered in this book.

QUESTIONS

Covering the Reading

1. *True or false.* The graph of any circular function and its image under a translation are congruent.

2. Consider the function $y = \cos\left(x + \frac{\pi}{3}\right)$.
   a. Identify the phase shift from $y = \cos x$.
   b. Sketch two cycles of the curve.

3. Consider the translation $T(x, y) \to \left(x + \frac{3\pi}{4}, y - 3\right)$.
   a. Find an equation for the image of the sine function under T.
   b. Find the amplitude, the period, and the phase shift of the image.

In 4 and 5, write an equation for the function that is graphed.

4. **5.**

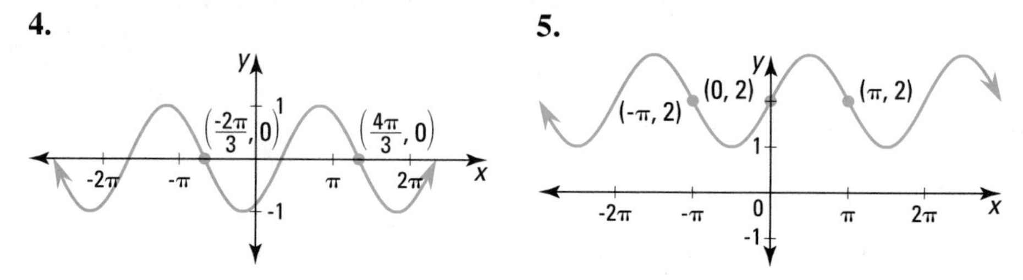

6. The graph below represents a translation image of $y = \tan x$. Find an equation for the function.

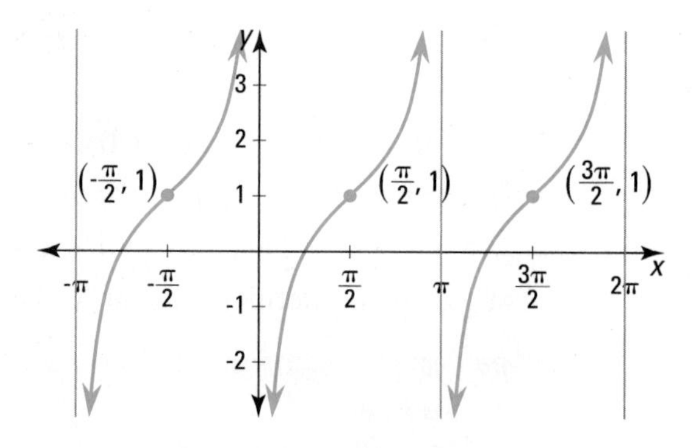

In 7–9, match the equation with its graph.

7. $y = \sin\left(x + \frac{\pi}{3}\right)$ **8.** $y = \sin\left(x - \frac{\pi}{2}\right)$ **9.** $y = \sin x - 1$

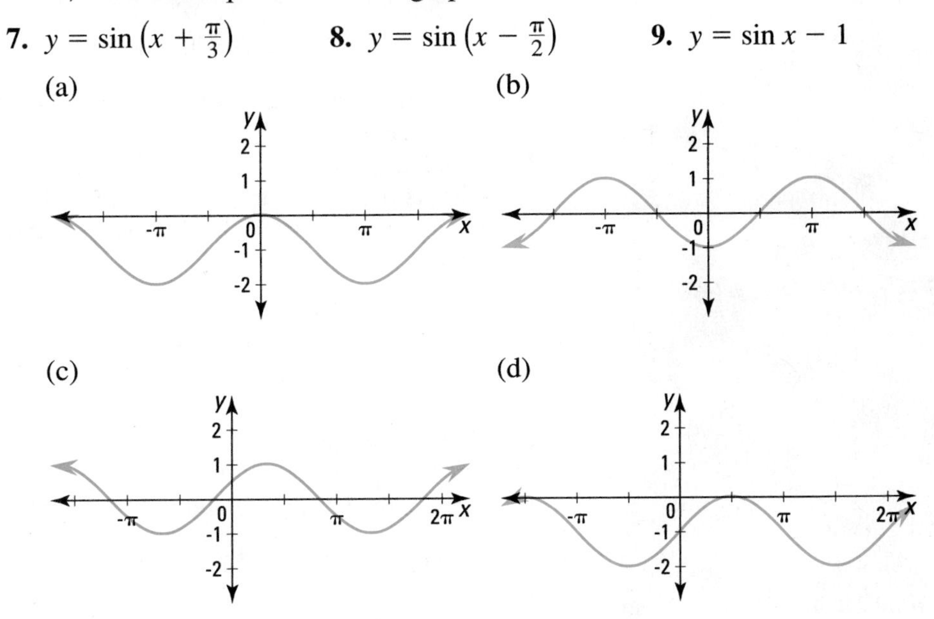

10. Write your answer to the Activity.

11. a. Sketch by hand two cycles of $y = \sin(x + \pi) + 2$ on the interval $-2\pi \le x \le 2\pi$. Label all x- and y-intercepts.

b. Check your work by using an automatic grapher.

12. Refer to the graphs of $y = \sin x$, $y = \sin\left(x - \frac{\pi}{2}\right)$, $y = \cos x$, and $y = \cos\left(x - \frac{\pi}{2}\right)$ drawn at the end of the lesson.

a. Which graph(s) are out of phase with the graph of $y = \sin x$?

b. By how much are they out of phase?

Applying the Mathematics

13. Maximum *capacitance* occurs in an alternating current circuit when the current flow leads the voltage by $\frac{\pi}{2}$. If the voltage wave is modeled by $y = 2\cos x$, give an equation for the current flow that maximizes capacitance.

14. *True or false.* If true, prove using appropriate theorems; if false, give a counterexample.

For all real numbers x, $\sin\left(x - \frac{\pi}{2}\right) = -\cos x$.

15. a. Sketch or print a hard copy of the graph of $f(\alpha) = \tan\left(\alpha - \frac{\pi}{6}\right)$ on the interval $-\frac{\pi}{2} \le \alpha \le 2\pi$.

b. Give equations for the asymptotes of the function on this interval.

Low tide on the Pacific coast.

16. The height in meters of the tide in a harbor is given by

$$h = 0.8 \cos \tfrac{\pi}{6}t + 6.5,$$

where t is the time in hours after high tide.

a. Calculate h at $t = 0$, $t = 1$, and $t = 2$.

b. Sketch a graph of this function for $0 \le t \le 24$.

c. What is the minimum height of the tide during a 24-hour period?

d. At what times during the 24 hours after high tide does the minimum height occur?

Review

17. Consider the graph of $f(x) = 2 \sin (3x)$.

a. Graph f and its parent on the same set of axes.

b. Identify the amplitude and the frequency of f. *(Lesson 4-7)*

18. a. Graph $y = \cos 8x$ and $y = 8 \cos x$ on the same axes.

b. Approximate to the nearest hundredth at least one value of x between 0 and 2π where $\cos 8x = 8 \cos x$. *(Lesson 4-7)*

In 19 and 20, refer to the unit circle at the right. *(Lesson 4-4)*

y, x, O, $(c, d) = (\cos \theta_1, \sin \theta_1)$, θ_1, $(1, 0)$, θ_2, $(e, f) = (\cos \theta_2, \sin \theta_2)$

19. a. If $c = d$, find the exact value of each.

b. Find two possible values of θ_1.

20. If $\theta_2 = \frac{-2\pi}{3}$, find e and f.

21. Given $g(x) = |x|$ and $p(x) = 1 - x^2$, let $c(x) = g(p(x))$.

a. Write an expression for $c(x)$.

b. State the domain and range of c. *(Lesson 3-7)*

22. *Skill sequence.* Simplify. *(Previous course)*

a. $\dfrac{x - 2}{\frac{1}{2}}$ **b.** $\dfrac{x - \frac{1}{2}}{\frac{1}{4}}$ **c.** $\dfrac{x - \frac{\pi}{2}}{\frac{1}{8}}$

23. *Skill sequence.* Each expression below is of the form $ax - h$. Rewrite each in the form $\dfrac{x - \frac{h}{a}}{\frac{1}{a}}$. *(Previous course)*

a. $2x - 4$ **b.** $4x - 2\pi$ **c.** $3x + \pi$ **d.** $\frac{1}{2}x + \frac{3}{2}$

Exploration

24. Find out how phase shift is interpreted in the study of sound.

LESSON

4-9

The Graph-Standardization Theorem

Rubberband Transformations

In this lesson you will learn how composites of scale changes and translations affect circular functions.

We examine a non-periodic function first. Consider the parabola $y = x^2$. Apply the scale change $S(x, y) = (3x, 2y)$. This stretches the parent function by a factor of 3 in the x-direction and by a factor of 2 in the y-direction. To this image apply the translation $T(x, y) = (x - 4, y + 1)$. This translates the image 4 units to the left, and one unit up.

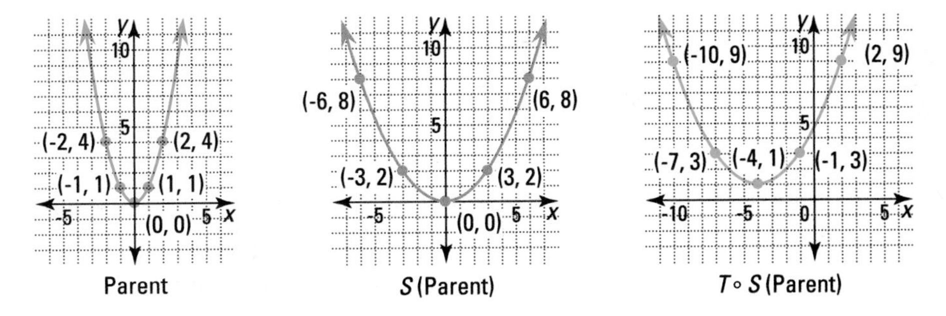

By the Graph Scale-Change Theorem, the image of the graph of $y = x^2$ under the scale change $S: (x, y) \rightarrow (3x, 2y)$ is

$$\frac{y}{2} = \left(\frac{x}{3}\right)^2.$$

By the Graph-Translation Theorem, the image of the graph of this new equation under $T: (x, y) \rightarrow (x - 4, y + 1)$ is

$$\frac{y - 1}{2} = \left(\frac{x + 4}{3}\right)^2.$$

This is an equation for the image of the graph of $y = x^2$ under the composite $T \circ S$.

In general, a **rubber band transformation** is the composite of scale changes and translations. Suppose S is a scale change and T a translation with

$$S(x, y) = (ax, by), \text{ where } a \neq 0 \text{ and } b \neq 0,$$
$$\text{and } T(x, y) = (x + h, y + k).$$

Then the rubber band transformation

$$\begin{aligned} T \circ S(x, y) &= T(S(x, y)) \\ &= T(ax, by) \\ &= (ax + h, by + k). \end{aligned}$$

Thus, $T \circ S$ maps (x, y) to $(ax + h, by + k)$. Put another way, under $T \circ S$,

$$(x', y') = (ax + h, by + k).$$

This equation for $T \circ S$ helps to determine how a rubber band transformation affects the equation of a relation. We are interested in how x' and y' are related but we are given only how x and y are related.

Since $\quad x' = ax + h \quad$ and $\quad y' = by + k.$

it follows that $\quad \frac{x' - h}{a} = x \quad$ and $\quad \frac{y' - k}{b} = y.$

This justifies the following theorem.

Graph-Standardization Theorem

In a relation described by a sentence in x and y, the following processes yield the same graph:

(1) replacing x by $\frac{x - h}{a}$ and y by $\frac{y - k}{b}$ in the sentence;

(2) applying the scale change $(x, y) \rightarrow (ax, by)$, where $a \neq 0$ and $b \neq 0$, followed by applying the translation $(x, y) \rightarrow (x + h, y + k)$ to the graph of the original relation.

The Graph-Standardization Theorem and Circular Functions

The Graph-Standardization Theorem can be applied to the graph of a circular function in exactly the same way it can be applied to any other graph.

Example 1

a. Use the Graph-Standardization Theorem to sketch a graph of $y = \cos\left(\frac{x + \pi}{3}\right)$.

b. Check your work using an automatic grapher.

c. Identify the amplitude, period, and phase shift of this function.

▶

CHAPTER REVIEW

Questions on SPUR Objectives

SPUR stands for **S**kills, **P**roperties, **U**ses, and **R**epresentations. The Chapter Review questions are grouped according to the SPUR Objectives for this chapter.

SKILLS DEAL WITH THE PROCEDURES USED TO GET ANSWERS.

Objective A: *Convert between degrees, radians, and revolutions.* *(Lesson 4-1)*

In 1 and 2, a rotation is given. **a.** Convert to degrees. **b.** Convert to radians.

1. $\frac{1}{5}$ revolution counterclockwise

2. $\frac{2}{3}$ revolution clockwise

In 3 and 4, convert to degrees without using a calculator.

3. $-\frac{\pi}{6}$ radians **4.** $\frac{7\pi}{12}$ radians

In 5 and 6, convert to radians without using a calculator.

5. 135° **6.** 300°

In 7 and 8, tell how many revolutions are represented by each rotation.

7. $\frac{2\pi}{3}$ **8.** 540°

Objective B: *Find lengths of circular arcs, and areas of sectors.* *(Lesson 4-2)*

9. Find the length of the arc of a 120° central angle in a circle with radius 9 inches.

10. The arc of a central angle of $\frac{\pi}{6}$ radians has a length of 3π feet. Find the radius of the circle.

11. Find the area of the sector whose central angle is $\frac{\pi}{6}$ radians in a circle whose radius is 10 meters.

12. The area of a sector in a circle of radius 6 inches is 48 square inches. Find the measure of the central angle to the nearest tenth of a degree.

Objective C: *Find sines, cosines, and tangents of angles.* *(Lessons 4-3, 4-5)*

In 13–15, give exact values.

13. $\cos\left(\frac{\pi}{4}\right)$

14. $\sin\left(\frac{\pi}{3}\right)$

15. $\tan\left(\frac{\pi}{6}\right)$

In 16–18, approximate to the nearest thousandth.

16. tan 1.1

17. sin .0926

18. cos .4563

In 19–21, evaluate to the nearest hundredth.

19. sin 3

20. cos (-42.2°)

21. tan 151°

In 22–25, give exact values.

22. $\cos\left(\frac{5\pi}{4}\right)$ **23.** sin 210°

24. $\tan\left(-\frac{\pi}{4}\right)$ **25.** $\sin\left(\frac{9\pi}{2}\right)$

26. Give three values of θ from -2π to 2π such that $\cos\theta = 1$.

In 27 and 28, let $P = R_\theta(1, 0)$. Find the coordinates of P when θ is the following.

27. 7π

28. $\frac{3}{5}$ of a revolution clockwise

29. Solve $\sin x = -\frac{1}{2}$ exactly in the interval $-\frac{\pi}{2} \le x \le \frac{5\pi}{2}$.

PROPERTIES DEAL WITH THE PRINCIPLES BEHIND THE MATHEMATICS.

Objective D: *Apply the definitions of the sine, cosine, and tangent functions.* *(Lessons 4-3, 4-4, 4-6)*

30. For the sine function identify each.

a. domain **b.** range

31. For what values of θ is $\tan\theta$ undefined?

In 32 and 33, let $f(x) = \cos x$. *True or false.*

32. f is an even function.

33. The maximum value of f is 1.

34. In what interval(s) between 0 and 2π are both the cosine and tangent functions negative?

35. *Multiple choice.* For what values of θ is $\sin\theta < 0$ and $\cos\theta > 0$?

(a) $0 < \theta < \frac{\pi}{2}$ (b) $\frac{\pi}{2} < \theta < \pi$

(c) $\pi < \theta < \frac{3\pi}{2}$ (d) $\frac{3\pi}{2} < \theta < 2\pi$

Objective E: *Apply theorems about sines, cosines, and tangents.* *(Lessons 4-4, 4-5)*

36. Why is the statement that for all θ, $\sin(\pi - \theta) = \sin\theta$ called the Supplements Theorem?

In 37–40, given $\sin\theta = k$, without using a calculator, find each.

37. $\cos\left(\frac{\pi}{2} - \theta\right)$

38. $\sin(\pi - \theta)$

39. $\sin(\theta - \pi)$

40. $\sin(\pi + \theta)$

41. Use theorems about sines and cosines to prove that $-\sin\left(\frac{\pi}{2} - \theta\right) = \cos(\pi - \theta)$.

In 42–44, *true or false*. Justify your answer.

42. For all θ, $\cos(\theta + 3\pi) = \cos\theta$.

43. For all θ, $\sin(\theta + 6\pi) = \sin\theta$.

44. For all θ, $\cos^2\theta + \sin^2\theta = \tan^2\theta$.

45. If $\cos\theta = \frac{1}{4}$, without using a calculator find all possible values of each.

a. $\sin\theta$ **b.** $\tan\theta$

Objective F: *Identify the amplitude, period, frequency, phase shift, and other properties of circular functions.* *(Lessons 4-7, 4-8, 4-9)*

In 46–49, give, if it exists, **a.** the period, **b.** the amplitude, and **c.** the phase shift.

46. $\frac{y}{5} = \sin\frac{x}{2}$

47. $y = 2\cos(3\pi x)$

48. $y = 2\cos\left(x - \frac{\pi}{3}\right)$

49. $h(\theta) = \frac{1}{2}\tan(2\theta)$

50. Identify each for the function given by the equation $y = -4\cos\frac{x}{3}$.

a. amplitude **b.** period **c.** frequency

51. State **a.** the maximum and **b.** the minimum values of the function $f(t) = 10 + 5\sin 2t$.

52. Suppose the transformation $(x, y) \to \left(2x + 1, \frac{y}{3} - 1\right)$ is applied to the function $y = \sin x$.

a. State an equation for the image.

b. Find the amplitude, period, phase shift, and vertical shift of the image.

53. Let $S(x, y) = \left(\frac{x}{3}, -2y\right)$ and $T(x, y) = (x + 6, y)$.

a. Find the image of $y = \cos x$ under the composite transformation $T \circ S$.

b. Find a single transformation that maps $y = \cos x$ to the function in part **a**.

USES DEAL WITH APPLICATIONS OF MATHEMATICS IN REAL SITUATIONS.

Objective G: *Solve problems involving lengths of arcs or areas of sectors.* *(Lesson 4-2)*

54. A radar screen represents a circle of radius 40 miles. If the arm shown below makes 25 revolutions per minute, what area is mapped by the radar in each second?

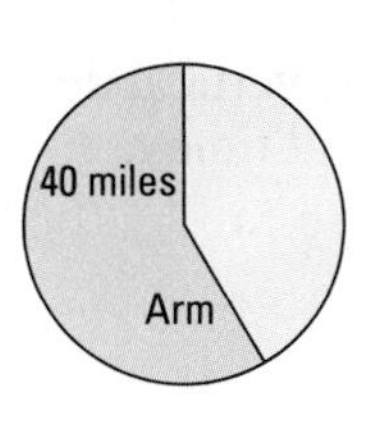

55. A theater is planned as shown. The internal radius of the building is $AO = 26$ meters and $m\angle AOB = 160°$. If the stage area has a radius of 5 meters, find the area of the seating section.

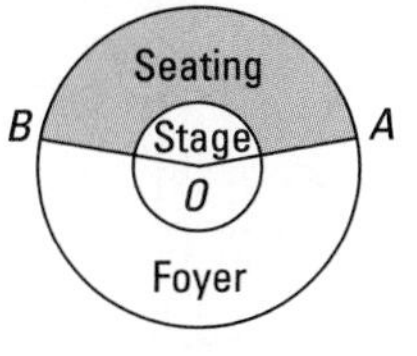

Objective H: *Use equations of circular functions to solve problems about real phenomena.* *(Lessons 4-7, 4-8, 4-9)*

56. An alternating current I in amps of a circuit at time t in seconds ($t > 0$) is given by the formula $I = 40 \cos 60\pi t$.

a. Find the maximum and minimum values of the current.

b. How many times per second does the current reach its maximum value?

57. The voltage V in volts in a circuit after t seconds ($t > 0$) is given by $V = 120 \cos 60\pi t$.

a. Find the first time the voltage is 100.

b. Find three times at which the voltage is maximized.

58. A certain sound wave has equation $y = 60 \sin 20\pi t$. Give an equation of a sound wave with twice the frequency and half as loud as this one.

59. A simple pendulum is shown at the right. The angular displacement from vertical (in radians) as a function of time t in seconds is given by

$$f(t) = \frac{1}{2}\sin\left(2t + \frac{\pi}{2}\right).$$

a. What is the initial angular displacement?

b. What is the frequency of f?

c. How long will it take for the pendulum to make 5 complete swings?

Objective I: *Find equations of circular functions to model periodic phenomena.* *(Lessons 4-10)*

60. Suppose the height h in meters of a tide at Greenwich Mean Time t is given in the table below.

t	0	5	6	12	18	24
h	3.7	0.1	0.2	3.6	0.3	3.7

a. Fit a sine wave to these data.

b. What is the period of the sine wave?

c. What is the amplitude of the sine wave?

61. The length of the day from sunrise to sunset in a city at 30° N latitude (such as Baton Rouge, Louisiana, or Cairo, Egypt) is given in the table below.

a. Find an equation using the sine function to model these data.

b. What is the period of the function used to model these data?

c. Predict the length of the day on December 21, the winter solstice, at 30° N latitude.

Date	Jan 1	Feb 1	Mar 1	Apr 1	May 1	June 1	July 1	Aug 1	Sept 1	Oct 1	Nov 1	Dec 1	Jan 1
Days after January 1	0	31	59	90	120	151	181	212	243	273	304	334	365
Length in hours	10.25	10.77	11.53	12.47	13.32	13.93	14.05	13.58	12.77	11.88	11.00	10.37	10.25

Source: *The Weather Almanac*

62. The figure below shows a waterwheel rotating at 4 revolutions per minute. The distance d of point P from the surface of the water as a function of time t in seconds can be modeled by a sine wave with equation of the form

$$\frac{d-k}{b} = \sin\left(\frac{t-h}{a}\right).$$

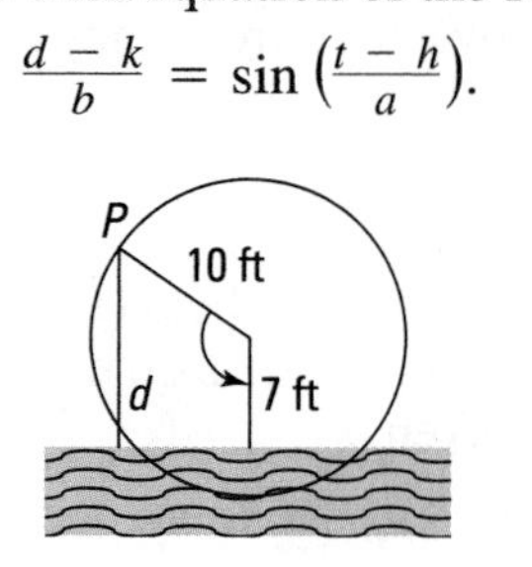

a. What is the amplitude of the distance function?

b. What is the period of the distance function?

c. If point P emerges from the water just as you start a stopwatch, write an equation for the distance function.

d. Approximately when does point P first reach its highest point?

63. A gear with a 4 cm radius rotates counterclockwise at a rate of 120 revolutions per minute. The gear starts with point A on the tooth level with the center of the wheel as shown below.

a. Write an equation to give the vertical distance y that point A is above or below the starting position at time t.

b. How far above or below the starting position will point A be after 5 minutes?

c. Write an equation for the vertical distance h point A is above point B at time t.

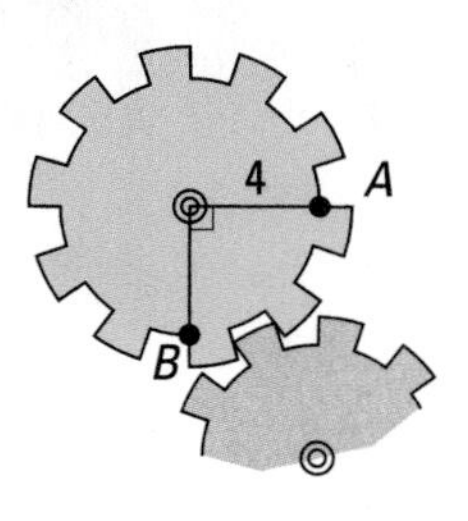

REPRESENTATIONS DEAL WITH PICTURES, GRAPHS, OR OBJECTS THAT ILLUSTRATE CONCEPTS.

Objective J: *Use the unit circle to find values of sines, cosines and tangents.* *(Lesson 4-3)*

In 64–67, refer to the unit circle at the right. Which letter could represent the value given?

(c, d) y (a, b)
(e, f)
(g, h)
x

64. sin 70°

65. cos (-160°)

66. $\cos\left(\frac{11\pi}{18}\right)$

67. $\sin\left(\frac{26\pi}{9}\right)$

In 68 and 69, let P' be the reflection image of P over the y-axis, as shown in the unit circle at the right. State the value of the following.

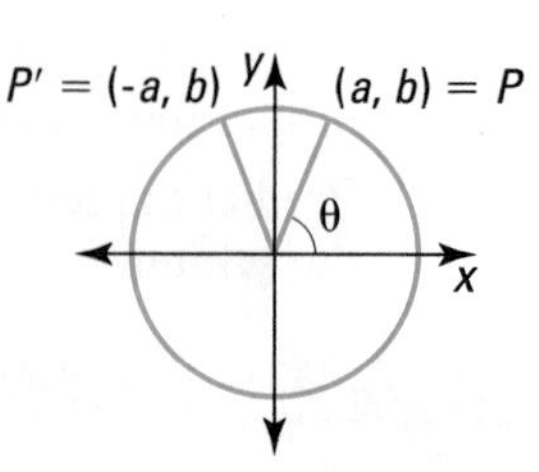

68. $\sin(\pi - \theta)$

69. $\tan(-\theta)$

70. Draw a picture using a unit circle to show why the cosine function is an even function.

Objective K: *Draw or interpret graphs of the parent sine, cosine, and tangent functions.* *(Lesson 4-6)*

71. Consider the function $f(x) = \sin x$.

a. Sketch a graph of f without using an automatic grapher.

b. What is the period of f?

72. Below is part of the graph of a function f. Which of the following could be an equation for f: $f(x) = \cos x$ or $f(x) = \sin x$? Justify your answer.

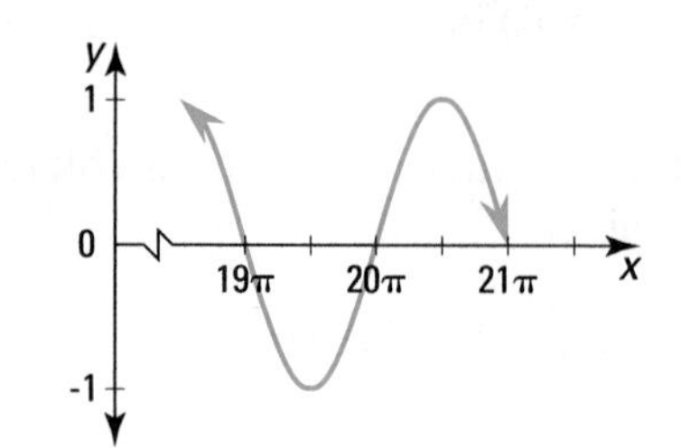

CHAPTER FOUR

73. Consider the graphs of $S(x) = \sin x$ and $C(x) = \cos x$. What translation maps

a. S to C? **b.** C to S?

74. a. Use an automatic grapher to draw

$$y = \cos x$$
$$y = \cos(-x)$$
and $$y = \cos(\pi - x)$$

on the same set of axes.

b. Describe the relations among the curves.

c. What theorems do the relations between these three graphs represent?

75. Let $g(\theta) = \tan \theta$.

a. Sketch a graph of $y = g(\theta)$.

b. State its period.

c. Write equations for two of the asymptotes of g.

Objective L: *Graph transformation images of circular functions.* *(Lessons 4-7, 4-8, 4-9)*

In 76–79, sketch one cycle of the graph without using an automatic grapher.

76. $y = \frac{1}{2} \sin\left(\frac{1}{2}x\right)$

77. $y = 8 \cos(\pi x)$.

78. $y = \tan\left(x - \frac{\pi}{2}\right) + 3$

79. $y = \sin(x + 4) - 1$

80. a. Write an equation for the image of $y = \sin x$ under a phase shift of $\frac{\pi}{6}$.

b. Check by graphing.

81. a. Write an equation for the image of $y = \cos x$ under a phase shift of $-\frac{4\pi}{3}$.

b. Check by graphing.

In 82 and 83, **a.** sketch a graph of the function. **b.** State the period and maximum value if it exists.

82. $\frac{y - 1}{2} = \cos(x - \pi)$

83. $y = 6 - 5 \sin(4x + 2)$

Objective M: State equations for graphs of circular functions. *(Lessons 4-7, 4-8, 4-9)*

In 84–86, match each equation with its graph.

84. $y = \sin\left(x - \frac{\pi}{3}\right)$

85. $y = 1 + \sin x$

86. $y = \cos\left(x - \frac{\pi}{2}\right)$

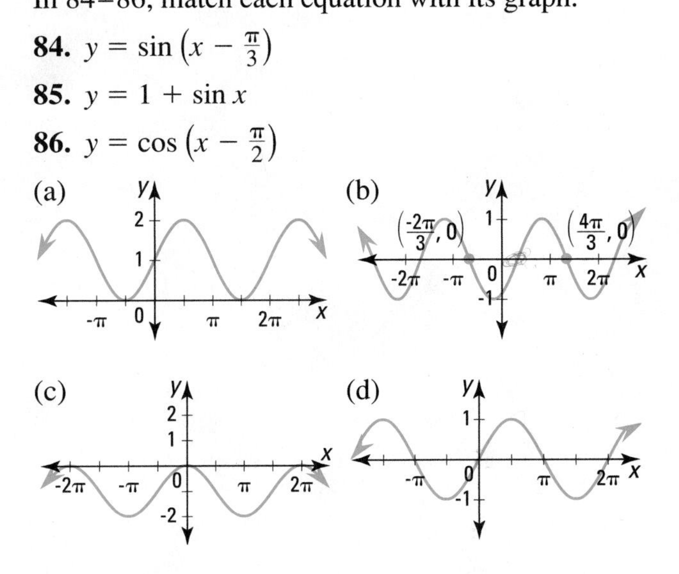

87. Give an equation for the sine wave below.

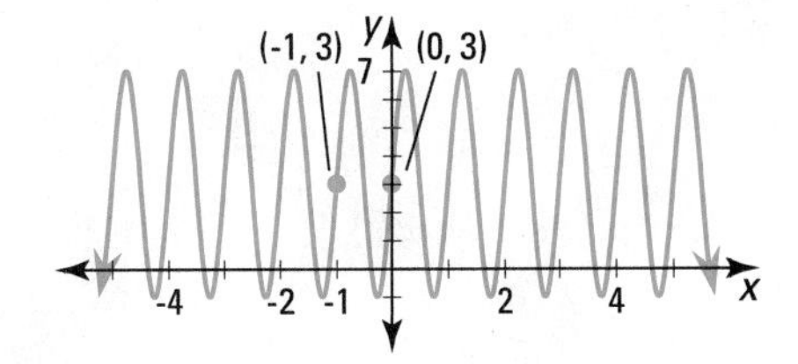

88. Find an equation for the graph below, which is a translation image of the graph of $y = \tan x$.

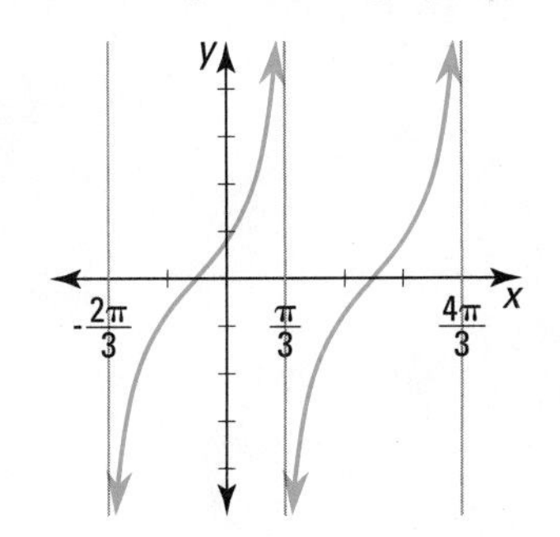

CHAPTER

5

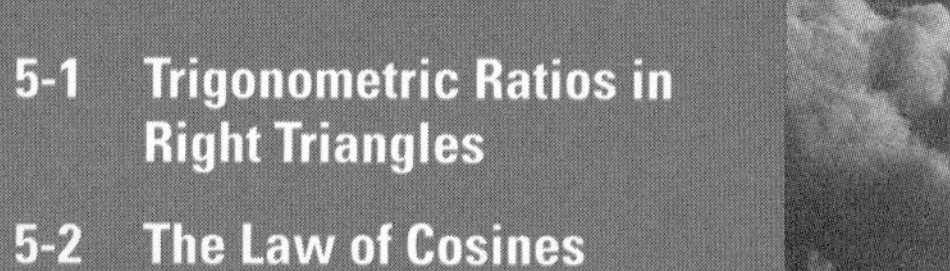

TRIGONOMETRIC FUNCTIONS

In Chapter 4, you studied the use of the sine, cosine, and tangent functions in describing circular motion and other periodic phenomena such as sound waves or tides. However, the first known uses of these functions arose from the need of people to solve practical, everyday problems in which lengths or angles in triangles had to be found. Thus, the study of the sine, cosine, and tangent functions is called **trigonometry**, a word derived from Greek words meaning "triangle measurement," and these functions are often called **trigonometric functions**.

The origins of trigonometry have been traced back to the Egyptians of the 13th century B.C., whose tables of shadow lengths correspond to today's tangent and *cotangent* functions. The Babylonians and Greeks used trigonometry to study the heavens. Travelers of recent centuries used trigonometry to navigate.

In this chapter, you will study additional properties of these functions and you will use trigonometry to solve problems, such as the following, that are based on triangle measurement.

How long is a throw from 10 feet behind second base to first base?

What is the diameter of the moon?

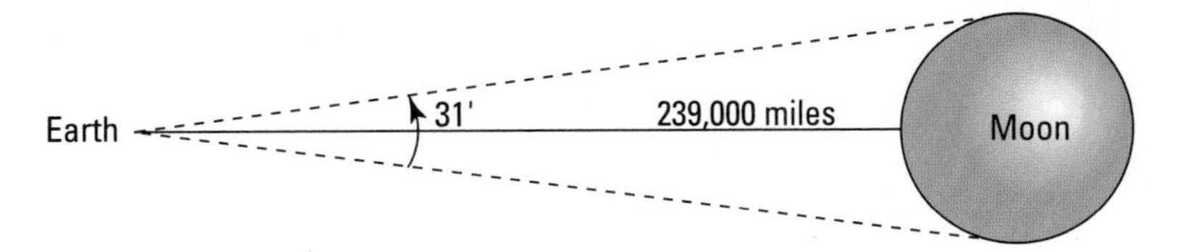

How far is it from Washington, D.C., to Beijing, China?

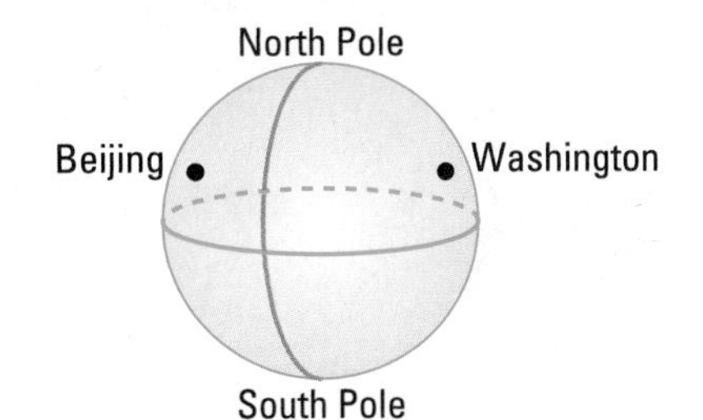

LESSON

5-1

Trigonometric Ratios in Right Triangles

Geomatics. *The work of surveyors is a part of geomatics, the art, science, and technologies related to geographically-referenced information. This surveyor is on Mount St. Helens in the state of Washington.*

The picture below reviews some terminology about right triangles which may be familiar to you. Examine it closely. Each leg is opposite one acute angle and adjacent to the other.

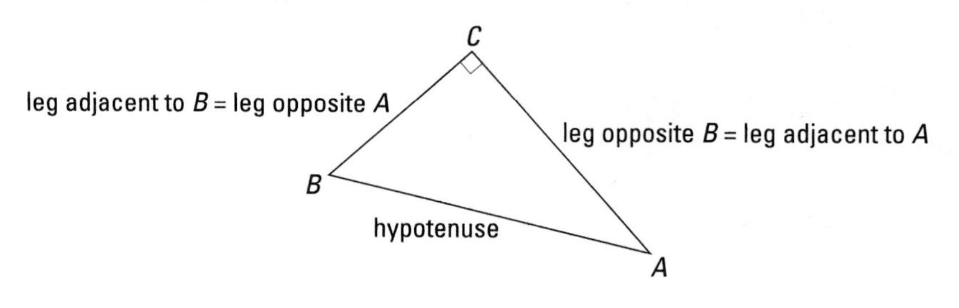

Relating Sines, Cosines, and Tangents to Sides in Right Triangles

In an earlier course, you may have seen sines, cosines, and tangents defined in terms of the sides of right triangles. These relationships can be *proved* from the definitions of sine, cosine, and tangent that you studied in Chapter 4.

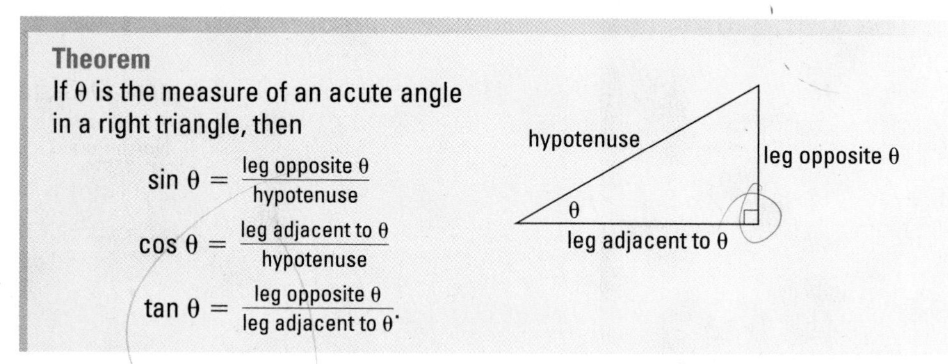

Theorem

If θ is the measure of an acute angle in a right triangle, then

$$\sin \theta = \frac{\text{leg opposite } \theta}{\text{hypotenuse}}$$

$$\cos \theta = \frac{\text{leg adjacent to } \theta}{\text{hypotenuse}}$$

$$\tan \theta = \frac{\text{leg opposite } \theta}{\text{leg adjacent to } \theta}.$$

Proof

Place right $\triangle ABC$ on a coordinate system with A at (0, 0) and C on the positive ray of the x-axis. Let D be the intersection of $\overrightarrow{AB}$ and the unit circle and draw $\overline{DE} \perp \overline{AC}$. We wish to prove:

$$\sin\theta = \frac{\text{leg opposite }\theta}{\text{hypotenuse}} = \frac{BC}{AB}$$

$$\cos\theta = \frac{\text{leg adjacent to }\theta}{\text{hypotenuse}} = \frac{AC}{AB}$$

$$\tan\theta = \frac{\text{leg opposite }\theta}{\text{leg adjacent to }\theta} = \frac{BC}{AC}.$$

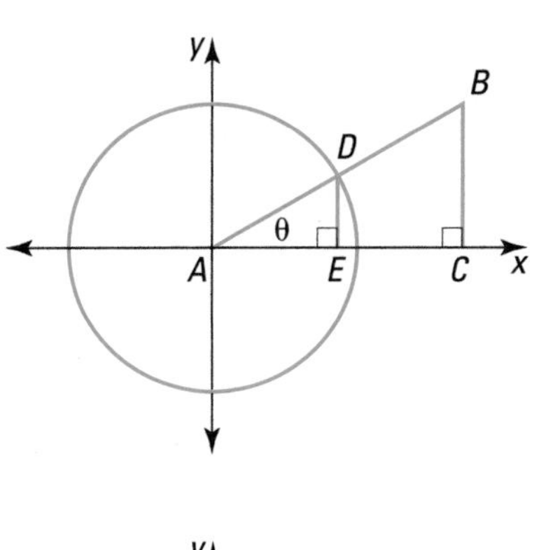

From the definitions of cosine and sine, $D = (\cos\theta, \sin\theta)$. Since θ is the measure of an acute angle, D is in the first quadrant. So $AE = \cos\theta$ and $DE = \sin\theta$. And since the circle is a unit circle, $AD = 1$. Now, by similar triangles, $\frac{DE}{AD} = \frac{BC}{AB}$, so $\frac{\sin\theta}{1} = \frac{BC}{AB}$, and thus $\sin\theta = \frac{\text{leg opposite }\theta}{\text{hypotenuse}}$.

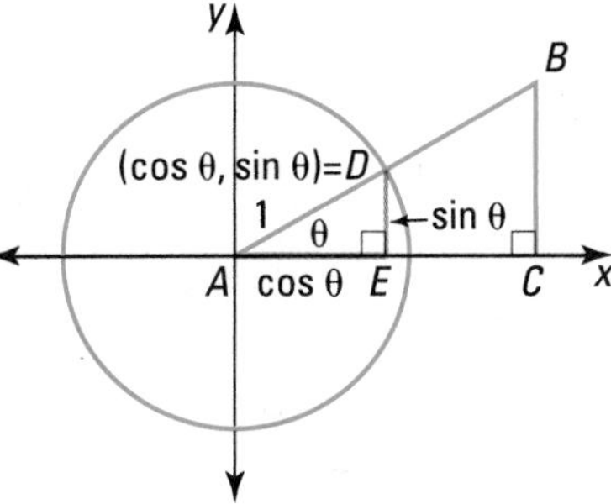

Activity

Finish the above proof for $\cos\theta$ and $\tan\theta$ by modifying the last sentence of the proof twice.

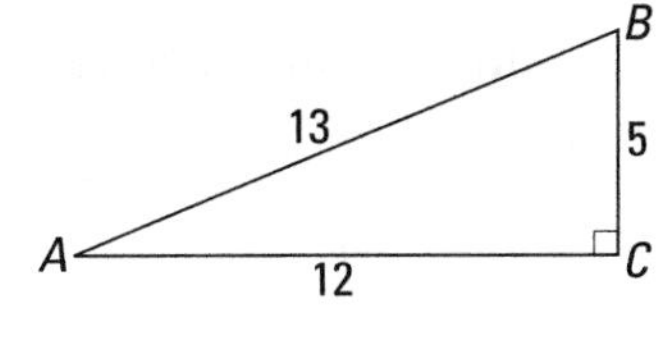

For instance, in the triangle at the left, the leg opposite A has length 5, the leg adjacent to A has length 12, and the hypotenuse has length 13.

So $\sin A = \frac{5}{13}$,

$\cos A = \frac{12}{13}$,

and $\tan A = \frac{5}{12}$.

Finding Sides in Right Triangles

In many situations you know only the length of one side and the measure of one acute angle in a right triangle. By choosing the appropriate trigonometric ratio, you can determine the length of either other side.

Example 1

Suppose that the distance along the slope from the top of the bank of a river to the edge of the water is 23.6 m, and a surveyor finds that the land slopes downward at an angle of 26° from the horizontal. (Such an angle is called an **angle of depression**.) Find d, the horizontal distance from the top of the bank to the river's edge.

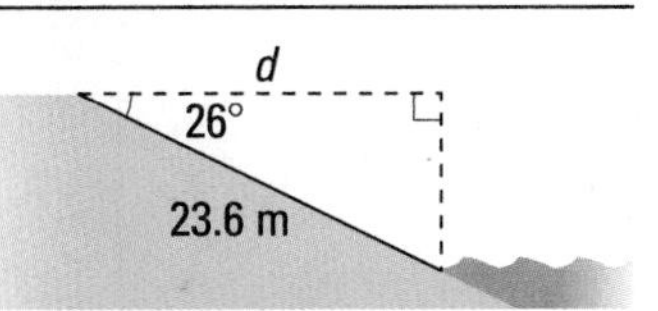

Solution

You are given the measure of an acute angle and the length of the hypotenuse in a right triangle. You must find the side adjacent to the acute angle. Use the cosine ratio, and solve for *d*.

$$\cos 26° = \frac{d}{23.6}$$
$$d = (23.6)(\cos 26°)$$
$$d \approx 23.6 \cdot 0.899$$
$$d \approx 21.2$$

So the horizontal distance from the bank of the river to the edge of the water is about 21.2 meters.

Degrees, Minutes, and Seconds

A degree may be subdivided into *minutes* and *seconds*. One degree equals sixty **minutes**. One minute equals sixty **seconds**. Minutes are represented by a single tick mark and seconds by a double tick mark. For instance, 5 degrees, 22 minutes, 30 seconds is written as 5°22'30", and represents $5 + \frac{22}{60} + \frac{30}{3600}$ degrees. It is often inconvenient to work with these fractions. They can be converted to decimals as follows:

$$\begin{aligned} 5°22'30" &= 5 + \tfrac{22}{60} + \tfrac{30}{3600} \\ &= 5 + .3\overline{6} + .008\overline{3} \\ &= 5.375°. \end{aligned}$$

Your calculator may have a key, sometimes labeled DMS, for converting between degrees, minutes, and seconds and decimal degrees. You should learn how it works. This conversion is helpful because minutes and seconds are still commonly used in geography, as in Example 2.

Example 2

A surveying instrument is 4.5 feet above the ground. A surveyor marks a point 50 feet from the base of a cliff, and measures the **angle of elevation** to its top to be about 61°39'. Find the height of the cliff.

Solution

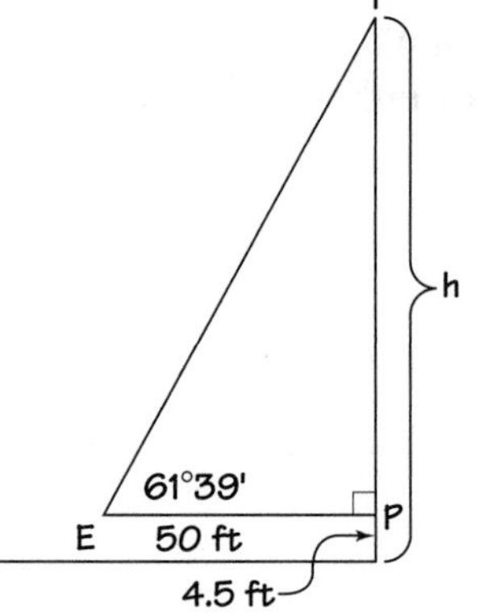

Draw a diagram showing the right triangle formed by the top *T* of the cliff, the eye *E* of the surveyor, and the point *P* where a horizontal line through *E* intersects the cliff. You are given $m\angle TEP$ and *EP*, the length of the side adjacent to it. You must find *TP*, the length of the side opposite $\angle E$. Use the tangent ratio and solve for *TP*.

$$61°39' = 61.65°$$
$$\tan 61.65° = \frac{TP}{50}$$
$$50 \tan 61.65° = TP$$
$$TP \approx 92.67$$

So the height $h = TP + 4.5 \approx 92.7 + 4.5 = 97.2$ feet.

Example 3

Federal law specifies that every new public building must be accessible by a ramp with slope $\frac{1}{12}$ or less. What is the maximum angle of elevation for a ramp?

Solution

First draw a picture.

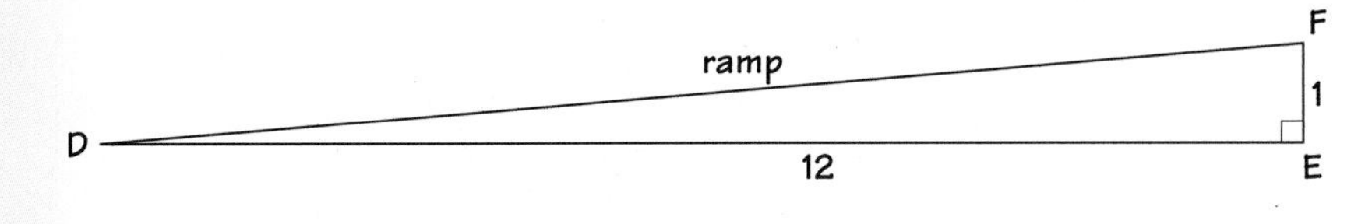

In this situation, $\tan D = \frac{1}{12}$. The inverse of the tangent function, $\tan^{-1}$, can be used to find $m\angle D$. Specifically, $m\angle D = \tan^{-1}\left(\frac{1}{12}\right)$.

The following key sequence works on many calculators.

2nd TAN (1 ÷ 12) ENTER

If your calculator is set to radians, you will see .0831412... displayed. If your calculator is set to degrees, you will see 4.763641 .... These displays indicate

$$m\angle D \approx .0831 \text{ radians} \approx 4.7636°.$$

Check

Does $\tan 4.7636° = \frac{1}{12}$? $\tan 4.7636° = .0833326\ldots$ and $\frac{1}{12} = .08\overline{3}$. It checks.

QUESTIONS

Covering the Reading

In 1 and 2, use your work on the Activity in this lesson.

1. Finish the proof of the theorem in this lesson for cos θ.

2. Finish the proof of the theorem in this lesson for tan θ.

In 3 and 4, use $\triangle ABC$ at the right.

3. Give the exact value for each.
 a. $\sin A$
 b. $\cos A$
 c. $\tan A$

4. a. Find the exact value of $\tan B$.
 b. Find $m\angle B$ to the nearest tenth of a degree.

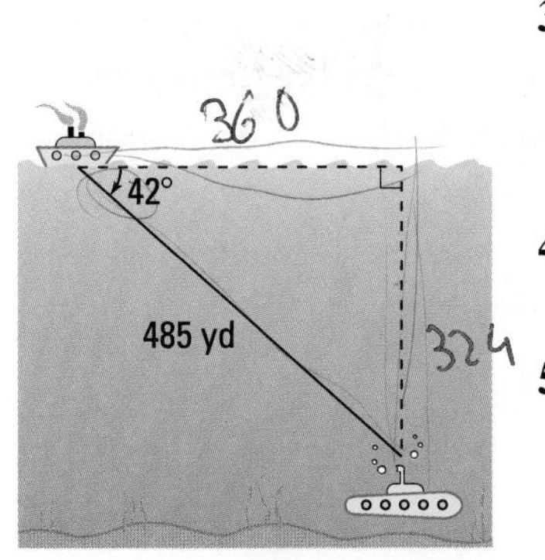

5. Sonar on a ship sights an object at an angle of depression of 42° and a distance of 485 yards.
 a. How far below sea level is the object?
 b. How far must the ship sail to be directly over the object?

6. In $\triangle DEF$ at the left, find DE and EF to the nearest hundredth.

In 7 and 8, change to decimal degrees.

7. 50°6'15" **8.** 32°40"

9. Use a calculator to evaluate tan 16°35' to the nearest hundredth.

In 10 and 11, find $m\angle A$ to the nearest tenth of a degree.

10. **11.**

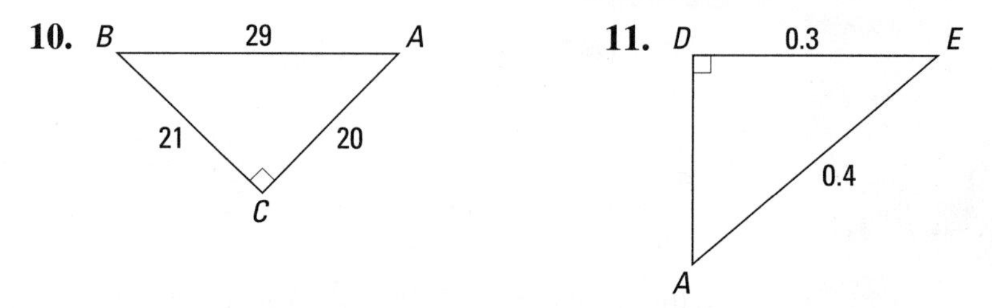

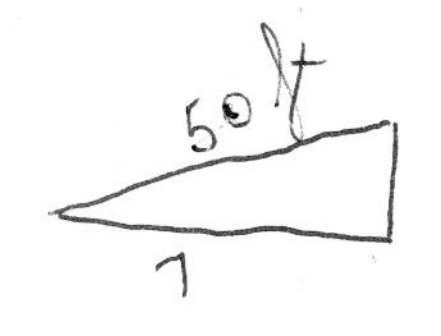

12. Suppose a road rises 50 feet in a mile. What is its average angle of elevation?

Applying the Mathematics

13. From a distance, a surveyor measures the angle of elevation of Shanghai's Oriental Pearl Television Tower (China's tallest structure with a height of 1535 feet) to be about 6°.

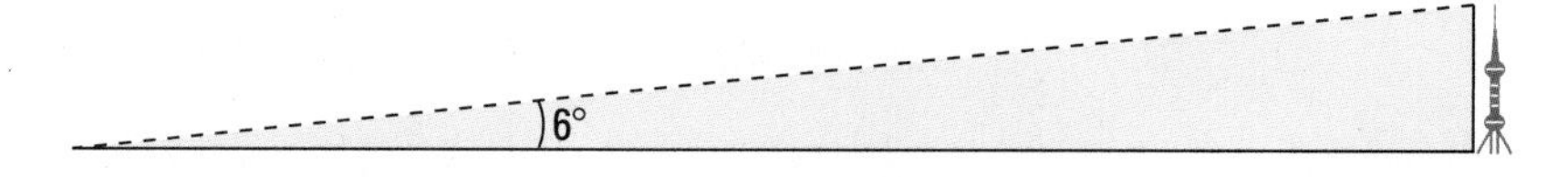

a. Assuming the measurement of 6° is correct, how far is the surveyor from the building, to the nearest 100 feet?

b. If the elevation is only correct to the nearest degree (i.e., the elevation is 6° ± 1°), give the maximum and minimum values for the surveyor's distance from the Oriental Pearl Television Tower.

14. The sails of the windmill illustrated at the left measure 13.5 meters from the tip of a blade to the tip of the opposite blade. The pivot O is 8.1 meters off the ground. How far off the ground is point P after the sail rotates 70° from the horizontal as shown?

15. Lumber sold in the U.S. as 12" is actually only $11\frac{1}{4}$" wide. Suppose you need to cut a 72° angle on a piece of lumber for a woodwork project, but you don't have a protractor. How far on the length of the board will the cut reach? (See the drawing below.) Give your answer to the nearest $\frac{1}{8}$ inch.

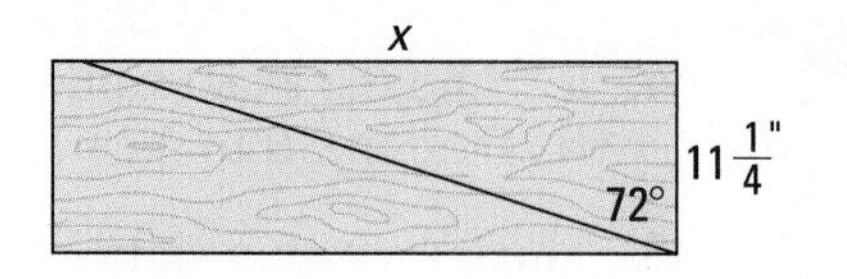

16. A ship is on a bearing of 47°. (A *bearing* is the angle measured clockwise from due north.)
   a. How far has the ship sailed if it is 200 km north of its original position?
   b. How far east of its original position is the ship?
   c. If the ship's average speed is 12 km per hour, for how long has it been sailing?

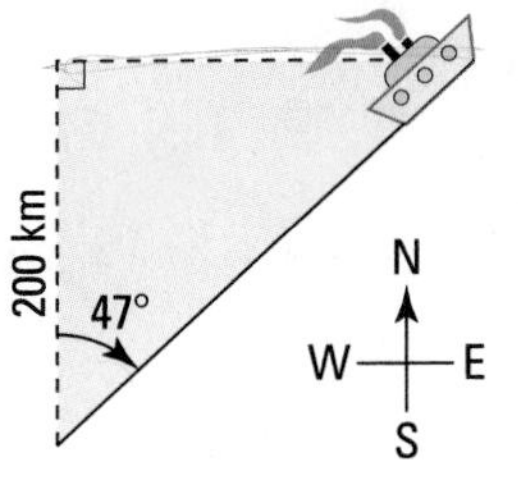

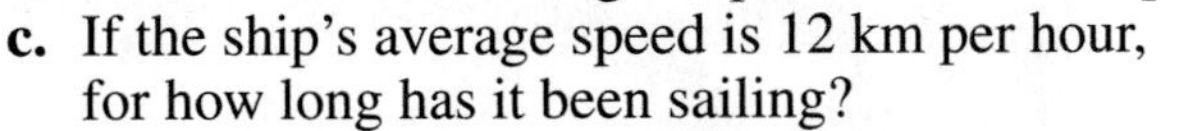

Review

17. For what values of θ between 0 and 2π is $\cos\theta < 0$? *(Lessons 4-3, 4-6)*

18. New York City is due north of Bogota, Colombia. The latitude of New York City is 40°47' N and the latitude of Bogota is 4°36' N. Approximate the distance between them in miles. Use 7926 miles for Earth's diameter. *(Lesson 4-2)*

19. Consider the graph of a function f defined for $0 \le x \le 10$, and graphed at the right.
   a. Sketch a graph of the inverse of f.
   b. Is the inverse of f a function? Why or why not? *(Lesson 3-8)*

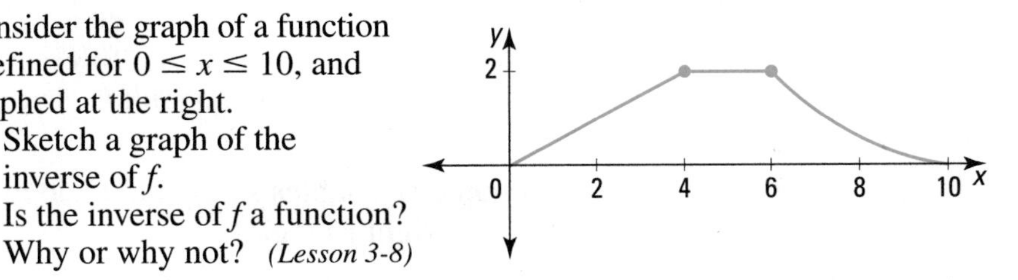

20. If functions F and G are inverses of each other, how are their domains and ranges related to each other? *(Lesson 3-8)*

Exploration

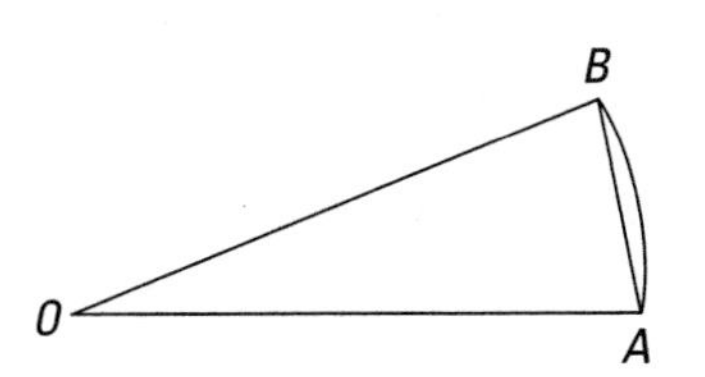

$AB \approx$ length of $\overset{\frown}{AB}$

21. For small angles, the length of an arc and the length of the associated chord of a circle are approximately equal. Astronomical measurements are commonly made by measuring the small angle formed by lines of sight to the extremities of a distant object. Earth's moon covers an angle of 31' when it is about 239,000 miles away.
   a. Use this information to estimate the diameter of the moon.

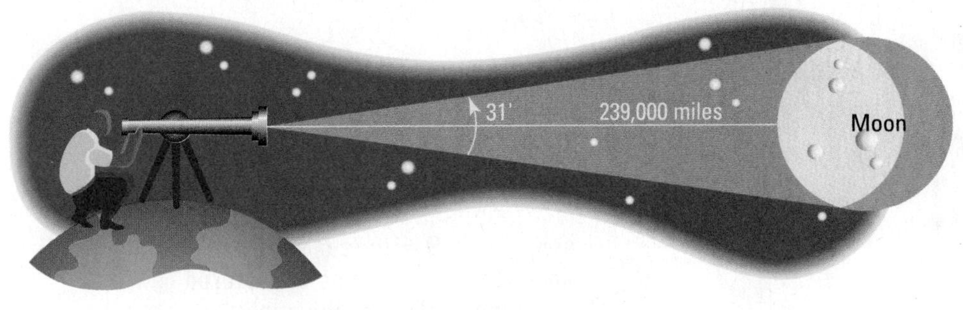

   b. Compare your estimate to the value found in an almanac or other reference book.

LESSON

5-2

The Law of Cosines

Brave play. *Mark Lemke, second baseman for the Atlanta Braves, perhaps does not think about the Law of Cosines while fielding the ball, but it wouldn't hurt if he did.*

Trigonometry enables sides and angle measures to be found in triangles other than right triangles.

Consider this problem: A baseball player catches a line drive at a point 10 feet directly behind second base. How far must the player throw the ball to get it to first base to complete a double play?

The problem can be solved using a powerful theorem called the *Law of Cosines*. In stating this theorem, we name the side opposite each vertex by the small letter of that vertex. For example, opposite vertex B is side b.

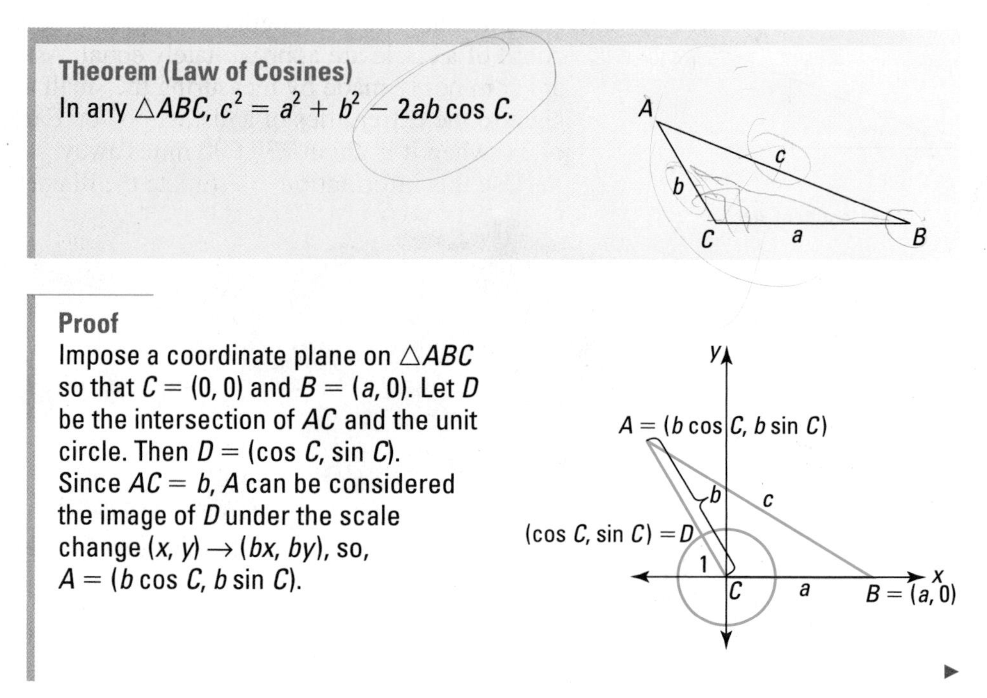

Theorem (Law of Cosines)
In any $\triangle ABC$, $c^2 = a^2 + b^2 - 2ab \cos C$.

Proof
Impose a coordinate plane on $\triangle ABC$ so that $C = (0, 0)$ and $B = (a, 0)$. Let D be the intersection of $\overline{AC}$ and the unit circle. Then $D = (\cos C, \sin C)$. Since $AC = b$, A can be considered the image of D under the scale change $(x, y) \rightarrow (bx, by)$, so, $A = (b \cos C, b \sin C)$.

By the distance formula, $c = \sqrt{(b \cos C - a)^2 + (b \sin C - 0)^2}$.
The rest of the proof involves rewriting the above equation so that it has the form in which it appears in the theorem.

Square both sides.	$c^2 = (b \cos C - a)^2 + (b \sin C - 0)^2$
Expand the binomials.	$c^2 = b^2\cos^2 C - 2ab \cos C + a^2 + b^2\sin^2 C$
Apply the Commutative Property of Addition.	$c^2 = a^2 + b^2\sin^2 C + b^2\cos^2 C - 2ab \cos C$
Factor.	$c^2 = a^2 + b^2(\sin^2 C + \cos^2 C) - 2ab \cos C$
Use the Pythagorean Identity.	$c^2 = a^2 + b^2 - 2ab \cos C$

Using the Law of Cosines to Find a Side of a Triangle

Notice the power of the Law of Cosines. Given two sides and the included angle of a triangle (the SAS condition), you can find the third side.

Example 1

A baseball player is 10 feet behind second base. How far is it from that position to first base?

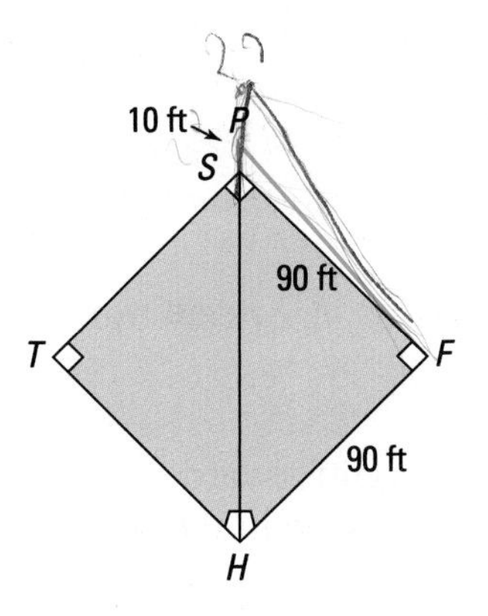

Solution

To solve this problem, recall that the bases on a baseball diamond are vertices of a square of side 90 ft. In the figure at the left, the distance PF is needed. Because $m\angle TSF = 90°$ and $\overline{PH}$ bisects $\angle TSF$, $m\angle PSF = 135°$. Also, $PS = 10$ and $SF = 90$. Since two sides and the included angle are given, the Law of Cosines can be used. For this situation,

$$\begin{aligned} PF^2 &= PS^2 + SF^2 - 2 \cdot PS \cdot SF \cos S \\ &= 10^2 + 90^2 - 2 \cdot 10 \cdot 90 \cdot \cos 135° \\ &\approx 8200 - 1800 \cdot (-.707) \\ &\approx 9473. \end{aligned}$$

So $$PF \approx \sqrt{9473} \approx 97 \text{ feet.}$$

Check

Since $\angle PSF$ is obtuse, PF should be the longest side of $\triangle PSF$ and, by the Triangle Inequality, $PF < 100$. So the answer is reasonable.

The Law of Cosines can be considered as a generalization of the Pythagorean Theorem. Notice that if $m\angle C = 90°$ in $\triangle ABC$, then

$$c^2 = a^2 + b^2 - 2ab \cos 90°.$$

Since $\cos 90° = 0$, $$c^2 = a^2 + b^2.$$

The first appearance of the Law of Cosines that we know about is in Book II of Euclid's *Elements*, written around 300 B.C.

Using the Law of Cosines to Find an Angle of a Triangle

Example 1 shows how the Law of Cosines can be used given SAS. Because each angle between 0 and 180° has a unique cosine, the Law of Cosines can also be used to find the measure of any angle of a triangle if the lengths of all three sides are known (the SSS condition).

Example 2

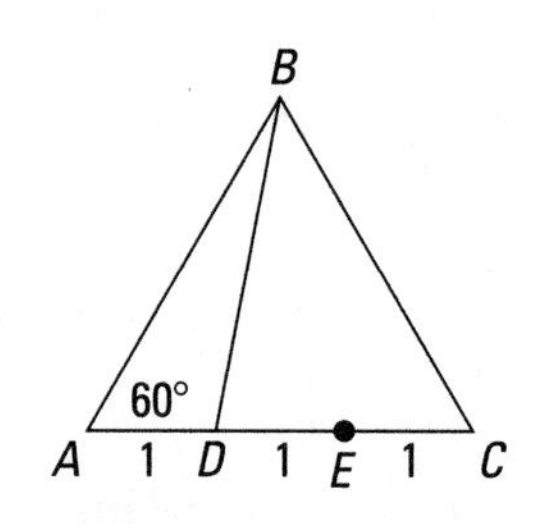

A student tries to trisect $\angle ABC$ in equilateral $\triangle ABC$ by trisecting $\overline{AC}$ with points D and E and then drawing $\overline{BD}$. Show that $\angle ABC$ is not trisected by this construction.

Solution

Suppose AB = 3. Then AD = 1. By the Law of Cosines,

$$\begin{aligned} BD^2 &= AB^2 + AD^2 - 2 \cdot AB \cdot AD \cdot \cos 60° \\ &= 3^2 + 1^2 - 2 \cdot 3 \cdot 1 \cdot (0.5) \\ &= 7 \end{aligned}$$

So $\quad BD = \sqrt{7}.$

Now use the Law of Cosines with $\angle ABD$ as the included angle.

$$\begin{aligned} AD^2 &= AB^2 + BD^2 - 2 \cdot AB \cdot BD \cdot \cos \angle ABD \\ 1 &= 9 + 7 - 2 \cdot 3 \cdot \sqrt{7} \cdot \cos \angle ABD \\ -15 &= -6\sqrt{7} \cdot \cos \angle ABD \\ .944911 &\approx \cos \angle ABD \\ \cos^{-1} .944911 &\approx m\angle ABD \\ 19.1° &\approx m\angle ABD \end{aligned}$$

$m\angle ABD$ would be 20° if $\angle ABC$ were trisected. So, $\overline{BD}$ does not trisect $\angle ABC$.

Using the Law of Cosines to solve for an angle is straightforward, but the algebra can be tricky. Be sure that you understand each step in the solution to Example 2.

QUESTIONS

Covering the Reading

1. Refer to Example 1. Suppose that an infielder is standing 20 feet behind second base. To the nearest foot, how far is the player from third base?

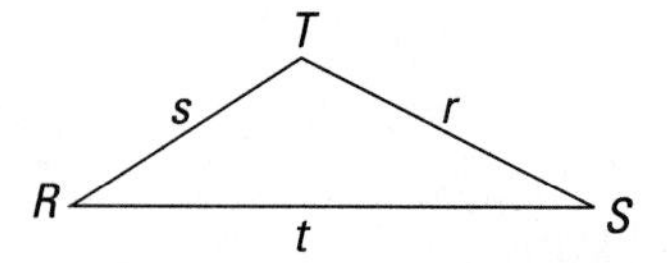

2. Refer to $\triangle RST$ at the left.
   a. Write a formula for t in terms of $m\angle T$, r, and s.
   b. Suppose $r = 6$, $s = 5$, and $m\angle T = 120°$. Find the exact length t.

3. In $\triangle XYZ$, $x = 10$, $y = 15$, and $z = 20$. Find each.
   a. $m\angle Z$ **b.** $m\angle X$

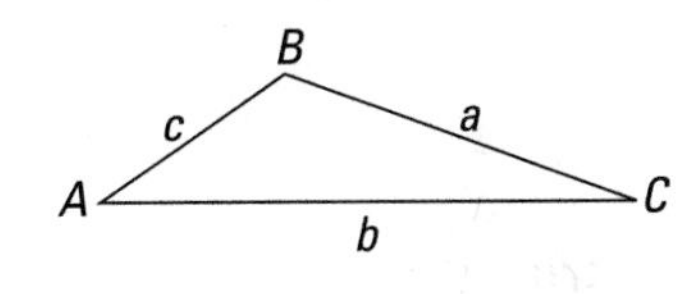

In 4–7, *multiple choice.* Refer to $\triangle ABC$ at the left. Which formula can be used to find the required measure directly?

(a) $a^2 = b^2 + c^2 - 2bc \cos A$ (b) $b^2 = a^2 + c^2 - 2ac \cos B$
(c) $c^2 = a^2 + b^2 - 2ab \cos C$ (d) none of (a)-(c)

4. Given: a, b, c.
Find: $m\angle A$.

5. Given: a, b, $m\angle A$.
Find: c.

6. Given: a, b, $m\angle C$.
Find: c.

7. Given: a, b, $m\angle C$.
Find: $m\angle A$.

In 8 and 9, refer to the proof of the Law of Cosines.

8. a. Find the slope of $\overline{CD}$. **b.** Find the slope of $\overline{CA}$.
c. Use the results of parts **a** and **b** to show that A, D, and C are collinear.

9. Use the distance formula to show that $AC = b$.

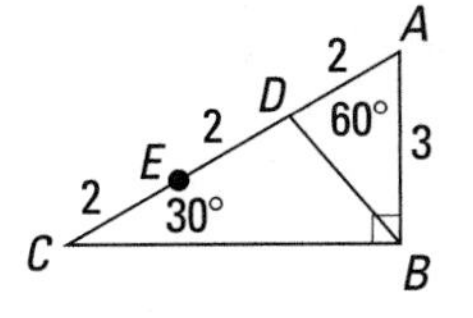

10. In the right triangle ABC at the left, D and E trisect the hypotenuse. Show that $\overline{BD}$ does not trisect $\angle CBA$.

Applying the Mathematics

11. Find the length of a diagonal of a regular pentagon which has a side of length 10.

12. The sides of a triangle have lengths 5.9 m, 2.8 m, and 5.9 m. Find the measure of the smallest angle.

13. Show that there is no triangle with sides 5 cm, 9 cm, and 15 cm using the given property.
a. the Law of Cosines **b.** the Triangle Inequality

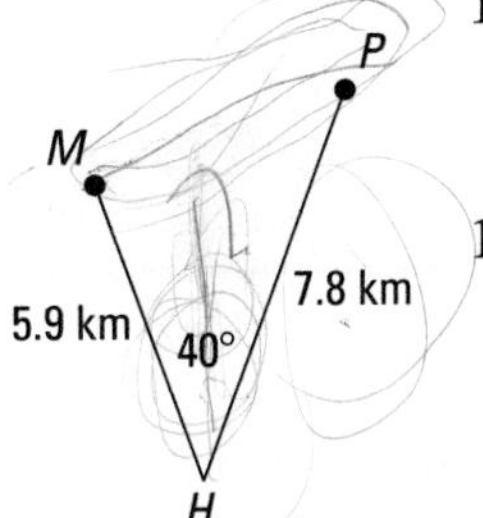

14. A sign at a mountain overlook indicates that a hiker H is 5.9 km from a microwave tower M and 7.8 km from the highest visible peak P. The hiker estimates the angle between M and P from her position to be 40°. Find MP.

Review

15. A plane flying at 32,000 feet starts its descent 100 miles from an airport A. At what angle θ does the plane descend? *(Lesson 5-1)*

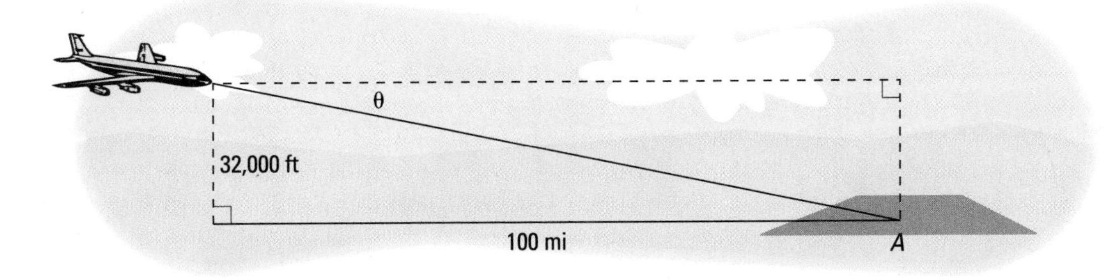

16. A 28-foot ladder leans against the side of a building at an angle of 75°. How far does the ladder reach up the building? *(Lesson 5-1)*

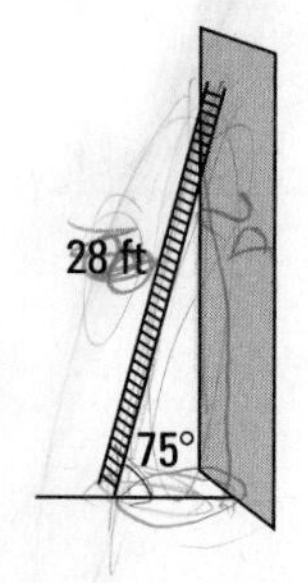

17. Two sightings are taken of a TV tower. The first gives an elevation of 23°. The second sighting is taken 400 feet farther from the tower and gives an elevation of 20°30'. How tall is the tower? (Hint: Write two equations in h and x involving the tangent function and solve the system.) *(Lesson 5-1)*

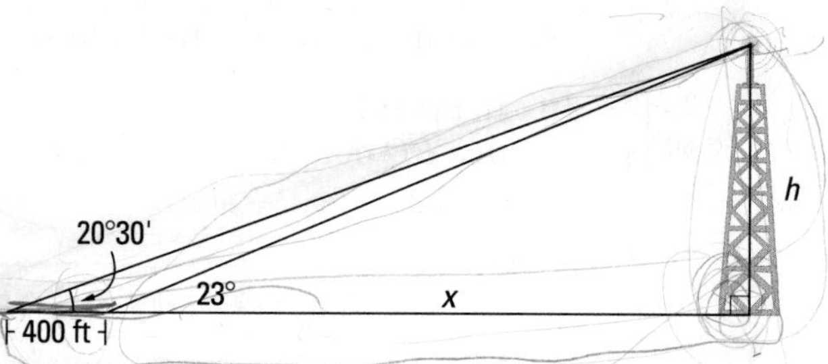

18. Graph on the same set of axes for $0 \le x \le 2\pi$. *(Lessons 4-6, 4-7, 4-8)*

a. $y = \cos x$ **b.** $y = 2 \cos x$ **c.** $y = 3 + 2 \cos x$

19. Suppose $f: x \rightarrow \frac{1}{3}x - 12$.

a. Find an equation for $f^{-1}(x)$.

b. Explain how the graphs of $y = f(x)$ and $y = f^{-1}(x)$ are related to each other.

c. Evaluate $f(f^{-1}(x))$. *(Lesson 3-8)*

Exploration

20. Let a, b, and c be the sides of a triangle, and suppose that c is the longest side.

a. If $c^2 > a^2 + b^2$, what is true about $\triangle ABC$?

b. If $c^2 < a^2 + b^2$, what can you conclude?

c. Prove your conjectures in parts **a** and **b**.

LESSON

5-3

The Inverse Cosine Function

Inclined to load the truck. *A ramp can be a huge asset in loading a truck if the angle of elevation is small.*

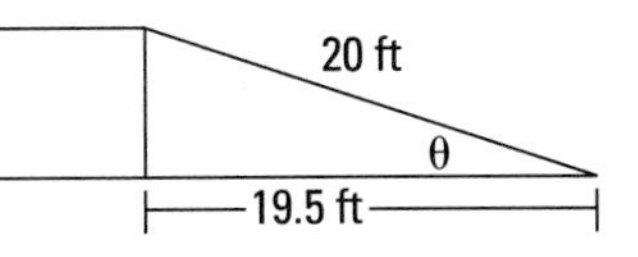

In the first two lessons of Chapter 5 you solved problems in which you had to find the measure of an angle in a triangle. For instance, to find the measure of angle θ made when a 20-foot ramp is placed 19.5 feet from a loading dock, you could write $\cos\theta = \frac{19.5}{20}$. You can use the $\boxed{\cos^{-1}}$ or $\boxed{\text{Acos}}$ key on a calculator to determine that $\theta \approx 12.8°$. In this lesson, properties of the inverse cosine function, $\cos^{-1}$, are examined.

The Domain of the Inverse Cosine Function

Recall the graph of $y = \cos x$.

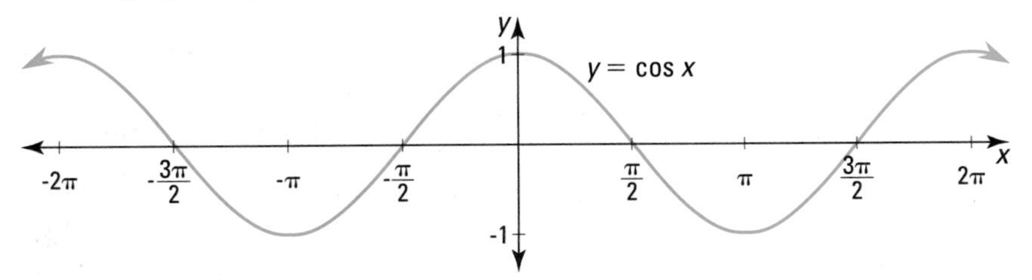

Because $y = \cos x$ does not pass the horizontal line test, its inverse is not a function. For this reason, in order for the inverse of the cosine function to be a function, the domain of $y = \cos x$ must be restricted. There are many possible restricted domains. Here are three criteria for an appropriate domain:

1. The domain should include the angles between 0 and $\frac{\pi}{2}$ because they are the measures of the acute angles of a right triangle.
2. On the restricted domain, the function should take on all the values of the range, that is, all real numbers from -1 to 1.
3. If possible, the function should be continuous in the restricted domain.

The graphs below show several ways to restrict the domain of $y = \cos x$. Each graph fails to meet the above criteria in some way.

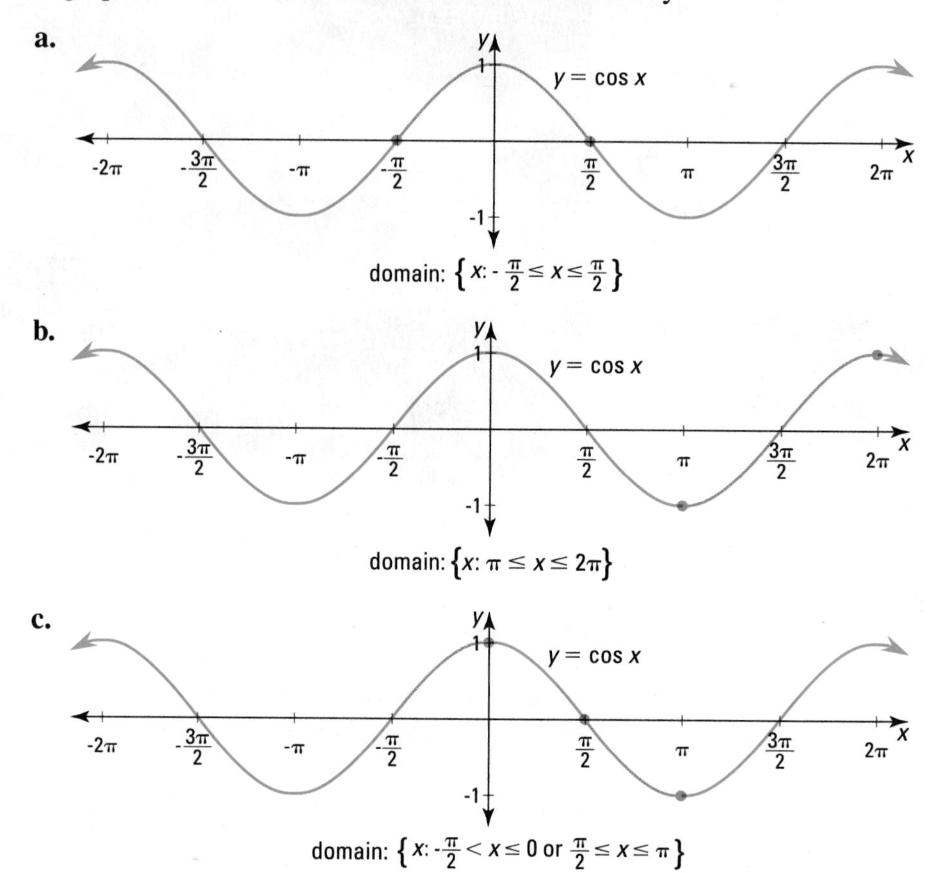

The domain chosen in graph **a** does not give an inverse function since it does not pass the horizontal line test. The domain in graph **b** is rejected because it does not include acute angles. The domain in graph **c** is rejected because it is discontinuous.

Only one domain fits all three criteria mentioned above. It is $\{x: 0 \le x \le \pi\}$. The function that is the inverse of this restricted cosine function is denoted $\mathbf{cos^{-1}}$ and called the **inverse cosine function.**

Definition

$y = \mathbf{cos^{-1}}\, x$ if and only if $x = \cos y$ and $0 \le y \le \pi$.

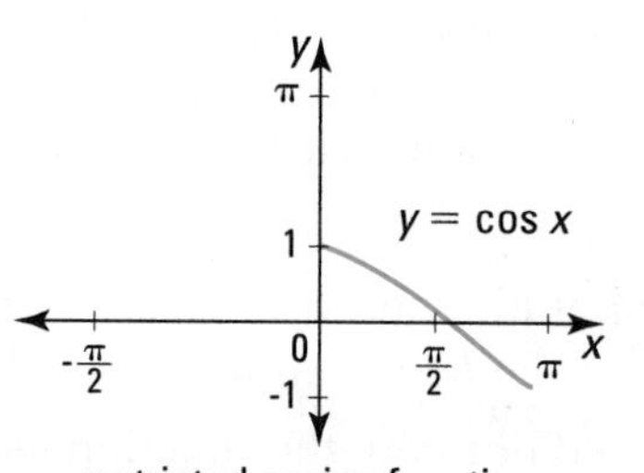

restricted cosine function
domain: $\{x: 0 \le x \le \pi\}$
range: $\{y: -1 \le y \le 1\}$

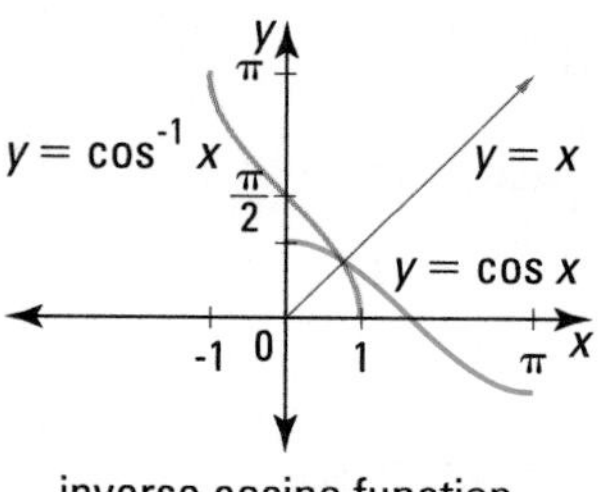

inverse cosine function
domain: $\{x: -1 \le x \le 1\}$
range: $\{y: 0 \le y \le \pi\}$

Recall that the graph of the inverse of a function is the reflection image of the graph of the original function across the line $y = x$. Notice that, as with all inverse functions, the domain of $y = \cos^{-1} x$ is the range of $y = \cos x$ and the range of $y = \cos^{-1} x$ is the restricted domain of $y = \cos x$. Also recall that if f and f^{-1} are inverse functions, then $f \circ f^{-1}(x) = x$ for all x in the domain of f^{-1}, and $f^{-1} \circ f(x) = x$ for all x in the domain of f.

The notation **Arccos** is sometimes used in place of $\cos^{-1}$.

When using the inverse cosine function to evaluate an expression, your answer must lie in the range of $y = \cos^{-1} x$, that is, from 0 to π (radians), or from 0° to 180°.

Evaluating Inverse Cosines

Example 1

Evaluate $\cos^{-1}\left(\frac{\sqrt{2}}{2}\right)$. Give an exact answer in radians.

Solution

Recall the unit circle. If $y = \cos^{-1}\left(\frac{\sqrt{2}}{2}\right)$, then, by definition of $\cos^{-1}$, y is the unique number on the interval $0 \leq y \leq \pi$ whose cosine is $\frac{\sqrt{2}}{2}$. Because $\cos \frac{\pi}{4} = \frac{\sqrt{2}}{2}$ and $0 \leq \frac{\pi}{4} \leq \pi$, $\cos^{-1}\left(\frac{\sqrt{2}}{2}\right) = \frac{\pi}{4}$.

Check

Use a calculator set to radians. Ours gives $\cos^{-1}\left(\frac{\sqrt{2}}{2}\right) = .7853981634$. Multiply this value by 4 and compare it to π.

Example 2

Evaluate $\cos^{-1}(-0.7924)$. Give your answer in degrees.

Solution

$y = \cos^{-1}(-0.7924)$ if and only if $\cos y = -0.7924$ and $0° \leq y \leq 180°$. Use a calculator.

$$\cos^{-1}(-0.7924) \approx 142.4°$$

Check

Is $0° \leq 142.4° \leq 180°$? Yes, so the answer from the calculator is in the correct range. Now evaluate cos 142.4°. Our calculator gives the answer as -0.7922896, which is about -0.7924.

Applications of the Inverse Cosine

Wherever there are situations involving the cosine function, applications of the inverse cosine function may appear.

Example 3

The Landsat 2 satellite can only see a portion of Earth's surface (bounded by a horizon circle as shown below at the left) at any given time. Imagine looking at a cross section of the satellite and Earth, as shown below at the right. Point C is the center of Earth, H is a point on the horizon circle, and S is the location of the satellite. Let $\theta = m\angle HCS$. The altitude a of the satellite is the distance in km of the satellite above Earth. Notice that $\angle CHS$ is a right angle.

a. Write a formula for θ in terms of r and a.

b. The radius of Earth is about 6378 km. To the nearest tenth of a degree, what is θ when Landsat 2 is 956 km above Earth?

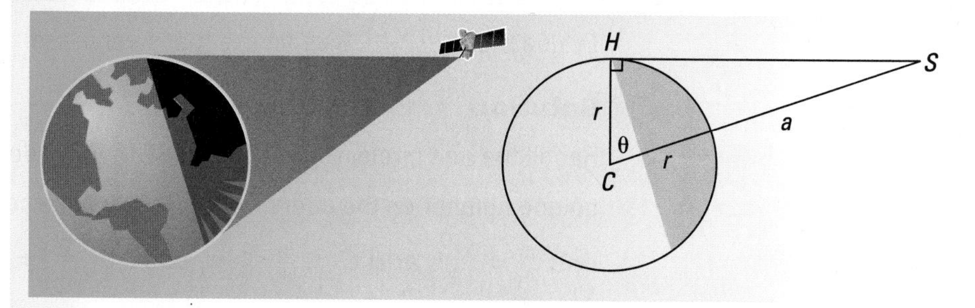

Solution

a. Since the hypotenuse of $\triangle CHS$ and the side adjacent to θ involve r and a, use the cosine of θ.

$$\cos\theta = \frac{r}{r+a}$$

Solve for θ. $\quad \theta = \cos^{-1}\left(\frac{r}{r+a}\right)$

b. For $r = 6378$ and $a = 956$,

$$\theta = \cos^{-1}\left(\frac{6378}{6378+956}\right)$$
$$\approx \cos^{-1}(0.869648)$$
$$\approx 29.58°$$

So $\quad \theta \approx 29.6°$.

QUESTIONS

Covering the Reading

1. *True or false.* The inverse of the cosine function defined for $-2\pi \le x \le 2\pi$ is a function. Justify your answer.

2. Why is $\left\{x: 0 \le x \le \frac{\pi}{2}\right\}$ not used as the domain of the restricted cosine function so that it has an inverse?

3. How is the expression "$\theta = \cos^{-1} k$" read?

4. **a.** Copy and complete the table of values below. Round approximations to the nearest thousandth.
   b. Graph $y = \cos x$, $0 \le x \le \pi$, and $y = \cos^{-1} x$ on the same coordinate system. Use the same scale on each axis.
   c. State the domain and range of the function $y = \cos^{-1} x$.
   d. What transformation maps $y = \cos x$ with $0 \le x \le \pi$ to $y = \cos^{-1} x$?

point on $y = \cos x$	$(0, 1)$	$(\frac{\pi}{6}, ?)$	$(\frac{\pi}{4}, ?)$	$(\frac{\pi}{3}, ?)$	$(\frac{\pi}{2}, ?)$	$(\frac{2\pi}{3}, ?)$	$(\frac{3\pi}{4}, ?)$	$(\frac{5\pi}{6}, ?)$	$(\pi, ?)$
corresponding point on $y = \cos^{-1} x$	$(1, 0)$	$(?, ?)$	$(?, ?)$	$(?, ?)$	$(?, ?)$	$(?, ?)$	$(?, ?)$	$(?, ?)$	$(?, ?)$

In 5–7, find the exact value of the expression in radians.

5. $\cos^{-1}\left(\frac{\sqrt{3}}{2}\right)$ **6.** Arccos 1 **7.** $\cos^{-1}\left(-\frac{\sqrt{2}}{2}\right)$

In 8–10, find the value for the expressions in degrees.

8. $\cos^{-1}\left(\frac{\sqrt{3}}{2}\right)$ **9.** Arccos 1 **10.** $\cos^{-1}\left(-\frac{\sqrt{2}}{2}\right)$

In 11 and 12, estimate the value of the expression in radians.

11. $\cos^{-1}\left(\frac{\sqrt{3}}{3}\right)$ **12.** Arccos (-0.9)

13. Refer to Example 3. Give the measure of θ when the height of the satellite above Earth is 850 km.

Applying the Mathematics

14. Refer to Example 3.
   a. Give a formula for $m\angle HSC$ in terms of r and a. ($\angle HSC$ is called the *angular separation of the horizon.*)
   b. Give a relationship between $\cos \theta$ and $\sin \angle HSC$.

15. Suppose a parallelogram is made with sides of 8" and 15" from bars that are hinged so that the included angle θ between its sides can be changed.
   a. Use the Law of Cosines to write an equation for d in terms of θ.
   b. Solve the equation for θ.
   c. Set your calculator to degree mode. Find θ when $d = 17$, and when $d = 9$.
   d. Find an appropriate window and draw a complete graph of the equation in part **b**.

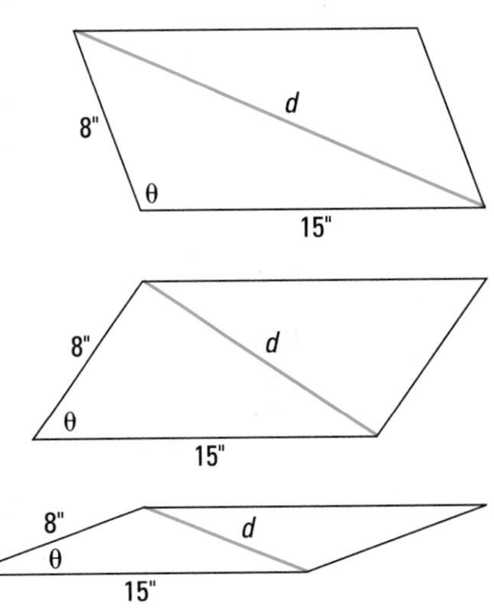

16. A 26" bicycle tire has a chalk mark at its top. As the bike moves forward, the height h of the chalk mark in terms of d, the distance traveled in inches, can be given by

$$h = f(d) = 13 + 13 \cos\left(\frac{d}{13}\right).$$

a. What is the period of f? Why?
b. Graph one period of f.
c. How far has the bike traveled the first time the chalk mark is 20" above ground? The second time?

In 17 and 18, compute without using your calculator.

17. $\cos\left(\cos^{-1}\left(-\frac{\sqrt{2}}{2}\right)\right)$

18. $\cos^{-1}(\cos 400°)$

Review

19. In $\triangle PQR$, $p = 19$, $q = 5$, and $r = 17$. Find $m\angle P$ and $m\angle Q$. *(Lesson 5-2)*

20. A fishing boat sails at a steady speed of 13 mph on a bearing of 67° (from north). If the boat set sail at 3:00 A.M., describe its location east and north of its port at 7:00 A.M. *(Lesson 5-1)*

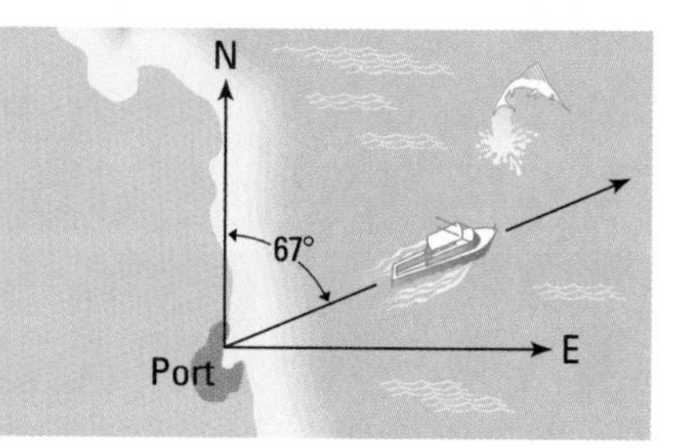

21. Consider $\triangle ABC$ at the right.
a. Find h, the altitude to side $\overline{BC}$, in terms of b and $m\angle ACB$.
b. Derive a formula for the area of $\triangle ABC$ in terms of a, b, and $m\angle ACB$. *(Lessons 4-4, 5-1)*

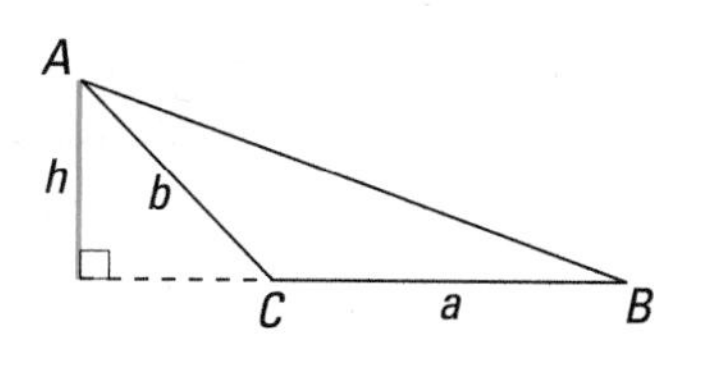

22. A data set consists of exactly four numbers. The mode of the data set is 5, the mean and median are 10 and 15. Which number is the mean? Explain how you can tell. *(Lesson 1-3)*

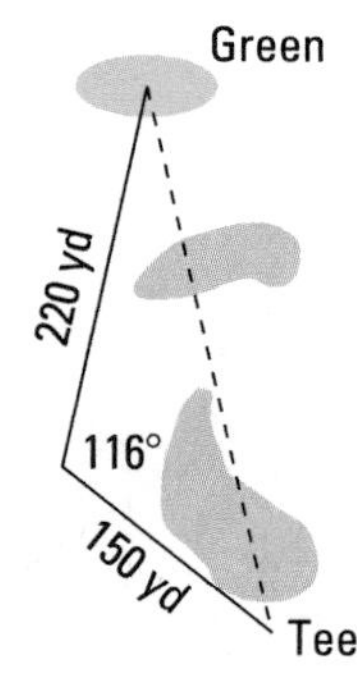

23. The figure at the left represents the way a golfer played a hole to avoid two water hazards. How far is it from the tee to the green directly over the water? Round your answer to the nearest yard. *(Lesson 5-2)*

Exploration

24. a. Find $\sin(\cos^{-1} 0.6)$.
b. Find $\sin\left(\cos^{-1}\left(\frac{8}{17}\right)\right)$.
c. Generalize the results above. That is, find $\sin(\cos^{-1} a)$ when $0° \le \cos^{-1} a \le 90°$.

LESSON

5-4

The Law of Sines

Are we lost? Are we there yet? Where are we? *Campers often use some mathematics to determine distances and locations both on land and on a map.*

The Law of Cosines is not always helpful in finding sides and angles in triangles. Consider this situation. Some campers want to find the distance f across a lake. They measure the distance from the flagpole to the edge of the headquarters and measure the angles as indicated. This provides them with the measures of two angles and the included side of $\triangle FBH$ as shown. Because the ASA condition is met, this is enough information to determine f.

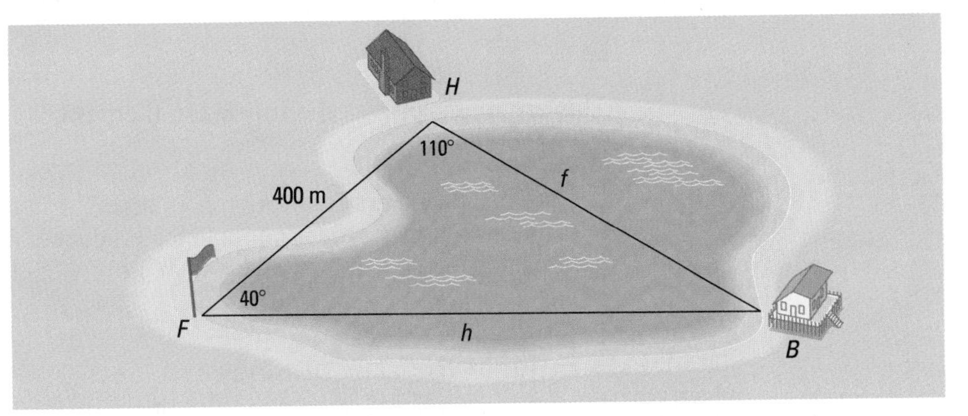

However, when the campers apply the Law of Cosines to find f, they get the following.

$$f^2 = b^2 + h^2 - 2bh \cos F$$
$$f^2 = 400^2 + h^2 - 2 \cdot 400 \cdot h \cos 40°$$
$$f^2 = 160{,}000 + h^2 - 800h \cos 40°$$

The result is a single equation with two unknowns, so the campers are unable to proceed any further with this solution.

Fortunately, there is another way to find f, using a theorem known as the *Law of Sines*. The proof of the Law of Sines involves the area of a triangle, so we first review area.

The SAS Area Formula for a Triangle

The area K of the triangle ABC as shown at the right is given by the familiar formula

$$K = \frac{1}{2}bh.$$

If h is not known, you can find h using the right triangle BCD.

$$\sin C = \frac{h}{a}$$

So $h = a \sin C$.

Substituting this value in the area formula gives

$$K = \frac{1}{2}ab \sin C.$$

Similarly, $\sin A = \frac{h}{c}$. So $h = c \sin A$, and so another formula is

$$K = \frac{1}{2}bc \sin A.$$

Activity

For $\triangle ABC$ at the right, use $\overline{AB}$ as the base and h as the altitude. Derive yet a third formula for the area of $\triangle ABC$.

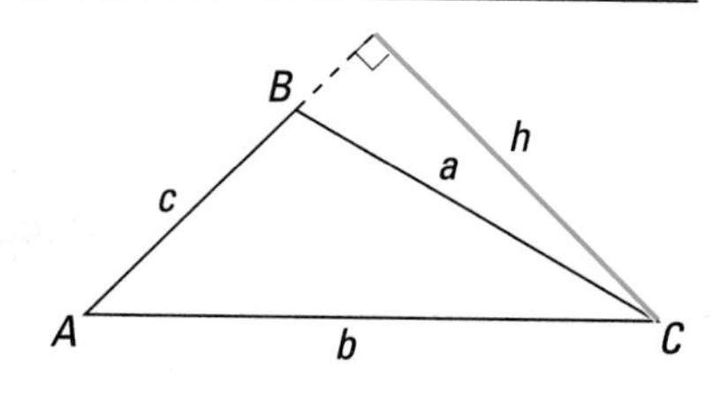

This argument proves the following theorem.

Theorem (SAS Area Formula for a Triangle)
In any triangle the area is one-half the product of the lengths of any two sides and the sine of their included angle.

A Proof of the Law of Sines

The Law of Sines is one of the most beautiful results in all of mathematics—simple and elegant.

Theorem (Law of Sines)
In any triangle ABC, $\frac{\sin A}{a} = \frac{\sin B}{b} = \frac{\sin C}{c}$.

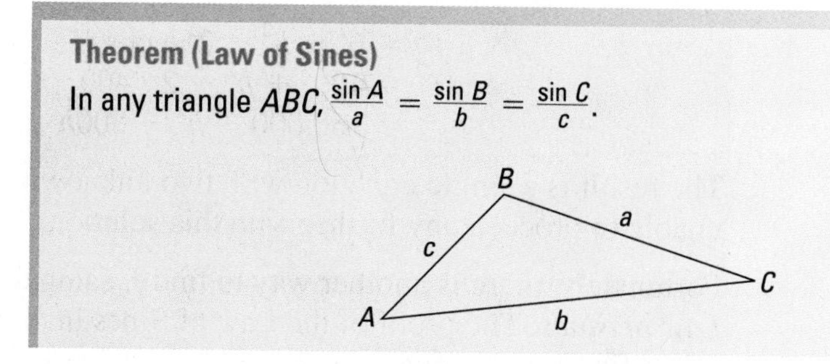

Proof

Let $\triangle ABC$ be any triangle. To find the area of $\triangle ABC$ with the SAS Formula, any two sides and their included angle may be used. Because the area of a given triangle is constant,

$$\frac{1}{2}bc \sin A = \frac{1}{2}ac \sin B = \frac{1}{2}ab \sin C.$$

	$\frac{1}{2}bc \sin A = \frac{1}{2}ac \sin B = \frac{1}{2}ab \sin C.$
Multiply by 2.	$bc \sin A = ac \sin B = ab \sin C$
Divide by abc.	$\frac{bc \sin A}{abc} = \frac{ac \sin B}{abc} = \frac{ab \sin C}{abc}$
Simplify.	$\frac{\sin A}{a} = \frac{\sin B}{b} = \frac{\sin C}{c}$

Using the Law of Sines with the ASA Condition

You can use the Law of Sines to find the length of a second side of a triangle given the measures of two angles and a side (the ASA or AAS conditions).

Example 1

Refer back to the situation at the beginning of the lesson. Find the distance f across the lake.

Solution

Use the Triangle-Sum Theorem to find the measure of $\angle B$.

$$m\angle B = 180 - (110 + 40) = 30°$$

Use the Law of Sines to find f.

$$\frac{\sin F}{f} = \frac{\sin B}{b}$$

$$\frac{\sin 40°}{f} = \frac{\sin 30°}{400}$$

$$f \sin 30° = 400(\sin 40°)$$

$$f = \frac{400(\sin 40°)}{\sin 30°}$$

$$f \approx 514$$

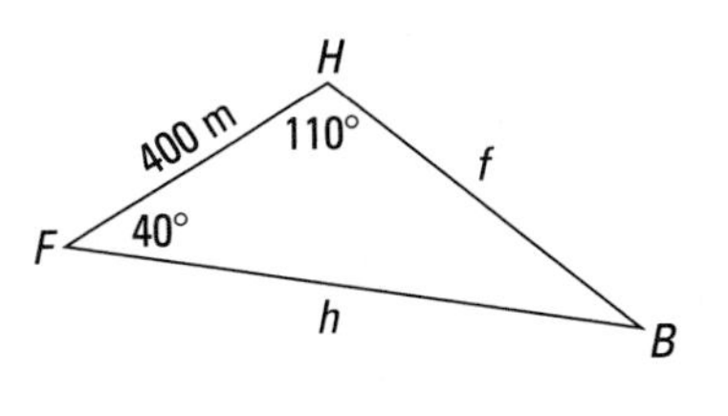

It is about 514 meters across the lake from the beach house to headquarters.

Check

Recall that in a triangle the longer sides are opposite the larger angles. The 514 m side is opposite the 40° angle, and the smaller 400 m side is opposite the (smaller) 30° angle, as it should be.

Using the Law of Sines with the SSA Condition

The Law of Sines can also be used to determine the measure of a second angle of a triangle when two sides and a nonincluded angle are known. This is the SSA condition. In general however, SSA is not a condition that guarantees congruence. Thus, when the Law of Sines is used in an SSA situation, no solution, one solution, or two solutions may result.

Example 2

In $\triangle ABC$, $m\angle A = 32°$, $AB = 8$, and $BC = 5$. Find all possible values of $m\angle C$ (to the nearest degree) and sketch the triangles determined by these values.

Solution

Make a rough sketch. Use the Law of Sines.

$$\frac{\sin 32°}{5} = \frac{\sin C}{8}$$

Solve for sin C. $$\sin C = \frac{8 \sin 32°}{5}$$

$$\sin C \approx 0.84787$$

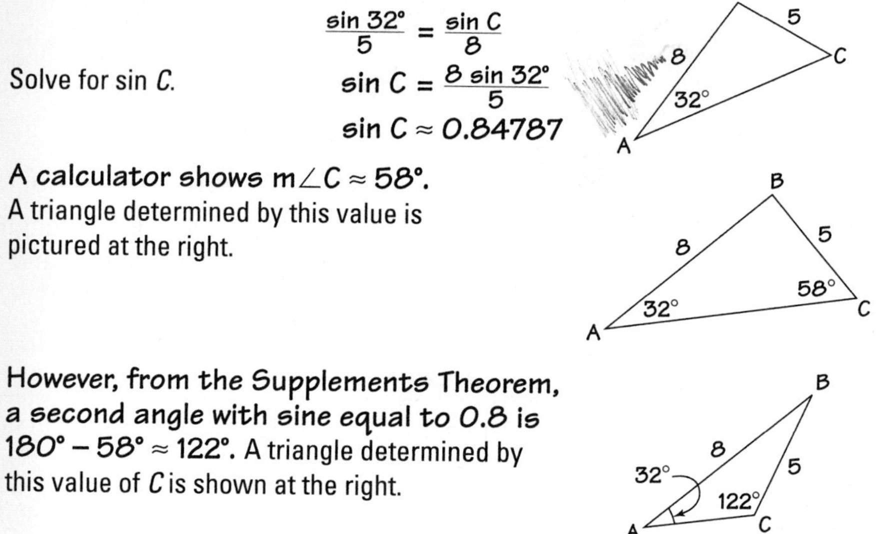

A calculator shows $m\angle C \approx 58°$.
A triangle determined by this value is pictured at the right.

However, from the Supplements Theorem, a second angle with sine equal to 0.8 is $180° - 58° \approx 122°$. A triangle determined by this value of C is shown at the right.

When the side opposite the given angle is larger than the other given side, the SSA condition leads to a unique triangle. We then call it the SsA condition.

Example 3

In $\triangle XYZ$, $x = 10$, $z = 3$, and $m\angle X = 42.5°$. Find $m\angle Z$ to the nearest tenth of a degree.

Solution

Make a rough sketch. Use the Law of Sines to get

$$\frac{\sin X}{x} = \frac{\sin Z}{z}$$

So $$\frac{\sin 42.5°}{10} = \frac{\sin Z}{3}$$

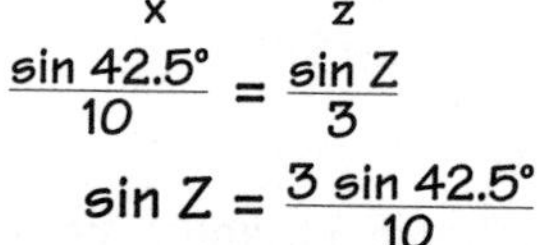

$$\sin Z = \frac{3 \sin 42.5°}{10}$$

$$\sin Z \approx 0.20268$$

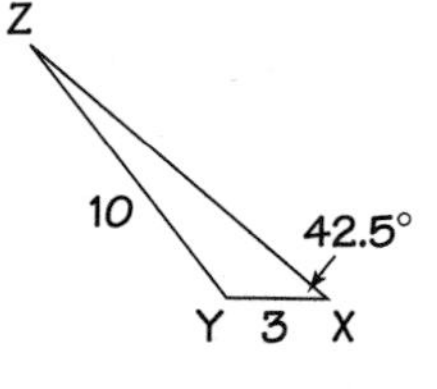

A calculator shows that

$$m\angle Z \approx 11.7°.$$

From the Supplements Theorem,

$$\sin 11.7° = \sin(180° - 11.7°) = \sin 168.3°.$$

But if 168.3° were a solution to this problem, then the sum of the measures of the angles of $\angle XYZ$ would be more than 180° ($m\angle X + m\angle Y \approx 42.5 + 168.3 = 210.8°$). So $m\angle Z = 11.7°$ is the only possible solution.

As you will see in the Questions, there are also SSA cases when no triangle is possible.

In general, when looking for measures of angles or sides in triangles, try methods involving simpler computations first. If these methods do not work, use the following.

1. If a triangle is a right triangle, use right triangle trigonometric ratios.
2. If a triangle is not a right triangle, consider the Law of Sines. It is useful for the ASA, AAS, and SSA conditions.
3. If the Law of Sines is not helpful, use the Law of Cosines. The Law of Cosines is most directly applicable to SAS and SSS conditions.

QUESTIONS

Covering the Reading

1. Show your work for the Activity in this lesson.

2. Find the area of $\triangle ABC$ where $a = 7$, $b = 12$, and $m\angle C = 52°$.

3. In any triangle, the ratio of the sine of an angle to __?__ is constant.

4. Tell if the statement is equivalent to the Law of Sines for $\triangle ABC$.

a. $\frac{A}{a} = \frac{B}{b} = \frac{C}{c}$

b. $\frac{a}{\sin A} = \frac{b}{\sin B} = \frac{c}{\sin C}$

c. $\frac{a}{b} = \frac{\sin A}{\sin B}, \frac{b}{c} = \frac{\sin B}{\sin C}, \frac{a}{c} = \frac{\sin A}{\sin C}$

d. $ab \sin C = bc \sin A = ac \sin B$

In 5 and 6, use the Law of Sines to find x.

5. **6.**

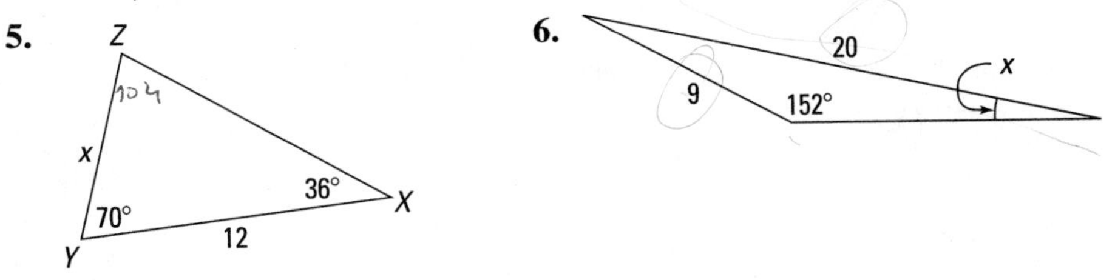

7. In $\triangle ABC$, suppose $m\angle C = 45°$, $m\angle A = 30°$, and $c = 12$. Find the exact lengths of the other two sides.

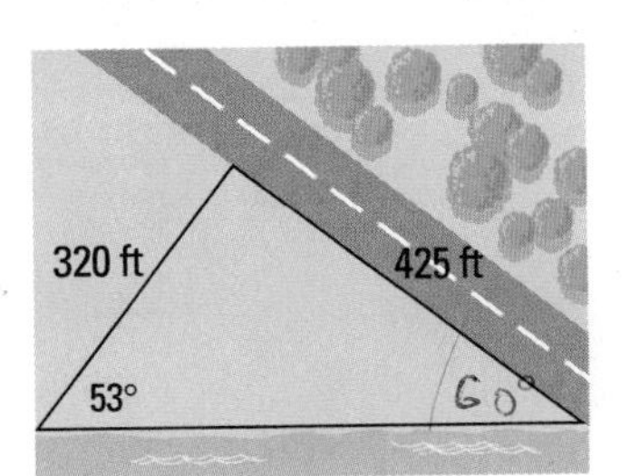

8. The Costas want to check the survey of a plot of land they are thinking of buying. The plot is triangular with one side on the lakefront, with dimensions as shown at the left.

a. Find the measure of the angle between the lakeshore and the 425-foot side.

b. About how many feet of lake frontage does the plot have?

9. In $\triangle XYZ$, $x = 14$, $z = 21$, and $m\angle X = 40°$.

a. Find the two possible measures of $\angle Z$.

b. Draw two noncongruent triangles satisfying the conditions of this question.

In 10 and 11, *true or false*.

10. When given SSA conditions, it is possible for two different triangles to be determined.

11. When given ASA conditions, it is possible for two different triangles to be determined.

In 12–17, *multiple choice*. A triangle is given with an unknown side or angle of measure x. Which strategy for finding x is computationally the easiest?

(a) definition of right triangle trigonometric ratios
(b) Law of Sines
(c) Law of Cosines

Do not solve for x.

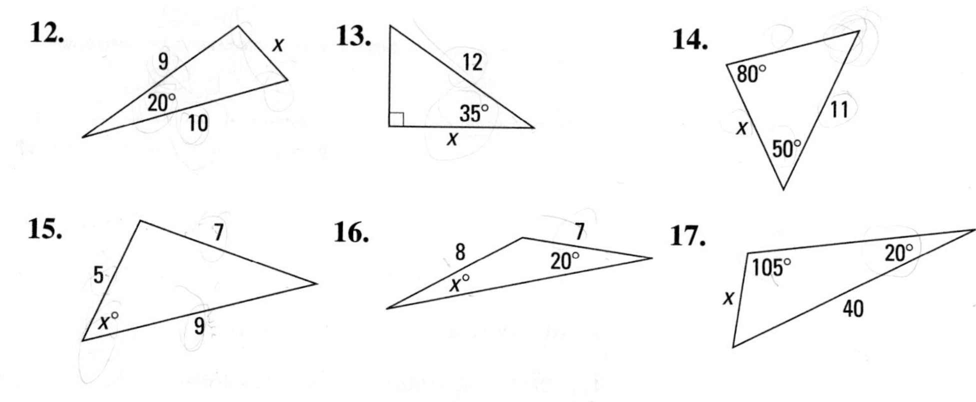

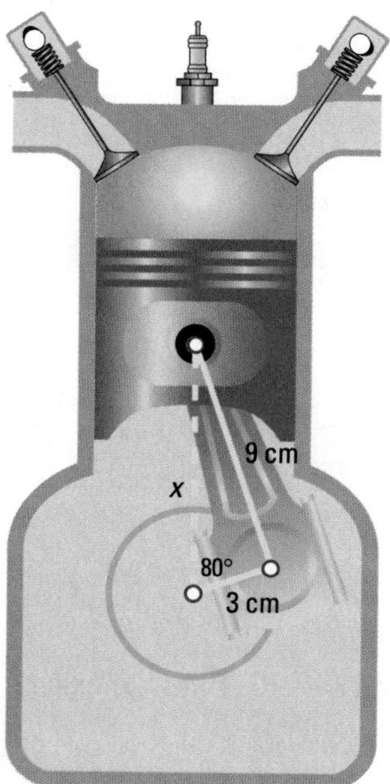

Applying the Mathematics

18. A piston driven by a 3 cm radial arm has length 9 cm. At the time that the radial arm is 80° off its axis, as pictured below, what is x?

19. To find the height h of a mountain, surveyors often find the angle of elevation to the top from two points at the same altitude a fixed distance apart. Suppose that the angles of elevation from two points 500 meters apart are 35°20' and 25°46'. Find h.

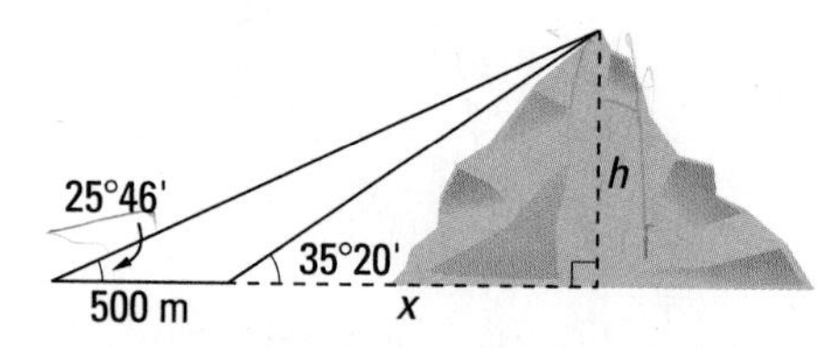

20. Use the Law of Sines to prove that the base angles of an isosceles triangle are congruent.

Review

21. **a.** State the domain and range of the inverse cosine function.
b. How are the domain and range related to the domain and range of the cosine function? *(Lesson 5-3)*

In 22 and 23, find exact values. *(Lesson 5-3)*

22. $\cos^{-1}\left(\cos\frac{5}{6}\right)$ **23.** $\sin\left(\cos^{-1}\frac{3}{5}\right)$

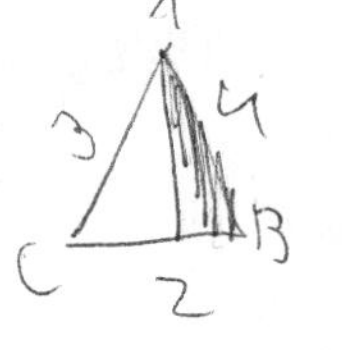

24. Find $m\angle B$ in $\triangle ABC$ if $a = 2$, $b = 3$, and $c = 4$. *(Lesson 5-2)*

25. A carpenter's square has two perpendicular rulers, as shown. It can be used for laying out angles. If the distance on the tongue is 9 in. and the distance on the blade is 13 in., find the measure of θ. *(Lesson 5-1)*

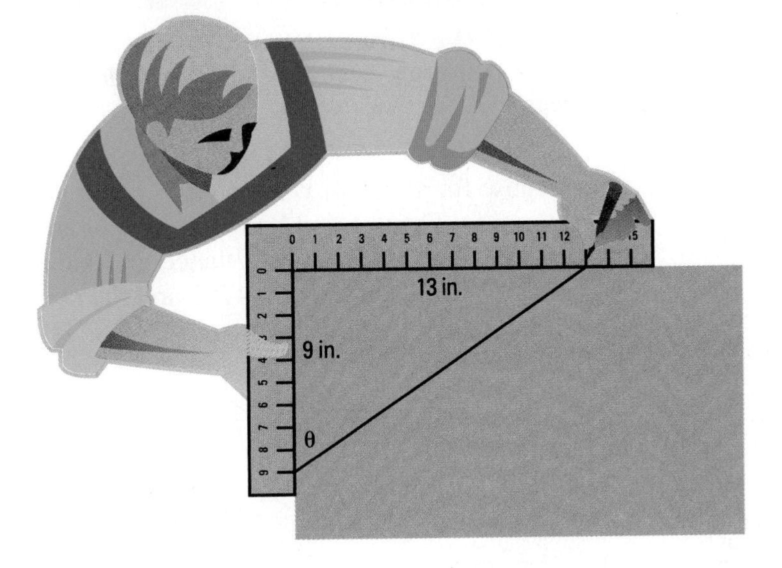

In 26 and 27, find the exact value without a calculator. *(Lesson 4-5)*

26. $\sin\left(-\frac{\pi}{6}\right)$ **27.** $\tan 495°$

Exploration

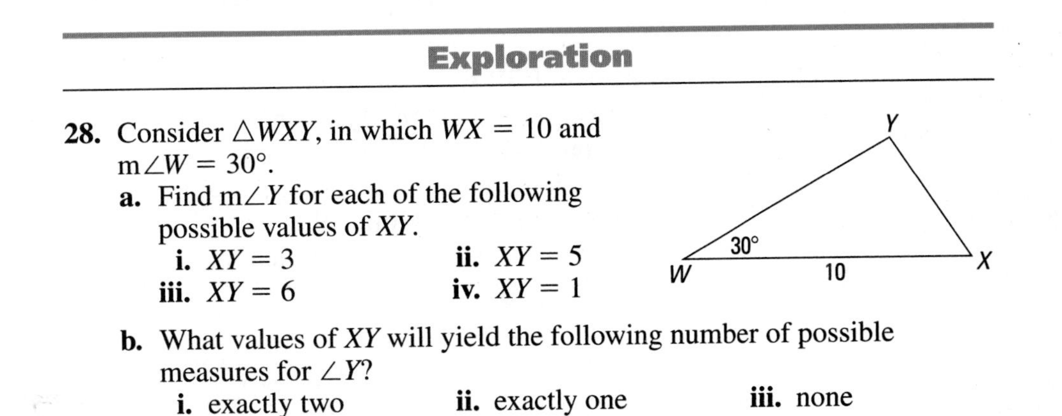

28. Consider $\triangle WXY$, in which $WX = 10$ and $m\angle W = 30°$.
a. Find $m\angle Y$ for each of the following possible values of XY.
i. $XY = 3$ **ii.** $XY = 5$
iii. $XY = 6$ **iv.** $XY = 1$
b. What values of XY will yield the following number of possible measures for $\angle Y$?
i. exactly two **ii.** exactly one **iii.** none

LESSON

5-5

The Inverse Sine Function

Sine of the Times. *NASA's Mission Control in Houston displays the tracks of satellites and spacecraft on screen. The paths shown here are approximately sinusoidal. See Question 24.*

Because for all x, $\sin x = \sin(\pi - x)$, an angle and its supplement have the same sine. Thus, if you know the sine of an angle, the angle may not be uniquely determined. For instance, in Example 2 of Lesson 5-4 you saw that in $\triangle ABC$, $\sin C \approx 0.84787$ and the measure of $\angle C$ could be about 58° or about 122°.

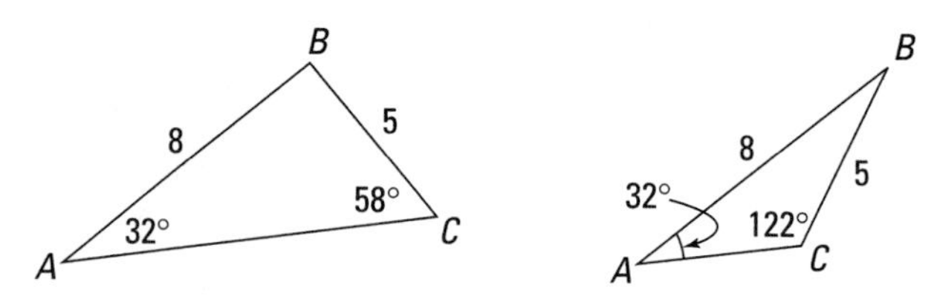

However, if you use the sin⁻¹ or Asin key on a calculator and enter 0.84787, it will return only one value, approximately 58°. That is the value of the function called the *inverse sine function*, $y = \sin^{-1} x$, when $x = 0.84787$. In this lesson, we examine this function.

The Domain of the Inverse Sine Function

At the right is a graph of the sine function $y = \sin x$ (in blue), and its reflection image $x = \sin y$ (in orange) over the line $y = x$. Notice that the inverse of $y = \sin x$ is not a function.

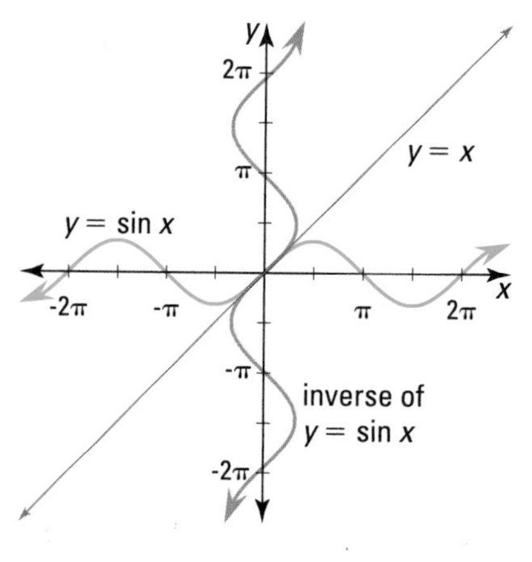

However, as with the cosine function, it is possible to restrict the domain of the sine function so that its inverse is a function. The following three criteria stated in that lesson can again be met.

1. The domain should include the angles between 0 and $\frac{\pi}{2}$ because these are the measures of the acute angles in a right triangle.
2. On the restricted domain, the function should take on all values in its range.
3. If possible, the function should be continuous on the restricted domain.

These criteria lead to restricting the domain of $y = \sin x$ to $\left\{x: -\frac{\pi}{2} \le x \le \frac{\pi}{2}\right\}$. The **inverse sine function**, denoted $\mathbf{sin^{-1}}$, is the inverse of this restricted sine function.

Definition
$y = \sin^{-1} x$ if and only if $x = \sin y$ and $-\frac{\pi}{2} \le y \le \frac{\pi}{2}$.

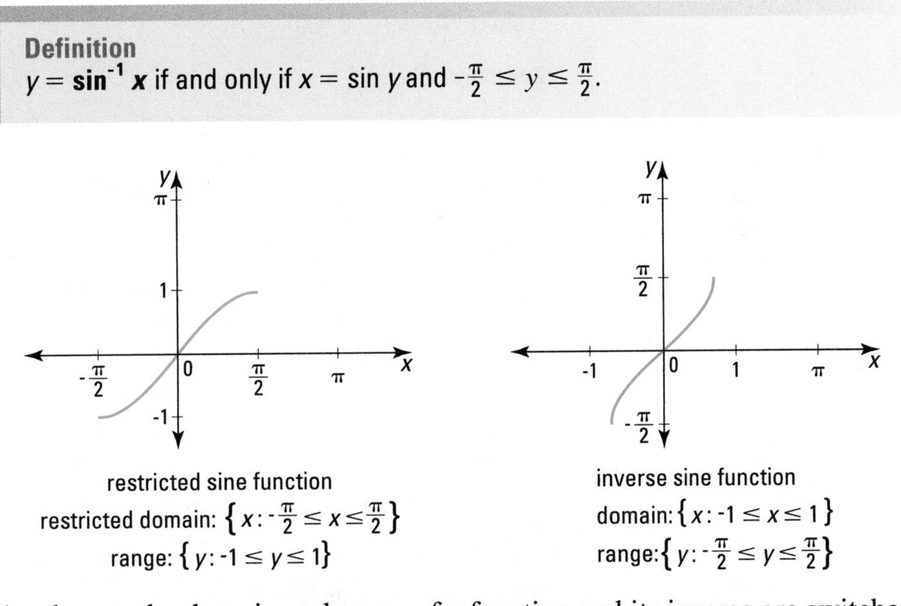

As always, the domain and range of a function and its inverse are switched. Thus, the domain of $y = \sin^{-1} x$ is $-1 \le x \le 1$, and the range is $-\frac{\pi}{2} \le y \le \frac{\pi}{2}$. That is, when $y = \sin^{-1} x$, y is the number from $-\frac{\pi}{2}$ to $\frac{\pi}{2}$ whose sine is x. The notation **Arcsin** is sometimes used in place of $\sin^{-1}$.

Evaluating Inverse Sines

Some values of the inverse sine function can be found exactly without using a calculator.

Example 1

Evaluate $\sin^{-1}\frac{1}{2}$.

Solution

If $y = \sin^{-1}\frac{1}{2}$, then y is the unique number in the interval $-\frac{\pi}{2} \leq y \leq \frac{\pi}{2}$ whose sine is $\frac{1}{2}$. Because $\sin\frac{\pi}{6} = \frac{1}{2}$ and $-\frac{\pi}{2} \leq \frac{\pi}{6} \leq \frac{\pi}{2}$, $y = \frac{\pi}{6}$. Thus, $\sin^{-1}\frac{1}{2} = \frac{\pi}{6}$.

All values of the inverse sine function can be estimated using a calculator.

Example 2

Evaluate Arcsin (-0.833).

Solution

If your calculator is in radian mode, the appropriate key sequence will show Arcsin $(-0.833) \approx -0.985$. If your calculator is in degree mode, you should get Arcsin $(-0.833) \approx -56.408°$.

Check

In radian mode, evaluate sin (-0.985) on your calculator. Because the display shows $-.8332720904 \approx -.833$, it checks.

Because the restricted sin and its inverse $\sin^{-1}$ are functions, $\sin(\sin^{-1} x) = x$ in the domain of $\sin^{-1}$, and $\sin^{-1}(\sin x) = x$ for x in the restricted domain of sin.

Example 3

Explain why $\sin^{-1}\left(\sin\frac{5\pi}{4}\right) \neq \frac{5\pi}{4}$.

Solution 1

Evaluate directly.

$$\sin\frac{5\pi}{4} = -\frac{\sqrt{2}}{2}$$

$$\sin^{-1}\left(\sin\frac{5\pi}{4}\right) = \sin^{-1}\left(-\frac{\sqrt{2}}{2}\right) = -\frac{\pi}{4}$$

Thus, $$\sin^{-1}\left(\sin\frac{5\pi}{4}\right) \neq \frac{5\pi}{4}.$$

Solution 2

Notice that $\frac{5\pi}{4}$ is not in the restricted domain of the sine function necessary for the inverse to be a function. Thus, $\sin^{-1}\left(\sin\frac{5\pi}{4}\right) \neq \frac{5\pi}{4}$.

An Application of the Inverse Sine Function

The inverse sine function has applications in all situations involving the sine function.

Example 4

An 18-foot ladder leans against a building as shown at the right.

a. Express y, the measure of the angle the ladder makes with the ground, as a function of x, the height of the top of the ladder.

b. What are the domain and range of the function that maps x onto y?

Solution

a. From the diagram you can see that

$$\sin y = \frac{x}{18}.$$

So
$$y = \sin^{-1}\left(\frac{x}{18}\right).$$

b. x can be no larger than the length of the ladder, so **the domain is $\{x: 0 \le x \le 18\}$.** y can be any measure from 0° (when the ladder is on the ground) to 90° (when the ladder is flush with the wall). **So the range is $\{y: 0° \le y \le 90°\}$.**

Check

Graph the function $y = \sin^{-1}\left(\frac{x}{18}\right)$. By the Graph Scale-Change Theorem, you should expect to see the image of $y = \sin^{-1} x$ under the scale change $(x, y) \to (18x, y)$. At the left is the graph produced on an automatic grapher using the window $-20 \le x \le 20$, $-\frac{3\pi}{2} \le y \le \frac{3\pi}{2}$.

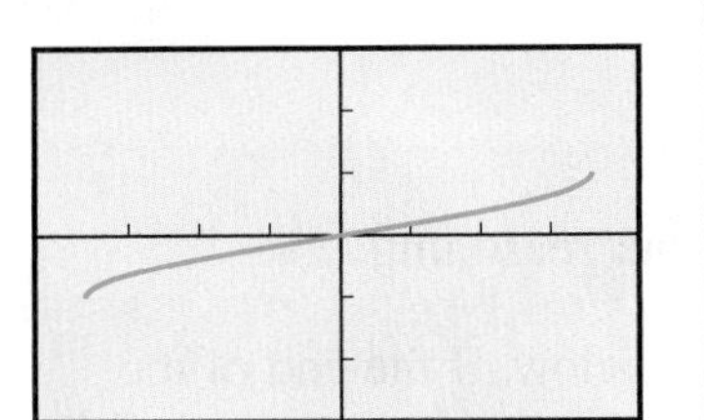

$-20 \le x \le 20$, x-scale = 5
$-\frac{3\pi}{2} \le y \le \frac{3\pi}{2}$, y-scale = $\frac{\pi}{2}$

The graph shows that for the domain $\{x: 0 \le x \le 18\}$, the range is $\left\{y: 0 \le y \le \frac{\pi}{2}\right\}$. It checks.

QUESTIONS

Covering the Reading

1. Explain how the Horizontal Line Test tells you that the inverse of $y = \sin x$ is not a function.

2. How is the expression "$\theta = \sin^{-1} k$" read?

3. Evaluate $\sin^{-1}\left(\frac{1}{2}\right)$ to the nearest degree without using a calculator.

4. Explain how to check the solution to Example 2 found by a calculator in degree mode.

5. **a.** Complete the table of values below. Round approximations to the nearest thousandth.
b. Graph $y = \sin x$, $-\frac{\pi}{2} \le x \le \frac{\pi}{2}$, and $y = \sin^{-1} x$ on the same coordinate system. Use the same scale on each axis.
c. State the domain and range of the function $y = \sin^{-1} x$.
d. What transformation maps the graph of $y = \sin x$ with $-\frac{\pi}{2} \le x \le \frac{\pi}{2}$, to the graph of $y = \sin^{-1} x$?

point on $y = \sin x$	$(-\frac{\pi}{2}, -1)$	$(-\frac{\pi}{3}, ?)$	$(-\frac{\pi}{4}, ?)$	$(-\frac{\pi}{6}, ?)$	(0, 0)	$(\frac{\pi}{6}, ?)$	$(\frac{\pi}{4}, ?)$	$(\frac{\pi}{3}, ?)$	$(\frac{\pi}{2}, ?)$
corresponding point on $y = \sin^{-1} x$	$(-1, -\frac{\pi}{2})$	(?, ?)	(?, ?)	(?, ?)	(?, ?)	(?, ?)	(?, ?)	(?, ?)	(?, ?)

In 6–8, find an exact value in radians.

6. $\sin^{-1}\left(\frac{\sqrt{3}}{2}\right)$ **7.** Arcsin 1 **8.** $\sin^{-1}\left(-\frac{\sqrt{2}}{2}\right)$

In 9–11, find an exact value for the expression in degrees.

9. $\sin^{-1}\left(\frac{\sqrt{3}}{2}\right)$ **10.** Arcsin 1 **11.** $\sin^{-1}\left(-\frac{\sqrt{2}}{2}\right)$

In 12–14, use a calculator to estimate the value.

12. $\sin^{-1}\left(\frac{\sqrt{3}}{3}\right)$ **13.** Arcsin (-0.9) **14.** $\sin^{-1}$ (-0.88)

15. *True or false.*
a. If $\theta = \sin^{-1} n$, then $n = \sin \theta$.
b. If $n = \sin \theta$, then $\theta = \sin^{-1} n$.

16. *True or false.* $\sin^{-1}\left(\sin\left(\frac{7\pi}{4}\right)\right) = \frac{7\pi}{4}$. Explain your reasoning.

17. A 15-foot ramp is placed as shown in the figure below. If the end of the ramp is x feet above the ground, express y, the angle the ramp makes with the ground, as a function of x.

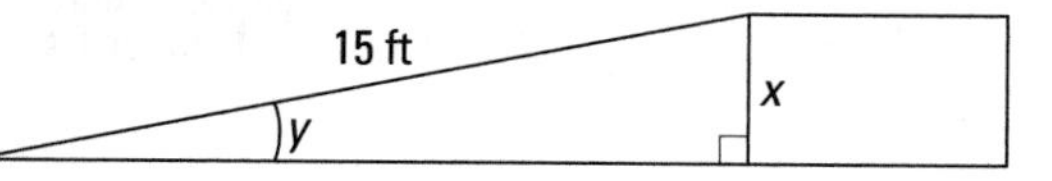

18. Compute $\sin\left(\sin^{-1}\left(-\frac{\sqrt{2}}{2}\right)\right)$ without using a calculator.

19. Find Arcsin (sin 0.6) without using a calculator.

Applying the Mathematics

20. Explain why $\{x: 0 \le x \le \pi\}$ is not used as the domain of the restricted sine function.

21. Prove that $\sin(\sin^{-1} x) = x$ for all x such that $-1 \le x \le 1$.

22. **a.** Evaluate $\cos(\sin^{-1} 0.6)$ on your calculator.
b. Draw an appropriate triangle to show how the answer to part **a** could have been found without a calculator.
c. Evaluate $\cos\left(\sin^{-1}\left(\frac{b}{c}\right)\right)$, where $b \ne 0$, $c \ne 0$.

23. The equation $E = 4 \sin(60\pi t)$ describes the electrical voltage E in a circuit at a time t.
   a. Solve for t in terms of E.
   b. How is the graph of t as a function of E related to the graph of the inverse of the sine function?

24. A satellite orbits Earth. At time $t = 0$ hours it is farthest from Earth, at a height of 600 miles. At $t = 1$ hour it is closest to Earth, at a height of 450 miles.
   a. Assume that the height h varies sinusoidally with time. Write an equation using the sine function to model this situation.
   b. Solve this equation for t in terms of h.
   c. What are the first four times the satellite is 500 miles above Earth?

Review

25. A hill slopes upward at an angle of 5° with the horizontal. A tree grows vertically on the hill. When the angle of elevation of the sun is 30°, the tree casts a shadow downhill that is 32 m long. If the shadow is entirely on the hill, how tall is the tree? *(Lesson 5-4)*

26. A ship travels 300 km along a bearing of $\theta°$ where $0 < \theta < 90$. Give an equation for the bearing as a function of x, the distance north of the original position. *(Lesson 5-3)*

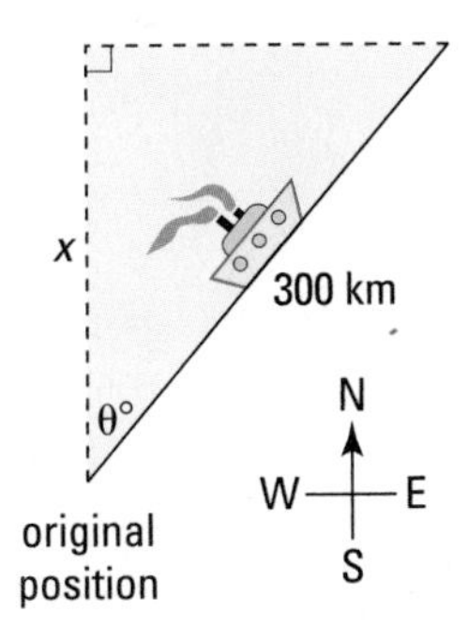

27. A triangular field has sides of length 270 ft, 405 ft, and 541 ft. What is the measure of the smallest angle of this field? *(Lesson 5-2)*

28. Find the length w of the guy wire pictured below. *(Lesson 5-1)*

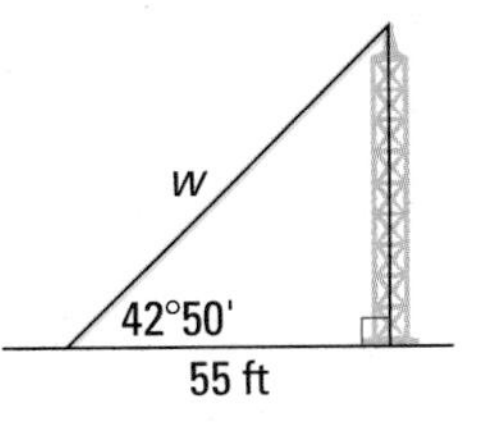

29. For the function $y = \tan\left(x + \frac{\pi}{4}\right)$, determine each. *(Lesson 4-8)*
   a. domain
   b. range
   c. period

Exploration

30. Prove: For all real numbers x from -1 to 1, $\cos^{-1} x = \frac{\pi}{2} - \sin^{-1} x$.

LESSON

5-6 The Inverse Tangent Function

You have seen situations in which the tangent function is used to find an angle measure in a triangle. For instance, if a plane flying at an altitude of 5.5 miles begins its descent 90 miles from an airport, the angle of the path of descent can be determined by using the tangent ratio.

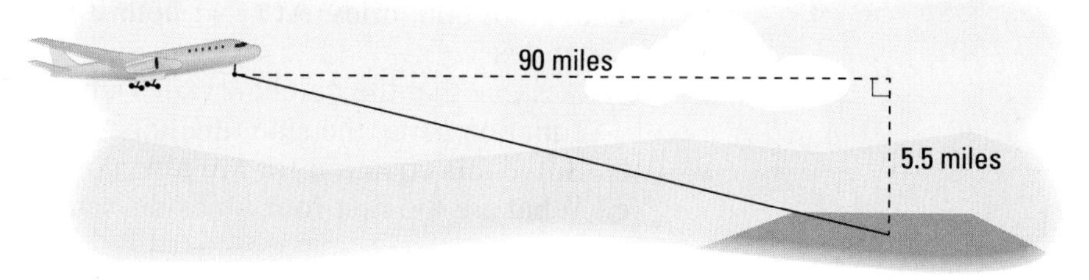

To find θ, the angle whose tangent is $\frac{5.5}{90}$, you can use the tan^{-1} or Atan key on a calculator. The calculator returns the value of the function called the *inverse tangent function.*

Defining the Inverse Tangent Function

At the right is a graph of the tangent function $y = \tan x$ (in blue) and $x = \tan y$ (in orange) its reflection image over the line $y = x$. Like the sine and cosine functions, the inverse of the tangent function is not a function, but it is possible to restrict the domain of the tangent function so that its inverse is a function.

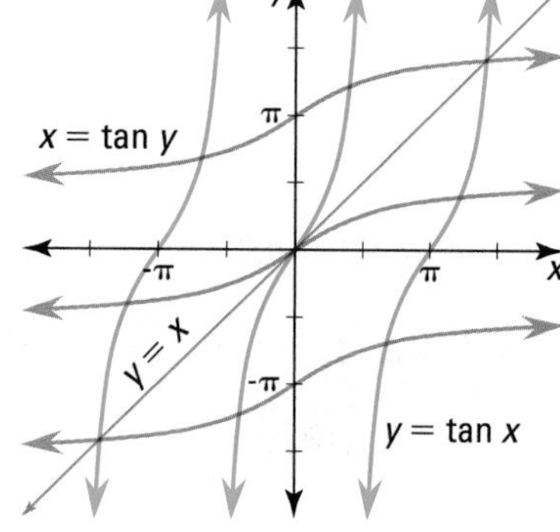

Using the criteria for choosing an appropriate domain used in Lessons 5-3 and 5-5 leads to restricting the domain of the tangent function to $-\frac{\pi}{2} < x < \frac{\pi}{2}$. This **inverse tangent function**, denoted as **tan^{-1}**, is the inverse of this restricted function.

Definition

$y = \tan^{-1} x$ if and only if $x = \tan y$ and $-\frac{\pi}{2} < y < \frac{\pi}{2}$.

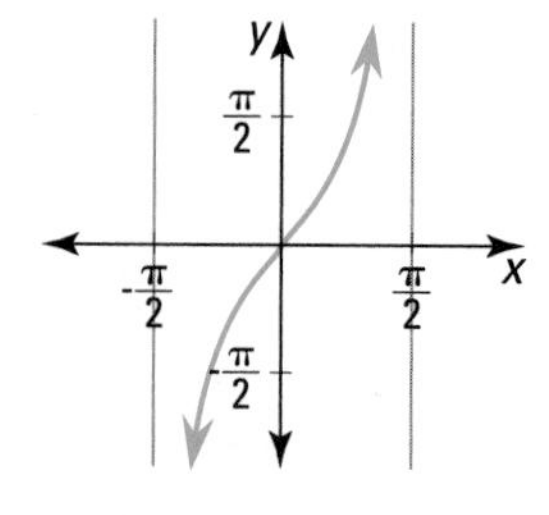

restricted tangent function
domain: $\{x: -\frac{\pi}{2} < x < \frac{\pi}{2}\}$
range: set of all real numbers

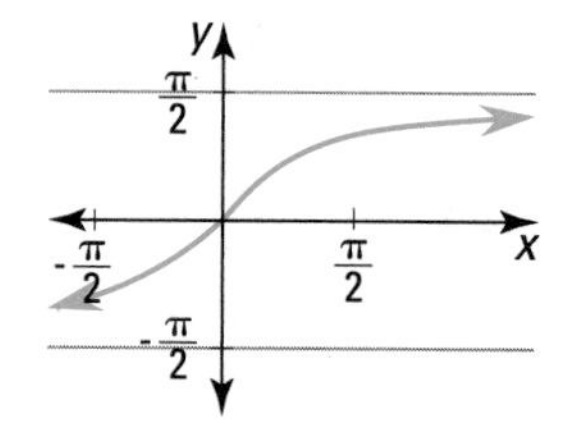

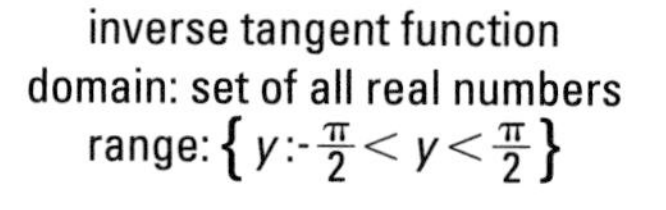

inverse tangent function
domain: set of all real numbers
range: $\{y: -\frac{\pi}{2} < y < \frac{\pi}{2}\}$

It has the set of real numbers as its domain and $-\frac{\pi}{2} < y < \frac{\pi}{2}$ as its range.

You can read $y = \tan^{-1} x$ as "y is the number (or angle) whose tangent is x." The notation **Arctan** is sometimes used in place of $\tan^{-1}$.

Evaluating Inverse Tangents

Some values of the inverse tangent function can be found exactly without using a calculator.

Example 1

Evaluate $\tan^{-1}(-1)$.

Solution

If $y = \tan^{-1}(-1)$, then by definition of $\tan^{-1}$, y is the unique number in the interval $-\frac{\pi}{2} < y < \frac{\pi}{2}$ whose tangent is -1. Because $\tan\left(-\frac{\pi}{4}\right) = -1$ and $-\frac{\pi}{2} < -\frac{\pi}{4} < \frac{\pi}{2}$, $y = -\frac{\pi}{4}$. Thus, $\tan^{-1}(-1) = -\frac{\pi}{4}$.

All values of the inverse tangent function can be estimated using a calculator.

Example 2

Evaluate Arctan 3.7.

Solution

Apply the definition of the inverse tangent function: $y = \text{Arctan } 3.7$ if and only if $\tan y = 3.7$ and $-\frac{\pi}{2} < y < \frac{\pi}{2}$. In radian mode, a calculator displays Arctan $3.7 \approx 1.3068$.

Check

Evaluate tan 1.3068 with a calculator. This results in a display of about 3.6995. It checks.

Applications Involving the Inverse Tangent Function

Example 3

A plane flying at an altitude of 32,000 feet (about 6 miles) descends at a constant angle θ in radians to an airport runway x miles away.

a. Write an equation for θ as a function of x.

b. If $x = 40$, find θ to the nearest degree.

Solution

a. Draw a diagram. Let P = the position of the plane before descent, A = the point of contact on the airport runway, and T = the point above A needed to form a right triangle. Then $\theta = m\angle APT$.

Then $\tan \theta \approx \frac{6}{x}$

and $\theta \approx \tan^{-1} \frac{6}{x}$.

b. When $x = 40$, $\theta \approx \tan^{-1}\left(\frac{6}{40}\right) \approx 8.53°$. The angle of descent is close to 9°.

The angle of descent in Example 3 is quite large. This is why planes flying higher than 30,000 feet often begin their descent as far away as 180 miles from their destination.

QUESTIONS

Covering the Reading

1. a. Find θ to the nearest tenth of a degree if $\tan \theta = 0.0611$.

b. Interpret your answer to part **a** in the situation of the first paragraph of this lesson.

2. How is the expression "$\theta = \tan^{-1} k$" read?

3. a. Copy and complete the table of values below. Round approximations to the nearest thousandth.

point on $y = \tan x$	(-1.5, -14.1)	$(-\frac{\pi}{3}, ?)$	$(-\frac{\pi}{4}, ?)$	$(-\frac{\pi}{6}, ?)$	(0, 0)	$(\frac{\pi}{6}, ?)$	$(\frac{\pi}{4}, ?)$	$(\frac{\pi}{3}, ?)$	(1.5, ?)
corresponding point on $y = \tan^{-1} x$	(-14.1, -1.5)	(?, ?)	(?, ?)	(?, ?)	(?, ?)	(?, ?)	(?, ?)	(?, ?)	(?, ?)

b. Plot the points above, and graph $y = \tan x$, $-\frac{\pi}{2} < x < \frac{\pi}{2}$, and $y = \tan^{-1} x$ on the same coordinate system. Use the same scale on each axis.

c. State the domain and range of the function $y = \tan^{-1} x$.

d. What transformation maps the graph of $y = \tan x$ with $-\frac{\pi}{2} < x < \frac{\pi}{2}$ to the graph of $y = \tan^{-1} x$?

In 4–6, find the exact value of the expression in radians.

4. $\tan^{-1}(\sqrt{3})$ **5.** Arctan 1 **6.** $\tan^{-1}\left(\frac{\sqrt{3}}{3}\right)$

In 7–9, find the exact value of the expression in degrees.

7. $\tan^{-1}(\sqrt{3})$ **8.** Arctan 1 **9.** $\tan^{-1}\left(\frac{\sqrt{3}}{3}\right)$

In 10–12, use a calculator to estimate the value in degrees.

10. $\tan^{-1}\left(\frac{\sqrt{3}}{3}\right)$ **11.** Arctan (-.9) **12.** $\tan^{-1} 2001$

13. Refer to Example 3.

a. Graph $y = \tan^{-1}\left(\frac{6}{x}\right)$ on the window $-5 \le x \le 100$, $-5 \le y \le 2$.

b. Trace along the graph to estimate y when $x = 70$.

c. Explain what the answer to part **b** means in relation to the context of the problem.

14. If a plane flying at 35,000 feet begins a constant descent 180 miles from its destination, find the angle of descent to the nearest tenth of a degree.

Applying the Mathematics

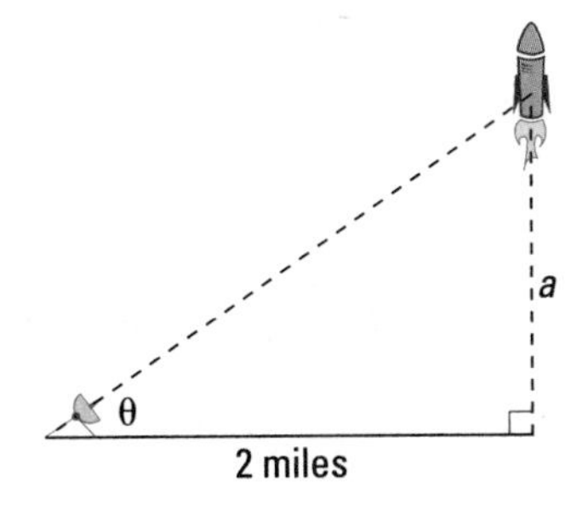

15. A radar tracking station is located 2 miles from a rocket launching pad. If a rocket is launched straight upward, express the angle of elevation θ of the rocket from the tracking station as a function of the altitude a (in miles) of the rocket.

16. A rectangular picture 80 cm high is hung on a vertical wall so that the bottom edge is at your eye level. Your angle of vision, y, of this picture is determined by your eye and the top and bottom edges of the picture.

a. Write an equation for y as a function of the distance x in cm between your eye and the wall.

b. Suppose now that the rectangular picture is hung on a vertical wall so that the bottom edge is 30 cm above your eye level. Express y as a function of x.

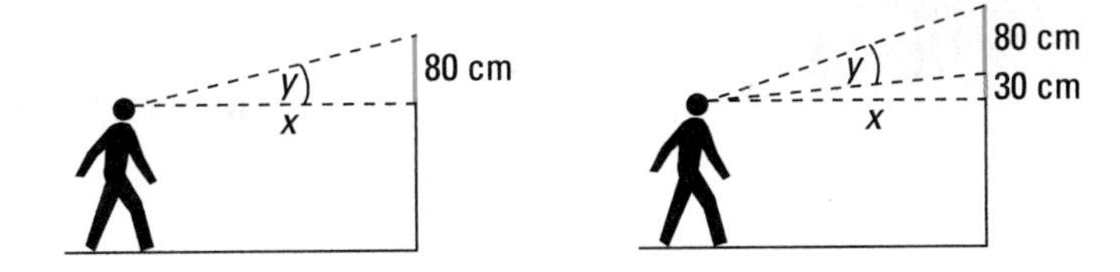

Picture Hang Ups.
Museums, such as the Philadelphia Museum of Art, often hang a picture so that its center is at "eye level," about 5 feet 8 inches above the floor.

In 17 and 18, compute without using your calculator.

17. $\tan(\tan^{-1}(-19))$ **18.** $\tan^{-1}\left(\tan\left(\frac{2\pi}{3}\right)\right)$

19. Consider the expression $\tan^{-1}\left(\frac{x}{y}\right) + \tan^{-1}\left(\frac{y}{x}\right)$.

a. Choose several values for x and y and evaluate this expression.

b. Make a conjecture about the value of this expression in terms of x and y.

c. Prove this conjecture.

d. Explain how this expression can be related to right triangles.

Review

In 20 and 21, evaluate in degrees. Do not use a calculator.

20. $\sin^{-1} 1$ *(Lesson 5-5)* **21.** $\cos^{-1}\left(-\frac{\sqrt{2}}{2}\right)$ *(Lesson 5-3)*

22. Solve for θ, given that θ is an angle of a triangle. *(Lessons 4-3, 5-3, 5-5)*
a. $\cos \theta = 0.5$ **b.** $\sin \theta = 0.5$

23. Consider the parent function $y = \sin^{-1} x$.
a. Apply the scale change $S(x, y) \to \left(2x, \frac{y}{2}\right)$ to the parent function. Then apply the translation $T(x, y) \to (x - 2, y + 1)$. Give an equation for $T \circ S$.
b. Draw a graph of the function $y = T(S(x))$.
c. Give the domain and range of the function in part **b**. *(Lessons 4-9, 5-5)*

24. Owners of some land wished to determine the distance from A to B. They began by walking from A 250 feet directly towards B but encountered a small swamp. So they turned left at an angle of 50° and walked 160 feet, then turned right 63° and walked directly to B. How far is it from A to B? *(Lesson 5-4)*

Fakahatchee State Preserve, Florida

25. The height h in meters of a tide in a harbor is given by $h = \cos\left(\frac{\pi}{6}t\right) + 5$, where t is the time in hours after high tide. *(Lessons 4-7, 4-8)*
a. Sketch a graph of this function for $0 \le t \le 24$.
b. What is the maximum height of the tide during this 24-hour period?
c. At what times during the 24-hour period does the highest tide occur?

26. Suppose $0 \le x \le \pi$. *(Lesson 4-7)*
a. Graph $y = \cos\left(\frac{x}{2}\right)$ and $y = \sin(3x)$ on this interval.
b. Give approximate solutions correct to the nearest hundredth to $\cos\left(\frac{x}{2}\right) = \sin(3x)$.
c. Check your answers by substituting into the original equations.

27. How many solutions between 0 and 2π are there to $\tan x = -\sqrt{3}$? *(Lesson 4-5)*

28. *Skill sequence.* Solve for x. *(Previous course)*
a. $(7x - 7)(x - 3) = 0$ **b.** $6x^2 = 5 - 7x$ **c.** $6x^4 = 5 - 7x^2$

Exploration

29. In 1671, James Gregory discovered that when $-1 \le x \le 1$,

$$\tan^{-1} x = \sum_{i=0}^{\infty} \frac{(-1)^i x^{(2i+1)}}{2i + 1} = x - \frac{x^3}{3} + \frac{x^5}{5} - \frac{x^7}{7} + \frac{x^9}{9} - \dots.$$

In 1981, the Japanese mathematicians Kazunori Miyoshi and Kazuhiko Nakayama calculated π to 2,000,000 decimal places using Gregory's series and the formula (proved using geometry) that

$$\pi = 32 \tan^{-1}\left(\frac{1}{10}\right) - 4 \tan^{-1}\left(\frac{1}{239}\right) - 16 \tan^{-1}\left(\frac{1}{515}\right).$$

a. Use a calculator to verify that the formula used by Miyoshi and Nakayama seems to be correct.
b. Use the first three terms of Gregory's series to estimate each of the three Arctangents and thus come up with an estimate for π. To how many decimal places is this estimate accurate?
c. Use more terms of Gregory's series to come up with an estimate accurate to more decimal places.

Introducing Lesson 5-7

Solving Trigonometric Equations Graphically

You will need an automatic grapher for this activity. Work with a partner and discuss your results.

1 Graph $y = \tan(2x)$ on the interval $-\frac{\pi}{2} < x < \frac{\pi}{2}$.

2 How many solutions does the equation $\tan(2x) = 3$ have on the interval $-\frac{\pi}{2} < x < \frac{\pi}{2}$?

3 Use your graph to estimate these solutions to the nearest hundredth.

4 Check your answers by substituting into the original equation.

5 Use a graph to estimate all solutions to the equation $\tan(2x) = 3$ on the interval $-2\pi \leq x \leq 2\pi$.

6 Explain how you could have found all the solutions in step 5 without graphing.

7 Write one or more expressions that give *all* real solutions to the equation $\tan(2x) = 3$.

LESSON

5-7

General Solutions to Trigonometric Equations

Sinusoidal Solutions. *This roller coaster track is sinusoidal. The cars will be even with the top of the tree on the left more than once during the ride.*

A **trigonometric equation** is an equation in which the variable to be found is in an argument of a sine, cosine, or tangent function. Examples are: $\cos \theta = 0.8$, $10 = 12 \sin (2\pi t)$, $\tan (2x) = 3$, and $2 \sin^2 \theta = 1 - \sin \theta$. As you saw in the previous In-class Activity, the number of solutions to a trigonometric equation can vary significantly, depending on the domain of the variable.

Three types of domains commonly arise:

(1) the restricted domains of the sine, cosine, and tangent functions that are used in obtaining their inverse functions;
(2) an interval equal in size to the period of the function under study;
(3) the set of all real numbers for which the function is defined.

Using the inverse trigonometric function $\cos^{-1}$, $\sin^{-1}$, or $\tan^{-1}$ on your calculator will help you find solutions for domains of type (1). To find the solutions for types (2) and (3), you may need to use the properties of the trigonometric functions studied in Chapter 4, and you will find it helpful to graph the function. For type (3), the periodic nature of the functions generates infinitely many solutions in the set of real numbers.

The solution set that arises from domains of type (3), considering all real values of the variable, is called the **general solution** to the trigonometric equation.

The Simplest Trigonometric Equations

The simplest trigonometric equations are of the form $af(x) = b$, where f is the sine, cosine, or tangent function.

Example 1

Consider the equation $\cos\theta = 0.8$. Round all solutions to the nearest thousandth.

a. Find all solutions from 0 to π.

b. Solve the equation when $0 \le \theta \le 2\pi$.

c. Find the general solution.

Solution

a. By definition of the inverse cosine function, $\theta = \cos^{-1} 0.8$. In radians, $\theta \approx 0.644$.

b. On the same set of axes graph $y = \cos x$ and $y = 0.8$. Each point of intersection corresponds to a solution to the equation $\cos x = 0.8$.

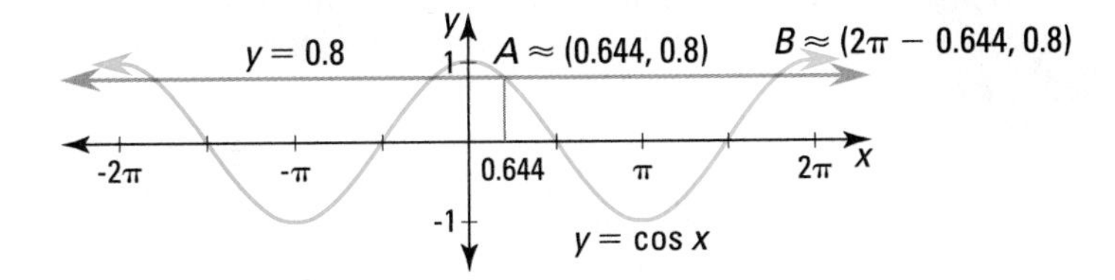

Point A represents the solution found in part **a**. Point B shows another solution in the interval $\{x: 0 \le x \le 2\pi\}$. The symmetry of the graph of the cosine function to the line $x = \pi$ shows this solution to be approximately $2\pi - 0.644$, or about 5.639. Thus, when $\cos\theta = 0.8$ and $0 \le \theta \le 2\pi$, then $\theta \approx 0.644$ or $\theta \approx 5.639$.

c. The general solution follows from part **b** and the Periodicity Theorem. Adding or subtracting multiples of 2π to the two solutions in part **b** generates all solutions to $\cos\theta = 0.8$.

$\theta \approx 0.644 + 2\pi$	$\theta \approx 5.639 + 2\pi$
$\theta \approx 0.644 + 4\pi$	$\theta \approx 5.639 + 4\pi$
$\vdots$	$\vdots$
$\theta \approx 0.644 - 2\pi$	$\theta \approx 5.639 - 2\pi$
$\theta \approx 0.644 - 4\pi$	$\theta \approx 5.639 - 4\pi$
$\vdots$	$\vdots$

Thus, the general solution to $\cos\theta = 0.8$ is

$$\theta \approx 0.644 + 2\pi n \text{ or } \theta \approx 5.639 + 2\pi n$$

for all integers n.

These solutions are represented by the set of all points of intersection of the line $y = 0.8$ and the graph of $y = \cos x$.

The process used in Example 1 can be employed to solve many trigonometric equations. That is, first find one solution using an inverse trigonometric function, and then use other properties of these functions, particularly the Periodicity Theorem, to find all the solutions.

Something Shocking.
The benefits and hazards of 110-volt alternating current (AC) versus 220-volt direct current (DC) were debated when cities first began to be wired for electricity.

Example 2

The output voltage E (in volts) of a circuit at t seconds ($t \geq 0$) is given by

$$E = 12 \sin (2\pi t).$$

To the nearest .01 second, at which times in the first three seconds does $E = 10$?

Solution

Substitute 10 for E in the given equation.

$$10 = 12 \sin (2\pi t)$$

Solve for $\sin(2\pi t)$. $\quad \sin (2\pi t) = \frac{10}{12}$

Think of $2\pi t$ as a "chunk" representing θ and solve for $2\pi t$. Use a calculator (in radian mode) to find a first quadrant solution.

$$2\pi t = \sin^{-1}\left(\frac{10}{12}\right)$$

$$\approx 0.9851$$

So, a first solution is $\quad \theta_1 \approx 0.9851.$

Another solution can be found using the Supplements Theorem, $\sin \theta = \sin (\pi - \theta)$. Thus,

$$\sin (2\pi t) = \sin (\pi - 2\pi t) \approx \sin (\pi - 0.9851) \approx \sin 2.1565.$$

So, $\sin 2.1565 \approx \frac{10}{12}$, from which a second solution is

$$\theta_2 \approx 2.1565.$$

Because the period of the sine function is 2π, if multiples of 2π are added to or subtracted from 0.9851 and 2.1565, other solutions are generated. So the general solution is

$$2\pi t \approx 0.9851 + 2n\pi \quad \text{or} \quad 2\pi t \approx 2.1565 + 2n\pi, \text{ for all integers } n.$$

Thus, $t \approx 0.1568 + n \quad$ or $\quad t \approx 0.3432 + n$, for all integers n.

Specifically, in the interval $0 \leq t \leq 3$,

$$t \approx 0.1568 + 0 \quad \text{or} \quad t \approx 0.3432 + 0$$
$$\approx 0.1568 + 1 \quad\quad \approx 0.3432 + 1$$
$$\approx 0.1568 + 2 \quad\quad \approx 0.3432 + 2.$$

So, 0.1568, 1.1568, 2.1568, 0.3432, 1.3432, and 2.3432 are the solutions in the interval $0 \leq t \leq 3$. E equals 10 volts after approximately 0.16, 0.34, 1.16, 1.34, 2.16, and 2.34 seconds.

Check 1

Substitute these six values of t in the original equation, and verify that $E \approx 10$ for each value. For instance, for the first value, $12 \sin (2\pi(0.1568)) \approx 10.00061$.

Check 2

Graph $y = 12 \sin (2\pi t)$ and $y = 10$. Notice that the maximum and minimum values of this function are 12 and -12, respectively. So use the window $0 \leq x \leq 3$, $-12 \leq y \leq 12$. Note also that $E = 12 \sin (2\pi t)$ has period equal to $\frac{2\pi}{2\pi} = 1$. There are two solutions per period for a total of 6 solutions for $0 \leq t \leq 3$.

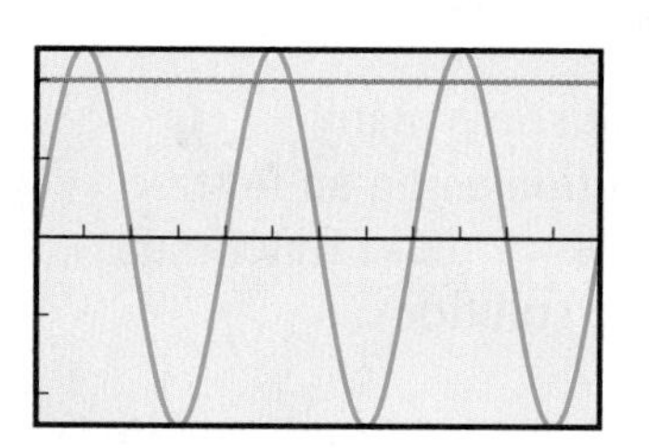

$0 \leq x \leq 3$, x-scale = .25
$-12 \leq y \leq 12$, y-scale = 5

Activity 1

Complete Check 1 of Example 2.

Trigonometric Equations with Quadratic Form

Recall that equations of the form $ax^2 + bx + c = 0$, where $a \neq 0$, are called quadratic equations. If x is replaced by an unknown value of a trigonometric function, the resulting equation is a trigonometric equation with quadratic form.

Example 3

Consider the equation $2 \sin^2 \theta = 1 - \sin \theta$.

a. Find all solutions such that $0 \leq \theta \leq 2\pi$.

b. Find the general solution.

Solution

a. Think of $\sin \theta$ as a single entity, a chunk. Notice that the equation has quadratic form. So, rewrite the equation with one side equal to 0, and solve by factoring or by using the quadratic formula.

$$2 \sin^2 \theta = 1 - \sin \theta$$

$$2 \sin^2 \theta + \sin \theta - 1 = 0$$

$$(2 \sin \theta - 1)(\sin \theta + 1) = 0$$

So $\quad 2 \sin \theta - 1 = 0 \quad$ or $\quad \sin \theta + 1 = 0.$

$$\sin \theta = \frac{1}{2} \quad \text{or} \quad \sin \theta = -1$$

One solution to each of these equations can be found using the inverse sine function.

$$\sin^{-1}\left(\frac{1}{2}\right) = \frac{\pi}{6} \quad \text{or} \quad \sin^{-1}(-1) = -\frac{\pi}{2}$$

$$\theta = \frac{\pi}{6} \quad \text{or} \quad \theta = -\frac{\pi}{2}$$

By the Supplements Theorem, $\sin \theta = \sin (\pi - \theta)$. Thus, $\pi - \frac{\pi}{6} = \frac{5\pi}{6}$ and $\pi - \left(-\frac{\pi}{2}\right) = \frac{3\pi}{2}$ also satisfy the given equation. Even though $-\frac{\pi}{2}$ is not in the target interval, $\frac{3\pi}{2}$ is. **So the solutions to $2 \sin^2 \theta = 1 - \sin \theta$ for $0 \leq \theta \leq 2\pi$ are $\frac{\pi}{6}$, $\frac{5\pi}{6}$, and $\frac{3\pi}{2}$.**

b. By the Periodicity Theorem, adding or subtracting multiples of the period 2π does not change the value of the sine. So the general solution is

$$\theta = \frac{\pi}{6} + 2\pi n,$$

$$\theta = \frac{5\pi}{6} + 2\pi n, \text{ or}$$

$$\theta = \frac{3\pi}{2} + 2\pi n, \text{ for any integer } n.$$

Check 1

Substitute $\frac{\pi}{6}$ for θ in the original equation. Does $2\sin^2\left(\frac{\pi}{6}\right) = 1 - \sin\frac{\pi}{6}$?

$$2\sin^2\left(\frac{\pi}{6}\right) = 2\left(\frac{1}{2}\right)^2 = 2 \cdot \frac{1}{4} = \frac{1}{2}$$

$$1 - \sin\left(\frac{\pi}{6}\right) = 1 - \frac{1}{2} = \frac{1}{2}$$

This solution checks, and the other solutions can be checked in the same way.

Check 2

Graph $y = 2(\sin x)^2$ and $y = 1 - \sin x$ on the same set of axes. Notice that there are three points of intersection on $0 \le x \le 2\pi$. The x-coordinates of these points are the solutions found in part **a**.

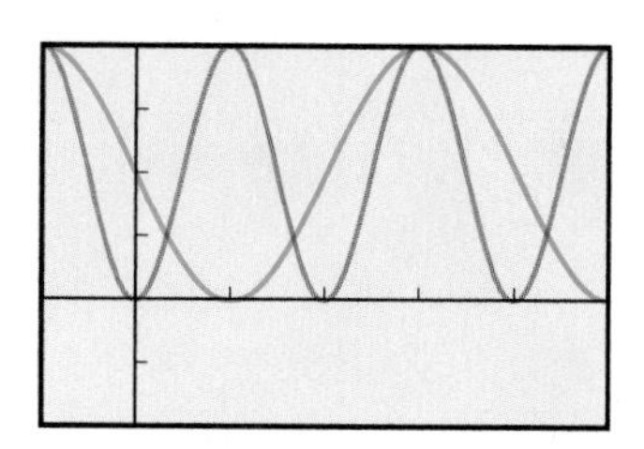

$-\frac{\pi}{2} \le x \le \frac{5\pi}{2}$, x-scale $= \frac{\pi}{2}$
$-1 \le y \le 2$, y-scale $= 0.5$

Activity 2

Do Check 1 of Example 3 for $\theta = \frac{3\pi}{2}$.

QUESTIONS

Covering the Reading

1. Give the three commonly used types of domains for solutions to trigonometric equations.

2. Consider the equation $\cos\theta = 0.24$.
a. Find the solution between 0 and π.
b. Find all solutions between 0 and 2π.
c. Draw a graph to illustrate the solutions in part **b**.
d. Give a general solution to the equation.

3. Show your work for Activity 1.

4. Refer to Example 2.
a. How many solutions are there to the equation $12\sin(2\pi t) = 10$ when $0 \le t \le 5$?
b. Use a graph to justify your answer to part **a**.
c. Give all solutions to $12\sin(2\pi t) = 10$ when $3 \le t \le 5$.

5. Show your work for Activity 2.

6. The output voltage E (in volts) of a circuit at t seconds ($t > 0$) is given by $E = 20\cos(4\pi t)$. To the nearest 0.01 second, at which times in the first 2 seconds is E equal to 15?

In 7 and 8, find all values of θ on the interval $0 \le \theta < 2\pi$ that satisfy the equation.

7. $5 \cos \theta + 1 = 0$

8. $4 \sin^2 \theta - 1 = 0$

9. Solve $2 \cos^2 x - 3 \cos x + 1 = 0$ for x in the indicated domain.
a. $\{x: 0 \le x < 2\pi\}$
b. the set of all real numbers

Applying the Mathematics

10. Solve $\cos \theta = 0.34$ to the nearest degree for θ in the indicated domain.
a. $\{\theta: 0° \le \theta < 90°\}$
b. $\{\theta: 0° \le \theta < 360°\}$
c. the set of all real numbers

11. The number of hours y of daylight in Seattle as a function of x, the number of days after March 21, can be modeled by the equation $y = 12.25 + 3.75 \sin\left(\frac{2\pi x}{365}\right)$.
a. Find the first two times after March 21 that there will be 11.5 hours of daylight.
b. Convert your answers to dates.

12. a. Give the general solution to $3 \cos \theta = 7$.
b. Under what conditions will $a \cos \theta = b$ have solutions?

In 13 and 14, solve for θ, given that $0 \le \theta \le 2\pi$.

13. $\tan \theta = 3$

14. $\tan \theta - \sqrt{3} = 2 \tan \theta$

Review

15. Mariah sits in the center seat of the first row of the Palace Movie Theater, as shown in the figure at the right. She is 8.5 feet away from the wall where the screen is. When seated, the height of her eyes is 3.1 feet above the floor. The bottom of the screen is 6.2 feet above the floor, and the top of the screen is 15.6 feet above the floor. Her angle of vision is formed by the bottom and top of the screen and her eyes. Find the measure of her angle of vision. *(Lesson 5-6)*

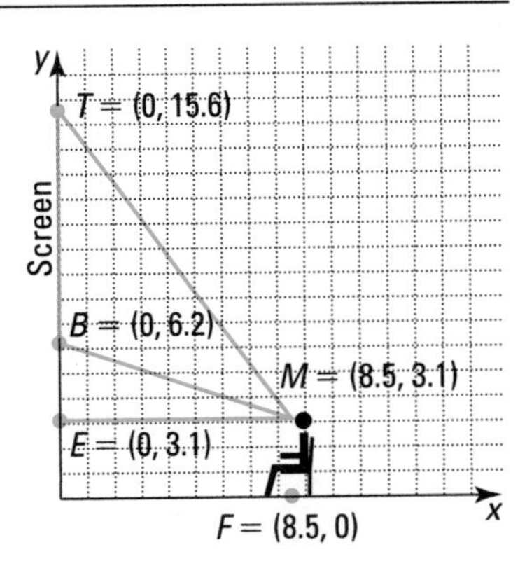

16. In $\triangle XYZ$, $x = 12$, $z = 10$, and $m\angle Z = 43°$. Find all possible values for $m\angle X$, $m\angle Y$, and XZ. *(Lesson 5-4)*

17. Wheelchair ramps are commonly required to have angles of elevation between about 2.9° and 4.8°. Find the angle of elevation of the ramp illustrated at the right and determine if it is within the specified range.
(Lessons 5-1, 5-6)

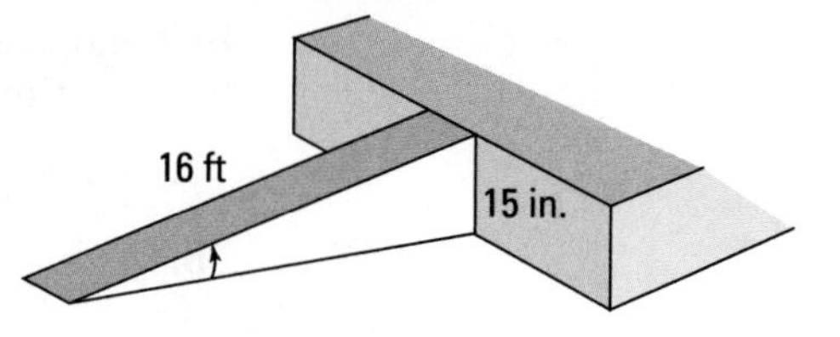

18. A portion of a roller-coaster track is to be sinusoidal as illustrated at the right. The high and low points of the track are separated by 60 meters horizontally and 35 meters vertically. The low point is 5 meters below ground level.

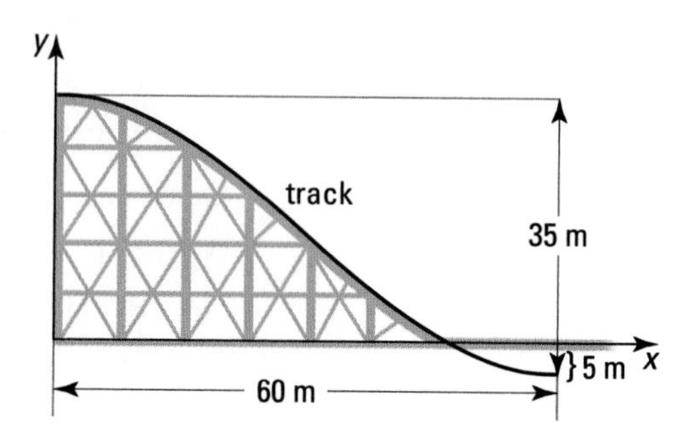

a. Write an equation for the height y in meters of a point on the track at a distance x meters from the high point.

b. The contractor building the roller coaster is preparing to cut the timbers to be set vertically every 5 meters starting at the foot of the high point as pictured. How long should the timbers be? *(Lesson 4-10)*

19. Write an equation for the sine curve below. *(Lesson 4-9)*

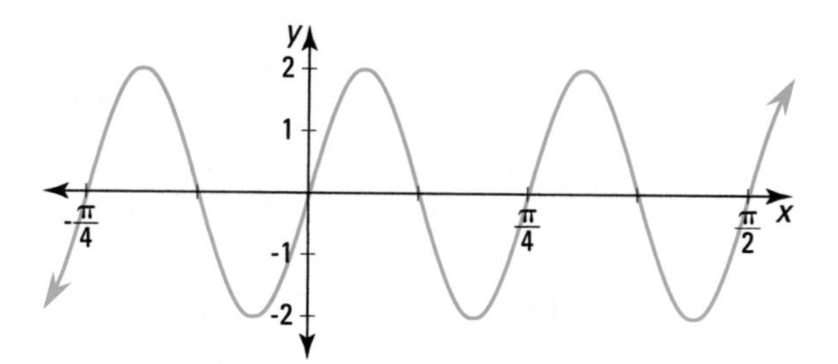

20. What type of symmetry must an even function have? *(Lesson 3-4)*

In 21–26, tell whether the function is odd, even, or neither. *(Lessons 3-4, 4-6)*

21. $y = |x|$ **22.** $y = \sqrt{x}$ **23.** $y = x^{10}$

24. $y = 10^x$ **25.** $y = \cos x$ **26.** $y = \tan x$

Exploration

27. a. How many solutions are there to the given equation on the interval $0 \le \theta < 2\pi$?

i. $\cos \theta = 0.3$ ii. $\cos (2\theta) = 0.3$

iii. $\cos (3\theta) = 0.3$ iv. $\cos (4\theta) = 0.3$

b. Generalize your results in part **a**.

c. How many solutions are there to the equation $\sin (n\theta) = a$, where $|a| < 1$, n is a positive integer, and $0 \le \theta < 2\pi$?

LESSON

5-8

From Washington to Beijing

Jefferson Memorial, Washington D.C.

Some passengers flying from Washington, D.C., to Beijing, China, were surprised to learn about halfway through their journey that they were passing over part of Alaska. Neither Washington nor Beijing is that far north, so why were they going this way? In this lesson we use ideas from trigonometry to find distances on a sphere. First we review some geography and define "shortest distances" on a sphere. Then we use these ideas to find the shortest distance between two cities having the same longitude or latitude. Finally, we calculate the shortest distance between Washington, D.C., and Beijing to illustrate how you can use trigonometry to find the shortest distance between any two cities on Earth.

Circles on a Sphere

If a plane contains a point in the interior of a sphere, then the intersection of the plane and the sphere is a circle. A **great circle** of a sphere is the intersection of a sphere and a plane containing the center of the sphere. This circle has the same center as the sphere. Thus, a great circle has the same radius and circumference as the sphere. Great circles are important because the shortest distance between two points on a sphere is measured along the great circle containing them.

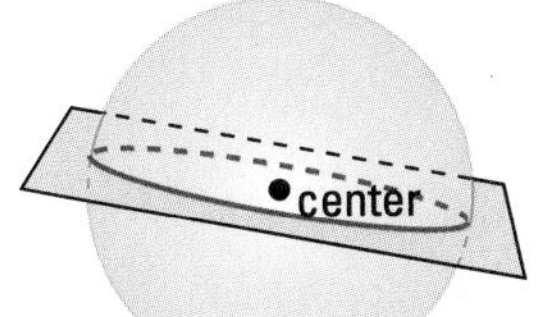

great circle

center of circle

center of sphere

not a great circle

Prime Location. *Cross hairs in the eyepiece of the Transit Circle telescope in the Greenwich Observatory's Meridian Building officially define 0° Longitude. It is indicated by this British postage stamp's red line.*

On Earth, which is approximately a sphere of radius 3960 mi, the equator is a great circle. There are infinitely many great circles containing the north pole N and the south pole S. Each semicircle with endpoints N and S is called a "line" of longitude, or **meridian**. The meridian through Greenwich, England, is called the **Greenwich meridian** or **prime meridian**. *Longitudes* are measured using angles east or west of Greenwich, and so all longitudes are between 0° and 180°. In the figure above, the longitude of P is φ (this is the Greek letter phi). Because P is east of Greenwich, φ measures longitude east. The meridian which is 180°W (and 180°E) is called the **International Date Line**.

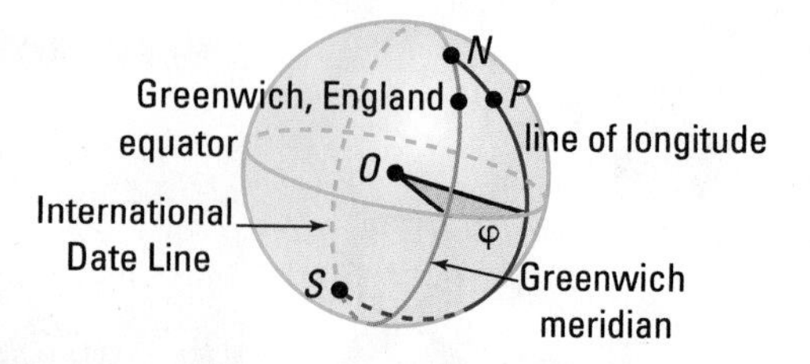

Latitudes measure the extent to which a point is north or south of the equator. They are determined by the angle subtended at the center of Earth by an arc on a line of longitude; so all latitudes are between 0° and 90°. In the diagram at the right, the latitude of P is θ. Because P is north of the equator, θ measures latitude north. The equator itself can be considered at 0°N latitude or 0°S latitude. Notice that a "line" of latitude is a circle, but, except for the equator, lines of latitude are *not* great circles.

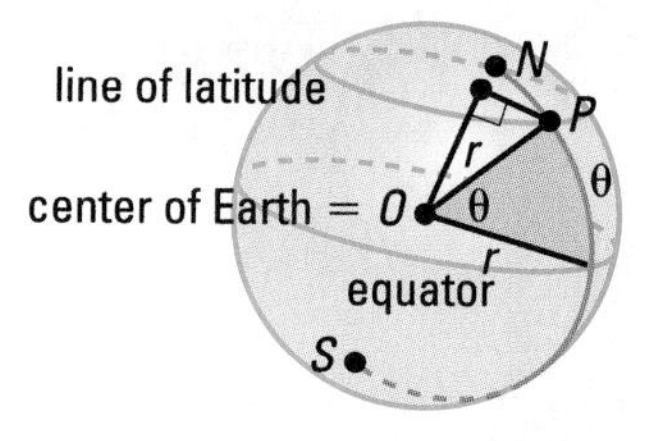

Distances Between Points at the Same Longitude

The position of any point on Earth can be determined by its longitude and latitude. In the figure at the right, W represents Washington, D.C. Its location is specified by 77°0'W, 38°55'N. This means that Washington, D.C., is on a line of longitude 77°0' west of the Greenwich meridian and on a line of latitude 38°55' north of the equator.

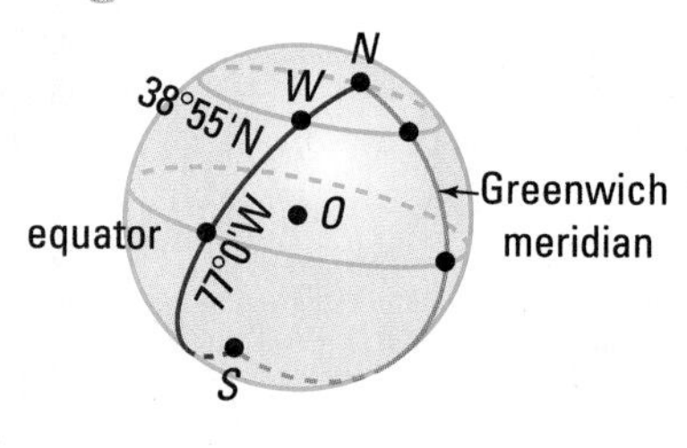

What is the shortest distance from the North Pole to Washington? On any sphere the shortest distance between two points is the length of the minor arc of the great circle connecting them. So, the shortest way to go from the North Pole to Washington is to go along the 77° 0'W meridian.

Let E be the point on the equator at 77° 0' west longitude, and let N be the north pole. As you can see from the diagram at the right, because $m\angle WOE = 38°55'$, $m\angle NOW = 51°5'$. So, the length of $\overset{\frown}{NW}$ is

$$\frac{51°5'}{360°} \cdot 2 \cdot \pi \cdot 3960 \text{ mi} \approx 3530 \text{ mi}.$$

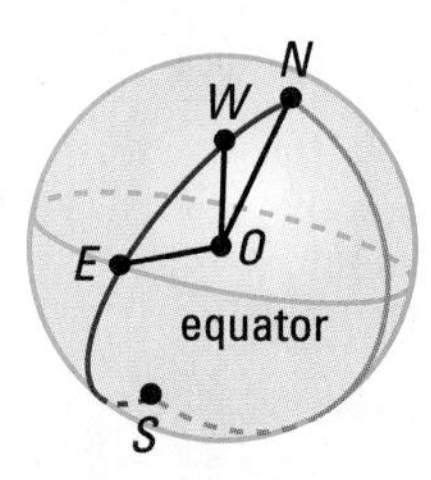

Washington, D.C., is about 3530 miles from the North Pole.

In this way you can find the shortest distance between any two places on Earth that are on the same line of longitude.

Example 1

Jackson, Mississippi (90°12'W, 32°22'N), and St. Louis, Missouri (90°12'W, 38°35'N), are on the same meridian. They are points J and L in the figure at the right. Estimate the distance from Jackson to St. Louis.

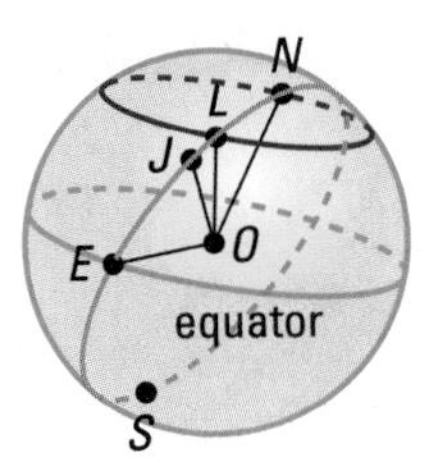

Solution

Because J and L are on the same great circle, the shortest distance between them is the length of $\overset{\frown}{JL}$ on the meridian that is 90°12'W.

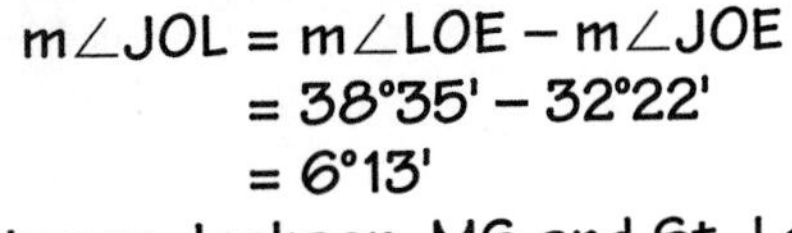

$$\begin{aligned} m\angle JOL &= m\angle LOE - m\angle JOE \\ &= 38°35' - 32°22' \\ &= 6°13' \end{aligned}$$

So, the distance between Jackson, MS and St. Louis, MO, is

$$\frac{6°13'}{360°} \cdot 2 \cdot \pi \cdot 3960 \text{ mi} \approx 430 \text{ mi.}$$

Distances Between Points at the Same Latitude

However, we cannot find the shortest distance between cities with the same latitude in this way. Consider Ankara, Turkey (32°55'E, 39°55'N), and Beijing, China (116°25'E, 39°55'N). Many people think that the shortest distance between Ankara and Beijing is along the 39°55'N line of latitude, but this is not the case, because lines of latitude are not great circles.

Greenwich meridian

To show this, we first find the distance between Ankara (A) and Beijing (B) along the 39°55' N line of latitude. Let R be the point on the Greenwich meridian at latitude 39°55'. If Q is the center of the circle that is this "line" of latitude,

$$m\overset{\frown}{AB} = m\angle AQB.$$

So,

$$\begin{aligned} m\overset{\frown}{AB} &= m\angle RQB - m\angle RQA \\ &= 116°25' - 32°55' \\ &= 83°30'. \end{aligned}$$

To find the length of $\overset{\frown}{AB}$, we need the radius of circle Q. One radius of this circle is $\overline{RQ}$.

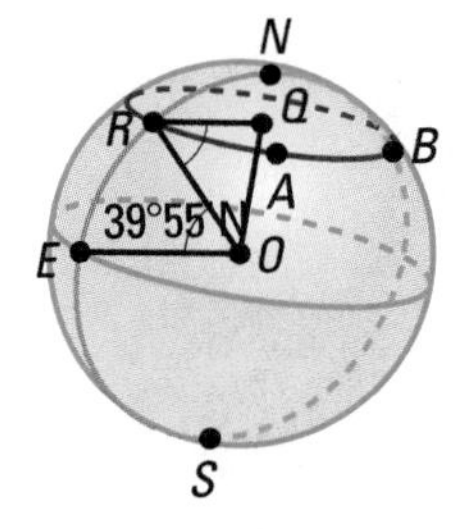

Because $\overline{RQ} \parallel \overline{EO}$, $m\angle QRO = 39°55'$. Also,

$$\frac{RQ}{RO} = \cos \angle QRO.$$

Hence, $RQ = RO \cdot \cos \angle QRO.$

But RO is the radius of Earth. Therefore,

$$\begin{aligned} RQ &= 3960 \cdot \cos 39°55' \\ &\approx 3040 \text{ mi.} \end{aligned}$$

Hence the distance between Ankara and Beijing along the line of latitude is about

$$\frac{83°30'}{360°} \cdot 2 \cdot \pi \cdot 3040 \text{ mi} \approx 4430 \text{ mi}.$$

Now compare this distance with the great circle distance between Ankara and Beijing. For this, we must use *spherical triangles*, that is, triangles whose sides are arcs of great circles measured in degrees, and a *Spherical Law of Cosines*, which is presented here without proof.

Spherical Law of Cosines

If ABC is a spherical triangle with sides a, b, and c, then

$$\cos c = \cos a \cos b + \sin a \sin b \cos C.$$

You can use the Spherical Law of Cosines to find the great circle distance between Ankara and Beijing. The key is to let Ankara and Beijing be two vertices of the spherical triangle and to let one of the poles be the third vertex of the spherical triangle. In this case, the North Pole is used.

Example 2

Find the length of n, the great circle arc from Ankara to Beijing.

Solution

Let A = Ankara, B = Beijing, and N = North Pole. In spherical $\triangle ABN$, from the Spherical Law of Cosines:

$$\cos n = \cos a \cos b + \sin a \sin b \cos N.$$

$m\angle N$ is the same as $m\angle AQB$ that was found before in calculating the distance from Ankara to Beijing along the line of latitude. Arc measures a and b are easy to find.

$$\begin{aligned} b &= 90° - \text{latitude of Ankara} \\ &= 90° - 39°55' \\ &= 50°5' \end{aligned}$$

Because Ankara and Beijing have the same latitude, $a = 50°5'$ also. Now substitute into the Spherical Law of Cosines.

$$\begin{aligned} \cos n &= \cos 50°5' \cos 50°5' + \sin 50°5' \sin 50°5' \cos 83°30' \\ &\approx 0.4783 \\ n &\approx 61.4° \end{aligned}$$

So, the length of the great circle through Ankara and Beijing is about $\frac{61.4°}{360°} \cdot 2 \cdot \pi \cdot 3960 \text{ mi} \approx 4240 \text{ mi}.$

Notice that this is about 190 mi shorter than the path from A to B along the line of latitude.

Distance between Any Two Points on a Sphere

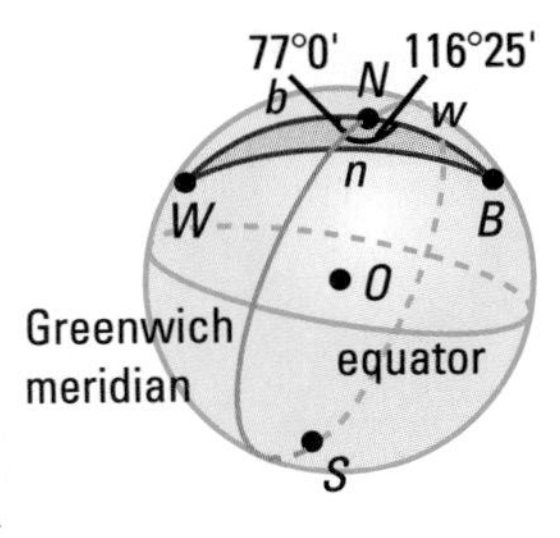

The most general and most common problem of this type is to find the shortest distance between two cities not on the same latitude or longitude, for instance, Washington, D.C., (W) and Beijing (B).

To use the Spherical Law of Cosines, we need to find b, w, and $m\angle N$, where b is the great circle arc measure from Washington to the North Pole (N), and w is the great circle arc measure from Beijing to the North Pole. Earlier we found that $w = 50°5'$ and $b = 51°5'$. Finding $m\angle N$ is more complicated. You might think that

$$\begin{aligned} m\angle N &= 77°0' + 116°25' \\ &= 193°25'. \end{aligned}$$

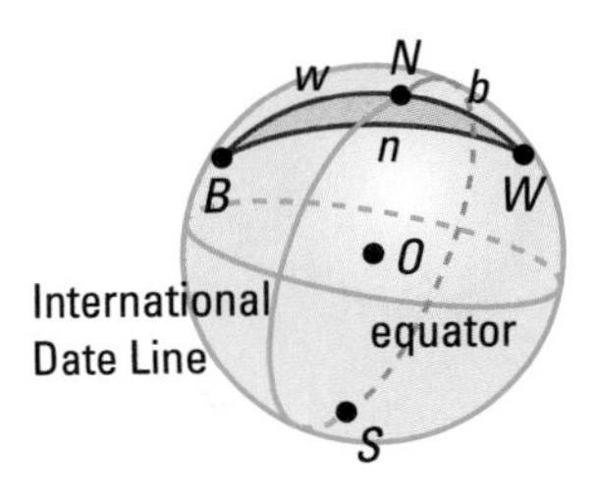

But angles in spherical triangles, like those in plane triangles, must have measures less than 180°. This means that the shortest great circle arc from Washington to Beijing crosses the International Date Line instead of the Greenwich meridian, and

$$\begin{aligned} m\angle N &= 360° - 193°25' \\ &= 166°35'. \end{aligned}$$

Now substitute into the Spherical Law of Cosines.

$$\begin{aligned} \cos n &= \cos b \cos w + \sin b \sin w \cos N \\ &= (\cos 51°5')(\cos 50°5') + (\sin 51°5')(\sin 50°5')(\cos 166°35') \\ &\approx -0.1774 \\ n &\approx 100.2° \end{aligned}$$

So, the shortest distance from Washington to Beijing is about

$$\frac{100.2°}{360°} \cdot 2 \cdot \pi \cdot 3960 \text{ mi} \approx 6930 \text{ mi}.$$

Problems involving distances in navigation and astronomy have been important for millennia and led to the development of trigonometry. Spherical trigonometry, in fact, developed in ancient Greece before plane trigonometry. Euclid knew some of its fundamentals, and by the time of Menelaus (about 100 A.D.), Greek trigonometry reached its peak. Nasir-Eddin (1201–1274), an Arabian mathematician, systematized both plane and spherical trigonometry, but his work was unknown in Europe until the middle fifteenth century. Johannes Muller (1436–1476), also known as Regiomontanus, presented the Spherical Law of Cosines given in this lesson and also a *Spherical Law of Sines*, an amazing theorem that we leave for you to find as an exploration.

QUESTIONS

Covering the Reading

In 1 and 2, *multiple choice.* Tell whether the figure is (a) always, (b) never, or (c) sometimes (but not always) part or all of a great circle.

1. line of longitude

2. line of latitude

In 3 and 4, state the common name of the meridian.

3. 0°W

4. 180°E

5. What is the name of the great circle which is 0°N latitude?

6. Find the distance from Kinshasa, Zaire (15°17'E, 4°18'S), to the South Pole.

7. Find the distance between Fresno, California (119°48'W, 36°44'N), and Reno, Nevada (119°49'W, 39°30'N). Assume that the cities are on the same meridian.

8. *True or false.* An arc of a line of latitude (other than the equator) can be the side of a spherical triangle.

9. Use the distances calculated in the text from Ankara to Beijing. If an airplane flies at 550 mph along the line of latitude instead of the great circle arc, about how much longer will the flight take?

In 10 and 11, consider Chicago, Illinois (88°W, 42°N), Providence, RI (71°W, 42°N), and Rome, Italy (12°E, 42°N).

10. **a.** Find the distance from Chicago to Providence along the line of latitude.
b. Find the great circle distance from Chicago to Providence.
c. How much longer is the line of latitude distance?

11. **a.** Find the distance from Chicago to Rome along the line of latitude.
b. Find the great circle distance from Chicago to Rome.
c. How much longer is the line of latitude distance?
d. To the nearest percent, how much longer is the line of latitude distance?

12. Find the great circle distance between Prague, Czechoslovakia (14°26'E, 50°5'N), and Rio de Janeiro, Brazil (43°12'W, 22°57'S).

Prague, Czechoslovakia

Review

13. Solve $\tan^2 x - 1 = 0$ over the indicated interval.
a. $\left\{x: -\frac{\pi}{2} < x < \frac{\pi}{2}\right\}$
b. $\{x: -2\pi \leq x \leq 2\pi\}$
c. all real values of x in radians *(Lesson 5-7)*

14. Given $2\cos\left(\frac{\pi t}{2}\right) = -1$.

a. Solve for t in the interval $-2 \le t \le 2$.

b. On the same set of axes, graph $y = 2\cos\frac{\pi t}{2}$ and $y = -1$, and verify your answer in part **a**. *(Lesson 5-7)*

15. A sea wall rises 6 feet above the ocean floor. The height of the water above the ocean floor at the wall, h, can be modeled by the equation

$$h = 1.5\sin\left(\frac{t-4}{\frac{6}{\pi}}\right) + 3.5,$$

where t is the number of hours after midnight.

a. Sketch a graph of this function.

b. Solve this equation for t in terms of h.

c. At what times is the tide the highest? *(Lesson 5-7)*

In 16–18, give the domain and range. *(Lessons 5-3, 5-5, 5-6)*

16. $y = \tan^{-1} x$

17. $y = \sin^{-1} x$

18. $y = \cos^{-1} x$

19. To draw a map, a cartographer needed to find the distances between point Z across the lake and each of point X and Y on another side. The cartographer found $XY \approx 0.3$ miles, $m\angle X \approx 50°$, and $m\angle Y \approx 100°$. Find the distances from X to Z and from Y to Z. *(Lesson 5-4)*

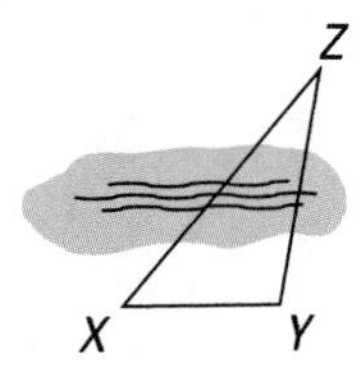

20. In $\triangle PAM$, $a = 13$, $m = 11$, and $m\angle P = 38°$. Find AM. *(Lesson 5-2)*

21. Air traffic controllers need to know the distance between the clouds and the ground. This is called the "ceiling." This can be done by shining a beam of light perpendicular to the ground up at the clouds, and measuring the angle of elevation from a fixed location, such as the control tower to the point where the beam hits the clouds. If the control tower is 2000 feet from the beam and the angle of elevation is 70˚, what is the ceiling? *(Lesson 5-1)*

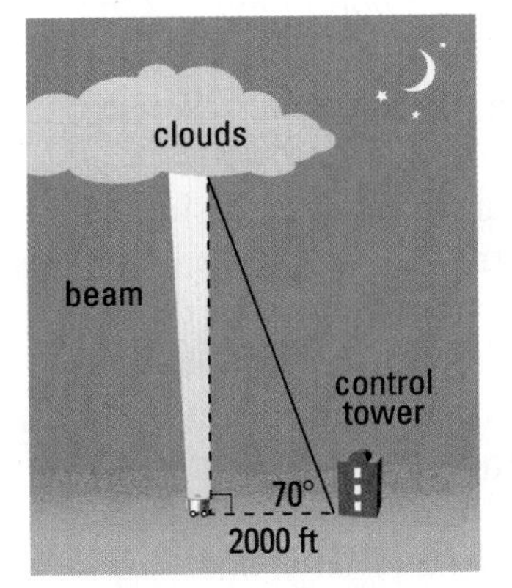

In 22 and 23, solve for x. *(Previous course)*

22. a. $x^2 = 1024$ **b.** $2^x = 1024$

23. a. $x^3 = 531{,}441$ **b.** $3^x = 531{,}441$

Exploration

24. Consult an encyclopedia or a book on spherical trigonometry. What is the Spherical Law of Sines?

A project presents an opportunity for you to extend your knowledge of a topic related to the material of this chapter. You should allow more time for a project than you do for a typical homework question.

1 Applications of the Law of Sines

Use the Law of Sines to prove five of the following statements for every triangle ABC.

a. $\frac{a-c}{c} = \frac{\sin A - \sin C}{\sin C}$

b. $\frac{a}{b} = \frac{\sin A}{\sin B}$

c. $\frac{b+c}{b-c} = \frac{\sin B + \sin C}{\sin B - \sin C}$

d. The bisector of an interior angle of a triangle divides the opposite side into parts whose ratio is equal to the ratio of the sides adjacent to the angle bisected. That is, if $\overrightarrow{AD}$ bisects $\angle BAC$, then $\frac{x}{y} = \frac{c}{b}$.

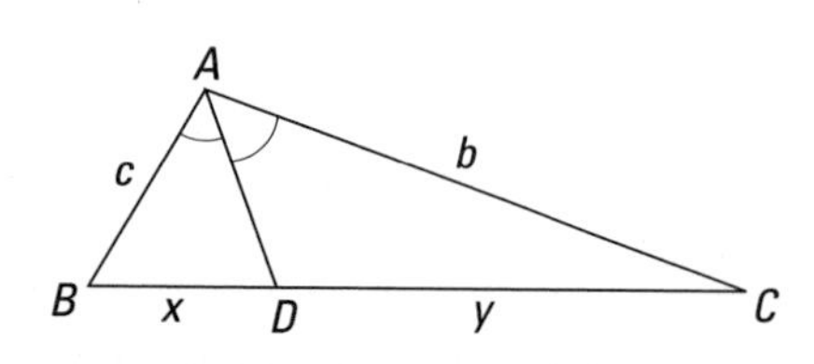

e. In a scalene triangle, the largest angle is opposite the longest side.

f. A triangle is equilateral if and only if it is equiangular.

2 Bond Angles in Molecules

In the methane molecule (CH_4), a single carbon atom lies at the center of a regular tetrahedron $ABDE$ whose vertices are four hydrogen atoms, as shown chemically at left and geometrically at right.

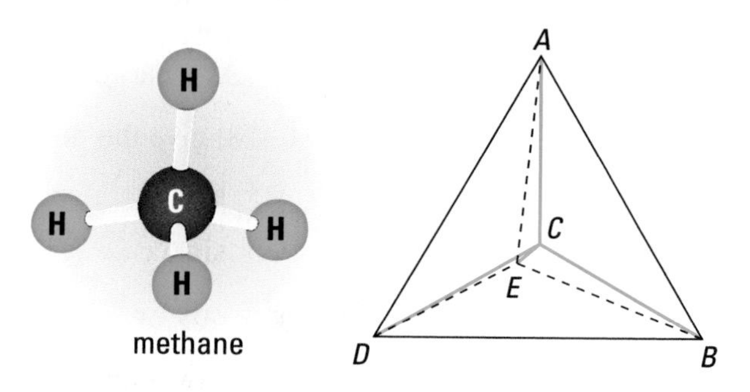

Because of this, the hydrogen atoms can achieve their maximum separation in space. The angles with vertex at C and sides passing through the vertices of the tetrahedron are *bond angles*. One such bond angle is ACB. These bond angles all have the same measure, a measure characteristic of many organic molecules.

a. Find the measure of this bond angle using geometry and trigonometry.

b. Consult a chemistry textbook or some other source to check your answer to part **a** and also to find the carbon-hydrogen bond length in the methane molecule. Find the bond lengths and bond angles in the molecules ethane (C_2H_6), ethylene (C_2H_4), acetylene (C_2H_2), and cyclpropane (C_3H_6), and write a short report on why bond angles are important to chemists.

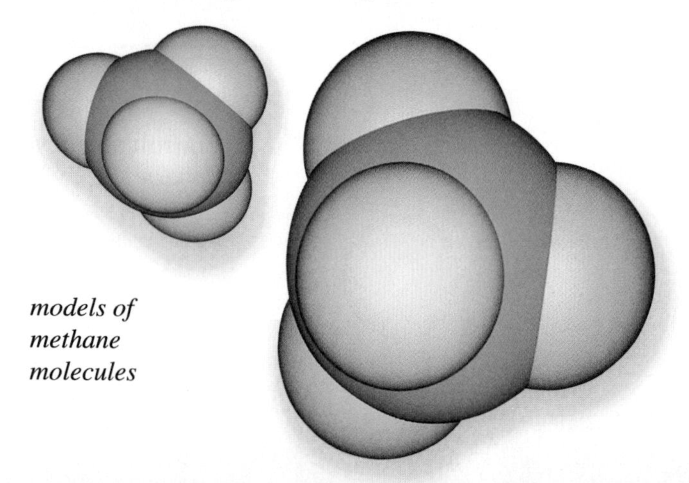

models of methane molecules

3 The Gregory Series

As noted in Lesson 5-6, the Scottish mathematician James Gregory (1638–1675) found the following series for $\tan^{-1} x$, where $-1 \le x \le 1$.

$$\tan^{-1} x = \sum_{i=0}^{\infty} \frac{(-1)^i x^{(2i+1)}}{2i+1}$$

$$= x - \frac{x^3}{3} + \frac{x^5}{5} - \frac{x^7}{7} + \frac{x^9}{9} - \dots$$

Here is a calculator program to approximate $\tan^{-1} x$ using the first 100 terms of Gregory's series.

```
0→X
Disp "ENTER A NO.", "FROM -1 TO 1"
Input X
X→S
X→T
For (N, 3, 199, 2)
-X*X*(N – 2)/N *T→T
S+T→S
End
Disp S
```

a. The variable T represents the term of the series. What is its first value? How is it changed within the loop?

b. Run the program with $x = 1$ to find an approximation for $\frac{\pi}{4}$. Run the program with some other value of x ($-1 \le x \le 1$), and compare your output with the value of $\tan^{-1} x$ given by your calculator. Check that the formula does *not* work when $|x| > 1$.

c. Modify the program to evaluate more terms of the series. Use your modification to evaluate $\tan^{-1} 1$. Compare the calculator's output to the exact value of $\tan^{-1} 1$.

d. The astronomer Abraham Sharp (1651–1742) used this series to find $\tan^{-1}\left(\frac{\sqrt{3}}{3}\right)$ to approximate π to 71 decimal places. Use the program to find $\tan^{-1}\left(\frac{\sqrt{3}}{3}\right)$. Compare the rate of convergence with that for $\tan^{-1} 1$ obtained in part **c**. (Notice that a programmable calculator can do calculations of this kind with only limited precision. Special programs and more powerful computers are needed to evalute to more than about 12-decimal-place precision.)

e. Read about these, and other, uses of Gregory's Arctan series to evaluate π in Petr Beckmann's *A History of π* or Howard Eves' *An Introduction to the History of Mathematics*. Summarize your work in a report.

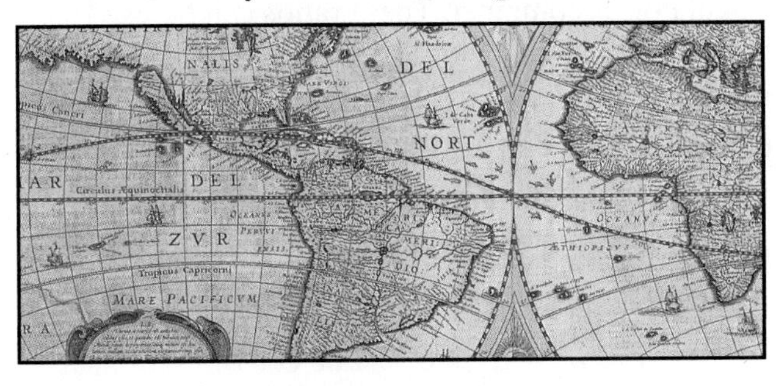

4 Landmarks and Surveying

Surveyors and cartographers use trigonometry extensively to locate points on Earth and to represent points on maps. In particular, they use a network of fixed *benchmarks* to locate property lines and other landmarks.

a. Find out how benchmarks are determined.

b. Find some benchmarks in your neighborhood.

c. Describe how these locations are used to locate other places.

d. Present your findings in a report.

Eilean Donan-Loch Duich, Scotland

SUMMARY

The sine, cosine, and tangent of θ, when $0° < \theta < 90°$ or $0 < \theta < \frac{\pi}{2}$, are ratios of side lengths of right triangles. In a right triangle,

$$\cos\theta = \frac{\text{adjacent leg}}{\text{hypotenuse}},$$

$$\sin\theta = \frac{\text{opposite leg}}{\text{hypotenuse}}$$

$$\tan\theta = \frac{\text{opposite leg}}{\text{adjacent leg}}.$$

These ratios can be evaluated exactly for some angles. All values can be approximated using a calculator or computer. These ratios can be used to find sides and angles of right triangles.

Trigonometric ratios can also be used to find unknown sides and angles in all triangles.

The following two theorems are helpful.

Law of Cosines: In any $\triangle ABC$,

$$a^2 = b^2 + c^2 - 2bc\cos A,$$
$$b^2 = a^2 + c^2 - 2ac\cos B,$$
and
$$c^2 = a^2 + b^2 - 2ab\cos C.$$

Law of Sines: In any $\triangle ABC$,

$$\frac{a}{\sin A} = \frac{b}{\sin B} = \frac{c}{\sin C}.$$

The Law of Cosines is helpful when the SAS or the SSS condition is met. The Law of Sines is helpful when the ASA or AAS condition is met. In the case of SSA, zero, one, or two triangles may result.

The inverses of the parent sine, cosine, and tangent functions are not functions. However, if the domains of the parent functions (and equivalently the range of their inverses) are restricted as noted below, the inverses are functions.

$y = \cos^{-1} x = \text{Arccos } x$ is defined when $0 \le y \le \pi$.

$y = \sin^{-1} x = \text{Arcsin } x$ is defined when $\frac{-\pi}{2} \le y \le \frac{\pi}{2}$.

$y = \tan^{-1} x = \text{Arctan } x$ is defined when $\frac{-\pi}{2} < y < \frac{\pi}{2}$.

The inverse trigonometric function keys on a calculator typically give values only in the above intervals.

Equations involving the circular functions are called trigonometric equations. Solving trigonometric equations involves the use of the inverses of the circular functions. This leads to solutions in a restricted domain. Due to the periodic nature of circular functions, a general solution can be obtained by using the period of the parent function, and the properties of sines, cosines, and tangents.

VOCABULARY

Below are the most important terms and phrases for this chapter. You should be able to give a general description and a specific example of each and a precise definition for those marked with an asterisk (*).

Lesson 5-1
trigonometry
trigonometric functions
*sine, *cosine, *tangent
angle of depression, elevation
minutes of degrees
seconds of degrees

Lesson 5-2
*Law of Cosines

Lesson 5-3
*inverse cosine function
*$\cos^{-1}$, *Arccos

Lesson 5-4
*SAS Area Formula for a Triangle
*Law of Sines

Lesson 5-5
*inverse sine function
*$\sin^{-1}$, *Arcsin

Lesson 5-6
*Inverse tangent function
*$\tan^{-1}$, *Arctan

Lesson 5-7
trigonometric equation
general solution

PROGRESS SELF-TEST

Take this test as you would take a test in class. You will need an automatic grapher. Then check the test yourself using the solutions at the back of the book.

1. Write 16°35' to the nearest hundredth of a degree.

In 2–4, consider $\triangle JBM$ at the right.

2. Find $\sin M$ exactly.

3. Find $\tan B$ exactly.

4. Find $m\angle B$ to the nearest tenth of a degree.

In 5 and 6, evaluate without a calculator, and describe your method.

5. $\cos^{-1}\left(\frac{1}{2}\right)$

6. $\tan^{-1}\left(\tan\left(\frac{\pi}{4}\right)\right)$

7. Explain why $\cos^{-1}\left(\cos\left(-\frac{\pi}{3}\right)\right) \neq -\frac{\pi}{3}$.

8. a. Draw a graph of $y = \sin^{-1} x$.

b. Give the domain and range of $y = \sin^{-1} x$.

In 9 and 10, a ladder is 12 feet long.

9. If the ladder is placed against a wall so that its base is 2 feet from the wall, find, to the nearest degree, the acute angle the ladder makes with the ground.

10. Suppose the base of the ladder is x feet from the wall. Find an expression for θ, the angle the ladder makes with the ground.

11. A certain variety of wheat forms a mound in the shape of a cone as shown. If the wheat is dry and allowed to fall naturally, then $m\angle\theta = 41°$. How high is the mound when its diameter is 12 feet?

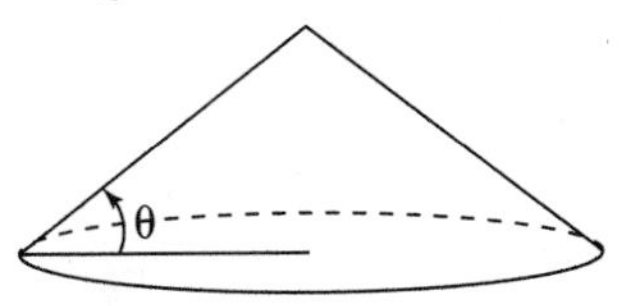

12. Find x in the triangle below. Round your answer to the nearest tenth.

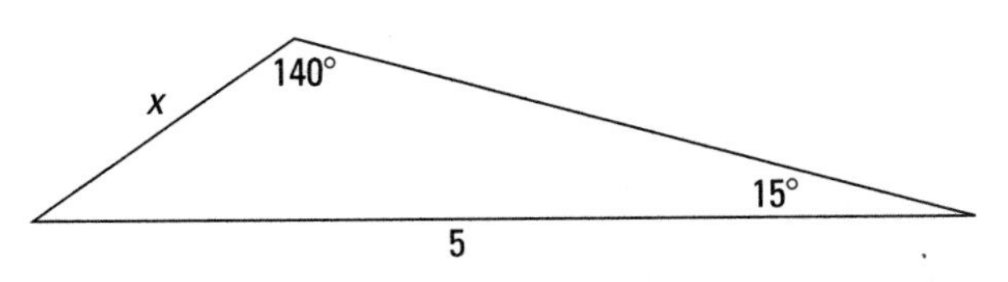

13. A surveyor wishes to find the distance between a public marina and a private pier. His measurements are shown at the right. What is the distance between the marina and the pier?

14. In $\triangle ABC$, $a = 12$, $b = 7$, and $m\angle B = 35.5°$. Find all possible values for $m\angle A$. Round your answer(s) to the nearest tenth of a degree.

15. Solve $\cos\theta = -0.125$ over each domain.

a. $\{\theta: 0 \le \theta \le \pi\}$

b. $\{\theta: 0 \le \theta \le 2\pi\}$

c. θ is any real number.

16. Give a general solution to $2\sin\theta - \sqrt{2} = 0$.

17. For what value(s) of k does the equation $10\cos\theta = k$ have no solutions?

18. Explain why applying the Law of Cosines always leads to a situation with only one answer.

19. The output voltage V (in volts) of a circuit at t seconds ($t \ge 0$) is given by $V = 25\sin(3\pi t)$.

a. Graph this equation for $0 \le t \le 2$.

b. What is the maximum output in volts in this time?

c. How often during the first two seconds is the voltage at maximum output?

d. Find the first four times the voltage is equal to 20 volts.

20. Suppose that the wheel on a child's wagon has a pebble stuck in its tread. Assume that the pebble is now exactly at the top of the wheel, 6" off the ground. If the wheel is turning at the rate of 1 revolution every 10 seconds, a model for the height of the pebble over time is given by

$$h(t) = 3 + 3\cos\left(\frac{\pi t}{5}\right).$$

Find the first two times the pebble is 4 inches off the ground.

CHAPTER REVIEW

Questions on SPUR Objectives

SPUR stands for **S**kills, **P**roperties, **U**ses, and **R**epresentations. The Chapter Review questions are grouped according to the SPUR Objectives for this chapter.

SKILLS DEAL WITH THE PROCEDURES USED TO GET ANSWERS.

Objective A: *Find sines, cosines, and tangents of angles.* *(Lesson 5-1)*

1. Refer to triangle TRY below. Find each.

a. $\sin R$

b. $\sin Y$

c. $\cos R$

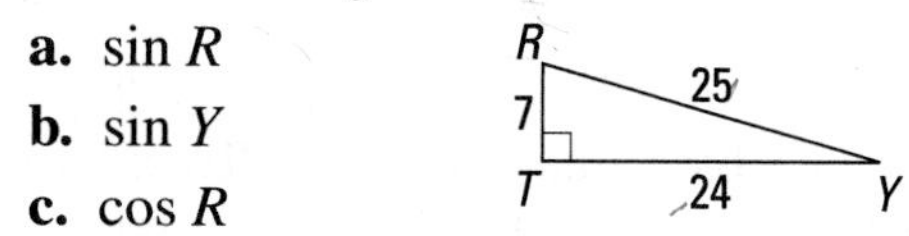

In 2–4, approximate to the nearest thousandth.

2. $\tan 42°$ **3.** $\sin 16°40'$ **4.** $\cos 82.13°$

In 5–7, find the exact value without using a calculator.

5. $\cos 60°$ **6.** $\sin 45°$ **7.** $\tan 30°$

Objective B: *Evaluate inverse trigonometric functions.* *(Lessons 5-3, 5-5, 5-6)*

In 8–10, evaluate without a calculator. State angle measures in degrees.

8. $\sin^{-1}\left(\frac{1}{2}\right)$ **9.** Arctan 1 **10.** $\cos^{-1}\left(-\frac{\sqrt{2}}{2}\right)$

In 11–13, give the value to the nearest tenth of a radian.

11. Arcsin 0.1895 **12.** $\tan^{-1}10$

13. $\cos^{-1}(-0.8753)$

In 14 and 15, evaluate without a calculator.

14. $\cos\left(\text{Arccos}\left(\frac{4}{5}\right)\right)$ **15.** $\sin^{-1}\left(\sin\left(\frac{3\pi}{4}\right)\right)$

Objective C: *Use trigonometry to find lengths, angles, or areas.* *(Lessons 5-1, 5-2, 5-4)*

In 16 and 17, find x.

16. **17.**

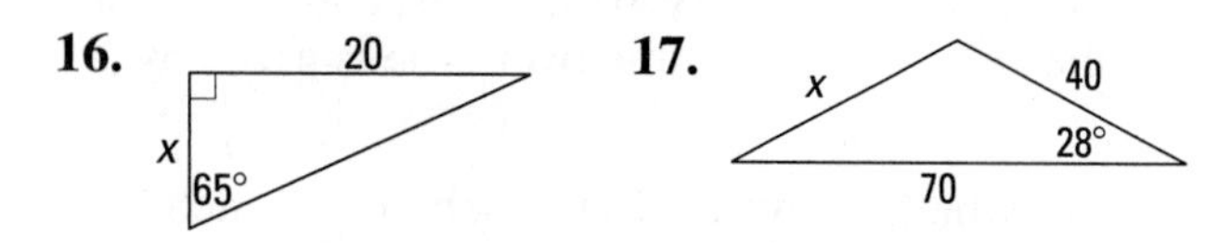

18. Find, to the nearest tenth of a degree, the measures of the angles of a 5-12-13 triangle.

19. Find, to the nearest tenth of a degree, the measure of the largest angle in a triangle whose sides are 4, 5, and 6 cm.

20. In $\triangle XYZ$, $m\angle X = 48°$, $m\angle Y = 68°$, and $y = 10$. Find x.

21. In $\triangle ABC$, $a = 3$, $b = 5$, and $m\angle A = 20.7°$. Find all possible values of $m\angle B$ to the nearest tenth of a degree.

22. Calculate the area of the triangle.

23. Find the area of the parallelogram.

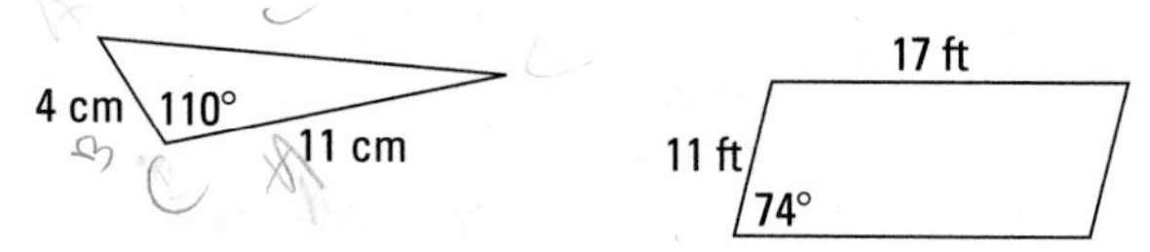

Objective D: *Solve trigonometric equations.* *(Lessons 5-3, 5-5, 5-6, 5-7)*

In 24–26, find θ, where $0° < \theta < 90°$, to the nearest hundredth.

24. $\tan \theta = 1.5$ **25.** $\sin \theta = 0.32$

26. $\cos \theta = 0.1234$

27. Find the exact degree measure such that $\sin \theta = \frac{\sqrt{3}}{2}$ given $0 \le \theta \le \frac{\pi}{2}$.

28. Give the number of solutions to the equation for $0 \le x \le 2\pi$. Justify your reasoning.

a. $8 \sin x = 5$ **b.** $5 \sin x = 8$

c. $5 \tan x = 8$

In 29–32, solve given that $0 \le \theta \le 2\pi$.

29. $\sin \theta = -0.34$ **30.** $\cos \theta = \frac{7}{15}$

31. $\sin^2 \theta + 3 \sin \theta + 1 = 0$

32. $\tan \theta = -0.4$

In 33–38, describe the general solution.

33. $\cos x = 0.24$

34. $4 \sin x = -1$

35. $3 \tan \theta - 5 = 0$

36. $\cos (3x) = 0.724$

37. $\sin (2\pi x) = -0.341$

38. $2 \cos^2(3x) - \cos (3x) = 1$

PROPERTIES DEAL WITH THE PRINCIPLES BEHIND THE MATHEMATICS.

Objective E: *Interpret the Law of Sines, Law of Cosines, and related theorems.* *(Lessons 5-2, 5-4)*

39. Explain why the two triangles below have the same area.

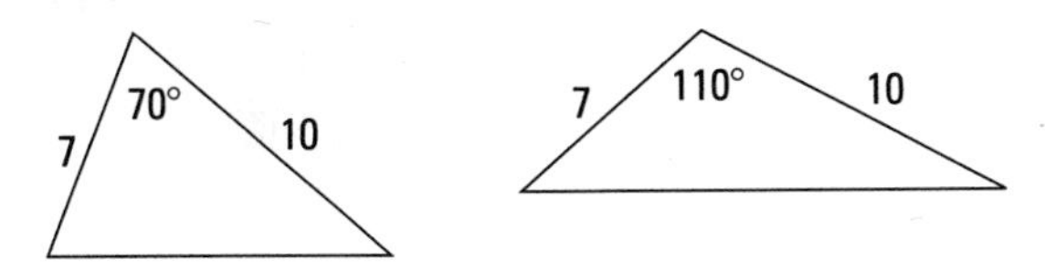

40. Explain how the Pythagorean Theorem follows from the Law of Cosines.

41. In $\triangle EFG$, $m\angle E = 35°$, $EF = 4$, and $FG = 9$. Tom claims that there is exactly one triangle satisfying these conditions. Karen claims that there are two. Who is correct? Why?

42. Applying the Law of Sines sometimes lead to a situation with two answers. Explain why.

Objective F: *State properties of inverse trigonometric functions.* *(Lessons 5-3, 5-5, 5-6)*

43. For what values of θ is the following statement true? If $k = \sin \theta$, then $\theta = \sin^{-1} k$.

44. *Multiple choice.* If $\sin 5x = a$ and $-\frac{\pi}{2} \le 5x \le \frac{\pi}{2}$, then x equals __?__.

(a) $5 \sin^{-1} a$

(b) $\sin^{-1}\left(\frac{a}{5}\right)$

(c) $\sin^{-1} (5a)$

(d) $\frac{1}{5} \sin^{-1} a$

45. Why must the domain of $y = \cos x$ be restricted in order to define $y = \cos^{-1} x$?

46. State the domain and the range of $y = \sin^{-1} x$.

47. *True or false.* The function $y = \text{Arctan}\, x$ has period π.

48. Explain why $\cos^{-1}\left(\cos\left(-\frac{\pi}{4}\right)\right) \neq -\frac{\pi}{4}$.

USES DEAL WITH APPLICATIONS OF MATHEMATICS IN REAL SITUATIONS.

Objective G: *Solve problems using trigonometric ratios in right triangles.* *(Lesson 5-1)*

49. A ladder against a wall makes a 75° angle with the ground. If the base of the ladder is 4 feet from the wall, find the length of the ladder.

50. A school building casts a shadow 18 m long when the elevation of the sun is 41° as shown at the right. How high is the building if $AB = 16$ m?

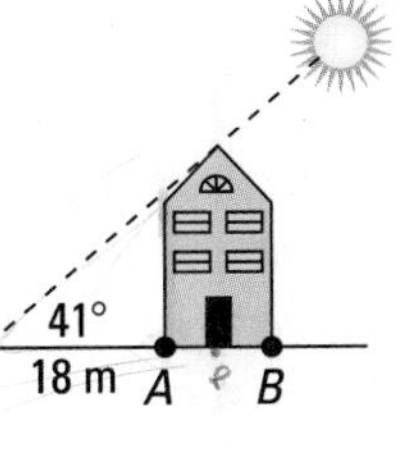

51. Guy wires 60 feet long are to be used to steady a flagpole 50 feet tall. What acute angle θ will the wires make with the ground?

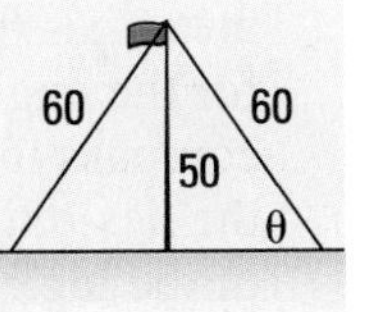

52. Two sightings 80' apart are taken to the top of a canyon wall. The angles of elevation are shown. How high is the top above the canyon floor?

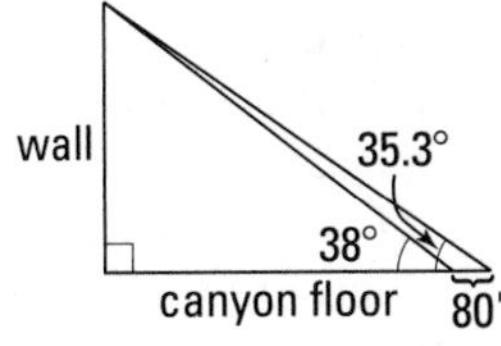

53. From ancient to modern times, carpenters and masons have used a 3-4-5 right triangle to mark right angles. Suppose that each measurement could be as much as 3% off. One worst case scenario occurs when the sides are each 3% longer and the hypotenuse is 3% shorter.

a. Find the measures of the three angles of a 3-4-5 triangle.

b. Calculate the measure of the largest angle for the worst case scenario described above. Do you think the 3-4-5 triangle method is accurate enough?

54. A tanker sails due west from port at 1 P.M. at a steady speed. At 2:15 P.M., the bearing of a lighthouse from the ship is 37° (from north).

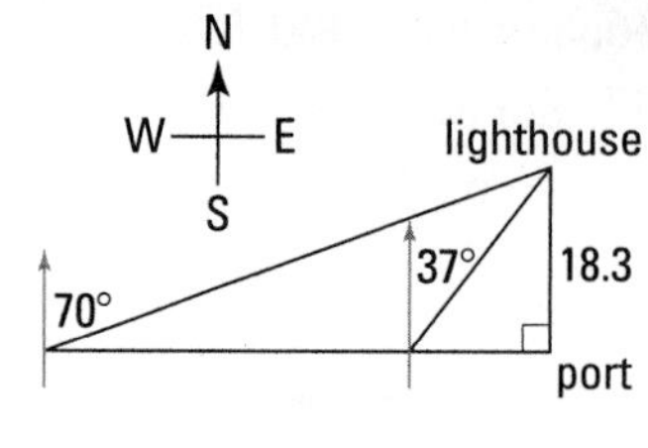

a. If the lighthouse is 18.3 miles due north of the port, how far out to sea is the ship?

b. Find the speed of the ship.

c. At what time will the lighthouse lie on a bearing of 70° from the ship, assuming that the speed of the ship is constant?

Objective H: *Solve problems involving the Laws of Sines and Cosines.* *(Lessons 5-2, 5-4)*

55. A team of surveyors measuring from A to B across a pond places a vertical stake at S, a point from which they can measure distances to A and B across dry ground. The measures are shown in the diagram. Find AB.

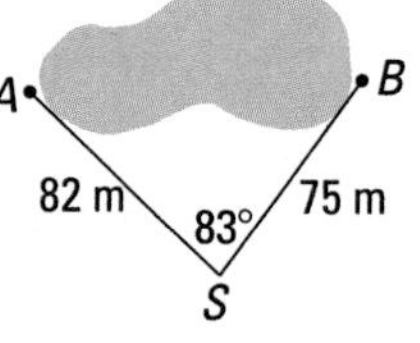

56. a. Find the length of the longer diagonal of a parallelogram with one angle of 39° and sides of 8.2 cm and 10.1 cm.

b. Find the length of the shorter diagonal of this parallelogram.

57. An airport controller notes from radar that one jet 12° west of south and 20 miles from the airport is flying toward a private plane which is 27 miles directly south of the airport. How far apart are the planes?

58. Forest ranger towers at A and B are 10 miles apart. The ranger in A spots a fire 10° east of north. She calls the ranger at B, who locates the fire as 30° north of west with respect to B.

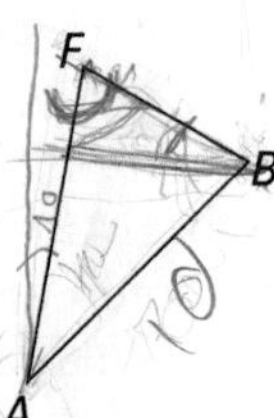

a. If B is directly northeast of A, find the distance of the fire from A.

b. Find the distance of the fire from B.

59. In the diagram at the right, $\overline{AB} \parallel \overline{CD}$. The circle has diameter 40 mm and $AB = CD = 35$ mm.

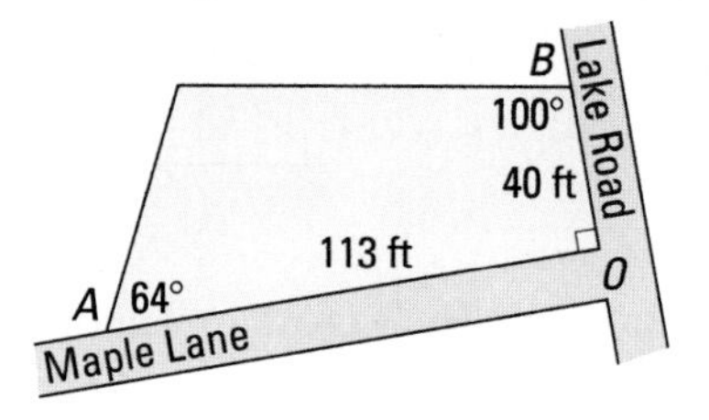

a. Find θ to the nearest tenth of a degree.

b. Find the shaded area.

60. An irregularly shaped plot of land has certain known dimensions. It borders two roads which meet at right angles. Frontage on Lake Road measures 40' and frontage on Maple Lane measures 113'. Property lines run away from the roads at angles of 64° and 100°, as shown.

a. Find the lengths of the other two sides of the plot of land.

b. What is the area of the property?

61. In order to sail against the wind, a sailor must take an indirect path—what is called "tacking." Suppose a boat sails from point A to an upwind point B following the path shown below, where $AC = 690$ yd, $CD = 955$ yd, $DB = 410$ yds. What is the actual distance between A and B? Round your answer to the nearest yard.

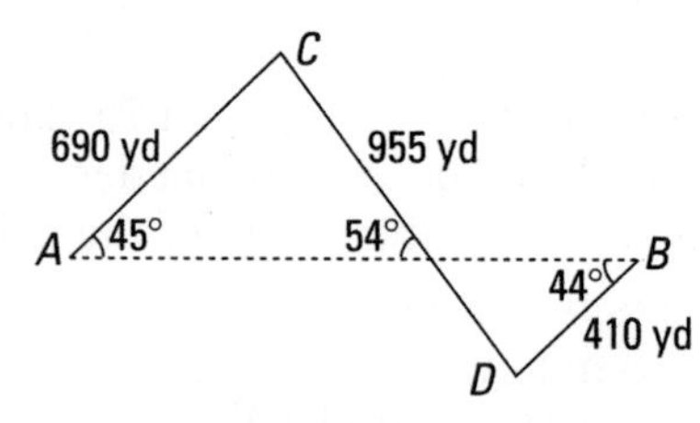

Objective I: *Write and solve equations for phenomena described by trigonometric and circular functions.* *(Lesson 5-3, 5-4, 5-5, 5-6, 5-7)*

62. On a compass used to draw arcs, the leg which holds the pencil measures 6.2". Find a formula for the angle θ at the top of the compass in terms of the radius of the desired circle and the length of the leg.

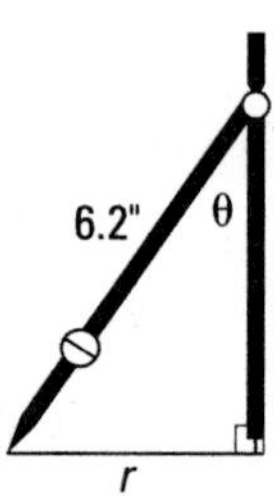

63. The vertical displacement d of a mass oscillating at the end of a spring is given by the equation $d = 3 \cos (\pi t)$ where t is time in seconds.

a. Solve this equation for t.

b. At what time does d first equal 2 cm?

64. c, the length of chord $\overline{AB}$ in $\odot O$, depends on the magnitude of central angle θ.

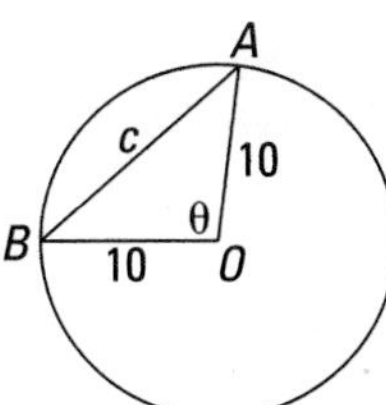

a. Use the Law of Cosines to write an equation for c in terms of θ.

b. Solve the equation of part **a** for θ.

c. What is an appropriate domain for c?

d. Use your equation to find the value of θ when $c = 15$.

65. The measured voltage E in a circuit at t seconds ($t \geq 0$) is given by $E = 20 \cos (4\pi t)$. Find, to the nearest .01 second, the first five times that $E = 16$.

66. New Orleans has about 14 hours of daylight at the summer solstice and 9.3 hours at the winter solstice. An equation for number of hours h of daylight as a function of days d after March 21 is given by

$$h = 11.65 + 2.35 \sin \left(\frac{d}{\frac{365}{2\pi}} \right).$$

a. Find the next four times New Orleans has 13.6 hours of daylight. Give your answer in days after March 21.

b. Does New Orleans have a day in the calendar year before March 21 with 10 hours of daylight?

67. The distance from ground level to a paddle on an old wooden mill wheel can be modeled by $d = 11 + 15 \sin (\pi(t - 3))$, where t = time in minutes.

a. Graph the function. Why does it dip below the t-axis?

b. On your graph mark the first two times ($t > 0$) that the paddle is 5' above the ground.

c. Find the first two times the paddle is 5' above the ground by solving $5 = 11 + 15 \sin (\pi(t - 3))$.

REPRESENTATIONS DEAL WITH PICTURES, GRAPHS, OR OBJECTS THAT ILLUSTRATE CONCEPTS.

Objective J: *Graph or identify graphs of inverse trigonometric functions.* *(Lessons 5-3, 5-5, 5-6)*

68. Graph $y = \cos x$ and $y = \cos^{-1} x$ for $0 \leq x \leq \pi$ on the same set of axes.

69. *Multiple choice.* Which function is graphed at the right?

(a) $y = \tan^{-1} x$

(b) $y = \cos^{-1} x$

(c) $y = \sin x$

(d) $y = \sin^{-1} x$

70. *True or false.* The graph of $y = \tan^{-1} x$ has asymptotes.

71. Sarah graphed $y = \cos^{-1} x$ on her calculator in degree mode. Her screen looked like the one drawn below. She thought her calculator was broken, but G. J. fixed it in 30 seconds.

a. What might G. J. have done to display the graph?

b. What would the display look like?

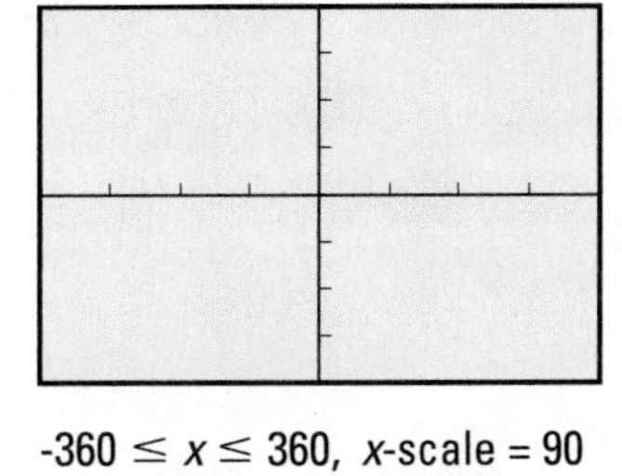

$-360 \leq x \leq 360$, x-scale = 90
$-4 \leq y \leq 4$, y-scale = 1

CHAPTER

Root, Power, and Logarithm Functions

Solving an equation of the form $x^y = z$ for one of the variables when the other two are known leads to *root functions*, *power functions*, and *logarithm functions*. These functions describe real-world situations and are used for solving problems like the three given here.

(1) For a ship, the speed s in knots varies directly with the seventh root of the horsepower p of the engines. Write a formula for s as a function of p.

(2) Carbon-14 has a half-life of about 5730 years. A human thigh bone is found with 41% of the original quantity of carbon-14 remaining. How old is the bone?

(3) The pH of a water solution is defined by the equation $\text{pH} = -\log C$, where C is the concentration of hydrogen ions (in moles per liter). Find the pH of pineapple juice which has a hydrogen ion concentration of 4×10^{-6} moles/liter.

Properties of root, power, and logarithm functions are derived from properties of powers, that is, properties of expressions of the form x^y that you have studied in previous courses.

LESSON

6-1

nth Root Functions

What Is an *n*th Root?

Powers and roots are intimately connected. If $x^2 = k$, then x is called a **square root** of k. If $x^3 = k$, then x is a **cube root** of k. Higher powers lead to 4th roots, 5th roots, and so on.

> **Definition**
> Let n be an integer with $n \geq 2$. x is an ***n*th root** of k if and only if $x^n = k$.

Here are a few examples.

15 is a cube root of 3375 because $15^3 = 3375$.

$-\frac{1}{2}$ is a cube root of $-\frac{1}{8}$ because $\left(-\frac{1}{2}\right)^3 = -\frac{1}{8}$.

6 is a fourth root of 1296 because $6^4 = 1296$.

-6 is a fourth root of 1296 because $(-6)^4 = 1296$.

-9 has no real square root since $x^2 = -9$ has no solution in the set of real numbers.

How Many Real *n*th Roots Does a Real Number Have?

Examination of the graphs of the nth power functions can indicate how many real roots a number k has. The number of intersections of $y = k$ with $y = x^n$ is the number of real roots of k. The graphs have different forms depending on whether n is odd or even.

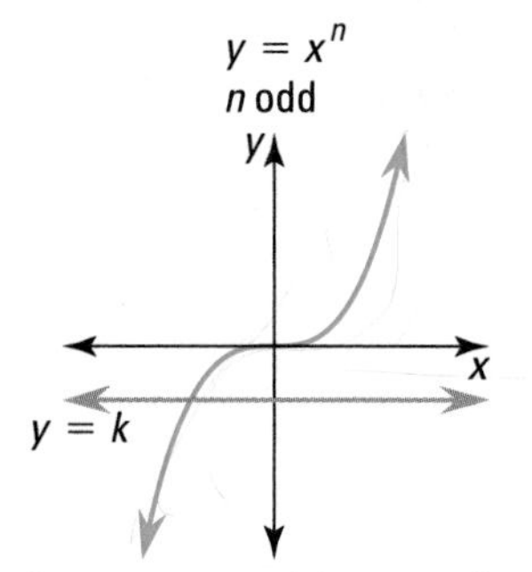

intersects $y = k$ in one point regardless of value of k

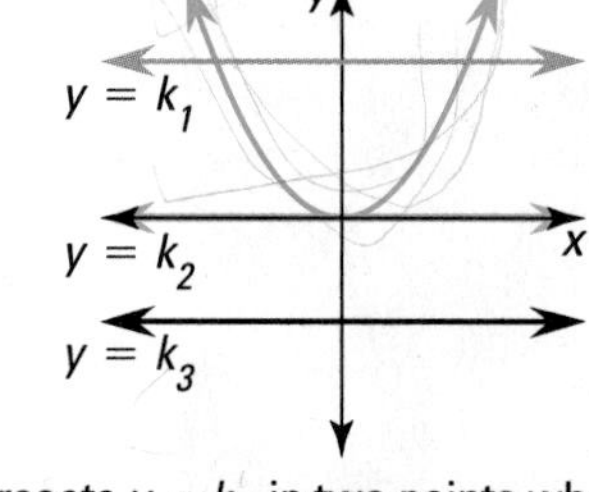

intersects $y = k_1$ in two points when $k_1 > 0$
intersects $y = k_2$ in one point when $k_2 = 0$
intersects $y = k_3$ in no points when $k_3 < 0$

Consequently, when n is odd, k has exactly one real nth root. For example, when $n = 5$, $3^5 = 243$ while $(-3)^5 = -243$, so 3 is the only real 5th root of 243. However, when n is even and k is positive, k has two real nth roots. For example, for $n = 4$, $3^4 = (-3)^4 = 81$, so both 3 and -3 are 4th roots of 81. Also, those two fourth roots are opposites. If n is even and k is negative, k has no real nth roots. For example, suppose $n = 4$ and $k = -81$. There is no real number x for which $x^4 = -81$ because the 4th power of a real number cannot be negative. In contrast, if n is even and $k = 0$, then there is exactly one nth root of k. That root is 0 since $x^n = 0$ if and only if $x = 0$.

The Exponent $\frac{1}{n}$

Notice that when $x > 0$, the graphs of $y = x^n$ look about the same whether n is even or odd. They are increasing and lie entirely in the first quadrant. Thus, when k is positive and x is restricted to be positive, the equation $x^n = k$ has exactly one positive solution. This solution is $k^{1/n}$. To prove that this is a solution, recall the Power of a Power Property.

Postulate (Power of a Power Property)
For any nonnegative base x and any nonzero real exponents m and n,

$$(x^m)^n = x^{mn}.$$

Thus, $$(k^{1/n})^n = k^{(1/n)\cdot n} = k^1 = k.$$

Consequently, $k^{1/n}$ is the positive solution to the equation $x^n = k$. For example, $25^{1/2}$ is the positive solution to $x^2 = 25$, so $25^{1/2}$ is the positive square root of 25. That is, $25^{1/2} = 5$. Similarly, $8^{1/3}$ is the positive cube root of 8, so $8^{1/3} = 2$.

*n*th Root Functions

Taking the nth power and taking the nth root of a number are *inverse operations*. Each "undoes" the result of the other. For instance, start with the number 10; raise it to the 4th power ($10^4 = 10{,}000$). Then take the 4th root ($10{,}000^{1/4} = 10$). You end up with the original number, 10. In general, the functions f and g with

$$f(x) = x^n \text{ and } g(x) = x^{1/n}$$

and domain $\{x: x \geq 0\}$ are inverses of each other.

Activity 1

a. Use an automatic grapher to plot $f(x) = x^4$ and $g(x) = x^{1/4}$ on the window $-2.5 \leq x \leq 2.5$, $-2.5 \leq y \leq 2.5$. Sketch what you see.
b. Use the graph of f to evaluate $f(1.2)$.
c. Use the graph of g to evaluate $g(x)$ when $x = f(1.2)$.

The functions with equations of the form $y = x^{1/n}$, where n is an integer and $n \geq 2$, are called ***n*th root functions**. Because $x^{1/n}$ is defined only when $x \geq 0$, the domain of all these functions is the set of nonnegative real numbers. The range is also the set of nonnegative reals. Some nth root functions are graphed below.

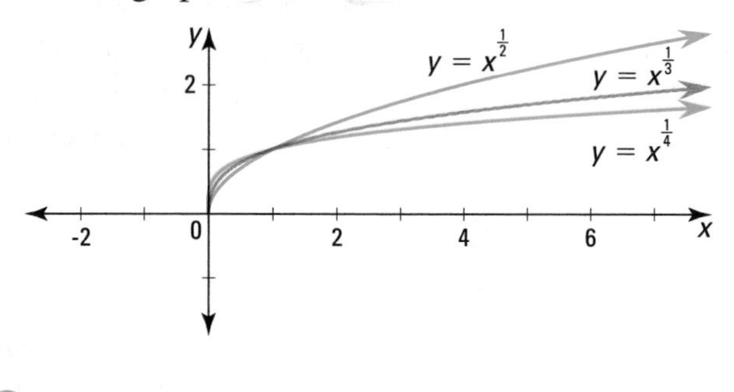

Activity 2

Graph the functions above and two more nth root functions on the window $-1 \leq x \leq 6$, $0 \leq y \leq 3$. Other than their common domains and ranges, list three characteristics that all the functions share.

Radical Notation for *n*th Roots

An nth root can also be expressed using the **radical** symbol $\sqrt{}$. The square root of 2 can be written as $\sqrt{2}$, the cube root of 2 as $\sqrt[3]{2}$, and the positive nth root of a positive number x as $\sqrt[n]{x}$. That is, $\sqrt[n]{x} = x^{1/n}$. But there is a bonus in using radical notation. If x is *negative* and n is odd, then $\sqrt[n]{x}$ stands for the unique real nth root of x. For example, $\sqrt[3]{-8} = -2$.

The formula for the radius r *of a cylinder with the same height and radius is* $r = (V/\pi)^{1/3}$, *where* V *is the volume of the cylinder.*

Definition

When $x \geq 0$, and n is an integer with $n \geq 2$,

$$\sqrt[n]{x} = x^{1/n} = \text{the positive } n\text{th root of } x.$$

When $x < 0$, and n is an odd integer with $n \geq 3$,

$$\sqrt[n]{x} = \text{the real } n\text{th root of } x.$$

Note that the definition of $\sqrt[n]{x}$ does not include the case of $x < 0$ and n is even because, for example, $\sqrt[4]{-81}$ is not a real number. This case yields complex numbers; they are discussed in Chapter 9.

Example 1

Evaluate each expression.

a. $1296^{1/4}$ **b.** $\sqrt[5]{-32}$

Solution

a. From the examples at the beginning of the lesson, you know that both 6 and -6 are 4th roots of 1296. By definition, $1296^{1/4}$ represents the positive 4th root, so $1296^{1/4} = 6$.

b. $\sqrt[5]{-32} = -2$, because $(-2)^5 = -32$.

All scientific calculators give accurate estimates of nth roots of positive numbers. On most graphics calculators, you have a choice of ways to evaluate nth roots; use the ∧ or the a^b key or choose $\sqrt[x]{\ }$ from a menu. Although we have not defined $x^{1/n}$ for $x < 0$ and n an even integer, some calculators will evaluate the expression if put into complex mode.

Activity 3

Which of the following are real numbers? Evaluate these on your calculator. Show what your calculator displays for the nonreal number(s).

a. $\sqrt[4]{33}$ **b.** $33^{1/4}$ **c.** $-33^{1/4}$ **d.** $(-33)^{1/4}$

Caution: Some calculators treat $\sqrt[n]{x}$ as identical to $x^{1/n}$ when n is odd. For reasons we explain in the next lesson, we do not do so.

Example 2

Below are the graphs of $f(x) = x^3$ and $g(x) = x^{1/3}$ produced by two different graphers. On each, the graph of $f(x) = x^3$ is in blue; the graph of $g(x) = x^{1/3}$ is in orange.

I.

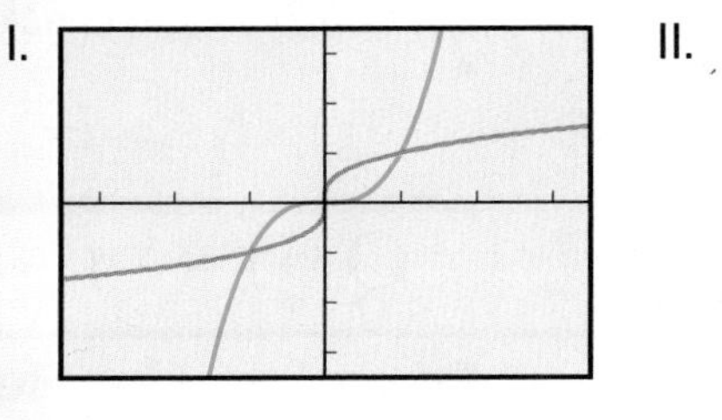

$-3.5 \leq x \leq 3.5$, x-scale = 1
$-3.5 \leq y \leq 3.5$, y-scale = 1

II.

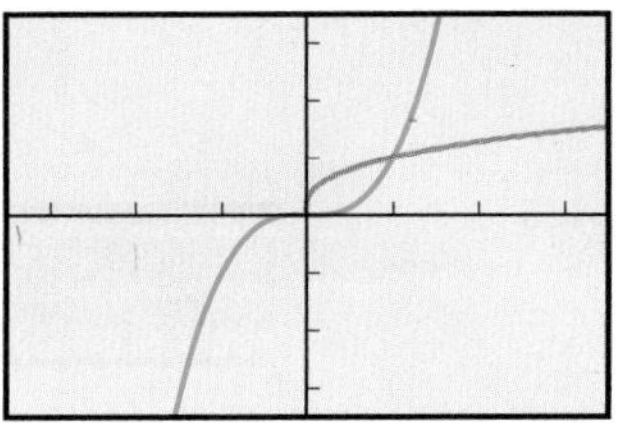

$-3.5 \leq x \leq 3.5$, x-scale = 1
$-3.5 \leq y \leq 3.5$, y-scale = 1

a. Which is consistent with our definition of $x^{1/n}$? Justify your answer.

b. For what values of x is $f(x) = g^{-1}(x)$? Draw a graph of f and g for these values of x.

Solution

a. Graph I shows the cube root function $g(x) = x^{1/3}$ defined for all real values of x. But $x^{1/3}$ is defined in this book only for $x \geq 0$. So only graph II agrees with our definition of $x^{1/n}$.

b. The function g is not defined for $x < 0$. So g can only be the inverse of f if the domain of each is limited to nonnegative real numbers. The graphs on this restricted domain are drawn at the left.

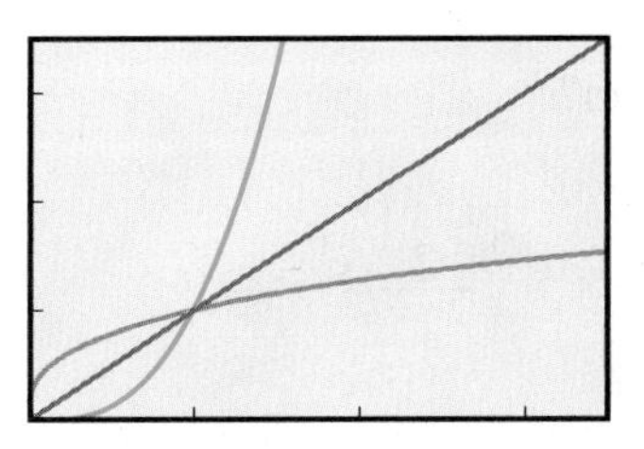

$0 \leq x \leq 3.5$, x-scale = 1
$0 \leq y \leq 3.5$, y-scale = 1

Suppose $x \geq 0$. Then

$$f(g(x)) = f(x^{1/3}) = (x^{1/3})^3 = x$$

and $$g(f(x)) = g(x^3) = (x^3)^{1/3} = x.$$

Thus, $$f = g^{-1} \text{ and } g = f^{-1}.$$

Graphically, $f(x) = x^3$ and $g(x) = x^{1/3}$ are reflection images over the line $y = x$, whose graph we have shown in gray at the left.

Applications of nth Roots

Because of their inverse relationship, every formula with nth powers can lead to the calculation of nth roots.

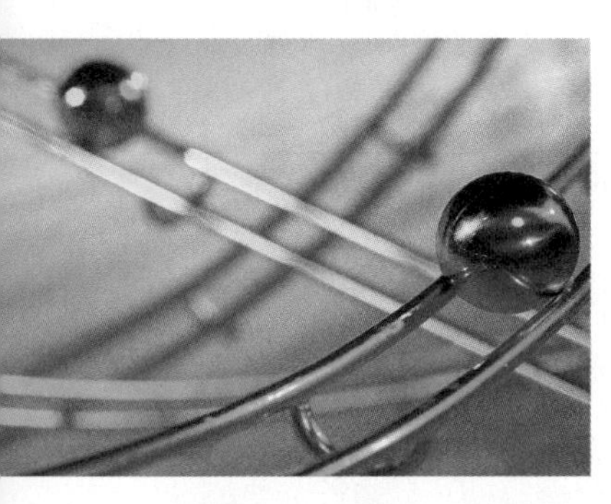

Ball bearings are milled to be as spherical as possible.

Example 3

Express the radius r in mm of a spherical ball bearing as a function of the volume V in mm^3.

Solution

The volume V is given by

Solve for r.

So, the radius is given by

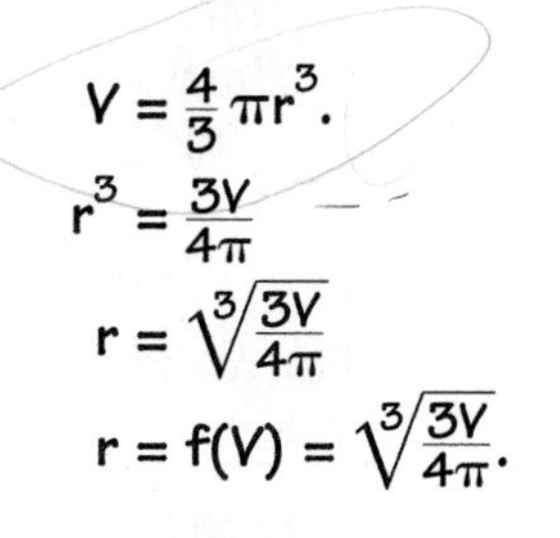

Check

Substitute a value for V, say $V = 2$, in the formula for r. Then $f(2) = \sqrt[3]{\frac{3 \cdot 2}{4\pi}} \approx 0.782$. Now check that this value works in the original formula. Since $V = \frac{4}{3} \cdot \pi \cdot (0.782)^3 \approx 2$, it checks.

QUESTIONS

Covering the Reading

1. Show that 7 is a fifth root of 16,807.

2. a. Show that 3.5 is a fourth root of 150.0625.
b. Give the other real fourth root of 150.0625.

In 3 and 4, a number x and a value of n are given. **a.** Give the number of real nth roots x has. **b.** Find all real nth roots of the number.

3. $x = 4096$, $n = 4$

4. $x = 243$, $n = 5$

5. Evaluate $1000^{1/3}$ without a calculator.

6. *True or false.* $36^{1/2} = -6$

7. Calculate $(17^{1/7})^7$.

8. Write your answers to Activity 1.

9. a. Write your answers to Activity 2.
b. What is the domain of every nth root function?

10. Place a $<$ or $>$ sign in the blank.
a. For $0 < x < 1$, $x^{1/3}$ _?_ $x^{1/7}$.
b. For $x > 1$, $x^{1/3}$ _?_ $x^{1/7}$.

In 11 and 12, evaluate without a calculator.

11. $\sqrt[4]{625}$

12. $\sqrt[3]{-216}$

13. For what values of x and n are $x^{1/n}$ and $\sqrt[n]{x}$ equal?

14. *True or false.* $125^{1/3} > \sqrt[3]{-125}$ 15. Write your answers to Activity 3.

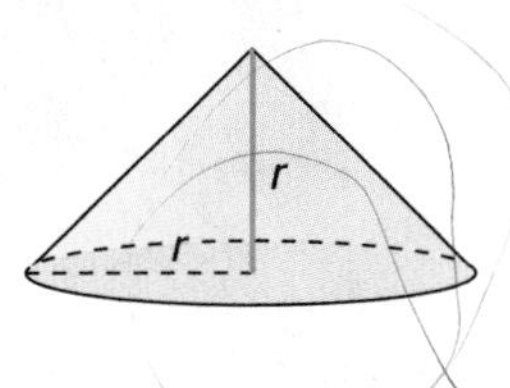

16. The volume V of a cone with radius r and height equal to the radius is given by $V = \frac{1}{3}\pi r^3$.
   a. Give a formula for the radius in terms of V.
   b. A cone with equal radius and height has volume 60 mm^3. Use the formula in part **a** to find its height.

Applying the Mathematics

17. It has been found that the speed s in knots of a ship is a function of the horsepower p developed by its engines, with $s = 6.5p^{1/7}$. How fast will a ship travel with engines producing 650 horsepower?

18. The ancient Greeks wanted to construct a cube that would have twice the volume of a cube at the altar at Delos. If the given cube had side of length one unit, to the nearest thousandth what should be the length of a side of the constructed cube?

In 19 and 20, use an automatic grapher.

19. a. Plot $f(x) = x^{1/2}$ and $g(x) = -x^{1/2}$ on one set of axes.
   b. What single equation describes the union of these two graphs?

20. a. Plot $f(x) = \sqrt[5]{x}$ and $g(x) = \sqrt[5]{x+2} + 3$ on one set of axes.
   b. What transformation maps f to g?
   c. What transformation maps g to f? d. What is the domain of g?

Review

21. Are the functions f and g with $f(x) = \frac{2}{x}$ and $g(x) = \frac{x}{2}$ inverse functions? Justify your answer. *(Lesson 3-8)*

22. Given $g(x) = 4x$ and $h(x) = x^5$, find each composite. *(Lesson 3-7)*
   a. $h \circ g(3)$ b. $g(h(3))$ c. $h \circ g(x)$ d. $g \circ h(x)$

Year	% reporting smoking
1975	73.6
1980	71.0
1986	67.6
1987	67.2
1988	66.4
1990	64.4
1991	63.1
1992	61.8
1993	61.9
1994	62.0
1995	64.2

Source: *World Almanac 1997*

23. The table at the left gives the percentage of high school seniors from 1975 through 1995 who reported having ever smoked a cigarette. Use statistics to predict the percentage of high school seniors who will report in the year 2001 that they have ever smoked. How accurate do you think your prediction is? *(Lessons 2-2, 2-3, 2-8)*

24. *Skill sequence.* Solve. *(Previous course)*
   a. $3^z = 81$ b. $3^{(y-1)} = 81$ c. $3^{x^2-3x} = 81$

25. *Skill sequence.* Simplify. *(Previous course)*
   a. $x^7 \cdot x^9$ b. $(2x^7)^9$ c. $\frac{x^7}{x^9}$

Exploration

26. Consider all functions of the form $y = x^{1/n}$, where n is an integer greater than or equal to 2. Theoretically, there is no largest n possible. Experiment with an automatic grapher. Plot $y = x^{1/n}$ for some large values of n. What is the largest value of n your machine can handle before memory or screen resolution is overloaded?

LESSON

6-2

Rational Power Functions

The Meaning of Rational Exponents

According to a certain microwave cookbook, whenever you double the amount being cooked, the cooking time should be multiplied by 1.5. For example, if it takes 6 minutes to cook one portion, it takes 9 minutes to cook two portions or 13.5 minutes to cook four portions. Using techniques you will learn in Lesson 6-7, it can be shown that if it takes 10 minutes to cook one portion, then the approximate time $T(p)$ it takes to cook p portions is given by

$$T(p) = 10p^{0.585}.$$

What is the time needed to cook 5 portions? From the formula, $T(5) = 10 \cdot 5^{0.585}$. Use your calculator to get $5^{0.585} \approx 2.56$. So $T(5) \approx 10 \cdot 2.56 = 25.6$ minutes.

But what does it *mean* to find the 0.585 power of a number? As it does with the exponent $\frac{1}{n}$, the Power of a Power Property enables us to deduce how other rational exponents can be interpreted.

For instance, consider the expression $x^{3/5}$, where $x \geq 0$. Then,

$$\begin{aligned} x^{3/5} &= x^{(1/5)\cdot 3} && \text{definition of division} \\ &= (x^{1/5})^3 && \text{Power of a Power Property} \\ &= \left(\sqrt[5]{x}\right)^3. && \text{definition of } \sqrt[n]{x} \end{aligned}$$

Similarly,

$$\begin{aligned} x^{3/5} &= x^{3\cdot(1/5)} && \text{definition of division} \\ &= (x^3)^{1/5} && \text{Power of a Power Property} \\ &= \sqrt[5]{x^3}. && \text{definition of } \sqrt[n]{x} \end{aligned}$$

Thus $x^{3/5} = \left(\sqrt[5]{x}\right)^3 = \sqrt[5]{x^3}$. This result can be generalized.

Rational Exponent Theorem

For all positive integers m and n, and all real numbers $x \geq 0$,

$x^{m/n} = \left(x^{1/n}\right)^m = \left(\sqrt[n]{x}\right)^m$, the mth power of the positive nth root of x, and

$x^{m/n} = \left(x^m\right)^{1/n} = \sqrt[n]{x^m}$, the positive nth root of the mth power of x.

Thus, by writing $5^{0.585}$ as $5^{\frac{585}{1000}} = 5^{\frac{117}{200}}$, $5^{0.585}$ can be interpreted either as the 200th root of 5^{117} or as the 117th power of the 200th root of 5. You would not compute $5^{0.585}$ by hand, but some rational powers can be computed by hand.

Example 1

Evaluate $128^{3/7}$.

Solution 1

To evaluate without a calculator, first take the 7th root, and then cube the result.

$$128^{3/7} = \left(\sqrt[7]{128}\right)^3 = 2^3 = 8$$

Solution 2

Use a calculator. First cube 128, and then take the 7th root.

$$128^{3/7} = \sqrt[7]{128^3} = \sqrt[7]{2097152} = 8$$

Solution 3

Use a calculator to evaluate 128 [a^b] [(] 3 [/] 7 [)] directly. Again the display shows 8.

Generally, when evaluating rational powers, it is easier to take roots before powering. As Solutions 2 and 3 show, using a calculator sometimes masks exact answers. Most numbers raised to rational exponents can only be approximated by a decimal. Thus, an exact value of $132^{2/5}$ is $\left(\sqrt[5]{132}\right)^2$, while an approximation to three decimal places is 7.051.

Properties of Powers

From other properties of exponents you can also deduce how zero and negative exponents must be used. Recall the following properties.

Postulates for Powers

For any nonnegative bases x and y and nonzero exponents, or any nonzero bases and integer exponents:

Product of Powers Property	$x^m \cdot x^n = x^{m+n}$	
Power of a Product Property	$(xy)^n = x^n y^n$	
Quotient of Powers Property	$\frac{x^m}{x^n} = x^{m-n}$	$(x \neq 0)$
Power of a Quotient Property	$\left(\frac{x}{y}\right)^n = \frac{x^n}{y^n}$	$(y \neq 0)$.

These properties can be used to rewrite numbers with rational powers. For instance, $\frac{2^5}{2^5} = 2^{5-5} = 2^0$ by the Quotient of Powers Property. But $\frac{2^5}{2^5} = 1$ because any nonzero number divided by itself equals one. So $2^0 = 1$.

In general, by the Quotient of Powers Property, when $x \neq 0$ and x^n is defined, the expression $\frac{x^n}{x^n} = x^{n-n} = x^0$. But because $x^n \neq 0$, you also know that $\frac{x^n}{x^n} = 1$. This proves the following result.

Zero Exponent Theorem
If x is any nonzero real number, $x^0 = 1$.

Properties of negative exponents can also be deduced from the Postulates for Powers. Consider x^{-n}. What does this mean? By the Product of Powers Property, whenever x^n is defined,

$$x^n \cdot x^{-n} = x^{n+(-n)}$$
$$= x^0.$$

So $\quad x^n \cdot x^{-n} = 1. \quad$ Zero Exponent Theorem

Dividing each side of the equation by x^n gives

$$x^{-n} = \frac{1}{x^n}.$$

This result is the following theorem.

Negative Exponent Theorem
For all $x > 0$ and n a real number, or for all $x \neq 0$ and n an integer,

$$x^{-n} = \frac{1}{x^n}.$$

So x^n and x^{-n} are reciprocals. For example, 9^{-2} and 9^2 are reciprocals:

$$9^{-2} = \frac{1}{9^2} = \frac{1}{81},$$

$$9^2 = \frac{1}{9^{-2}} = \frac{1}{\frac{1}{81}} = 81.$$

Example 2

Evaluate $27^{-5/3}$. Give an exact answer.

Solution

Some calculators will not display an exact answer. So use properties of powers to simplify.

$$27^{-5/3} = (27^{1/3})^{-5} = \frac{1}{(\sqrt[3]{27})^5} = \frac{1}{3^5} = \frac{1}{243}$$

Check

Use a calculator, with 27 as the base and $-\frac{5}{3}$ as the exponent. Our display shows 0.0041152263. On the same calculator, we get the same display for $\frac{1}{243}$.

An indirect proof can be used to show why rational exponents are not used with negative bases. By the Rational Exponent Theorem, if $(-125)^{1/3}$ were defined, it must equal $\sqrt[3]{-125}$, which is -5. But $\frac{1}{3} = \frac{2}{6}$, so $(-125)^{1/3} = (-125)^{2/6}$. We calculate $(-125)^{2/6}$ using the Power of a Power Property: $(-125)^{2/6} = ((-125)^2)^{1/6} = (15625)^{1/6} = 5$. This is a contradiction; the same expression cannot have two values. This contradiction can occur each time a negative base is used with a rational exponent.

Graphs of Rational Power Functions

Any function f with equation of the form $f(x) = x^{m/n}$, where m and n are nonzero integers, is a **rational power function**. Because we must have $x \geq 0$, the domain of a rational power function is the set of nonnegative real numbers. And since $x \geq 0$ implies $x^{m/n} \geq 0$, so is the range.

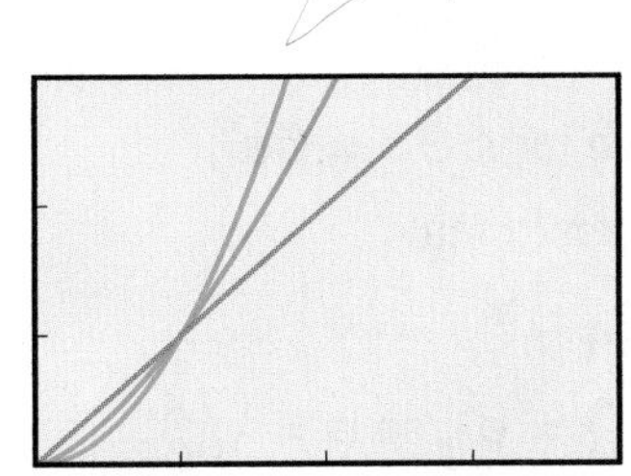

$0 \leq x \leq 4$, x-scale = 1
$0 \leq y \leq 3$, y-scale = 1

Graphs of rational power functions can be drawn using an automatic grapher. At the left are the graphs of $y = x^{3/2}$ in blue, $y = x$ in orange, and $y = x^2$ in green. Notice that for all $x \neq 1$, the graph of $y = x^{3/2}$ lies between the graphs of $y = x^1$ and $y = x^2$. This is expected, since $\frac{3}{2}$ is between 1 and 2.

Example 3

Suppose $f: x \rightarrow x^{5/3}$.

a. Find an equation for the inverse of f.
b. Is the inverse a function?
c. Use an automatic grapher to plot f and its inverse g.

Solution

a. Recall that an equation for the inverse of a function can be found by switching y and x. So, an equation for the inverse of $y = x^{5/3}$ is $x = y^{5/3}$.

b. Solve the equation in part **a** for y. Raise each side to the $\frac{3}{5}$ power.
$x^{3/5} = (y^{5/3})^{3/5} = y^1$.
So another equation for the inverse of f is $y = x^{3/5}$. Now we see that to each $x \geq 0$, there corresponds a unique value of y in $y = x^{3/5}$. So the inverse is a function.

c. The graphs are produced at the right.

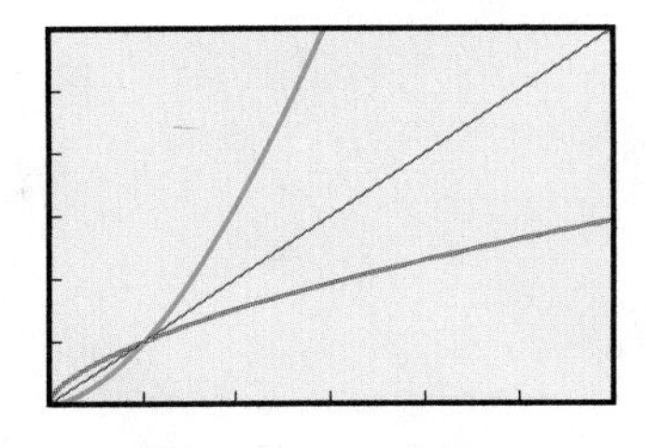

$0 \leq x \leq 6$, x-scale = 1
$0 \leq y \leq 6$, y-scale = 1

Check

The graphs of f and g are reflection images of each other over the line $y = x$, verifying that f and g are inverses. The graph of g passes the vertical line test, verifying that g is a function.

An Application of Rational Power Functions

Combining two formulas with integer powers may result in a formula with a non-integer rational power, as the next example illustrates.

Example 4

a. Find the volume of a cube with surface area 93 square inches.

b. Express the volume V of a cube as a function of its surface area A.

Solution

a. Let s be the length of one edge of the cube. You should be familiar with formulas for the volume and surface area.

$$V = s^3$$
$$A = 6s^2$$

Substitute 93 for A in the second formula, and solve for s. $93 = 6s^2$, so $s = \sqrt{\frac{93}{6}} = \sqrt{\frac{31}{2}} = \sqrt{15.5}$. Now use the first formula.

$$V = s^3 = (\sqrt{15.5})^3 \approx 61.024 \text{ in}^3$$

b. Generalize the process in part **a**. Since $A = 6s^2$, $\frac{A}{6} = s^2$, so $s = \sqrt{\frac{A}{6}}$.

Then $V = s^3 = \left(\sqrt{\frac{A}{6}}\right)^3 = \left(\frac{A}{6}\right)^{3/2}$. So $V = \left(\frac{A}{6}\right)^{3/2}$.

Check

Let $A = 93$ in the formula found in part **b**. Then $V = \left(\frac{93}{6}\right)^{3/2}$. A calculator gives the same value as found in part **a**.

The exponent $\frac{3}{2}$ in the formula in Example 4, part **b** signifies the change in dimension from surface area (a 2-dimensional measure) to volume (a 3-dimensional measure).

QUESTIONS

Covering the Reading

In 1–3, suppose the variables represent positive numbers. Rewrite each expression using rational exponents in fraction form.

1. $(\sqrt[3]{r})^5$ **2.** $\sqrt[4]{t^9}$ **3.** $k^{-0.3}$

In 4 and 5, rewrite each expression using a radical sign. Assume $x > 0$.

4. $x^{7/8}$ **5.** $x^{-8/5}$

6. Refer to the formula $T(p) = 10p^{0.585}$ on page 376 where $T(p) =$ the time in minutes needed to cook p portions in a microwave. Use two different methods to find the approximate time needed to cook six portions.

In 7–10, simplify without using a calculator. Check with a calculator.

7. a. $64^{1/3}$ **b.** $64^{-2/3}$ **8. a.** $64^{1/2}$ **b.** $64^{3/2}$

9. $16^{-3/4}$ **10.** $125^{-5/3}$

11. a. Use an automatic grapher to graph $f: x \rightarrow x^{5/2}$ for $0 \leq x \leq 3$.
b. State the range of f.
c. Write an equation for the inverse of f.
d. Plot the graph of $y = f^{-1}(x)$ on the same set of axes.

12. a. Use an automatic grapher to plot $f(x) = x^{2/3}$ and $g(x) = x^{3/2}$ on the same set of axes.
b. How are the graphs related? **c.** Find $f(g(x))$ and $g(f(x))$.

13. Refer to Example 4. Find the volume of a cube whose surface area is 500 square inches.

Applying the Mathematics

14. a. Find the surface area of a cube whose volume is 50 m^3.
b. Express the surface area of a cube as a function of its volume.
c. Interpret the exponent in the formula you find in part **b** as a change in dimension.

Up, up, and away. *As a helium-filled weather balloon rises, it expands due to decreasing atmospheric pressure. Such a balloon may reach an altitude of over 45 km.*

15. Earth's atmospheric pressure decreases as you ascend from the surface. It can be shown that at an altitude of h kilometers $(0 < h < 80)$, the pressure P in grams per square centimeter (g/cm^2) is approximately given by the formula

$$P = 1035 \cdot 2^{-10h/58}.$$

Give the approximate pressure at each altitude.
a. sea level **b.** 30 km above Earth **c.** 50 km above Earth

16. a. Without using a calculator, decide which is larger, $0.1^{0.3}$ or $0.1^{-0.3}$.
b. Explain how you made your decision.

17. Use trial and error and a calculator to solve $7^x = 20$ for x to the nearest tenth.

In 18 and 19, use an automatic grapher to plot each pair of functions on the same axes.

18. a. Sketch graphs of $f(x) = x^2$ and $g(x) = x^{2.2}$ for $x \geq 0$.
b. Where do the graphs intersect?
c. For what values of x is $g(x) > f(x)$?
d. For what values of x is $g(x) < f(x)$?

19. a. Sketch graphs of $f(x) = x^{0.4}$ and $g(x) = x^{-0.4}$ for $x \geq 0$.
b. *True or false.* The graphs are reflection images of each other.

Review

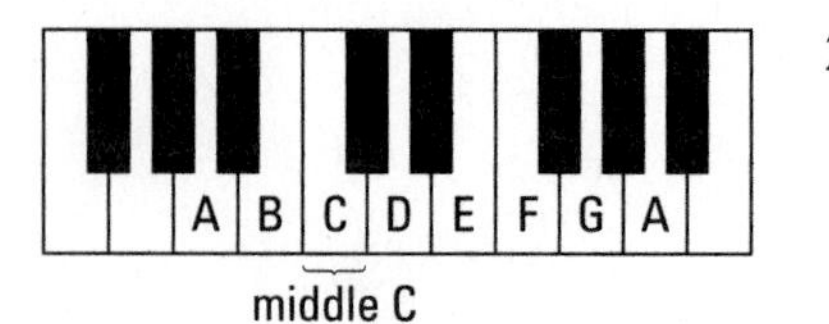

20. The keys of a piano are tuned to have frequencies in cycles per second (cps) so that each key (white *and* black) has a frequency $2^{1/12}$ times that of the previous key. The A to the left of middle C has a frequency of 220 cps.

a. Find the frequency of middle C.

b. Find the frequency of the A above middle C, which is one octave (12 notes) higher than the A below middle C. *(Lessons 2-4, 6-1)*

21. For what values of x is $\sqrt[n]{x} > x$? *(Lesson 6-1)*

22. Consider the function f with $f(x) = \sqrt[3]{x} - 2$.

a. Give an equation for the inverse of f.

b. Sketch f and its inverse on the same set of axes.

c. What is the largest domain on which both f and its inverse can be defined so each is a function? *(Lessons 3-8, 6-1)*

23. Order from smallest to largest. *(Previous course, Lesson 6-1)*

$$3^4, 3^{-4}, 4^{-3}, 3^{1/4}, \frac{3}{4}$$

24. Ahmed scored 86 on his math exam. The class mean on the math exam was 80 and the standard deviation was 5.5. That same week he scored 77 on a chemistry exam while the class mean was 65.5 and the standard deviation was 7.2. On which exam did he do better relative to his classmates? Justify your answer. *(Lesson 3-9)*

25. *Multiple choice.* Let f, g, and h be defined so that $f(x) = 2^x$, $g(x) = 3^x$, and $h(x) = 9^x$. Which characteristics are true of all three functions? *(Lesson 2-4)*

I. The function passes through the point (0, 1).
II. The domain is the set of all real numbers.
III. The x-axis is a horizontal asymptote.

(a) I only (b) II only (c) I and III
(d) II and III (e) I, II, and III

Exploration

26. The expression 0^0 is sometimes called an *indeterminate form* because more than one value might be reasonable for 0^0.

a. Compute the values of this sequence.
$0^2, 0^1, 0^{1/2}, 0^{1/4}, 0^{1/8}, 0^{1/16}, \ldots$
What does this imply as a reasonable value for 0^0?

b. Compute the values of this sequence.
$2^0, 1^0, \left(\frac{1}{2}\right)^0, \left(\frac{1}{4}\right)^0, \left(\frac{1}{4}\right)^0, \left(\frac{1}{16}\right)^0, \ldots$
What does this imply as a reasonable value for 0^0?

c. Compute the values of this sequence.
$2^2, 1^1, \left(\frac{1}{2}\right)^{1/2}, \left(\frac{1}{4}\right)^{1/4}, \left(\frac{1}{8}\right)^{1/8}, \ldots$
What does this sequence imply?

d. Evaluate 0^0 using the powering key on different calculators. What do you get?

LESSON

6-3

Logarithm Functions

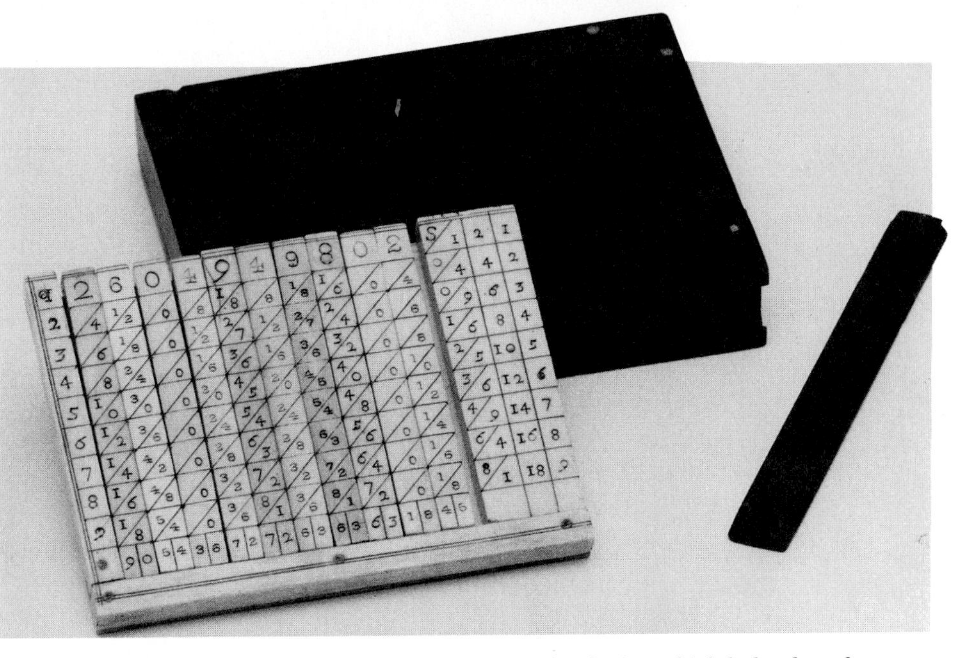

Napier's Bones. *In 1617, John Napier invented a device which helped perform multiplication. His creation was called Napier's Rods or "Bones" because of its appearance.*

The simplest exponential functions have equations of the form $y = b^x$, where x can be any real number, $b > 0$, and $b \neq 1$. If y is given and we wish to find x, then we are dealing with the inverses of these functions. To obtain the inverse, we switch x and y. So its inverse has equation $x = b^y$. The exponent y is called the *logarithm of x to the base b*.

> **Definition**
> Let $b > 0$ and $b \neq 1$. Then y is the **logarithm of x to the base b**, written $\mathbf{y = \log_b x}$, if and only if $b^y = x$.

In words, the logarithm of x to the base b is the power of b that equals x.

The word "logarithm" was first used by John Napier (1550–1617) of Scotland, who is usually credited with being the inventor of logarithms because of his 1614 brochure, *Mirifici logarithmorum canonis descriptio* (A Description of the Wonderful Law of Logarithms). Logarithm is often abbreviated as "log" in both spoken and written mathematics.

Evaluating Logarithms

To find the logarithm of a number with a particular base, you sometimes can use the definition directly. First you need to write the argument of the log function as a power; that is, as the given base raised to an exponent.

Example 1

Evaluate.

a. $\log_5 125$ **b.** $\log_5 \sqrt{5}$ **c.** $\log_5 0.04$

Solution

Because each base is 5, write each argument as a power of 5, and apply the definition of logarithm. The exponent is the logarithm.

a. Think: What power of 5 equals 125? $125 = 5^3$. So $\log_5 125 = 3$.

b. Think: What power of 5 equals $\sqrt{5}$? $\sqrt{5} = 5^{\frac{1}{2}}$. So $\log_5 \sqrt{5} = \frac{1}{2}$.

c. Think: What power of 5 equals 0.04? $0.04 = \frac{4}{100} = \frac{1}{25} = \frac{1}{5^2} = 5^{-2}$.
So $\log_5 0.04 = -2$.

In Example 2, you must solve an equation before applying the definition of logarithm.

Example 2

Evaluate $\log_4 8$.

Solution

From the definition, $\log_4 8$ is the power of 4 that equals 8. So, write 8 as a power of 4. That is, if $y = \log_4 8$, then

$$4^y = 8.$$

To solve this equation, express each side as a power to the same base, in this case 2.

$$(2^2)^y = 2^3 \quad \text{substitution}$$
$$2^{2y} = 2^3 \quad \text{Power of a Power Property}$$

The exponents must be the same if the two expressions are equal. So,

$$2y = 3.$$
$$y = \frac{3}{2}.$$

Thus $\log_4 8 = \frac{3}{2}$.

Check

Does $4^{3/2} = 8$? $4^{3/2} = (\sqrt{4})^3 = 2^3 = 8$. It checks.

John Napier

Common Logarithms

Unlike Examples 1 and 2, most logarithms cannot be evaluated directly. However, many calculators have a `log` key which calculates values of logarithms to base 10. Base 10 logarithms are sometimes called **common logarithms**. The first table of common logarithms was produced by Henry Briggs (1561–1630) of England, who worked with Napier. In 1624 he published *Arithmetica logarithmica*, containing common logarithms to fourteen decimal places.

Caution: Common logarithms are often *written* without indicating the base 10. In this book, when you see an expression like log 100, you can assume it means $\log_{10} 100$. Common logarithms of integer powers of 10 can be found without using a calculator. For instance, to find log 100, think: if $\log 100 = x$, then $10^x = 100$. Thus $x = 2$, and so $\log 100 = 2$.

Activity

Evaluate without a calculator.

a. log 1000 **b.** log 1 **c.** log 0.01

Common logarithms can be used to solve equations of the form $10^x = a$, where $a > 0$.

Example 3

Solve $10^x = 4$ to the nearest tenth.

Solution

Use the definition of a logarithm to rewrite the equation as $x = \log_{10} 4$. Find $\log_{10} 4$ with a calculator.

$$\log_{10} 4 \approx 0.60206 \approx 0.6$$

Check

Use a calculator to verify that $10^{0.6} \approx 3.98 \approx 4$.

Using the definition of logarithm, it is easy to find the number that has a given common logarithm.

Example 4

Solve $\log x = 3.724$ to the nearest tenth.

Solution

Because no base is written, the base is 10. Apply the definition.

$$\log_{10} x = 3.724 \text{ if and only if } x = 10^{3.724}.$$

Use a calculator to calculate the power.

$$x \approx 5296.6$$

Check

Does $\log 5296.6 \approx 3.724$? A calculator verifies that it does.

Graphs and Properties of Logarithm Functions

The graph of the exponential function f with $f(x) = 2^x$ is shown on page 386 in blue. Its inverse has equation $x = 2^y$ which is equivalent to $y = \log_2 x$. That is, the inverse of the exponential function with base 2 is the logarithm function with base 2. In symbols, $f^{-1}(x) = \log_2 x$. In general, the function which maps x onto $\log_b x$ is called the **logarithm function with base *b***. It is the inverse of the exponential function with base b.

That is, if for all real numbers x, $f(x) = b^x$, then for all positive x, $f^{-1}(x) = \log_b x$.

Below are graphed three exponential functions and their inverses, the corresponding logarithm functions.

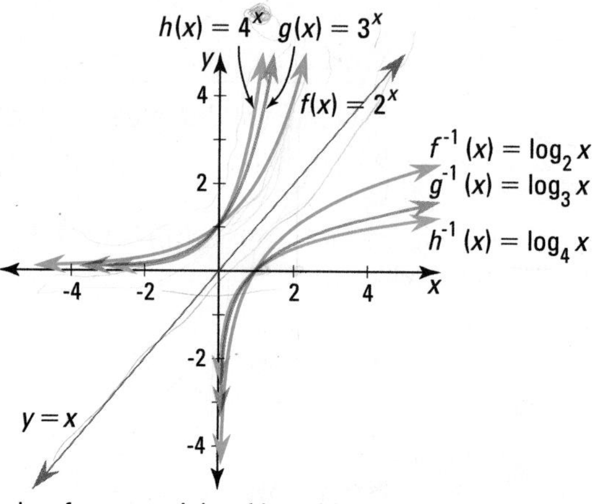

Graphs of exponential and logarithm functions with bases 2, 3, and 4

Like the family of exponential functions, studied in Chapter 2, the graphs of logarithm functions also form a *family* of curves with a characteristic shape and similar properties. From the graphs of the various functions above, you can see that all logarithm functions with base $b > 1$ share certain properties.

(1) The domain is the set of positive real numbers.
(2) The range is the set of all real numbers.
(3) The graph contains (1, 0); that is, $\log_b 1 = 0$.
(4) The function is strictly increasing.
(5) The end behavior, as x gets larger, is to increase without bound.
(6) As x gets smaller and approaches 0, the values of the function are negative with larger and larger absolute values.
(7) The line $x = 0$ (the y-axis) is an asymptote of the graph.

Recall the fourth property listed above, that logarithm functions with base $b > 1$ are strictly increasing. That is, if $x_2 > x_1$, then $\log_b x_2 > \log_b x_1$. This property allows you to deduce the solution to logarithmic equations, because if $\log_a x = \log_a y$, then it must be true that $x = y$.

n	$\log_{10} n$
$1 = 10^0$	0
$10 = 10^1$	1
$100 = 10^2$	2
$1000 = 10^3$	3
$10{,}000 = 10^4$	4

For another result of the "strictly increasing" property, note that $\log_{10} 100 = 2$, $\log_{10} 1000 = 3$, and so on. Consequently, all 3-digit integers greater than 100 have common logarithms between 2 and 3. For example, since 826 is between 10^2 and 10^3, $\log_{10} 826$ is between 2 and 3. In general, common logarithms of numbers between successive powers of 10 are numbers between successive integers. This property can be used in reverse. A number with a logarithm between 3 and 4 must be between 1000 and 10,000. (Look back at Example 4 for an instance of this generalization.) This relationship can be used to determine the number of digits in large numbers. (See Question 20.)

QUESTIONS

Covering the Reading

1. *Multiple choice.* Which statement is read "p is the logarithm of q to the base s"?
(a) $\log_q p = s$
(b) $\log_p q = s$
(c) $p = \log_q s$
(d) $p = \log_s q$

2. Write an equation equivalent to $2^7 = 128$ using logs.

3. Write an equation equivalent to $\log_6 216 = 3$ using exponents.

In 4–7, use the definition of logarithm to evaluate.

4. $\log_4 256$

5. $\log_7 1$

6. $\log_5 0.2$

7. $\log_9 27$

8. Give your answers to the Activity.

In 9–12, solve.

9. $9^x = 243$

10. $10^x = 8$

11. $\log_{10} x = 3.121$

12. $\log_{10} x = -1.4$

13. *True or false.* The function with equation $y = \log_4 x$ is the inverse of the function with equation $y = 4^x$.

14. Consider the function $f(x) = \log_{7.5} x$.
a. State the domain of f.
b. *True or false.* The graph contains the point $(1, 0)$.
c. Which axis is an asymptote of the graph?

15. *Multiple choice.* If $\log_{10} p = 1.6274$, then p must be between which of the following? (Do not use a calculator.)
(a) 0 and 1
(b) 1 and 2
(c) 1 and 10
(d) 10 and 100

Applying the Mathematics

16. *Multiple choice.* In which interval is $\log_7 62$? Justify your answer.
(a) $\{x: 0 \leq x < 1\}$
(b) $\{x: 1 \leq x < 2\}$
(c) $\{x: 2 \leq x < 3\}$
(d) $\{x: 8 \leq x < 9\}$

In 17 and 18, use this information. The pH level of blood having bicarbonate concentration b and carbonic acid concentration c is given by $\text{pH} = 6.1 + \log\left(\frac{b}{c}\right)$. Find the pH level of blood with the given concentrations.

17. $b = 32, c = 3$

18. $b = 20c$

19. Consider the numbers 1492, 149,200, and 14,920,000,000,000.
a. Write each number in scientific notation.
b. Find the common logarithm of each number.
c. How are the answers to parts **a** and **b** related?

20. **a.** Find the common logarithm of 2^{100}.
b. How many digits does 2^{100} have?

21. Solve for x: $\log_7 (4x - 3) = \log_7 5$.

Review

22. Let $f(x) = x^{3/7}$.
a. State the domain and range of f.
b. Give the inverse of f.
c. Graph $y = f(x)$ and its inverse on the window $-2.5 \le x \le 2.5$, $-2.5 \le y \le 2.5$. *(Lesson 6-2)*

23. Give the exact value of $512^{-2/3}$. *(Lesson 6-2)*

Radio actors. *Before television, performers such as George Burns and Gracie Allen entertained studio audiences as well as listeners over the airwaves.*

24. Rewrite $\sqrt[5]{x^2y}$ without a radical. *(Lesson 6-2)*

25. The intensity I of a sound varies inversely as the square of the distance d from its source. That is, $I = \frac{k}{d^2}$.
a. Solve for d, writing your solution with radicals.
b. Write your solution without radical notation. *(Lessons 6-1, 6-2)*

26. A five-year certificate of deposit is purchased for \$5000. If the certificate pays 5.5% interest compounded quarterly, find the value of the certificate at maturity. *(Previous course, Lesson 2-4)*

Exploration

27. Find out what prompted Napier and Briggs to invent logarithms.

Introducing Lesson 6-4

The Number e

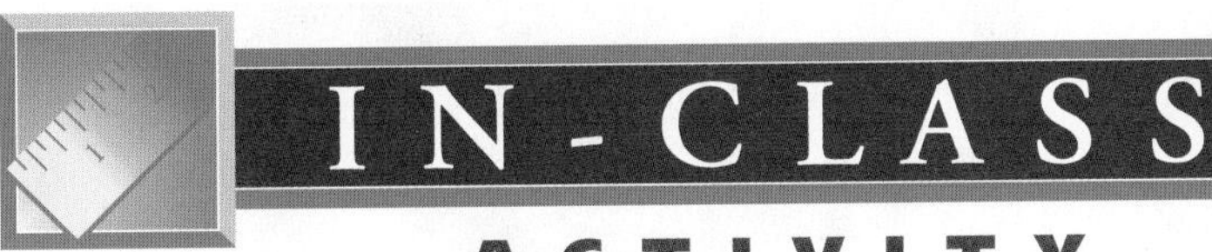

Recall the compound interest formula $A = P\left(1 + \frac{r}{n}\right)^{nt}$, where A is the value of an investment of P dollars earning interest at rate r, compounded n times per year for t years. Suppose you invest \$1 for 1 year at a huge 100% annual interest rate. What is your balance after 1 year? Savings institutions may compound daily ($n = 365$), monthly ($n = 12$), or quarterly ($n = 4$). Applying the Compound Interest Formula with $P = 1$, $r = 100\% = 1$, and $t = 1$ gives

$$A = 1\left(1 + \frac{1}{n}\right)^{n \cdot 1} = \left(1 + \frac{1}{n}\right)^n.$$

Thus, the value of the investment depends on the number of times the savings institution compounds.

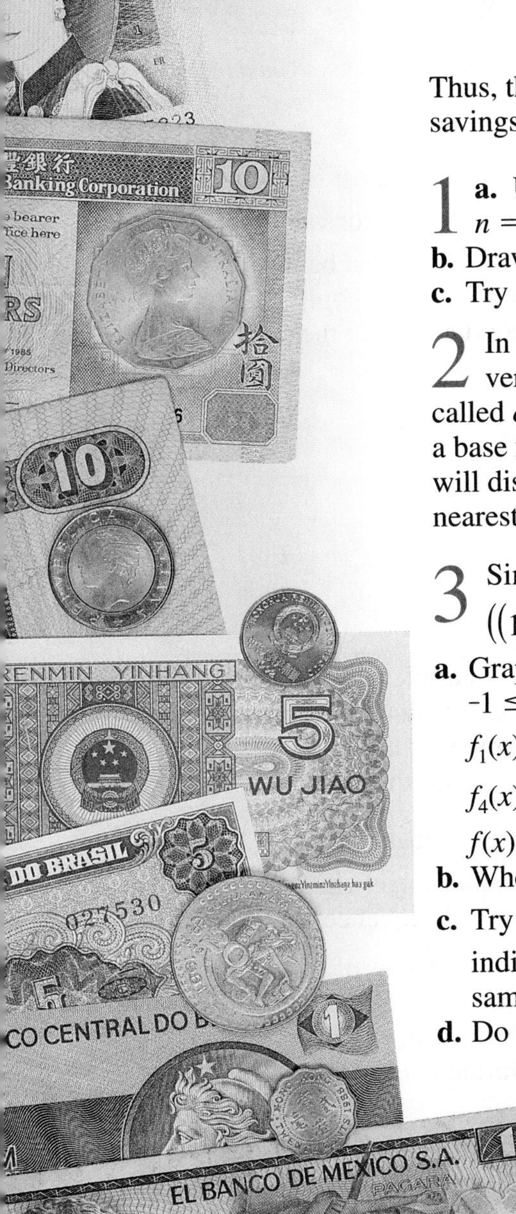

1 **a.** Use the compound interest formula to find the value of A for $n = 1, 2, 4, 6, 12, 24, 36$, and 365 compounding periods per year.
b. Draw a conclusion about the value of A as n increases.
c. Try a value for n greater than 365. Is your conclusion confirmed?

2 In Step 1 you should have found that as n increases and becomes very large, A gets closer and closer to the particular real number called e. You may have studied e in a previous course and know that it is a base for natural logarithms. Find e on your calculator. The calculator will display an approximate value. Record this value, correct to the nearest hundred-thousandth.

3 Since as n increases, $\left(1 + \frac{1}{n}\right)^n$ comes closer and closer to e, $\left(\left(1 + \frac{1}{n}\right)^n\right)^x$ comes closer and closer to e^x as n increases.
a. Graph the following functions on the window $-3 \le x \le 3$, $-1 \le y \le 10$.

$f_1(x) = \left(\left(1 + \frac{1}{1}\right)^1\right)^x$ $\quad f_2(x) = \left(\left(1 + \frac{1}{2}\right)^2\right)^x$

$f_4(x) = \left(\left(1 + \frac{1}{4}\right)^4\right)^x$ $\quad f_{12}(x) = \left(\left(1 + \frac{1}{12}\right)^{12}\right)^x$

$f(x) = e^x$

b. When $x = 0$, what is true about all the graphs?
c. Try to find a value of n so that $y = e^x$ and $y = \left(\left(1 + \frac{1}{n}\right)^n\right)^x$ are indistinguishable on the window used in part **a**. Are they the same graph?
d. Do you think that $\left(1 + \frac{1}{n}\right)^n$ is ever equal to e? Why or why not?

LESSON

6-4

e and Natural Logarithms

A perfect ten. *Swiss mathematician Leonhard Euler is pictured on this Swiss 10-franc note.*

In the In-class Activity, you used the compound interest formula $A = P\left(1 + \frac{r}{n}\right)^{nt}$ with $P = \$1$, $r = 100\%$, $t = 1$ year, for values of n ranging from 1 to 365. These values of A correspond to interest being compounded from annually to daily. Values for A as the number of compoundings increases from one per day to one per second appear in the table below.

Compounding Schedule	n	$P\left(1 + \frac{r}{n}\right)^{nt}$	Balance in \$ after 1 year (A)
daily	365	$1\left(1 + \frac{1}{365}\right)^{365}$	2.71457
hourly	8760	$1\left(1 + \frac{1}{8760}\right)^{8760}$	2.71813
every second	31,536,000	$1\left(1 + \frac{1}{31{,}536{,}000}\right)^{31{,}536{,}000}$	2.71828

As you might expect, the balance after one year increases with greater numbers of compounding periods. However, no number of compoundings yields an infinite sum of money. As the number of compoundings increases, the value of the investment approaches the number e.

We say that ***e*** is the *limiting value* of the sequence $a_n = \left(1 + \frac{1}{n}\right)^n$ and mean by this a number to which the terms of a sequence get closer and closer as n increases. You will learn more about limits of sequences in Chapter 12.

The letter e was chosen to name this number in honor of the mathematician Leonhard Euler (1707–1783), who discovered its importance. The number e is irrational; its decimal expansion, like that of π, is known to many places. A decimal approximation of e to thirteen decimal places is

$$e \approx 2.7182818284590 \ldots.$$

e and Continuous Change

Examine the banking advertisement below carefully. Notice that a distinction is made between the *interest rate* and the annual *yield*.

FIRST SAVINGS BANK
introduces Money Market Plus.

BALANCE	RATE	YIELD
\$1,000 to \$9,999	5.75%	5.904%
\$10,000 to \$24,999	5.75%	5.904%
\$25,000 to \$49,999	5.90%	6.062%
\$50,000 Plus	6.10%	6.273%

All you need to open a Money Market Plus Account is \$1,000.00. First Savings Bank starts giving right away, with current rates* paid on your entire balance and with interest that compounds monthly.
First Savings Bank knows how to give.

*Rates subject to change without notice.

FIRST SAVINGS BANK

Here is how the yield is calculated from the rate. The ad states that interest compounds monthly, so on an investment of P dollars between \$1,000 and \$25,000, the bank uses the *prorated* monthly interest rate of $\frac{0.0575}{12}$. After one month, the total interest earned is $P \cdot \frac{0.0575}{12}$. So, after one month the total in the account is $P + P \cdot \frac{0.0575}{12} = P\left(1 + \frac{0.0575}{12}\right)$. Thus, the monthly scale factor is $\left(1 + \frac{0.0575}{12}\right)$. If no deposits or withdrawals are made, then the balance after one year is

$$P\left(1 + \frac{0.0575}{12}\right)^{12} \approx 1.05904P,$$

indicating the effective annual "yield" of 5.904% stated in the advertisement.

In general, when the principal (the initial investment) P is invested at an annual interest rate r compounded n times per year, the interest rate in each period is prorated as $\frac{r}{n}$. The balance at the end of one year is $P\left(1 + \frac{r}{n}\right)^n$ and the annual yield is $\left(1 + \frac{r}{n}\right)^n - 1$. At the end of t years, the amount A the investment is worth is given by

$$A = P\left(1 + \frac{r}{n}\right)^{nt}.$$

Activity 1

Calculate to the nearest millionth.

a. $\left(1 + \frac{.05}{365}\right)^{365}$ and $e^{.05}$ **b.** $\left(1 + \frac{.06}{365}\right)^{365}$ and $e^{.06}$ **c.** $\left(1 + \frac{.085}{365}\right)^{365}$ and $e^{.085}$

It can be shown that, when n is very large,

$$\left(1 + \frac{r}{n}\right)^n \approx e^r.$$

Since $\left(1 + \frac{r}{n}\right)^n - 1$ is the annual yield, the limit indicates that, as the number of compounding periods increases, the annual yield is $e^r - 1$. When this yield is used to calculate interest, the interest is said to be *compounded continuously*.

Example 1

If $500 is put in a saving account at an 8% *rate* compounded continuously, find the following.

a. the annual yield

b. the value of the investment after one year

Solution

a. The annual yield at an interest rate r is $e^r - 1$, and here $r = .08$. So the yield is

$$e^{.08} - 1 \approx 1.083287 - 1$$
$$\approx 8.329\%.$$

b. After one year the account grows to

$$500 + 500(e^{.08} - 1) = 500(e^{.08})$$
$$\approx \$541.64.$$

After t years the amount would be $500(e^{.08})^t = 500e^{.08t}$. This is an instance of the following general formula.

Continuous Change Model

If a quantity P grows or decays continuously at an annual rate r, the amount $A(t)$ after t years is given by

$$A(t) = Pe^{rt}.$$

Example 2

Suppose $500 is invested in an account paying an 8% annual interest rate.

a. What is the balance after 4.5 years if interest is compounded continuously?

b. How does this balance compare with quarterly compounding over 4.5 years?

Solution

a. Use the Continuous Change Model $A(t) = Pe^{rt}$ where $P = 500$, $r = 0.08$, and $t = 4.5$.

$$A(4.5) = 500e^{0.08(4.5)}$$
$$= 500e^{0.36}$$
$$\approx 500(1.433329)$$
$$\approx 716.66$$

The balance after 4.5 years is $716.66.

b. Use the formula $A = P\left(1 + \frac{r}{n}\right)^{nt}$, with $P = 500$, $r = 0.08$, $n = 4$, and $t = 4.5$.

$$A = 500\left(1 + \frac{0.08}{4}\right)^{4 \cdot 4.5}$$
$$= 500(1.02)^{18}$$
$$\approx \$\,714.12$$

Continuous compounding earns $2.54 more in this case.

Check

You should expect continuous compounding to give a slightly greater balance. It does.

Many situations in the everyday world involve continuous change, or close approximations to it. Examples are radioactive decay and many natural growth processes. The growth of large human populations is approximately continuous.

Gnu growth. *The growth of large populations of animals in the wild, such as wildebeest in Kenya, is also approximately continuous.*

The Graph of $y = e^x$

In the preceding In-class Activity, you should have found that as n increased, the exponential curves

$$f_n(x) = \left(1 + \frac{1}{n}\right)^{nx} = \left(\left(1 + \frac{1}{n}\right)^n\right)^x$$

approach the graph of the function with equation $f(x) = e^x$. This function is the **exponential function with base *e***.

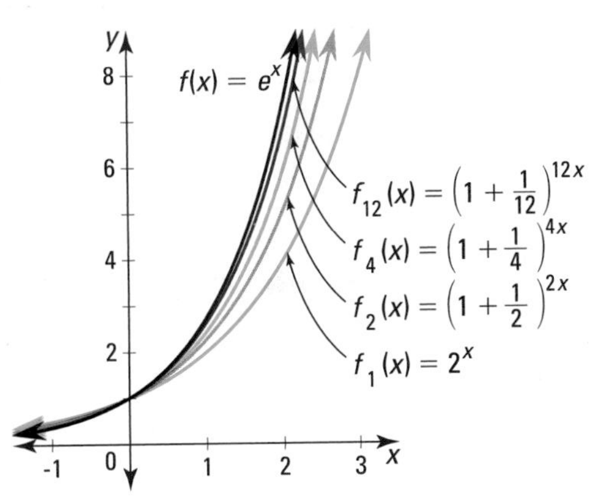

Like other exponential functions, the exponential function with base e has the set of real numbers as its domain, and the set of positive real numbers as its range. The x-axis is a horizontal asymptote. Although its graph gets steep for large x-values, the graph of $y = e^x$ does not have any vertical asymptotes.

Also, like other exponential functions, it has an inverse, with equation $x = e^y$. This equation is equivalent to $y = \log_e x$. That is, the inverse of $f(x) = e^x$ has equation

$$f^{-1}(x) = \log_e x.$$

It is the logarithm function to the base e. The values of this function are so important that they have a special name and symbol.

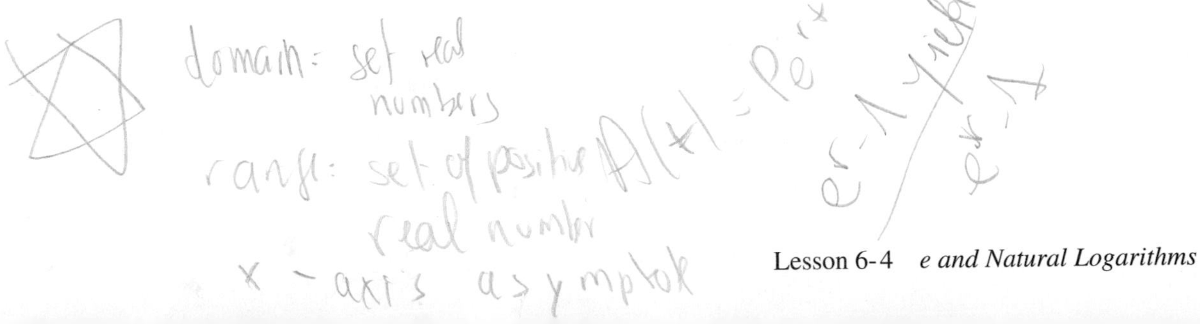

Natural Logarithms

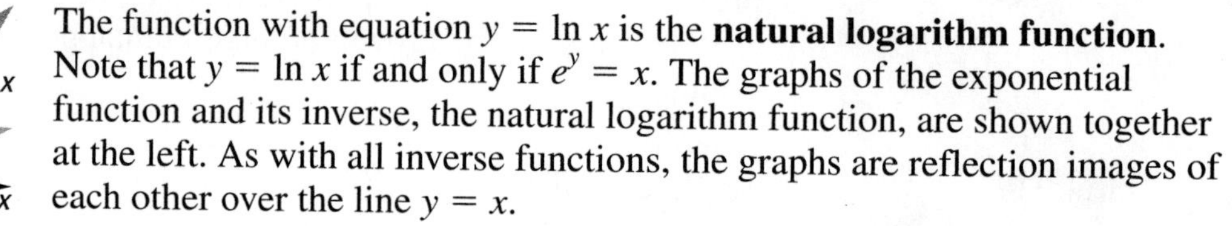

Definition

The **natural logarithm** of x is the logarithm to the base e, written **ln x**. That is, for all x, $\ln x = \log_e x$.

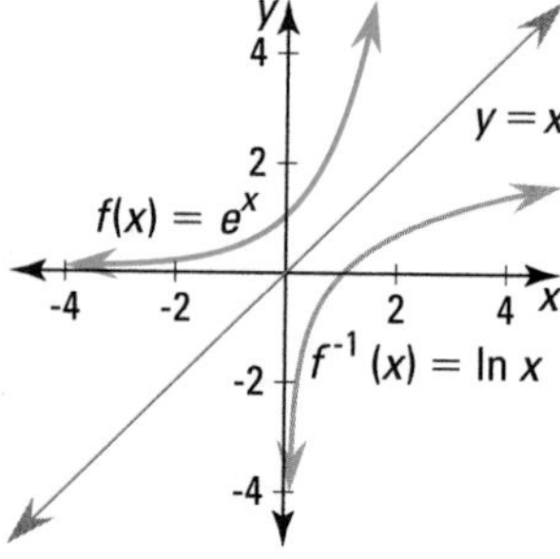

The function with equation $y = \ln x$ is the **natural logarithm function.** Note that $y = \ln x$ if and only if $e^y = x$. The graphs of the exponential function and its inverse, the natural logarithm function, are shown together at the left. As with all inverse functions, the graphs are reflection images of each other over the line $y = x$.

On calculators, the key for natural logarithms is usually marked [ln] or [ln x], while [log] is used to refer to common logarithms.

Activity 2

a. Without using a calculator, predict which of ln 10 and log 10 will be larger, and why.

b. Check by using your calculator.

Natural logarithms are often used in applications. Example 3 illustrates one situation.

Space Pressure. *Astronaut James E. van Hoften traveled in a pressurized cabin and wore a pressurized suit to survive the atmosphere of space travel. Here he is shown outside Discovery with the coast of Brazil in the background.*

Example 3

Under certain conditions, the height h in feet above sea level can be approximated from the atmospheric pressure P in pounds per square inch (psi) using the equation

$$h = \frac{\ln P - \ln 14.7}{-0.000039}.$$

Human blood "boils" at 0.9 psi, and such a situation is fatal. At what height above sea level will blood boil in an unpressurized cabin?

Solution

Substitute 0.9 for P, and evaluate.

$$h = \frac{\ln 0.9 - \ln 14.7}{-0.000039} \approx \frac{-0.10536 - 2.6878}{-0.000039} \approx 71{,}621$$

Without a pressurized cabin, heights greater than 72,000 feet above sea level would be fatal.

QUESTIONS

Covering the Reading

1. a. Estimate $\left(1 + \frac{1}{n}\right)^n$ to the nearest millionth for the given value of n.

  i. 1000 **ii.** 1,000,000

b. As n gets larger and larger, what number does $\left(1 + \frac{1}{n}\right)^n$ approach?

2. Give your answers to Activity 1.

3. a. Evaluate.

i. $\left(1 + \frac{5}{1000}\right)^{1000}$ **ii.** $\left(1 + \frac{5}{1000000}\right)^{1000000}$

b. As n increases, what number does $\left(1 + \frac{5}{n}\right)^n$ approach?

In 4 and 5, suppose $2000 is invested in an account paying 6% annual interest for 5 years.

4. If interest is compounded continuously, find each of the following.

a. the annual yield

b. the amount the investment is worth after one year

5. Suppose the account is left for 5 years. Give the balance if interest is compounded as follows.

a. continuously **b.** monthly

In 6–8, evaluate using a calculator.

6. $e^{1.64}$ **7.** $e^{-0.8}$ **8.** $\ln 0.45$

In 9–11, evaluate without a calculator.

9. e^0 **10.** $\ln 1$ **11.** $\ln e$

12. Give your answer to Activity 2.

13. a. State the domain and range of $f: x \to e^x$.

b. State the domain and range of $g: x \to \ln x$.

14. Refer to Example 3. A geologist measured atmospheric pressure to be about 10 psi. Estimate the altitude of the geologist.

Applying the Mathematics

15. a. The population of New Zealand in 1992 was about 3,381,000 with an average growth rate of 1.3%. If this growth rate continues, use the Continuous Change Model to predict New Zealand's population in 2010.

b. Compare your answer to Example 1 in Lesson 2-4. Explain any similarities or differences.

Hubble Telescope with its gold solar power panels

In 16 and 17, a particular satellite has a radioisotope power supply, with power output given by

$$P = 60e^{-t/300},$$

where t is the time in days and P is the power output in watts.

16. What is the power output at the end of its first year?

17. When the power output drops below 8 watts, there will be insufficient power to operate the satellite. Use an automatic grapher to estimate how long the satellite will remain operable.

18. a. Without using a calculator, evaluate $\ln e^5$.

b. Explain how you got your answer.

19. It can be shown that the velocity V reached by a rocket when all its propellant is burned is given by $V = c \ln R$, where c is the exhaust velocity of the engine and R is the ratio $\frac{\text{takeoff weight}}{\text{burnout weight}}$ for the rocket. (The burnout weight is the takeoff weight minus the weight of the fuel.) Space Shuttle engines produce exhaust velocities of 4.6 kilometers per second. If the ratio R for a Space Shuttle is 3.5, what velocity can the Shuttle reach with its own engines?

20. a. Use an automatic grapher to graph the functions

$$f: x \to e^{3x},\ g: x \to \ln(3x), \text{ and } h: x \to \tfrac{1}{3} \ln x.$$

b. Which, g or h, is the inverse of f?

c. Show algebraically that your answer to part **b** is correct.

Review

In 21 and 22, give an equation for the inverse of the function with the given equation. *(Lesson 6-3)*

21. $f(x) = 7^x$

22. $g(x) = \log_6 x$

23. Write an equation equivalent to $\left(\frac{1}{8}\right)^{1/3} = \frac{1}{2}$ using logarithms. *(Lesson 6-3)*

24. Evaluate $\log_{10} \sqrt[3]{10}$ without a calculator. *(Lesson 6-3)*

25. Which symbol, =, >, or <, makes this sentence true?
$900^{3/5}$ ___?___ $\left(\sqrt[3]{900}\right)^5$ *(Lesson 6-2)*

26. In the unit circle O at the right, $\overset{\frown}{PQ}$ has length 1.4. Give the following measures. *(Lessons 4-1, 4-2)*

a. the radian measure of $\angle POQ$

b. the degree measure of $\angle POQ$

c. the length of major arc $\overset{\frown}{PRQ}$

d. the area of the sector $PRQO$.

P
1.4
O
Q
R

Exploration

27. The value of e^x is given by the following infinite series:

$$e^x = 1 + \sum_{n=1}^{\infty} \frac{x^n}{n!} = 1 + \frac{x}{1!} + \frac{x^2}{2!} + \frac{x^3}{3!} + \frac{x^4}{4!} + \dots,$$

where $3! = 3 \cdot 2 \cdot 1$, $4! = 4 \cdot 3 \cdot 2 \cdot 1$, and so on.

a. Evaluate e^1 using the five terms shown in the sum above. How close is your answer to the value given in this lesson?

b. Compute $e^{0.15}$ using the formula above. Compare to a calculator value.

c. How many terms of the sum are needed to obtain an estimate for e accurate to the thousandths place?

Introducing Lesson 6-5

Sums, Differences, and Logarithms

IN-CLASS ACTIVITY

Clear the screen before each step.

1 **a.** Graph $f(x) = \log(2x)$ and $g(x) = \log 2 + \log x$ on the same set of axes. How are the graphs of f and g related?

b. Pick another constant $c > 0$. Graph $f(x) = \log(cx)$ and $g(x) = \log c + \log x$.

c. Make a conjecture about the relation between $\log(cx)$ and $\log c + \log x$.

2 **a.** Graph $f(x) = \log\left(\frac{x}{15}\right)$ and $g(x) = \log x - \log 15$ on the same set of axes.

b. Pick another constant $d > 0$. Graph $f(x) = \log\left(\frac{x}{d}\right)$ and $g(x) = \log x - \log d$ on the same set of axes.

c. Make a conjecture about an identity involving $\log\left(\frac{x}{d}\right)$.

3 Look back at the conjectures you made in Steps 1 and 2. Does either conjecture appear to be true if log is replaced by ln?

LESSON

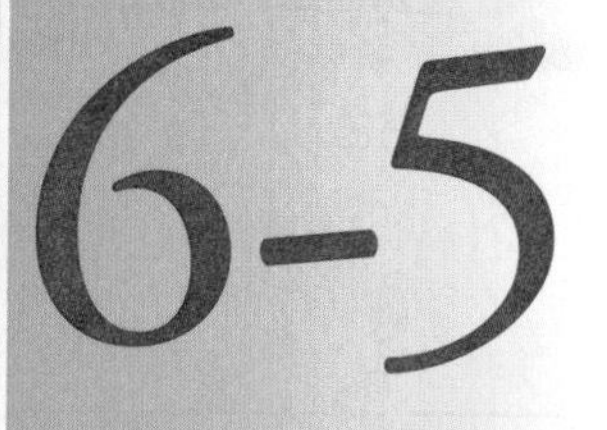

Properties of Logarithms

Recall that any positive number except 1 can be the base b of a logarithm, and that

$$x = \log_b m \text{ if and only if } b^x = m.$$

From this definition you can deduce properties of logarithms corresponding to properties of exponents in Lesson 6-2.

For example, because $b^0 = 1$ for any nonzero b, then by the definition of logarithm, $\log_b 1 = 0$. In words, the logarithm of 1 to any base is zero. For this reason, the graph of $f(x) = \log_b x$ contains (1, 0) for any base b.

> **Theorem (Logarithm of 1)**
> For any base b, $\log_b 1 = 0$.

In the In-class Activity preceding this lesson, you examined pairs of functions whose graphs were the same. This should have led you to some conjectures involving the values of these functions. By applying properties of exponents, we now show why these conjectures are true.

Logarithms of Products and Quotients

Suppose you know two positive numbers x and y and their logarithms to base b.

Given: $\log_b x = m$ and $\log_b y = n$.

Then $x = b^m$ — definition of $\log_b x$

and $y = b^n$. — definition of $\log_b y$

To find the logarithm of the product xy, express xy as a power of that base b.

$xy = b^m \cdot b^n$ — Multiplication Property of Equality

$xy = b^{m+n}$ — Product of Powers Property

Therefore,

$\log_b (xy) = m + n.$ — definition of $\log_b (xy)$

But $m + n = \log_b x + \log_b y.$

This proves the following theorem.

> **Theorem (Logarithm of a Product)**
> For any base b and for any positive real numbers x and y,
> $$\log_b (xy) = \log_b x + \log_b y.$$

This theorem establishes what you should have seen graphically in Step 1 of the In-class Activity. In words, the log of a product is the sum of the logs of its factors. The Logarithm of a Product Theorem can also be used to simplify sums of logs.

Example 1

Evaluate $\log 250 + \log 4$ without a calculator.

Solution

$\log 250 + \log 4 = \log (250 \cdot 4) = \log 1000 = 3$

Check

Use a calculator.
$\log 250 + \log 4 \approx 2.3979 + 0.6021 = 3.0000$

Since $\log 250 + \log 4 = \log 1000$, it is also the case that $\log 1000 - \log 4 = \log 250$. That is, $\log 1000 - \log 4 = \log \frac{1000}{4}$. The general property can be proved using the corresponding exponential property $\frac{b^m}{b^n} = b^{m-n}$. You are asked to prove this in the Questions.

Theorem (Logarithm of a Quotient)
For any base b and for any positive real numbers x and y,

$$\log_b \left(\frac{x}{y}\right) = \log_b x - \log_b y.$$

The magnitude of an earthquake is measured on a logarithmic scale. The 1995 earthquake in Kobe, Japan, measured 7.2 in magnitude on the Richter scale. That is 100 times more powerful than one with a magnitude of 5.2. See Question 16.

Logarithms of Powers

Some numbers are too large even for many calculators or computers to write all the digits. For example, in 1996, the number $2^{1257787} - 1$ was found to be prime. If you try to evaluate $2^{1257787}$ using a powering key, an "overflow" error will occur on most machines. However, the Logarithm of a Power Theorem can be used to approximate this large power.

Theorem (Logarithm of a Power)
For any base b, any positive real number x, and any real number p,

$$\log_b x^p = p \log_b x.$$

The proof of this theorem uses the Power of a Power Property: $(b^m)^n = b^{mn}$. You are asked to prove the theorem in the Questions.

Using Properties of Logarithms

The properties of logarithms can be used to solve or rewrite *logarithmic equations*.

Example 2

If $t > 0$ and $\ln P = \frac{1}{2} \ln t - \ln 6$, write an expression for P without logarithms. ▶

Solution

$$\ln P = \frac{1}{2} \ln t - \ln 6 \qquad \text{Given}$$

The goal is to write the right side as a single logarithm.

$$= \ln t^{1/2} - \ln 6 \qquad \text{Log of a Power Theorem}$$
$$= \ln \sqrt{t} - \ln 6 \qquad \text{definition of rational power}$$
$$= \ln \left(\frac{\sqrt{t}}{6}\right) \qquad \text{Log of a Quotient Theorem}$$

Then $P = \frac{\sqrt{t}}{6}$. If $\log_b x = \log_b y$, then $x = y$.

Example 3

Estimate $2^{1257787} - 1$, the prime found in 1996.

Solution

Let $x = 2^{1257787}$

Take the log of each side.

$$\log x = \log (2^{1257787})$$
$$\log x = 1257787 \log 2 \qquad \text{Log of a Power Theorem}$$
$$\approx 1257787(0.3010299957)$$
$$\log x \approx 378631.6152$$
$$x \approx 10^{378631.6152} \qquad \text{definition of log } x$$
$$= 10^{378631} \cdot 10^{0.6152} \qquad \text{Product of Powers Property}$$
$$\approx 10^{378631} \cdot 4.123.$$

So $2^{1257787} - 1$ is about $4.123 \cdot 10^{378631}$, a 378632-digit number beginning 412 . . . .

Equivalent Exponential and Linear Equations

The properties of logarithms can be used to rewrite *exponential equations*, a skill needed for the applications in Lesson 6-7. The general idea is as follows. Suppose

$$y = ab^x.$$

Take the natural log of each side.

$$\ln y = \ln (ab^x)$$
$$= \ln a + \ln b^x \qquad \text{Log of a Product Theorem}$$

So $\ln y = (\ln b)x + \ln a.$ Log of a Power Theorem

If a and b are constant, this is a linear model for $\ln y$ with slope $\ln b$ and y-intercept $\ln a$.

The idea of rewriting an exponential equation as a linear equation can be reversed.

Example 4

Rewrite $\log y = 3.1 + 0.03x$ as an exponential equation in the form $y = a \cdot b^x$.

Solution

$\log y = 3.1 + .03x$ Given

$y = 10^{3.1 + .03x}$ definition of base 10 logarithm

From this point, no properties of logs are needed.

$= 10^{3.1} \cdot 10^{.03x}$ Product of Powers Property

$= 10^{3.1} \cdot (10^{.03})^x$ Power of a Power Property

$y \approx 1258.93(1.072)^x$ Estimate rational powers using a calculator.

QUESTIONS

Covering the Reading

In 1–3, evaluate without using a calculator.

1. $\log 5 + \log 2$ **2.** $\log 100^6$ **3.** $\log 2000 - \log 2$

4. Prove the Logarithm of a Quotient Theorem.

5. Prove the Logarithm of a Power Theorem.

In 6–8, use the facts that $\log_6 11 \approx 1.3383$ and $\log_6 4 \approx 0.7737$ to estimate.

6. $\log_6 44$ **7.** $\log_6 \left(\frac{11}{4}\right)$ **8.** $\log_6 \sqrt[3]{121}$

9. If $\log a = 3 \log b - 2 \log c$, find an expression for a that does not involve logarithms.

10. Write a linear function for $\ln y$ which is equivalent to $y = 700(1.05)^x$.

11. Write an exponential equation in the form $A = cd^t$ equivalent to $\ln A = 1.3t + 6.2$.

12. **a.** Evaluate 13^{100} by each of the following methods.
- **i.** using the powering key on your calculator
- **ii.** using common logs
- **iii.** using natural logs

b. Which of the methods in part **a** do you think is best? Why?

c. How many digits does 13^{100} have?

Applying the Mathematics

13. Given $F = \frac{GmM}{d^2}$, write $\ln F$ in terms of $\ln G$, $\ln m$, $\ln M$, and $\ln d$.

14. **a.** For $x > 0$, graph $f(x) = \log\left(\frac{x^2}{9}\right)$ and $g(x) = 2 \log x - \log 9$ on the same set of axes.

b. Use properties of logarithms to explain why the graphs are the same.

15. *True or false.* For all $x > 0$ and $y > 0$, $\log(x - y) = \log x - \log y$. Justify your answer.

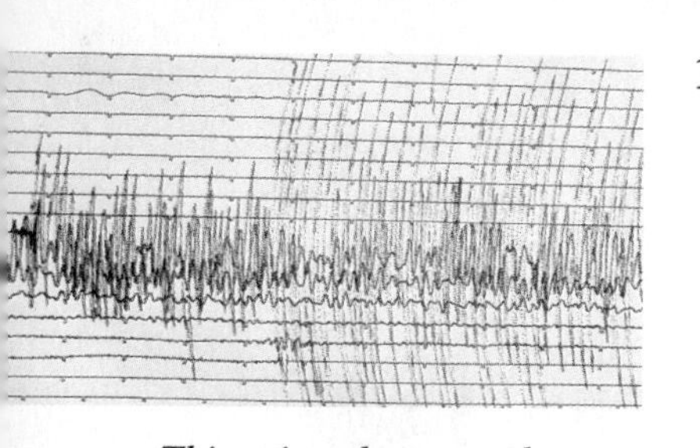

This seismology graph shows the oscillation of the ground during the Loma Prieta earthquake in Columbia, CA, in 1989. Seismic readings help locate the center of a quake.

16. The Richter scale for measuring the magnitude of earthquakes has been used since its invention in 1932 by Charles F. Richter (1901–1985). The scale values are common logarithms. The Japanese earthquake of 1933 measured 8.9 on the Richter scale. The 1906 San Francisco earthquake is estimated to have been 8.3. If $\log x = 8.9$ and $\log y = 8.3$, x is how many times as large as y? (This gives you an idea of how many times more powerful the Japanese earthquake was.)

17. Prove that for all bases b and positive n, $\log_b\left(\frac{1}{n}\right) = -\log_b n$.

18. Is 300^{400} larger than 400^{300}? Justify your answer.

Review

19. If t is the number of years and r is the annual interest rate, match the interest formulas to their compounding periods. *(Lessons 2-4, 6-4)*

a. $A(t) = Pe^{rt}$ **I.** annual compounding

b. $A(t) = P\left(1 + \frac{r}{n}\right)^{nt}$ **II.** periodic compounding

c. $A(t) = P(1 + r)^t$ **III.** continuous compounding

20. The population of Ethiopia was estimated to be 55,979,000 in 1995, with an average annual growth rate of 2.9%.

a. Use the Continuous Change Model, $A(t) = Pe^{rt}$ where $A(t)$ is the population t years after 1995 and P is the 1995 population, to find an equation for Ethiopia's population in future years.

b. On what main assumption does this formula rest?

c. Use the equation to estimate the population of Ethiopia in 2010. *(Lesson 6-4)*

In 21 and 22, evaluate without a calculator. *(Lessons 6-3, 6-4)*

21. $\log_2 32$ **22.** $\ln e^4$

23. List three properties that all logarithm functions share. *(Lessons 6-3, 6-4)*

24. *Skill sequence.* Solve for x. *(Lesson 6-3)*

a. $\log_3 x = 4$ **b.** $\log_3 (x + 1) = 2$ **c.** $\log_3 (2x) = \log_3 (3x - 1)$

25. Let A = the set of even integers from 10 to 25 and B = the set of integers from 20 to 30.

a. Find $A \cap B$. **b.** Find $A \cup B$. *(Previous course)*

Exploration

26. Given $\log 2 \approx 0.3010$, $\log 3 \approx 0.4771$, and $\log 7 \approx 0.8451$, it is possible to use the properties of logs to find the common logs of most positive integers less than or equal to 40.

a. Use these values to find each.

i. $\log 5$ **ii.** $\log 27$ **iii.** $\log 28$

b. Give five numbers whose logarithms *cannot* be found easily from $\log 2$, $\log 3$, and $\log 7$.

LESSON

6-6 Solving Exponential Equations

You already know how to solve some equations that contain constant exponents. For example, $x^3 = 15$ can be solved by taking the cube root of each side. However, when an equation has a variable as the exponent, such as $3^x = 15$, different techniques are needed. An equation to be solved for a variable in an exponent is called an **exponential equation**.

Numerical and Graphical Methods

Approximate solutions to exponential equations may be found by using guess-and-check or graphing strategies. Consider the equation $3^x = 15$. It must have a solution between 2 and 3, because $3^2 = 9$ and $3^3 = 27$. A first guess might be $x = 2.4$; a calculator shows that $3^{2.4} \approx 13.97$, a little low. A calculator also shows that $3^{2.5} \approx 15.59$, a little high. Thus, $2.4 < x < 2.5$. Further guesses and checks can be used to narrow the interval that contains the solution, thus increasing the level of accuracy of the answer.

To solve the equation $3^x = 15$ graphically, examine the point on the graph of $y = 3^x$ that has y-coordinate 15. At the right are graphs of $y = 3^x$ and $y = 15$. From the graph you can see that when $y = 15$, $x \approx 2.5$.

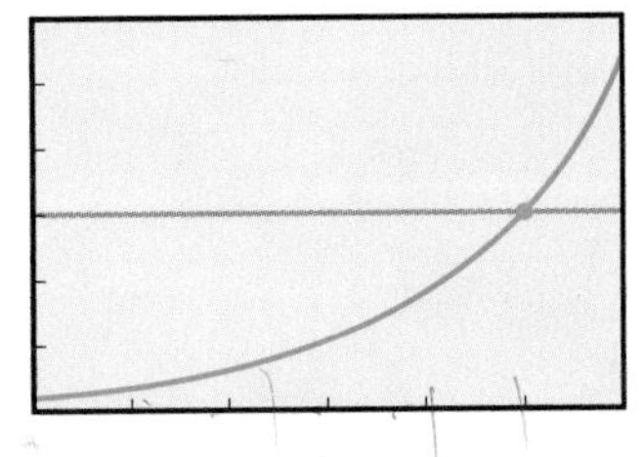

$0 \le x \le 3$, x-scale = 0.5
$0 \le y \le 30$, y-scale = 5

By changing the size of the viewing rectangle on an automatic grapher or by reading the coordinates of a point on the curve marked by a cursor, you can increase the accuracy of your estimated solution. At the right are the graphs of $y = 3^x$ and $y = 15$ in the window $2 \le x \le 3$, $10 \le y \le 20$. The coordinates of the cursor suggest that when $3^x = 15$, $x \approx 2.46$.

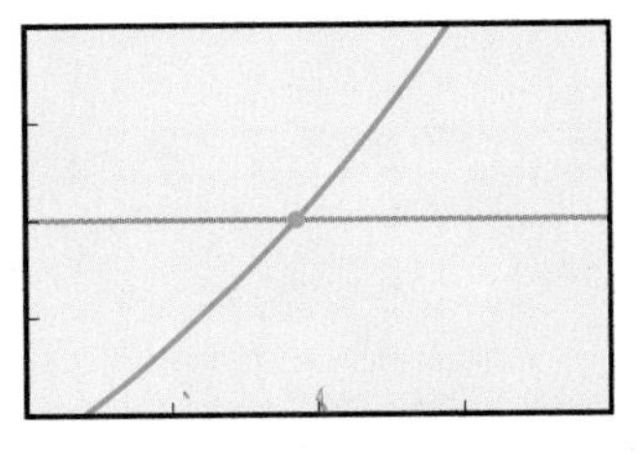

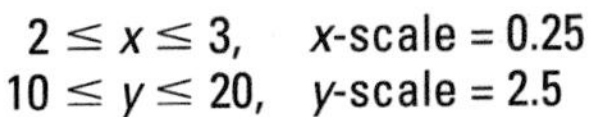

$2 \le x \le 3$, x-scale = 0.25
$10 \le y \le 20$, y-scale = 2.5

Using Logarithms to Solve Exponential Equations

Any equation of the form $b^x = a$, where $b > 0$, $b \neq 1$, and $a > 0$, can be solved by using logarithms. If you take the logarithm of both sides of an exponential equation, the exponent will become a factor in a linear equation.

Example 1

Solve $3^x = 15$ to four decimal places.

Solution

	$3^x = 15$	Given
	$\log (3^x) = \log 15$	Take the log of each side.
	$x \log 3 = \log 15$	Log of a Power Theorem
	$x = \frac{\log 15}{\log 3}$	Divide each side by log 3.
So	$x \approx 2.46497 \approx 2.4650$	

Check

Use a calculator. $3^{2.4650} \approx 15.00044 \approx 15$

Although any base for logarithms can be used to solve an exponential equation, sometimes one base is preferred over others. For example, the Continuous Change Model from Lesson 6-4 gives rise to equations involving e. When you begin with these equations, $\ln e = \log_e e = 1$, so using natural logarithms makes the solution easier.

Example 2

The 1995 population of Mexico was estimated at 94 million. Its annual growth rate is 1.9%. Estimate when the population will reach 110 million.

Solution

Assume the growth rate stays constant. Use the Continuous Change Model

$$A(t) = Pe^{rt},$$

where t represents the number of years after 1995. Then $A(t) = 110$ million, $P = 94$ million, and $r = 0.019$. Substitute these values.

$110 = 94 e^{0.019t}$	
$\frac{110}{94} = e^{0.019t}$	Divide both sides by 94.
$\ln \left(\frac{110}{94}\right) = \ln \left(e^{0.019t}\right)$	Take the natural log of each side.
$\ln \left(\frac{110}{94}\right) = 0.019t$	Log of a Power, and $\ln e = 1$
$t = \frac{\ln\left(\frac{110}{94}\right)}{0.019} \approx 8.273$	

So, if the growth rate remains constant, the population is expected to reach 110 million in about 8.27 years. Since 0.27 of a year is about 3 months, we say **Mexico's population will reach 110 million in about 2003, 8 years from 1995.**

The assumption of continuous change would not be a good one over a long period of time for a country like Mexico, but it is reasonable over a short term like eight years.

An assumption of continuous change is frequently appropriate in physical situations like those of decay.

Of Mammoth Interest. *This skeleton of a mammoth was preserved in ice in Siberia for over 10,000 years. The skull is still covered with skin.*

Example 3

Assuming carbon-14 has a half-life of 5730 years, give the approximate age of a skull found by an archaeologist if the skull has 63% of its original carbon-14 concentration.

Solution

Use the Continuous Change Model,

$$A(t) = Pe^{rt}$$

with $P = 1$. The information about half-life implies that $A(5730) = 0.5$. From this, you can determine r.

$$0.5 = 1 \cdot e^{5730r} \qquad \text{substitution}$$

$$\ln 0.5 = 5730r \qquad \text{Take the natural log of each side.}$$

$$r = \frac{\ln 0.5}{5730} \approx -0.000121$$

Thus, for carbon-14, $A(t) \approx e^{-0.000121t}$. We wish to know when $A(t) = 0.63$. Again, substitute.

$$0.63 \approx e^{-0.000121t}$$

$$\ln 0.63 \approx -0.000121t \qquad \text{Take the natural log of each side.}$$

$$t \approx \frac{\ln 0.63}{-0.000121} \approx 3818$$

So the skull is about 3800 years old.

Check

More than half the carbon-14 was left, so the age should be less than the half-life. The answer is reasonable.

Notice in Example 3 that the rate of growth is negative, indicating decay. The technique of radiocarbon dating, as well as dating by other radioactive substances, is very important to archaeologists and anthropologists interested in early civilizations. The results are only approximations, however, since they depend on an assumption that the decay rates are constant. Although most scientists believe carbon-14 dating is an accurate dating technique for about 10 half-life periods (up to about 50,000 years), there is some question of its accuracy for over 20 half-life periods (more than one hundred thousand years).

The Change of Base Theorem

In general, here is how to solve $b^x = a$ for x using an arbitrary base c. Take the logarithm of each side of the equation to that base.

$$b^x = a \qquad \text{Given}$$

$$\log_c (b^x) = \log_c a \qquad \text{Take } \log_c \text{ of each side.}$$

$$x \log_c b = \log_c a \qquad \text{Log of a Power Theorem}$$

$$x = \frac{\log_c a}{\log_c b} \qquad \text{Divide both sides by } \log_c b.$$

So the solution to $b^x = a$ is $x = \frac{\log_c a}{\log_c b}$. However, the given equation is also equivalent to $x = \log_b a$. This proves a theorem about the quotient of logs with the same base.

Theorem (Change of Base)
For all values of a, b, and c for which the logarithms exist,

$$\log_b a = \frac{\log_c a}{\log_c b}.$$

The Change of Base Theorem allows you to evaluate any logarithm on your calculator, even though only common logs and natural logs are built in.

Example 4

Evaluate $\log_4 150$.

Solution 1

Use the Change of Base Theorem. You may choose any base for c. Choose either $c = 10$ to use common logarithms, or $c = e$ to use natural logarithms. We use common logs.

$$\log_4 150 = \frac{\log 150}{\log 4} \approx 3.61441$$

Solution 2

Use natural logarithms.

$$\log_4 150 = \frac{\ln 150}{\ln 4} \approx 3.61441$$

Check

Use a calculator.

$$4^{3.61441} \approx 150.00014$$

Caution: In a problem like that in Example 4 using a quotient of logarithms, use your calculator to find $\frac{\log 150}{\log 4}$ in one step, and do not round until the final step. That reduces the round-off error.

QUESTIONS

Covering the Reading

1. **a.** Solve the equation $3^x = 15$ using natural logarithms.
   b. Check your solution against that in Example 1.

2. Consider the equation $5^x = 650$.
   a. Use guess-and-check to find the solution rounded to the nearest tenth.
   b. Draw a graph that justifies your answer to part **a**.
   c. Solve the equation using logarithms.

In 3 and 4, solve and check.

3. $7^x = 30$

4. $6^z = 0.4$

In 5 and 6, evaluate.

5. $\log_6 20$

6. $\log_{12} 7$

7. In 1996, the population of the United States was estimated at 266 million, with an annual growth rate of 0.9%. If this rate continues, estimate when the population will reach 300 million.

8. Suppose an art dealer in 1996 used carbon-14 dating to determine whether a painting was likely to have been painted by the great Italian artist and scientist Leonardo da Vinci (1452–1519). A specimen of paint was found to have 96% of the original amount of carbon-14. Is it plausible that the painting could be a Leonardo da Vinci? Justify your answer.

Applying the Mathematics

9. *Multiple choice.* Which expression(s) could be entered into an automatic grapher to produce a graph of $y = \log_7 x$?
(a) $y = \frac{\log 7}{\log x}$ (b) $y = \frac{\log x}{\log 7}$ (c) $y = \frac{\ln x}{\ln 7}$ (d) $y = \left(\frac{x}{7}\right)$

10. If you invest money at 7% interest compounded continuously, how long will it take for your money to double?

11. **a.** Find $\log_6 7776$. **b.** Find $\log_{7776} 6$.
c. What is the relationship of the answers to parts **a** and **b**?
d. Use the Change of Base Theorem to explain the relationship in part **c**.

12. The following formula is commonly used for estimating the age t in years of a specimen using the original number N_0 of radioactive atoms in the sample, the number N of radioactive atoms in the sample today, and the half-life $t_{0.5}$ of the substance.

$$t = \frac{t_{0.5}}{0.693} \ln \left(\frac{N_0}{N}\right)$$

a. Check that this formula works for Example 3 by replacing $\frac{N_0}{N}$ with $\frac{P}{A(t)}$.
b. Prove that the formula is correct.

Review

13. Suppose $N = \frac{A}{B^3}$. Use the laws of logarithms to express $\log N$ in terms of $\log A$ and $\log B$. *(Lesson 6-5)*

14. Rewrite $\log_2 R = 2.5p + 1.7$ as an exponential equation. *(Lesson 6-5)*

In 15 and 16, use this situation from psychology. Learning and forgetting are often modeled with logarithm functions. In one experiment, subjects studied nonsense syllables (like "gpl") and were asked to recall them after t seconds. A model for remembering was found to be

$$P = 92 - 25 \ln t \qquad \text{for } t \geq 1,$$

where P is the percent of students who remembered a syllable after t seconds.

15. **a.** What percent of students remembered after 1 second?
b. What percent remembered after 10 seconds?

16. Use an automatic grapher to give the approximate time after which only half of the students remembered a syllable. *(Lesson 6-4)*

In 17–19, evaluate without a calculator. *(Lesson 6-3)*

17. $\log_2 128$ **18.** $\log 0.001$ **19.** $\log 10^{0.03}$

20. Match each function with its graph. Assume $a > 0$. *(Lessons 2-4, 6-1, 6-2, 6-3)*

(a) $y = a^x$ (b) $y = \sqrt{x}$ (c) $y = \log_2 x$ (d) $y = x^{3/2}$

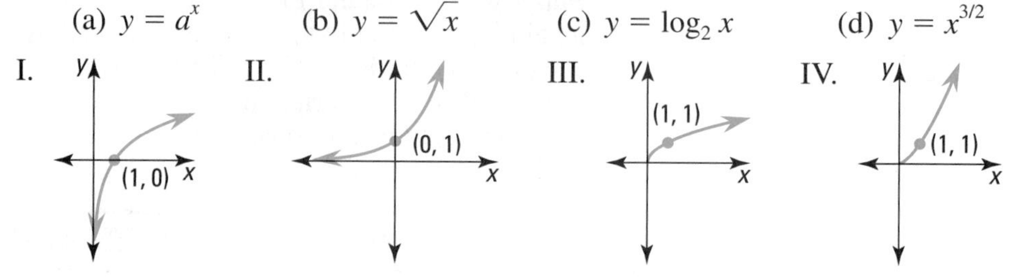

Channel Catfish, *an oil painting by Herman Menzel*

21. Use the mean lengths of Illinois channel catfish of various ages given below.

Age (years)	1	2	3	4	5	6	7	8	9	10
Length (inches)	6.4	9.6	12.6	14.3	16.7	18.5	21.0	22.6	25.6	26.6

Source: Illinois Department of Conservation.

a. Find an equation of the line of best fit for predicting length from age.
b. Interpret the slope of the line.
c. Use the line to predict the length of a twelve-year-old channel catfish in Illinois.
d. Suggest a reason for being cautious about your prediction in part **c**.
e. Find the correlation coefficient r between the age of the fish and its mean length.
f. Interpret the sign of the correlation. *(Lessons 2-2, 2-3)*

22. Refer to the Venn diagram at the right.
a. Give $N(A)$, the number of elements in set A.
b. What is $A \cup B$?
c. What is $A \cap B$? *(Previous course)*

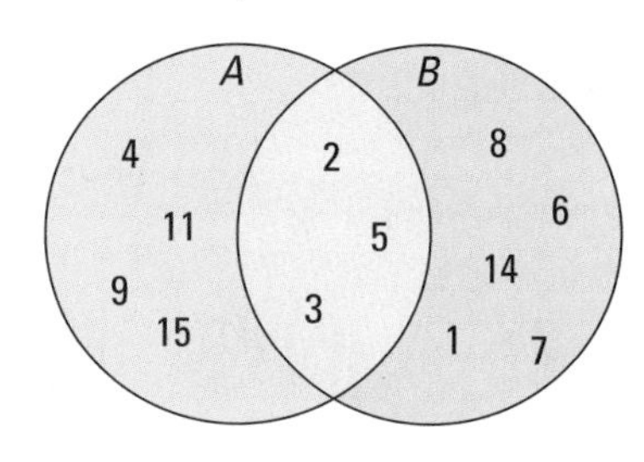

Exploration

23. a. Generalize the answer to Question 10. That is, give a rule for the length of time t it takes to double an investment at interest rate r assuming continuous compounding.
b. A rule of thumb used by some people to determine the length of time t in years it would take to double their money at $r\%$ interest is called the *Rule of 72*. The time t is estimated to be $t = \frac{72}{r}$. To see how this compares with your rule for part **a**, graph the two rules on an automatic grapher simultaneously.
c. State how well the rule of thumb approximates the continuous compounding case.

LESSON

6-7

Linearizing Data to Find Models

Alligator comeback. *In the 1960s, American alligators were an endangered species, but protective legislation and scientific monitoring of their population has helped restore their number in the wild.* *See page 410.*

In Chapter 2, linear, quadratic, and exponential functions were used to model sets of data. All of these models were generated with a statistics utility. Some of these models were theory-based because they depended on some theoretical assumption, that population growth is exponential or that area involves some quadratic function. Others were based only on the impression made by the scatterplot of the data set.

Often the shape of the scatterplot offers clues to choosing a function to model the data set. For instance, you can tell whether a power function $y = x^n$ with $n > 1$ or a logarithm function $y = \log_b x$ with $b > 1$ is more suitable by the shape of the curve.

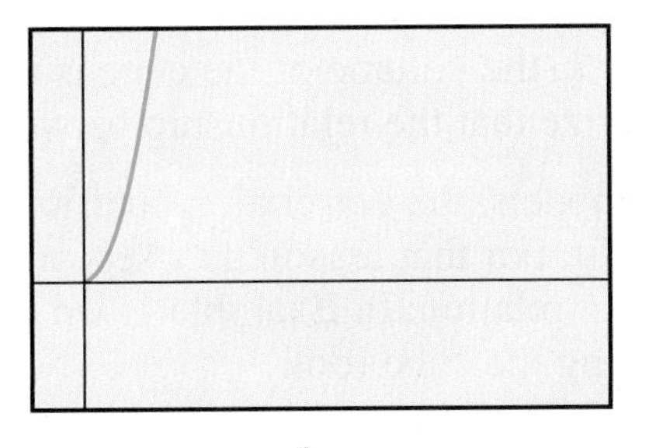

$y = x^n, n > 1$

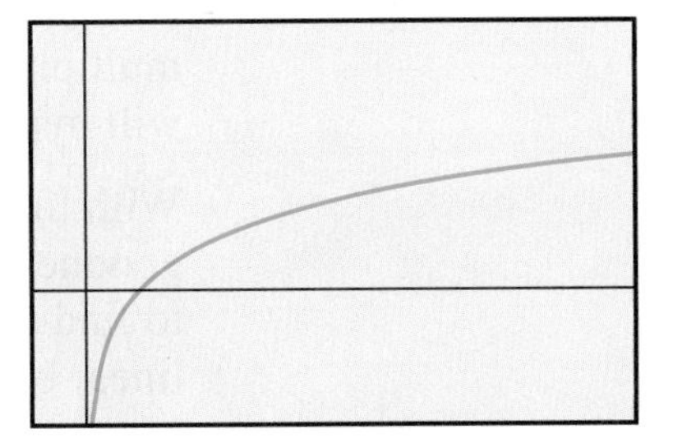

$y = \log_b x, b > 1$

However, you cannot always tell which power function to use, or whether an exponential function might be more appropriate than a power function, by looking at a graph. For example, the graphs of $y = x^2$ in blue, $y = x^3$ in orange, and $y = 2^x$ in green drawn at the right each show about the same growth when $0 \le x \le 2.5$.

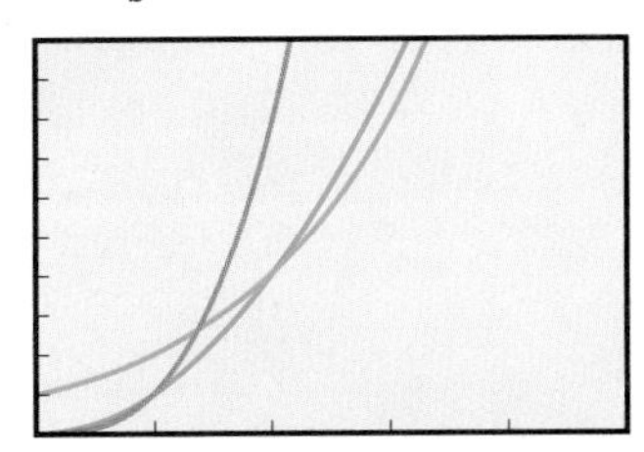

$0 \le x \le 5$, x-scale = 1
$0 \le y \le 10$, y-scale = 1

Linearizing Data Using the Cube Root

Wildlife biologists study the characteristics of the population of certain animal species. For example, in Florida knowing the number and size of alligators in a region is essential to monitor the health of the alligator population, and to protect humans and other animals. The biologists monitor alligators by taking aerial photographs and counting the number of animals. From an aerial photograph an alligator's length can be determined by measuring and scaling. However, its weight is difficult to determine, so a model relating length and weight is needed.

Consider the data in the table and scatterplot below from thirteen alligators which were captured, measured, and weighed.

Alligator Length and Mass

Length (cm)	239	188	373	147	218	239	160	218	175	183	325	216	208
Mass (kg)	59	23	290	13	39	50	15	41	16	17	166	38	36

From the scatterplot it is clear that the relationship between the variables is not linear. However, it is not clear what curve should be fit to the data. Either a power function of the form $y = ax^n$ or an exponential function of the form $y = ab^x$ is a possible model.

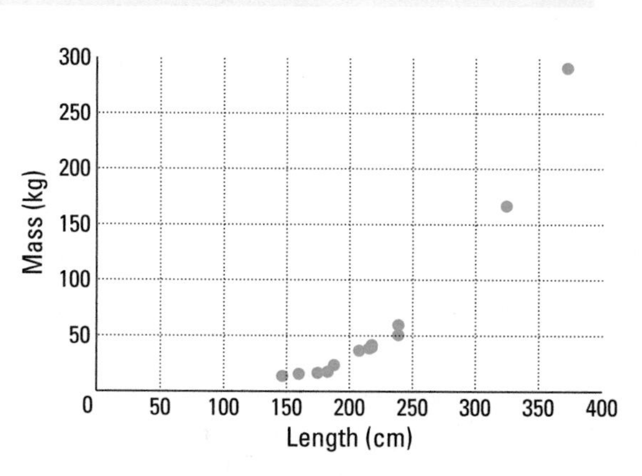

A theory-based model for the data comes from geometry. Recall that mass (weight) is directly proportional to volume, and that if the edge of a cube is multiplied by k, the volume of the cube is multiplied by k^3. Therefore, we will hypothesize that the relationship between length and mass is cubic.

With linear models, the correlation coefficient r gives a measure of goodness of fit. For that reason data sets are often rewritten or transformed to find a linear relation. In Example 1, we transform the data from cubic to linear by taking the cube root.

Example 1

Consider the data on length L and weight M of alligators given above.

a. Show that when the mass data are transformed, $(L, \sqrt[3]{M})$ can be described by a linear equation, and find the line of best fit for that data.

b. Use the line of best fit in part **a** to find a cubic equation in L and M.

c. If an alligator measures 270 cm, give its approximate mass.

Solution

a. Calculate the cube roots of the mass, and make a scatterplot of $(L, \sqrt[3]{M})$.

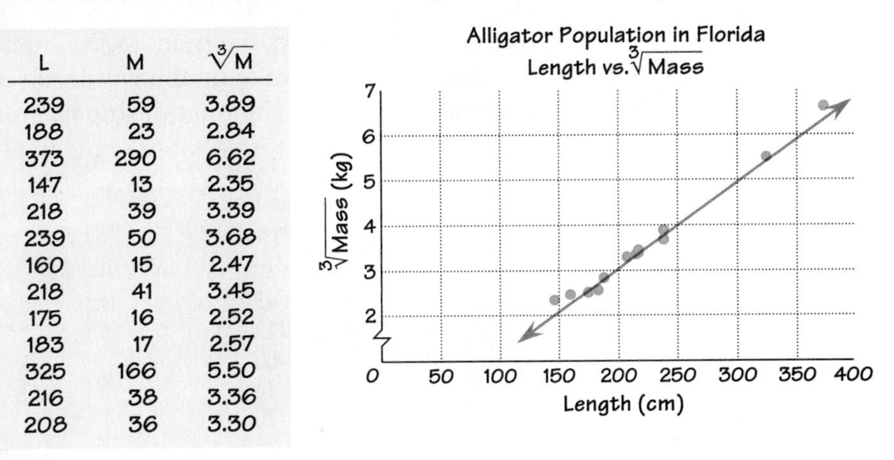

L	M	$\sqrt[3]{M}$
239	59	3.89
188	23	2.84
373	290	6.62
147	13	2.35
218	39	3.39
239	50	3.68
160	15	2.47
218	41	3.45
175	16	2.52
183	17	2.57
325	166	5.50
216	38	3.36
208	36	3.30

A statistics utility gives the equation $y = 0.019x - 0.791$ as the line of best fit for (Length, $\sqrt[3]{\text{Mass}}$) with $r \approx .9942$. The linear fit is very good. The scatterplot of $(L, \sqrt[3]{M})$ looks approximately linear.

b.

$$y = 0.019x - 0.791$$

$$\sqrt[3]{M} = 0.019L - 0.791 \quad \text{Substitute } L \text{ for } x \text{ and } \sqrt[3]{M} \text{ for } y.$$

$$M = (0.019L - 0.791)^3 \quad \text{Cube both sides.}$$

c. Substitute 270 for L in the equation in part **b**.

$$M = (0.019(270) - 0.791)^3$$

$$M \approx 82 \text{ kilograms}$$

Check

A scatterplot of the original data and $M = (0.019L - 0.791)^3$ is at the right. The fit is good.

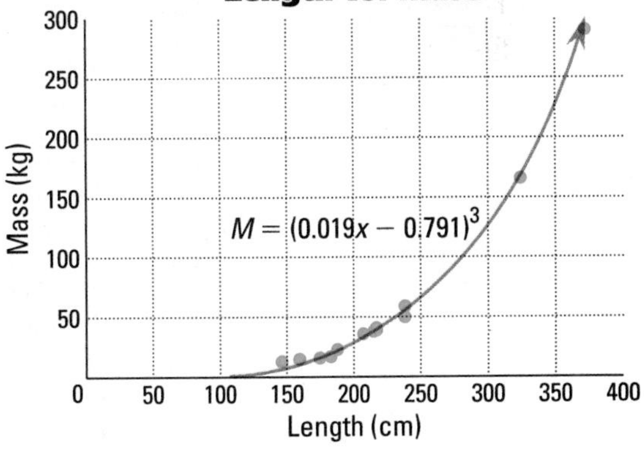

white alligator, one of a clutch found in Louisiana

To study the relationship between L and M for the alligator data, the first step was to replace each M value by $\sqrt[3]{M}$. In that step, the dependent variable M was transformed into the new variable $\sqrt[3]{M}$.

Linearizing Data Using a Logarithmic Transformation

The following data and scatterplot are from an experiment on the effect of practice time t in seconds on the percent P of unfamiliar words correctly recalled. For instance, the point (5, 53) means that when people were given 5 seconds to concentrate on the words, on average they recalled 53% of the meanings correctly. The relationship between P and t is clearly nonlinear.

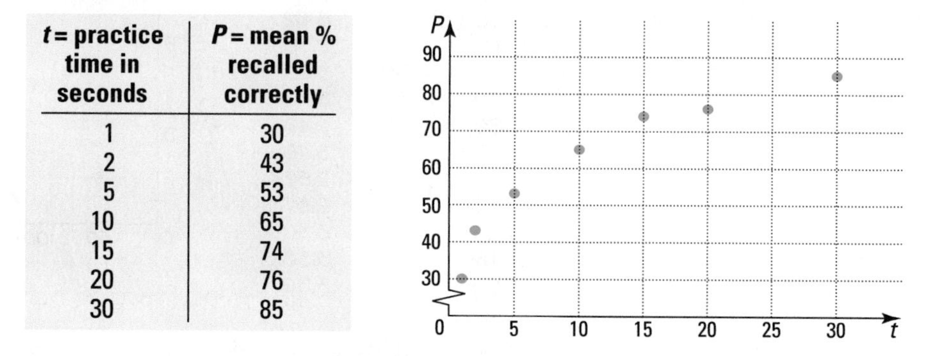

t = practice time in seconds	P = mean % recalled correctly
1	30
2	43
5	53
10	65
15	74
20	76
30	85

The shape of the graph suggests that an appropriate model may be logarithmic of the form

$$P = a \log t + b$$

for some positive a and b.

Example 2

a. Find an equation of the form $P = a \log t + b$ to model the practice time data.

b. Approximate the amount of practice time needed for the mean percentage of meanings recalled to exceed 95%.

Solution

a. First find the logarithms of the values of t. Any base is suitable. We use natural logarithms. Then plot the points ($\ln t$, P).

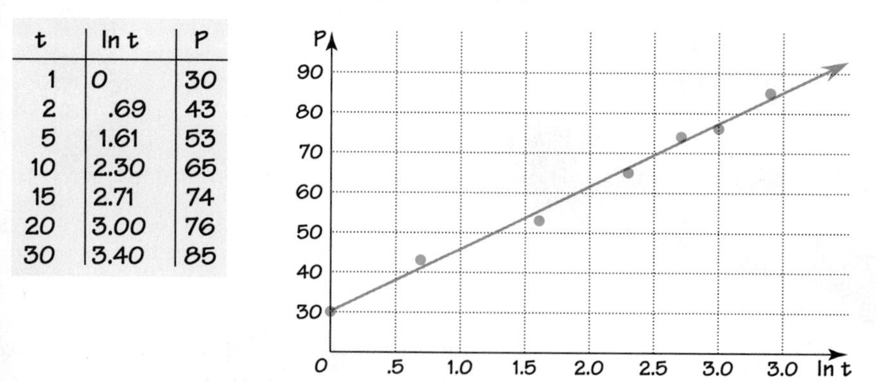

t	ln t	P
1	0	30
2	.69	43
5	1.61	53
10	2.30	65
15	2.71	74
20	3.00	76
30	3.40	85

The effect of the transformation is to show a near linear relationship between P and $\ln t$. So, a logarithmic model is appropriate for these data. A statistics utility gives $y = 15.7x + 30.1$ as the equation for the line of best fit, with $r \approx .996$. Substituting P and $\ln t$ for y and x, respectively, an equation that models the practice time data is

$$P \approx 15.7 \ln t + 30.1.$$

b. Substitute 95 for P and solve for t.

$$95 \approx 15.7 \ln t + 30.1$$
$$64.9 \approx 15.7 \ln t$$
$$\ln t \approx 4.133758$$

So by definition of $\ln t$, $t \approx e^{4.133758}$

$$\approx 62.4.$$

The model predicts that people will exceed 95% accuracy after about 62 seconds of practice.

Check

Extend the line on the graph. When $P = 95$, $\ln t$ is a little less than 4.2. So t is a little less than $e^{4.2} \approx 67$, consistent with the solution.

As with all real data, it is important to keep equations and predictions like those in Examples 1 and 2 in perspective. For instance, in Example 2 perhaps it is not reasonable to assume most people will ever achieve 95% recall of the words. It may be that after a certain number of seconds of practice, boredom becomes a factor and the percentage of meanings recalled actually declines. However, for practice times within the range observed, the model seems to be quite accurate. As always, it is usually more defensible to interpolate than to extrapolate.

Also, other nonlinear models may also describe the data well. In particular, in Example 2 a square root model might describe the data well. In the absence of a theory-based model, trial and error, the goodness of the linear fit, and an analysis of residuals serve as guidelines for choosing one model over another. A decision to prefer an exponential or logarithm function over other possible models is often made because one model is predicted by, or consistent with, other theories or hypotheses.

QUESTIONS

Covering the Reading

In 1–3, refer to the alligator population data and the model in Example 1.

1. Why was a cubic model used to model these data?

2. An aerial photograph reveals that an alligator is 10 feet long. What is its mass?

3. Find the length of an alligator with a mass of 30 kg.

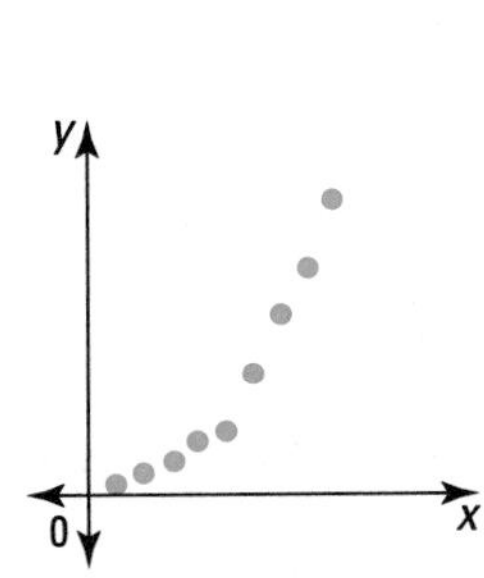

4. *Multiple choice.* Data from an experiment are plotted at the left. Which equation could not model these data?

(a) $y = ax^2$ (b) $y = a \cdot 2^x$

(c) $y = ax^3$ (d) $y = a \log_2 x$

5. Rewrite the equation $\sqrt{y} = ax + b$ to show y as a function of x.

In 6 and 7, refer to the word-recall experiment and Example 2.

6. According to the model, what is the expected percent recall after 4 seconds of practice?

7. What is the expected amount of practice time needed for 90% recall?

Applying the Mathematics

8. Solve for y.

a. $\log y = .5x + 1$ **b.** $\log y = .5 \log x + 1$

9. The table below lists the estimates of expected life span for people of various ages.

Current age (years)	Expected life span (years)	Current age (years)	Expected life span (years)
1	76.2	45	78.6
5	76.3	50	79.2
10	76.4	55	79.9
15	76.5	60	80.9
20	76.7	65	82.3
25	77.1	70	84.0
30	77.3	75	85.9
35	77.7	80	88.3
40	78.1	85	91.0

a. Draw a scatterplot of current age x versus expected life span y.

b. Which of the two functions, $y = ab^x$ or $y = a \log x$, seems to fit these data better?

c. Determine an equation of one of the forms in part **b** to fit these data.

d. For the data above, a statistics utility calculated the equation $y = 0.152x + 73.668$ for the line of best fit. Which of the models, the linear model or the model from part **c**, better predicts the expected life span of a 40-year-old?

e. Comment on the suitability of the models in parts **c** and **d** for predicting the expected life span of a 90-year-old.

10. The table below shows the trend in life expectancy for a child born in the given year in the United States.

year, t	1900	1915	1930	1945	1960	1990
life expectancy, L (in years)	47.3	54.5	59.7	65.9	69.7	75.4

a. Find a logarithm function with equation of the form $L = a \ln t + b$ to fit these data.

b. Find a square root function with equation of the form $L = a\sqrt{t} + b$ to fit these data.

c. Based on an analysis of correlation coefficients and residuals, which of the models—logarithmic or square root—do you think is better? Why?

d. Based on the model you chose in part **c**, predict the life expectancy for a child born in the year of your birth.

11. It has been suggested that the time taken t (seconds) for a rowing shell to cover 2000 m is related to the number x of oarsmen in the boat, according to the power function

$$t = cx^n.$$

Here are the winning times for various rowing events at the 1996 Olympics.

x	1	2	4	8
t	404.85	376.98	366.37	342.74

a. Take the log of each side of the equation for t above.
b. Graph log t (vertical axis) against log x (horizontal axis).
c. Find an equation for the line of best fit for the graph in part **b**.
d. Interpret the slope of your line in part **c**.
e. Give a model of the form $t = cx^n$ for the 1996 Olympics data.

Review

12. Graph $y = \log_{11} x$ using the Change of Base Theorem. *(Lesson 6-6)*

In 13 and 14, solve and check. *(Lesson 6-6)*

13. $6^x = 70$ **14.** $\log_5 376 = t$

15. Assuming carbon-14 has a half-life of 5730 years, give the approximate age of a wooden spear found by an anthropologist, if the spear has 34% of the original carbon-14 concentration. *(Lesson 6-6)*

16. Find a formula for the length of time it takes to triple an investment under continuous compounding at $r\%$ interest. *(Lesson 6-6)*

17. The graph of $y = \log_2 x$ is scaled by $S(x, y) = \left(x, \frac{1}{\log_2 3} y\right)$.
a. Use the Graph Scale-Change Theorem to write an equation for the image as a quotient of logarithms.
b. Use the Change of Base Theorem to write the equation in part **a** as a single logarithm function. *(Lessons 3-5, 6-6)*

18. *True or false.* For $b \geq 0$, $c > 0$, $\log \left(\frac{b}{c}\right)^2 = 2 \log b - \log c$. Justify your answer. *(Lesson 6-5)*

19. **a.** For what values of x is $x^{1/2}$ less than $x^{1/4}$?
b. For what values of x is $x^{1/2}$ greater than $x^{1/4}$?
c. Generalize your answers to parts **a** and **b**. *(Lesson 6-1)*

Exploration

20. Collect data on the number of cases reported for AIDS or some other disease in recent years for your city or state. Which type of function—linear, exponential, or logarithm—best models the data?

A project presents an opportunity for you to extend your knowledge of a topic related to the material of this chapter. You should allow more time for a project than you do for a typical homework question.

1 Change of Base and Exponent

Just as logarithms can be converted from one base to another using the Change of Base Theorem, so can exponential functions be converted from one base to another.

a. Use an automatic grapher to graph $f(x) = 8^x$ and $g(x) = e^{2.07944x}$ on the same graph. What do you notice?

b. Graph $f(x) = 8^x$ and $h(x) = 6^{1.16056x}$ on the same graph. What do you notice?

c. Prove that $8^x = e^{x \ln 8}$ by starting with $y = 8^x$. Use this result to account for what you observed about the graphs in part **a**.

d. Explain your observations in part **b**.

e. Rewrite $f(x) = 8^x$ as an exponential function with base 3.

f. Any exponential function of the form $f(x) = ab^x$ can be rewritten as an exponential function of the form $g(x) = ae^{kx}$. Develop a method of doing this. (This means you never need to find any powers except powers of the number e. That is, the power key on your calculator is unnecessary if you have e^x!)

2 Using Logs to Calculate—the Old Way

Lesson 6-5 mentions that logarithms and the slide rule were once used to simplify complex calculations. Do *one* of the following.

a. Find an advanced algebra or trigonometry book published before 1965. Find out how logarithms were used. Write a description of what you find.

b. Locate a slide rule and instruction book. Find out how to multiply, divide, and take powers of numbers. Demonstrate this skill to your class.

c. Before the slide rule was invented, John Napier invented a calculation aid now called "Napier's Bones." Find a description and make a set. Show how they were used for computations.

3 Semilog Graphing

The graph below shows the U.S. population from 1790 to 1860 on special paper called semilog graph paper. The scale on the y-axis is graduated in proportion with the logarithms of the numbers represented. The x-axis is scaled uniformly, which is why the paper is only "semi" logarithmic. With such paper, you do not need a calculator or computer to do a logarithmic transformation. You merely graph the populations directly (watch the scale carefully; the halfway mark between vertical measures is the geometric mean of those values, not the arithmetic mean).

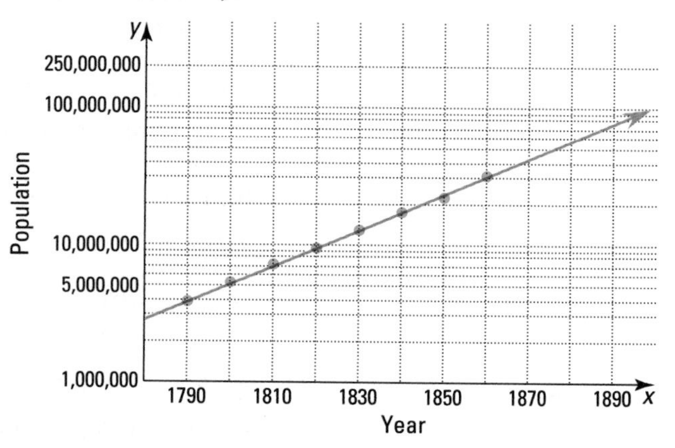

Similarly, you can read values directly from either scale. Extending the line in this case, the predicted 1890 population is about 80 million.

a. Obtain some semilog graph paper. Notice carefully the numbers on the vertical axis. Label the vertical axis from 1 to 100 and the horizontal axis from 1 to 10. Graph the function $f(x) = 1.6^x$. What shape is your graph? Graph $g(x) = 3(1.6)^x$ on the same set of axes. What kind of transformation maps f to g? Explain why.
b. Graph other exponential functions on semilog paper, such as, $m(x) = e^{2x}$ and $n(x) = 1.8^x$. Describe the graph of any exponential function that is plotted on semilog paper.
c. Log-log paper has logarithmic scales on both the x- and y-axes. Find some log-log paper and graph $f(x) = x^3$, $g(x) = x^{1.5}$, and $h(x) = x^{-2.2}$ on it on the same set of axes. What do you notice? What is true about the graph of any power function when it is plotted on log-log paper?

4 Population Density

Use an almanac to find data on the density (number of people per square mile) of the U.S. population for the census years from 1790 to 1990.

a. Produce a scatterplot with year on the horizontal axis and density on the vertical axis.
b. Rewrite the data using square root, cube root, and logarithmic transformations. In each transformation produce a scatterplot and find the line of best fit.
c. Find a residual plot for each linear fit. Use both the residual plot and the correlation coefficient to decide which transformation gives the best fit.
d. Use the equation for the line of best fit to find an equation that relates year and population density. Make a residual plot to show that the equation fits the data well.
e. Predict U.S. population density in 2000 and 2020. Will your model hold for the first 20 years of the 21st century? Why or why not?

5 Population and Walking Speed

Below is a set of data relating the population of various cities and the walking time of an average person in that city. The walking time was calculated by measuring the time it took to walk 50 feet on a busy street under controlled conditions. Several measures were taken and a mean time calculated.

City	Population (in 1982)	Mean Time (in seconds)
Brno, Czechoslovakia	341,950	10.4
Prague, Czechoslovakia	1,092,760	8.5
Certe, Corsica	5,490	15.1
Bastia, France	49,380	10.2
Munich, Germany	1,340,000	8.9
Psychio, Crete	370	18.1
Itea, Greece	2500	22.0
Iraklion, Greece	78,000	13.0
Athens, Greece	867,020	9.6
Safed, Israel	14,000	13.5
Dimna, Israel	23,700	15.3
Netaneya, Israel	70,700	11.6
Jerusalem, Israel	304,500	11.3
New Haven, Connecticut	138,000	11.4
Brooklyn, New York	2,602,000	9.9

Source: *UMAP Journal, Vol. 3 #2, 1982*

a. Produce a scatterplot of population (in thousands) against mean walking time. What shape is the scatterplot?
b. Attempt to linearize the data by (i) using the logarithm of the population and (ii) using the square root of the population. For each, find the line of best fit and the correlation coefficient. Make residual plots using the line of best fit.
c. Compare the two transformations in part **b.** Which fit is best?
d. Use the best fitting line to predict the mean walking time in your town and in three other towns in your state. Do you think the predictions are accurate? Explain why population size would influence mean walking time. What other factors might influence it as well? Explain these factors in a paragraph.

SUMMARY

This chapter discusses functions of the form $f(x) = x^n$, $x > 0$, $n \neq 0$; and logarithm functions, base b, with general form $f(x) = \log_b x$, $x > 0$, $b > 0$, $b \neq 1$.

The functions f with equations of the form $f(x) = x^n$ have special names depending on the value of n. If n is a positive integer and $n \geq 2$, they are *nth power functions*. If n is the reciprocal of an integer and greater than or equal to 2, they are *nth root functions*. If n is a rational number, they are *rational power functions*. The rational power functions are defined only for nonnegative values of x and $n \neq 0$ if $x = 0$. The nth root functions are inverses of the corresponding nth power functions restricted to $x \geq 0$.

An exponent that is the reciprocal of a positive integer n is equivalent to an nth root.

$$x^{1/n} = \sqrt[n]{x} \text{ for all } x \geq 0$$

A rational exponent is equal to the root of a power, or the power of a root.

$$x^{p/q} = \sqrt[q]{x^p} = \left(\sqrt[q]{x}\right)^p \text{ for all } x \geq 0$$

Logarithm functions are inverses of exponential functions. Although any positive base other than 1 is possible, common logarithms (base 10) are especially convenient because the decimal number system also has base 10, so $\log 100 = 2$, $\log 1000 = 3$, and so on. Natural logarithms (base e) are often used because they are easily calculated from infinite series. The Continuous Change Model $A(t) = Pe^{rt}$, gives the amount $A(t)$ of a substance after t years when growth or decay is continuous with initial value P and annual growth rate r. Several natural phenomena follow this model.

Laws of exponents can be used to prove theorems about logarithms of products, quotients, and powers, and these in turn can be used to solve exponential equations that you could previously only solve through trial and error. The Change of Base Theorem allows you to convert logarithms from one base to another and to graph $y = \log_b x$ for values of b other than 10 and e.

Both nth root and logarithm functions can model real situations. When a relationship between two variables is curvilinear, a log or nth root transformation can rewrite one or both variables. When the transformation results in a near linear relationship, a line of best fit can be calculated. From this a power or exponential relationship involving the original data can be found.

VOCABULARY

Below are the most important terms and phrases for this chapter. You should be able to give a general description and a specific example of each and a precise definition for those marked with an asterisk (*).

Lesson 6-1
square root
cube root
nth root
nth root functions
radical
$\sqrt[n]{x}$, $x^{1/n}$

Lesson 6-2
rational exponent, $x^{m/n}$, x^0, x^{-n}
rational power functions

Lesson 6-3
*logarithm, base, $\log_b x$
*common logarithm
logarithm function with base b

Lesson 6-4
*e
interest rate, yield
compounded continuously
*Continuous Change Model
exponential function with base e
*natural logarithm, $\ln x$
natural logarithm function

Lesson 6-5
*Logarithm of 1 Theorem
*Logarithm of a Product Theorem
*Logarithm of a Quotient Theorem
*Logarithm of a Power Theorem

Lesson 6-6
exponential equation
*Change of Base Theorem

 CHAPTER SIX

PROGRESS SELF-TEST

Take this test as you would take a test in class. You may want to use a scientific calculator and an automatic grapher. Then check the test yourself using the solutions at the back of the book.

In 1–4, evaluate without a calculator. Show your work or explain your reasoning.

1. $64^{2/3}$ **2.** $\left(\frac{9}{25}\right)^{-1/2}$ **3.** $\log_3 27$ **4.** $\ln e^2$

5. State the domain and range of $f(x) = x^{4/5}$.

6. Simplify $\sqrt[5]{x^{10}y^5}$ for $x > 0$, $y > 0$.

7. Solve $7^x = 2401$.

8. Solve $5^x = 47$ to the nearest thousandth.

9. Approximate $\log_5 16$ to the nearest thousandth.

10. Given $\log_{12} 15 \approx 1.090$ and $\log_{12} 3 \approx .4421$, explain how to use these to find $\log_{12} 5$.

11. Strontium-90 has a half-life of 25 years. How long will it take 10 grams of strontium-90 to decay to 3 grams?

12. Consider $g(t) = \log_3 t$.

a. Graph $y = g(t)$ and $y = g^{-1}(t)$ on an appropriate interval.

b. Give the equation(s) of any asymptotes of g.

c. Find an equation for g^{-1}.

13. Rewrite without logarithms:
$\frac{1}{2} \log a + \log b = \frac{1}{3} \log c$.

14. *True or false.* $10^{\log x} = e^{\ln x}$ for any positive number x. Justify your response.

15. a. Graph $f(x) = x^{5/3}$.

b. On the same set of axes, graph f^{-1}, the inverse of f.

c. Give an equation for f^{-1}.

16. It is conjectured that the number L of a softball team's losses varies inversely as the square of the number of runs R scored in a season.

$$L = \frac{k}{R^2}$$

Write R as a function of L.

In 17 and 18, refer to the graphs of $f(x) = x^{7/4}$ and $g(x) = x^{9/4}$, shown below.

17. Which of y_1 or y_2 is the graph of g?

18. *Multiple choice.* For which values of x is $f(x) < g(x)$?

(a) all values of x

(b) $x < 1$

(c) $x > 1$

(d) no value of x

19. Rewrite $A = 3.75(.054)^t$ as a linear equation in $(t, \log A)$.

20. At the beginning of an experiment, a cup of coffee at 100° C was placed in a 20° C room. At various times t in minutes the temperature of the coffee was measured, and the difference in temperature y from room temperature recorded. The results are in the table below.

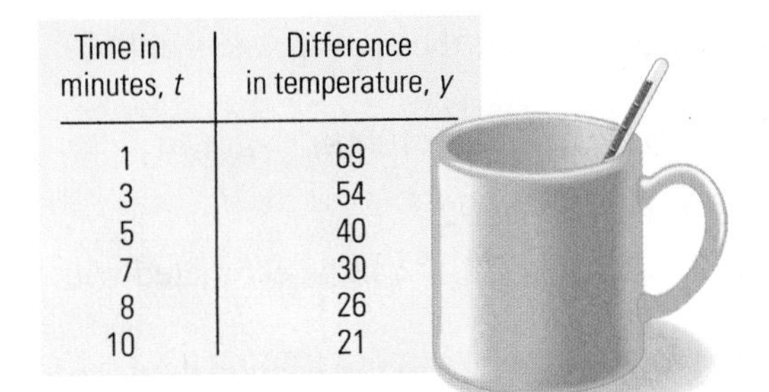

Time in minutes, t	Difference in temperature, y
1	69
3	54
5	40
7	30
8	26
10	21

a. Transform the data by finding the natural log of y.

b. Draw a graph of the ordered pairs $(t, \ln y)$.

c. Find an equation for the line of best fit for the scatterplot in part **b**.

d. Use the line of best fit to find an exponential equation to fit the original set of data.

CHAPTER REVIEW

Questions on SPUR Objectives

SPUR stands for **S**kills, **P**roperties, **U**ses, and **R**epresentations. The Chapter Review questions are grouped according to the SPUR Objectives for this chapter.

SKILLS DEAL WITH THE PROCEDURES USED TO GET ANSWERS.

Objective A: *Evaluate $b^{m/n}$ for $b > 0$.* *(Lessons 6-1, 6-2)*

For 1–4, evaluate without a calculator.

1. $125^{1/3}$ **2.** $125^{5/3}$

3. $125^{-2/3}$ **4.** $\sqrt[3]{-125}$

In 5 and 6, assume a and t are positive. Rewrite using a radical sign.

5. $a^{2/3}$ **6.** $t^{-3/7}$

In 7 and 8, assume all variables are positive. Write without a radical sign.

7. $\sqrt[5]{st^7}$ **8.** $\frac{1}{\sqrt[6]{a^2b^3}}$

In 9 and 10, insert the appropriate symbol (>, <, =).

9. $(10{,}000)^{3/4}$ _?_ $(1000)^{4/3}$

10. $\sqrt[10]{(-2)^{10}}$ _?_ -2

11. Explain how $8^{1.96}$ can be estimated without a calculator.

12. Estimate $3 \cdot 7^{0.5}$ to the nearest thousandth.

Objective B: *Solve exponential equations.* *(Lesson 6-6)*

In 13–16, solve and check.

13. $e^m = 8$ **14.** $5^n = 9$

15. $7(2.3)^x = 100$ **16.** $15(1.08)^n = 40$

Objective C: *Evaluate logarithms.* *(Lessons 6-3, 6-4, 6-5, 6-6)*

In 17–22, evaluate without using a calculator.

17. $\log_{10} 10{,}000$ **18.** $\log_3\left(\frac{1}{27}\right)$ **19.** $\ln e^{-1.73}$

20. $\log_2 2048$ **21.** $\log_a\left(\sqrt[3]{a^4}\right)$ **22.** $e^{\ln 5.3}$

23. Explain how you can tell without using a calculator which of log 5 or ln 5 is larger.

24. Order from smallest to largest without using a calculator. $\log_5 10$, $\log_2 10$, $\log_7 10$

In 25–28, evaluate and round to the nearest hundredth.

25. log 73 **26.** ln 22.8

27. $\log_{12} \pi$ **28.** $\log_6 73$

PROPERTIES DEAL WITH THE PRINCIPLES BEHIND THE MATHEMATICS.

Objective D: *Describe properties of rational power, nth root, and logarithm functions.* *(Lessons 6-1, 6-2, 6-3, 6-4, 6-5)*

29. Give the domain and range of the rational power function f, where $f(x) = x^{4/3}$.

30. a. What restrictions can be made on the domain of the function $g: x \rightarrow x^5$ so that its inverse is an nth root function?

b. Describe g^{-1}.

31. Why do we restrict rational exponents to positive bases?

In 32 and 33, let h be the logarithm function with base 5.

32. a. State the domain of h.

b. State the range of h.

33. Find an equation for the inverse of h.

34. *Multiple choice.* Which of the following is the inverse of $y = \log_3 x$?

(a) $y = 3 \log x$ (b) $y = 3^x$

(c) $y = x^3$ (d) $y = \sqrt[3]{x}$

35. Define e.

36. What point(s) is (are) on the graph of every function with equation $f(x) = \log_b x$?

Objective E: *Use properties of logarithms.* *(Lessons 6-5, 6-6, 6-7)*

In 37–39, use the fact that $\log_8 5 \approx 0.774$ and $\log_8 12 \approx 1.195$ to evaluate the expression.

37. $\log_8 60$ **38.** $\log_8 \left(\frac{25}{12}\right)$ **39.** $\log_8 \sqrt[5]{12}$

In 40 and 41, rewrite as a single logarithm.

40. $\frac{1}{2} \log 4 - 2 \log 3$ **41.** $5 \ln x + 2 \ln y - \ln z$

42. Explain how $\log 80 + \log 2.5 - \log 2$ can be evaluated without using a calculator.

43. If $A = \frac{C^3}{D}$, express $\log A$ in terms of $\log C$ and $\log D$.

44. If $y = 8(5)^x$, then write $\ln y$ as a linear function of x.

In 45 and 46, *true or false.*

45. $\log_{1/2} 8 = \log_2 \frac{1}{8}$

46. For $x > 0$, $\log_{10} x = (\log_{10} e)(\ln x)$.

In 47 and 48, rewrite as an expression that does not involve logarithms.

47. $\log y = 3 \log x + \log 17$

48. $\ln t = \frac{3}{2} \ln a - \ln p$

49. A line of best fit for $\log b$ in terms of c is given by $\log b = 0.38c - 0.9$. Rewrite the equation to give b as a function of c.

50. A line of best fit for $y^{1/4}$ in terms of x is given by $y^{1/4} = 5.2x + 1.79$. Rewrite the equation to give y as a function of x.

51. 18^{150} is an n-digit number. Find n.

52. Prove that when a, x, y, and z are positive, $\log_a \left(\frac{x}{y}\right) + \log_a \left(\frac{y}{z}\right) + \log_a \left(\frac{z}{x}\right) = 0$.

USES DEAL WITH APPLICATIONS OF MATHEMATICS IN REAL SITUATIONS.

Objective F: *Use rational exponents to model situations.* *(Lessons 6-1, 6-2)*

53. One model of the number of AIDS cases N as a function of time T in years is $N^{1/3} = kT$ where k is a constant. Write N as a function of T.

54. The weight W of an object varies inversely as the square of its distance from the center of Earth: $W = \frac{k}{d^2}$. Write d as a function of W.

55. $T(d) = \left(\frac{1}{2}\right)^{d/10} T_0$ gives the toxicity of sewage after d days of treatment. T_0 is the initial value of toxicity.

a. Evaluate $T(4)$.

b. What value of d would give a toxicity of 10% of T_0?

c. A chemical accident causes the toxicity to rise to 5 times the safe level. How many days will it take to restore the quality of water to a safe level?

56. An estimate for Earth's population P in billions is $P = 4(2)^{(Y - 1975)/35}$ where Y is the year.

a. Evaluate P for $Y = 1975$.

b. Estimate P in 2000.

c. When will the 1990 population be doubled?

Objective G: *Solve problems arising from exponential or logarithmic models.* *(Lessons 6-4, 6-6, 6-7)*

57. The half-life of a certain substance is 30 hours. About how many hours will it take for an initial amount of 8 grams to decay to 2.5 grams?

58. A family has $9,000 saved for college tuition. They will need $14,000 for college expenses five years from now. If they place their money in an account with continuous compounding, what rate must they find to assure them of the needed $14,000 in tuition?

59. The intensity of sunlight at points below the ocean is thought to decrease exponentially with the depth of the water. One model for this situation is $I = 100(.325)^d$. If special equipment is needed for divers to see when the intensity drops below 0.2 units, at what depth is this equipment needed?

CHAPTER SIX

60. The population of Tanzania in 1995 was about 28.7 million, with an annual growth rate of 2.6%. Assume the population changes continuously.

a. Give an equation for the population n years after 1995.

b. Predict the population in 2000.

c. Predict when the population will reach 35 million.

61. A certain radioactive substance has a half-life of 4 hours. Let A be the original amount of the substance, and L the amount left after h hours.

a. Give an exponential model for L in terms of A and h.

b. What percent of the original amount of the substance will remain after 7 hours?

62. The formula $\log w = -2.866 + 2.722 \log h$ estimates the normal weight w in pounds of a girl h inches tall. Estimate the normal weight of a girl who is 55 inches tall.

Objective H: *Use rational power functions or logarithm functions to model data.* *(Lesson 6-7)*

63. In 1619, Kepler observed that the length a of the semi-major axis of a planet's elliptical orbit was directly related to the time T it took for the planet to complete a revolution around the sun. When T is measured in days, and a in millions of kilometers, the logarithms of the data for the first six planets (Mercury, Venus, Earth, Mars, Jupiter, and Saturn) produce almost collinear points. The equation for the line is

$$\ln T = \frac{3}{2} \ln a - 1.72.$$

Write T as a function of a. (This is Kepler's Third Law of Planetary Motion.)

64. In the manufacture of glass, the hardening process is called *gelling*. Below is a graph on semilog paper showing the time it takes glass to gel at temperatures ranging from 100° to 300°C.

a. *Multiple choice.* If the curve were drawn for the data on normal graph paper, the graph

(i) still decreases but much more rapidly.

(ii) still decreases but not as rapidly.

(iii) increases at about the same rate.

(iv) does not change.

b. Estimate the gel time of glass at 150° C.

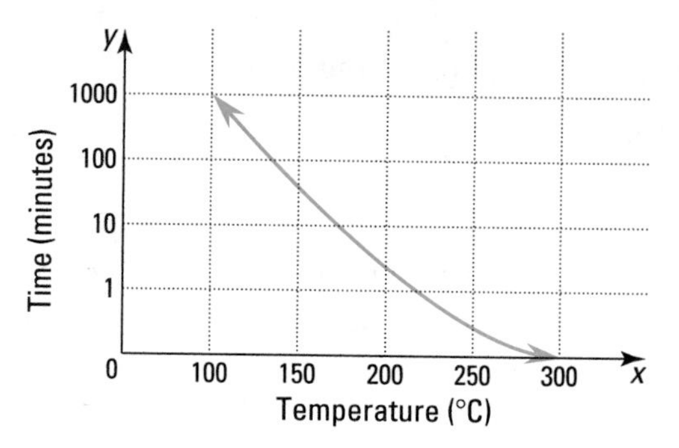

65. When Julie began to practice bowling, she recorded her average score s after w weeks. The results are shown at the right.

Week (w)	Average score (s)
1	155
3	174
5	183
7	186
15	198
20	204
25	211
30	213

a. Draw a scatterplot of the ordered pairs (w, s).

b. Which of the following function(s) might be used to linearize the data?

i. $(\ln w, s)$ ii. $(\log w, s)$

iii. $(w, \log s)$ iv. $(w, \ln s)$

c. Draw a scatterplot of $(\ln w, s)$.

d. Find a line of best fit for the scatterplot in part **c**, and give the correlation coefficient.

e. Use the relationship in part **d** to predict Julie's average bowling score after a year of practice, if it continues to improve in a similar way to the first 30 weeks.

66. Scientists measured and found the diameter and volume of 12 Ponderosa pine trees, as listed below.

Diameter (d) (inches)	Volume (v) (cubic inches)
36	192
28	113
41	294
19	28
32	123
22	51
38	252
25	56
17	16
31	141
20	32
25	86

a. Draw a scatterplot of the points (d, v).

b. Find the line of best fit for these points.

c. Replace v by $\log v$. Find the line of best fit for the transformed data. Is the fit a better one?

d. Replace v by $\sqrt[3]{v}$ and then by $\sqrt{v}$. Find the best-fitting line for each of the sets of pairs $(d, \sqrt[3]{v})$ and $(d, \sqrt{v})$.

e. Which transformation provides the best fit? Why?

REPRESENTATIONS DEAL WITH PICTURES, GRAPHS, OR OBJECTS THAT ILLUSTRATE CONCEPTS.

Objective I: *Graph nth root, rational power, and logarithm functions.* *(Lessons 6-1, 6-2, 6-3, 6-4)*

67. a. Graph $f(x) = x^{4/3}$ and $g(x) = x^{8/3}$ for $0 \le x \le 5$.

b. For what values of x is $f(x) = g(x)$?

c. For what values of x is $f(x) > g(x)$?

d. For what values of x is $f(x) < g(x)$?

68. a. Graph $f(x) = \log x$ for $0 \le x \le 10$.

b. Use the graph in part **a** to estimate log 2 and log 7 to the nearest tenth.

69. How is the graph of $f(t) = \log_3 t$ related to the graph of $g(t) = 3^t$?

70. a. Sketch the graph of $f(x) = \log_5 x$ for $0 < x \le 5$.

b. Sketch f^{-1} on the same set of axes, and give an equation for f^{-1}.

71. a. Predict the shape of the graph of $f(x) = \ln e^x$.

b. Check using an automatic grapher.

72. What line is an asymptote of the graph of every equation of the form $y = \log_b x$, $b > 0$, $b \neq 1$?

Objective J: *Interpret graphs of nth root, rational power, and logarithm functions.* *(Lessons 6-1, 6-2, 6-3, 6-4)*

In 73–76, *multiple choice.* Which graph is of the given equation?

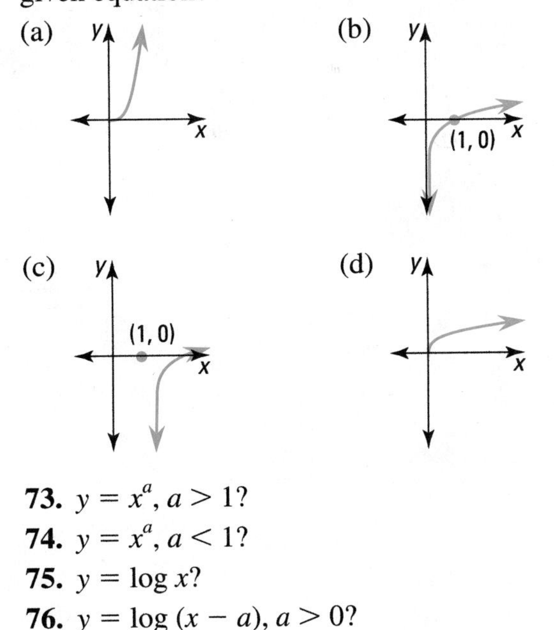

73. $y = x^a, a > 1$?

74. $y = x^a, a < 1$?

75. $y = \log x$?

76. $y = \log (x - a), a > 0$?

CHAPTER 7

PROBABILITY AND SIMULATION

Many situations in life involve uncertainty. Will it rain on the day of the class picnic? Will there be enough people at a student council meeting to have a quorum? Can you expect to win a lottery once in your life if you play each week? Answers to these questions involve *probabilities*, numbers which measure the likelihood of an event.

The mathematics of probability theory is usually considered to have begun in a series of letters between the French mathematicians Pascal and Fermat in 1654 concerning dice games. Nowadays, probability theory has many applications beyond the analysis of games of chance, including setting insurance rates, weather forecasting, and political polling.

The simplest of probability questions can be answered by direct counting. Sometimes the situations can be pictured and probabilities calculated by comparing lengths of segments or areas of regions. In complicated situations, theorems are applied to calculate the number of ways in which things can happen. Probabilities arising from still more complex situations, such as weather forecasting, cannot be calculated directly, but they can be estimated from *simulations* of the situation.

In this chapter, you will study a broad range of situations involving probability, from counting to simulation.

LESSON

7-1

Basic Principles of Probability

Weather or Not. *A precipitation probability is determined by mathematical models based upon what has happened in the past.*

Probability theory is the branch of mathematics that studies chance. In your earlier mathematics courses, you have calculated probabilities of some events. In this course, you will study probability in more detail, and in later chapters you will see connections to polynomials and even to the number e, the base of natural logarithms. To begin this study we define some of the basic vocabulary you should be certain to know.

The Outcomes and Sample Space of an Experiment

Probabilities occur when something happens and various results are possible. That "something" is called an *experiment*. Specifically, an **experiment** is a situation that has several possible results. The results are called **outcomes**. Here are some familiar experiments and outcomes.

Experiment	Outcomes
tossing a coin	heads, tails
tossing a coin twice	HH, HT, TH, TT
rolling a die	1, 2, 3, 4, 5, 6
rolling two dice and considering the sum of the numbers on the top faces	2, 3, 4, 5, 6, 7, 8, 9, 10, 11, 12

The set of possible outcomes of an experiment is the **sample space** for the experiment. For the experiment "tossing a coin," the usual sample space is {heads, tails}, or $\{H, T\}$ for short. For "rolling two dice and considering the sum of the numbers on the top faces," the natural sample space is the set of integers from 2 to 12. But if you were interested in all possible results of rolling two dice, then you might consider a different sample space, as is done in Example 1.

Example 1

Two different dice (red and white) are rolled and the numbers that appear are recorded. Describe an appropriate sample space.

Solution

There are 6 ways that each die might land. So there are $6 \cdot 6 = 36$ ways two dice can come up. All the possible outcomes of this experiment are shown below.

The fact that rolling two dice can have different sample spaces illustrates an important point. *The sample space depends on the reason for the experiment.* For instance, in tossing a coin, if you want to allow the possibility that the coin might land on its edge, then the sample space for "tossing a coin" would be {heads, tails, edge}.

The above sample spaces are all finite, but sample spaces can be infinite. For instance, if a dart is thrown at a dartboard, we can think of the sample space as being the set of points on the board.

Events and Probabilities

In the dartboard at the left, you might be particularly interested in the *bull's eye*. This is an example of an *event*. In general, an **event** is any subset of the sample space of an experiment.

Example 2

For the experiment of tossing two dice, list the outcomes in the event "doubles," that is, getting the same number on each die.

Solution

The event "doubles" consists of the outcomes (1, 1), (2, 2), (3, 3), (4, 4), (5, 5), and (6, 6). You could write

Doubles = {(1, 1), (2, 2), (3, 3), (4, 4), (5, 5), (6, 6)}.

The *probability of an event* is a number from 0 to 1 that measures the likelihood that the event will occur. Probabilities may be written in any way that numbers are written. An event which is expected to happen one-quarter of the time has a probability which can be written as $\frac{1}{4}$ or $\frac{2}{8}$ or .25 or 25%, and so on.

Let $N(E)$ be the number of elements in a set E, and S be a sample space. For the experiment "rolling a die," $S = \{1, 2, 3, 4, 5, 6\}$, and $N(S) = 6$. If E = "rolling an even number with a die," $E = \{2, 4, 6\}$ and $N(E) = 3$. So if all outcomes were equally likely, you would expect to roll an even number half the time. This idea is generalized in the definition of probability.

Definition

Let E be an event in a finite sample space S. If each outcome in S is equally likely, then the **probability that E occurs**, denoted **$P(E)$**, is given by

$$P(E) = \frac{\text{number of outcomes in the event}}{\text{number of outcomes in the sample space}}.$$

Note that in order to apply this definition, each element in the sample space must be *equally likely*. You must pay attention to this requirement when you set up or interpret sample spaces. For example, if you toss two fair coins, and record all possible orders of heads and tails, there are four equally likely outcomes in the sample space: HH, HT, TH, and TT.

Thus, $P(HH) = P(HT) = P(TH) = P(TT) = \frac{1}{4}$.

Now suppose you were interested in the number of *heads* that come up when you toss two fair coins. You might pick the sample space to be {2 heads, 1 head, 0 heads}. There are three outcomes, but they are not equally likely because

$$P(\text{1 head}) = \frac{2}{4} = \frac{1}{2}, \text{ whereas } P(\text{2 heads}) = P(\text{0 heads}) = \frac{1}{4}.$$

If a sample space has n outcomes all of which are equally likely, then the experiment is called **fair** or **unbiased** and each outcome has probability $\frac{1}{n}$. The outcomes are said to occur *at random* or *randomly*.

Example 3

Suppose two fair dice are rolled.

a. Find $P(\text{sum of dice} = 7)$.

b. Find $P(\text{sum of dice} < 10)$.

c. Find $P(\text{sum of dice} = 1)$.

d. Find $P(\text{sum of dice} < 50)$.

Solution

The sample space, first shown on page 427, is repeated here. $N(S) = 36$. Because the dice are fair, each outcome is equally likely.

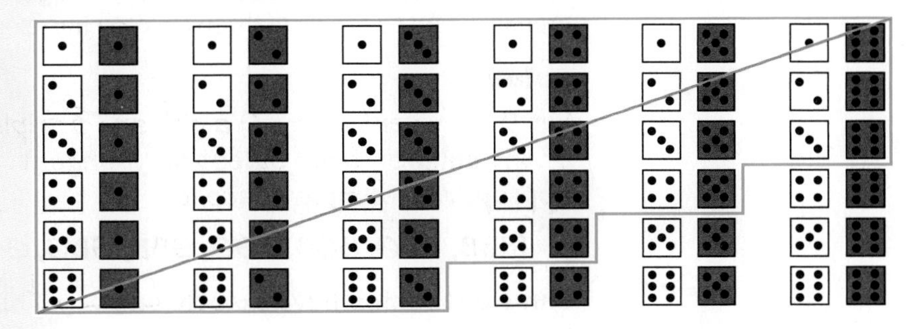

a. Let E = "sum of dice = 7." The outcomes in E are identified above by the orange line through them. $N(E) = 6$. So $P(E) = \frac{N(E)}{N(S)} = \frac{6}{36} = \frac{1}{6}$.

b. Let E = "sum of dice < 10." E consists of 30 outcomes outlined above by the blue polygon. $P(E) = \frac{N(E)}{N(S)} = \frac{30}{36} = \frac{5}{6}$.

c. Let E = "sum of dice = 1." There are no outcomes in E. So $E = \emptyset$, and $N(E) = 0$. Thus $P(E) = \frac{N(E)}{N(S)} = \frac{0}{36} = 0$.

d. Let E = "sum of dice < 50." Every outcome of S is also in E. So $N(E) = 36$. Thus $P(E) = \frac{N(E)}{N(S)} = \frac{36}{36} = 1$.

Part **c** illustrates that in a finite sample space, if an event is impossible, then its probability is 0. Part **d** illustrates that if an event must happen, then it will contain all the possible outcomes in the sample space, and so $N(E) = N(S)$. Then $P(E) = \frac{N(E)}{N(S)} = 1$. So the probability of a "sure thing" is 1.

Relative Frequencies and Probabilities

Probabilities are determined in a variety of ways. When tossing a coin, you might assume that heads and tails are equally likely. From this assumption, it follows that the probability of a head is $\frac{1}{2}$ and the probability of a tail is $\frac{1}{2}$. In 2500 tosses of the coin you would expect about 1250 heads. If you do not wish to toss the coin so many times, you might simulate the tossing with a computer or calculator. In contrast, if you have some reason to expect that a particular coin is unbalanced, you might toss the coin a large number of times and take the long-term relative frequency of heads as an estimate of the probability. For instance, if it comes up heads 1205 times in 2500 tosses, then the relative frequency of heads is $\frac{1205}{2500} = 48.2\%$, and you might pick 48% as the probability of getting a head for that coin.

Example 4

A researcher is studying the number of boys and girls in families with three children. Assume that the birth of a boy or a girl is equally likely. Find the probability that a family of three children has exactly one boy.

Solution

Let B represent a boy, G a girl, and a triple of letters, the genders of the children from oldest to youngest. List the outcomes. Then an appropriate sample space is

{BBB, BBG, BGB, BGG, GBB, GBG, GGB, GGG}.

Three outcomes have exactly one boy. Thus, the probability of exactly one boy in a three-child family is $\frac{3}{8}$. So P(one boy) = $\frac{3}{8}$.

Activity

Find the probability that a family of three children has exactly two girls.

Actually, more boys than girls are born. In the U.S. the relative frequency of the birth of a boy in a single birth is closer to 51%. So the assumption in Example 4 is a little off. Later in this chapter you will see how to calculate probabilities when the outcomes are not equally likely.

Relative frequencies and probabilities have important similarities and differences. For example, both yield values from 0 to 1. However, the meanings of the two values differ. A relative frequency of 0 means an event *has not occurred*; for example, the relative frequency of snow on July 4 in Florida since 1900 is 0. In contrast, a probability of 0 in a finite sample space means the event is *impossible*. For example, the probability of tossing a sum of 17 with two normal dice is 0. A relative frequency of 1 means that an event *has occurred* in each known trial. In contrast, a probability of 1 means that an event *must always occur*. For example, the probability is 1 that the toss of a single die gives a number less than 7. Notice that this event consists of the whole sample space of the experiment. These properties are summarized below.

Theorem (Basic Properties of Probability)
Let S be the sample space associated with an experiment, and let $P(E)$ be the probability of E. Then:

(i) $0 \leq P(E) \leq 1$.
(ii) If $E = S$, then $P(E) = 1$.
(iii) If $E = \emptyset$, then $P(E) = 0$.

QUESTIONS

Covering the Reading

1. Which mathematicians are credited with beginning the study of probability?

2. Define *experiment.*

3. To test a new package design, a carton of a dozen eggs is dropped from a height of 18 inches. The number of broken eggs is counted. Determine a sample space for this experiment.

In 4–7, suppose two fair dice are rolled. **a.** List the outcomes of the named event. **b.** Give the probability of the event.

4. The sum is 11.

5. The absolute value of the difference of the numbers shown on the dice is 1.

6. At least one die shows a 3.

7. The product of the numbers shown on the dice is 7.

8. Give the answer to the Activity.

9. Consider the experiment of tossing 3 fair coins.
a. Give a sample space for the experiment.
b. Find $P(2 \text{ heads})$.
c. *True or false.* $P(3 \text{ heads}) = P(0 \text{ heads})$
d. Find $P(\text{at least 2 heads})$.

10. State the difference between a probability of zero and a relative frequency of zero.

11. Give an example different from the one in the lesson of an event V such that $P(V) = 1$.

12. In 1994, 483,000 of the 1,678,000 men and women in the U.S. armed forces were in the Navy. What was the relative frequency of Navy personnel in the armed forces in 1994?

Applying the Mathematics

13. Let A be an event. If $P(A) = .25$ and there are 200 equally likely outcomes in the sample space, how many outcomes are in A?

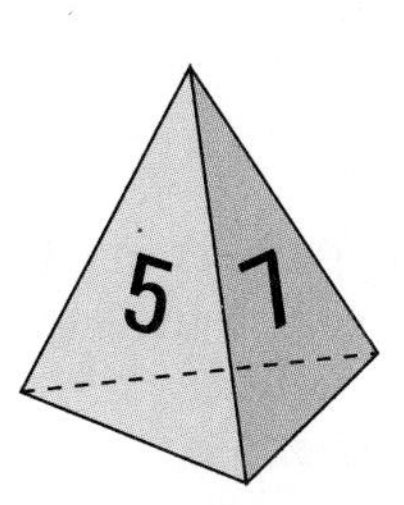

14. All human blood can be typed as one of O, A, B, or AB, but the distribution of the blood type varies with race. Among African Americans, 49% have type O, 27% have type A, and 20% have type B. What is the probability that an African American has type AB blood?

15. Consider a fair tetrahedral die with faces numbered 1, 3, 5, 7. Two of these dice are tossed. Find each probability.
a. $P(\text{sum is even})$ **b.** $P(\text{sum is odd})$ **c.** $P(\text{sum is 8})$

16. The definition of probability can be extended to infinite sample spaces. If every outcome in an infinite sample space is equally likely, and E is an event in that space, then

$$P(E) = \frac{\text{measure of event}}{\text{measure of sample space}},$$

where the measure may be length, area, volume, and so on.

a. Due to a storm, the electricity went out at 2:13, so both hands of a clock stopped between 2 and 3. If all times are equally likely, what is the probability that both hands would be between the same two consecutive numbers on the face of the clock?

b. Think of the minute hand as a spinner. If the dial is fair and the minute hand spun, what is the probability it lands between 6 and 8?

In 17 and 18, if the *odds against* an event are x to y, the probability of the event is $\frac{y}{x + y}$.

17. If the odds against winning a wager are 5 to 1, what is the probability of winning?

18. Suppose the probability of having exactly one boy in a family of three children is $\frac{3}{8}$. What are the odds against having exactly one boy in a family of three children?

19. A baseball player with a batting average of .318 for the first 85 at-bats gets up to bat for the 86th time.

a. Estimate the probability that this batter gets a hit.

b. Suppose the batter gets a hit. What is the new batting average?

Review

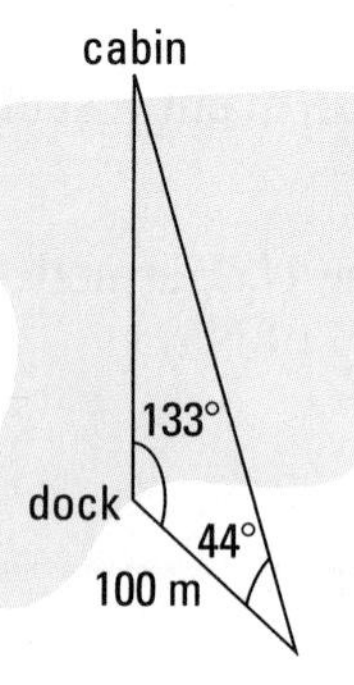

20. From the town dock and another point 100 m away, Mr. Wu sights his cabin and takes angle measures as indicated on the drawing. Find the distance from the cabin to the dock. *(Lesson 5-4)*

21. If the half-life of a drug in the body is 10 hours, what percent of the drug remains after the given amount of time?

a. 10 hours **b.** 24 hours *(Lesson 2-5)*

22. *True or false.* The graphs of $f(x) = 6^x$ and $g(x) = x^6$ are reflection images of each other over the y-axis. Explain why or why not. *(Lessons 2-4, 3-4)*

23. Evaluate $\sum_{k=1}^{10} k$. *(Lesson 1-3)*

Exploration

24. Simulate the experiment of Example 4 by tossing three coins. Call one side of each coin a boy and the other side a girl. Repeat the experiment a large number of times. How close is the relative frequency of "one boy" that you find to the probability calculated in the example?

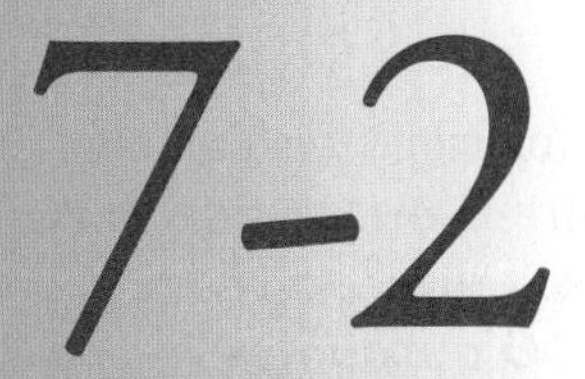

LESSON

7-2 Addition Counting Principles

Because probabilities are often calculated by dividing one count by another, being able to count elements of sets is an important skill. This and the next lesson cover the fundamental principles of counting.

Recall that $A \cup B$, the **union** of sets A and B, contains all elements that are either in A or in B. If A and B have no elements in common, they are called **disjoint** or **mutually exclusive**. If two events are not mutually exclusive, then they *overlap*. Recall that the **intersection** $A \cap B$ of two sets A and B is the set of elements in both A and B.

The *Venn diagrams* below show $A \cup B$ for two types of events: mutually exclusive, and not mutually exclusive.

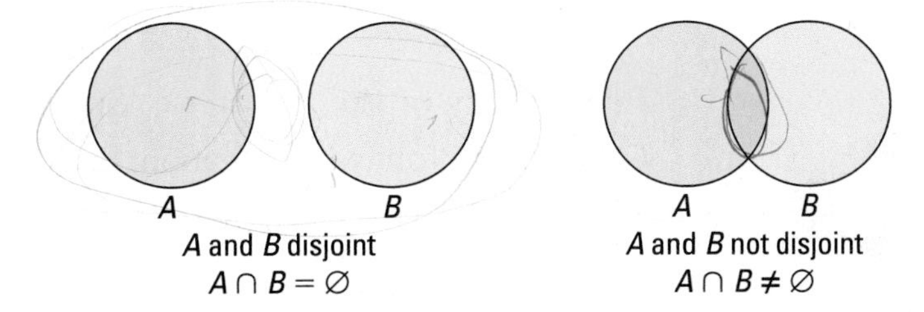

A and B disjoint
$A \cap B = \varnothing$

A and B not disjoint
$A \cap B \neq \varnothing$

Probability of the Union of Mutually Exclusive Sets

The first counting principle is a restatement of the Putting-Together Model for addition that you first learned in elementary school.

Addition Counting Principle (Mutually Exclusive Form)
If two finite sets A and B are mutually exclusive, then

$$N(A \cup B) = N(A) + N(B).$$

Now think of A and B as events in a finite sample space S. Divide both sides of the equation in the Addition Counting Principle by $N(S)$.

$$\frac{N(A \cup B)}{N(S)} = \frac{N(A)}{N(S)} + \frac{N(B)}{N(S)}$$

A basic theorem about probability is obtained.

Theorem (Probability of the Union of Mutually Exclusive Events)
If A and B are mutually exclusive events in the same finite sample space, then

$$P(A \cup B) = P(A) + P(B).$$

Example 1

If two fair dice are tossed, what is the probability of a sum of 7 or 11?

Solution 1

Let A = "tossing a 7" and B = "tossing an 11." You might wish to refer to the list of outcomes in the previous lesson. There are 6 outcomes in A and 2 outcomes in B. A and B are mutually exclusive, so there are 8 outcomes in A ∪ B. Because there are 36 outcomes in the sample space, N(S) = 36.

$$P(A \cup B) = \frac{N(A \cup B)}{N(S)} = \frac{8}{36} \approx 0.22$$

Solution 2

Let A and B be defined as in the first solution.

$$P(A) = \frac{N(A)}{N(S)} = \frac{6}{36} \quad \text{and} \quad P(B) = \frac{N(B)}{N(S)} = \frac{2}{36}$$

Because A and B are mutually exclusive,

$$P(A \cup B) = P(A) + P(B) = \frac{6}{36} + \frac{2}{36} = \frac{8}{36} \approx 0.22.$$

Probability of the Union of Any Two Sets

Consider the following situation. Participants at a two-day conference could register for only one of the days or both. There were 231 participants on Friday; 252 on Saturday. The total number of people who registered for the conference was 350. Because $231 + 252 \neq 350$, there must have been people who attended both days.

Every year teachers who use UCSMP textbooks are invited to a two-day conference at the University of Chicago.

Symbolically, if F is the set of Friday attendees and S is the set of Saturday attendees, then $N(F) = 231$, $N(S) = 252$, and $N(F \cup S) = 350$.

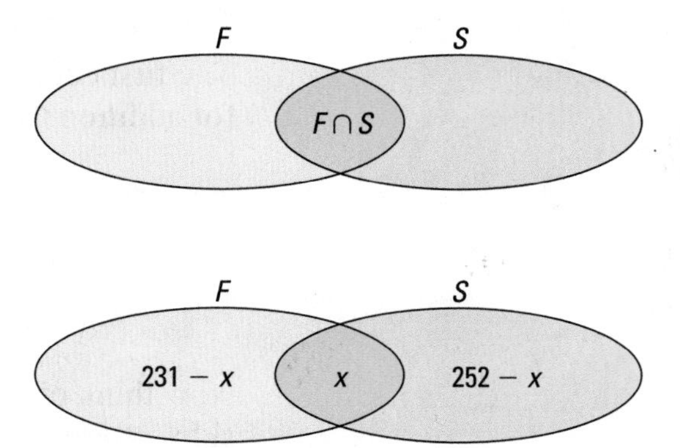

Let x be the number of people who registered for both days. Then the number of people who registered only for Friday is $231 - x$, and the number of people who registered only for Saturday is $252 - x$. Thus,

$$N(F \cup S) = (231 - x) + x + (252 - x)$$
$$= 483 - x.$$

Because $N(F \cup S) = 350$,

$$350 = 483 - x.$$

So, $x = 133$. Thus, there were 133 people who registered for both days.

This situation is a special case of a more general result. If $N(A \cap B) = x$, then the number of elements in A which are not in the intersection is $N(A) - x$. Similarly, there are $N(B) - x$ elements in B which are not in the intersection, as shown below. Then

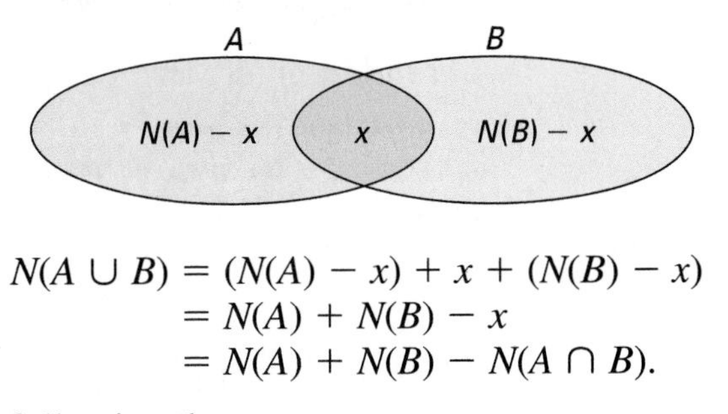

$$\begin{aligned} N(A \cup B) &= (N(A) - x) + x + (N(B) - x) \\ &= N(A) + N(B) - x \\ &= N(A) + N(B) - N(A \cap B). \end{aligned}$$

This proves the following theorem.

Addition Counting Principle (General Form)
For any finite sets A and B,

$$N(A \cup B) = N(A) + N(B) - N(A \cap B).$$

If A and B are two events in the same finite sample space S, then dividing by $N(S)$ yields

$$\frac{N(A \cup B)}{N(S)} = \frac{N(A)}{N(S)} + \frac{N(B)}{N(S)} - \frac{N(A \cap B)}{N(S)}.$$

The fractions all stand for probabilities, identified in the next theorem.

Theorem (Probability of a Union of Events—General Form)
If A and B are any events in the same finite sample space, then

$$P(A \text{ or } B) = P(A \cup B) = P(A) + P(B) - P(A \cap B).$$

Example 2

The name of a participant in the conference described on page 434 is drawn for a door prize. What is the probability that this person attended on both days?

Solution 1

Use the definition of probability. Since 133 of the 350 participants attended both days,

$$P(\text{winner attended both days}) = \frac{133}{350} = 0.38.$$

▶

Solution 2

Use the Probability of a Union of Events Theorem. $P(A) = \frac{231}{350}$ and $P(B) = \frac{252}{350}$. Because everyone who attended the conference attended on either Friday or Saturday $P(A \cup B) = 1 = \frac{350}{350}$.

By the above theorem,

$$P(A \cup B) = P(A) + P(B) - P(A \cap B).$$

$$\frac{350}{350} = \frac{231}{350} + \frac{252}{350} - P(A \cap B)$$

$$-\frac{133}{350} = -P(A \cap B)$$

So $$P(A \cap B) = \frac{133}{350} = 0.38.$$

Activity

In Example 2, find the probability that the winner attended only on Saturday.

Example 3

A pair of dice is thrown. What is the probability that the dice show doubles or a sum over 7?

Solution

Use the sample space shown on page 427 for a pair of dice. Find the probability of each event.

$$P(\text{doubles}) = \frac{6}{36},$$

$$P(\text{sum over } 7) = \frac{15}{36}, \text{ and}$$

$$P(\text{doubles and sum over } 7) = \frac{3}{36} \text{ (double 4's, 5's, or 6's)}$$

Now compute the probability of their union using the theorem on page 435.

So, $P(\text{doubles or sum over } 7) = P(\text{doubles}) + P(\text{sum over } 7) - P(\text{both})$

$$= \frac{6}{36} + \frac{15}{36} - \frac{3}{36}$$

$$= \frac{18}{36} = \frac{1}{2}.$$

Notice that the Probability of the Union of Mutually Exclusive Events Theorem on page 433 is a special case of the Probability of a Union of Events Theorem. When A and B are mutually exclusive events, $A \cap B = \emptyset$ and so $P(A \cap B) = 0$. Then

$$P(A \cup B) = P(A) + P(B) - P(A \cap B)$$

reduces to $$P(A \cup B) = P(A) + P(B).$$

Complementary Events

In the next example, the events are mutually exclusive and their union is the entire sample space. Such events are called **complementary events.** The complement of an event A is called **not** $\textbf{\textit{A}}$.

Example 4

Two dice are tossed. Find the probability of each event.

a. Their sum is seven. **b.** Their sum is *not* seven.

Solution

a. Use the diagram of the two-dice experiment on page 427. There are 6 possibilities on the diagonal from lower left to upper right.

So $P(\text{sum is } 7) = \frac{6}{36} = \frac{1}{6}$.

b. You could count again. Or you could recognize that "sum is 7" and "sum is not 7" are mutually exclusive events whose union is the entire sample space. Then

$P(\text{sum is 7 or sum is not 7}) = P(\text{sum is 7}) + P(\text{sum is not 7})$.

So, $1 = P(\text{sum is 7}) + P(\text{sum is not 7})$,

or $P(\text{sum is not 7}) = 1 - P(\text{sum is 7})$

$= 1 - \frac{1}{6}$.

Thus, the probability that the sum of two dice is not seven is $\frac{5}{6}$.

The reasoning in Example 4 leads to the following general theorem.

Theorem (Probability of Complements)
If A is any event, then $P(\text{not } A) = 1 - P(A)$.

QUESTIONS

Covering the Reading

In 1 and 2, suppose two fair dice are rolled. **a.** State whether X and Y are mutually exclusive. **b.** Find $N(X \cup Y)$. **c.** Find $N(X \cap Y)$.

1. $X =$ The first die shows 6. $Y =$ The sum of the dice is 10.

2. $X =$ The first die shows 5. $Y =$ The sum of the dice is 3.

In 3 and 4, refer to the sample space for tossing two fair dice on page 427.

3. What is the probability that white shows an even number or red shows a multiple of 3?

4. What is the probability that at least one of the dice shows a 4?

5. Give your answer to the Activity.

6. Suppose that the probability that a manufactured computer chip is usable is 0.993. What is the probability that it is not usable?

7. The probability that Carol wins the election for the Student Government presidency is 0.4 and the probability that Carl wins is 0.5.
a. What is the probability that Carol or Carl will win?
b. What is the probability that Carl will not win?
c. What is the probability that neither Carl nor Carol will win?

In 8–10, assume that A and B are in the same sample space. Under what conditions are the following true?

8. $P(A \text{ or } B) = P(A) + P(B) - P(A \cap B)$

9. $P(A \text{ or } B) = P(A) + P(B)$

10. $P(\text{not } A) = 1 - P(A)$

11. *True or false.* Complementary events are a special case of mutually exclusive events.

12. Write an argument explaining why $P(\text{not } A) = 1 - P(A)$.

Applying the Mathematics

13. Give an example of two mutually exclusive events that are not complementary.

14. Name a sport in which "win the game" and "lose the game" are not complementary events.

15. The manager of a little league baseball team contacted the local meteorological office regarding the likely weather for the opening day of the season, and was given the table of probabilities below.

	Wind Speed (mph)		
	Less Than 10	10–30	More Than 30
Sunny	0.30	0.16	0.08
Partly cloudy	0.14	0.08	0.06
Overcast	0.09	0.06	0.03

a. What is the probability that opening day will be sunny?
b. What is the probability that the wind speed will be 30 mph or less?
c. What is the probability that the weather will be overcast or the wind speed will be greater than 30 mph?
d. What is the probability that the weather will not be overcast and the wind speed will be less than 10 mph?

16. A whole number from 1 to 300 is chosen at random. Find the probability of each event.
a. The number is divisible by 3.
b. The number is divisible by 4.
c. The number is divisible by 3 or by 4.

17. Consider the dartboard pictured here. The radii of the concentric circles are 2", 6", 10", and 11". You get 10, 20, 30, 40, or 50 points if your dart lands in the regions as indicated. Suppose you always hit the interior of the square when you throw, you are equally likely to hit any point within the square, and you cannot land on a boundary. Determine the probability of each event.

a. Your score is over 30 points.

b. Your score is under 30 points.

In 18 and 19, refer to the probabilities in the Venn diagram of events A and B at the right.

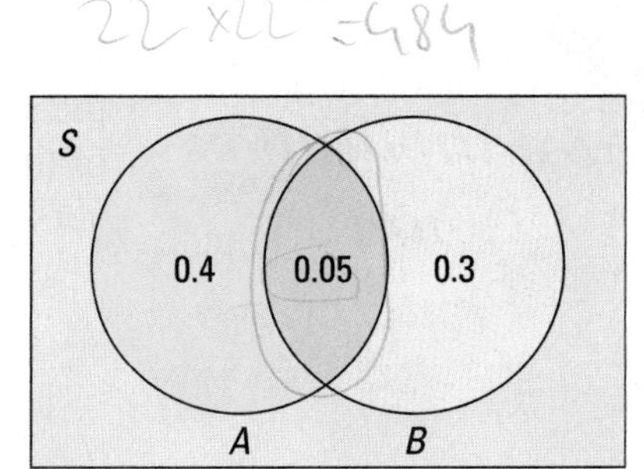

18. Are A and B mutually exclusive? Why or why not?

19. Calculate the following probabilities.

a. $P(A \cap B)$ b. $P(A)$

c. $P(A \cup B)$ d. $P(\text{not } B)$

Michael Jordan has made about 85% of his free throws.

Review

20. A basketball player shoots two free throws. Each is either made or missed. Determine the sample space for the experiment under each circumstance.

a. You record the result of each shot in order.

b. You count the number of baskets made. *(Lesson 7-1)*

21. The table below estimates the probability that a randomly chosen M&M® peanut candy is a particular color.

Color	Brown	Red	Yellow	Green	Orange	Blue
Probability	.2	x	.2	x	x	.3

If no other color is possible, find the value of x. *(Lesson 7-1)*

22. If a whole number from 1 to 50 is picked at random, what is the probability that it is a perfect square? *(Lesson 7-1)*

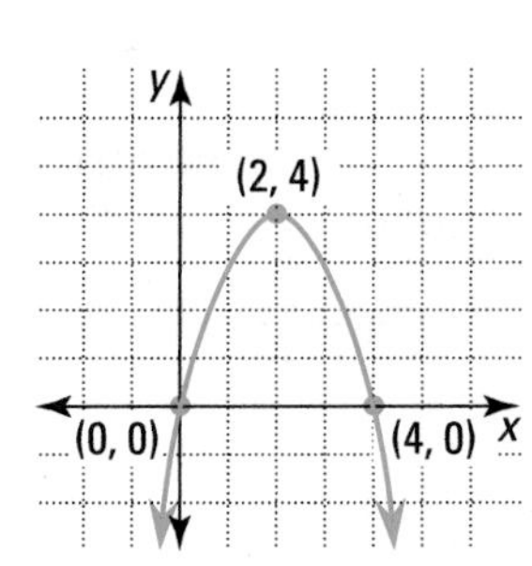

23. Give an equation for the parabola at the left. *(Lessons 2-6, 3-2)*

24. Solve $t^2 - 100t = 21$. *(Previous course)*

Exploration

25. a. Draw a Venn diagram for $A \cup B \cup C$.

b. Extend the Probability of a Union of Events Theorem to cover any 3 events in the same sample space. That is, give a formula for $P(A \cup B \cup C)$.

c. Give an example of the use of the formula you find in part **b.**

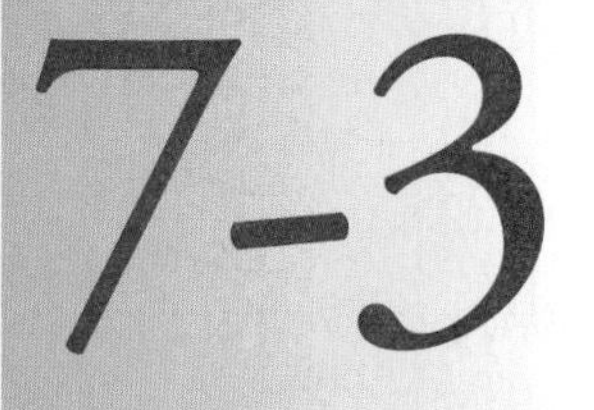

Multiplication Counting Principles

The Multiplication Counting Principle

Pete Seria decided to offer a special on his famous pizza pies. He limited the special to cheese pizzas with or without pepperoni and with a choice of thin crust, thick crust, or stuffed. Pete wondered how many different versions of pizza were possible, so he sketched this *tree diagram*.

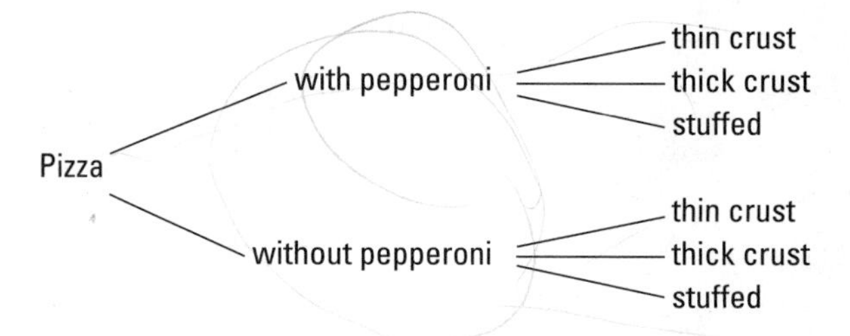

Counting the paths, Pete saw there were only six different possible pizzas, and thought that offer wasn't attractive enough. So he decided to advertise that each pizza came in one of four sizes: individual, small, medium, and large. Rather than continuing with the tree (since he'd run out of room on his paper), Pete noticed that for each of 2 choices about pepperoni there were 3 choices of crust and $2 \cdot 3 = 6$ possible pizzas. And for each of these there were 4 possible sizes; so that gave $6 \cdot 4 = 24$ total choices.

Pete did not have to diagram or list all the possible choices because he knew a fundamental use of multiplication.

> **The Multiplication Counting Principle**
> Let A and B be any finite sets. The number of ways to choose one element from A and then one element from B is $N(A) \cdot N(B)$.

The Multiplication Counting Principle has an obvious extension to choices made from more than two sets. The number of ways to choose one element from set A_1, one element from set A_2, . . . , and one element from set A_k is $N(A_1) \cdot N(A_2) \cdot \ldots \cdot N(A_k)$.

Selections with Replacement

Example 1

a. How many ways are there of answering a test having 5 true-false questions?

b. If you guess on each question, what is the probability of answering all 5 questions correctly?

Solution

a. There are two ways to respond to each of the five questions. Think of each response as a choice from a set with 2 elements in it, T or F. $A_1 = \{T, F\}$, $A_2 = \{T, F\}$, $A_3 = \{T, F\}$, $A_4 = \{T, F\}$, and $A_5 = \{T, F\}$. The number of ways to answer the test equals

$N(A_1) \cdot N(A_2) \cdot N(A_3) \cdot N(A_4) \cdot N(A_5) = 2 \cdot 2 \cdot 2 \cdot 2 \cdot 2 = 2^5 = 32.$

b. When you guess, all outcomes are equally likely. One of those 32 outcomes is "all answers correct," so **the probability of answering all questions correctly is $\frac{1}{32}$, or about 3%.**

Check

a. Below is a list of the 16 possible ways to answer the 5 questions if the first is answered T.

TTTTT	TTFTT	TFTTT	TFFTT
TTTTF	TTFTF	TFTTF	TFFTF
TTTFT	TTFFT	TFTFT	TFFFT
TTTFF	TTFFF	TFTFF	TFFFF

In the Questions you are asked to list the other 16.

The situation in Example 1 is an instance of making 5 choices *with replacement* from a set, here the set $\{T, F\}$. That is, you may give the same response as many times as you wish. Each way of answering the 5 questions gives rise to an **arrangement** of the 2 symbols T and F. Two choices for each of 5 questions gives 2^5 arrangements. In general:

Theorem (Selections with Replacement)
Let S be a set with n elements. Then there are n^k possible arrangements of k elements from S *with replacement.*

Proof
Use the Multiplication Counting Principle. Here $N(S) = n$, so the number of possible ways to choose one element from S, each of k times, is

$$\underbrace{N(S) \cdot N(S) \cdot \ldots \cdot N(S)}_{k \text{ times}} = \underbrace{n \cdot n \cdot \ldots \cdot n}_{k \text{ factors}} = n^k.$$

Example 2

There are two multiple-choice parts to the mathematics section of the PSAT (Preliminary Scholastic Aptitude Test). One has 25 multiple-choice questions with 5 options each, and the other has 15 multiple-choice questions with 4 options each. How many ways are there to answer the multiple-choice parts of the PSAT mathematics section?

Solution

First, determine how many ways there are of answering each part of the test. 5 choices for 25 questions gives 5^{25} possible arrangements on the first part, and 4 choices for 15 questions gives 4^{15} arrangements on the second part. Now use the Multiplication Counting Principle again. There are $5^{25} \cdot 4^{15}$, or $3.2 \cdot 10^{26}$ different ways of answering these two parts of the PSAT mathematics section.

Selections Without Replacement

Example 3 illustrates that when repeated choices from a set are made *without replacement*, the Multiplication Counting Principle can still be applied.

Example 3

Susita decides to rank order the five colleges to which she plans to apply. How many rankings can she make?

Solution

For her first choice there are 5 possibilities. For her second choice there are 4 remaining colleges. For her third choice there remain 3 colleges. There are 2 colleges left for the fourth choice, and 1 school is left for fifth. Altogether there are $5 \cdot 4 \cdot 3 \cdot 2 \cdot 1 = 120$ possible rankings.

The answer to Example 3 is often denoted as 5!, read "five *factorial*."

Definition
For n a positive integer, ***n* factorial** is the product of the positive integers from 1 to n. In symbols, $n! = n \cdot (n-1) \cdot (n-2) \cdot (n-3) \cdot \ldots \cdot 3 \cdot 2 \cdot 1$.

Most scientific and graphing calculators have a factorial function. Check yours and find out how to use it to calculate factorials.

The result of Example 3 can easily be generalized.

Theorem (Selections without Replacement)
Let S be a set with n elements. Then there are $n!$ possible arrangements of the n elements *without replacement.*

QUESTIONS

Covering the Reading

1. If each of Pete Seria's pizzas came in only 3 sizes, how many different specials would he have had?

2. In how many ways can a sample of two children (one boy and one girl) be chosen from a class of 12 boys and 14 girls?

Nite Owl Diner, Fall River, MA

3. A diner serves a bargain breakfast which includes eggs (over-easy, poached, or scrambled); pancakes or toast; and juice (orange, tomato, or grapefruit). A breakfast must include eggs and one selection from each of the other categories.

a. Draw a tree diagram showing the different possible breakfasts.

b. How many possible breakfasts are there?

4. Refer to Example 1, part **a.** Write the other 16 ways to answer the test.

5. A test has 10 true-false questions. If you know three answers and guess on seven, what is the probability that you will get them all correct?

6. How many ways are there of answering a test (assuming you answer all items) if the test has 10 multiple-choice questions, each with 4 choices?

7. How many ways are there of answering a test with 10 true-false and 20 multiple-choice questions, each with 5 choices, if you must answer each question?

8. Refer to Example 2. The PSAT mathematics section has a penalty for guessing, so if you don't know an answer you should leave the question blank. Each five-option multiple-choice question therefore really has six possible responses (A, B, C, D, E, or blank), and each four-option multiple-choice question has five possible responses (A, B, C, D, or blank). Write an expression for the number of ways of answering the multiple-choice part of the PSAT mathematics section.

9. Evaluate 6! without using a calculator.

10. Evaluate 12! using a calculator.

Applying the Mathematics

11. In how many ways can the batting order of a 10-person softball team be set?

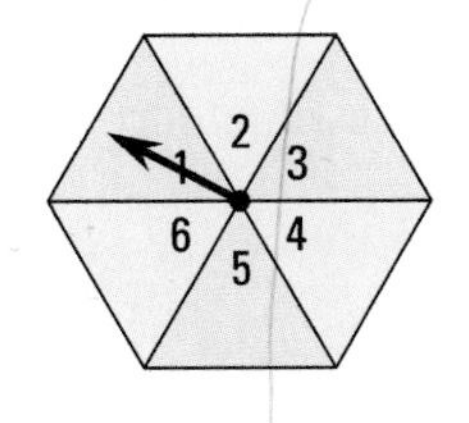

12. The spinner at the left has 6 congruent regions.

a. If it is spun twice, list the possible outcomes.

b. If it is spun 10 times, how many possible outcomes are there?

c. If the spinner is fair, what is the probability of ten 1s in a row?

13. An 18-speed bicycle gets its 18 speeds by selecting one gear from each of two sets of gears. The front set has three gears. How many gears does the rear set have?

14. Solve $\frac{8!}{p} = 6!$

15. Consider $\frac{n!}{r!} = 72$, where n and r are positive integers.

a. To find all possible solutions (n, r), how many different pairs of numbers must you check if $10 \geq n \geq 6$ and $8 \geq r \geq 5$?

b. Solve $\frac{n!}{r!} = 72$, where n and r satisfy the conditions of part **a**.

16. Evaluate $\frac{10000!}{9998!}$ without using a calculator.

Ansel Adams (1902–1984), renowned wilderness photographer, increased public acceptance of photography as an art. At the California School of Fine Arts, he established the first academic department to teach photography as a profession.

Review

17. A record store receives a new shipment of albums. Of these, r can be cataloged as rock, c can be cataloged as country, and b can be cataloged as either rock or country. How many records are in the shipment? *(Lesson 7-2)*

18. Of the 37 books on a bookstore shelf labeled "Photography & Painting," 18 books contain chapters on photography, and 23 books have chapters on painting. What is the probability that a randomly selected book has chapters both on photography and painting? *(Lesson 7-2)*

19. **a.** What is the probability of rolling a sum of 10 with two fair dice?

b. What are the odds against rolling a sum of 10 with two fair dice? *(Lesson 7-1)*

In 20 and 21, give exact values without using a calculator. *(Lessons 5-3, 5-6)*

20. $\tan^{-1} 1$

21. $\cos^{-1}\left(\frac{-\sqrt{2}}{2}\right)$

22. Refer to the graph below. *(Lessons 2-1, 4-6)*

a. What are the domain and range of f?

b. Give the maximum and minimum values of f.

c. What is the period of f?

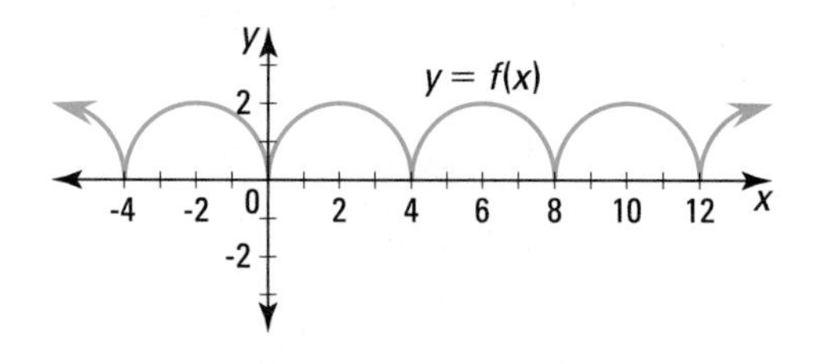

Exploration

23. **a.** What is the largest factorial your calculator can display without going into scientific notation?

b. What is the largest factorial your calculator can estimate in scientific notation?

Permutations

Northridge	Northridge	Northridge	Northridge
Sacramento	Sacramento	Sacramento	Sacramento
E. Washington	E. Washington	E. Washington	E. Washington
Idaho State	Idaho State	Idaho State	Idaho State
Montana	Montana	Montana	Montana
Montana State	Montana State	Montana State	Montana State
N. Arizona	N. Arizona	Portland State	Portland State
Portland State	Weber State	N. Arizona	Weber State
Weber State	Portland State	Weber State	N. Arizona

Permutations of *n* Objects Taken *n* at a Time

In 1996, the Big Sky Basketball Conference had nine teams: California State Northridge, California State Sacramento, Eastern Washington, Idaho State, Montana, Montana State, Northern Arizona, Portland State, and Weber State. Assuming no ties, how many different possible standings could result?

The answer is given by the Selections without Replacement Theorem from the last lesson; for the nine teams, the number of different standings is

$$9! = 9 \cdot 8 \cdot 7 \cdot 6 \cdot 5 \cdot 4 \cdot 3 \cdot 2 \cdot 1 = 362{,}880.$$

Each different arrangement of a set of objects is called a **permutation**. Four of the 362,880 possible permutations of the teams in the Big Sky Conference are listed above. In general, the Selections without Replacement Theorem can be restated as a theorem about permutations.

Permutation Theorem
There are $n!$ permutations of n different elements.

Permutations of *n* Objects Taken *r* at a Time

Similar reasoning can be used when not all of the n original objects are selected for arrangement.

Example 1

Seven horses are in a race at Churchill Downs. You want to predict which horse will finish first, which second, and which third (called *win*, *place*, and *show*, respectively). How many different predictions are possible?

Solution

Unlike the standings situation, only three of the seven horses are selected. Use the Multiplication Counting Principle.

	win		place		show
Any of the 7 horses can be first.	7				
For each of these, 6 horses can be second.	7	·	6		
For each of these, 5 horses can be third.	7	·	6	·	5

So there are $7 \cdot 6 \cdot 5 = 210$ possible predictions.

Thus, in Example 1, if you picked the horses blindly, the probability of predicting the first, second, and third place finishers correctly is $\frac{1}{210}$.

When the order of the subjects is taken into account, the number of ways of arranging 3 objects out of a set of 7 objects is referred to as the number of permutations of 7 objects taken 3 at a time. In general, the number of permutations of ***n* objects taken *r* at a time** is denoted $_nP_r$ and can be calculated by multiplying n by the consecutive integers less than itself, until r factors have been taken. The second factor is $n - 1$, the third factor is $n - 2$, and so on. So the rth factor is $n - (r - 1)$, which equals $n - r + 1$.

Theorem (Formula for $_nP_r$)
The number of permutations of n objects taken r at a time is

$$_nP_r = n(n-1)(n-2) \cdot \ldots \cdot (n-r+1).$$

Notice that $7 \cdot 6 \cdot 5 = \frac{7 \cdot 6 \cdot 5 \cdot 4 \cdot 3 \cdot 2 \cdot 1}{4 \cdot 3 \cdot 2 \cdot 1} = \frac{7!}{4!}$, and $4 = 7 - 3$. In a similar way, any product of consecutive integers can be written as a quotient of factorials. This provides an alternate way of calculating $_nP_r$.

Theorem (Alternate Formula for $_nP_r$)

$$_nP_r = \frac{n!}{(n-r)!}$$

Example 2

How many different five-letter words can be formed from the word BIRTHDAY? (The words do not have to make sense in English or any other language.)

Solution 1

One such word is BIRTH. Other words are RABID and YDRIA. The question essentially asks for the number of permutations of 8 objects taken 5 at a time. Use the first formula for $_nP_r$.

$$_8P_5 = \underbrace{8 \cdot 7 \cdot 6 \cdot 5 \cdot 4}_{\text{5 factors}} = 6720 \text{ words}$$

Solution 2

Use the Alternate Formula for $_nP_r$.

$$_8P_5 = \frac{8!}{(8-5)!} = 6720 \text{ words}$$

When all n objects are selected, the alternate formula for $_nP_r$ gives $_nP_n = \frac{n!}{(n-n)!} = \frac{n!}{0!}$. Because $_nP_n$ should be $n!$, $0!$ is defined to equal 1.

Definition

$$0! = 1$$

Example 3

Solve ${}_nP_5 = 7 \cdot {}_nP_4$.

Solution 1

Use the Formula for ${}_nP_r$.

$$n(n-1)(n-2)(n-3)(n-4) = 7n(n-1)(n-2)(n-3)$$

Divide each side of the equation by $n(n-1)(n-2)(n-3)$.

$$n - 4 = 7$$
$$n = 11$$

Solution 2

Use the Alternate Formula for ${}_nP_r$.

Rewrite. $$\frac{n!}{(n-5)!} = 7\frac{n!}{(n-4)!}$$

Divide by $n!$ and multiply means by extremes.

$$(n-4)! = 7(n-5)!$$

A key step is to use the fact that $n! = n(n-1)!$, or, more generally, $(n-a)! = (n-a)(n-a-1)!$

Rewrite. $$(n-4)(n-5)! = 7(n-5)!$$
$$n - 4 = 7$$
$$n = 11$$

Check

Find the ${}_nP_r$ function on your calculator. Then compute ${}_{11}P_5 = 55440$, ${}_{11}P_4 = 7920$, and $7 \cdot {}_{11}P_4 = 55440$. So ${}_{11}P_5 = 7 \cdot {}_{11}P_4$.

QUESTIONS

Covering the Reading

1. List all the permutations of the letters in USA.

2. Doc, Grumpy, Happy, Sleepy, Bashful, Sneezy, and Dopey go to work whistling in a different order each day. How many days can they go without repeating an order?

3. Write $_{11}P_3$ in each way.
   a. as a product of integers
   b. as a ratio of two factorials

In 4 and 5, evaluate.

4. $_{12}P_5$

5. $_7P_2$

6. Refer to the 9 teams in the Big Sky Basketball Conference. In how many ways can the first 5 positions in the standings be filled?

7. a. How many permutations consisting of two letters each can be formed from the letters of UCSMP?
   b. List them all.

In 8 and 9, an expression is given. **a.** Evaluate it. **b.** Explain your answer to part **a** in terms of choosing items from a set.

8. $_nP_1$

9. $_nP_n$

10. Explain why 0! is defined to equal 1.

11. Solve for n: $_nP_3 = 5 \cdot {_nP_2}$.

Applying the Mathematics

12. a. How many ID numbers are there consisting of a permutation of four of the digits 1, 2, 3, 4, 5 and 6?
    b. If one of the ID numbers is chosen at random, what is the probability that it is 3416?

13. An exhibition hall has eight doors. In how many ways can you enter and leave the hall through different doors?

14. Each row of an aircraft has three seats on each side of the aisle. In how many different ways can a woman, her husband, and four children occupy a row of seats if the two parents sit in the aisle seats?

15. A curator at a museum wants to hang six portraits and four landscapes in a line on a wall.
    a. In how many ways can the paintings be arranged?
    b. In how many ways can the paintings be arranged if the portraits are kept together and the landscapes are kept together?

16. a. Show that $_6P_4 = 6 \cdot {_5P_3}$.
    b. Prove that $_nP_r = n \cdot {_{n-1}P_{r-1}}$ for all integers n and r with $1 \le r \le n$.

$_nC_n = \frac{n!}{(n-n)!\,n!}$

Review

In 17–19, consider Chuck's Restaurant, which has the following items on its menu. *(Lesson 7-3)*

17. **a.** If you order milk, an entrée, and a dessert, how many possible orders are there?
b. Show them in a tree diagram.

18. How many ways are there to order an entrée, beverage, and dessert?

19. If you cannot eat either hamburger or chicken, how many ways are there to order an entrée, beverage, and dessert?

In 20 and 21, evaluate. *(Lesson 7-3)*

20. $6 \cdot 5!$

21. $\frac{395!}{392!}$

22. *True or false.* If A and B are nonempty mutually exclusive events, then $P(A \cap B) = P(A) + P(B)$. Explain your reasoning. *(Lesson 7-2)*

23. There are nine felt-tip and nine ball-point pens in a box, with three red, three blue, and three black of each kind. A pen is selected at random from the box. What is the probability that it is black or has a ball-point? *(Lessons 7-1, 7-2)*

24. If x is randomly chosen from the set $\{1, 2, 3, \dots, 50\}$ of integers, what is the probability that $\log_2 x$ is an integer? *(Lessons 6-3, 7-1)*

25. **a.** Graph $f(x) = \cos x$ and $g(x) = \sin\left(x + \frac{5\pi}{2}\right)$, for $-\pi \leq x \leq 2\pi$, on the same axes.
b. *True or false.* For all x, $\sin\left(x + \frac{5\pi}{2}\right) = \cos x$. *(Lesson 4-8)*

Exploration

26. $7 \cdot 6 \cdot 5 = 15 \cdot 14$. Find two other sets of consecutive integers greater than 1 whose products are equal.

LESSON

7-5

Independent Events

Sure Thing. *Whether they are made of wool, cotton, or polyester, socks are ususally stored in pairs so the probability of selecting a matching pair is one.*

What Are Independent Events?

When you flip a fair coin twice, the result of the first flip has no bearing on the result of the second flip. This is sometimes expressed by saying "the coin has no memory." Thus *if a coin is fair*, even if 10 heads have occurred in a row, the probability of heads on the 11th toss is still $\frac{1}{2}$. The tosses of the coin are called *independent events* because the result of one toss does not affect the results of other tosses.

Similarly, selections with replacement are considered to be independent events because later selections do not remember what happened with earlier selections. For instance, suppose that six socks are in a drawer: four of them orange, two blue. We name them 1 2 3 4 1 2. If a first sock is blindly taken, put back, and then a second sock is taken, what is the probability that both are blue?

Let A be the event that the first sock is blue, and B be the event that the second sock is blue. Thus $A \cap B$ is the event that both socks are blue. Since in each selection there are 2 blue socks among the 6, $P(A) = \frac{2}{6}$ and $P(B) = \frac{2}{6}$. To calculate $P(A \cap B)$, a rectangular array can be drawn as was done for the dice in Lesson 7-1. Each pair in the array is an outcome of the event $A \cap B$. For instance, 4 1 means that the orange sock #4 is the first sock and blue sock #1 is the second sock.

Sample Space with Replacement

11	12	13	14	11	12
21	22	23	24	21	22
31	32	33	34	31	32
41	42	43	44	41	42
11	12	13	14	11	12
21	22	23	24	21	22

In 4 of the 36 pairs, both socks are blue. So $P(A \cap B) = \frac{4}{36}$. This is the product of $P(A)$ and $P(B)$.

More generally, if S_1 is the sample space for the first event A, and S_2 is the sample space for the second event B, and the events are independent, then an array formed like the one above will have $N(S_1) \cdot N(S_2)$ elements, of which $N(A) \cdot N(B)$ are in $A \cap B$. So

$$P(A \cap B) = \frac{N(A) \cdot N(B)}{N(S_1) \cdot N(S_2)} = \frac{N(A)}{N(S_1)} \cdot \frac{N(B)}{N(S_2)} = P(A) \cdot P(B).$$

This relationship between the probabilities of A, B, and $A \cap B$ is taken as the definition of independent events.

Definition

Events A and B are **independent events** if and only if $P(A \cap B) = P(A) \cdot P(B)$.

Example 1

The circular region around a fair spinner is divided into six congruent sectors and numbered as shown at the right. Consider spinning it twice. (Suppose the spinner cannot stop on a boundary line.) Define two events as follows.

A: The first spin stops on an even number.

B: The second spin stops on a multiple of 3.

Decide whether or not events A and B are independent.

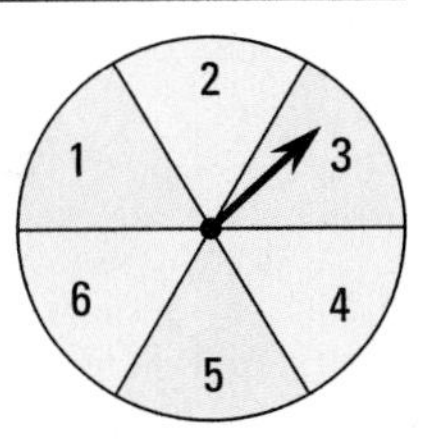

Solution

A and B are independent if $P(A \cap B) = P(A) \cdot P(B)$.

$$P(A) = \frac{3}{6} = \frac{1}{2}$$

$$P(B) = \frac{2}{6} = \frac{1}{3}$$

$P(A \cap B)$ can be obtained from the sample space illustrated at the right. The six circled points represent those for which both A and B are true.

So $\quad P(A \cap B) = \frac{6}{36} = \frac{1}{6}$.

Because $P(A) \cdot P(B) = \frac{1}{2} \cdot \frac{1}{3} = \frac{1}{6} = P(A \cap B)$, events A and B are independent.

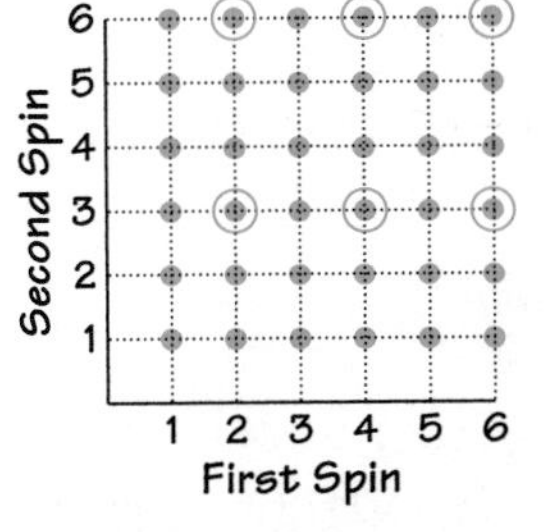

Check

Because the spinner does not have a memory, the outcome of the first spin does not influence the second spin. Thus, we would expect the events to be independent.

What Are Dependent Events?

Now examine what happens if two socks are blindly taken *without replacement* from a drawer with four orange socks and two blue socks. $P(A)$, the probability that the first sock is blue, is still $\frac{2}{6}$. But $P(B)$, the probability that the second is blue, depends on whether the first one taken was blue or was orange. If the first one taken was blue, then there are four orange socks and one blue sock left, so the probability that the second is blue is $\frac{1}{5}$. If the first one taken was orange, then there are three orange and two blue socks left, so the probability that the second sock is blue is $\frac{2}{6}$. The value of $P(B)$ depends on the outcome of event A. For this reason, selections without replacement are considered to be *dependent events.*

It is possible to calculate $P(A \cap B)$ even when A and B are dependent.

At the right is a listing for the sock experiment without replacement. These outcomes consist of all those in the independent case except those with the same sock selected twice. Thus there are only 30 outcomes. In only two are both socks blue, so $P(A \cap B) = \frac{2}{30}$. This confirms that in this case, $P(A \cap B) \neq P(A) \cdot P(B)$, because $P(A) \cdot P(B) = \frac{2}{6} \cdot \frac{2}{6} = \frac{4}{36}$.

Sample Space without Replacement				
12	13	14	11	12
21	23	24	21	22
31	32	34	31	32
41	42	43	41	42
11	12	13	14	12
21	22	23	24	21

Example 2

Consider spinning the spinner in Example 1 twice. Define the events

A: the first spin shows a number less than 3;

B: the sum of the spins is less than 5.

Decide whether events *A* and *B* are independent.

Solution

We need to determine whether $P(A \cap B) = P(A) \cdot P(B)$. The sample space has the 36 elements shown in the solution to Example 1, and copied at the left.

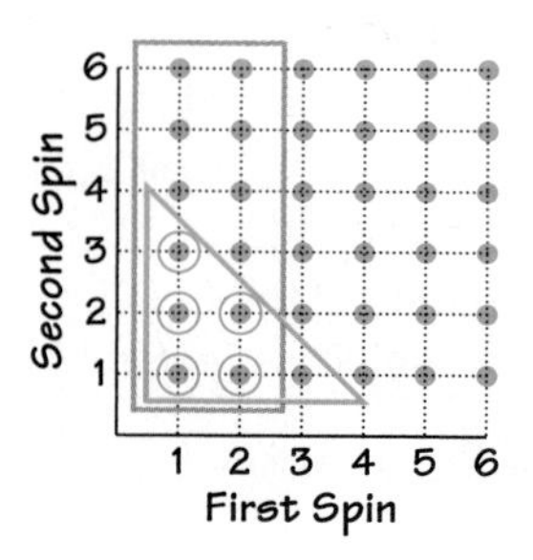

A consists of the 12 outcomes inside the orange rectangle.

So, $$P(A) = \frac{12}{36} = \frac{1}{3}.$$

B is the set of outcomes {(1, 1), (1, 2), (1, 3), (2, 1), (2, 2), (3, 1)} inside the green triangle.

So, $$P(B) = \frac{6}{36} = \frac{1}{6}.$$

The five circled points represent $A \cap B$.

So, $$P(A \cap B) = \frac{5}{36}.$$

In this case, $$P(A) \cdot P(B) = \frac{1}{3} \cdot \frac{1}{6} \neq P(A \cap B).$$

So, the events A and B are not independent.

Check

The event B requires small numbers on both spins, so if event A occurs, B seems more likely to occur. This makes us expect that B is dependent on A.

An Example from Aviation

The notion of independence can be extended to more than two events. Consider this true story.

In May, 1983, an airline jet carrying 172 people between Miami and Nassau lost its engine oil, power, and 12,000 feet of altitude over the Atlantic Ocean before a safe recovery was made. When the warning lights indicating low oil pressure on all three engines lit up at nearly the same time, the crew's initial reaction was that something was wrong with the warning system, not the oil pressure. As one person stated in *The Miami Herald* of May 5, 1983,

"They considered the possibility of a malfunction in the indication system because it's such an unusual thing to see all three with low pressure indications. The odds are so great that you won't get three indications like this. The odds are way out of sight, so the first thing you'd suspect is a problem with the indication system."

Boeing 727 cockpit

Example 3

Aviation records show that for the most common engine on a Boeing 727 airliner, there is an average of 0.04 "inflight shutdowns" per 1000 hours of running time. So the probability of an engine's failure in a particular hour is about 0.00004. Suppose the failures of the three engines were independent. What is the probability of three engines failing in the same hour?

Solution

Let A, B, and C be the engines. If they are independent events,

$$\begin{aligned} P(\text{A, B and C fail}) &= P(\text{A fails}) \cdot P(\text{B fails}) \cdot P(\text{C fails}) \\ &= (0.00004) \cdot (0.00004) \cdot (0.00004) \\ &= 6.4 \times 10^{-14}. \end{aligned}$$

The number 6.4×10^{-14} is the sort of "out of sight" probability the writer of the article mentioned. This probability could be interpreted that *if* failures were independent, then about once in every 16,000,000,000,000 hours of flight would all three engines fail simultaneously.

After the incident, it was discovered that a mechanic doing routine maintenance on the plane had failed to install six tiny rubber seals on the engines' oil plugs. The gaps this error created allowed all the oil to leak out when the engines were fired up.

The crew members assumed that oil pressure problems in the three engines were independent events. Had this in fact been the case, they would have been correct in their assumption that the probability of all three engines failing simultaneously was extremely small. But the three failures were all due to one cause, a mechanic's error. So the failures were dependent events, and the event was not as unlikely as the crew thought.

Can Events Be Independent and Mutually Exclusive?

Suppose that A and B are two events which have a nonzero probability of occurring, that is, $P(A) > 0$ and $P(B) > 0$. If the events are independent, then $P(A \cap B) = P(A) \cdot P(B)$, and so $P(A \cap B) > 0$. For the events to be mutually exclusive, $A \cap B = \emptyset$, and so $P(A \cap B) = P(\emptyset) = 0$. This proves that events which have a nonzero probability of occurring cannot be both independent and mutually exclusive.

As an example, consider two candidates running for the office of President of the United States, one a Republican and one a Democrat. Because they cannot both win the election, the event of the Republican winning and the event of the Democrat winning are mutually exclusive. Yet, these two events are clearly not independent of one another.

QUESTIONS

Covering the Reading

1. A drawer contains five socks, three red and two blue.

a. If you pick a sock randomly, replace it, and pick another, what is the probability that both socks are red?

b. If you pick two socks randomly without replacing the first, what is the probability that both are red?

c. If F = the first sock is red, and S = the second sock is red, in which of parts **a** and **b** are F and S independent events?

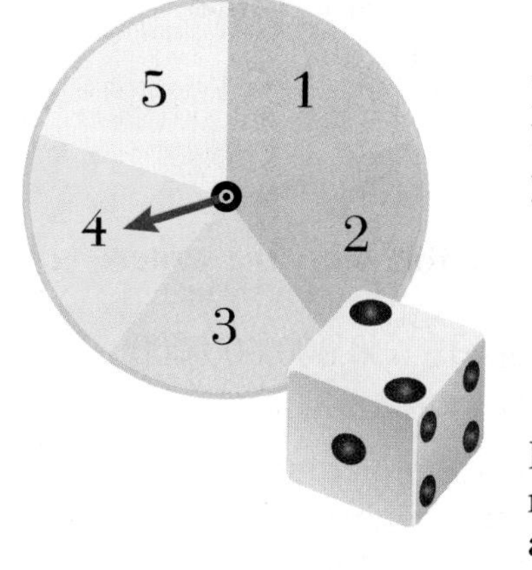

In 2 and 3, suppose you have a spinner with five congruent areas and a die, both fair. Decide whether or not the two events are independent. Justify your answer.

2. A = the spinner shows 4. B = the die shows 4.

3. A = the spinner shows 4. B = the sum of the spinner and die is over 6.

4. When are three events A, B, and C independent?

In 5 and 6, refer to the reporting of the airline incident. Suppose the failure rate per hour of each engine is 0.0005, and assume failures of the engines are independent events.

5. What is the probability that all three engines fail at the same time?

6. What is the probability that none of the engines fails?

7. Give an example of two events different from the ones in the text which have nonzero probabilities and are not both independent and mutually exclusive.

Applying the Mathematics

8. Two fair dice are tossed. Use the definition of independence to classify the following pairs of events as independent, mutually exclusive, or neither.

a. One die shows 2. The other die shows 3.

b. One die shows 2. The same die does not show 3.

c. One die shows 2. The same die shows 3.

9. A fair coin is tossed three times. Consider the events:

A: at most one head occurs;

B: heads and tails occur at least once.

Are A and B independent? Justify your answer using the definition of independence.

African fish eagle in Okavango, Botswana

10. The information booklet about a wildlife reservation park states that the probability of observing an eagle on a given day is 0.21, and the probability for a hawk is 0.17. The booklet also indicates that, based on records, 2% of the visitors observe both of these birds of prey on the same day. In this park, are observing an eagle and observing a hawk independent events? Explain your answer.

11. A motorist has recorded some data while commuting on a section of road with five traffic lights. In 50 trips on this road, the five lights stopped the motorist 20, 22, 25, 19, and 24 times, respectively. The five lights all stopped the motorist once. Do you think the lights are operating independently? Explain your reasoning.

12. An auto manufacturer buys plastic molded parts from two companies: Ace and Best. Here is the frequency distribution of parts by quality that the auto company has received.

	Ace	Best
Excellent	60	24
Acceptable	272	20
Unacceptable	16	8

a. What is the probability that a randomly selected part is from Ace?

b. What is the probability that a randomly selected part is excellent?

c. What is the probability that a randomly selected part is both from Ace and excellent?

d. Are the quality of parts and their sources independent?

13. A roulette wheel in Europe has 37 compartments numbered 0, 1, 2, . . . , 36. Find the probability that the number 29 will come up at least once in each case.

a. a single spin

b. two successive spins

c. three successive spins

Review

14. **a.** In how many ways can the 23 members of a club line up for a photo?
b. In how many ways can four of these people be chosen to be president, vice president, secretary, and treasurer of the club? *(Lesson 7-4)*

15. Suppose you wish to visit all six large islands in the state of Hawaii: Hawaii, Kauai, Lanai, Maui, Molokai, and Oahu. If you are to visit each island once, in how many different orders might you travel? *(Lesson 7-4)*

16. Solve for n: $17! = n \cdot 16!$ *(Lesson 7-4)*

17. Solve for n and r: ${}_nP_r = 600$. *(Lesson 7-4)*

18. When one coin is tossed there are two possible outcomes—heads or tails. How many outcomes are possible when the following numbers of coins are tossed? *(Lesson 7-3)*
a. 2 **b.** 5 **c.** 8 **d.** n

19. Suppose a basketball player has a free throw shooting average of 0.75. What is the probability that the player will not make his next free throw? *(Lesson 7-2)*

In 20 and 21, two bags each contain five slips of paper. An angle has been drawn on each slip. The measures of the angles on the slips in each bag are 10°, 30°, 45°, 60°, and 90°. Let a and b be the measures of the angles drawn from bags 1 and 2, respectively. *(Lessons 4-3, 7-1)*

20. Find $P(a + b \geq 90°)$.

21. Find $P(\sin(a + b) \geq \sin 90°)$.

Exploration

22. The so-called "Law of Averages" is often used to lead people to expect that if event E occurs often, then its complement E' is more likely to occur the next time the experiment is undertaken. Test this "law." Toss a coin at least 200 times and record each result. Count the number of times that each of the following occurs: *HH*, *HT*, *TH*, *TT*. (In the sequence *HHHT*, you would count *HH* twice and *HT* once.) Does your data suggest more switches than would be expected?

LESSON

7-6

Probability Distributions

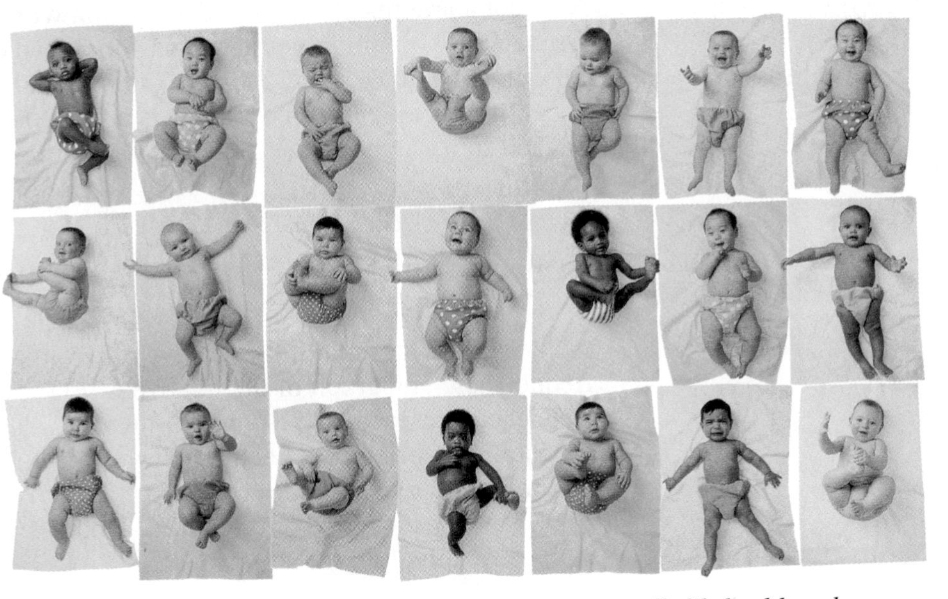

Observation shows that births of boys and girls are not equally likely although we often assume that they are. See Example 2.

What Is a Probability Distribution?

In Lesson 7-1, the 36 possible outcomes for the tossing of two dice are listed. If the dice are fair, then the probabilities of obtaining each possible sum are given in the table below. Check that the sum of the probabilities is 1, so no possible outcome has been excluded.

x (sum of dice)	2	3	4	5	6	7	8	9	10	11	12
$P(x)$ (probability of outcome)	$\frac{1}{36}$	$\frac{2}{36}$	$\frac{3}{36}$	$\frac{4}{36}$	$\frac{5}{36}$	$\frac{6}{36}$	$\frac{5}{36}$	$\frac{4}{36}$	$\frac{3}{36}$	$\frac{2}{36}$	$\frac{1}{36}$

In this situation, let x = the sum of the top faces of two dice. Then x is a *random variable*. In general, a **random variable** is a variable whose values are numbers determined by the outcome of an experiment. The pairs of numbers in the table above represent a *probability distribution*. A **probability distribution** is a function which maps each value of a random variable onto its probability.

The probability distribution P for the sum of two dice is graphed at the right. From both the table and the graph, you can see that the domain of P is the set of integers from 2 to 12; the range is the set

$$\left\{\frac{1}{36}, \frac{2}{36}, \frac{3}{36}, \frac{4}{36}, \frac{5}{36}, \frac{6}{36}\right\}.$$

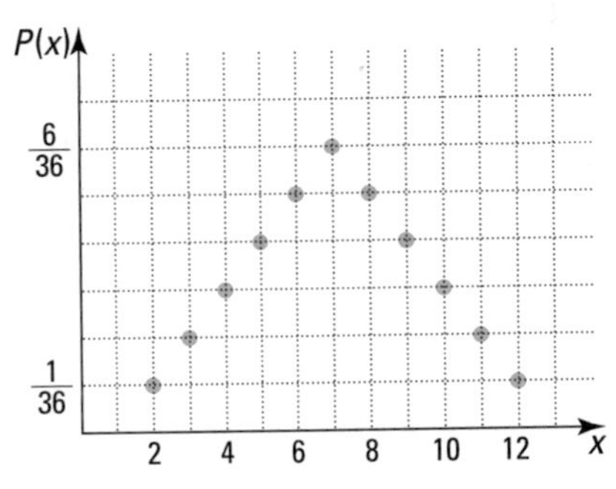

Now compare this probability distribution with the distribution of relative frequencies you might get if you performed an experiment. In an experiment, two dice were tossed 78 times and the sum of the numbers on the top faces was found. Below is a table of the relative frequencies of each sum.

x (sum of dice)	2	3	4	5	6	7	8	9	10	11	12
$R(x)$ (relative frequency)	$\frac{2}{78}$	$\frac{4}{78}$	$\frac{6}{78}$	$\frac{6}{78}$	$\frac{13}{78}$	$\frac{12}{78}$	$\frac{14}{78}$	$\frac{11}{78}$	$\frac{5}{78}$	$\frac{2}{78}$	$\frac{3}{78}$

At the right is a graph of the relative frequencies. The graph of the relative frequencies resembles the graph of the probability distribution. Each graph shows that for $x = 2$ or 12 both $P(x)$ and $R(x)$ are small; and for $x = 6, 7,$ or 8 both $P(x)$ and $R(x)$ are relatively large.

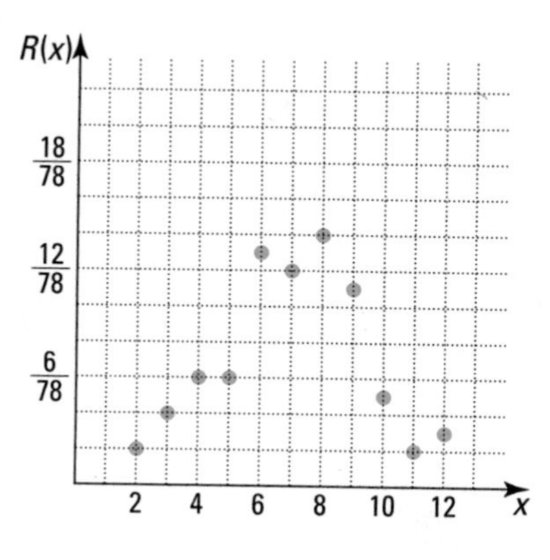

Expected Value

The distributions can be compared further by calculating their means. To find the mean sum $\bar{x}$ resulting from the experiment, add all 78 outcomes and divide by 78. There were two 2s, four 3s, six 4s, etc., so the total is

$$2 \cdot 2 + 3 \cdot 4 + 4 \cdot 6 + 5 \cdot 6 + 6 \cdot 13 + 7 \cdot 12 + 8 \cdot 14 + 9 \cdot 11 + 10 \cdot 5 + 11 \cdot 2 + 12 \cdot 3 = 551.$$

Thus, the mean sum is $\bar{x} = \frac{551}{78} \approx 7.06$.

Alternatively, you could divide each outcome by 78 before adding. Then the mean sum is

$$\bar{x} = 2 \cdot \tfrac{2}{78} + 3 \cdot \tfrac{4}{78} + 4 \cdot \tfrac{6}{78} + 5 \cdot \tfrac{6}{78} + 6 \cdot \tfrac{13}{78} + 7 \cdot \tfrac{12}{78} + 8 \cdot \tfrac{14}{78} + 9 \cdot \tfrac{11}{78} + 10 \cdot \tfrac{5}{78} + 11 \cdot \tfrac{2}{78} + 12 \cdot \tfrac{3}{78}$$

$$= \frac{551}{78} \approx 7.06.$$

Think of the 11 possible values of the random variable x as $x_1, x_2, \ldots, x_{11}$. This way of calculating the mean generalizes to the following formula for computing the mean $\bar{x}$ of n numbers x_i, if the relative frequency $R(x_i)$ of each x_i is known.

$$\bar{x} = x_1 \cdot R(x_1) + x_2 \cdot R(x_2) + \ldots + x_n \cdot R(x_n) = \sum_{i=1}^{n} (x_i \cdot R(x_i))$$

The *mean* or *expected value of a probability distribution* is found by using the probability $P(x_i)$ instead of the relative frequency $R(x_i)$. The expected value of the probability distribution is usually denoted by μ, the lowercase Greek letter mu (pronounced "mew").

Definition

Let $\{(x_1, P(x_1)), (x_2, P(x_2)), \ldots, (x_n, P(x_n))\}$ be a probability distribution. The **mean** or **expected value** μ of the distribution is

$$\mu = \sum_{i=1}^{n} (x_i \cdot P(x_i)).$$

The mean of the probability distribution is also called the mean or expected value of the random variable. It indicates the average value of the random variable you may expect as an experiment is repeated. As with a probability, an expected value is a fixed theoretical value which is not necessarily obtained every time an experiment is repeated.

Example 1

Consider the experiment of rolling two dice and adding the numbers on the top faces.

a. Calculate the expected value of the probability distribution.

b. What is the percent error between the mean sum $\overline{x}$ of the relative frequencies, calculated on page 458, and the expected value?

Solution

a. Refer to the table of values of x_i and $P(x_i)$ at the beginning of the lesson. The expected value

$$\mu = \sum_{i=1}^{11} (x_i \cdot P(x_i))$$

$$= 2 \cdot \frac{1}{36} + 3 \cdot \frac{2}{36} + 4 \cdot \frac{3}{36} + 5 \cdot \frac{4}{36} + 6 \cdot \frac{5}{36} + 7 \cdot \frac{6}{36} + 8 \cdot \frac{5}{36} + 9 \cdot \frac{4}{36} + 10 \cdot \frac{3}{36} + 11 \cdot \frac{2}{36} + 12 \cdot \frac{1}{36}$$

$$= \frac{2}{36} + \frac{6}{36} + \frac{12}{36} + \frac{20}{36} + \frac{30}{36} + \frac{42}{36} + \frac{40}{36} + \frac{36}{36} + \frac{30}{36} + \frac{22}{36} + \frac{12}{36}$$

$$= 7.$$

b. The mean sum for the experiment at the beginning of the lesson is 7.06. This differs by only 0.06 from the expected value, so **the percent error from the expected value is $\frac{0.06}{7} \approx 0.0086 = 0.86\%$, less than 1%.**

A probability distribution is a function. So it can be described by identifying its domain and by giving a table or rule for the function. Frequently, a probability distribution is graphed as a histogram. It is common in such cases to center a bar of width 1 over the individual value of the random variable. The height of each bar is the corresponding probability.

Example 2

Consider a family with three children. Assume that births of boys and girls are equally likely. Let the random variable of the distribution stand for the number of boys.

a. Give the domain of the random variable.
b. Find the probability for each value of the random variable.
c. Construct a histogram of the probability distribution.
d. Find the expected value of the distribution.

Solution

a. There may be 0, 1, 2, or 3 boys, so the random variable takes on the values 0, 1, 2, and 3.

b. The sample space consists of 8 outcomes, the ordered triples BBB, BBG, BGB, BGG, GBB, GBG, GGB, and GGG.

Since each outcome is equally likely, we use $\frac{N(E)}{N(S)}$ to determine each probability.

x = number of boys	0	1	2	3
P(x)	$\frac{1}{8}$	$\frac{3}{8}$	$\frac{3}{8}$	$\frac{1}{8}$

c. Graph with bars centered over the values of x.

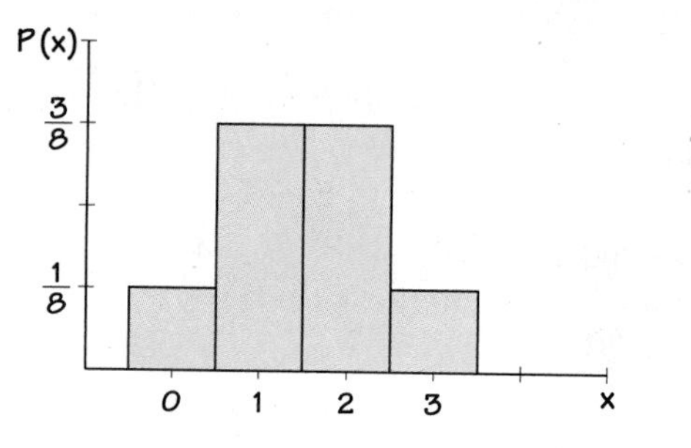

d. Use the definition of expected value. Here x_i is the event "having i boys."

$$\mu = \sum_{i=0}^{3}(x_i \cdot P(x_i)) = 0 \cdot \frac{1}{8} + 1 \cdot \frac{3}{8} + 2 \cdot \frac{3}{8} + 3 \cdot \frac{1}{8}$$
$$= \frac{12}{8}$$
$$= 1.5 \text{ boys}$$

Check

For part **d**, if the births of boys and girls are equally likely, they each happen half of the time. In a family of three children, $\frac{1}{2}$ of 3 *is* 1.5, the expected value calculated in part **d**.

Look back at the histogram above. Notice that each bar has an area of $1 \cdot P(x_i) = P(x_i)$. So the area of each bar is the probability of the event to which it corresponds; and thus the sum of the areas of the bars is 1. This property is true for *all* probability distributions, and will be applied in Chapter 10.

QUESTIONS

Covering the Reading

1. What is a *random variable*?

2. What is a *probability distribution*?

3. *True or false.* In a probability distribution, each element in the range must be a number between 0 and 1, inclusive.

In 4 and 5, explain why the given table does not define a probability distribution.

4.

x	3	4	5	6	7
$f(x)$	$\frac{1}{16}$	$\frac{11}{16}$	$-\frac{1}{16}$	$\frac{2}{16}$	$\frac{3}{16}$

5.

x	0	1	2	3
$f(x)$	$\frac{1}{4}$	$\frac{2}{4}$	$\frac{3}{4}$	$\frac{1}{4}$

6. Find the expected value of the following probability distribution.

x	5	6	7	8	9	10
$P(x)$	$\frac{1}{15}$	$\frac{2}{15}$	$\frac{3}{15}$	$\frac{4}{15}$	$\frac{4}{15}$	$\frac{1}{15}$

The British royal family in the 1970s: Queen Elizabeth, Prince Philip, and their children, Charles, Anne, Andrew, and Edward.

7. Consider a family with four children.
   a. List all possible outcomes in the sample space.
   b. Let x = the number of girls in the family. Find the probability for each value of the random variable assuming that births of boys and girls are equally likely.
   c. Make a histogram of the probability distribution.
   d. Find the expected value of x.

8. What is the total area of the bars in a histogram for a probability distribution?

9. *True or false.* The mean of a probability distribution is always a value of the random variable of the experiment.

Applying the Mathematics

10. Copy the graph of the probability distribution on page 457 associated with rolling two dice and recording the sum.
    a. Superimpose two lines which contain the points of the graph.
    b. Show that the area enclosed by the x-axis and the two lines in part **a** is 1 square unit.
    c. Determine the equations for the two lines in part **a**.

In 11 and 12, an experiment involves rolling two dice and recording the absolute value of the difference between the numbers showing on the two dice. For example, if you roll a 4 and a 6, the outcome is $|4 - 6| = 2$.

11. The following table of relative frequencies was formed after 360 trials.

Difference	0	1	2	3	4	5
Relative frequency	$\frac{62}{360}$	$\frac{98}{360}$	$\frac{77}{360}$	$\frac{60}{360}$	$\frac{38}{360}$	$\frac{25}{360}$

a. Make a scatterplot of these data.
b. Find the mean difference.

12. Let X = the absolute value of the difference between the numbers showing on two dice.
a. Make a table of values of the probability distribution for X.
b. Make a scatterplot of the distribution.
c. Find the expected value of X.
d. What is the percent error between the mean difference in Question 11, part **b** and the expected value of X?

13. In a lottery, the *value* of a ticket is a random variable, defined to be the amount of money you win less the cost of playing. Suppose that in a lottery with 125 tickets, each ticket costs \$1. First prize is \$50, second prize is \$30, and third prize is \$20. Then the possible values of the random variable are \$49, \$29, \$19, and -\$1.
a. Why is one of the values negative?
b. The probability of winning first prize is $\frac{1}{125}$. The same probability holds for second and third prizes. Find the probability of winning nothing.
c. Find the expected value of a ticket.

14. An ecologist collected the data shown in the table below on the life span of a species of deer. Based on this sample, what is the expected life span of this species?

Age at death (years)	1	2	3	4	5	6	7	8
Number	2	30	86	132	173	77	40	10

15. The dot frequency graph at the right is of the probability function in Example 2. The graph of $f(x) = -\frac{1}{4}\left|x - \frac{3}{2}\right| + \frac{1}{2}$ is superimposed.
a. Verify that each of the four points $(x_i, P(x_i))$ is on the graph of f.
b. Verify that the equation above for f is produced from $y = |x|$ by the rubberband transformation $L(x, y) = \left(x + \frac{3}{2}, -\frac{1}{4}y + \frac{1}{2}\right)$.

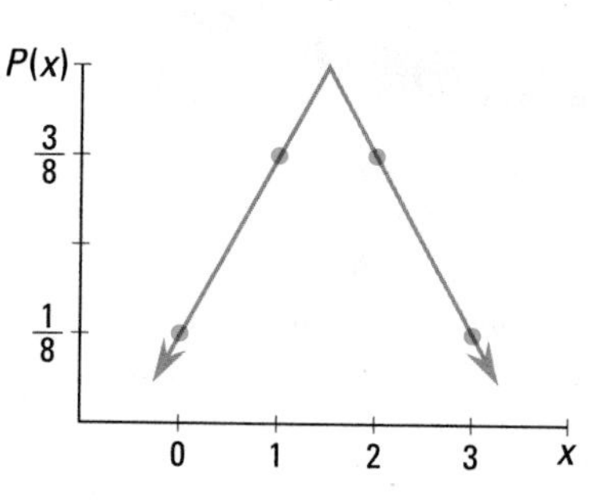

Review

16. The wheel on the TV program *Wheel of Fortune* is first divided equally into 24 compartments with one labeled "Lose A Turn." Find the probability that the wheel stops at "Lose A Turn" for each of the following.
a. a single spin
b. two successive spins
c. three successive spins *(Lesson 7-5)*

17. Consider the experiment of tossing a fair coin five times.
a. Determine the probability of at least one tail.
b. Determine the probability of exactly two heads.
c. *True or false.* The two events in parts **a** and **b** are independent. *(Lessons 7-1, 7-2, 7-3, 7-5)*

18. In how many different ways can a class with 18 students be seated in a room containing 24 desks? *(Lesson 7-4)*

19. Write $\frac{(n + 2)!}{n!}$ as a polynomial in n. *(Lesson 7-3)*

20. The *Statistical Abstract of the United States 1996* states that in 1991 there were 31,041,000 freshwater anglers and 8,885,000 saltwater anglers. The total number of anglers, however, is 35,578,000.
a. How many anglers in 1991 were in both categories?
b. If there were 252,131,000 people in the U.S. in 1991, determine the probability of randomly picking a person in the population who fished in saltwater but not in freshwater. *(Lesson 7-2)*

21. A person recorded the following scores on an electronic game: 810, 670, 630, 820, 710, 590, 6450, 920, 610, 770.
a. Find the mean of these scores.
b. Find the median score.
c. Which is the better measure of center—the mean or the median? Why?
d. Find the standard deviation of the scores.
e. How does the score of 6450 affect the size of the standard deviation of the scores? *(Lessons 1-3, 1-7)*

Exploration

22. a. Find the life expectancy for a person of your age and sex.
b. Find out how life expectancies are determined.

Introducing Lesson 7-7

The Monty Hall Problem

Work with a partner on this problem. You will need three playing cards, two of one color and a third of a different color.

Monty Hall was the host of the TV game show called *Let's Make a Deal!* Contestants were told that behind each of three doors was a prize, not all of which were considered desirable. The contestant was asked to pick a door, and then Monty Hall would offer money to the contestant, who could take it or choose what was behind the door, sight unseen.

Here is a variation of that game. Suppose that behind two of the doors is a goat and behind the third door is a new car. You are the contestant and you pick one door, say Door Number 2. The host, *who knows what is behind each door*, then opens one of the other two doors and shows you a goat. The host now asks you, "Do you want to stay with the door you chose or do you wish to choose the other unopened door?" The problem is to determine whether it is to your advantage to switch.

1 Decide who will play the role of the host, and who will play the contestant. Let the two cards of the same color represent the goats, and the card with the unique color represent the car.

2 The host should shuffle the cards, place them face down without the other person's watching, and remember which card represents the car.

3 The contestant will then choose one of the cards. The host will not turn over that card, but the host will turn over a remaining card which represents a goat.

4 The contestant will then decide to keep the first choice or to switch. Then the host will turn over the final choice to see if the contestant won the game (got the car) or lost the game (got a goat).

5 Play the game (that is, repeat steps 2–4) 15 times. Keep a tally on a chart similar to the one below. Then reverse roles and play the game 15 more times, and record your results on the same tally chart.

Contestant's Strategy	Number of Wins	Number of Losses
Keeps the Original Card		
Switches Cards		

6 On the basis of your data, what should the strategy of the contestant be?

7 Under the direction of your teacher, incorporate your data with that of the rest of the class. On the basis of the class data, what should be the strategy of the contestant?

LESSON

7-7 *Designing Simulations*

The In-class Activity on the preceding page is a *simulation* of what happened on the TV show. A **simulation** of a real situation is an experimental model of the situation that attempts to capture all aspects of the situation that affect the outcomes. Simulations appear in all areas of our lives. They are used by car manufacturers to test safety features in cars, by governments to examine procedures in the case of major emergencies, by toymakers to estimate how long a toy will last. A poll before an election is a simulation of the election. A fire drill in a school is a simulation; not only does a fire drill alert you to what to do in case of fire, but it also provides an estimate of how long it takes to evacuate the school. The PSAT exam is a simulation of the SAT; the PLAN exam is a simulation of the ACT.

When it is possible, people repeat simulations so that probabilities of the various outcomes can be estimated. When an experiment is repeated, the repetitions are called **trials**. In the Monty Hall situation, you were asked to perform 30 trials, that is, 30 simulations of the same real situation. By combining your data with the data of others, hundreds of simulations could be run. It is possible to compute the probability of choosing the door with the car behind it, but the repeated trials provide a relative frequency that may be a fairly good estimate of that probability without using any laws of probability.

Monte Carlo Simulations

The use of relative frequencies obtained from repeated trials to answer a mathematical problem is often called a **Monte Carlo method**, named after the well-known Monte Carlo Casino in the principality of Monaco. Monte Carlo methods were pioneered by John von Neumann (1903–1957), one of the inventors of modern computer programming. These methods make it possible to estimate solutions to a variety of problems.

There are three steps to the Monte Carlo method.

1. Determine how the situation will be simulated.
2. Define what constitutes a single trial and what data will be recorded.
3. Specify the number of trials that will be run and how the estimated answer will be obtained.

We first use a Monte Carlo method to simulate a problem for which you already know the answer.

Example 1

A researcher is studying the number of boys and girls in families with three children. Assume that the birth of a boy or a girl is equally likely. Design a simulation with 100 trials to estimate the probability that a family of three children has exactly one boy. (This is the situation of Example 4 of Lesson 7-1.)

Solution 1

Follow the three steps on page 465.

1. To simulate the situation, flip a coin. If the coin comes up heads, call it a boy. If it comes up tails, call it a girl.
2. A trial is to flip the coin three times and count the number of heads.
3. Repeat the trial 100 times. Calculate the percent of trials in which exactly one head occurs.

Solution 2

1. Use a die. If it comes up 1, 2, or 3, call it a boy. If it comes up 4, 5, or 6, call it a girl.
2. A trial is to roll the die three times and count the number of times a 1, 2, or 3 occurs.
3. Repeat the trial 100 times. Calculate the percent of trials in which exactly one of the three throws shows a 1, 2, or 3.

Activity

Run one of these simulations to estimate the probability of having exactly one boy in a family with three children.

Using Random Numbers for Simulation

A set of numbers is **random** if each number has the same probability of occurring, each pair of numbers has the same probability of occurring, each triple of numbers has the same probability of occurring, and so on. A fair die is a device for generating random numbers from {1, 2, 3, 4, 5, 6}, and for this reason dice are used for playing games in which you want everyone to have the same chance. However, cards, coins, and dice are often not efficient for running a simulation. Using random numbers takes less time and energy.

The Table of Random Numbers in Appendix C is such a set of numbers. It was constructed so that each digit from 0 to 9 has the same probability of being selected, each pair of digits from 00 to 99 has the same probability of being selected, each triple of digits from 000 to 999 has the same probability of being selected, and so on.

To use a Table of Random Numbers, you must start randomly as well. One way to do this is to close your eyes, point to a pair of digits on the page, and use that pair as the row. Then close your eyes again, point to a pair of digits on the page, and use that pair as the column. For instance, if you point to 03 and then to 12, start at the 3rd row, 12th column. Then choose to go up, down, right, or left—perhaps by rolling a die. If you point to a pair of digits which does not refer to a row or column, point again.

Example 2

A researcher is studying the number of boys and girls in families with three children. Assume that the birth of a boy or a girl is equally likely. Use the Table of Random Numbers to estimate the probability that a family of three children has exactly one boy.

Solution

1. To simulate the sex of a child, read a single digit in the table. Let an even number represent the birth of a boy and an odd number represent the birth of a girl.
2. The table starting at row 3 is shown below. A trial is to read three consecutive digits and to count the number of even numbers. For instance, if you started at row 3, column 12 and read to the right, the digits 196 would represent the first trial, a family with two girls and one boy.

										Begin		
24130	48360	22527	97265	76393	64809	15179	24830	49340	32081	30680	19655	63348	58629
42167	93093	06423	61680	17856	16376	39440	53537	71341	57004	00849	74917	97758	16379
37570	39975	81837	16656	06121	91782	60468	81305	49684	60672	14110	06927	01263	54613
77921	06907	11008	42751	27756	53498	18602	70659	90655	15053	21916	81825	44394	42880
99562	72905	56420	69994	98872	31016	71194	18738	44013	48840	63213	21069	10634	12952
96301	91977	05463	07972	18876	20922	94595	56869	69014	60045	18425	84903	42508	32307
End													

3. Repeat the trial 100 times, and record your results. Some of the trials are shown below.

Trial	Digit Simulating Births	Number of Boys (evens)	Exactly 1 Boy
1	196	1	Yes
2	556	1	Yes
3	334	1	Yes
4	858	2	No
5	629	2	No
6	421	2	No
7	679	1	Yes
⋮	⋮	⋮	⋮
17	405	2	No
18	353	0	No
⋮	⋮	⋮	⋮
99	296	2	No
100	301	1	Yes

There are 47 trials with exactly 1 boy. So, the relative frequency is $\frac{47}{100} = .47$.

As you know from Example 4 in Lesson 7-1, the probability in the situation of Examples 1 and 2 is $\frac{3}{8}$ =.375. We would usually want a closer estimate than .47, and probably should have done a larger simulation, but with 100 trials, even being off by 10% is not a rare event. For this reason, simulations like the ones above typically involve thousands of trials and require programming a calculator or computer. These ideas are discussed in the next lesson.

Entire probability distributions can be estimated by considering the relative frequencies of all possible events in a simulation. For instance, in the simulation of Example 2, it happens that 10 trials yield 0 boys, 47 trials yield 1 boy (as we stated earlier), 30 trials yield 2 boys, and 13 trials yield 3 boys. We compare the relative frequencies of these events with their probabilities when boys and girls are equally likely.

Number of Boys	0	1	2	3
Relative Frequency from Simulation	.10	.47	.30	.13
Probability	$\frac{1}{8}$ = .125	$\frac{3}{8}$ = .375	$\frac{3}{8}$ = .375	$\frac{1}{8}$ = .125

A Table of Random Numbers can be used to simulate any event with a known probability.

Example 3

Explain how to use a Table of Random Numbers for an event that has the given probability.

a. 0.2 **b.** 0.25

Solution

a. We want to assign 0.2 of the possible digits to the event. Choose two of the digits from 0 to 9 to represent the event occurring, and the other eight to represent the event not occurring. One way to do this is to examine single digits in the table of random numbers. If the digit is:

0 or 1 the event occurs;
2, 3, 4, 5, 6, 7, 8, or 9 the event does not occur.

b. Because the probability involves hundredths, use the 100 pairs of digits from 00 to 99. One way to do the simulation is to examine pairs of digits in the table of random numbers. If the pair is:

00, 01, 02, ..., 23, or 24 the event occurs;
25, 26, 27, ..., 98, or 99 the event does not occur.

QUESTIONS

Covering the Reading

1. Define *simulation.*

2. What are the results that you obtained in the Activity?

3. Explain how to use a regular tetrahedral die to run a Monte Carlo simulation of the situation of Example 1.

4. When using the Table of Random Numbers, how should the user decide where to start?

5. a. Give the results for trials 8–16 of Example 2.
b. Graph the relative frequencies from trials 1–25 to estimate the probability distribution for this example.

In 6 and 7, explain how to define a trial using the Table of Random Numbers for an event that has the given probability.

6. 0.6 **7.** 0.57

Applying the Mathematics

8. Suppose a person with a certain medical condition has probability 0.7 of recovering fully, if the person undergoes surgery. Also suppose that 100 surgeries for this condition are performed.
a. Design a simulation for this situation.
b. Run the simulation to estimate the number of patients who underwent surgery and recovered fully.

9. A softball player has a batting average of .300. This means

$$\frac{\text{number of hits}}{\text{number of official at-bats}} = .300.$$

a. Design a simulation to illustrate the next ten at-bats of this player without using the Table of Random Numbers. Run this simulation.
b. Design a simulation for the next ten at-bats using the Table of Random Numbers. Run this simulation.
c. Run 100 trials of the simulation for ten at-bats using either method.

10. Without using a simulation, explain why, in the Monty Hall problem, the probability of the contestant winning is $\frac{2}{3}$ if he or she switches doors. (Hint: Remember that the host always knows what is behind the first door chosen and then shows a different door with a goat behind it.)

Village of Foroglio in Switzerland

Review

11. The distribution of family sizes in a small village is given in the table below.

S = family size	2	3	4	5	6	7	8
$R(S)$ = relative frequency	$\frac{2}{87}$	$\frac{9}{87}$	$\frac{19}{87}$	$\frac{31}{87}$	$\frac{15}{87}$	$\frac{8}{87}$	$\frac{3}{87}$

a. Graph this distribution.
b. How can this be considered as a probability distribution?
c. What is the average size of a family in this village? *(Lesson 7-6)*

12. On January 8, 1989, a two-engine plane crashed in England after both engines shut down. Reporters quoted experts as saying that the probability of both engines failing was 10^{-6}. Assume the engines' performances are independent. *(Lesson 7-5)*

a. What is the probability of one engine failing?

b. Are the engines on this plane more or less reliable than the ones described in Lesson 7-5?

c. Give a reason why the engine failures may *not* have been independent events.

In 13–15, identify the events as independent, mutually exclusive, complementary, or none of these. *(Lessons 7-1, 7-2, 7-5)*

13. One student is chosen from a class, then another student is chosen.

14. Fumbling in the dark, a person tries one key from his key ring, drops the ring, then tries a key again.

15. Kevin is early for class; Kevin is late for class.

16. Consider eight athletes in a 100 m dash heat as shown at left. *(Lessons 7-3, 7-4)*

a. In how many ways can the runners finish the race?

b. If three of the athletes are neck and neck at the finish line, in how many ways might the eight finish?

17. A kindergarten teacher has 20 felt-tip pens, which are evenly divided among the colors yellow, green, red, blue, and purple. Find the probability that the first six pens chosen by the children have the following characteristics. *(Lessons 7-1, 7-3)*

a. Each pen has a color different from the others.

b. Three pens are red and the other three are blue.

18. *Skill sequence.* Solve for x. *(Previous course, Lesson 5-7)*

a. $2x - 5 = 3$ **b.** $2x^2 - 5x = 3$ **c.** $2\sin^2 x - 5\sin x = 3$

19. a. Evaluate $\lfloor 3x \rfloor$ for $x = 0, 0.25, 0.5$, and 0.75.

b. For what values of x is $1 \le \lfloor 3x \rfloor < 2$? *(Lesson 2-7)*

Exploration

20. Find three different tables of random numbers.

a. Select three samples of 100 consecutive digits (horizontally, vertically, or diagonally) in each table. Calculate the relative frequency of the digits 0 through 9 in each sample.

b. Discuss the differences and similarities between the frequencies you calculated in part **a**.

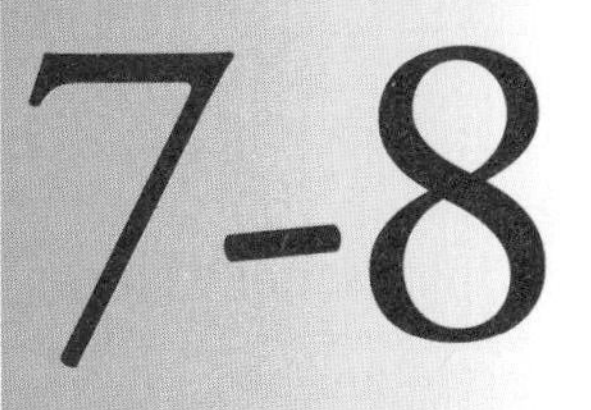

Simulations with Technology

As you saw in the last lesson, running a simulation can be very tedious, even if you use a table of random numbers. Fortunately, technology makes it easier and more efficient to obtain random numbers.

There is no known way to generate a set of random numbers. Computers and graphics calculators can generate numbers that are close to random. For this reason, the numbers generated are called *pseudo-random*. ("Pseudo" means "false" or "pretended".) However, we will use the convention of talking about random numbers even though we know they are pseudo-random.

Generating Random Numbers with Technology

In BASIC, pseudo-random numbers with decimal values between 0 and 1 can be obtained using the RND function. In some versions of BASIC, this function always has an argument, usually 1. In other versions the argument may be optional. The computer program below will print ten random numbers, with a different set printed each time it is run.

```
10 FOR I = 1 TO 10
20 PRINT RND(1)
30 NEXT I
40 END
```

In some versions of BASIC it is necessary to *seed* the random number generator first, in order to avoid getting the same numbers every time RND is used. In this case, add the line

```
5 RANDOMIZE
```

to the program above and provide a seed value when the computer asks

```
RANDOM NUMBER SEED (-32768 TO 32767)?
```

We assume that a seed is either not needed or has already been given for the programs in the rest of this lesson.

Many calculators can generate random numbers. The function on your calculator might be called **rand**, **RANDOM**, or something similar. As in BASIC, the range of this function is $0 \le y < 1$. In this text, **rand** will be used to denote this function.

It may be necessary to seed your calculator. Find out how to do that. In the rest of this lesson we shall assume that your calculator does not need a seed or has been seeded.

Simulating a Probability

Once you have learned how to generate random integers with your technology, you can perform simulations, as the following example shows.

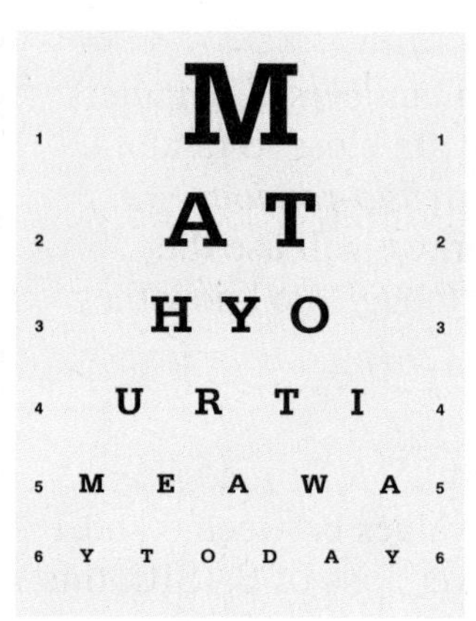

Example 1

A new operation to restore eyesight is thought to be successful 85% of the time when performed well on appropriate patients. Explain how to use technology to generate data to simulate the results of 60 operations.

Solution

Use the three steps of the Monte Carlo method.

1. *Use a graphics calculator as the tool.* **rand** will generate random numbers y such that $0 \leq y < 1$. **round** can be used to round to the nearest hundredth. On some calculators the key sequence **round** (**rand**, 2), will randomly generate a number in the set {.00, .01, .02, .03, ..., .98, .99}.
2. *A trial can be run by pressing* ENTER. *If the trial gives .00 to .84, call it a success. If the trial gives .85 to .99, call it a failure.*
3. *Repeat for 60 trials.*

Check

Here are the data from a simulation on one calculator.

.96	.31	.28	.08	.73	.02	.67	.05	.75	.81
.77	.4	.21	.96	.91	.01	.02	.79	.96	.04
.28	.22	.48	.7	.58	.35	.84	.65	.96	.97
.88	.9	.7	.47	0	.09	.78	.24	.09	.19
.72	.64	.58	.15	.16	.89	.9	.71	.05	.54
.76	.66	.68	.64	.29	.48	.52	.75	.85	.18

49 of the results are from 0 to .84, and $\frac{49}{60} \approx 82\%$. The simulation seems to be generating a random sample.

Generating Random Integers

The range of the **rand** function is $0 \leq y < 1$. This is a convenient range if the function is used to simulate an event with a certain probability, as in Example 1. If you need a different range, you can use the floor function and transformations to generate random numbers within an appropriate range.

Suppose, for instance, you want to select numbers randomly from the set {1, 2, 3}. The value of **rand** will lie in each of the equal-sized intervals $0 \leq y < \frac{1}{3}$, $\frac{1}{3} \leq y < \frac{2}{3}$, and $\frac{2}{3} \leq y < 1$ about one-third of the time. So 3 * **rand** will lie in each of the intervals $0 \leq y < 1$, $1 \leq y < 2$, and $2 \leq y < 3$ about one-third of the time. Now apply the floor function.

INT (3 * **rand**) will generate each of the integers 0, 1, and 2 about one-third of the time. Finally, **INT** (3 * **rand**) + 1 will generate the correct integers 1, 2, and 3 with the appropriate frequencies. The following table summarizes this reasoning.

Function	Range	Graph
rand	$\{y: 0 \le y < 1\}$	0 1 2 3
3 * **rand**	$\{y: 0 \le y < 3\}$	0 1 2 3
INT(3 * **rand**)	{0, 1, 2}	0 1 2 3
INT(3 * **rand**) + 1	{1, 2, 3}	0 1 2 3

The procedure can be generalized to any set of the form $\{1, 2, \ldots, n\}$.

Using Random Integers for Simulations

It is a common practice for airline companies to accept more reservations than there are available seats, to compensate for the fact that many people do not show up for their scheduled flights. If the airline accepts too many reservations, it is likely that some passengers will not be able to travel, despite having reserved seats. If they accept too few reservations, many flights will depart with empty seats. Neither situation is desirable from the company's viewpoint.

Suppose that an airline has a small commuter aircraft with a 24-seat capacity. How many reservations should it accept for each flight?

The company could solve this problem by experimenting with accepting different numbers of reservations. However, they may find this too expensive if too many planes depart with empty seats. If too many planes are overbooked, the company may lose many future customers. So, a simulation is a good idea here.

Suppose, based on past records, that the probability of arrival for each passenger is 0.9 and further that each passenger acts without regard to what other passengers do. That is, assume the events are independent.

A means of simulating a probability of .9 is needed. One way to do this is to generate random integers from 0 to 9. This can be done by using a BASIC program or **INT**(10 * **rand**) on a calculator. We generated 24 random numbers, and let '0' represent a no-show. (A no-show could be coded with any digit since each has a 0.1 probability of appearing, the same as that of a passenger failing to show up for a flight.) We ran the experiment 6 times.

Trial 1:	71194	18738	44013	48840	6321
Trial 2:	94595	56869	69014	60045	1842
Trial 3:	57740	84378	25331	12566	5867
Trial 4:	38867	62300	08158	17983	1643
Trial 5:	56865	05859	90106	31595	7154
Trial 6:	18663	72695	52180	20847	1223

The results, if only 24 reservations are accepted, are shown at the right. This suggests that the airline might reasonably accept 25 reservations and seldom be overbooked. But how often is seldom? The following shows a way to find out.

trial	arrived	not arrived (no-shows)
1	22	2
2	21	3
3	23	1
4	21	3
5	21	3
6	22	2

Example 2

Run 10 simulations to estimate how many reservations are needed to fill the plane.

Solution

Use the same plan as just described, except now generate random integers until all 24 seats are full. Our results are shown below.

	Reservations	
Trial	Simulated (0 means no-show)	Needed
1	24130 48360 22527 97265 76393 6	26
2	42167 93093 06243 61680 37856 16	27
3	37570 39975 81837 16656 06121 9	26
4	77921 06907 11008 42751 27756 534	28
5	09429 93969 52636 92737 88974	25
6	10365 61129 87529 85689 48237	25
7	07119 97336 71048 08178 77233 13	27
8	51085 12765 51821 51259 77452	25
9	82368 21382 52474 60268 89368	25
10	01001 54092 33362 94904 31273 04147	30

Accepting less than 25 reservations will leave empty seats. Accepting 26 reservations may lead to overbooking in some cases but will fill the plane most of the time.

By using a computer, thousands of trials can be run and the probability of people with no seat estimated rather closely. The company then has the information it needs to decide how many reservations to accept.

This same idea is used by hotels in deciding how many reservations they can accept.

Simulation Used for Purely Mathematical Problems

A problem of great importance in mathematics is that of finding the area enclosed by curves on the coordinate plane. The great mathematician Archimedes (287–212 B.C.) was the first to solve the problem of finding the area of the region under the parabola $y = x^2$ between $x = 0$ and $x = 1$, shown shaded in the graph at the right.

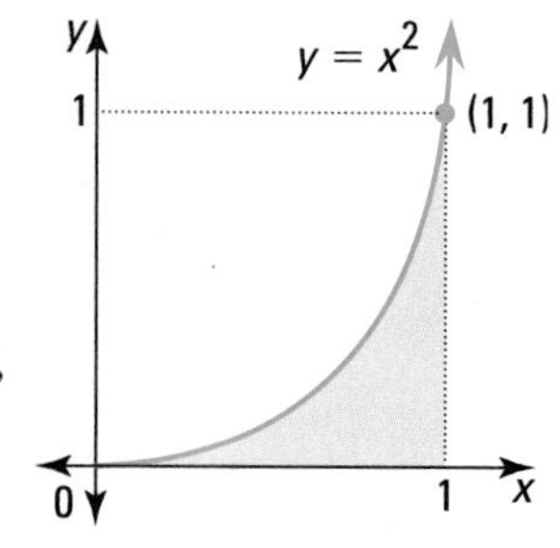

At first, this may not look like a problem which can be approached by a simulation. However, it can be done! The idea is that if a point is randomly selected in the unit-square region bounded by (0, 0), (0, 1), (1, 1), and (1, 0), then the probability it lies in the shaded area is the ratio of the shaded area to the area of the square:

$$P(\text{point is in the shaded area}) = \frac{\text{shaded area}}{\text{area of square}}.$$

Notice that in the shaded area, $y < x^2$. Using this fact, it is possible to use a spreadsheet or a graphics calculator with a spreadsheet feature to conduct a Monte Carlo simulation. Randomly select a large number n of points at random in the unit-square region and test whether $y < x^2$. If c of the points lie in the shaded area, then a good estimate of P(point is in the shaded area) is $\frac{c}{n}$. Because the area of the square is known to be 1, the shaded area under the parabola is easily estimated.

One way to do this is to use the **rand** function to assign 100 random numbers to column L1 and 100 random numbers to column L2. The numbers in column L1 are the x-values and those in column L2 are the y-values of 100 random points in the unit-square region. Have the spreadsheet or the calculator test when the numbers in column L2 are smaller than the squares of the numbers in column L1. When this is so, let 1 be the result. When this is not so, let the result be 0. Store these answers in column L3. The sum of the numbers in column L3 is the number c of points in the shaded area. Below are the first seven points of our output for one trial.

L1	L2	L3
.81957	.61630	1
.77186	.87352	0
.42401	.62674	0
.53215	.70656	0
.91212	.35701	1
.96849	.54378	1
.04107	.07178	0

The table shows that 3 of the first 7 randomly chosen points were in the shaded region.

We ran this simulation 100 times (thus randomly choosing $100 \cdot 100 = 10{,}000$ points in the unit square). The number of times our point was in the shaded region was 3282. Thus, an estimate for the area is $\frac{3282}{10000} = .3282$.

Using calculus, it can be shown that the area under the parabola between $x = 0$ and $x = 1$ is exactly $\frac{1}{3}$. Thus our simulation is accurate to within about .005. In any simulation, you need to conduct a large number of trials to obtain accurate results.

QUESTIONS

Covering the Reading

1. Explain the meaning of *pseudo-random numbers*.

2. What function on your calculator yields random numbers between 0 and 1?

3. Suppose in Example 1 the probability of success was .9. Modify the procedure to run the simulation.

In 4–7, give the range of possible values of the calculator key sequence.

4. 12 * **rand**

5. **INT** (2 * **rand**)

6. **INT** (**rand**) + 1

7. **INT** (2 * **rand**) + 1

8. Refer to the six trials of the airline reservations problem before Example 2. Suppose that 4 is used instead of a 0 to represent a no-show. What difference does this make in the results?

9. Refer to Example 2. Run the simulation for five more trials. Comment on any differences in the results.

In 10–13, suppose that a simulation is run to find the area under the parabola $y = x^2$ between $x = 0$ and $x = 1$. What is the approximation produced if the following points are chosen?

10. (0.3, 0.8), (0.6, 0.2), (0.4, 0.1), (0.9, 0.5)

11. (0.16, 0.74), (0.77, 0.68), (0.88, 0.96), (0.04, 0.71), (0.85, 0.37), (0.2, 0.01)

12. **13.**

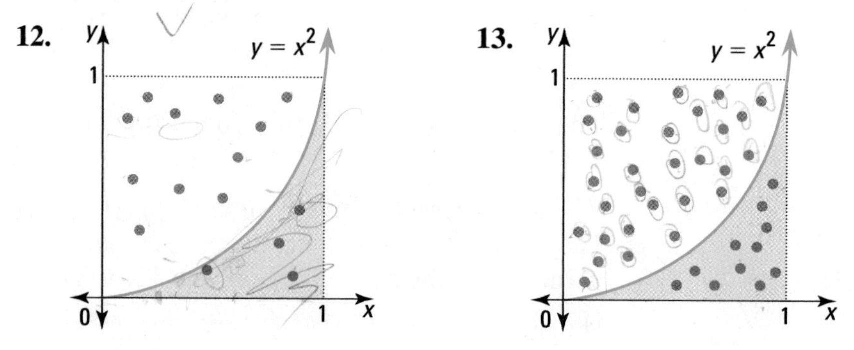

14. Adapt the simulation to find the area under the parabola $y = x^2$ between $x = 0$ and $x = 2$ using 1000 points.

Applying the Mathematics

15. Run a simulation of Example 2 of Lesson 7-7 using technology.

16. Run a simulation to approximate the area bounded by the graphs of $y = \sin x$, $x = 0$, $x = \pi$, and the x-axis.

17. Suppose that a manufacturer knows that 2% of the nails he makes are defective. Design and run a simulation to determine how many nails his company should put in each box in order to have at least 100 good nails in a box.

Review

18. **a.** Use the Table of Random Numbers to simulate rolling two dice 100 times.
b. What fraction of the time did a sum of 7 occur? *(Lesson 7-7)*

19. A bag contains 5 black, 4 orange, and 3 green marbles. Three marbles are drawn in succession, each marble being replaced before the next one is drawn. What is the probability of drawing a black, then an orange, and then a green marble? *(Lessons 7-1, 7-5)*

20. **a.** How many four-letter permutations can be made using the letters in the word COMPANY?
b. List five of these permutations which have a meaning in English. *(Lesson 7-4)*

21. **a.** Show that ${}_8P_5 = 56 \cdot {}_6P_3$.
b. Prove that ${}_nP_r = (n^2 - n) \cdot {}_{n-2}P_{r-2}$. *(Lesson 7-4)*

22. Consider the experiment of tossing a fair coin four times. *(Lessons 7-1, 7-2)*
a. Determine the probability of at least two heads.
b. Determine the probability of exactly one head.
c. *True or false.* The two events in parts **a** and **b** are complementary events. Justify your answer.

Exploration

23. **a.** Use a simulation to approximate the area under the curve $y = x^n$ from $x = 0$ to $x = 1$ for $n = 3, 4$, and 5.
b. Make a conjecture for the area under the curve $y = x^n$ from $x = 0$ to $x = 1$ for positive integers n.

A project presents an opportunity for you to extend your knowledge of a topic related to the material of this chapter. You should allow more time for a project than you do for a typical homework question.

1 Fair Dice?

Obtain a pair of dice distinguishable from each other (for instance, two dice of different sizes or colors).

a. Throw the dice fifty times, recording the results of each die on each throw.

b. Construct a relative frequency distribution for each of the two dice separately.

c. Construct a relative frequency distribution for the sum of the two dice.

d. Repeat steps **a–c** at least three more times. Calculate the total relative frequency distribution for the sum of the two dice.

e. For a larger number of tosses, describe how close the relative frequencies of occurrence of the numbers 1 to 6 on a single die and of the sums from 2 to 12 on the pair of dice are to their probabilities. Do your dice seem to be fair? Why or why not?

2 Insurance Rates

Statistics and probability are used in determining insurance premiums (the amounts that people pay for insurance). Pick a type of insurance (for example, automobile or life).

a. Find out all the variables that affect the premiums you would have to pay if you wanted this type of insurance and what it would cost you to obtain this type of insurance.

b. Write an essay summarizing how insurance companies use statistics and probability to determine these rates.

3 The Birthday Problem

a. Calculate the probability that n people have n different birthdates, for $n = 2, 3, 4,$ and k.

b. What is the smallest value of k for which this probability is less than .5? (This is known as the **birthday problem.**)

c. Test the result of part **b** on a group of people or with a set of birthdays of famous people.

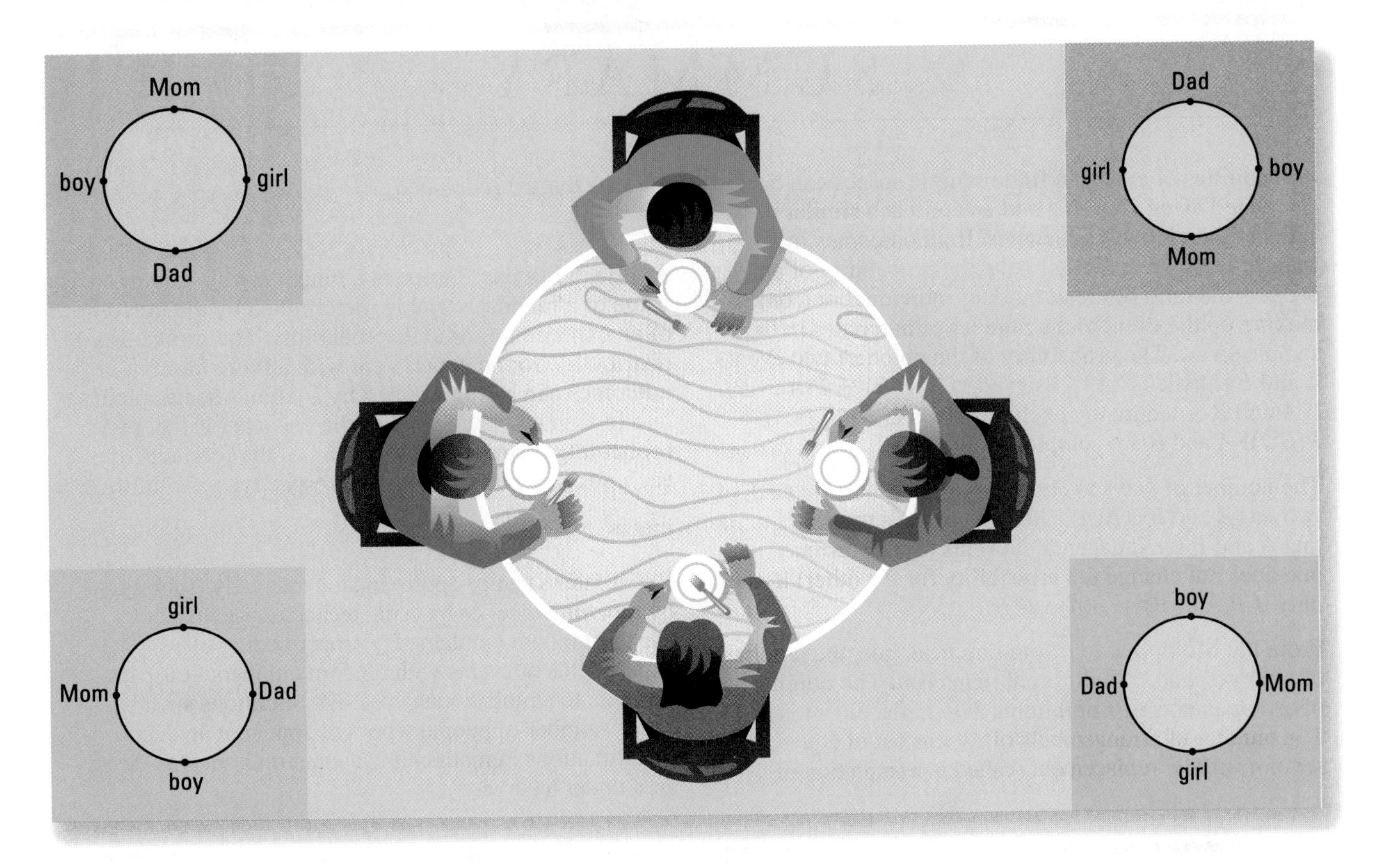

4 Seating Arrangements

a. The Grump family, consisting of two parents and two children, are about to sit down together at a circular table with four seats. In how many different ways can they do this if rotation images as shown in the corners above are regarded as the same?

b. Generalize your answer to part **a**. That is, in how many different ways can n people be seated at a circular table? Make drawings and write mathematical arguments to support your answer.

5 Probabilistic Analysis of Functions

Investigate the following situation. If r and s are numbers from 0 to 9, what is the probability P that the function $f(x) = x^2 + rx + s$ has real roots?

a. Consider the case where r and s are integers, and conduct an experiment. Randomly choose 20 pairs (r, s) of integers from 0 to 9, calculate the relative frequency of the number of functions having real roots, and estimate P. Repeat the experiment and revise your estimate as necessary.

b. Calculate the probability of having real roots if r and s are integers from 0 to 9. (Hint: There are 100 outcomes in the sample space.)

c. Assume r and s are real numbers from 0 to 9. Modify the method of Lesson 7-8 to estimate the probability that f has real roots.

d. Repeat parts **b** and **c** allowing r and s to lie in the interval from -10 to 10. Compare the probabilities you get with those found in parts **b** and **c**.

SUMMARY

Probabilities of events in finite sample spaces can be calculated using counting and an approach similar to calculating relative frequencies. If all outcomes in a sample space are equally likely, the probability of an event is the ratio of the number of individual outcomes making up the event to the number of outcomes in the sample space. The probability of the union of two events A and B satisfies $P(A \cup B) = P(A) + P(B) - P(A \cap B)$. If A and B are mutually exclusive, $P(A \cup B) = P(A) + P(B)$. If A and B are complementary, $P(B) = 1 - P(A)$.

The number of ways to choose one element from each of two sets A and B is $N(A) \cdot N(B)$. This leads to the definition that A and B are independent events (the occurrence of one does not change the probability for the other) if and only if $P(A \cap B) = P(A) \cdot P(B)$.

From the Multiplication Counting Principle, the number of arrangements of n different items is $n!$ The number of arrangements of r of n items *with* replacement is n^r. The number of arrangements of r items out of a given set of n *without* replacement (called a permutation of r out of n things) is denoted ${}_nP_r$.
$${}_nP_r = n(n-1)\ldots(n-r+1) = \frac{n!}{(n-r)!}.$$

A probability distribution is a function which maps each value of a random variable (determined by the outcome of an experiment) onto its probability. The probability distribution for an experiment with a finite number of outcomes can be represented by a table, a scatterplot, or a histogram. The mean, or the expected value, of a probability distribution is the sum of the products of each possible outcome with its respective probability; that is, $\mu = \sum_{i=1}^{n} (x_i \cdot P(x_i))$.

Randomness can be approximated manually (such as by throwing dice) or by using technology-generated pseudo-random numbers. By proper coding of experiments or events with random numbers, it is possible to simulate many real-life situations such as the number of people who will appear at an event, or estimations in mathematical situations such as the area under a curve.

VOCABULARY

Below are the most important terms and phrases for this chapter. You should be able to give a general description and a specific example of each and a precise definition for those marked with an asterisk (*).

Lesson 7-1
probability theory, experiment
outcome, *sample space
event
*probability of an event
fair, unbiased, at random, randomly
Basic Properties of Probability Theorem

Lesson 7-2
union of sets
*disjoint sets, mutually exclusive sets
intersection of sets, Venn diagram
Addition Counting Principle (mutually exclusive form; general form)
Probability of a Union Theorem (for mutually exclusive events; general form)
complementary events, not A
Probability of Complements Theorem

Lesson 7-3
tree diagram
Multiplication Counting Principle
arrangement
Selections with Replacement Theorem
*n factorial, $n!$
Selections without Replacement Theorem

Lesson 7-4
*permutation
Permutation Theorem
*permutations of n objects taken r at a time, ${}_nP_r$
Formula for ${}_nP_r$ Theorem
Alternate Formula for ${}_nP_r$ Theorem

Lesson 7-5
*independent events
dependent events

Lesson 7-6
random variable
probability distribution
*mean of a probability distribution
expected value of a probability distribution

Lesson 7-7
simulation
trial
Monte Carlo method
*random numbers

Lesson 7-8
pseudo-random numbers
rand

PROGRESS SELF-TEST

Take this test as you would take a test in class. Then check the test yourself using the solutions at the back of the book.

1. Assume that each of the two spinners shown below is equally likely to land in each of the three regions.

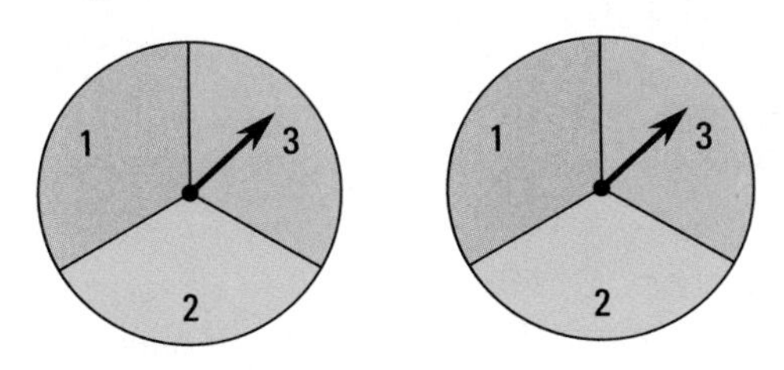

a. Give the sample space for the result of spinning *both* spinners.

b. What is the probability that the sum of the two spinners is greater than 4?

2. When two fair dice of different colors are rolled, what is the probability that the red die will show an odd number and the green die will show an even number?

3. Suppose $P(A \cap B) = 0.5$, $P(A) = 0.6$, and $P(B) = 0.8$. Find $P(A \cup B)$.

4. a. Determine the number of permutations of the letters in the word MASTER.

b. How many of these permutations begin with A and end with T?

In 5 and 6, evaluate.

5. $\frac{9!}{3!}$ **6.** ${}_5P_3$

7. *True or false.* If an event A contains all the possible outcomes of an experiment, then $P(A) = 1$.

8. Consider the events of scoring under 50 and scoring from 50 to 100 on a test. Determine if the events are mutually exclusive, complementary, or both, if the maximum possible score on the test is the following.

a. 100 **b.** 120

9. Solve ${}_nP_4 = 56{}_nP_2$.

10. A consumer protection group reports that 25% of 5-lb bags of sugar of a certain brand are underweight. Three bags of sugar are selected at random. Assume that the report is correct.

a. What is the probability that all three bags are underweight?

b. What is the probability that none of the bags is underweight?

11. If you have three pairs of jeans, two pairs of sneakers, and five sweatshirts, how many different outfits consisting of jeans, a sweatshirt, and sneakers can you make?

12. A test contains 10 true-false questions and 5 multiple-choice questions, each with four choices. Assuming a student answers all questions, how many different answer sheets are possible?

13. Susie Shoorschott makes $\frac{1}{3}$ of her three-point shots in basketball. Design a simulation which does not use random digits to estimate how many three-point shots she would make if she shot 100 times.

14. It is known that the probability of contracting a certain children's disease by coming into contact with an infected person is 0.12. Use the random number table in Appendix C to estimate the probability that if all five children in a family come in contact with their infected cousin, at least two of the children in the family will get the disease from the cousin. Conduct 25 trials.

15. Explain how to use technology to approximate the area between the graph of $y = \cos x$ and the x-axis from $x = 0$ to $x = \frac{\pi}{2}$.

16. a. Verify that the table below shows a probability distribution.

x	1	2	3	4	5
$P(x)$	.03	.47	.22	.05	.23

b. Graph the probability function in part **a**.

c. Calculate the mean of the distribution.

CHAPTER SEVEN

CHAPTER REVIEW

Questions on SPUR Objectives

SPUR stands for **S**kills, **P**roperties, **U**ses, and **R**epresentations. The Chapter Review questions are grouped according to the SPUR Objectives for this chapter.

SKILLS DEAL WITH THE PROCEDURES USED TO GET ANSWERS.

Objective A: *List sample spaces and events for probabilistic experiments.* *(Lesson 7-1)*

In 1–3, consider the experiment of tossing three different coins.

1. Write the sample space for the experiment.
2. List the outcomes in the event "at least two tails show up."
3. *True or false.* The event "no tails show up" consists of a single outcome.

In 4–6, assume that a right-hand page of this book is picked at random and the page number if it has one is recorded.

4. What is the sample space for this experiment?
5. Write the set of outcomes in the event "the page is the first page of a chapter."
6. *True or false.* The event "the page has an even number" is the empty set.

Objective B: *Compute probabilities.* *(Lessons 7-1, 7-2, 7-3)*

In 7 and 8, consider rolling two fair dice, and recording the numbers on the top faces. Find each probability.

7. P(each die is even)
8. P(the sum is even)
9. Consider the experiment of tossing a coin and a fair die. The coin is marked "1" (heads) and "2" (tails). Find the probability that the sum is less than 5.

In 10 and 11, let x be a randomly selected number from {1, 2, 3, 5, 8, 13, 21, 34, 55, 89}. Calculate the probability.

10. $P(x \text{ is even or } x < 2^5)$
11. $P(x \text{ is even and } x < 2^5)$
12. When two fair dice are tossed, what is the probability the first is a 3 or the second is odd?

Objective C: *Find the number of ways of selecting or arranging objects.* *(Lessons 7-3, 7-4)*

13. A coin is tossed seven times. How many possible outcomes are there?
14. List all the permutations of the digits 4, 0, and 7.
15. a. Determine the number of permutations of the letters of the word NUMBER.
    b. How many of these permutations end in BER?
16. a. How many permutations consisting of four letters each can be formed from the letters of DINOSAUR?
    b. How many of the permutations in part **a** end in R?
    c. How many of the permutations in part a start with D and end in R?

Objective D: *Evaluate expressions using factorials.* *(Lessons 7-3, 7-4)*

In 17–19, evaluate without using a calculator.

17. 7!
18. 0!
19. $\frac{21!}{20!}$
20. Write $\frac{16!}{12!}$ as a product of integers.
21. Evaluate $\frac{120!}{116!}$.
22. *True or false.* $\frac{12!}{6!6!} = \frac{12!}{8!4!}$

In 23 and 24, evaluate.

23. ${}_{10}P_4$
24. ${}_{5}P_5$

PROPERTIES DEAL WITH THE PRINCIPLES BEHIND THE MATHEMATICS.

Objective E: *State and use properties of probabilities.* *(Lessons 7-1, 7-2, 7-5)*

25. If $P(A) = .23$ in an experiment, determine $P(\text{not } A)$.

26. Explain why $P(E) = 1.5$ cannot be a correct statement for any event E.

In 27–30, *true or false.*

27. If A and B are mutually exclusive events, and $P(A) = .7$, then $P(B) = .3$.

28. If A and B are complementary events and $P(A) = k$, then $P(B) = 1 - k$.

29. If A and B are independent events, then $P(A \text{ or } B) = 1$.

30. If the sample space of A is $\emptyset$, then $P(A) = 0$.

Objective F: *Determine whether events are mutually exclusive, independent, or complementary.* *(Lessons 7-2, 7-5)*

In 31 and 32, determine if the pair of events are mutually exclusive.

31. Scoring an 80 on a test and scoring a 95 on the same test.

32. Throwing a sum of 9 on two dice and throwing a 2 on at least one die.

33. *True or false.* Selecting a king from a deck of cards and then picking a king from the remaining cards are two independent events.

34. In selecting a TV viewer, are "finding an adult" and "finding a teenager" complementary events? Explain your reasoning.

In 35–38, you are given information about the probabilities of events A and B. Deduce which (if any) of the terms below apply to the events.

(a) mutually exclusive

(b) complementary

(c) independent

35. $P(A) = .5$, $P(B) = .2$, $P(A \cup B) = .6$

36. $P(A) = .5$, $P(B) = .2$, $P(A \cup B) = .7$

37. $P(A) = .4$, $P(B) = .6$, $P(A \cup B) = 1$

38. $P(A) = .33$, $P(B) = .3$, $P(A \cup B) = .099$

Objective G: *Solve equations using factorials.* *(Lesson 7-4)*

In 39–42, solve.

39. $\frac{x!}{56} = 6!$

40. $\frac{t!}{(t-1)!} = 19$

41. ${}_nP_5 = 12{}_nP_4$

42. ${}_5P_c = {}_6P_3$

USES DEAL WITH APPLICATIONS OF MATHEMATICS IN REAL SITUATIONS.

Objective H: *Calculate probabilities in real situations.* *(Lessons 7-1, 7-2, 7-5)*

In 43 and 44, consider the following situation. An ornithologist feeds a special nutrient to 26 of the 257 pelicans in a bird sanctuary and tags them. A week later, she captures a pelican in the sanctuary. Assume the special nutrient does not affect the behavior of the birds.

43. What is the probability that the pelican is a tagged one?

44. If the pelican is not tagged, what is the probability that the next one she catches will be tagged if she

a. releases the first bird?

b. does not release the first bird?

CHAPTER SEVEN

In 45 and 46, consider a business which needs computer diskettes. Of the two independent suppliers they usually use, U has a .4 probability and C has a .7 probability of filling any given order in three days. They order diskettes from both suppliers.

45. What is the probability that both U and C will fill the order in 3 days?

46. What is the probability that the order will be filled by at least one of the suppliers in 3 days?

Objective I: *Use counting principles and theorems to find the number of ways of arranging objects.* *(Lessons 7-3, 7-4)*

47. How many different ways can a student answer 20 multiple-choice questions, each of which has four choices?

48. Susan has a choice of n math classes, five science classes and two history classes. In how many ways can she select one of each of the three kinds of classes?

49. In how many ways can the starting five on a basketball team line up in a row?

50. A committee of two students is to be chosen from a school with 340 juniors and 330 seniors. In how many ways can the committee be chosen to include both a junior and a senior?

51. How many automobile license plates consisting of two letters followed by four digits are there if repetitions of letters or digits are allowed?

52. A certain car seats five people, two in front and three in back.

a. In how many ways can a family of five be seated in the car?

b. In how many ways can a family of five be seated in the car for a trip if only two of the family members have driver's licenses?

Objective J: *Design and conduct simulations without technology.* *(Lesson 7-7)*

In 53–54, design and conduct a simulation without using a random number table or technology.

53. Simulate selecting 5 samples of 16 corn stalks each from a field which is estimated to be 25% damaged because of a drought. What percentage of corn in each sample is damaged?

54. Manuel doesn't have any idea how to answer 15 questions on a multiple-choice test for which there are 3 possible choices for each question. Simulate his answering these questions by guessing, running 10 trials. What is the estimated probability that he gets 7 or more correct?

In 55–56, design and conduct a simulation using a random number table to answer each question.

55. John has a batting average of .325. What is the estimated probability of his getting 4 or more hits in his next 10 at-bats?

56. A washer manufacturer knows that 3% of the washers made are defective. How many washers should be put in each box sold to have at least 50 good washers in each box?

CHAPTER SEVEN

Objective K: *Design and conduct simulations using technology.* (*Lesson 7-8*)

57. Design and conduct an experiment to simulate rolling three dice 1000 times. What is your experimental probability that the sum is greater than or equal to 15?

58. Suppose that in a lacrosse playoff series of 5 games, team *A* has a .6 probability of winning the game over team *B*. Design and conduct a simulation of 1000 such series between the two teams. About how many times does *A* win the series?

In 59–60, estimate the area between the graph of the function and the *x*-axis.

59. $f(x) = x^2 + 3$ from $x = 0$ to $x = 1$

60. $f(x) = \sin x + \cos x$ from $x = 0$ to $x = \frac{\pi}{2}$

REPRESENTATIONS DEAL WITH PICTURES, GRAPHS, OR OBJECTS THAT ILLUSTRATE CONCEPTS.

Objective L: *Construct, graph, and interpret probability distributions.* (*Lesson 7-6*)

61. On a fair die, the faces contained 0, 1, 2, 1, 2, and 4 dots.

a. Find the probability of each of the outcomes 0, 1, 2, and 4.

b. Graph the distribution as a histogram.

c. Find the mean of the probability distribution.

62. Tell why this table does *not* show a probability distribution.

x	-1	0	1	4
$P(x)$	$\frac{1}{2}$	$\frac{1}{4}$	$\frac{1}{8}$	$\frac{1}{5}$

63. Construct a graph of the probability distribution for the function *P* where *P*(*s*) is the probability that when two fair dice are rolled, the number *s* showing on one die is greater than or equal to the number showing on the other die.

64. In a lottery, 120 tickets are sold at $1 each. First prize is $50 and second prize is $20. Find the expected value of a ticket.

x = profit in dollars	-1	19	49
$P(x)$	$\frac{118}{120}$	$\frac{1}{120}$	$\frac{1}{120}$

65. The clerk in charge of textbooks took a sample of books that were returned at the end of the year and judged whether they were reusable. Here is the distribution of books that were not reusable.

x = age of book in years	1	2	3	4	5	6
Number destroyed	3	10	10	12	20	30

On the basis of this data, what is the expected life span of a book?

CHAPTER

Sequences, Series, and Combinations

Although few hereditary diseases can be cured at present, tests have been developed to detect carriers of many genetic disorders. By assessing the probabilities that various genetic diseases will arise in their family, couples can make informed decisions concerning their future.

For instance, suppose that Mr. and Mrs. Washington each had siblings with cystic fibrosis, a disease now known to be hereditary. If the Washingtons have two children, what is the probability that one will have the disease? This situation can be analyzed as a *binomial experiment*, a type of situation which you will study in this chapter.

Probabilities in binomial experiments can be calculated from just a few pieces of information. In the case of cystic fibrosis, two out of three people who have siblings with cystic fibrosis are carriers of the disease. Also, the probability that two carriers of the disease have an afflicted child is 25%. From this information, it can be found that if Mr. and Mrs. Washington have two children, then the probability that at least one has the disease is about 21%. (Of course, if detection tests show that either Mr. or Mrs. Washington is not a carrier, the probability is drastically reduced.)

Binomial experiments such as this one appear in business, politics, and sports, as well as medicine, and they require a knowledge of counting techniques. In this chapter, these techniques are developed through a discussion of sequences, series, and combinations.

LESSON

8-1

Formulas for Sequences

In a *Nautshell*. *The shell of a chambered nautilus maintains its shape as it grows along a logarithmic spiral. The sizes of the chambers, shown in this cross section, form a sequence which is closely related to the Fibonacci sequence.*

What Is a Sequence?

Consider the following example. Let R_n be the number of dots in a rectangular array of dots with n columns and $n + 1$ rows.

$R_1 = 2$ $\quad R_2 = 6$ $\quad R_3 = 12$ $\quad R_4 = 20$ $\quad R_5 = 30$

In general, the nth array has n dots in each of $n + 1$ rows, so $R_n = n(n + 1)$.

$R_n = n(n + 1)$ is a formula that pairs each positive integer n with the corresponding number R_n. Specifically, the function R contains the ordered pairs (1, 2), (2, 6), (3, 12), (4, 20), (5, 30), and so on. It is an example of a type of function called a *sequence*.

Definition
A **sequence** is a function whose domain is a set of consecutive integers greater than or equal to k.

Each element in the range of a sequence is called a **term** of the sequence. The corresponding positive integer in the domain is its **position** in the sequence. Often, the letter n is used to denote the position of a term, and a subscripted variable such as R_n or a_n is used to denote the term itself.

A formula such as $R_n = n(n + 1)$, which shows the nth term of a sequence in terms of n, is called an **explicit formula**. In contrast, a **recursive**

formula is one in which the first term or first few terms are given, and then the nth term is expressed using the preceding term(s).

For the sequence R on page 488, notice that each term other than the first is the sum of the previous one and some even number.

$$\begin{aligned} R_2 &= 6 = 2 + 4 = R_1 + 4 \\ R_3 &= 12 = 6 + 6 = R_2 + 6 \\ R_4 &= 20 = 12 + 8 = R_3 + 8 \\ R_5 &= 30 = 20 + 10 = R_4 + 10 \end{aligned}$$

In each case the even number added is twice the subscript of R_n. That is, $R_n = R_{n-1} + 2n$. So a recursive formula for this sequence is

$$\begin{cases} R_1 = 2 \\ R_n = R_{n-1} + 2n, \text{ for all integers } n > 1. \end{cases}$$

The pattern in the recursive formula can be pictured.

$R_1 = 2$ $\quad R_2 = R_1 + 2 \cdot 2$ $\quad R_3 = R_2 + 2 \cdot 3$ $\quad R_4 = R_3 + 2 \cdot 4$ $\quad R_5 = R_4 + 2 \cdot 5$

Example 1

a. Calculate R_6 using the explicit formula.
b. Assume R_5 is known. Calculate R_6 using the recursive formula.
c. Find R_{14} using either formula.

Solution

a. Use the explicit formula $R_n = n(n + 1)$.

$$R_6 = 6(6 + 1) = 6 \cdot 7 = 42$$

b. Use the recursive formula $R_n = R_{n-1} + 2n$.

$$\begin{aligned} R_6 &= R_{6-1} + 2 \cdot 6 \\ &= R_5 + 12 \\ &= 30 + 12 \\ &= 42 \end{aligned}$$

c. To use the recursive formula, you would need to know R_{13}. So use the explicit formula.

$$\begin{aligned} R_{14} &= 14(14 + 1) \\ &= 14 \cdot 15 = 210 \end{aligned}$$

Check

a. and **b.** Draw an array. As shown at the right, $R_6 = 42$.
c. Find the first 13 terms: 2, 6, 12, 20, 30, 42, 56, 72, 90, 110, 132, 156, 182. So $R_{13} = 182$. Now use the recursive definition. $R_{14} = R_{13} + 2 \cdot 14$. So $R_{14} = 182 + 28 = 210$. It checks.

Arithmetic Sequences

Two important types of sequences are *arithmetic* and *geometric* sequences. An **arithmetic sequence** is one in which the difference between consecutive terms is constant. For example, the sequence with first term equal to -7 and a constant difference of 3 is an arithmetic sequence whose first six terms are

$$-7, -4, -1, 2, 5, 8.$$

Each term beyond the first is three more than the previous term. Each term is also equal to -7 plus some number of 3s. If the nth term of this sequence is called a_n, then

$$a_n = -7 + 3 \cdot (n - 1).$$

In general, any arithmetic sequence can be generated both explicitly and recursively.

Theorem

Let n be a positive integer and a_1 and d be constants. The formulas

$$a_n = a_1 + (n - 1)d \quad \text{and} \quad \begin{cases} a_1 \\ a_n = a_{n-1} + d, n > 1 \end{cases}$$

generate the terms of the arithmetic sequence with first term a_1 and constant difference d.

The explicit formula in the theorem shows that arithmetic sequences are linear functions of n. Given such a function as an explicit formula, you can find a recursive formula.

Example 2

Write the first three terms, and give a recursive formula for the sequence whose nth term is $a_n = 27 - 4n$.

Solution

The formula for a_n is linear, so from the previous theorem it generates an arithmetic sequence. The first term is $a_1 = 27 - 4(1) = 23$.
The second term is $a_2 = 27 - 4(2) = 19$.
The third term is $a_3 = 27 - 4(3) = 15$.
The constant difference confirms that the sequence is linear.
The constant difference is $d = a_2 - a_1 = 19 - 23 = -4$.
So a recursive formula is

$$\begin{cases} a_1 = 23 \\ a_n = a_{n-1} - 4, \text{ for all integers } n > 1. \end{cases}$$

Check

Find the first few terms, using both the explicit and recursive definitions. For both methods, you get 23, 19, 15, 11, 7, ...

In an explicit formula for an arithmetic sequence, if any three of the numbers d, n, a_1, and a_n are known, the fourth can always be found.

Example 3

What position does 127 have in the arithmetic sequence below?
16, 19, 22, ..., 127, ...

Solution

The constant difference d is 3, $a_1 = 16$, and $a_n = 127$. Substitute into the explicit formula from the preceding theorem and solve for n.

$$a_n = a_1 + (n - 1)d$$
$$127 = 16 + (n - 1)3$$
$$127 = 3n + 13$$
$$n = 38$$

127 is the 38th term of the sequence.

Check

Find the 38th term directly from the formula. $a_{38} = 16 + (38 - 1)3 = 127$. It checks.

Geometric Sequences

A **geometric sequence** is one in which the *ratio* of consecutive terms is constant. For instance, in the geometric sequence $3, \frac{3}{2}, \frac{3}{4}, \frac{3}{8}, \ldots$, the constant ratio is $\frac{1}{2}$. Below at the left is an explicit formula for the nth term of this sequence; at the right is a recursive formula.

$$g_n = 3\left(\frac{1}{2}\right)^{n-1} \qquad \begin{cases} g_1 = 3 \\ g_n = \frac{1}{2}g_{n-1}, \text{ for all integers } n > 1 \end{cases}$$

Generalizing for any geometric sequence gives the following.

Theorem

Let n be a positive integer and g_1 and r be constants. The formulas

$$g_n = g_1 r^{n-1} \qquad \text{and} \qquad \begin{cases} g_1 \\ g_n = rg_{n-1}, n > 1 \end{cases}$$

generate the terms of the geometric sequence with first term g_1 and constant ratio r.

Notice that geometric sequences are exponential functions if $r > 0$ and $r \neq 1$.

Example 4

A particular car depreciates 25% in value each year. Suppose the original cost is $14,800.

a. Find the value of the car in its second year.

b. Write an explicit formula for the value of the car in its nth year.

c. In how many years will the car be worth about $1000?

Solution

a. Let g_n = the amount the car is worth in dollars in year n. So, the initial amount $g_1 = 14800$. In year 2, it is worth 75% of the previous amount, so $g_2 = 14800(.75) = 11100$.

b. The situation generates a geometric sequence. Find g_n when $g_1 = 14800$ and $r = .75$.

$$g_n = 14800(0.75)^{n-1}$$

c. Find n so that

$$g_n \approx 1000.$$

$$14800\,(.75)^{n-1} = 1000$$

$$(.75)^{n-1} \approx 0.06757.$$

Take the logarithm of each side.

$$(n-1)\log .75 \approx \log 0.06757$$

$$n - 1 \approx 9.37$$

$$n \approx 10.37$$

That is, in year 10, the car will be worth about $1000.

Some calculators have a SEQUENCE mode that allows you to generate sequences either recursively or explicitly. On these calculators, the terms of the geometric sequence in Example 4 might be generated by inputting either of the following formulas.

Recursive Formula	Explicit Formula
$U_n = .75 * U_{n-1}$	$U_n = U_n\text{Start} * (.75)\wedge(n-1)$

At the right is the output from a calculator when the window variables U_nStart = 14800 and nStart = 1. The variable nStart sets the value of n at which the calculation begins, and the variable U_nStart sets the value of U_n when $n = n$Start.

n	U_n
1	14800
2	11100
3	8325
4	6243.75
5	4682.813
6	3512.109
7	2634.082
8	1975.562
9	1481.671
10	1111.253
11	833.440

The 10th and 11th terms of the sequence provide a check to the work in part **c** of Example 4.

Explicit formulas are useful because they allow you to calculate values directly. There are, however, several reasons for using recursive formulas.

First, sometimes an explicit formula cannot be found. Second, some biological processes, such as the genetic instructions for the spiral growth of certain shells, work recursively. Third, calculator and computer programs often run faster using recursive rather than explicit formulas, particularly when the number of terms generated is large. Throughout this chapter, you will need to find many terms of a sequence quickly. You should learn to use programs or to use list features of a calculator to generate sequences.

QUESTIONS

Covering the Reading

In 1 and 2, refer to the sequence R in the lesson.

1. What is the 7th term?

2. Find R_{30}.

In 3 and 4, *true or false.*

3. The domain of every sequence is the set of positive numbers.

4. The terms of a sequence are elements of its range.

5. If t_n is a term in a sequence, what is the following term?

In 6–8, an explicit or recursive formula for a sequence is given. **a.** Determine the first three terms of the sequence. **b.** Identify the sequence as arithmetic, geometric, or neither.

6. $\begin{cases} C_1 = 2 \\ C_n = C_{n-1} - 2, \text{ for all integers } n > 1 \end{cases}$

7. $b_n = \dfrac{n(n+1)}{2}$

8. $d_n = -(1.05)^{n-1}$

9. Find the first term and the constant difference of the arithmetic sequence defined by $k_n = \frac{4-n}{2}$.

10. What is the position of 3282 in the arithmetic sequence 6, 18, 30, . . . , 3282, . . . ?

11. Consider the sequence generated by the following.

$$\begin{cases} t_1 = 18 \\ t_n = \frac{1}{2}t_{n-1}, \text{ for all integers } n > 1 \end{cases}$$

a. Write the first four terms of the sequence.
b. Write an explicit formula for t_n.
c. Find t_{20} using either the explicit or recursive formula.

12. Suppose a car bought for \$25,000 depreciates 20% per year.
a. Find the value of the car in its 3rd year.
b. In what year will the value of the car first fall below \$5000?

Applying the Mathematics

13. **a.** Complete the lines below so that a calculator in SEQUENCE mode will generate the geometric sequence 36, 24, 16, ... recursively.

$U_n =$?

U_nStart = ?

nStart = ?

b. Use a calculator to find the first twenty terms of the sequence in part **a**.

14. How many terms are in the finite geometric sequence 6, 12, 24, ..., 768?

15. Several long distance runners are on a special ten-day exercise program. They are to run three miles on the first day, and on each successive day of the program they are to increase their distance by 10% over the previous day's distance. How far must they run on the sixth day?

In 16 and 17, consider the following sequence of dots in rectangular arrays.

$O_1 = 3$ $O_2 = 8$ $O_3 = 15$ $O_4 = 24$

16. *Multiple choice.* Recall that n is the index of O_n. Which of the following describes those rectangles?

(a) The width and length equal the index.

(b) The width equals the index and the length is one more than the index.

(c) The width equals the index and the length is two more than the index.

17. **a.** Write an explicit formula for O_n.

b. What is O_{100}?

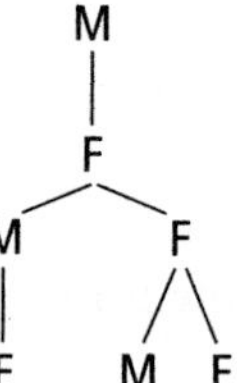

18. A female bee has both female and male parents; but a male bee has only a female parent.

a. At the left is part of the ancestral tree of a male bee. The number of bees in consecutive generations are 1, 1, 2, 3. Continue the ancestral family tree for the male bee for three more generations.

b. Complete the recursive formula for the number of bees in the nth generation of the male's ancestral tree.

$$\begin{cases} b_1 = 1 \\ b_2 = 1 \\ b_n = \underline{\ ?\ } \end{cases}$$

c. Make an ancestral tree for 3 generations of a female bee.

d. Write a recursive formula for the number of bees in the nth generation of the female's ancestral tree.

19. **a.** Use a calculator or computer to generate the first 20 terms of the arithmetic sequence with $a_1 = -97$ and $d = 4$.

b. Which term of this sequence is the number -1?

Review

20. *Multiple choice.* Refer to the graph below. Which can be an equation for the graph? *(Lesson 4-8)*

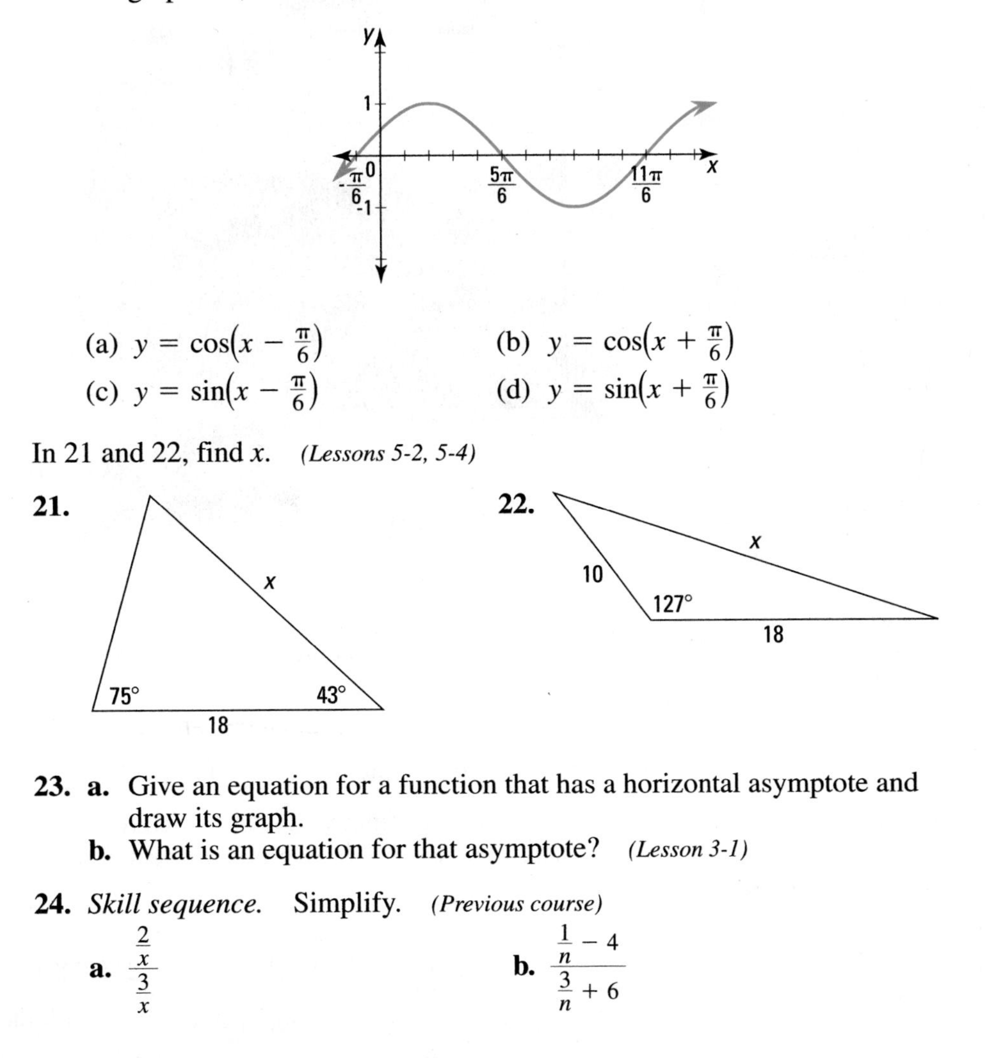

(a) $y = \cos\left(x - \frac{\pi}{6}\right)$ (b) $y = \cos\left(x + \frac{\pi}{6}\right)$

(c) $y = \sin\left(x - \frac{\pi}{6}\right)$ (d) $y = \sin\left(x + \frac{\pi}{6}\right)$

In 21 and 22, find x. *(Lessons 5-2, 5-4)*

21.

22.

23. **a.** Give an equation for a function that has a horizontal asymptote and draw its graph.

b. What is an equation for that asymptote? *(Lesson 3-1)*

24. *Skill sequence.* Simplify. *(Previous course)*

a. $\dfrac{\frac{2}{x}}{\frac{3}{x}}$ **b.** $\dfrac{\frac{1}{n} - 4}{\frac{3}{n} + 6}$

Exploration

25. Consider the right triangle with sides 3, 4, and 5. Notice that the lengths of the sides form an arithmetic sequence.

a. Determine three other right triangles with side lengths in arithmetic sequence.

b. Let the sides of a right triangle be a, $a + d$, and $a + 2d$ units long. Use the Pythagorean Theorem to determine a relation between a and d.

c. Based on the result in part **b**, make a general statement about all the right triangles whose sides form an arithmetic sequence.

LESSON

8-2

Limits of Sequences

Each image of the boy is half the height of the previous one. The limit of the sequence of images is a single point. The height of any image is the sum of the heights of the smaller images.

Notation for Limits

In Lesson 6-4, we defined the number e as the *limiting value* of the sequence

$$s_n = \left(1 + \frac{1}{n}\right)^n.$$

That is, e is the number to which $\left(1 + \frac{1}{n}\right)^n$ gets closer and closer as n increases. At that time, you were asked to calculate s_n for various values of n. Here are some other values of the sequence.

n	s_n
10	$\left(1 + \frac{1}{10}\right)^{10} = 1.1^{10} \approx 2.593742460\ldots$
100	$\left(1 + \frac{1}{100}\right)^{100} = 1.01^{100} \approx 2.704813829\ldots$
1000	$\left(1 + \frac{1}{1000}\right)^{1000} = 1.001^{1000} \approx 2.716923932\ldots$
10000	$\left(1 + \frac{1}{10000}\right)^{10000} = 1.0001^{10000} \approx 2.7181459268\ldots$

The limiting value, to 13 decimal places, is 2.7182818284590. We write

$$\lim_{n \to \infty} \left(1 + \frac{1}{n}\right)^n = e,$$

read "the limit of $\left(1 + \frac{1}{n}\right)$ to the nth power, as n approaches infinity, is e."

The sequence for e is a complicated sequence, and so we have to *tell* you it has a limiting value because proving that fact is beyond the scope of this course.

Divergent Sequences

A description of what happens to the values t_n of a sequence as n gets very large is called the **end behavior** of the sequence. Examine the following two sequences and the graphs of their first few terms. There are important similarities in the end behaviors of these sequences.

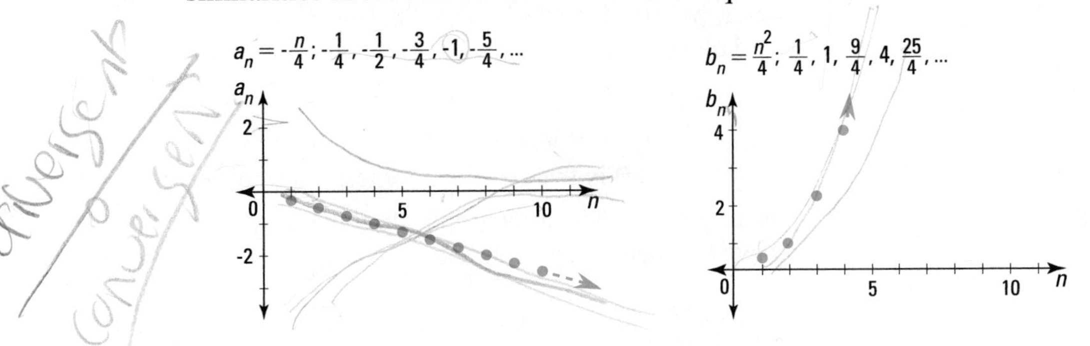

The sequence with terms $a_n = -\frac{n}{4}$ is an arithmetic sequence whose terms decrease steadily as n increases. Each term is $\frac{1}{4}$ less than its predecessor; the points all lie on a line. The terms of $b_n = \frac{n^2}{4}$ increase as n increases; all points of the graph lie on a parabola. Sequence a has a maximum value but no minimum value. Sequence b has a minimum value but no maximum value. As n increases, the terms in the former decrease without bound and those in the latter increase without bound.

Because neither sequence a nor b approaches a constant value as n increases, neither sequence has a limit as n approaches infinity. Another way of saying this is "the limit does not exist." This is consistent with the lack of horizontal asymptotes to the graphs of a and b. A sequence which does not have a finite limit is said to be **divergent** or to **diverge**. Sequences a and b are divergent.

The Harmonic Sequence

A sequence which has a finite limit L is said to be **convergent** or to **converge to L**. In this book, we do not give an algebraic definition of the limit of a sequence. Usually such a definition is studied in calculus. But we assume some properties of limits from which it can be determined whether some sequences are divergent or convergent.

The sequence of reciprocals of the positive integers, $1, \frac{1}{2}, \frac{1}{3}, \frac{1}{4}, \ldots$, sometimes called the **harmonic sequence**, is convergent.

Limit Property 1

(1) $\lim_{n \to \infty} \left(\frac{1}{n}\right) = 0$

The limit of the harmonic sequence is 0.

Why does the harmonic sequence converge to 0? Because no matter how small a number near zero you might pick, after a while the terms of the harmonic sequence are all nearer 0 than your number. This is what we mean by the phrase "getting closer and closer" to 0.

Graphically, the terms of the harmonic sequence lie on one branch of the hyperbola $y = \frac{1}{n}$. That 0 is the limit is geometrically represented by the fact that $y = 0$ is an asymptote to this graph. In general, graphs of convergent sequences have horizontal asymptotes.

The Alternating Harmonic Sequence

The **alternating harmonic sequence** with terms $c_n = \frac{(-1)^n}{n}$ is like the harmonic sequence, but every other term is negative. For example, $c_{99} = \frac{(-1)^{99}}{99} = -.\overline{01}$ and $c_{100} = \frac{(-1)^{100}}{100} = 0.01$. Although the terms alternate between positive and negative values, this sequence also has a limit of 0. Its graph has $y = 0$ as a horizontal asymptote, as shown at the right.

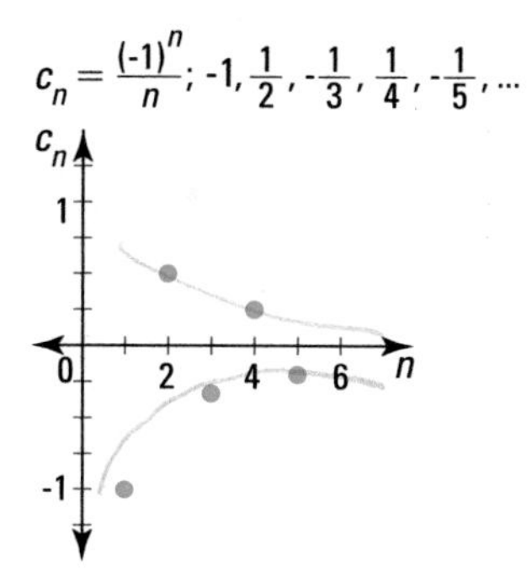

More Properties of Limits

Consider the three sequences defined by

$$e_n = 2, \qquad f_n = \frac{2}{n}, \qquad \text{and} \qquad d_n = \frac{2n+1}{n},$$

for all integers $n \geq 1$. The sequence e has all terms equal to 2, so $\lim_{n \to \infty} e_n = 2$. The sequence f is just twice the harmonic sequence, so its limit is twice the limit of the harmonic sequence; that is, $\lim_{n \to \infty} f_n = 0$.

The first few terms of the sequence defined by $d_n = \frac{2n+1}{n}$ are $\frac{3}{1}, \frac{5}{2}, \frac{7}{3}, \frac{9}{4}, \ldots$. To find out if $\lim_{n \to \infty} \left(\frac{2n+1}{n}\right)$ exists, you can rewrite $\frac{2n+1}{n}$ as a sum of fractions and simplify.

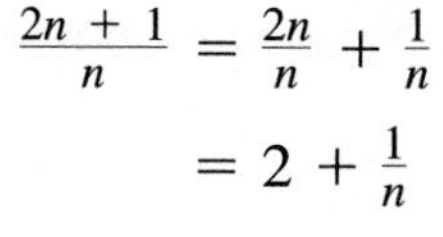

$$\frac{2n+1}{n} = \frac{2n}{n} + \frac{1}{n}$$
$$= 2 + \frac{1}{n}$$

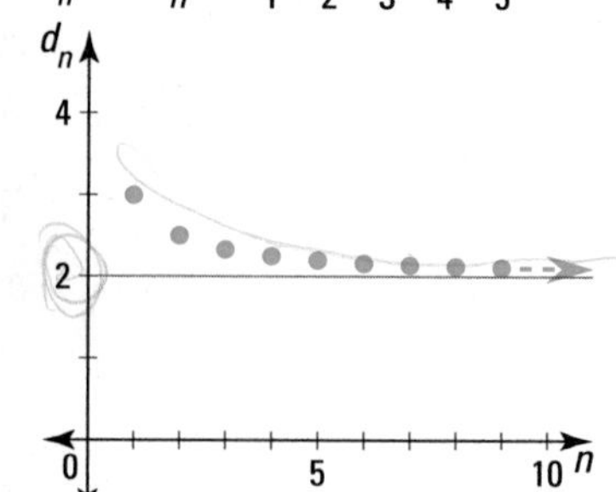

So each term of this sequence is 2 more than the corresponding term of the harmonic sequence. So its limit is 2 more than 0, or 2.

In general, limits possess the following properties.

Limit Properties 2–5

If $\lim_{n\to\infty} a_n$ and $\lim_{n\to\infty} b_n$ exist and c is a constant, then:

(2) $\lim_{n\to\infty} c = c$

The limit of a constant sequence is that constant.

(3) $\lim_{n\to\infty} (a_n + b_n) = \lim_{n\to\infty} a_n + \lim_{n\to\infty} b_n$

(4) $\lim_{n\to\infty} (a_n b_n) = \lim_{n\to\infty} a_n \cdot \lim_{n\to\infty} b_n$

The limit of a sum or product is the sum or product of the individual limits.

(5) $\lim_{n\to\infty} (ca_n) = c \cdot \lim_{n\to\infty} a_n$

The limit of a constant times the terms of a sequence equals the product of the constant and the limit of the sequence.

From Limit Properties 2 and 4, we can deduce two more properties. Suppose that a sequence b is convergent and that $\lim_{n\to\infty} b_n \neq 0$.

$$\begin{aligned}\lim_{n\to\infty} b_n \cdot \lim_{n\to\infty}\left(\tfrac{1}{b_n}\right) &= \lim_{n\to\infty}\left(b_n \cdot \tfrac{1}{b_n}\right) && \text{Limit Property 4}\\ &= \lim_{n\to\infty} 1 \\ &= 1 && \text{Limit Property 2}\end{aligned}$$

Dividing both sides of the equation by $\lim_{n\to\infty} b_n$ gives

$$\lim_{n\to\infty}\left(\tfrac{1}{b_n}\right) = \frac{1}{\lim_{n\to\infty} b_n}.$$

This proves Limit Property 6. The proof of Limit Property 7 is left for the Questions.

Limit Properties 6 and 7

If $\lim_{n\to\infty} a_n$ and $\lim_{n\to\infty} b_n$ exist and $\lim_{n\to\infty} b_n \neq 0$, then:

(6) $\lim_{n\to\infty}\left(\frac{1}{b_n}\right) = \frac{1}{\lim_{n\to\infty} b_n}$

The limit of a reciprocal is the reciprocal of the limit.

(7) $\lim_{n\to\infty}\left(\frac{a_n}{b_n}\right) = \frac{\lim_{n\to\infty} a_n}{\lim_{n\to\infty} b_n}$

The limit of a quotient is the quotient of the individual limits.

In the following example, the limit is found by rewriting the expression in terms of $\frac{1}{n}$ and then applying Property 7.

Example

Find $\lim_{n\to\infty}\left(\frac{2-n}{4-3n}\right)$.

Solution

Rewrite the expression after dividing numerator and denominator by n.

$$\lim_{n\to\infty}\left(\frac{2-n}{4-3n}\right) = \lim_{n\to\infty}\left(\frac{\frac{2}{n}-1}{\frac{4}{n}-3}\right)$$

$$= \lim_{n\to\infty}\left(\frac{2\left(\frac{1}{n}\right)-1}{4\left(\frac{1}{n}\right)-3}\right) = \frac{\lim_{n\to\infty}\left(2\left(\frac{1}{n}\right)-1\right)}{\lim_{n\to\infty}\left(4\left(\frac{1}{n}\right)-3\right)} \qquad \text{Limit Property 7}$$

Now use Limit Properties 3, 5, 1 and 2.

So, the limit is $\frac{2(0)-1}{4(0)-3} = \frac{-1}{-3} = \frac{1}{3}$.

Check

Substitute some large values for n. For instance, if $n = 1000$, $\frac{2-n}{4-3n} = \frac{2-1000}{4-3000} = \frac{-998}{-2996} \approx 0.3331 \approx \frac{1}{3}$.

QUESTIONS

Covering the Reading

1. What is the *end behavior* of a sequence?

2. Consider the five sequences a, b, c, d, and the harmonic sequence in this lesson.
   a. Which have limits? **b.** Which converge?

In 3 and 4, *true or false*.

3. If each term in a sequence is less than the preceding term, the sequence has a limit.

4. If a sequence has a limit, then the graph of the sequence has a horizontal asymptote.

5. Consider the sequence s

$$\frac{5}{1}, \frac{8}{3}, \frac{11}{5}, \frac{14}{7}, \ldots, \text{ where } s_n = \frac{3n+2}{2n-1}.$$

   a. Find the tenth term of the sequence. Write it as a fraction and as a decimal.
   b. Evaluate s_{100} and s_{1000} to three decimal places.
   c. Graph the sequence.
   d. Does the graph appear to have a horizontal asymptote? If so, what is its equation?
   e. Find the limit of the sequence using the idea of the Example.

6. **a.** Graph the sequence with nth term $\frac{3n - 7}{4n}$.
b. Is the sequence convergent or divergent? If it is convergent, give its limit.

7. Does the sequence generated by $t_n = \frac{n^2 + 3}{n^2 + 1}$ converge or diverge? If it converges, state its limit.

In 8 and 9, decide whether the sequence is convergent or divergent. If it is convergent, give its limit.

8. $-1, 1, \frac{3}{7}, \frac{2}{7}, \ldots, \frac{n}{n^2 - 2}, \ldots$

9. $0, \frac{6}{4}, \frac{24}{9}, \frac{60}{16}, \ldots, \frac{n^3 - n}{n^2}, \ldots$

In 10–13, find the limit by using properties of limits.

10. $\lim_{n \to \infty} \left(\frac{3}{n}\right)$

11. $\lim_{n \to \infty} \left(\frac{11 - 5n}{6n + 23}\right)$

12. the constant sequence 8, 8, 8, 8, ...

13. the sequence of decimals formed by an increasing number of 3s: 0.3, 0.33, 0.333, 0.3333, 0.33333, ...

Applying the Mathematics

14. Let $t_n = \frac{24{,}000}{n}$.
a. Find t_1, t_2, t_3, t_4, and $t_{10{,}000}$.
b. This sequence has a limit L. Use the theorems in the lesson to determine L.
c. Find a number x such that for all $n > x$, t_n is within 0.1 of L.

15. In parts **a–d**, tell whether the limit exists. If it does, state it.
a. $\lim_{n \to \infty} \left(\frac{2}{3}\right)^n$
b. $\lim_{n \to \infty} \left(\frac{3}{2}\right)^n$
c. $\lim_{n \to \infty} (-4)^n$
d. $\lim_{n \to \infty} (-0.99)^n$
e. Make a conjecture about $\lim_{n \to \infty} r^n$.

16. **a.** Find $\lim_{n \to \infty} \left(\frac{1}{n} - 5\right)$.
b. Give an equation of the horizontal asymptote to the graph of $y = \frac{1}{x} - 5$.
c. How are the answers to parts **a** and **b** related?

17. Assume $\lim_{n \to \infty} a_n$ and $\lim_{n \to \infty} b_n$ exist and $\lim_{n \to \infty} b_n \neq 0$. Provide the justifications for Steps 2–4 in the proof of Limit Property 7 below.

	Conclusions	Justifications
Step 1:	$\lim_{n \to \infty} \left(\frac{a_n}{b_n}\right) = \lim_{n \to \infty} \left(a_n \cdot \frac{1}{b_n}\right)$	Algebraic Definition of Division
Step 2:	$= \lim_{n \to \infty} a_n \cdot \lim_{n \to \infty} \left(\frac{1}{b_n}\right)$	?
Step 3:	$= \lim_{n \to \infty} a_n \cdot \frac{1}{\lim_{n \to \infty} b_n}$	?
Step 4:	$= \frac{\lim_{n \to \infty} a_n}{\lim_{n \to \infty} b_n}$	?

Review

18. For the geometric sequence 100, -50, 25, -12.5, . . . , write each.
  a. an explicit formula
  b. a recursive formula *(Lesson 8-1)*

19. For the arithmetic sequence $3x + 2y$, $4x + y$, $5x$, . . . , find each.
  a. the constant difference
  b. the 50th term *(Lesson 8-1)*

20. What is the position of 105 in the arithmetic sequence 10, 15, 20, . . . , 105, . . . ? *(Lesson 8-1)*

21. Consider the geometric sequence with terms 5, 15, 45, 135, 405, ...
  a. Find a formula for t_n, the nth term.
  b. Write the log of the first five terms in the geometric sequence.
  c. Prove that the numbers found in part **b** form an arithmetic sequence. *(Lessons 6-3, 8-1)*

22. Find the other measures of the sides and angles of two non-congruent triangles in which $a = 20$, $m\angle C = 25°40'$, and $c = 10$. *(Lesson 5-4)*

23. *Skill sequence.* Represent using summation notation.
  a. $a_1 + a_2 + a_3 + a_4$
  b. $b_2 + b_3 + b_4 + \ldots + b_{10}$
  c. $m_1 + m_2 + m_3 + \ldots + m_n$ *(Lesson 1-3)*

24. Evaluate $\frac{2(2^{13} - 1)}{2 - 1}$. *(Previous course)*

Exploration

25. Consider the sequences whose terms are defined by $\left(1 + \frac{r}{n}\right)^n$, where r is a constant.
  a. Use a computer or calculator to estimate, to the nearest thousandth, the limit of the sequence when $r = 1$, 3, and 8.
  b. Each of the limits in part **a** is related to a power of e. Determine the relation and generalize what you observe.

LESSON

8-3

Arithmetic Series

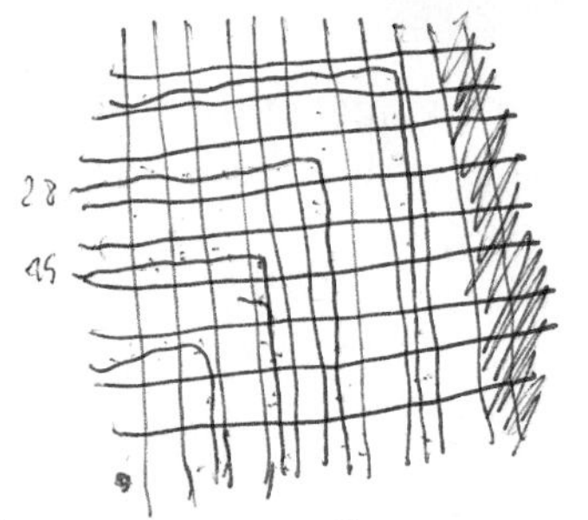

A **series** is an indicated sum of terms of a sequence. If the number of terms added is infinite, the resulting series is an **infinite series**. If a finite number of terms is added, the resulting series is called a **finite series**.

For example, consider the sequence t with $t_n = \frac{1}{n!}$. Then

$$\sum_{n=1}^{5} t_n = \frac{1}{1!} + \frac{1}{2!} + \frac{1}{3!} + \frac{1}{4!} + \frac{1}{5!}$$

is a finite series, while

$$\sum_{n=1}^{\infty} t_n = \frac{1}{1!} + \frac{1}{2!} + \frac{1}{3!} + \ldots$$

is an infinite series.

If $a_1, a_2, a_3, \ldots, a_n$ are terms in an arithmetic sequence, then

$$S_n = a_1 + a_2 + a_3 + \ldots + a_n = \sum_{i=1}^{n} a_i$$

is called a **finite arithmetic series**, or simply, an **arithmetic series**.

Examples of Arithmetic Series

Suppose a child builds a figure with colored blocks in stages as illustrated below.

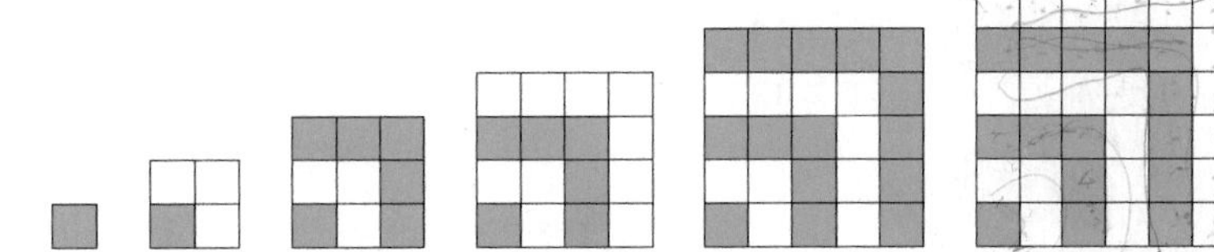

The number of blocks set down in each stage is a term in the arithmetic sequence of odd numbers 1, 3, 5, ... The final pattern consists of a 6×6 square of 36 blocks. So the number of blocks in the sixth pattern is the sum of the first six odd numbers.

$$1 + 3 + 5 + \ldots + 11 = 36$$

If a_n is the number of blocks added in the nth stage and S_n is the total number of blocks in the nth figure, then

$$S_6 = a_1 + a_2 + a_3 + \ldots + a_6 = \sum_{n=1}^{6} a_n.$$

Recall that an explicit formula for the nth odd number is $a_n = 2n - 1$. So

$$S_6 = \sum_{n=1}^{6} (2n - 1).$$

To evaluate this expression, replace n with each of the integers 1 through 6, and add the resulting terms.

$$\begin{aligned}\sum_{i=1}^{6}(2n-1) &= (2\cdot 1-1)+(2\cdot 2-1)+(2\cdot 3-1)+(2\cdot 4-1)+\\ &\quad (2\cdot 5-1)+(2\cdot 6-1)\\ &= 1+3+5+7+9+11\\ &= 36\end{aligned}$$

Note the importance of the parentheses in $\sum_{i=1}^{6}(2n-1)$. In the expression $\sum_{i=1}^{6}2n-1$, the 1 is not part of the summation, and a different sum is indicated.

Example 1

Evaluate $\sum_{n=1}^{6}2n-1$.

Solution

Each of the six terms is of the form $2n$. Add them and then subtract one from the result.

$$\begin{aligned}\sum_{n=1}^{6}2n-1 &= \left(\sum_{n=1}^{6}2n\right)-1\\ &= (2(1)+2(2)+2(3)+2(4)+2(5)+2(6))-1\\ &= (2+4+6+8+10+12)-1\\ &= 41\end{aligned}$$

A Story about Gauss

Carl Friedrich Gauss as a youth was specially tutored in advanced mathematics and supplied with hard-to-get texts such as the algebra book shown above.

To find the sum of the terms of a finite arithmetic sequence, one method is to add every term. Another way was discovered by the great mathematician Carl Friedrich Gauss (1777–1855) while he was in the third grade. As punishment for misbehavior, everyone in his class was asked to add the integers from 1 to 100. Here is what Gauss did.

Suppose S_{100} represents the sum of the first 100 integers. So

$$S_{100} = 1 + 2 + 3 + \ldots + 99 + 100.$$

He rewrote the series beginning with the last term.

$$S_{100} = 100 + 99 + 98 + \ldots + 2 + 1$$

Then he added the two equations.

$$2S_{100} = 101 + 101 + 101 + \ldots + 101 + 101$$

The right side of the equation has 100 terms, each equal to 101. Thus

$$2S_{100} = 100(101).$$

He divided each side of the equation by 2.

$$S_{100} = 5050.$$

It is said that Gauss wrote nothing but the answer of 5050 on his slate, having done all the previous work in his head. Imagine the reaction of his teacher, who thought this would take a long time!

A Formula for the Sum of Any Arithmetic Series

Gauss's strategy can be used to find a formula for the sum S_n of any arithmetic series. First, write S_n starting with the first term a_1 and successively add the constant difference d. Second, write S_n starting with the last term a_n and successively subtract the constant difference d.

$$S_n = a_1 + (a_1 + d) + (a_1 + 2d) + \ldots + (a_1 + (n - 1)d)$$
$$S_n = a_n + (a_n - d) + (a_n - 2d) + \ldots + (a_n - (n - 1)d)$$

Now add the two preceding equations.

$$2S_n = \underbrace{(a_1 + a_n) + (a_1 + a_n) + (a_1 + a_n) + \ldots + (a_1 + a_n)}_{n \text{ terms}}$$

The right side has n terms each equal to $a_1 + a_n$.

$$2S_n = n(a_1 + a_n)$$

Divide both sides by 2. $\quad S_n = \frac{n}{2}(a_1 + a_n)$

This formula for S_n is useful if you know the first and nth terms of the series. If you do not know the nth term, you can find it using $a_n = a_1 + (n - 1)d$ from Lesson 8-1. This leads to an alternative formula which you are asked to prove in the Questions.

Theorem

The sum $S_n = a_1 + a + \ldots + a_n$ of an arithmetic series with first term a_1 and constant difference d is given by

$$S_n = \frac{n}{2}(a_1 + a_n) \quad \text{or} \quad S_n = \frac{n}{2}(2a_1 + (n - 1)d).$$

Uses of Arithmetic Series

Example 2

A student borrowed \$4000 for college expenses. The loan was repaid over a 100-month period, with monthly payments as follows:

\$60.00, \$59.80, \$59.60, . . . , \$40.20.

How much did the student pay over the life of the loan?

Solution

Find the sum $60.00 + 59.80 + 59.60 + \ldots + 40.20$. Because the terms show a constant difference ($d = 0.20$), this sum is an arithmetic series with $a_1 = 60.00$, $n = 100$, and $a_{100} = 40.20$.

Use the formula $\quad S_n = \frac{n}{2}(a_1 + a_n)$.

So $\quad S_{100} = \frac{100}{2}(60.00 + 40.20)$

$\quad = 5010.$

The student paid back a total of \$5010.

Example 3

In training for a marathon, an athlete runs 7500 meters on the first day, 8000 meters the next day, 8500 meters the third day, each day running 500 m more than on the previous day. How far will the athlete have run in all at the end of thirty days?

Solution

The distances form an arithmetic sequence, with $a_1 = 7500$ and $d = 500$. Because the final term is not known, use the second formula in the theorem.

$$\begin{aligned} S_{30} &= \frac{30}{2}(2a_1 + (30-1)d) \\ &= \frac{30}{2}(2(7500) + (30-1)500) \\ &= 442{,}500 \text{ m} \end{aligned}$$

The athlete runs 442.5 km in thirty days.

The formulas for S_n are also useful if S_n is known and you must find one of a_1, a_n, n, or d, as shown in Example 4.

Example 4

A woman is building a log playhouse for her children, with the design at the left for part of the roof. How should she cut a ten-foot log to get the five logs needed, if each log is to be eight inches longer than the one before it?

Solution

The lengths of the logs form an arithmetic sequence. You have $n = 5$, $d = 8$, and $S_5 = 120$. If you knew a_1, you would know how to cut the logs. Substitute into the formula for S_n and solve for a_1.

$$S_5 = \frac{5}{2}(2a_1 + (5-1)8)$$

$$120 = \frac{5}{2}(2a_1 + 32)$$

$$120 = 5a_1 + 80$$

Thus, $a_1 = 8.$

She should cut the top log 8 inches long. The other logs should be 16, 24, 32 and 40 inches long.

Check

$8 + 16 + 24 + 32 + 40 = \frac{5}{2}(8 + 40) = 120$

QUESTIONS

Covering the Reading

In 1 and 2, refer to the child's pattern of blocks at the start of the lesson.

1. *Multiple choice.* Which expression represents the number of green blocks in the 6 × 6 square?

(a) $\sum_{n=1}^{3} (2n - 1)$ (b) $\sum_{n=1}^{3} (4n - 1)$

(c) $\sum_{n=1}^{3} (4n - 3)$ (d) $\sum_{n=0}^{3} (2n + 1)$

2. Suppose the pattern is continued to form a 10 × 10 square.
a. How many blocks are green? **b.** How many blocks are white?

3. What is the main difference between a sequence and a series?

In 4 and 5, evaluate.

4. a. $\sum_{n=1}^{5} (2n + 1)$ **b.** $\sum_{n=1}^{5} 2n + 1$

5. a. $\sum_{n=1}^{5} (2^n + 3)$ **b.** $\sum_{n=1}^{5} 2^n + 3$

6. Find the sum of the first one thousand positive integers.

7. A woman borrowed \$6000 for 5 years. Her monthly payments were
\$145, \$144.25, \$143.50, \$142.75, . . . , \$100.75.
a. How much did she pay over the life of the loan?
b. How much interest did she pay on this loan?

8. Refer to Example 3. How far will the athlete have run after two weeks?

9. Refer to Example 4. How should a 12-foot log be cut to get five logs whose lengths form an arithmetic sequence with constant difference equal to 8 in.?

Applying the Mathematics

In 10 and 11, evaluate.

10. $\sum_{p=1}^{7} \left((-1)^p p\right)$ **11.** $\sum_{p=1}^{7} p^p$

12. Use the formulas $S_n = \frac{n}{2}(a_1 + a_n)$ and $a_n = a_1 + (n - 1)d$ to prove that the sum of the first n terms of an arithmetic series with first term a_1 and constant difference d can also be written $S_n = \frac{n}{2}(2a_1 + (n - 1)d)$.

In 13 and 14, suppose a display of cans in a supermarket is built with one can on top, two cans in the next row, and one more can in each succeeding row.

13. If there are 12 rows of cans, how many cans are in the display?

14. If 200 cans are available to be displayed, how many rows are needed, and how many cans will be left over?

15. As part of a sales promotion, a large flag was made by attaching strips of plastic ribbon three inches wide to a pole. If the first strip is six inches long and each successive strip is four inches longer than the previous one, how many strips were cut from a roll of plastic ribbon 966 inches long?

16. Write an expression for the sum of the first k terms of an arithmetic sequence with first term f and kth term m.

Review

In 17 and 18, decide whether the sequence is convergent or divergent. If it is convergent, give its limit. *(Lesson 8-2)*

17. $\frac{8}{3}, \frac{11}{15}, \frac{16}{35}, \ldots, \frac{n^2 + 7}{4n^2 - 1}, \ldots$

18. $\frac{8}{3}, \frac{11}{7}, \frac{16}{11}, \ldots, \frac{n^2 + 7}{4n - 1}, \ldots$

19. Let $t_n = \cos\left(\frac{\pi}{6}n\right)$.

a. Write the first five terms of the sequence generated by this formula.
b. State whether the sequence is arithmetic, geometric, or neither.
c. Does $\lim_{n \to \infty} t_n$ exist? If so, what is it? *(Lessons 4-5, 8-1, 8-2)*

20. Life scientists often test animals' responses to doses of drugs or nutrients in amounts that form a geometric sequence. To test the content of vitamin A in carrots, pieces are fed to rats. Six dosage levels are arranged in a geometric sequence. If the lowest dose is 20 mg and the highest is 200 mg, find the other four doses. *(Lesson 8-1)*

21. According to the U.S. Bureau of the Census's International Data Base, the population of Indonesia was estimated to be 206.6 million in 1996, and the annual growth rate was 1.5%.

a. Use this information to write a recursive formula for the sequence of annual Indonesian populations.
b. Estimate the population of Indonesia in the year 2010.
c. Give two reasons why the annual growth rate may not, in fact, remain constant. *(Lesson 8-1)*

22. Solve $3^x = 120$. *(Lesson 6-6)*

Exploration

23. Consider the arithmetic sequence of positive odd integers, 1, 3, 5, 7, . . . , and the new sequence formed by adding consecutive terms of the sequence

$$S_1 = \sum_{n=1}^{1} a_n = 1,$$

$$S_2 = \sum_{n=1}^{2} a_n = 1 + 3 = 4,$$

$$S_3 = \sum_{n=1}^{3} a_n = 1 + 3 + 5 = 9, \text{ and so on.}$$

a. Determine S_4, S_5, and S_6.
b. Based on the results in part **a**, write a rule for the sum of the first n odd integers S_n.
c. Deduce your rule in part **b** from the general formula $S_n = \frac{n}{2}(a_1 + a_n)$.

LESSON

8-4

Geometric Series

Royal Game. *Chess originated in India or China. When an opponent's king is about to be captured, the winning player declares "checkmate", which comes from the Persian words* shāh *"king" and* māt *"dead."*

An Example of Geometric Series

The story about Gauss in Lesson 8-3 is generally considered to be a true story. The example that begins this lesson is legend.

The game of chess was invented between 1500 and 2500 years ago. A story is told that the king of Persia, after learning how to play, offered the game's inventor a reward. Clearing a chessboard, the inventor asked for one single grain of wheat on the first square, twice that on the second square, twice that again on the third, twice that again on the fourth, and so on for the whole board. The king, ready to give jewelry, gold, and other riches, thought that this was a modest request, easily granted. Was it?

The numbers of grains on the squares are $2^0, 2^1, 2^2, \ldots, 2^{63}$. They form a geometric sequence with $g_1 = 1$ and $r = 2$, and so the nth term is $g_n = 2^{n-1}$. Representing the total award for the entire chessboard by S_{64},

$$S_{64} = \sum_{n=1}^{64} 2^{n-1} = 1 + 2 + 4 + 8 + \ldots + 2^{63}.$$

S_{64} is a *finite geometric series*, analogous to the finite arithmetic series of the previous lesson.

To evaluate S_{64} without adding every term, you can use an approach similar to the one used for arithmetic series. First, write the series and then multiply each side of the equation by the constant ratio, 2.

$$S_{64} = 1 + 2 + 4 + \ldots + 2^{62} + 2^{63}$$

So, $$2S_{64} = 2 + 4 + \ldots + 2^{62} + 2^{63} + 2^{64}$$

Then, subtract the second equation from the first, term by term.

$$S_{64} - 2S_{64} = 1 + (2 - 2) + (4 - 4) + \ldots + (2^{62} - 2^{62}) + (2^{63} - 2^{63}) - 2^{64}$$

Simplify.

$$-S_{64} = 1 - 2^{64}$$

So, $S_{64} = 2^{64} - 1$.

Thus the total number of grains of wheat on the chessboard is $2^{64} - 1$, or 18,446,744,073,709,551,615. If you assume that each grain has the volume of a 4 mm × 1 mm × 1 mm rectangular box, the total volume of wheat would be about 74 cubic kilometers, many many times the amount of wheat in the world! Various versions of the story exist—what do you think happened to the inventor?

A Formula for the Sum of Any Geometric Series

In general, a **geometric series** is an indicated sum of terms of a geometric sequence. Suppose the sequence has first term g_1 and constant ratio r. The sum S_n of the first n terms of the sequence is called the ***n*th partial sum** and is written

$$S_n = g_1 + g_1 r + g_1 r^2 + \ldots + g_1 r^{n-1}$$
$$= \sum_{i=1}^{n} g_1 r^{i-1}$$

The procedure used to find S_{64} can be generalized.

$$S_n = g_1 + g_1 r + g_1 r^2 + \ldots + g_1 r^{n-1}$$

$$rS_n = g_1 r + g_1 r^2 + \ldots + g_1 r^{n-1} + g_1 r^n \quad \text{Multiply } S_n \text{ by } r.$$

$$S_n - rS_n = g_1 - g_1 r^n \quad \text{Subtract the preceding equations.}$$

$$(1 - r)S_n = g_1(1 - r^n) \quad \text{Factor each side.}$$

And, if $r \neq 1$, $S_n = \frac{g_1(1 - r^n)}{1 - r}$ — Divide each side by $1 - r$.

This proves the following theorem.

Theorem

The sum $S_n = g_1 + g_2 + \ldots + g_n$ of the finite geometric series with first term g_1 and constant ratio $r \neq 1$ is given by

$$S_n = \frac{g_1(1 - r^n)}{1 - r}.$$

Example 1

Evaluate $\sum_{i=1}^{7} 18\left(\frac{1}{3}\right)^{i-1}$.

Solution 1

This sum is a geometric series with $g_1 = 18$, $r = \frac{1}{3}$, and $n = 7$. Use the theorem on page 510.

$$S_n = \frac{g_1(1 - r^n)}{1 - r}$$

Substitute:

$$S_n = \frac{18\left(1 - \left(\frac{1}{3}\right)^7\right)}{1 - \frac{1}{3}}$$

$$= \frac{18\left(1 - \frac{1}{2187}\right)}{\frac{2}{3}}$$

$$= \frac{2186}{81}$$

$$= 26\frac{80}{81}$$

Solution 2

Evaluate each term and add them.

$18 + 6 + 2 + \frac{2}{3} + \frac{2}{9} + \frac{2}{27} + \frac{2}{81} = 26\frac{80}{81}$

Uses of Geometric Series

If you multiply the numerator and denominator of the formula for the sum of a geometric series by -1, you get an equivalent formula useful for situations where $r > 1$.

$$S_n = \frac{g_1(r^n - 1)}{r - 1}$$

Example 2

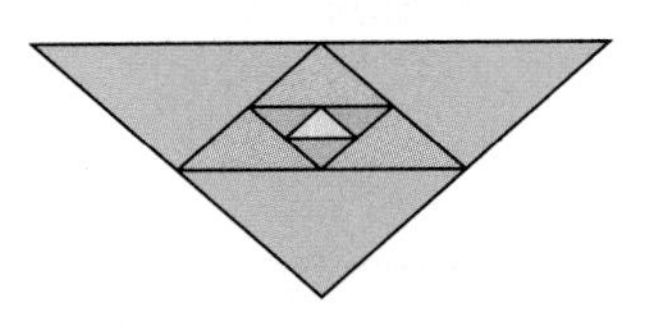

The set of a music show includes a backdrop in a design of nested triangles; the first four are shown at the left. The innermost triangle is the first built, having a perimeter of 0.55 meters. Each successive triangle has perimeter twice the previous one. What is the sum of the perimeters of the first eight nested triangles?

Solution

The sum begins $0.55 + 2 \cdot 0.55 + 4 \cdot 0.55 + \ldots$. Thus, the sum is the value of the finite geometric series g with $g_1 = 0.55$, $r = 2$, and $n = 8$.

$$S_n = \sum_{n=1}^{8} (0.55 \cdot 2^{n-1}).$$

Use the alternative formula for S_n.

$$S_n = \frac{g_1(r^n - 1)}{r - 1}$$

$$= \frac{0.55(2^8 - 1)}{2 - 1}$$

$$= 0.55(256 - 1)$$

$$= 140.25$$

The sum of the perimeters is 140.25 meters.

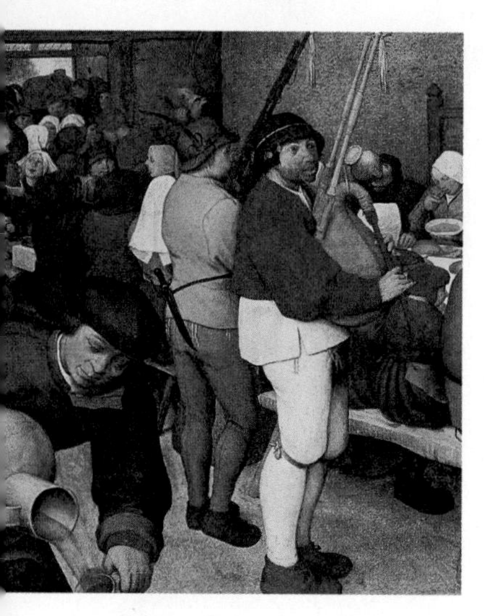

Great-Great- . . . Great-Grandparents. *About 19 generations ago, Pieter Bruegel depicted family gatherings in many of his paintings. Shown is a detail from* Peasant Wedding, *painted in 1565.*

Example 3

The maximum number of natural ancestors that you could have are 2 parents, 4 grandparents, 8 great-grandparents, and so on. Assuming that no one appears twice in your ancestral tree, in the last n generations you have S_n natural ancestors, where $S_n = 2 + 4 + 8 + \ldots + 2^n$. How many generations must you go back before you have a million natural ancestors, assuming that no one appears twice?

Solution

Use the alternate formula for S_n. Here $g_1 = 2$, $r = 2$, and n is unknown.

Solve
$$1,000,000 = \frac{2(2^n - 1)}{2 - 1}.$$
$$1,000,000 = 2(2^n - 1)$$
$$500,000 = 2^n - 1$$
$$2^n = 500,001$$
$$n = \frac{\ln 500,001}{\ln 2}$$
$$\approx 18.9$$

So, assuming no one appears twice on your ancestral tree, if you go back 19 generations, you have over a million ancestors.
(It is almost certain that many people have appeared twice on your tree.)

Check

Use a calculator or computer. The left column is the number of generations back. The right column is the maximum number of ancestors.
So it checks.

1	2
⋮	⋮
17	262142
18	524286
19	1048574
20	2097150

QUESTIONS

Covering the Reading

In 1 and 2, refer to the chessboard story at the beginning of the lesson.

1. Explain why the numbers of grains on the squares of the chessboard form a geometric sequence.

2. *True or false.* The total number of grains on the first 63 squares of the chessboard is about half that on all 64 squares.

3. *Multiple choice.* The expression $\sum_{i=1}^{n} a_1 r^{i-1}$ equals

(a) $\frac{a_1(1 - r)^n}{1 - r}$. (b) $\frac{a_1(1 - r^n)}{1 - r}$.

(c) $\frac{a_1(1 - r)^n}{r - 1}$. (d) $\frac{a_1(1 - r^n)}{r - 1}$.

4. a. Write the first six terms of the geometric sequence with first term -2 and constant ratio 3.

b. Evaluate $\sum_{i=1}^{6} (-2)3^{i-1}$ by adding the numbers in part **a**.

c. Evaluate $\sum_{i=1}^{6} (-2)3^{i-1}$ using the theorem in the lesson.

In 5 and 6, find the sum.

5. $\sum_{n=1}^{8} 3(0.5)^{n-1}$

6. $\sum_{i=1}^{20} 10(1.5)^{i-1}$

7. As first prize winner in a lottery, you are offered a million dollars in cash, or a prize consisting of one cent on July 1, two cents on July 2, four cents on July 3, and so on, with the amount doubling each day until the end of July. Which prize is more valuable? Justify your choice.

8. Refer to Example 2.
a. What is the sum of the perimeters of the first seven triangles?
b. Use your answer in part **a** to give the perimeter of the eighth triangle.

9. a. At most, how many different natural ancestors does a person have 5 generations ago?
b. At most, how many different natural ancestors does a person have in the last 5 generations?

10. How many generations must you go back before you have 10,000 ancestors assuming that no one appears twice?

11. Consider the geometric sequence 32, 24, 18, ...
a. Use logarithms to find how many terms must be added to give a sum of more than 127.
b. Check with a computer or a calculator.

Applying the Mathematics

12. Consider the expression $p + mp + m^2p + \ldots + m^{k-1}p$.
a. Rewrite the expression using Σ-notation.
b. Write the sum as a single fraction.

In 13 and 14, find the sum of the geometric series.

13. $3200 + 800 + 200 + \ldots + 3.125$

14. $8 + -12 + \ldots + -60.75$

15. a. Give an example of a geometric sequence with common ratio one.
b. Explain why the theorem for finding the sum of the first n terms of a geometric sequence does not apply to your answer in part **a**.
c. Give the sum of the first n terms of your answer to part **a**.

16. Find an explicit formula for the nth term of a geometric sequence with common ratio 1.5 for which the sum of the first four terms is 65.

17. A Superball bounces to three-quarters of the height from which it falls. What is the total distance traversed by a Superball dropped nearly vertically from 10 feet above the ground before it hits the ground for the eighth time? (The actual bounce would be closer to vertical. The bounces are shown spread out to help you visualize the problem.)

Review

18. Consider these sums: $\sum_{i=1}^{10} (2i + 1)$ and $\sum_{i=1}^{10} (2i - 1)$.
Which is larger, and by how much? (Try to answer without calculating the value of either series.) *(Lesson 8-3)*

19. A new graduate accepts a job as a data processing clerk at a starting salary of \$18,500 per annum, with an annual increment of \$750. Suppose he stays in the job for ten years.

a. How much will he earn in the 10th year?

b. How much will he earn in total after ten years? *(Lessons 8-1, 8-3)*

20. Let $t_n = \frac{2^n}{2^n - 1}$.

a. Write the first five terms of the sequence generated by t_n.

b. Does $\lim_{n \to \infty} t_n$ exist? If so, what is it? *(Lessons 8-1, 8-2)*

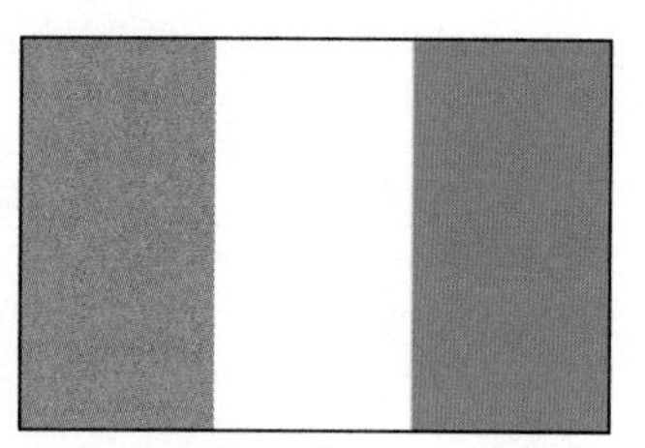

Ireland

Ivory Coast

21. Some countries have flags consisting of three stripes of different colors. The flags of Ireland and the Ivory Coast use the same colors, but in a different order. How many different flags can be designed consisting of three congruent stripes, either horizontal or vertical, where one is orange, one is white, and one is green? *(Lesson 7-4)*

22. Imagine tossing a fair coin four times and recording heads or tails each time.

a. How many elements are there in the sample space?

b. *True or false.* $P(\text{2 heads}) = \frac{1}{2}$. Explain your answer. *(Lesson 7-1)*

23. Let $f(x) = \frac{1}{x + 8} + 5$. *(Lessons 3-1, 3-2)*

a. What transformation maps the graph of $y = \frac{1}{x}$ to the graph of $y = f(x)$?

b. Give equations for the asymptotes of the graph of $y = f(x)$.

Exploration

24. Refer to the chessboard story at the start of this lesson.

a. Express the volume for a single grain of wheat in terms of cubic kilometers, and explain how the approximate volume 74 km^3 was obtained.

b. If 74 cubic kilometers of wheat were spread evenly over the area of the 50 states of the United States, how deep would the wheat be?

Introducing Lesson 8-5

Exploring Infinite Series

ACTIVITY

You will need a graphing calculator or a computer for this activity.

1 Consider the sequence $4, -\frac{4}{3}, \frac{4}{5}, -\frac{4}{7}, \frac{4}{9}, \dots$ and the *partial sums* that result from adding the first n terms of the sequence.

n	S_n
1	4
2	$4 - \frac{4}{3} \approx 2.666666667$
3	$4 - \frac{4}{3} + \frac{4}{5} \approx 3.466666667$
4	$4 - \frac{4}{3} + \frac{4}{5} - \frac{4}{7} \approx 2.895238095$
5	$4 - \frac{4}{3} + \frac{4}{5} - \frac{4}{7} + \frac{4}{9} \approx 3.33968254$

a. Calculate S_n for $n = 6$ to 10.

b. What pattern(s) do you notice in the *sequence of partial sums*?

c. Do you think the sequence of partial sums converges? Why or why not? If the sequence converges, its limit is considered to be the sum of the *infinite series*

$$4 - \frac{4}{3} + \frac{4}{5} - \frac{4}{7} + \frac{4}{9} - \dots$$

Do you think this sequence has a limit?

In 2 and 3, an infinite series is given. **a.** Find the first six partial sums for the infinite series. **b.** Make a conjecture about whether the infinite series converges or diverges.

2 $\sum_{i=0}^{\infty} 1.5^i = 1 + 1.5 + (1.5)^2 + (1.5)^3 + (1.5)^4 + \dots$

3 $\sum_{i=0}^{\infty} 12 \cdot 0.5^{i-1} = 24 + 12 + 6 + 3 + \frac{3}{2} + \frac{3}{4} + \dots$

LESSON

8-5

Infinite Series

What Is an Infinite Series?

In general, an *infinite series* is a sum that can be expressed in the form

$$\sum_{i=1}^{\infty} a_i = a_1 + a_2 + a_3 + \dots$$

In the preceding In-class Activity you encountered three infinite series. As you saw in the In-class Activity, an important question about infinite series is whether the sum of the series exists. And if the sum does exist, what is it? These questions can be answered by looking at the sequence S_n of partial sums of the series, where the nth partial sum is given by $S_n = a_1 + a_2 + \dots + a_n$. That is,

$$\begin{aligned} S_1 &= a_1 \\ S_2 &= a_1 + a_2 \\ S_3 &= a_1 + a_2 + a_3 \\ S_4 &= a_1 + a_2 + a_3 + a_4 \\ &\vdots \\ S_n &= a_1 + a_2 + \dots + a_n \end{aligned}$$

If the sequence $S_1, S_2, S_3, \dots, S_n$ converges, then its limit $\lim_{n\to\infty} S_n$, written S_∞, is called *the sum of the series.*

Definition

The **sum S_∞** of the infinite series $\sum_{i=1}^{\infty} a_i$ is the limit of the sequence of partial sums S_n of the series, provided the limit exists and is finite. In symbols,

if $$S_n = \sum_{i=1}^{n} a_i,$$

then $$S_\infty = \sum_{i=1}^{\infty} a_i = \lim_{n\to\infty} S_n = \lim_{n\to\infty} \sum_{i=1}^{n} a_i.$$

If $\lim_{n\to\infty} S_n$ exists, the series is called **convergent** and its sum is S_∞. If the limit does not exist, the series is **divergent**. In the preceding In-class Activity you should have found two convergent and one divergent series.

Example 1

Consider the infinite geometric series $\sum_{i=1}^{\infty} \frac{3^{i-1}}{2}$. Find the first five partial sums.

Does the sequence of partial sums seem to converge? If so, what is the sum of the series?

Here are the first five terms: $\frac{1}{2} + \frac{3}{2} + \frac{9}{2} + \frac{27}{2} + \frac{81}{2} + \ldots$

Solution

$$S_1 = \frac{1}{2}$$

$$S_2 = \frac{1}{2} + \frac{3}{2} = 2$$

$$S_3 = \frac{1}{2} + \frac{3}{2} + \frac{9}{2} = \frac{13}{2} = 6.5$$

$$S_4 = \frac{1}{2} + \frac{3}{2} + \frac{9}{2} + \frac{27}{2} = \frac{40}{2} = 20$$

$$S_5 = \frac{1}{2} + \frac{3}{2} + \frac{9}{2} + \frac{27}{2} + \frac{81}{2} = \frac{121}{2} = 60.5$$

The sequence of partial sums appears to increase without a limit. So the infinite series diverges.

Example 2

With advanced mathematics it can be proved that the infinite series

$$\frac{1}{1^4} + \frac{1}{2^4} + \frac{1}{3^4} + \frac{1}{4^4} + \ldots$$

is convergent. Approximate its sum to the nearest thousandth.

Solution

Generate the sequence of partial sums. Examine the sums until several consecutive terms are the same. Our calculator gives the following output.

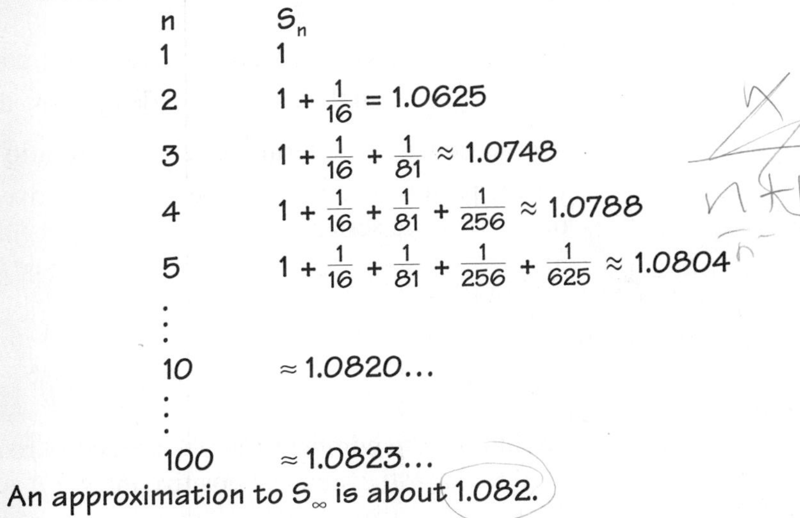

n	S_n
1	1
2	$1 + \frac{1}{16} = 1.0625$
3	$1 + \frac{1}{16} + \frac{1}{81} \approx 1.0748$
4	$1 + \frac{1}{16} + \frac{1}{81} + \frac{1}{256} \approx 1.0788$
5	$1 + \frac{1}{16} + \frac{1}{81} + \frac{1}{256} + \frac{1}{625} \approx 1.0804$
⋮	
10	$\approx 1.0820\ldots$
⋮	
100	$\approx 1.0823\ldots$

An approximation to S_∞ is about 1.082.

Recall that the harmonic series $\frac{1}{1} + \frac{1}{2} + \frac{1}{3} + \ldots + \frac{1}{n} + \ldots$ is the sum of the terms of the sequence of reciprocals of the natural numbers. Although the partial sums of the harmonic series change slowly for large values of n, they *do* continue to grow larger than any integer as n gets larger. That is, the series is divergent, and has no sum. Because partial sums may increase slowly, you should be careful and not leap to the conclusion that a series has converged just from examining the partial sums.

To analyze most infinite series thoroughly, more advanced mathematics is needed. However, you can analyze infinite *geometric* series thoroughly.

An Example of an Infinite Geometric Series

Fleance, a jumping flea, is at the center of a circular ring of radius 1 meter. Suppose the flea jumps along a radius toward the ring, but that each jump is half the previous jump (as Fleance gets tired). If the first jump is $\frac{1}{2}$ m long, will it ever reach the ring? If so, how many jumps will it take to reach the ring?

The jumps form a geometric sequence $\frac{1}{2}, \frac{1}{4}, \frac{1}{8}, \frac{1}{16}, \ldots$.

The total distance jumped equals $\frac{1}{2} + \frac{1}{4} + \frac{1}{8} + \ldots$.

The table at the right shows the total distances S_n after various numbers of jumps.

Number of Jumps	Total Distance Jumped
1	$S_1 = \frac{1}{2} \qquad = \frac{1}{2}$
2	$S_2 = \frac{1}{2} + \frac{1}{4} \qquad = \frac{3}{4}$
3	$S_3 = \frac{1}{2} + \frac{1}{4} + \frac{1}{8} \qquad = \frac{7}{8}$
4	$S_4 = \frac{1}{2} + \frac{1}{4} + \frac{1}{8} + \frac{1}{16} = \frac{15}{16}$
⋮	⋮
n	$S_n = \frac{1}{2} + \frac{1}{4} + \ldots + \frac{1}{2^n}$

The total distances $S_1, S_2, S_3, S_4, \ldots, S_n$ form a new sequence, $\frac{1}{2}, \frac{3}{4}, \frac{7}{8}, \frac{15}{16}, \ldots$. In the case of the flea jumps, the original sequence is geometric with first term $\frac{1}{2}$ and common ratio $\frac{1}{2}$. So you can find a formula for the partial sum S_n using the theorem proved in Lesson 8-4 for the sum of a geometric series.

$$S_n = \frac{\frac{1}{2}\left(1 - \left(\frac{1}{2}\right)^n\right)}{1 - \frac{1}{2}}$$
$$= 1 - \left(\frac{1}{2}\right)^n$$

To find out the number of jumps needed to reach the edge of the ring, you need to know the smallest positive integer n such that $S_n \geq 1$.

Substitute $1 - \left(\frac{1}{2}\right)^n$ for S_n and solve.

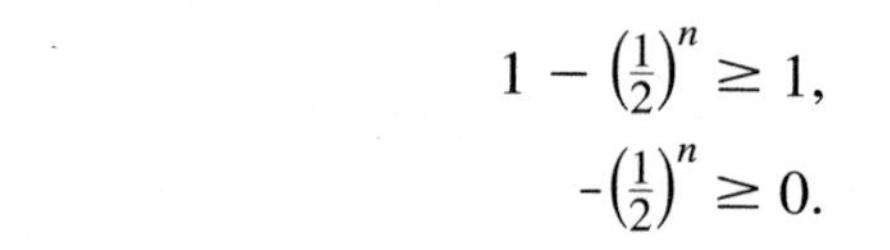

If $\qquad 1 - \left(\frac{1}{2}\right)^n \geq 1,$

then $\qquad -\left(\frac{1}{2}\right)^n \geq 0.$

Notice that the left side of the inequality is always negative. So the sentence $S_n \geq 1$ has no real solution. This means that Fleance never reaches the ring.

NO. OF JUMPS	DISTANCE JUMPED
1	0.5
2	0.75
3	0.875
•	•
•	•
•	•
6	0.984375
7	0.9921875
8	0.9960938
•	•
•	•
•	•
14	0.9999390
15	0.9999695
•	•
•	•
•	•
23	0.9999999
24	0.9999999
25	1
26	1

You can also use a computer or calculator to study $\lim_{n\to\infty} S_n$. At the left are some lines of output from a program that prints terms of the sequence generated by the formula $S_n = 1 - \left(\frac{1}{2}\right)^n$, where S_n represents the total distance jumped after n jumps.

From this output, you can see that although the flea never actually gets to the ring, it gets close enough for all practical purposes. Note that after 7 jumps, it is within 0.01 m of the ring; after 14 jumps it is within 0.0001 m and after 23 jumps, it is within 0.0000001 m of the ring. After 25 or more jumps, it is even closer than this, and the computer rounds off the total to 1, correct to 7 decimal places. This confirms that the sequence $\frac{1}{2}, \frac{3}{4}, \frac{7}{8}, \frac{15}{16}, \ldots$ of partial sums of the infinite series $\frac{1}{2} + \frac{1}{4} + \frac{1}{8} + \frac{1}{16} + \ldots$ converges to 1. That is,

$$\lim_{n\to\infty} \sum_{i=1}^{n} \frac{1}{2^i} = 1.$$

Thus, the total distance traveled by Fleance in a horizontal direction is 1 meter.

A Test for Convergence of Any Geometric Series

To examine infinite geometric series in general, consider the geometric sequence

$$g_1, g_1r, g_1r^2, \ldots, g_1r^{n-1}, \ldots.$$

For large values of n, $|g_1r^{n-1}|$ is large if $|r| > 1$, and $|g_1r^{n-1}|$ is small if $|r| < 1$. This suggests that the convergence or divergence of the geometric series depends on the absolute value of the common ratio r.

The sum of the first n terms of the geometric sequence with first term g_1 and common ratio r is

$$S_n = \frac{g_1(1 - r^n)}{1 - r},$$

or

$$S_n = \frac{g_1 - g_1r^n}{1 - r}.$$

For $|r| < 1$, r^n is very close to zero for very large values of n. In fact, it can be proved that

$$\lim_{n\to\infty} r^n = 0 \text{ whenever } |r| < 1.$$

So

$$\begin{aligned}
\lim_{n\to\infty} S_n &= \lim_{n\to\infty} \frac{g_1(1 - r^n)}{1 - r} = \frac{g_1}{1 - r} \lim_{n\to\infty} (1 - r^n) && \text{Limit Property 5} \\
&= \frac{g_1}{1 - r}\left(\lim_{n\to\infty} 1 - \lim_{n\to\infty} r^n\right) && \text{Limit Property 3} \\
&= \frac{g_1}{1 - r}(1 - 0) && \text{Limit Property 2 and } \lim_{n\to\infty} r^n = 0
\end{aligned}$$

Thus

$$S_\infty = \frac{g_1}{1 - r}.$$

When $|r| > 1$, the term g_1r^n is farther from zero for every successive value of n, and the infinite series is divergent. For $|r| = 1$, the sequence is either $g_1, g_1, g_1, \ldots$, for which $S_n = ng_1$, or the sequence is $g_1, {}^-g_1, g_1, {}^-g_1, \ldots$, for which S_n is either 0 or g_1; in each case, the series is divergent. The following theorem summarizes these results.

Theorem
Consider the infinite geometric series
$g_1 + g_1r + g_1r^2 + \ldots + g_1r^{n-1} + \ldots$, with $g_1 \neq 0$.

a. If $|r| < 1$, the series converges and $S_\infty = \frac{g_1}{1-r}$.

b. If $|r| \geq 1$, the series diverges.

Note that in the total distance of Fleance's jumps, $g_1 = \frac{1}{2}$ and $r = \frac{1}{2}$, so the series converges and $S_\infty = \frac{\frac{1}{2}}{1-\frac{1}{2}} = 1$. In contrast, in Example 1, $g_1 = \frac{1}{2}$ and $r = 3$, so the series diverges.

Example 3

Because of air resistance, the length of each swing of a certain pendulum is 95% of the length of the previous swing. If the first swing has length 40 cm, find the total length the pendulum will swing before coming to rest.

Solution

The lengths of successive swings, measured in cm, form a geometric sequence.

$$40, 40(0.95), 40(0.95)^2, \ldots$$

To find the sum of the series

$$40 + 40(0.95) + 40(0.95)^2 + \ldots,$$

where $g_1 = 40$ and $r = 0.95$, use the theorem above. Because $|r| < 1$, the sum exists.

$$S_\infty = \frac{g_1}{1-r} = \frac{40}{1-0.95} = 800 \text{ cm}$$

The pendulum swings through 800 cm, or 8 m.

A Swinging Time. *This Foucault pendulum in Chicago's Museum of Science and Industry is set in motion by burning a string which holds it stationary at night. It is in motion for the entire day.*

QUESTIONS

Covering the Reading

In 1 and 2, an infinite series is given. **a.** Write the first five partial sums. **b.** Does the sequence of partial sums appear to converge? If yes, what appears to be the sum of the series? If no, why do you think the series diverges?

1. $\frac{1}{2} + \frac{2}{3} + \frac{3}{4} + \ldots + \frac{n}{n+1} + \ldots$

2. $\frac{1}{1^3} + \frac{1}{2^3} + \frac{1}{3^3} + \frac{1}{4^3} + \ldots + \frac{1}{n^3} + \ldots$

In 3–5, refer to the series modeling the flea's jumps.

3. How far has the flea gone after 6 jumps?

4. What is the smallest value of n so that Fleance is within 0.001 m of the edge of the ring?

5. How close to the edge of the ring is the flea after 100 jumps?

6. Consider $\frac{1}{3} + \frac{1}{9} + \frac{1}{27} + \dots$

- **a.** Write the first three terms of the sequence of partial sums of this series.
- **b.** Write an explicit formula for the nth partial sum.
- **c.** Does the series converge? If so, what is its sum?

In 7–9, state whether or not the geometric series is convergent. If the series is convergent, give its sum.

7. $3 - \frac{9}{2} + \frac{27}{4} - \frac{81}{8} + \dots$

8. $5 + 4 + 3.2 + 2.56 + \dots$

9. $16 - 12 + 9 - 6.75 + \dots$

10. Refer to Example 3. How far would the pendulum travel if the length of each swing is 85% of the length of the previous swing?

Applying the Mathematics

11. **a.** Write the first five terms of the harmonic series.

- **b.** Use a calculator or a computer to find how many terms of the harmonic series must be added for the sum to exceed each of the following.
  i. 3 **ii.** 5
- **c.** *True or false.* The harmonic series is divergent.

12. Consider a pile driver driving a 3-meter pile into the ground. The first hit drives the pile in 50 cm, the second hit drives the pile in 40 cm further, and successive distances driven form a geometric sequence.

- **a.** How far will the pile be driven into the ground if the pile driver is allowed to run forever?
- **b.** What percent of the total distance driven is reached after 20 hits?

13. **a.** Under what condition(s) will the following geometric series converge?

$$b + \frac{b^2}{4} + \frac{b^3}{16} + \frac{b^4}{64} + \dots$$

- **b.** Under the condition(s) in part **a**, what is $\lim_{n \to \infty} \sum_{i=1}^{n} \frac{b^i}{4^{i-1}}$?

14. Find $\sum_{i=1}^{\infty} a_i$ for the sequence defined by

$$\begin{cases} a_1 = 3 \\ a_n = (0.6)a_{n-1}, \text{ for all integers } n \geq 2. \end{cases}$$

15. A ball dropped 60 feet rebounds on each bounce to $\frac{3}{4}$ of the distance from which it fell. How far will it travel before coming to rest?

16. Find the sum of the series $S = 1 + 3x + 5x^2 + 7x^3 + \dots$, given that $|x| < 1$. (*Hint:* Consider $S - Sx$.)

Review

17. A hot air balloon rises 60 ft in the first minute after launching. In each succeeding minute, it rises 80% as far as in the previous minute. *(Lessons 8-1, 8-4)*

a. How far does it rise during the sixth minute after launching?

b. How far will it have risen after 10 minutes?

c. How long will it take to reach a height of 260 feet?

18. Prove that the sum of the integral powers of 2 from 2^0 to 2^{n-1} is $2^n - 1$. *(Lesson 8-4)*

In 19 and 20, evaluate. *(Lessons 8-3, 8-4)*

19. $\sum_{k=1}^{6} 3^k$

20. $\sum_{k=1}^{6} (3 - k)$

21. Find the first positive term of the arithmetic sequence -101, -97, -93, ... *(Lesson 8-1)*

22. *Skill sequence.* *(Lesson 7-4)*

a. How many permutations are there of the letters in FLEAS?

b. How many of the permutations in part **a** begin with the letter A?

c. How many of them begin with A and end with S?

23. *True or false.* For $n \geq 1$, $n! = n \cdot (n - 1)!$ *(Lesson 7-3)*

Exploration

24. Consider the function defined by the infinite series

$$s(x) = x - \frac{x^3}{3!} + \frac{x^5}{5!} - \ldots + \frac{(-1)^{n-1}x^{2n-1}}{(2n - 1)!} + \ldots$$

a. Approximate $s(1)$ and $s\left(\frac{\pi}{2}\right)$ using the first five terms in the definition.

b. Write a computer or calculator program which accepts as input positive integers x and n, and produces as output $s(x)$ approximated by the nth partial sum of the series.

c. This series converges to $\sin(x)$ for any real value of x. Use the program you wrote in part **b** to determine how many terms of the series are needed to obtain an accuracy of three decimal places for all values of x in the interval $-\pi \leq x \leq \pi$.

LESSON

8-6

Combinations

Using Series to Solve Counting Problems

Sequences and series can be used to solve certain counting problems. Consider the following situation. Six friends, June, Kevin, Luis, Maria, Noor, and Olivia, leave a restaurant. Each person says good-bye to each of the others with a handshake. How many handshakes are needed?

To answer this question, you might consider one person at a time. Suppose June starts by shaking hands with each of the others: Kevin, Luis, Maria, Noor, and Olivia. Then, since Kevin and June have already said good-bye to each other, Kevin shakes hands with each of Luis, Maria, Noor, and Olivia. The following pattern develops:

	J	shakes hands with K, L, M, N, and O;
	K	shakes hands with L, M, N, and O;
	L	shakes hands with M, N, and O;
	M	shakes hands with N and O;
and	N	shakes hands with O.

Thus, the number of handshakes is $5 + 4 + 3 + 2 + 1 = 15$.

The number of handshakes can also be determined using the Multiplication Counting Principle. There are six choices for the first person in the pair and five choices for the second, so there are $6 \cdot 5 = 30$ ordered pairs of people. This set of thirty pairs are permutations of 2 objects chosen from 6. But the thirty pairs contain JK and KJ, NO and ON, and so on. Thus, the actual number of handshakes is only $\frac{1}{2}$ of 30, or 15.

Each of the above solutions is pictured at the left. The five blue segments, with J as an end-point, represent June's handshakes. The five segments with endpoint K, one blue and four orange, represent Kevin's handshakes, and so forth. The segments (5 blue, 4 orange, 3 green, 2 black, and 1 purple) represent $5 + 4 + 3 + 2 + 1$ handshakes. You can also count five segments ending or beginning at each of the six points. You might think there are 30 segments in all, but if you count them, you will see that there are only 15, because you have counted each segment twice.

The methods used to solve the preceding problem can be generalized.

Example 1

Suppose that n people meet at a wedding, and each person greets each of the others with a hug. How many hugs take place?

Solution 1

Consider the number of people each person hugs. No person greets himself or herself. So, the first person hugs $n - 1$ people; the second person, having already greeted the first, hugs each of the $n - 2$ other people; the third person then hugs each of the $n - 3$ others, etc. So the number of hugs is $(n - 1) + (n - 2) + (n - 3) + \ldots + 1$, an arithmetic series with first term $n - 1$, last term 1, and $n - 1$ terms. So the sum is $\left(\frac{n-1}{2}\right)((n - 1) + 1) = \left(\frac{n-1}{2}\right)n$.

Solution 2

There are $n(n - 1)$ ordered pairs of two people chosen from n people. So the number of unordered pairs, corresponding to the number of hugs, is $\frac{n(n-1)}{2}$.

What Is a Combination?

The preceding problems involve *combinations*. A **combination** is a collection of objects in which the order of the objects does not matter.

Example 2

Multiple choice. Which of the following situations involves a combination?

(a) Twenty students are semi-finalists for three scholarships—one for \$1500, one for \$1000, and one for \$500. In how many different ways can the scholarships be awarded?

(b) Twenty students are semi-finalists for three \$1000 scholarships. In how many different ways can the scholarships be awarded?

Solution

For choice (a), the amounts awarded are different, so the order of the winning students matters. For choice (b), the scholarships are equal, so the order of the winning students does not matter. The situation of choice (b) is a combination.

The answer to the question in choice (a) of Example 2 is the number of *permutations* of 20 things taken 3 at a time. In contrast, the answer to choice (b) is called the number of *combinations* of 20 people taken 3 at a time, written ${}_{20}C_3$. To calculate ${}_{20}C_3$, note that for any one of these combinations of 3 students, say A, B, and C, there are $3! = 6$ possible permutations: $A\ B\ C$, $A\ C\ B$, $B\ A\ C$, $B\ C\ A$, $C\ A\ B$, and $C\ B\ A$.

Thus, $3! \cdot {}_{20}C_3 = {}_{20}P_3 = 6840$. So ${}_{20}C_3 = \frac{6840}{3!} = 1140$. Thus there are 1140 different ways to award three \$1000 scholarships when choosing from 20 students.

In general, the **number of combinations of *n* things taken *r* at a time** is written ${}_nC_r$ or $\binom{n}{r}$. Some people read this as "n choose r." A formula for ${}_nC_r$ can be derived from the formula for ${}_nP_r$ by generalizing the argument in the previous paragraph. Each combination of r objects can be arranged in $r!$ ways.

So $\quad r!\,{}_nC_r = {}_nP_r$.

Thus, $\quad {}_nC_r = {}_nP_r \cdot \frac{1}{r!}$.

$\quad {}_nC_r = \frac{n!}{(n-r)!} \cdot \frac{1}{r!}$ $\quad$ Substitute from the Formula for ${}_nP_r$ Theorem.

So $\quad {}_nC_r = \frac{n!}{(n-r)!\,r!}$.

Theorem (Formula for ${}_nC_r$)
For all whole numbers n and r, with $r \le n$,

$$ {}_nC_r = \frac{1}{r!} \cdot {}_nP_r = \frac{n!}{(n-r)!\,r!}. $$

Example 3

A menu at a Chinese restaurant contains 48 main dishes. A group of friends chooses 6 different dishes. In how many different ways can they do this?

Solution

There are 48 dishes, from which 6 are to be chosen. Since the order in which the dishes are chosen does not matter, you want ${}_{48}C_6$. Use the Formula for ${}_nC_r$.

$$ {}_{48}C_6 = \frac{48!}{42!\,6!} $$

A calculator gives $\quad {}_{48}C_6 = 12{,}271{,}512$.

There are over 12 million different meals possible!

Activity

Graphics calculators usually have a built-in function for calculating ${}_nC_r$, which can be more convenient to use than the above formula. On some, you enter n first, then select the ${}_nC_r$ feature, and then enter r. On others you select the ${}_nC_r$ feature first.

a. Find out how the ${}_nC_r$ feature works on your calculator and use it to check Example 3.

b. If the restaurant adds two new dishes to its menu, how many more ways are there to choose six dishes?

Sometimes numbers resulting from computing a combination are too large for a calculator's memory. Or the display may only give you an approximate answer, because scientific notation has been used. In such cases, it may be necessary to do some calculation by hand first, as Example 4 shows.

Example 4

A football team with a roster of 60 players randomly selects 7 players from the roster for drug testing. What is the probability that its star quarterback and its star middle linebacker are both selected?

Solution

There are ${}_{60}C_7$ combinations of 7 players that could be picked. To determine how many of these combinations include the two star players, note that each such combination includes 5 players from the remaining 58 on the roster. There is only one way to select the star quarterback and linebacker (${}_2C_2 = 1$) and there are ${}_{58}C_5$ ways to select the other 5 players. Thus, the probability that these two stars are selected, assuming randomness, is

$$\frac{{}_2C_2 \cdot {}_{58}C_5}{{}_{60}C_7} = \frac{1 \cdot \frac{58!}{53!5!}}{\frac{60!}{53!7!}} = \frac{58!7!}{60!5!} = \frac{7 \cdot 6}{60 \cdot 59} \approx 0.012.$$

QUESTIONS

Covering the Reading

In 1–3, suppose the 26 students in a class each shake hands once with each other.

1. Use an arithmetic series to calculate the number of handshakes that take place.

2. Use the Multiplication Counting Principle to calculate the number of handshakes that take place.

3. *True or false.* The number of handshakes that takes place is ${}_{26}C_2$.

4. Match each item on the left with its description on the right.

a. combination (i) an arrangement of objects in order

b. permutation (ii) a selection of objects without regard to order

5. a. How many combinations of the letters UCSMP taken two at a time are possible?

b. List them all.

In 6–8, evaluate.

6. ${}_{18}C_3$ **7.** ${}_{14}C_1$ **8.** ${}_{103}C_0$

9. In how many ways can a person order eight different dishes from a list of 48?

10. What is your answer to part **b** of the Activity in the lesson?

11. Suppose 13 players from a track squad of 52 are chosen for drug testing.

a. What is the number of combinations of players that could be chosen?

b. How many of these combinations include both of the captains?

c. What is the probability that both captains are chosen?

Applying the Mathematics

In 12–14, evaluate the expression.

12. ${}_nC_n$ **13.** ${}_nC_1$ **14.** ${}_nC_0$

15. When $r > 1$, which is larger, ${}_nC_r$ or ${}_nP_r$? Justify your answer.

16. A lottery which requires guessing 6 numbers out of 50 in any order sells $1 tickets. A group of people decides to buy 12,000,000 tickets. Can they ensure that they win? Justify your answer.

17. Six points are in a plane so that no three are collinear, as shown at the left.

a. How many triangles can be formed having these points as vertices?

b. Generalize your result in part **a** to the case of n noncollinear points.

18. In the situation of Example 3, suppose that the 48 dishes are equally divided into seafood, meat, and vegetable. How many different meals are possible if the friends want two dishes from each group?

19. A standard deck of playing cards has 52 different cards: 13 each of clubs, diamonds, hearts, and spades.

a. How many different five-card hands are possible?

b. How many of the hands in part **a** contain only spades?

c. What is the probability of getting a five-card hand that is all spades?

20. a. Evaluate each expression.

i. ${}_9C_4$

ii. ${}_9C_5$

iii. ${}_8C_2$

iv. ${}_8C_6$

b. Find a value of k other than 3 for which ${}_{10}C_3 = {}_{10}C_k$.

c. Generalize the pattern observed in parts **a** and **b**.

d. Prove that your generalization is true.

Review

21. **a.** Determine the sum of the infinite geometric series

$$1 - \frac{1}{4} + \frac{1}{16} - \frac{1}{64} + \ldots + \left(-\frac{1}{4}\right)^{n-1} + \ldots.$$

b. Based on the result in part **a**, determine the sum $\sum_{i=1}^{\infty}\left(b\left(-\frac{1}{4}\right)^{i-1}\right)$, where b is any real number. *(Lessons 8-2, 8-5)*

22. **a.** Evaluate, giving your answer as a fraction.

$$\frac{3\left(1 - \left(\frac{1}{3}\right)^6\right)}{1 - \frac{1}{3}}$$

b. Write a geometric series having the value in part **a** as a sum. *(Lesson 8-4)*

23. Solve $6 \cdot {}_nP_2 = {}_9P_4 + 12$. *(Lesson 7-4)*

24. A test has 10 multiple-choice questions with five choices, 15 true-false questions, and 5 questions which require matching from a list of 6 choices. In how many ways can you answer the test in each situation?

a. You must answer each question.

b. You must answer the matching questions, but you have the option of leaving some true-false or multiple-choice questions blank. *(Lesson 7-3)*

Exploration

The Chicago Bulls won the 1997 NBA championship with a series of the form XXYYXX.

25. In professional baseball, basketball, and ice hockey the championship is determined by two teams playing a best of seven series. (The first team to win four games wins the series.) Call the two teams X and Y.

a. In how many different ways can the series occur if team X wins? For instance, two different 6-game series are $XXYXYX$ and $XYYXXX$. (Hint: Determine the different numbers of 4-game series, 5-game series, 6-game series, and 7-game series.)

b. There is a ${}_nC_r$ with n and r both less than 10 which equals the answer for part **a**. Find n and r.

c. Explain why the combination of part **b** answers the question of part **a**.

LESSON

8-7

Pascal's Triangle

The combinations of Lesson 8-6 came from counting problems but have important applications to powers of binomials and to probability. You will encounter these applications in the next two lessons. For this reason, it is helpful to know how combinations are related to each other. Many of the relationships among combinations can be seen in the array of numbers known as *Pascal's Triangle.*

What Is Pascal's Triangle?

For a given value of n, you can calculate ${}_nC_0, {}_nC_1, {}_nC_2, \ldots, {}_nC_n$, a total of $n + 1$ calculations. For instance, for $n = 4$, the 5 values are

$${}_4C_0 = 1 \quad {}_4C_1 = 4 \quad {}_4C_2 = 6 \quad {}_4C_3 = 4 \quad {}_4C_4 = 1.$$

When the values of ${}_nC_r$ are displayed systematically, a beautiful pattern emerges. Below, the values of ${}_nC_r$ with values of n and r from 0 to 6 are arranged in an array in the form of a right triangle. In the Western world this array is called **Pascal's Triangle**, after Blaise Pascal (1623–1662), a French mathematician and philosopher. Notice that the numbering starts with row 0 at the top.

n \ r	0	1	2	3	4	5	6
0	**1**						
1	**1**	**1**					
2	**1**	**2**	**1**				
3	**1**	**3**	**3**	**1**			
4	**1**	**4**	**6**	**4**	**1**		
5	**1**	**5**	**10**	**10**	**5**	**1**	
6	**1**	**6**	**15**	**20**	**15**	**6**	**1**

The isosceles triangle form of Pascal's Triangle is shown below.

row 0 → **1**
row 1 → **1 1**
row 2 → **1 2 1**
row 3 → **1 3 3 1**
row 4 → **1 4 6 4 1**
row 5 → **1 5 10 10 5 1**
row 6 → **1 6 15 20 15 6 1**
⋮

The arrays we call Pascal's Triangle were known to mathematicians long before Pascal studied them. They seem to have first appeared in the works of Abu Bakr al-Karaji, an Islamic mathematician, and Jia Xian, a Chinese mathematician, in the 11th century. The Persian mathematician and poet Omar Khayyam (c. 1048–1122) used them around the year 1100, and they were written about by the Chinese mathematician Chu Shih-Chieh, in books published in 1299 and 1303. Pascal wrote extensively about this triangular array of numbers and its properties in a 1653 publication, *Treatise on the Arithmetic Triangle*. It is for this reason that the triangle has his name.

Entries in Pascal's Triangle can be identified by row number (n) and column number (r), and so the terms can be considered as a 2-dimensional sequence. The following definition provides an explicit formula for the terms in the nth row, where n can be any whole number. It is an algebraic definition of the triangle.

Definition
Let n and r be nonnegative integers with $r \le n$. The **(r + 1)st term in row n of Pascal's Triangle** is ${}_nC_r$.

Example 1

Find the first four terms in row 7 of Pascal's Triangle.

Solution

By the definition of Pascal's Triangle, the first term of row 7 is ${}_7C_0$, the second term is ${}_7C_1$, the third term is ${}_7C_2$, and the fourth term is ${}_7C_3$.
From the formula for ${}_nC_r$, these are $\frac{7!}{7!0!}$, $\frac{7!}{6!1!}$, $\frac{7!}{5!2!}$, and $\frac{7!}{4!3!}$, or 1, 7, 21, and 35.

Blaise Pascal

Properties of Pascal's Triangle

Look closely at Pascal's Triangle. In its rows and columns and along the diagonals are many types of sequences, and many interesting patterns. Here are some properties which appear to be true for every row of Pascal's Triangle. The properties are described both in words and in symbols.

1. The first and last terms in each row are ones.
   That is, for each whole number n, ${}_nC_0 = {}_nC_n = 1$.
2. The second and next-to-last terms in the nth row equal n.
   For each whole number n, ${}_nC_1 = {}_nC_{n-1} = n$.
3. Each row is symmetric.
   For any whole number n, ${}_nC_r = {}_nC_{n-r}$.
4. The sum of the terms in row n is 2^n.
   For any whole number n, $\sum_{r=0}^{n} {}_nC_r = 2^n$.

You are asked to verify Property 1 in the Questions. Properties 2 and 3 are proved in Examples 2 and 3, respectively. You are asked to prove Property 4 in the next lesson.

Example 2

Prove that the second and next-to-last terms in the nth row of Pascal's Triangle equal n.

Solution

For any row n, the second entry is ${}_nC_1$.

$$ {}_nC_1 = \frac{n!}{(n-1)!1!} = \frac{n!}{(n-1)!} = \frac{n(n-1)(n-2)\dots 1}{(n-1)(n-2)\dots 1} = n $$

The next-to-last entry in the nth row is ${}_nC_{n-1}$.

$$ {}_nC_{n-1} = \frac{n!}{(n-(n-1))!(n-1)!} = \frac{n!}{(n-n+1)!(n-1)!} $$

$$ = \frac{n!}{1!(n-1)!} = n $$

So $\quad {}_nC_1 = {}_nC_{n-1} = n.$

Example 3 is a generalization of the result and proof of Example 2.

Example 3

Prove that for whole numbers n and r, where $r \le n$, ${}_nC_r = {}_nC_{n-r}$.

Solution

Use the Formula for ${}_nC_r$ Theorem.

$$ {}_nC_r = \frac{n!}{(n-r)!r!} $$

$$ {}_nC_{n-r} = \frac{n!}{(n-(n-r))!(n-r)!} $$

$$ = \frac{n!}{(n-n+r)!(n-r)!} $$

$$ = \frac{n!}{r!(n-r)!} $$

So for whole numbers n and r, where $r \le n$, ${}_nC_r = {}_nC_{n-r}$.

Another property not so easily seen, but easily checked, is the following:

5. Each element in Pascal's Triangle is the sum of the two elements nearest it in the preceding row. Specifically, for any whole numbers n and r with $1 \le r \le n$, ${}_nC_{r-1} + {}_nC_r = {}_{n+1}C_r$. For example, the 4 and 6 in row 4 generated by ${}_4C_1$ and ${}_4C_2$ add to 10, which is the entry just below in row 5 generated by ${}_5C_2$, as shown below.

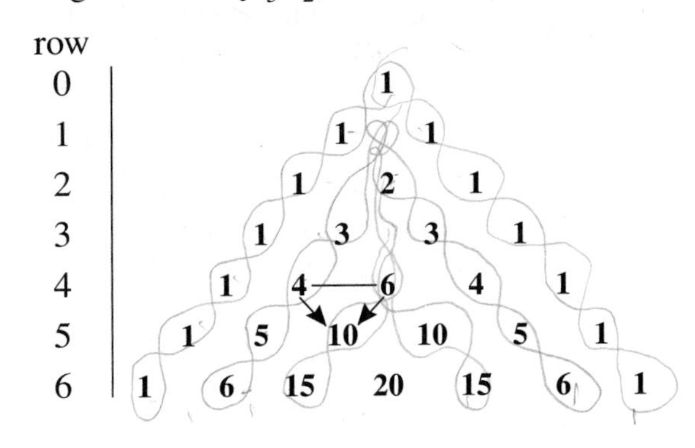

Pascal's Triangle, with the shaded hexagons representing odd numbers.

You are asked to prove this property algebraically in Question 14. Here is an argument using combinations that shows why the property works for a specific case. Suppose you wish to find ${}_7C_3$, the number of combinations of 7 objects taken 3 at a time. Call the objects A, B, C, D, E, F, and G. Now we split the problem into two parts. First, how many of these combinations contain G? We pick G and 2 objects from the remaining 6, so ${}_6C_2$ combinations contain G. Second, how many do not contain G? We pick all 3 objects from the remaining 6, so ${}_6C_3$ do not contain G. In this way, ${}_7C_3 = {}_6C_2 + {}_6C_3$.

Example 4

Use Properties 1, 3, and 5 to construct row 7 in Pascal's Triangle.

Solution

Start by copying row 6 from above. For row 7, Property 1 states that its first and last entries are 1. To find the second, third, and fourth entries in row 7, add consecutive pairs of terms in row 6 as described in Property 5; the results are $1 + 6 = 7$, $6 + 15 = 21$, and $15 + 20 = 35$. Use the symmetry property (or continue adding consecutive pairs of terms of row 6) to find the rest of the terms. Below is the result.

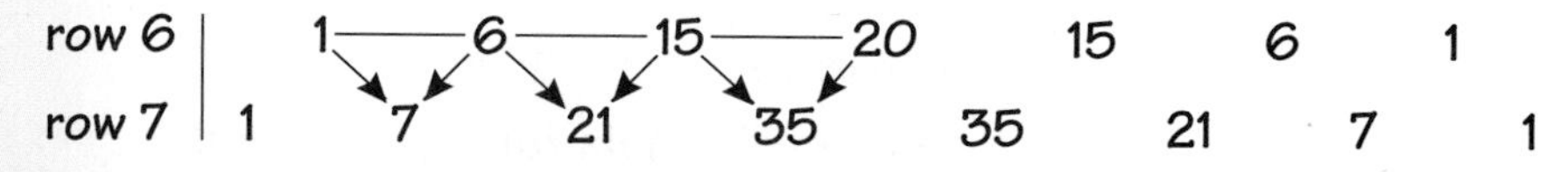

Check 1

Do the entries equal in order ${}_7C_0, {}_7C_1, {}_7C_2, \ldots$? In Example 1, it was shown that ${}_7C_0 = 1$, ${}_7C_1 = 7$, ${}_7C_2 = 21$, and ${}_7C_3 = 35$.

Check 2

Use Property 4.
Does $1 + 7 + 21 + 35 + 35 + 21 + 7 + 1 = 128 = 2^7$? Yes.

QUESTIONS

Covering the Reading

1. Refer to row 6 of Pascal's Triangle.
   a. How many terms are in the row?
   b. The third term is ${}_6C_r$. What is the value of r?
   c. The middle term is ${}_6C_s$. What is s?
   d. What is the sum of the numbers in this row?
   e. Express your answer to part **d** as a power of 2.

2. *True or false.* Blaise Pascal was the first person to study the triangle that now bears his name.

In 3–5, match the English description of the pattern in Pascal's Triangle to the description using combination notation.

(a) For each n, ${}_nC_1 = {}_nC_{n-1}$.
(b) For each n and each r $(r \leq n)$, ${}_nC_r = {}_nC_{n-r}$.
(c) For each n, ${}_nC_0 = {}_nC_n = 1$.

3. Each row in the isosceles triangle is symmetric to a vertical line.

4. The second and next-to-last entries in each row are equal.

5. The first and last entries in a row are 1.

6. Prove that for all whole numbers n, ${}_nC_0 = {}_nC_n = 1$.

7. Verify the property ${}_{n+1}C_r = {}_nC_{r-1} + {}_nC_r$ for $n = 8$, $r = 6$.

8. a. Give the entries in row 8 of Pascal's Triangle.
b. Check your answer to part **a** by showing the entries add to 2^8.

9. The first eight entries of row 14 of Pascal's Triangle are

1, 14, 91, 364, 1001, 2002, 3003, 3432.

a. How many other entries are there in row 14?
b. List the remaining entries.
c. What is the sum of the entries in row 14?
d. List the entries in row 15.

Applying the Mathematics

10. Find the first three numbers in the 100th row of Pascal's Triangle.

11. What are the last two terms in the row of Pascal's Triangle whose terms add to 2^{27}?

12. a. Expand the following.
i. $(x + y)^1$ **ii.** $(x + y)^2$ **iii.** $(x + y)^3$
b. Relate the coefficients of the results in part **a** to Pascal's Triangle.

13. Find a pattern in Pascal's Triangle that is not mentioned in this lesson.

14. Prove Property 5 in the lesson, which states that any entry in Pascal's Triangle is the sum of the two entries directly above it. That is, show that for all positive integers r and n with $1 \leq r \leq n$, ${}_{n+1}C_r = {}_nC_{r-1} + {}_nC_r$.

Review

15. A soccer league which has grown to include 22 teams is to be broken into two 11-team divisions. In how many ways can this be done? *(Lesson 8-6)*

16. Each year a company consisting of a president, vice-president, sales manager, financial manager, and 96 other employees holds a drawing in which four employees get a paid vacation to the South Pacific. What is the probability that the four employees chosen are the four executives? *(Lesson 8-6)*

Russian Matryoshka dolls

17. Consider a collection of Russian dolls of similar shapes and descending in size so that they fit into each other. Assume that each doll has $\frac{3}{4}$ the height of the next bigger one. *(Lessons 8-4, 8-5)*

a. What is the ratio of the volumes of two consecutive dolls?

b. If the biggest doll requires a wooden piece of 1400 cm^3, how much wood would be needed to carve out the given number of dolls?

i. 10 dolls **ii.** infinitely many dolls

In 18 and 19, a restaurant offers pizza with thick or thin crust, and with or without any of the following toppings: anchovies, mushrooms, onions, peppers, pepperoni, sausage. *(Lessons 7-3, 8-6)*

18. How many different kinds of pizza can be made?

19. How many thin crust pizzas can be made with exactly two toppings?

20. The first three terms of a sequence are 4, x, and $\frac{3}{2}x$.

a. Find x if the sequence is arithmetic.

b. Find x if the sequence is geometric. *(Lesson 8-1)*

21. *Skill sequence.* Find the exact volume. *(Previous course)*

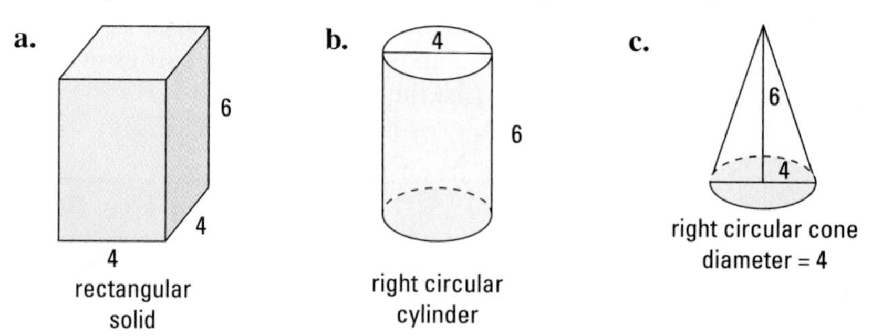

22. Of 210 horses in a herd, 48% are mares and 67% are brown. At least how many mares are brown? At most how many mares are brown? *(Previous course)*

Exploration

23. a. Use the definition $\begin{bmatrix} n \\ k \end{bmatrix} = \frac{1}{(n+1)\binom{n}{k}} = \frac{k!(n-k)!}{(n+1)!}$ to evaluate each term in the first four rows of the following triangle.

$$\begin{matrix} & & & \begin{bmatrix} 0 \\ 0 \end{bmatrix} & & & \\ & & \begin{bmatrix} 1 \\ 0 \end{bmatrix} & & \begin{bmatrix} 1 \\ 1 \end{bmatrix} & & \\ & \begin{bmatrix} 2 \\ 0 \end{bmatrix} & & \begin{bmatrix} 2 \\ 1 \end{bmatrix} & & \begin{bmatrix} 2 \\ 2 \end{bmatrix} & \\ \begin{bmatrix} 3 \\ 0 \end{bmatrix} & & \begin{bmatrix} 3 \\ 1 \end{bmatrix} & & \begin{bmatrix} 3 \\ 2 \end{bmatrix} & & \begin{bmatrix} 3 \\ 3 \end{bmatrix} \end{matrix}$$

b. This triangular array is called Leibniz's Harmonic Triangle. Where in the triangle does the harmonic sequence appear?

c. Describe some other pattern in this triangle.

LESSON

8-8

The Binomial Theorem

You saw in the previous lesson that Pascal's Triangle arises from evaluating ${}_nC_r$ for whole numbers n and r, $r \le n$. This lesson examines the connections between $(x + y)^n$ and Pascal's Triangle, as well as some applications of those connections.

To *expand* means to write a product of polynomials or a power of polynomials as a sum. Here are the *expansions* of $(x + y)^n$, for $n = 0, 1$, and 2.

$$(x + y)^0 = 1$$
$$(x + y)^1 = 1x + 1y$$
$$(x + y)^2 = 1x^2 + 2xy + 1y^2$$

Notice that the coefficients of the terms in the expansions are the entries in the 0th, 1st, and 2nd rows of Pascal's Triangle.

This pattern continues to hold. To see why, consider $(x + y)^3 = (x + y)(x + y)(x + y)$. You can find this product by multiplying each x and y term of the first factor by an x or y term of each of the other factors and then adding those partial products. In all, eight different partial products are computed and then added. These are highlighted in blue below.

Choice of Factors (in blue)		Partial Product		
$(x + y)(x + y)(x + y)$	$\rightarrow$	xxx	$\rightarrow$	x^3
$(x + y)(x + y)(x + y)$	$\rightarrow$	xxy	$\rightarrow$	x^2y
$(x + y)(x + y)(x + y)$	$\rightarrow$	xyx	$\rightarrow$	x^2y
$(x + y)(x + y)(x + y)$	$\rightarrow$	xyy	$\rightarrow$	xy^2
$(x + y)(x + y)(x + y)$	$\rightarrow$	yxx	$\rightarrow$	x^2y
$(x + y)(x + y)(x + y)$	$\rightarrow$	yxy	$\rightarrow$	xy^2
$(x + y)(x + y)(x + y)$	$\rightarrow$	yyx	$\rightarrow$	xy^2
$(x + y)(x + y)(x + y)$	$\rightarrow$	yyy	$\rightarrow$	y^3

Thus, $(x + y)^3 = 1x^3 + 3x^2y + 3xy^2 + 1y^3$. The coefficients are the entries in the third row of Pascal's Triangle.

To see why each coefficient is a combination, examine the eight partial products. The result x^3 occurs when x is used as a factor three times and y is used as a factor zero times. There are ${}_3C_0$ ways to choose 0 ys from the three y terms, so x^3 occurs in ${}_3C_0 = 1$ way. That is, x^3 occurs once, so its coefficient in the expansion is 1. The product x^2y occurs when x is chosen from two of the three factors and y from one. There are three y terms from which to choose, so this can be done in ${}_3C_1 = 3$ ways. So x^2y occurs three times and its coefficient in the expansion is 3. Similarly, xy^2 occurs when x

is chosen from one factor and y from two. There are three y terms from which to choose so this can be done in ${}_3C_2 = 3$ ways. So the coefficient of xy^2 in the expansion is 3. Finally, y^3 occurs when all three y terms are chosen, and this occurs in ${}_3C_3 = 1$ way. Thus

$$(x + y)^3 = x^3 + 3x^2y + 3xy^2 + y^3.$$

Using the language of combinations, we can write

$$(x + y)^3 = {}_3C_0x^3 + {}_3C_1x^2y + {}_3C_2xy^2 + {}_3C_3y^3.$$

What Is the Binomial Theorem?

Omar Khayyam (1048–1122)

In general, the expansion of $(x + y)^n$ has ${}_nC_0x^n = x^n$ as its first term and ${}_nC_ny^n = y^n$ as its last. The second term is ${}_nC_1x^{n-1}y = nx^{n-1}y$, and the second from the last is ${}_nC_{n-1}xy^{n-1} = nxy^{n-1}$. The sum of the exponents in each term is n, and the coefficient of $x^{n-k}y^k$ is ${}_nC_k$. These results are found in the following important theorem known to Omar Khayyam.

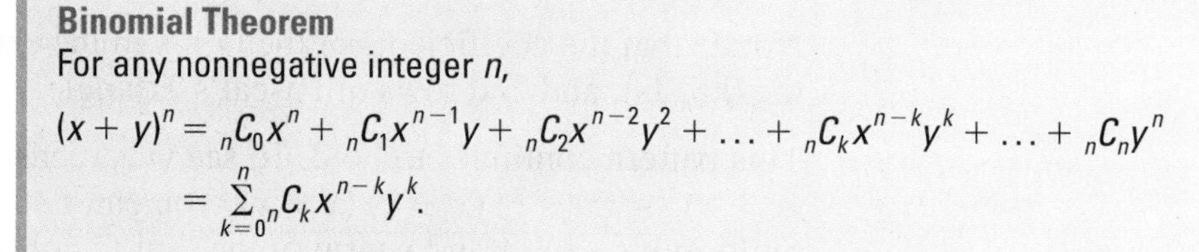

Binomial Theorem

For any nonnegative integer n,

$$(x + y)^n = {}_nC_0x^n + {}_nC_1x^{n-1}y + {}_nC_2x^{n-2}y^2 + \ldots + {}_nC_kx^{n-k}y^k + \ldots + {}_nC_ny^n$$
$$= \sum_{k=0}^{n} {}_nC_kx^{n-k}y^k.$$

For example,

$$\begin{aligned}(x + y)^4 &= (x + y)(x + y)(x + y)(x + y)\\ &= {}_4C_0x^4 + {}_4C_1x^3y + {}_4C_2x^2y^2 + {}_4C_3xy^3 + {}_4C_4y^4\\ &= x^4 + 4x^3y + 6x^2y^2 + 4xy^3 + y^4.\end{aligned}$$

Because of their application in this theorem, the combinations ${}_nC_k$ are sometimes called **binomial coefficients**.

Some Uses of the Binomial Theorem

The Binomial Theorem can be used to expand the power of any binomial.

Example 1

Find the coefficient of x^2y^3 in $(x + y)^5$.

Solution

From the five factors of $(x + y)^5$, y is to be chosen three times and x twice. This can be done in ${}_5C_3 = 10$ ways, so the coefficient of x^2y^3 is 10.

Check

$(x + y)^5 = x^5 + 5x^4y + 10x^3y^2 + \mathbf{10x^2y^3} + 5xy^4 + y^5$

Example 2

Expand $(2v - 3)^4$.

Solution

Use the Binomial Theorem with $n = 4$.

$(x + y)^4 = x^4 + 4x^3y + 6x^2y^2 + 4xy^3 + y^4$

Substitute $2v$ for x, and -3 for y.

$$(2v - 3)^4 = (2v)^4 + 4(2v)^3(-3) + 6(2v)^2(-3)^2 + 4(2v)(-3)^3 + (-3)^4$$
$$= 16v^4 + 4(8)(-3)v^3 + 6(4)(9)v^2 + 4(2)(-27)v + 81$$
$$= 16v^4 - 96v^3 + 216v^2 - 216v + 81$$

Check

Let $v = 2$. The power $(2v - 3)^4 = (2 \cdot 2 - 3)^4 = 1^4 = 1$. For $v = 2$, the series expansion has the value

$$16(2^4) - 96(2^3) + 216(2^2) - 216(2) + 81 = 256 - 768 + 864 - 432 + 81$$
$$= 1.$$

It checks.

The Binomial Theorem can also be used to solve counting problems involving experiments with only two outcomes.

Example 3

A coin is flipped five times. How many of the possible outcomes have at least two heads?

Solution

Substitute H for x, T for y, and 5 for n in the Binomial Theorem.

$$(H + T)^5 = {}_5C_0H^5 + {}_5C_1H^4T + {}_5C_2H^3T^2 + {}_5C_3H^2T^3 + {}_5C_4HT^4 + {}_5C_5T^5$$
$$= 1\,H^5 + 5\,H^4T + 10\,H^3T^2 + 10\,H^2T^3 + 5\,HT^4 + 1\,T^5$$

The coefficients correspond to the number of ways of obtaining 5 heads, 4 heads and 1 tail, . . . , and 5 tails, respectively. Thus, 5 heads can occur in 1 way, 4 heads and 1 tail can occur in 5 ways, and so on. The number of ways in which at least two heads occur is therefore $1 + 5 + 10 + 10 = 26$.

Check

Of the total $2^5 = 32$ outcomes, 1 has no heads and 5 have one head, so 6 have fewer than 2 heads. That leaves $32 - 6 = 26$ outcomes with at least 2 heads. It checks.

QUESTIONS

Covering the Reading

1. a. In the product $(x + y)(x + y)(x + y)$ what is the coefficient of x^2y?
b. Why can this coefficient be derived from a combination problem?

2. Expand $(a + b)^5$.

3. Expand $(a + b)^6$.

4. What is the coefficient of x^2y^4 in the expansion of $(x + y)^6$?

In 5–8, expand.

5. $(v + 2)^3$

6. $(x - 1)^6$

7. $(1 - 2q)^5$

8. $(10p + 2)^3$

9. How many of the possible outcomes of 5 tosses of a coin have the following?
   a. exactly 3 tails
   b. at least 3 tails

10. Use the Binomial Theorem to determine the number of ways 1, 2, 3, and 4 heads can occur when four fair coins are flipped.

Applying the Mathematics

In 11–13, suppose kx^py^q is a term in the series expansion of $(x + y)^n$. *True or false.*

11. $p + q = n$

12. $k = {}_nC_q$

13. $k = {}_nC_p$

14. Expand $(x^3 - y^2)^4$ and check by letting $x = 2$ and $y = 3$.

15. Mr. and Mrs. Ippy hope to have four children. Assuming that boys and girls are equally likely, what is the probability they will have at least two girls?

16. Rewrite $\sum_{i=0}^{7} \binom{7}{i} a^{7-i} 5^i$ in the form $(x + y)^n$.

17. Use the Binomial Theorem to prove that $\sum_{k=0}^{n} {}_nC_k = 2^n$. (This is Property 4 from Lesson 8-7.) Hint: Let $2^n = (1 + 1)^n$.

18. Alternately add and subtract the entries in the rows of Pascal's triangle as follows.

$$\begin{aligned} a_1 &= 1 - 1 \\ a_2 &= 1 - 2 + 1 \\ a_3 &= 1 - 3 + 3 - 1 \\ a_4 &= 1 - 4 + 6 - 4 + 1 \end{aligned}$$

Give an explicit formula for a_n.

Review

In 19 and 20, refer to the numbers below, which are the first six terms of row 10 of Pascal's Triangle. *(Lesson 8-7)*

1 10 45 120 210 252

19. Which term represents ${}_{10}C_4$?

20. **a.** Write the rest of row 10.
    b. Write row 11 in full.
    c. Write row 9 in full.

Paris, France

In 21 and 22, suppose that the names of four people in a baking competition are to be chosen from among a list of 100 finalists. **a.** Tell whether the situation represents a combination or permutation. **b.** State the number of possible outcomes. *(Lessons 7-4, 8-6)*

21. The first receives a \$10, 000 prize, the second receives \$5,000, the third \$1,000, and the fourth \$500.

22. All four people receive identical prizes: a trip to Paris, France.

23. Three integers from 1 to 100 are chosen at random. What is the probability that they are three consecutive integers? *(Lessons 7-1, 8-6)*

24. **a.** Under what conditions does the following infinite series have a sum?

$$\sum_{n=2}^{\infty} xy^n = xy^2 + xy^3 + xy^4 + xy^5 + \ldots$$

b. What is that sum, if it exists? *(Lesson 8-5)*

25. Before 1994, in all area codes, the first digit could not be a 0 or 1, the second digit had to be a 0 or 1, and the third digit could not be a 0 or 1. How many area codes were possible with these restrictions? *(Lesson 7-3)*

Exploration

26. **a.** Expand $(1 + .001)^5$ to obtain the decimal for 1.001^5.
b. How many terms of the expansion are needed to get an estimate of 1.001^5 accurate to the nearest thousandth?
c. Use your results from parts **a** and **b** to determine how many terms of the expansion of $(1 + .003)^8$ are needed to estimate 1.003^8 to the nearest millionth.
d. Give the complete decimal expansion of 1.003^8.
e. How close is your calculator value of 1.003^8 to the value of your answer in part **d**?

LESSON

8-9

Binomial Probabilities

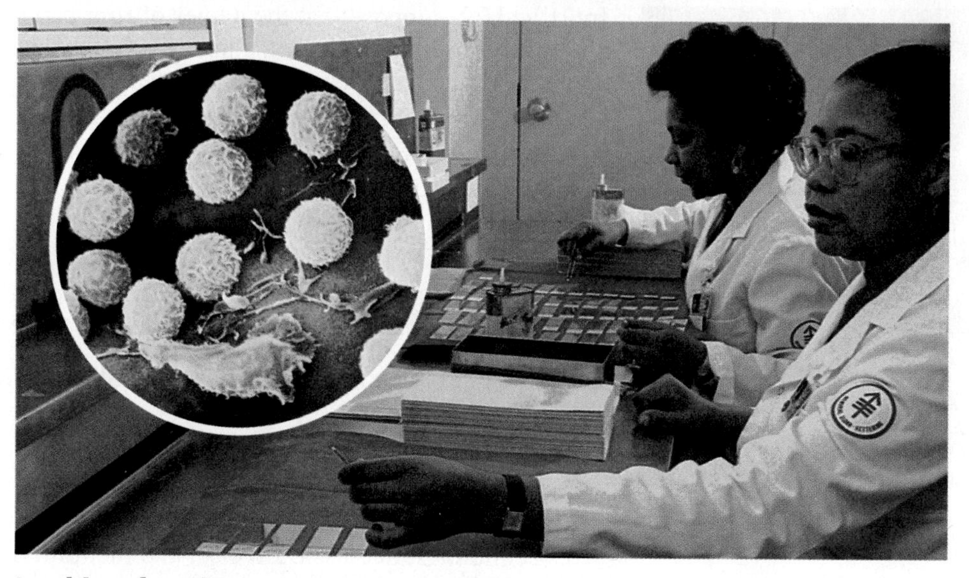

Looking for Signs. *The number of people whose cancer remains in remission follows a binomial distribution model. The inset shows a characteristic of leukemia: immature white blood cells in the bone marrow. See Example 1.*

What Is a Binomial Experiment?

In Example 3 of the preceding lesson, the expansion of $(H + T)^5$ helped to find how many ways 2 heads could occur in 5 tosses of a coin. This situation is an example of a *binomial experiment*, because, as you will learn later in this lesson, a formula for calculating the probabilities associated with such an experiment is related to the Binomial Theorem. A **binomial experiment** has the following features:

1. There are repeated situations, called *trials*.
2. There are only two possible outcomes, often called *success* (S) and *failure* (F), for each trial.
3. The trials are independent.
4. Each trial has the same probability of success.
5. The experiment has a fixed number of trials.

Listed below are all the possible outcomes for a binomial experiment with four trials.

Outcomes for a Binomial Experiment with 4 Trials				
exactly 0 successes	exactly 1 success	exactly 2 successes	exactly 3 successes	exactly 4 successes
FFFF	*FFFS*	*FFSS*	*FSSS*	*SSSS*
	FFSF	*FSFS*	*SFSS*	
	FSFF	*FSSF*	*SSFS*	
	SFFF	*SFFS*	*SSSF*	
		SFSF		
		SSFF		

Notice that the number of ways with exactly k successes among the 4 trials is ${}_4C_k$. That is, the number of outcomes in the columns above, 1, 4, 6, 4, 1, are precisely the numbers from row 4 of Pascal's Triangle.

The chart on page 540 should look familiar. It has 16 outcomes, similar to tossing four fair coins. However, in general, the 16 outcomes may not be equally likely, because the probability of success and the probability of failure may not be equal.

Example 1

Suppose that the probability for a certain cancer to remain in remission (undetectable) for at least one year after chemotherapy is 0.7 for all patients with that cancer.

a. Find the probability that exactly two of four patients currently being monitored are able to keep the cancer in remission for at least one year after chemotherapy.

b. Find the probability that two or three patients are able to sustain remission for at least one year.

Solution

a. For each patient, P(success) = 0.7; so P(failure) = 1 − 0.7 = 0.3.
Use the table on page 540. As listed in the column labeled *exactly 2 successes*, there are 6 combinations in which exactly 2 of the 4 patients sustain remission. The probability of each of these outcomes is $(0.7)^2(0.3)^2$. So

$$\begin{aligned} P(\text{exactly 2 successes in 4 trials}) &= 6(0.7)^2(0.3)^2 \\ &= 6(0.0441) \\ &= 0.2646. \end{aligned}$$

b. Because the outcomes are mutually exclusive,

$$\begin{aligned} P(\text{2 or 3 successes}) = \ &P(\text{exactly 2 successes}) + \\ &P(\text{exactly 3 successes}). \end{aligned}$$

From part **a**, P(exactly 2 successes) = 0.2646.
There are 4 ways to have exactly 3 successes. Each has probability $(0.7)^3(0.3)$. So

$$\begin{aligned} P(\text{exactly 3 successes}) &= 4(0.7)^3(0.3) \\ &= 0.4116. \end{aligned}$$

Thus,

$$\begin{aligned} P(\text{2 or 3 successes}) &= 0.2646 + 0.4116 \\ &= 0.6762. \end{aligned}$$

The results of Example 1 can be generalized. In a binomial experiment, if the probability of success is p, the probability of failure is $1 - p = q$. Then the probability of exactly 2 successes in 4 trials is ${}_4C_2q^2p^2 = 6q^2p^2$, and the probability of exactly 3 successes in 4 trials is ${}_4C_3qp^3 = 4qp^3$.

The General Binomial Experiment

These ideas can be generalized still further.

Binomial Probability Theorem
Suppose that in a binomial experiment with n trials the probability of success is p in each trial, and the probability of failure is q, where $q = 1 - p$. Then

$$P(\text{exactly } k \text{ successes}) = {}_nC_k \cdot p^k q^{n-k}.$$

Example 2

A quiz has eight multiple-choice questions, each with four alternatives. If a student guesses randomly on every question, what is the probability of getting five or more correct?

Solution

This is a binomial experiment. Answering each question is a trial; so there are $n = 8$ trials. The probability of success (getting a single question correct) is 0.25; the probability of failure is 0.75. Getting 5 or more correct is equivalent to the mutually exclusive events of getting exactly 5 or exactly 6 or exactly 7 or exactly 8 correct. So the desired probability is

$$\begin{aligned} P(5 \text{ or better}) \\ &= P(\text{exactly } 5) + P(\text{exactly } 6) + P(\text{exactly } 7) + P(\text{exactly } 8) \\ &= {}_8C_5\,(.25)^5(.75)^3 + {}_8C_6\,(.25)^6(.75)^2 + {}_8C_7\,(.25)^7(.75) + {}_8C_8(.25)^8 \\ &\approx 56(.000412) + 28(.000137) + 8(.000046) + 1(.000015) \\ &\approx .027291. \end{aligned}$$

So, sheer random guessing on a 8-item multiple-choice quiz yields a probability of less than 3% of getting 5 or more items correct. (Chances improve substantially with study!)

Binomial Probability Distributions

The probability distribution generated from the probability of x successes in a binomial experiment is called a **binomial probability distribution**. Here is an example.

Example 3

In a binomial experiment, suppose that the probability of success is 0.7. Determine and graph the probability distribution for the number of successes in five trials.

Solution

Let x be the number of successes. Then x can be any integer from 0 to 5. Let $P(x)$ = the probability of exactly x successes. By the preceding theorem, $P(x) = {}_5C_x\, p^x q^{5-x}$, where $p = 0.7$ and $q = 1 - p = 0.3$. Evaluate $p(x)$ for each possible value of x. The probability distribution is represented on page 543 in a table and with a graph.

▶

x	P(x)	
0	$q^5 = (.3)^5$	$= .00243$
1	$5pq^4 = 5(.7)(.3)^4$	$= .02835$
2	$10p^2q^3 = 10(.7)^2(.3)^3$	$= .1323$
3	$10p^3q^2 = 10(.7)^3(.3)^2$	$= .3087$
4	$5p^4q = 5(.7)^4(.3)$	$= .36015$
5	$p^5 = (.7)^5$	$= .16807$

Check

The sum of the probabilities should be 1. You should check this.

QUESTIONS

Covering the Reading

1. State four characteristics of a binomial experiment.

In 2–5, state whether or not the experiment is a binomial experiment. If not, identify the missing property or properties.

2. A die is rolled seven times. Success is rolling a 3.

3. Four cards are selected from a standard deck (of 52 cards) without replacement. Success is selecting an ace.

4. A bag contains two red, three green, and five blue marbles. The bag is shaken, a marble is selected, its color is recorded, and it is replaced. This is repeated five times.

5. One hundred people are selected at random and asked if they voted in the last presidential election. Success is if the person voted.

In 6 and 7, suppose, as in Example 1, that the probability of keeping a certain cancer in remission is 0.7.

6. What is the probability that all four of the patients will stay well?

7. What is the probability that at least two of the four will stay well?

8. Refer to Example 2.
   a. What is a trial in this situation?
   b. How do we know the trials are independent?
   c. Where in the solution is the requirement of independent events applied?
   d. Where in the solution is the fact that events are mutually exclusive applied?

9. Suppose a multiple-choice quiz has ten questions, each with five alternatives. If a student answers by random guessing, what is the probability that at least seven questions are answered correctly?

Have slogan, will campaign. *Campaign buttons with names or catchy slogans remind adults of their right and responsibility to vote.*

10. In a binomial experiment, suppose that the probability of success is 0.4. Determine and graph the probability distribution for the number of successes in 6 trials.

Applying the Mathematics

11. For the distribution of Example 3, give each.
a. mode **b.** expected value

12. Consider tossing a fair coin six times.
a. Construct a probability distribution for this experiment, where x is the number of heads that occurs.
b. Graph the probability distribution.
c. Find the probability of getting two or three heads.
d. Find the probability of getting at least one head.

13. Refer to the drawing below with six congruent sectors. On any one spin, the spinner is equally likely to land in any of the six sectors.
a. What is the probability of the spinner landing in a green sector?
b. Suppose a trial is a single spin, and that "success" means the spinner lands in a green sector. Complete the following probability distribution for the number of successes in four spins.

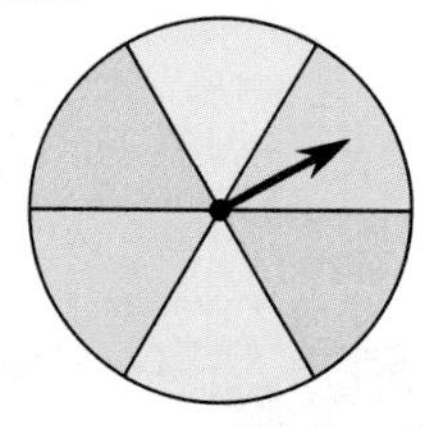

Probability Distribution of *x* Successes in 4 Spins

x = exact number of successes	0	1	2	3	4
$P(x)$					

c. Graph the distribution in part **b**.
d. Find P(at least 3 successes).
e. Find P(at least 1 success).

14. A baseball player has a batting average of .250. This can be interpreted to mean that the probability of a hit is $.250 = \frac{1}{4}$. Some people think this means that in 4 times at bat, the batter is *sure* to get a hit. Give the probability that this batter gets the following number of hits in 4 at-bats.
a. exactly 1 hit **b.** at least 1 hit

15. Suppose that in a binomial experiment P(success on one trial) = a.
a. Express P(failure on one trial) in terms of a.
b. Find P(success on exactly 3 of 7 trials).

16. A car rental company finds that, on the average, 86% of renters want small cars. Suppose 10 people at random come to rent cars.
a. Find the probability that exactly 7 of them want small cars.
b. Find the probability that no more than 3 of them want big cars.

Review

In 17 and 18, expand. *(Lesson 8-8)*

17. $(a + 2b)^6$

18. $(2 \sin \theta - \cos \theta)^3$

19. In a particular state lottery, you must pick 6 numbers correctly (in any order) out of 55. What is your probability of winning? *(Lesson 8-6)*

20. Solve ${}_{n+5}C_1 = {}_nC_2$. *(Lesson 8-6)*

21. An integer from 1 to 1000 is chosen at random. What is the probability that it is divisible by 7 or 11? *(Lessons 7-2, 8-3)*

22. Describe the end behavior of the sequence generated by $t_n = \frac{\sqrt{n}}{3 + \sqrt{n}}$. *(Lesson 8-2)*

23. Transliterated into English, the Hawaiian language has only the following letters: A, E, H, I, K, L, M, N, O, P, U, W. Every Hawaiian word and syllable ends with a vowel, and some words have no consonants. Two consonants never occur without a vowel between them. How many four-letter words are possible? *(Lessons 7-3, 7-4)*

24. *Skill sequence.* Solve for x. *(Lesson 6-6)*

a. $.2^x = .05$

b. $1 - .4^x = .95$

c. $1 - p^x = a, p > 0, a < 1$

Exploration

25. Binomial trials are sometimes called *Bernoulli trials.*

a. Who was Bernoulli?

b. What work of Bernoulli is related to binomial probabilities?

A project presents an opportunity for you to extend your knowledge of a topic related to the material of this chapter. You should allow more time for a project than you do for a typical homework question.

1 The Binomial Theorem for Rational Exponents

Isaac Newton generalized the Binomial Theorem to all rational exponents. That is, he derived series expansions for such expressions as $(x + y)^{-3}$, $(x + y)^{2/3}$, and $(x + y)^{-5/6}$. What did Newton find? What are the first four terms of the series expansions of the binomials above? How can this extended Binomial Theorem be used to aid in calculations?

2 Infinity in Art

The concept of infinity has intrigued people throughout history. In the last 100 years several artists and mathematicians have created spectacular works of art based on the infinite repetition of geometric forms. The Dutch artist Maurits Escher is probably most noted for his *tessellations*, which are tilings of the plane with congruent objects. Tessellations can be thought of as providing a finite pattern for covering the infinite plane. In other works of art, such as Square Limit, Escher represented infinite divisions within a finite space. Investigate Escher's use of mathematics in the representation of infinity.

3 A Prime Number Sieve

In 1934, a young Indian student named Sundaram devised the following "sieve" to identify some prime numbers. Here is the beginning of his table, in which each row (and column) is an arithmetic sequence.

4	7	10	13	16	19	22	...
7	12	17	22	27	32	37	...
10	17	24	31	38	45	52	...
13	22	31	40	49	58	67	...
16	27	38	49	60	71	82	...
.	.	.	.	.	.	.	...

Sundaram's table has the following properties: If N occurs in the table, then $2N + 1$ is not a prime number; if N does not occur in the table, then $2N + 1$ is a prime number.

a. Verify the first property for three numbers in the table and the second property for three numbers that are not (and never will be) in the table.

b. Identify the common difference d for each row. What is the pattern in these common differences as you read down the table?

c. Write an explicit formula for the kth term in the nth row. Use this result to prove that if N occurs in the table, then $2N + 1$ is composite.

d. Prove that if $2N + 1$ is not prime, then N is in the table. (This is the contrapositive of the second property stated above.)

e. Can all prime numbers be found by using Sundaram's table? Why or why not?

4 Probabilities and the Lottery

a. Obtain the rules, entry sheets, and an information sheet for a lottery. Use this information to find the number of different entries possible for each game, the probability that you will win first prize with a single entry, and the probability of winning *any* prize with a single entry. Would you advise someone to buy lottery tickets? Why or why not?

b. Repeat the steps in part **a** for another lottery. In which lottery does the person have a better chance of winning? Suggest some reasons why a particular game might be played.

(*Note:* Do not attempt to buy a ticket in your local Lotto competition without first checking that it is legal for you to do so. All states restrict sales to persons over a certain age.)

5 Recursively Defined Curves

Many interesting curves can be created by recursive definitions. For instance, begin with a square with a given side, say ———. At each stage, replace each side of the square with this shape:

. The original square and subsequent stages leading to a limit curve, sometimes called the *dragon curve,* are shown below.

a. Determine the perimeter, area, and dimension of the dragon curve. To determine the dimension, you will need to learn something about *fractals.*

b. Find out about other curves that are defined recursively. Some famous ones are called snowflake curves and space-filling curves.

c. Design your own curve.

6 A Test for Convergence

If an infinite series containing only positive terms is to converge, it is necessary that the terms approach 0 as n approaches infinity. However, this is not sufficient; the text points out that the harmonic series diverges even though the terms approach 0.

a. Explain why the following series diverges.

$$A = 1 + \frac{1}{2} + \underbrace{\frac{1}{4} + \frac{1}{4}}_{\text{2 terms}} + \underbrace{\frac{1}{8} + \frac{1}{8} + \frac{1}{8} + \frac{1}{8}}_{\text{4 terms}} +$$

$$\underbrace{\frac{1}{16} + \frac{1}{16} + \frac{1}{16} + \frac{1}{16} + \frac{1}{16} + \frac{1}{16} + \frac{1}{16} + \frac{1}{16}}_{\text{8 terms}} + \dots$$

b. Show that each term of the harmonic series

$$H = 1 + \frac{1}{2} + \frac{1}{3} + \frac{1}{4} + \frac{1}{5} + \frac{1}{6} + \dots$$

is greater than or equal to the corresponding term of series A. Explain how this result shows that the harmonic series diverges.

c. The following variation of the harmonic series, the *alternating harmonic series*, converges.

$$B = 1 - \frac{1}{2} + \frac{1}{3} - \frac{1}{4} + \frac{1}{5} - \frac{1}{6} + \dots + (-1)^{n+1}\frac{1}{n} + \dots$$

Use a calculator or computer to approximate B to six decimal places.

SUMMARY

A sequence is a function whose domain is the set of consecutive integers greater than or equal to k. An explicit formula allows you to find any specified term efficiently. A recursive formula describes each term in terms of previous ones and is often more efficient for generating the terms.

Two important kinds of sequences are arithmetic and geometric sequences. For an arithmetic sequence, the difference between successive terms is a constant, the constant difference. In a geometric sequence, the ratio of successive terms is a constant, the constant ratio. If an arithmetic sequence has first term a_1 and constant difference d, the nth term $a_n = a_1 + (n - 1)d$. If a geometric sequence has first term g_1 and constant ratio r, the nth term $g_n = g_1 r^{n-1}$.

Some infinite sequences converge to a limit while others diverge. A computer or calculator is useful for deciding whether or not a sequence is convergent, but it is not an infallible tool. Limits of some sequences can be found by applying properties of limits.

A series is the sum of the terms of a sequence. Explicit formulas for sums of arithmetic and geometric series exist. The sum S_n of the first n terms of an arithmetic sequence is given by $S_n = \frac{n}{2}(2a_1 + (n - 1)d)$ or $S_n = \frac{n}{2}(a_1 + a_n)$.

For a geometric series with $r \neq 1$, $S_n = \frac{g_1(1 - r^n)}{1 - r}$. To examine infinite series, it is useful to form a sequence $S_1, S_2, \ldots$ of partial sums. An infinite series may have a limit; some do not. For an infinite geometric series with first term g_1 and constant ratio r, the limit exists when $|r| < 1$; $S_\infty = \frac{g_1}{1 - r}$.

The number of ways to select r unordered items from a set of n elements is ${}_nC_r = \frac{{}_nP_r}{r!} = \frac{n!}{(n - r)!r!}$. Each selection is called a combination. A famous configuration of combinations is called Pascal's Triangle. Each row of Pascal's Triangle gives coefficients of terms in the expanded form of the power of a binomial. In particular, for all positive integers n,

$$(x + y)^n = {}_nC_0 x^n + {}_nC_1 x^{n-1}y + {}_nC_2 x^{n-2}y^2 + \ldots + {}_nC_n y^n.$$

A binomial experiment has a fixed number of trials, each with only two possible outcomes (success and failure), the probabilities of which are fixed and sum to 1. In a binomial experiment with n trials and probability of success p, the probability of exactly k successes is ${}_nC_k p^k(1 - p)^{n-k}$. By the Binomial Theorem, this is the $(k + 1)$st term in the expansion of $(x + y)^n$, where $x = p$ and $y = 1 - p$.

VOCABULARY

Below are the most important terms and phrases for this chapter. You should be able to give a general description and a specific example of each and a precise definition for those marked with an asterisk (*).

Lesson 8-1
*sequence, term, position
explicit formula, recursive formula
*arithmetic sequence
*geometric sequence

Lesson 8-2
limiting value, $\lim_{n \to \infty} s_n$
end behavior of a sequence
*divergent
*convergent, convergent to L
*harmonic sequence
alternating harmonic sequence

Lesson 8-3
*series
infinite series, finite series
arithmetic series

Lesson 8-4
*geometric series
nth partial sum

Lesson 8-5
sequence of partial sums
sum of an infinite series, S_∞
convergent, divergent series

Lesson 8-6
*combination, combinations of n things taken r at a time
${}_nC_r$, $\binom{n}{r}$
Formula for ${}_nC_r$ Theorem

Lesson 8-7
Pascal's Triangle
$(r + 1)$st term in row n of Pascal's Triangle

Lesson 8-8
expansion of $(x + y)^n$
Binomial Theorem
binomial coefficients

Lesson 8-9
*binomial experiment, success, failure
Binomial Probability Theorem
binomial probability distribution

PROGRESS SELF-TEST

Take this test as you would take a test in class. You will need a calculator. Then check the test yourself using the solutions at the back of the book.

In 1 and 2, consider this formula for a sequence.

$$\begin{cases} g_1 = 0 \\ g_n = g_{n-1} + n^2, \text{ for all integers } n > 1 \end{cases}$$

1. Is the sequence arithmetic, geometric, or neither?

2. Find the first four terms of the sequence.

3. The first term of an arithmetic sequence is -12 and the constant difference is d. Find the 15th term.

4. Consider the geometric sequence that begins 9, 3, ... Find the 7th term of the sequence.

5. An employee begins a job paying $19,000 per year with the guarantee of a 5% increase in salary each year.

a. What is the employee's salary during the fourth year?

b. What is the employee's salary during the *n*th year?

6. Consider the sequence given by

$$\begin{cases} a_1 = 3 \\ a_n = a_{n-1} - \frac{1}{2}n, \ n \geq 2. \end{cases}$$

a. Sketch a graph of this sequence.

b. Is the sequence convergent? If so, find its limit.

7. On each swing, a certain pendulum swings 70% of the length of its previous swing. How far will the pendulum swing before coming to rest if its first swing is 75 cm?

8. Estimate $\sum_{i=1}^{\infty} \frac{3}{i^3}$ correct to three decimal places.

9. Find the sum of all the integers from 100 to 200.

10. Find $\sum_{i=1}^{10} 7\left(\frac{3}{4}\right)^i$ to the nearest ten-thousandth.

11. Lillian has begun running every day for exercise. The first day she ran 0.5 miles. The 12th day she ran 3.25 miles. If each day she increased her distance by a constant amount, how many total miles did she run in all 12 days combined?

12. Prove that for all integers n greater than or equal to 1, ${}_nC_2 = {}_nC_{n-2} = \frac{n(n-1)}{2}$.

13. **a.** Expand $(x + y)^3$.

b. Explain how your answer to part **a** is related to Pascal's Triangle.

In 14 and 15, *multiple choice.*

14. The first term in the binomial expansion of $(2c - b)^{10}$ is $(2c)^{10}$. What is the 4th term?

(a) $(2c)^7$

(b) $(2c)^7(-b)^3$

(c) $10 \cdot 9 \cdot 8(2c)^7(-b)^3$

(d) $\frac{10 \cdot 9 \cdot 8}{3!}(2c)^7(-b)^3$

15. In a talent contest with 50 finalists (one from each state), the top three winners will be given identical prizes. How many different sets of possible winners are there?

(a) 3^{50} (b) 50^3

(c) $50 \cdot 49 \cdot 48$ (d) $\frac{50 \cdot 49 \cdot 48}{3!}$

16. Suppose the probability that a randomly selected heart transplant patient will survive more than one year is 0.86. Find the probability that at least 4 of 5 randomly selected heart patients will survive for longer than a year.

17. Show three places in Pascal's Triangle where the following property is displayed.

$${}_nC_0 + {}_nC_2 + {}_nC_4 + \ldots + {}_nC_{n-1} = {}_nC_1 + {}_nC_3 + {}_nC_5 + \ldots + {}_nC_n.$$

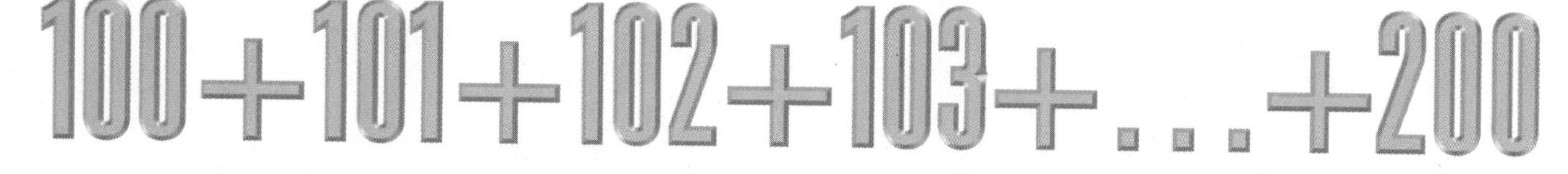

CHAPTER REVIEW

Questions on SPUR Objectives

SPUR stands for **S**kills, **P**roperties, **U**ses, and **R**epresentations. The Chapter Review questions are grouped according to the SPUR Objectives for this chapter.

SKILLS DEAL WITH THE PROCEDURES USED TO GET ANSWERS.

Objective A: *Find terms of sequences from explicit or recursive formulas.* *(Lesson 8-1)*

In 1–4, a sequence is described. **a.** Find the first 5 terms. **b.** Find the 12th term.

1. $R_n = n^2 - n$

2. $\begin{cases} B_1 = -6 \\ B_n = B_{n-1} + 3n,\ n \geq 2 \end{cases}$

3. $t_n = 3 \cdot 2^{n-1}$

4. $q_n = -10 + 3(n - 1)$

Objective B: *Find explicit or recursive formulas for the nth term of an arithmetic or geometric sequence.* *(Lesson 8-1)*

5. The first four terms of an arithmetic sequence are 84, 67, 50, 33. Find each.

a. the 50th term **b.** the nth term

6. The first three terms of a geometric sequence are 24, -84, 294. Find each.

a. the 15th term **b.** the nth term

7. Give an explicit formula for the sequence defined by

$$\begin{cases} k_1 = 22{,}000 \\ k_n = 0.8k_{n-1}, \text{ for all integers } n \geq 2. \end{cases}$$

8. Give a recursive formula for the sequence defined by $A_n = 32 - 5n$.

Objective C: *Evaluate arithmetic or geometric series.* *(Lessons 8-3, 8-4)*

In 9–12, evaluate the arithmetic or geometric series given.

9. $103 + 120 + 137 + 154 + \ldots + 290$

10. $(5u - v) + (4u + v) + (3u + 3v) + \ldots + (23v - 7u)$

11. $1 + 3 + 9 + 27 + \ldots + 3^{14}$

12. $x + x^2y + x^3y^2 + \ldots + x^{21}y^{20}$

13. Evaluate $\sum_{k=1}^{100} (4k - 13)$.

14. Evaluate $\sum_{n=1}^{20} 10(0.6)^{n-1}$.

Objective D: *Expand binomials.* *(Lesson 8-8)*

In 15–18, expand.

15. $(a + b)^3$

16. $(x - y)^6$

17. $(2x - 5)^4$

18. $\left(\frac{p}{2} + 2q\right)^5$

19. Find the second term in the binomial expansion of $(x - y)^{12}$.

20. Find the middle term in the binomial expansion of $(p + q)^{10}$.

PROPERTIES DEAL WITH THE PRINCIPLES BEHIND THE MATHEMATICS.

Objective E: *Determine whether a sequence is arithmetic or geometric.* *(Lesson 8-1)*

In 21–26, classify the sequence as possibly or definitely arithmetic, possibly or definitely geometric, or definitely neither.

21. 13, 24, 35, 46, ...

22. 44, 50, 57, 65, ...

23. $3u,\ u + v,\ 2v - u,\ 3v - 3u, \ldots$

24. $\begin{cases} a_1 = -2 \\ a_n = (a_{n-1})^2 + 1, \text{ for all integers } n > 1 \end{cases}$

25. $t_n = -8(-0.7)^n$

26. $\begin{cases} a_1 = x \\ a_n = y - a_{n-1}, \text{ for all integers } n \geq 2 \end{cases}$

Objective F: *Determine limits of certain sequences.* *(Lesson 8-2)*

In 27–30, decide whether the sequence has a limit, and if it does, determine the limit.

27. the geometric sequence 80, 60, 45, 33.75, ...

28. the arithmetic sequence 80, 60, 40, 20, ...

29. $h_n = \frac{7}{n}$

30. $\begin{cases} v_1 = 1 \\ v_n = (-1)^n \cdot v_{n-1}, \text{ for all integers } n > 1 \end{cases}$

31. Use a calculator or computer to evaluate terms of the sequence

$-\frac{19}{69}, -\frac{22}{67}, -\frac{25}{65}, \ldots, \frac{3n+16}{2n-71}, \ldots.$

a. Does the sequence seem to converge?

b. If the sequence is convergent, give its limit. If it is divergent, explain how you can tell.

32. Use a computer or calculator to decide whether the sequence below is convergent or divergent. If the sequence converges, give its limit as a fraction in lowest terms.

$1, \frac{11}{16}, \frac{16}{24}, \frac{23}{32}, \ldots, \frac{n^2+7}{8n}, \ldots$

Objective G: *Tell whether an infinite series converges. If it does, give the limit.* *(Lesson 8-5)*

In 33–35, for the geometric series shown, state whether or not the series is convergent. If the series is convergent, give its sum.

33. $8 - \frac{40}{3} + \frac{200}{9} - \frac{1000}{27} + \ldots$

34. $7 + 5.6 + 4.48 + \ldots$

35. $a - \frac{a}{5} + \frac{a}{25} - \frac{a}{125} + \ldots$

36. Use a computer or calculator to conjecture whether the series below is convergent. If it seems to be convergent, give what seems to be its limit.

$\frac{1}{1^5} + \frac{1}{2^5} + \frac{1}{3^5} + \frac{1}{4^5} + \ldots$

37. a. Under what condition does the following geometric series have a sum?

$a^3b^2 + a^3b^4 + a^3b^6 + a^3b^8 + \ldots$

b. Give an expression for the sum, when it exists.

Objective H: *Prove and apply properties involving combinations.* *(Lesson 8-7)*

In 38–40, prove the given identity.

38. ${}_nC_r = {}_nC_{n-r}$ for all positive integers n and r, $r \le n$

39. ${}_nC_1 = {}_nC_{n-1} = n$

40. ${}_nC_r = {}_{n-1}C_r + {}_{n-1}C_{r-1}$

41. *True or false.* For all positive integers n and r such that $r \le n$, ${}_nP_r > {}_nC_r$.

USES DEAL WITH APPLICATIONS OF MATHEMATICS IN REAL SITUATIONS.

Objective I: *Solve problems involving arithmetic and geometric sequences and series.* *(Lessons 8-1, 8-3, 8-4, 8-5)*

42. One sunflower produces 500 seeds. Each seed produces a flower which produces 500 seeds, and so on. Let a_n = the number of seeds after n generations.

a. Write an explicit formula for a_n.

b. Write a recursive formula for a_n.

c. Assuming no losses, how many sunflower seeds are produced at the end of five generations, starting with a first generation of 100 sunflowers?

43. The coach of a soccer team rewards the players on the team by putting stars on jerseys. Every time the coach increases the number of stars by two. For the first win, the coach gives 3 stars.

a. Determine how many times the team has won if each jersey has 17 stars.

b. Determine the least number of wins needed in order to have 100 stars on each jersey.

44. In mid-1996, the population of Iraq was about 21.4 million, with an average annual growth rate of 3.7%. Estimate the population in the middle of the year 2000, assuming that the population grows geometrically and the growth rate does not change.

45. In a certain housing complex, rents are increased by 4% every year. Consider a family which has been living at this complex for 15 years and assume that they paid $400 per month in the first year.

a. Determine the rent they are paying this year.

b. At the end of this year, how much will the family have paid during their 15 years of residency? (Hint: Consider the total rent the family has paid in each complete year.)

46. The tracks on an LP record can be approximated as concentric circles (rather than a continuous spiral) with a difference of .3 mm between the radii of consecutive circles. If the grooves on a record start 15 cm away from the center and end 3 cm away from it. What is the distance covered by the needle of a record player in one playing of this LP?

Objective J: *Use combinations to compute the number of ways of selecting objects.* *(Lesson 8-6)*

47. A committee of three is to be chosen from a faculty of 13 math teachers. How many ways of choosing the committee are there?

48. There are 20 members of a tennis club. If each must play the others exactly once in a tennis match, how many games must be played?

49. A euchre hand consists of five cards from a deck of 32 different cards. Half the cards are red, the other half are black.

a. How many different euchre hands are there?

b. How many euchre hands contain only red cards?

50. In how many ways can a DJ select eight hits from the top 40 to play in the next half hour?

51. A catering service can prepare 6 soups, 8 salads, 8 vegetables, and 10 entrees. In how many different ways can you select 1 soup, 3 salads, 4 vegetables, and 2 entrees?

Objective K: *Determine probabilities in situations involving binomial experiments.* *(Lesson 8-9)*

In 52 and 53, Mrs. McDonnell knows that each of her five children likes roughly 80% of the suppers she serves. Assume that the children's likes and dislikes are independent.

52. What is the probability that all five children will like a given supper?

53. What is the probability that at least one person will dislike supper?

54. If Mr. and Mrs. Washington both have siblings with cystic fibrosis, the probability that any given child born to them has the disease is $\frac{1}{9}$. If they have two children, what is the probability that at least one will have cystic fibrosis?

55. Fifteen percent of a certain species of young trees die during their first winter. A homeowner wants to plant a hedge with this species. If the homeowner plants 12 such trees, what is the probability that at least 10 will survive?

56. What is the probability that a student will get a perfect score by random guessing on an exam with 17 multiple-choice questions each of which has four options?

REPRESENTATIONS DEAL WITH PICTURES, GRAPHS, OR OBJECTS THAT ILLUSTRATE CONCEPTS.

Objective L: *Locate numerical properties represented by the patterns in Pascal's Triangle.* *(Lesson 8-7)*

In 57–60, show three places in Pascal's Triangle where the given property is represented.

```
          1
        1   1
      1   2   1
    1   3   3   1
  1   4   6   4   1
1   5  10  10   5   1
```

57. ${}_nC_r = {}_nC_{n-r}$

58. ${}_nC_r = {}_{n-1}C_r + {}_{n-1}C_{r-1}$

59. $\sum_{i=0}^{n}((-1)^i \cdot i \cdot {}_nC_i) = 0$

60. $\sum_{i=0}^{n}(i \cdot {}_nC_i) = n \cdot 2^{n-1}$

CHAPTER

POLYNOMIAL FUNCTIONS

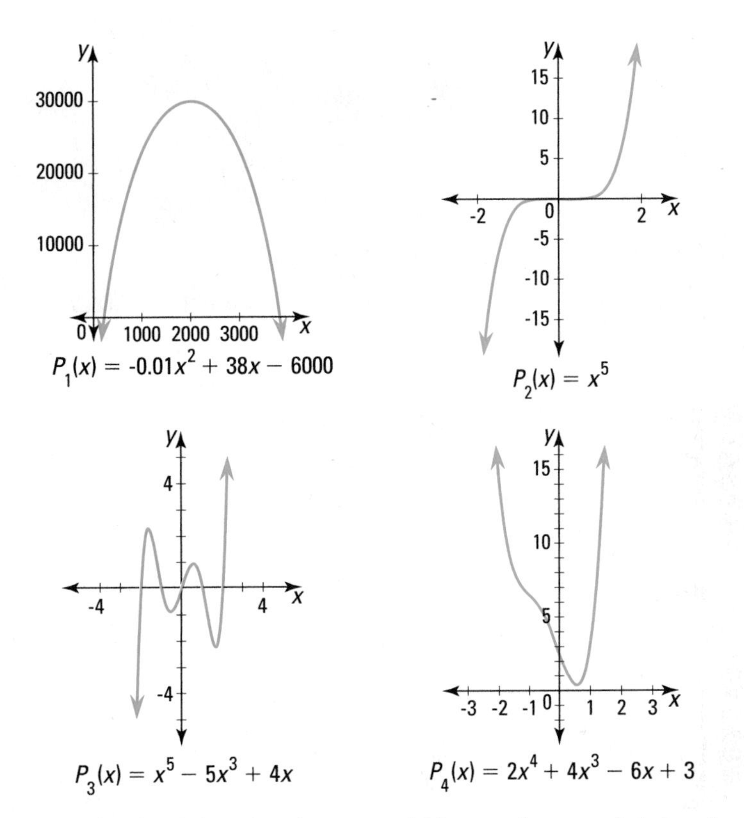

A polynomial function P_1 above could be used to model the shape of the nose of the space shuttle on the facing page.

A *polynomial* in one variable is a sum of multiples of nonnegative integer powers of that variable. The quadratic function P_1 and power function P_2 graphed above are examples of *polynomial functions*. Other polynomial functions such as P_3 and P_4 exhibit more complicated behavior.

The variety of polynomial functions makes them candidates for modeling many real-world situations. Some they model exactly and others they approximate. In this chapter, you will see applications of polynomial functions and their graphs in agriculture, economics, and other fields. You will also see some of the beautiful mathematical properties these functions possess. The theory underlying these properties involves complex numbers, division, and factoring.

LESSON

9-1

Polynomial Models

Uses of Paper. *In 1996, the U.S. paper industry produced enough paper for 2 billion books, 24 billion newspapers, and 372 billion square feet of corrugated cardboard.*

A Polynomial Model for Volume

A company has pieces of cardboard that are 60 cm by 80 cm. They want to make boxes from them (without a top) to hold equipment. Squares with sides of length x are cut from each corner and the resulting flaps are folded to make an open box as shown. In the language of geometry, this box is a right rectangular prism without one face, and its volume $V = \ell wh$.

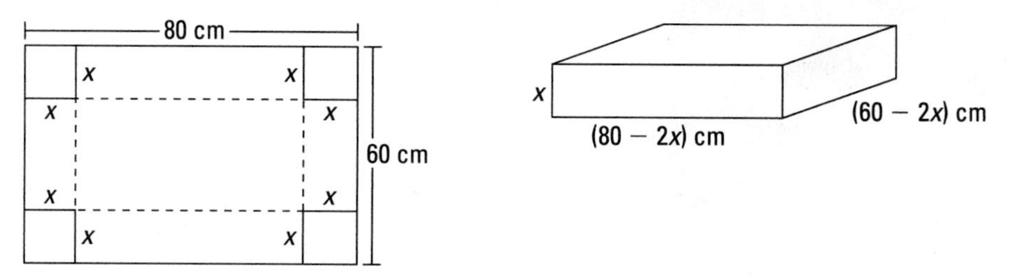

Is there a formula for the volume of the resulting box in terms of x? The cardboard has an original length of 80 cm. By cutting 2 corners, the length of the box is $(80 - 2x)$ cm. Similarly, the width of the box is $(60 - 2x)$ cm. When the flaps are folded to form the box, the height of the box is x cm. To find a formula for the volume of the box in terms of x, substitute these expressions for length, width, and height, respectively.

$$\begin{aligned} \text{Volume} &= \ell wh \\ V &= (80 - 2x)(60 - 2x)(x) \\ &= (4800 - 280x + 4x^2)(x) \\ &= 4800x - 280x^2 + 4x^3 \end{aligned}$$

The expression $4800x - 280x^2 + 4x^3$ is an instance of a *polynomial in the variable x.*

Terminology Associated with Polynomials

The **general form** of a polynomial in one variable is given in the following definiton.

Definition
A **polynomial in *x*** is an expression of the form

$$a_n x^n + a_{n-1}x^{n-1} + a_{n-2}x^{n-2} + \ldots + a_1 x + a_0$$

where n is a nonnegative integer and $a_n \neq 0$.

The number n is the **degree** of the polynomial and the numbers a_n, a_{n-1}, a_{n-2}, . . . , a_0 are its **coefficients**. The number a_n is called the **leading coefficient** of the polynomial. You might think that the leading coefficient of $4800x - 280x^2 + 4x^3$ is 4800, because it is the first coefficient, but it is not. For a polynomial in one variable, the leading coefficient comes first only when the terms of the polynomial are written in descending order of their exponents, as they are in the definition. This is called **standard form.** When the polynomial is written in standard form, $4x^3 - 280x^2 + 4800x$, the leading coefficient, 4, is the first coefficient and the degree, 3, is the first exponent. Note that all the exponents in a polynomial must be nonnegative integers.

The volume of the box depends on the length x of the side of the cut-out square, so the volume can be considered as a *polynomial function of x*.

$$V(x) = 4x^3 - 280x^2 + 4800x$$

In general, a **polynomial function** is a function whose rule can be written as a polynomial. In Lesson 9-2, you will see how to use this function to determine the value of x that gives the maximum volume of the box.

Example 1

If $V(x) = 4x^3 - 280x^2 + 4800x$, find $V(10)$ and state what it represents.

Solution

Substitute 10 for x in the formula for $V(x)$.

$$V(10) = 4(10)^3 - 280(10)^2 + 4800(10)$$
$$= 24{,}000$$

When the length of the side of the cut-out square is 10 cm, the volume of the box is 24,000 cm^3.

A Polynomial Model for an Annuity

An annuity is an investment involving money which is periodically deposited or withdrawn. Annuities give rise to polynomials.

Example 2

Tamara is saving her summer earnings for college. The table below shows the amount of money saved each summer.

After grade	Amount saved
8	\$ 600
9	\$ 900
10	\$1100
11	\$1500
12	\$1600

At the end of each summer, she put her money in a savings account with an annual yield of 7%. How much will be in her account when she goes to college, if no additonal money is added or withdrawn, and the interest rate remains constant?

Solution

Recall the compound interest formula, $A = P(1 + r)^t$ which gives the value of P dollars invested at an annual rate r after t years. The money Tamara put in the bank after grade 8 earns interest for 4 years. It is worth $600(1.07)^4$ when Tamara enters college. Similarly, the amount saved at the end of grade 9 is worth $900(1.07)^3$. Adding the values from each summer gives the total amount in the bank account.

$600(1.07)^4$	$+ \; 900(1.07)^3$	$+ \; 1100(1.07)^2$	$+ \; 1500(1.07)$	$+ \; 1600$
from summer after grade 8	from summer after grade 9	from summer after grade 10	from summer after grade 11	from summer after grade 12

Evaluating this expression shows that **Tamara will have about \$6353 when she goes to college.**

The amount Tamara has when she enters college depends on the interest rate she can get. Let her annual yield be r and $x = 1 + r$. Then her savings $A(x)$ is a polynomial function of x.

$$A(x) = 600x^4 + 900x^3 + 1100x^2 + 1500x + 1600$$

In the function A above, the coefficients of the terms of the polynomial represent the amount invested each successive year. The exponents represent the number of years each amount is on deposit. The value $A(x)$ of the function is the amount Tamara has when the annual interest rate is $x - 1$.

The Degree of a Polynomial

Recall that a **monomial** is a polynomial with one term; a **binomial** is a polynomial with two terms; and a **trinomial** is a polynomial with three terms. Monomials, binomials, and trinomials may be of any degree. For instance, the trinomial $4x^2 - 5x + 1$ is of degree 2, while $a^{10} - a^{20} + a^{30}$ is of degree 30.

Polynomials may also involve several variables. For instance, each of the following is a *polynomial in x and y*.

$$x^2y^3 - 3y^3 + 2x^2 - 6$$
$$x^3 + x^2y^2 + y^5$$

The **degree of a polynomial in more than one variable** is the largest sum of the exponents of the variables in any term. Each of the preceding two polynomials in x and y has degree 5.

Example 3

a. Express the surface area and volume of a cube with sides of length $a + b$ in terms of a and b.

b. State the degree of each polynomial.

Solution

a. The surface area S is six times the area of one face of the cube.

$$S = 6(a + b)^2$$

Use the Binomial Theorem to expand $(a + b)^2$.

$$S = 6(a^2 + 2ab + b^2)$$
$$S = 6a^2 + 12ab + 6b^2$$

The volume is the length of an edge cubed.

$$V = (a + b)^3$$

Use the Binomial Theorem to rewrite the right side.

$$V = a^3 + 3a^2b + 3ab^2 + b^3$$

b. For surface area, the largest sum of the exponents of the variables in any term is 2, so **S has degree 2.** For volume, the largest sum of the exponents of the variables in each term is 3, so **V has degree 3.**

Check

a. As illustrated in the figure above, the volume of the cube equals the sum of the volumes of 8 rectangular solids. In the top layer are two boxes with volumes equal to b^2a, and one each of volumes b^3 and a^2b. In the bottom layer, two of the visible boxes have volume a^2b, and the third has volume b^2a. The box hidden from view has volume a^3. So the total volume is

$$V = (2b^2a + b^3 + a^2b) + (2a^2b + b^2a + a^3)$$
$$= b^3 + 3b^2a + 3a^2b + a^3.$$

b. The polynomial for the volume of the cube, a 3-dimensional measure, is degree 3, and the polynomial for the surface area, a 2-dimensional measure, is degree 2.

QUESTIONS

Covering the Reading

In 1–3, refer to the description of making a box from a flat piece of cardboard. Another box is to be made from a 150-cm-by-100-cm piece of cardboard, by cutting squares of side x cm from the corners.

1. What are the length, width, and height of the box?

2. Write a polynomial function in x for the volume V of the box.

3. Evaluate $V(20)$ and state what it represents.

4. Consider the polynomial $3p^2 - 5p^6$.
a. What is its degree? **b.** What is its leading coefficient?
c. *True or false.* The polynomial is a binomial.

5. Let $p(x) = 6x^8 + 12x^5 - 4x^2 + 9$. If $p(x)$ is of degree n, state the value of each of the following.
a. n **b.** a_n **c.** a_0 **d.** a_2 **e.** a_{n-1}

6. Determine whether each expression can be written as a polynomial.
a. $3x^2$ **b.** 5^x **c.** $2x - 5$
d. $x^{1/2}$ **e.** $\frac{x^2 + x}{2}$ **f.** $\frac{x^2 + x}{x - 1}$

In 7 and 8, write the general form.

7. a 4th degree polynomial in y

8. an nth degree polynomial in x

9. Refer to Example 2. Suppose Tamara can invest her earnings at a 7.5% annual yield. Determine her savings when she enters college.

10. John saved his earnings for several summers just as Tamara did. A polynomial for his savings is

$$S(x) = 1000x^4 + 1250x^3 + 1300x^2 + 1400.$$

a. What did John deposit in the bank the first summer he saved?
b. One summer John did not save any money. Which summer was this?
c. Evaluate $S(1.0575)$ and explain what it represents.

11. Give the degree of the polynomial $7x^3y + 8y^2x^9$.

12. **a.** Find a polynomial for V, the volume of a cube with sides of length $x + 2y$.
b. State the degree of the polynomial.

Applying the Mathematics

In 13 and 14, give an example, if possible, of each of the following.

13. a binomial in three variables, with degree 5

14. a trinomial in two variables, of degree 4

15. The expression $\sum_{i=0}^{n} c_i x^i$ is a polynomial. Give its leading coefficient and its degree.

16. A box with a top is constructed from a piece of cardboard 150 cm by 250 cm. The shaded regions are cut out and the flaps are folded to make a box, as in the diagram below. Write a polynomial in x for the volume of the box.

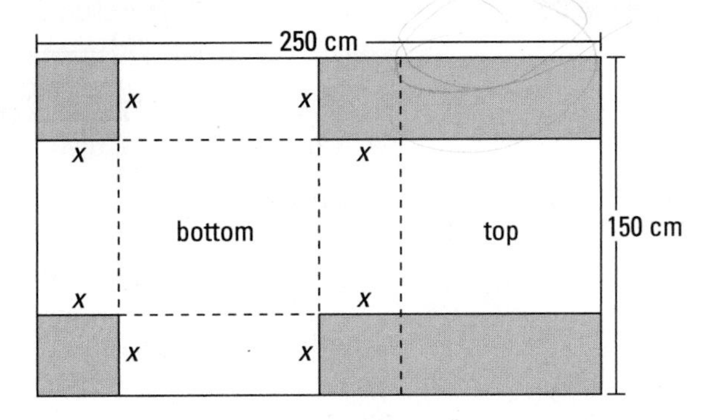

In 17–19, recall that the **square numbers**, 1, 4, 9, 16, 25, . . . , are the values of the function $s(n) = n^2$, when n is a positive integer. The **triangular numbers** $t(n) = \frac{1}{2}n(n+1)$ are the number of dots in shapes like those pictured below.

$t(1) = 1$ $t(2) = 3$ $t(3) = 6$ $t(4) = 10$

17. *True or false.* $s(n)$ is a polynomial function of n of degree 2.

18. *True or false.* $t(n)$ is a polynomial function of n of degree 1.

19. Prove: For all positive integers n, $s(n+1) = t(n) + t(n+1)$.

Review

20. The following table gives the average number of minutes of TV viewing per household per day.

a. Make a scatterplot of the data. Use the number of years since 1985–86 as the independent variable.

b. Use a quadratic regression to find a quadratic model for the data. Sketch a graph of the model on the scatterplot.

c. Is the model a theory-based model?

(Lesson 2-6)

Year	Minutes/Day
1985-86	430
1986-87	425
1987-88	415
1988-89	422
1989-90	415
1990-91	416
1991-92	424
1992-93	437
1993-94	441

Source: *1996 Information Please Almanac*

21. In a certain school, following a Board of Education policy, students must maintain a C average and have no failing grades to participate in extracurricular activities. The box plots below represent the percentage of students at 49 city high schools who were declared ineligible in five activities. *(Lesson 1-4)*

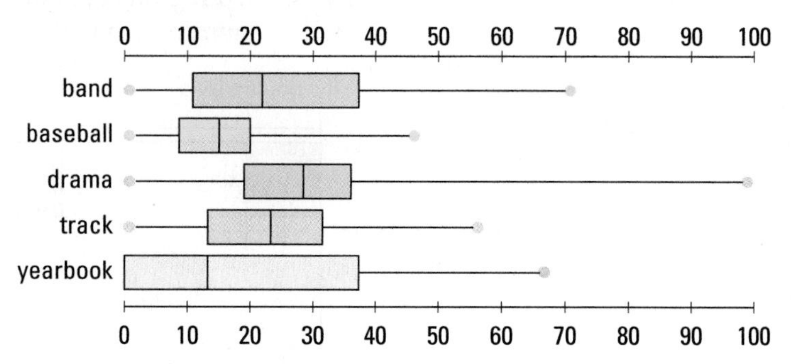

a. Which activity has the lowest median rate of ineligibility?
b. Write a paragraph or two comparing and contrasting the rates of ineligibility in these five activities.

22. Solve the system. *(Previous course, Lesson 2-6)*

$$\begin{cases} x + y + z = 0 \\ 9x + 3y + z = 12 \\ x - y + z = -4 \end{cases}$$

In 23 and 24, expand. *(Previous course)*

23. $(x + 3)(3x + 5)$

24. $(x - 2y)(2x + 8y)$

25. Draw an example of each geometric solid.
a. a regular tetrahedron
b. a pyramid with a square base *(Previous course)*

Exploration

26. a. Find the current annual yield on a certificate of deposit (CD) at a local bank.
b. Are the rates different for CDs depending on how long you invest the money? Are the rates different for the amount of money invested?
c. What are the penalties for early withdrawal and how do they work?

Introducing Lesson 9-2

Finding Some Key Points of a Polynomial Function

Use an automatic grapher.

In Lesson 9-1, a box was made from a 80-cm-by-60-cm piece of cardboard. The volume as a function of the length of a side of a cut-out square was found to be

$$V(x) = 4x^3 - 280x^2 + 4800x.$$

In order to utilize most of the cardboard, the company is interested in finding the maximum volume a box can have starting with cardboard 80 cm by 60 cm.

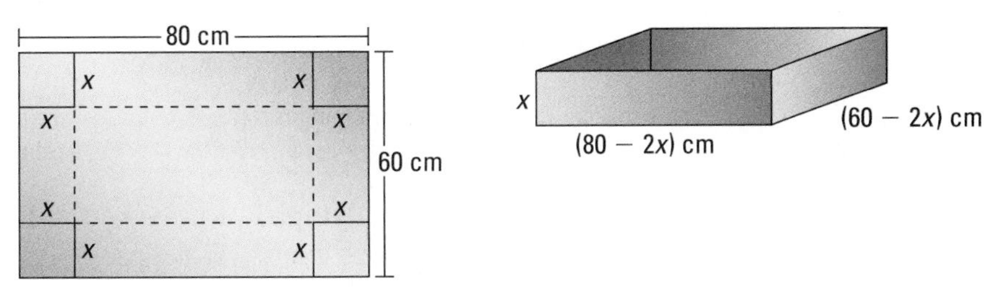

1 On what interval of x-values does the function V have meaning in this situation?

2 Make a table of values of ordered pairs on that interval.

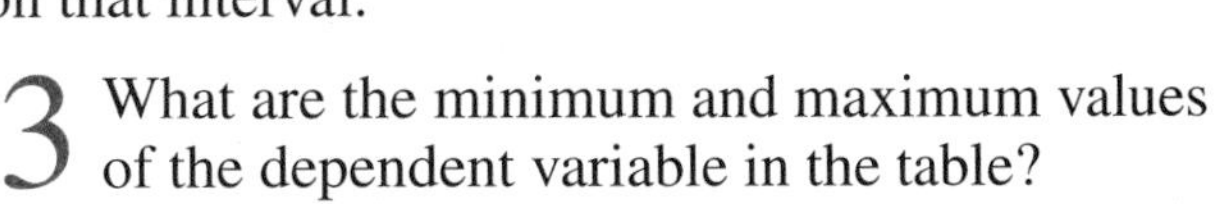

3 What are the minimum and maximum values of the dependent variable in the table?

4 Use the results of Steps 1 and 3 to set the window on your automatic grapher. Make a sketch of the function.

5 Find the maximum point of the graph. Mark it on the sketch along with its coordinates.

6 State the meaning of the coordinates of the maximum point relative to the problem.

LESSON

9-2

Graphs of Polynomial Functions

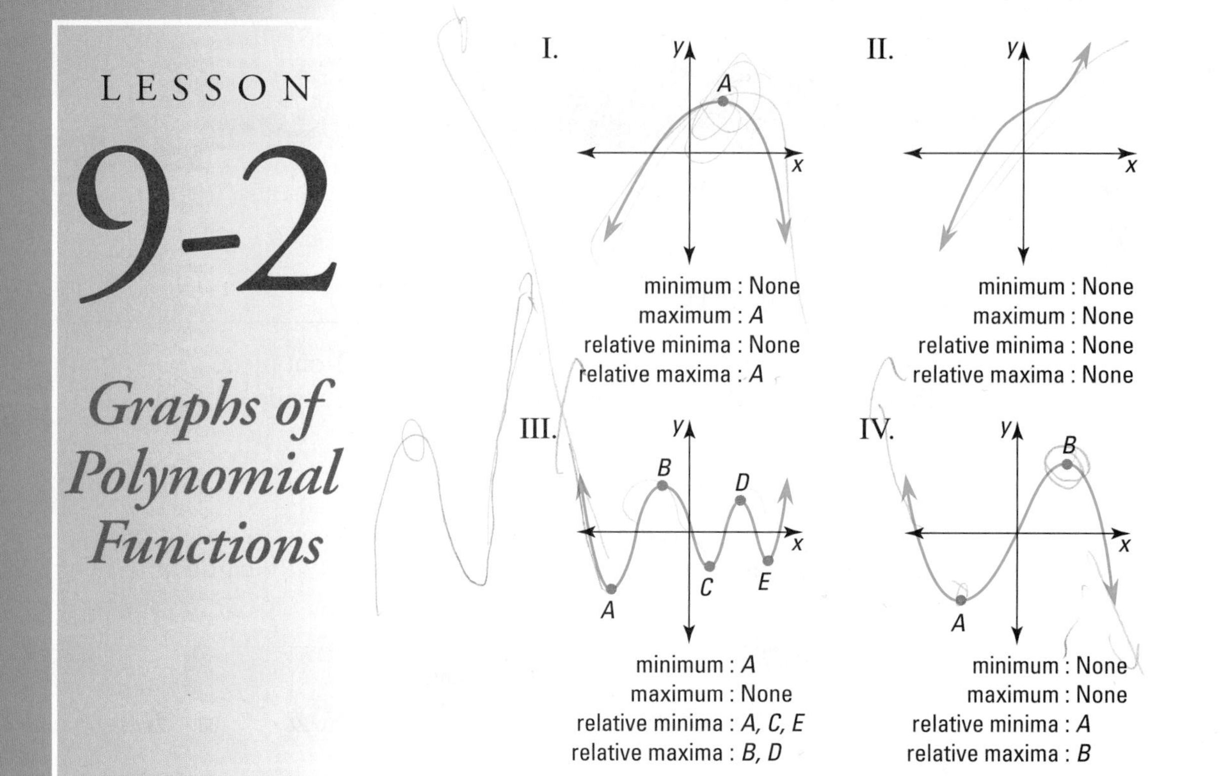

You are familiar with graphs of polynomial functions of degree 1 or 2. You know that the graph of every 1st degree polynomial is a line, and the graph of every quadratic function is a parabola. The graphs of higher degree polynomials do not have special names; nor do all polynomial functions of the same degree have graphs of the same shape. However, graphs of some higher degree polynomials do show a certain regularity, and like linear and quadratic functions, they can be described using key points and intervals.

Extrema of Functions

Recall that the range of a function is the set of possible values for the dependent variable. The **maximum value** of a function is the largest value in its range. Similarly, the **minimum value** of a function is the smallest value in its range. These are the **extreme values** or **extrema** of the function.

In figure I, the y-coordinate of A is the maximum value of the function. In Figures II and IV, the function has neither a maximum nor a minimum value. In Figure III, the y-coordinate of point A is the minimum value of the function, and there is no maximum value.

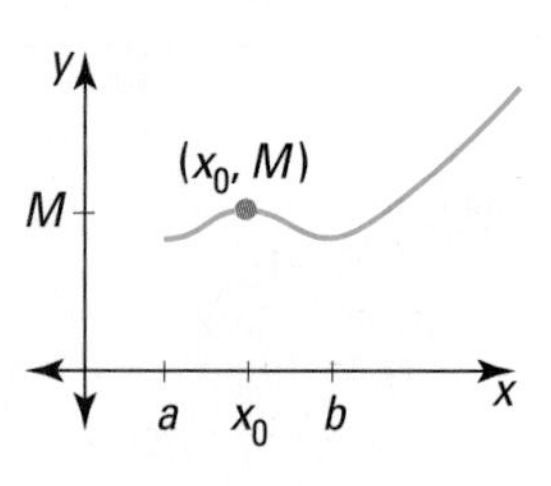

A **relative extremum** is a maximum or minimum value on an open interval $\{x: a < x < b\}$ of the function. Relative extrema are values at "turning points" of the function, as in Figures I, III and IV above. Specifically, a value M of a function f is a **relative maximum** for f if there is an open interval

$\{x: a < x < b\}$ in the domain of f containing a number x_0 such that $f(x_0) = M$ and for all other x in that interval, $f(x) \leq M$.

Every maximum value of a function on an open interval is a relative maximum, so in Figure I, the y-coordinate of A is a relative maximum. But in Figure III, the y-coordinates of B and D are relative maxima but not maxima.

Similarly, a value m of a function f is a **relative minimum** for f if there is an open interval $\{x: a < x < b\}$ in the domain of f containing a number x_0 such that $f(x_0) = m$ and for all other x in that interval, $f(x) \geq m$. Figure III has three relative minima, the y-coordinates of A, C, and E. The y-coordinate of A is the minimum value of the function.

Zeros of Polynomial Functions

Recall that the x-intercepts of the graph of a function are the *zeros* of the function itself. Given a polynomial function p with $p(x) = a_nx^n + a_{n-1}x^{n-1} + \ldots + a_1x + a_0$, the **zeros** or **roots of the polynomial function p** are all values of x such that $p(x) = 0$.

You already know how to find the exact zero of a polynomial of degree 1. This is a **linear polynomial function**, of the form $p(x) = ax + b$, and its zero is $\frac{-b}{a}$. A polynomial of degree 2, of the form $p(x) = ax^2 + bx + c$, is a **quadratic polynomial function**. Using the Quadratic Formula, you can also find its zeros exactly.

Though exact formulas for the zeros of polynomial functions of degrees 3 and 4 do exist, they are quite complicated, and there are no general formulas for finding the zeros of all polynomial functions of degree higher than 4. To find these zeros exactly, algebraic techniques, such as factoring, can sometimes be used. Algebraic techniques are discussed in Lessons 9-8 through 9-10.

To estimate the real zeros of a polynomial function, graphs and tables can be used. Consider a sketch and table of values of $f(x) = -x^3 + 5x + 2$ below.

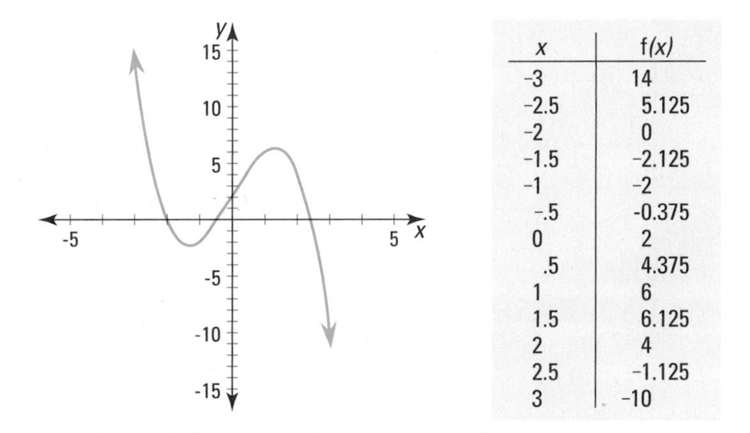

x	f(x)
-3	14
-2.5	5.125
-2	0
-1.5	-2.125
-1	-2
-.5	-0.375
0	2
.5	4.375
1	6
1.5	6.125
2	4
2.5	-1.125
3	-10

On the graph, you can see the x-intercepts by finding points where the graph crosses the x-axis. Notice that -2, an x-intercept on the graph, is verified by $x = -2, f(x) = 0$ in the table. There are no other places in the table where $f(x) = 0$, yet the graph clearly shows two other x-intercepts. Notice as x increases from -0.5 to 0, $f(x)$ increases from -0.375 to 2. Therefore, there exists a zero of the function between -0.5 and 0. Likewise, as x increases from 2 to 2.5, $f(x)$ decreases from 4 to -1.125. Another zero can be found between 2 and 2.5.

Intervals Where a Function Is Positive/Negative or Increasing/Decreasing

So far this lesson has focused on some key points of a polynomial function. The rest of this lesson focuses on what happens between key points. A function is **positive** on an interval when the values of the dependent variable are positive and **negative** on an interval when the values of the dependent variable are negative. A function is **increasing** on an interval if, for any two points on that interval, the slope between them is positive. A function is **decreasing** on an interval if, for any two points on that interval, the slope between them is negative.

Example

Consider the graph of $g(x) = \frac{1}{2}x^4 - 2x^3 + 3x - 4$ below. The x-coordinates of all key points (except the y-intercept) are labeled with a letter.

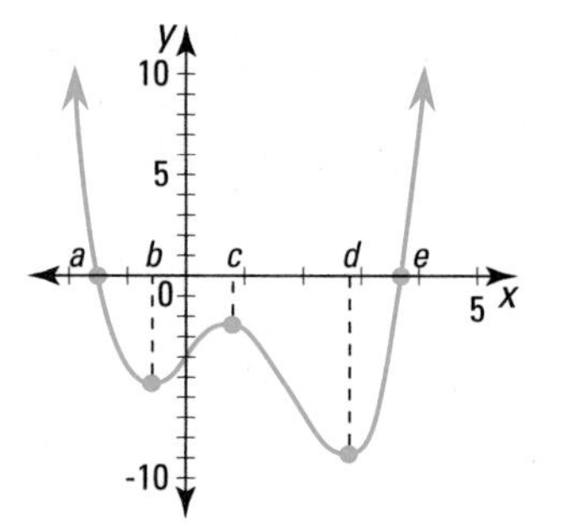

Use the letter labels to describe the interval(s) on which g satisfies the following conditions.

a. g is positive.

b. g is negative.

c. g is increasing.

d. g is decreasing.

e. Estimate the coordinates of the zeros and extrema to the nearest tenth. Redraw the graph with the coordinates of these key points.

Solution

a. The function g is positive when its graph is above the x-axis. This occurs when $x < a$ or $x > e$.

b. g is negative when its graph is below the x-axis. This occurs when $a < x < e$.

c. g is increasing when the graph goes up as you go to the right. This occurs when $b < x < c$ or $x > d$.

d. g is decreasing when the graph goes down as you go to the right. This occurs when $x < b$ or $c < x < d$.

e. Tracing on the graph shows $a \approx -1.5$, $b \approx -0.6$, $c \approx 0.8$, $d \approx 2.8$, and $e \approx 3.7$. The corresponding values of the function are shown on the graph at the right.

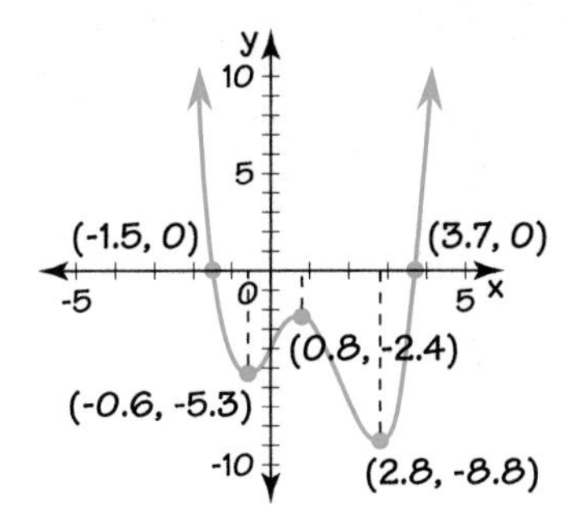

Notice that the description of where a function is positive/negative or increasing/decreasing is an interval of x-values and therefore only x-coordinates are needed.

QUESTIONS

Covering the Reading

In 1–3, refer to the In-class Activity on page 563.

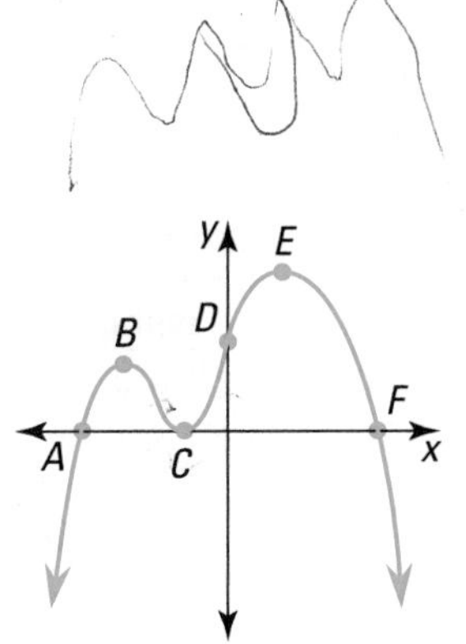

1. Graph $V(x) = 4x^3 - 280x^2 + 4800x$ on the default window of your automatic grapher. Describe what you see and why.

2. Graph V again for $-10 < x < 50$ and $-10{,}000 < y < 40{,}000$. Label all intercept points, zeros, and relative extrema. Give coordinates to the nearest integer.

3. Explain what $V(30) = 0$ means in this context.

4. Examine the graph at the left of a 4th degree polynomial with key points labeled. Classify each point as a zero, minimum, maximum, relative minimum, relative maximum, or none of the above.

5. Draw a sketch of a polynomial function which has a minimum, but no relative minimum.

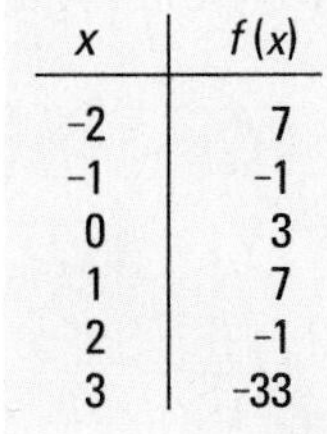

x	$f(x)$
-2	7
-1	-1
0	3
1	7
2	-1
3	-33

6. The table at the left gives values of a polynomial function.
a. Plot these points and sketch a possible graph of $y = f(x)$.
b. Between which pairs of consecutive integers must the zeros of f occur?

7. In this lesson a table of values for $f(x) = -x^3 + 5x + 2$ showed that there was a zero between 2.0 and 2.5. Make another table for x equal to 2.0, 2.1, 2.2, 2.3, 2.4, and 2.5. Between which two values of x in this table must a zero exist? Explain why.

8. At the right is a graph of f with various x-coordinates labeled. In what interval(s) does f satisfy the following conditions?
a. f is positive.
b. f is negative.
c. f is increasing.
d. f is decreasing.

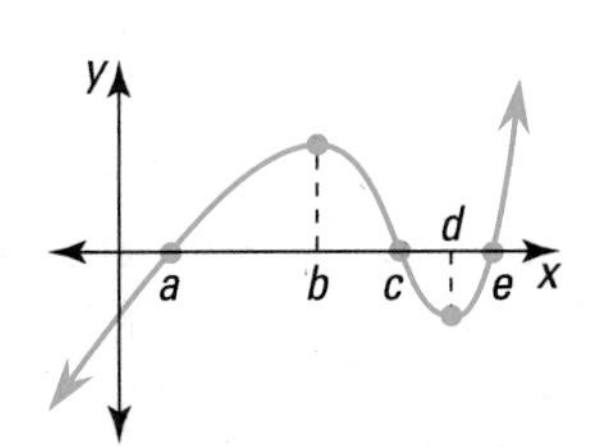

Applying the Mathematics

9. An open box is constructed by cutting squares of side x cm from the corners of a 100-cm-by-70-cm sheet of cardboard.

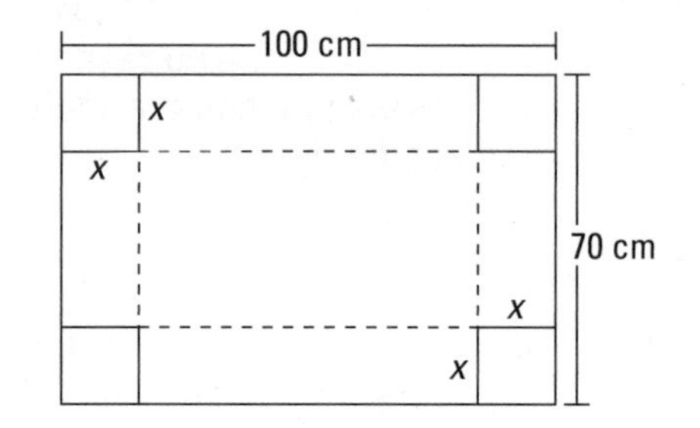

a. Write a polynomial function for the volume of the box.
b. Graph the function.
c. When is the function negative? What does this tell you?
d. Find the coordinates of the maximum of the function.
e. For what size square does the maximum volume occur?
f. What is the maximum volume the box can have?

10. Match each function with a characteristic.

a. $A(x) = 4 - x^2 - x$	I. no relative extrema
b. $B(x) = (x - 2)^3$	II. one relative maximum
c. $C(x) = 7x - 9$	III. one relative minimum
d. $D(x) = (x - 5)^2 - 6$	IV. both a relative maximum and a relative minimum
e. $E(x) = x^3 - 5x$	

11. A missile is fired from 10 ft above the ground with an initial velocity of 500 ft per sec and follows a projectile path. A function describing its height (vertical displacement) h at time t in seconds is $h(t) = -16t^2 + 500t + 10$.
a. After how many seconds will the missile be 3000 ft above the ground?
b. What will be the maximum height of the missile?
c. How many seconds after launching will the missile hit the ground?

In 12–15, use this information. It can be proved using calculus that every polynomial function of degree 4 has either one or three relative extrema. Sketch a graph of each function and tell how many relative maxima and relative minima the function has.

12. $f(x) = x^4$

13. $g(t) = (t - 3)^4 + 2$

14. $h(x) = x^4 - x^2$

15. $j(x) = x^4 - 5x^3 - 1$

16. Consider the function G, where $G(x) = x^3 - 8x + 1$.
a. Sketch a graph of G using an automatic grapher.
b. Identify and verify the y-intercept of G.
c. Estimate the zero(s) of G to the nearest tenth.
d. Estimate the coordinates of the relative extrema of G to the nearest hundredth.
e. In what interval(s) is G positive? negative?
f. In what interval(s) is G increasing? decreasing?

Review

17. The geometric series $g_1 + g_1r + g_1r^2 + \ldots + g_1r^{n-1}$ is a polynomial in the variable __a.__ of degree __b.__. *(Lesson 9-1)*

18. Isaiah M. Rich started saving on his 14th birthday. On that day he set aside \$100. On each successive birthday he has added to his account twice the amount that he deposited the previous birthday. His money is invested at 8% compounded annually and he makes no additional deposits or withdrawals.

a. How much money will he have in his account after making the deposit on his 21st birthday?

b. Write a polynomial in x to represent Isaiah's savings, where $x = 1 + \frac{r}{100}$ if the account pays r% interest.

c. What is the degree of the polynomial in part **b**?

d. What is the leading coefficient of the polynomial in part **b** and what does it represent? *(Lesson 9-1)*

19. Rose Gardner is expanding her garden. The original length and width of the rectangular plot were x meters and y meters. She is now adding h meters to each dimension. *(Lesson 9-1)*

a. Write a product of two binomials to express the area of her new garden.

b. Expand the product.

c. Make a diagram of the original plot and the expansion. Identify each of the areas represented by the terms in part **b**.

In 20 and 21, give the degree of the polynomial. *(Lesson 9-1)*

20. $(a - 5)(a - 2)^3$

21. $(x^2 - 5y)^3$

22. Consider the quadratic function $f(x) = x^2 - 3x - 10$.

a. Identify its y-intercept.

b. Identify its x-intercepts.

c. Identify its line of symmetry.

d. Sketch the graph from the information above.

e. Use the results of part **b** to factor $f(x)$.

(Previous course, Lesson 2-6)

23. Give the zeros of the function $f\colon x \to ax^2 + bx + c$. *(Previous course)*

In 24 and 25, factor each expression. *(Previous course)*

24. $x^2 - 10x + 25$

25. $x^2 - 11x + 30$

Exploration

26. Create some quintic (5th degree) polynomials of your own. Find functions fitting these criteria.

a. A quintic with exactly one real zero.

b. A quintic with exactly three real zeros.

c. A quintic with exactly five real zeros.

LESSON

9-3

Finding Polynomial Models

Fruit is sometimes displayed in layers of triangular numbers as shown above. The result is a *tetrahedral* array. The total number of points in a 3-dimensional tetrahedral array is called a **tetrahedral number**.

Below are the four smallest tetrahedral numbers and the arrays that give rise to them.

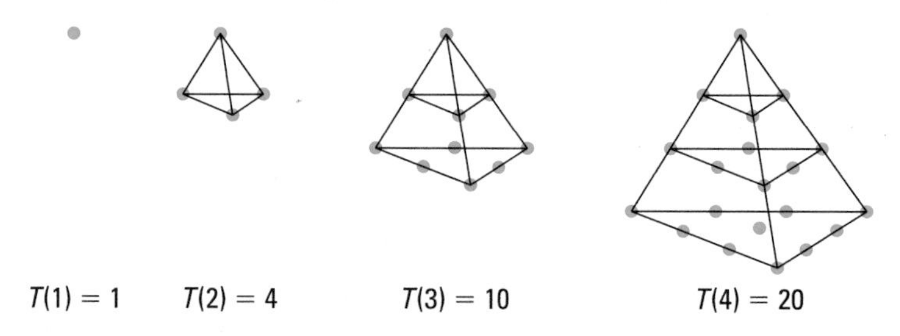

$T(1) = 1$ $T(2) = 4$ $T(3) = 10$ $T(4) = 20$

Notice that each tetrahedral number beyond the first is the sum of the previous tetrahedral number and a triangular number. For instance, the 3rd tetrahedral number is the sum of the 2nd tetrahedral number and the 3rd triangular number.

$$T(3) = 4 + 6 = 10$$

In general, if $T(n)$ represents the nth tetrahedral number, and $t(n)$ is the nth triangular number, a recursive formula for the nth tetrahedral number is

$$\begin{cases} T(1) = 1 \\ T(n) = T(n-1) + t(n), \text{ for all integers } n > 1. \end{cases}$$

Suppose that for the 25th anniversary of a store, the owner wants to arrange apples in a tetrahedral stack 25 rows high. The owner would like to know how many apples are needed.

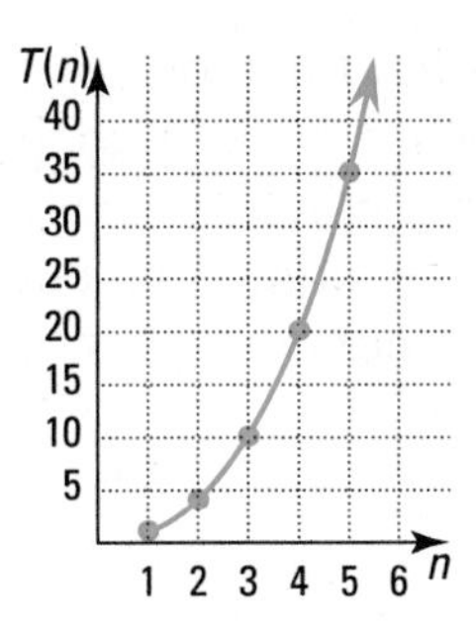

The owner would like an explicit formula for $T(n)$ and begins by graphing known values to see what kind of curve they suggest. At the left is a graph. This graph is clearly not linear. Is it a parabola? Is it part of a higher-degree polynomial? Or is it a part of an exponential curve?

The family of polynomial functions in one variable has a special property that enables you to predict from a table of values whether or not a function is polynomial, and if so, the degree of the polynomial. To examine this property, consider first some polynomials of small degree evaluated at consecutive integers. For instance, consider the first degree polynomial $f(x) = 5x + 3$.

Observe that the differences between consecutive values of $f(x)$, calculated as right minus left, are constant.

x	0		1		2		3		4		5
$f(x) = 5x + 3$	3		8		13		18		23		28
differences		5		5		5		5		5	

Notice that the constant difference is equal to the slope of the function $f(x) = 5x + 3$.

For second degree polynomial functions the differences in function values are not equal, but differences of these differences are constant. Here are the results when $f(x) = x^2 + x + 3$ is evaluated at integers from -1 to 5.

x	-1		0		1		2		3		4		5
$f(x) = x^2 + x + 3$	3		3		5		9		15		23		33
1st differences		0		2		4		6		8		10	
2nd differences			2		2		2		2		2		

Consider now a cubic polynomial, say $f(x) = 2x^3 + x - 10$. For the integers from 0 to 6 the following pattern of differences occurs.

x	0		1		2		3		4		5		6
$f(x) = 2x^3 + x - 10$	-10		-7		8		47		122		245		428
1st differences		3		15		39		75		123		183	
2nd differences			12		24		36		48		60		
3rd differences				12		12		12		12			

In this case, the 3rd differences are constant. Note also that 4th differences and beyond will all equal zero.

Each of the preceding examples is an instance of the following theorem. Its proof is beyond the scope of this book and is therefore omitted.

Polynomial Difference Theorem
The function $y = f(x)$ is a polynomial function of degree n if and only if, for any set of x-values that form an arithmetic sequence, the nth differences of corresponding y-values are equal and nonzero.

The Polynomial Difference Theorem tells you that if a function is polynomial in degree n, it will yield constant nth differences. Also, it tells you that if values of a function produce constant nth differences for an arithmetic sequence of x-values, then there is a polynomial function containing these points. Moreover, the degree of the polynomial is the n corresponding to the nth differences that are equal.

Example 1

Consider the tetrahedral number function T described on the first page of this lesson. Is T a polynomial function? If so, what is the degree of the polynomial?

Solution 1

Construct a table of consecutive tetrahedral numbers, and take differences between consecutive terms.

n	1		2		3		4		5		6
T(n)	1		4		10		20		35		56
1st differences		3		6		10		15		21	
2nd differences			3		4		5		6		
3rd differences				1		1		1			

Since the third differences are constant use the Polynomial Difference Theorem. The function $n \rightarrow T(n)$ is a polynomial function of degree 3.

Solution 2

On page 570, we noted that a recursive formula for T has $T(n) = T(n-1) + t(n)$, where $t(n)$ is the nth triangular number. Subtracting $T(n-1)$ from both sides, we have $T(n) - T(n-1) = t(n)$. This indicates that the 1st differences are the triangular numbers, which you can see in Solution 1. But it is known from Chapter 8 that the nth triangular number is $\frac{n(n+1)}{2}$, which is a quadratic polynomial. Since the 1st differences are quadratic, the 2nd differences must be linear, and so the 3rd differences are constant. Thus, T is a polynomial function of degree 3.

In order to find an explicit formula for this cubic polynomial, you can set up and solve a system of equations. You know the formula for $T(n)$ is of the form

$$T(n) = an^3 + bn^2 + cn + d.$$

You must find four coefficients a, b, c, and d to determine $T(n)$. So use any four data points in the table of tetrahedral numbers, and substitute them into the cubic form above. It is easiest if the values of n form an arithmetic sequence. Using $n = 4, 3, 2$, and 1 gives the following four equations.

$$\begin{aligned}
T(4)&:\quad 20 = 64a + 16b + 4c + d \\
T(3)&:\quad 10 = 27a + 9b + 3c + d \\
T(2)&:\quad 4 = 8a + 4b + 2c + d \\
T(1)&:\quad 1 = a + b + c + d
\end{aligned}$$

Solve this system. To eliminate d, subtract each successive pair of sentences above. This gives the following equivalent system.

$$10 = 37a + 7b + c$$
$$6 = 19a + 5b + c$$
$$3 = 7a + 3b + c$$

Repeating the same procedure with the sentences above eliminates c.

$$4 = 18a + 2b$$
$$3 = 12a + 2b$$

Subtracting these two equations gives $1 = 6a$; so $a = \frac{1}{6}$.

To find the other coefficients, substitute back.

$$3 = 12a + 2b, \text{ so when } a = \tfrac{1}{6},$$
$$3 = 12\left(\tfrac{1}{6}\right) + 2b. \text{ Thus, } b = \tfrac{1}{2}.$$

Similarly, $3 = 7a + 3b + c$, so when $a = \frac{1}{6}$ and $b = \frac{1}{2}$,

$$3 = 7\left(\tfrac{1}{6}\right) + 3\left(\tfrac{1}{2}\right) + c. \text{ Thus, } c = \tfrac{1}{3}.$$

Finally, $1 = a + b + c + d$, so when $a = \frac{1}{6}$, $b = \frac{1}{2}$, and $c = \frac{1}{3}$, $d = 0$.

The resulting polynomial formula for the nth tetrahedral number is

$$T(n) = \tfrac{1}{6}n^3 + \tfrac{1}{2}n^2 + \tfrac{1}{3}n.$$

Hence, to find the number of apples needed in a display 25 rows high, let $n = 25$. Then $T(n) = T(25) = 2925$. So almost 3000 apples are needed for the anniversary display.

As an alternative to finding the cubic model using a system of equations, it is possible to use the regression techniques learned in Chapter 2. Some statistical utilities include a quadratic, cubic, and quartic regression feature. Because the third differences were constant, we know that a cubic model is a good model. In fact, by examining the residuals we can verify that a cubic model is an exact model in this case.

Example 2

a. Use cubic regression to find a cubic model for the tetrahedral numbers.
b. Verify that the model is an exact model by examining the residuals.

Solution

a. Enter the table at the right in a statistics utility.

x	1	2	3	4
y	1	4	10	20

Our statistics utility gives the cubic regression model

$$y = 0.1666666667x^3 + 0.5x^2 + 0.3333333333x + (-3.7E12)$$

A cubic model is $y = \frac{1}{6}x^3 + \frac{1}{2}x^2 + \frac{1}{3}x$.

▶

b.

x	1	2	3	4
Observed y	1	4	10	20
Predicted y	1	4	10	20
Residuals	0	0	0	0

All of the residuals are 0, which verifies that a cubic model is an exact model.

To find the cubic model for the tetrahedral numbers, four noncollinear data points were used. Five noncollinear points are needed to determine a quartic (4th degree) model. In general, to find the equation for a polynomial of degree n you need $n + 1$ points, no three of which are collinear, no four of which are on the same parabola, and so on, which lead to a system of $n + 1$ equations in $n + 1$ unknowns.

QUESTIONS

Covering the Reading

In 1 and 2, a formula for a function f is given. **a.** Evaluate f for all integers from -1 to 7. **b.** Take differences between consecutive values until a nonzero constant is found.

1. $f(x) = -2x^2 + 5$

2. $f(x) = x^3 - x^2 + x + 1$

In 3 and 4, refer to the Polynomial Difference Theorem.

3. If the y-values are all equal to 7 for the 4th differences of consecutive integral x-values, what is the degree of the polynomial?

4. The theorem applies to differences of y-values taken from what sort of x-values?

In 5–7, use the data listed in each table. **a.** Determine if y is a polynomial function of x of degree less than 6. **b.** If so, find its degree.

5.

x	1	2	3	4	5	6	7	8	9
y	2	12	36	80	150	252	392	576	810

6.

x	1	2	3	4	5	6	7	8
y	9	26	47	66	77	74	51	2

7.

x	1	3	5	7	9	11	13
y	2	8	32	128	512	2048	8192

8. Show how to find the 7th tetrahedral number using each of the following.
a. Add the 7th triangular number to the 6th tetrahedral number.
b. Use the explicit formula for $T(n)$ developed in the lesson.

9. Consider a function f described by the data points below.

x	0	1	2	3	4	5	6
$f(x)$	0	5	14	33	68	125	210

a. Show that f may be a polynomial of degree less than 5, and find its degree.
b. Determine an equation for f.
c. Find $f(7)$.

Applying the Mathematics

10. Consider the sequence determined by the following:

$$\begin{cases} t_1 = 17; \\ t_n = t_{n-1} - 5, \text{ for integers } n > 1. \end{cases}$$

a. List the first six terms of the sequence.
b. Tell whether the sequence can be described explicitly by a polynomial.
c. If the answer to part **b** is yes, find the polynomial.

11. In Example 3 in Lesson 2-6, a store put an air conditioner normally selling for \$350 on sale. On the first day of the sale they reduced the price by \$10, the second day they took off an additional \$20, the third day took off an additional \$30, and so on.
a. Make a table of day vs. sale price for the first 6 days of the sale.
b. Use the polynomial difference theorem to find the degree of a polynomial function that maps day of sale to sale price.
c. Use regression to find a polynomial function to fit the data.
d. Find a recursive formula for the polynomial function in part **c**.

12. Suppose $f(x) = mx + b$.
a. Calculate $f(5) - f(4)$.
b. Evaluate $f(x + 1) - f(x)$.
c. Describe in words what the difference in part **b** represents.

13. a. If $f(x) = ax^3 + bx^2 + cx + d$, find $f(1), f(2), f(3), f(4), f(5)$, and $f(6)$.
b. Prove that the third differences of these values are constant.

14. Refer again to the tetrahedral numbers in the lesson. Suppose you try to model the data with a quadratic function.
a. Use $T(1)$, $T(2)$, and $T(3)$ to find a quadratic model for the data, and verify that this formula works for the first three numbers in the sequence.
b. Verify that this quadratic model does not predict the 4th tetrahedral number in the sequence.

Review

15. Does $f(x) = x^3 + 2$ have any relative extrema? If so, state the coordinates of each one. *(Lesson 9-2)*

16. Let h be the function defined by $h(x) = -50x^3 + 10x^2 + 150x + 250$. Draw a graph of the function. Label all intercepts and relative extrema. Give coordinates correct to the nearest tenth of the interval(s) on which h satisfies the following conditions. *(Lesson 9-2)*
a. h is positive.
b. h is negative.
c. h is increasing.
d. h is decreasing.

17. You invest \$750 at the ends of three consecutive years in an account whose annual yield is r. Your money is compounded annually and none is added or withdrawn.
a. Write a polynomial function describing the amount in the account at the end of the third year.
b. Determine the amount in part **a**, if $r = 4.8$. *(Lesson 9-1)*

18. a. In how many ways can you choose
i. 5 objects out of 6?
ii. 99 objects out of 100?
iii. 364 objects out of 365?
b. Generalize the results of part **a** and prove your answer. *(Lesson 8-6)*

Istanbul, Turkey

19. The population of Turkey in 1996 was about 62.5 million, with an annual growth rate of about 1.7%. Assume the population changes continuously.
a. Give a model for the population n years after 1996.
b. Predict the population in 2000.
c. Predict when the population will reach 100 million. *(Lesson 6-4)*

20. *Skill sequence.* Multiply and simplify.
a. $(x + 3)(4x)$
b. $(x + 3)(4x - 5)$
c. $(x + 3)(2x^2 + 4x - 5)$ *(Previous course)*

21. *Skill sequence.* Solve.
a. $x(x - 7) = 0$
b. $(y + 9)(3y - 7) = 0$
c. $(z - 5)(z + 8)(z + 15) = 0$ *(Previous course)*

Exploration

22. A complete set of dominoes of order n consists of t tiles with two halves each containing a number of dots according to the following criterion:

> Each whole number less than or equal to n (including the blank, representing 0) is paired with each other number exactly once.

Note that this means that each number is paired with itself exactly once.
a. Draw a complete set of dominoes of order 3.
b. Make a table of the number of dominoes in a complete set for orders 1, 2, 3, 4, 5, and 6.
c. Determine a formula for t in terms of n.

LESSON

9-4 Division and the Remainder Theorem

Parti 53497 per 83

53497 —— 83

Vienne 00644 — $\frac{45}{83}$

534
498
369
332
377
332
45
0 $\frac{45}{83}$

| 83

Divide and Conquer. *The first long division problem ever printed was in an arithmetic book by Philippi Calandri in 1491. It shows that 53497 ÷ 83 = 644$\frac{45}{83}$.*

In earlier courses you learned how to add, subtract, and multiply polynomials. Now you will learn how to divide them. The procedure is similar to dividing integers and relies on the same inverse relationship between multiplication and division.

For instance, because $5 \cdot 13 = 65$, from the definition of division you may conclude that $\frac{65}{13} = 5$. Recall that 65 is called the *dividend*, 13 is called the *divisor* and 5 is the *quotient*. Similarly for polynomials, because $(x + 3)(x + 5) = x^2 + 8x + 15$, you may conclude that $\frac{x^2 + 8x + 15}{x + 5} = x + 3$, provided $x \neq -5$.

If you do not recognize the factorization, then you can use long division. The procedure for long division of polynomials is illustrated in Example 1.

Example 1

Divide $6x^2 + 13x - 5$ by $3x - 1$.

Solution

Look at the first terms of both the dividend and divisor.

$$\begin{array}{r} 2x \\ 3x - 1 \overline{)\, 6x^2 + 13x - 5} \\ \underline{6x^2 - 2x} \\ 15x - 5 \end{array}$$

Think: $3x\overline{)6x^2} = 2x$. This is the first term in the quotient; write it above the dividend. Now multiply $3x - 1$ by $2x$ and subtract the product from $6x^2 + 13x - 5$.

▶

Now look at the first term of the divisor and the new dividend.

$$\begin{array}{r} 2x + 5 \\ 3x - 1\overline{)6x^2 + 13x - 5} \\ \underline{6x^2 - 2x} \\ 15x - 5 \\ \underline{15x - 5} \\ 0 \end{array}$$

Think: $3x\overline{)15x} = 5$. Thus 5 is the second term in the quotient; write it above the dividend adding it to $2x$. Multiply $3x - 1$ by 5 and subtract the product from $15x - 5$. Since 0 is left, the division is finished, and there is no remainder.

Check

Does $(2x + 5)(3x - 1) = 6x^2 + 13x - 5$? Yes. It checks.

If some of the coefficients in the dividend polynomial are zero, you need to fill in all the missing powers of the variable in the dividend, using zero coefficients. Example 2 demonstrates this and also shows two ways to check a long division solution.

Example 2

Divide $5x^3 - 2x - 36$ by $x - 2$.

Solution

The coefficient of x^2 in the polynomial is zero. Insert $0x^2$ so that all powers of x appear in the dividend.

$$\begin{array}{r} 5x^2 + 10x + 18 \\ x - 2\overline{)5x^3 + 0x^2 - 2x - 36} \\ \underline{5x^3 - 10x^2} \\ 10x^2 - 2x \\ \underline{10x^2 - 20x} \\ 18x - 36 \\ \underline{18x - 36} \\ 0 \end{array}$$

Think: $x\overline{)5x^3} = 5x^2$. Multiply $x - 2$ by $5x^2$ and subtract. Think: $x\overline{)10x^2} = 10x$. Multiply $x - 2$ by $10x$ and subtract. Think: $x\overline{)18x} = 18$. Multiply $x - 2$ by 18; subtract to get 0.

Check 1

Multiply quotient by divisor and use the distributive property to simplify.

$$\begin{aligned}(x - 2)(5x^2 + 10x + 18) &= x(5x^2 + 10x + 18) - 2(5x^2 + 10x + 18) \\ &= 5x^3 + 10x^2 + 18x - 10x^2 - 20x - 36 \\ &= 5x^3 - 2x - 36\end{aligned}$$

Check 2

Let $Y_1 = \frac{5x^3 - 2x - 36}{x - 2}$ and $Y_2 = 5x^2 + 10x + 18$. Make a table of values for $-3 \leq x \leq 3$. The output of a table utility is shown at the right. The Y-values of the table are identical except when $x = 2$. When $x = 2$, the denominator of Y_1 is zero and a division by zero "error" occurs. Mathematically we say Y_1 is undefined when $x = 2$. This confirms that $\frac{5x^3 - 2x - 36}{x - 2} = 5x^2 + 10x + 18$ except when $x = 2$.

X	Y_1	Y_2
-3	33	33
-2	18	18
-1	13	13
0	18	18
1	33	33
2	Error	58
3	93	93

Division of Polynomials Using a Symbol Manipulator

Most symbol manipulators can divide polynomials. The input and output from two different symbol manipulators are shown below.

INPUT	OUTPUT
$\dfrac{5x^3 - 2x - 36}{x - 2}$	$5 \cdot x^2 + 10 \cdot x + 18$
Simplify [(5x^3 − 2x − 36)/(x − 2)]	$18 + 10x + 5x^2$

The quotient polynomial is the same for both symbolic manipulators except that the first writes it in descending order of exponents; the second uses ascending order.

As in division of integers, not all polynomial division problems "come out even." In general, when a polynomial $f(x)$ is divided by a polynomial $d(x)$, it produces a quotient $q(x)$ and *remainder* $r(x)$. Either $r(x) = 0$ or $r(x)$ has degree less than the degree of the divisor, $d(x)$. In symbols,

$$f(x) = q(x) \cdot d(x) + r(x)$$

$$\text{dividend} = \text{quotient} \cdot \text{divisor} + \text{remainder}$$

or $$\frac{\text{dividend}}{\text{divisor}} = \text{quotient} + \frac{\text{remainder}}{\text{divisor}}.$$

Example 3

Divide $2x^4 - 8x^3 + 12$ by $x^2 - 2$.

Solution

$$\begin{array}{r}
2x^2 - 8x + 4 \\
x^2 - 2 \overline{) 2x^4 - 8x^3 - 0x^2 + 0x + 12} \\
\underline{2x^4 - 4x^2 } \\
- 8x^3 + 4x^2 + 0x \\
\underline{- 8x^3 + 16x } \\
4x^2 - 16x + 12 \\
\underline{4x^2 - 8} \\
- 16x + 20
\end{array}$$

Because the degree of $-16x + 20$ is less than that of $x^2 - 2$, the division is complete. You may write:

The quotient is $2x^2 - 8x + 4$ with remainder $-16x + 20$,

or $$\frac{2x^4 - 8x^3 + 12}{x^2 - 2} = 2x^2 - 8x + 4 + \frac{-16x + 20}{x^2 - 2}.$$

Check 1

Substitute a value for x and verify the last equation.

Check 2

Does dividend = quotient · divisor + remainder?

Does $2x^4 - 8x^3 + 12 = (2x^2 - 8x + 4)(x^2 - 2) + (-16x + 20)$?

Does $2x^4 - 8x^3 + 12 = (2x^4 - 8x^3 + 16x - 8) + (-16x + 20)$? Yes.

Consider the special case when the divisor $d(x)$ is linear and of the form $x - c$. For the remainder to be of a lower degree than the divisor, it must be a constant, possibly zero. Then

$$\text{dividend} = \text{quotient} \cdot \text{divisor} + \text{remainder}.$$

$$f(x) = q(x) \cdot (x - c) \qquad + r(x), \text{ where } r(x) \text{ is a constant}$$

This equation is true for all x. In particular, it is true when $x = c$. Then

$$f(c) = (c - c) \cdot q(c) + r(c).$$

This can be simplified.

$$f(c) = 0 \cdot q(c) + r(c)$$
$$f(c) = r(c)$$

This says that the value of the polynomial at $x = c$ is precisely the remainder when f is divided by $x - c$. These steps prove the Remainder Theorem.

Remainder Theorem
If a polynomial $f(x)$ is divided by $x - c$, then the remainder is $f(c)$.

Example 4

Find the remainder when $7x^5 - x^3 + 1$ is divided by $x - 2$.

Solution 1

Use the Remainder Theorem. Let $f(x) = 7x^5 - x^3 + 1$ and find $f(2)$.

$$f(2) = 7(2)^5 - (2)^3 + 1 = 217$$

So the remainder when $7x^5 - x^3 + 1$ is divided by $x - 2$ is 217.

Solution 2

Use polynomial long division.

$$\begin{array}{r|rrrrrr}
 & 7x^4 & +\ 14x^3 & +\ 27x^2 & +\ 54x & +\ 108 & \\
x - 2 & 7x^5 + 0x^4 & -\ x^3 & +\ 0x^2 & +\ 0x & +\ 1 & \\
 & 7x^5 - 14x^4 & & & & & \\ \hline
 & 14x^4 & -\ x^3 & & & & \\
 & 14x^4 & -\ 28x^3 & & & & \\ \hline
 & & 27x^3 & +\ 0x^2 & & & \\
 & & 27x^3 & -\ 54x^2 & & & \\ \hline
 & & & 54x^2 & +\ 0x & & \\
 & & & 54x^2 & -\ 108x & & \\ \hline
 & & & & 108x & +\ 1 & \\
 & & & & 108x & -\ 216 & \\ \hline
 & & & & & 217 &
\end{array}$$

Solution 3

Use a symbol manipulator. The first time we tried this, we were surprised. Nothing happened!

INPUT	OUTPUT
$\frac{7x^5 - x^3 + 1}{x - 2}$	$\frac{7x^5 - x^3 + 1}{x - 2}$

Instruct the symbol manipulator to rewrite the input as a proper fraction.

$\text{propFrac}\left(\frac{7x^5 - x^3 + 1}{x - 2}\right)$ $\quad \frac{217}{x - 2} + 7 \cdot x^4 + 14 \cdot x^3 + 27 \cdot x^2 + 54 \cdot x + 108$

Now the output is in the form $\frac{\text{dividend}}{\text{divisor}} = \frac{\text{remainder}}{\text{divisor}} + \text{quotient}$. **So the remainder is 217.**

Notice that the Remainder Theorem has limitations:

It only applies when dividing by a linear factor.

It does not produce a quotient.

But it provides a quick way to find the remainder. And the Remainder Theorem has a very useful consequence, the Factor Theorem, which you will study in Lesson 9-5.

QUESTIONS

Covering the Reading

In 1 and 2, find the quotient when the first polynomial is divided by the second.

1. $3x^2 - 16x - 35, x - 7$

2. $6z^4 - 3z^3 - 3z - 6, 2z^2 + 2$

3. Given that $(x - 3)(x^2 + 5x + 1) = x^3 + 2x^2 - 14x - 3$, write each quotient as a polynomial.

a. $\frac{x^3 + 2x^2 - 14x - 3}{x - 3}$

b. $\frac{x^3 + 2x^2 - 14x - 3}{x^2 + 5x + 1}$

4. In a division problem, state two relationships between the dividend, divisor, quotient, and remainder.

5. Suppose $f(x) = d(x) \cdot q(x) + r(x)$, $f(x) = x^2 + 3x + 7$, and $d(x) = x + 2$. Find possible polynomials for $q(x)$ and $r(x)$.

6. The input and output of a symbol manipulator are given below. Identify the dividend, divisor, quotient, and remainder.

INPUT	OUTPUT
$\text{Prop Frac}\ \frac{3b^5 + 16b^3 - 27b - 50}{b^3 - 7}$	$\frac{21 \cdot b^2 - 27 \cdot b + 62}{b^3 - 7} + 3 \cdot b^2 + 16$

In 7 and 8, two polynomials are given. **a.** Use the Remainder Theorem to find the remainder when the first polynomial is divided by the second. **b.** Check by dividing.

7. $y^3 + 4y^2 - 9y - 40, y - 3$

8. $2x^3 - 11x^2 - 2x + 5, x - 5$

9. Suppose you know that when $f(x)$ is divided by $x - 85$, the remainder is zero. What is $f(85)$?

Applying the Mathematics

10. Let $f(x) = x^5 - 32$ and $g(x) = x - 2$.

a. Express $\frac{f(x)}{g(x)}$ as a polynomial in simplest terms.

b. The expression in part **a** is a finite geometric series. Identify the first term and the common ratio of the series.

In 11 and 12, two polynomials are given. **a.** Find the quotient and remainder when the first polynomial is divided by the second. **b.** Show that the degree of the remainder is less than the degree of the divisor. **c.** Check by multiplying the divisor by the quotient and then adding the remainder.

11. $a^3 + 5a^2 - 10$, $a^2 - 5$ **12.** $x^4 - 9x^3 + 19x^2 - 2x - 3$, $x - 3$

13. What is the quotient if $x^3 + 2x^2y - 2xy^2 - y^3$ is divided by $x - y$?

14. Consider $g(x) = \frac{x^3 - 12x^2 + 48x - 64}{x^2 - 8x + 16}$.

a. *True or false.* For all $x \neq 4$, g is a linear function.

b. Justify your answer to part **a**.

15. a. Refer to Example 3. Use an automatic grapher to plot on the same set of axes

$$f(x) = \frac{2x^4 - 8x^3 + 12}{x^2 - 2}$$

$$g(x) = 2x^2 - 8x + 4$$

and $$h(x) = 2x^2 - 8x + 4 + \frac{-16x + 20}{x^2 - 2}.$$

b. Write several sentences comparing and contrasting the graphs.

Review

16. Consider the table of values below.

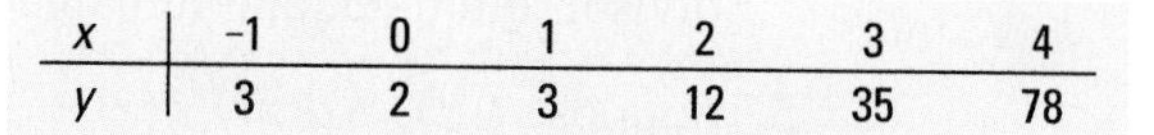

x	-1	0	1	2	3	4
y	3	2	3	12	35	78

a. Find a polynomial function to fit these data.

b. Find, to the nearest tenth, all zeros of the function in part **a**.

c. Find, to the nearest tenth, all relative extrema of the function. *(Lessons 9-2, 9-3)*

17. Let $h(x) = x^4 + 3x^3 - 11x^2 - 3x + 10$.

a. Graph $y = h(x)$ on a window that shows all zeros and relative extrema.

b. Identify the intervals where h is increasing, and the intervals where h is decreasing.

c. Identify the intervals where h is positive, and the intervals where it is negative. *(Lesson 9-2)*

18. The total daily revenue from a hot dog stand at a ball park is given by the equation $R(x) = x \cdot p(x)$, where x is the number of hot dogs sold and $p(x)$ is the price in cents of one hot dog. The price of a hot dog also depends on x, as given by the equation

$$p(x) = 250 + .002x - .00001x^2.$$

a. Find a polynomial expression equal to $R(x)$.
b. Draw a graph of R on a window that shows all relative extrema and x-intercepts for $x \geq 0$. (Hint: You will need values of x and y larger than 1000.)
c. Determine the number of hot dogs to be sold to produce the maximum daily revenue.
d. What is the maximum daily revenue possible?
e. What is the largest domain on which this model could hold?
(Lesson 9-2)

19. Let $g(x) = (2ax - 3b)^7$, where a and b are constants.
(Previous course, Lesson 9-1)
a. What is the degree of $g(x)$?
b. What is the leading coefficient of $g(x)$?
c. What is the constant term of $g(x)$?

20. Consider $f(x) = 6x^2 + 13x - 5$.
a. Solve $f(x) = 0$.
b. Factor $f(x)$.
c. State a relationship between the results of parts **a** and **b**.
(Previous course)

Exploration

21. a. Divide each polynomial by $x - y$.
i. $x^3 - y^3$
ii. $x^5 - y^5$
iii. $x^7 - y^7$
iv. $x^9 - y^9$
b. Generalize the pattern above.

LESSON

9-5 The Factor Theorem

How Are the Zeros of a Polynomial Function Related to the Factors of the Polynomial?

Consider the following polynomial functions in standard form. A symbol manipulator was used to find the factors of the polynomial and the zeros of the function.

INPUT	OUTPUT
Define $q(x) = x^2 - 3x - 10$	Done
factor(q(x), x)	$(x - 5) \cdot (x + 2)$
zeros(q(x), x)	$\{-2 \quad 5\}$

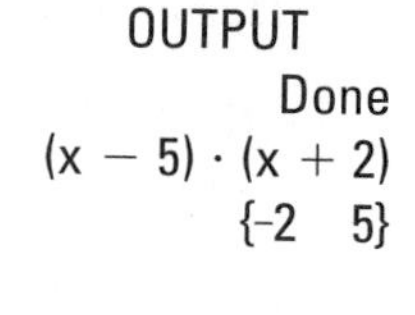

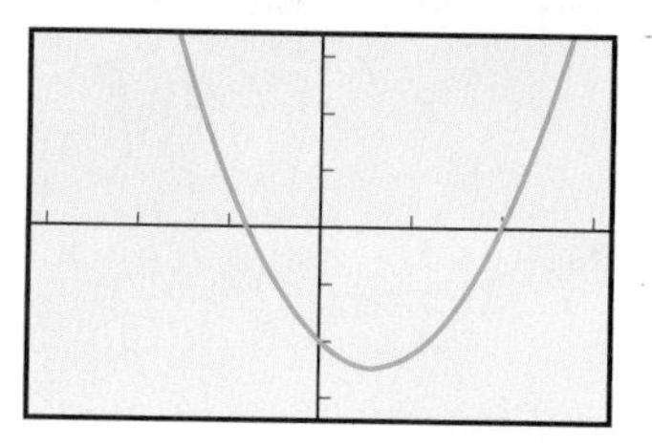

$-8 \le x \le 8$, x-scale = 2.5
$-17 \le y \le 17$, y-scale = 5

INPUT	OUTPUT
Define $r(x) = x^3 + x^2 - 12x$	Done
factor(r(x), x)	$x \cdot (x - 3) \cdot (x + 4)$
zeros(r(x), x)	$\{-4 \quad 0 \quad 3\}$

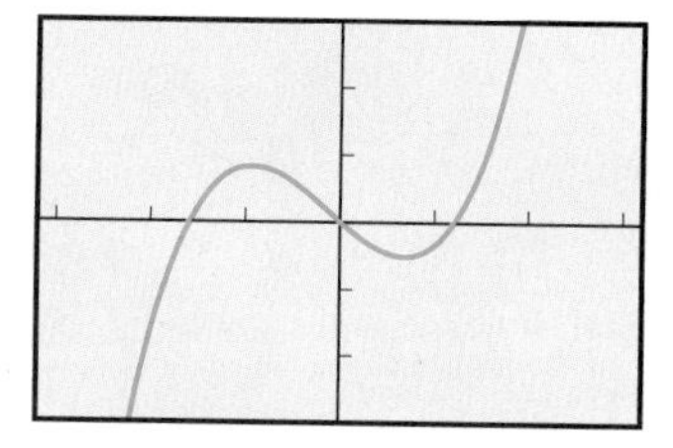

$-8 \le x \le 8$, x-scale = 2.5
$-75 \le y \le 75$, y-scale = 25

INPUT	OUTPUT
Define $s(x) = 2x^4 - 5x^3 - 57x^2 + 90x$	Done
factor(s(x), x)	$x \cdot (x - 6) \cdot (x + 5) \cdot (2 \cdot x - 3)$
zeros(s(x), x)	$\{-5 \quad 0 \quad \frac{3}{2} \quad 6\}$

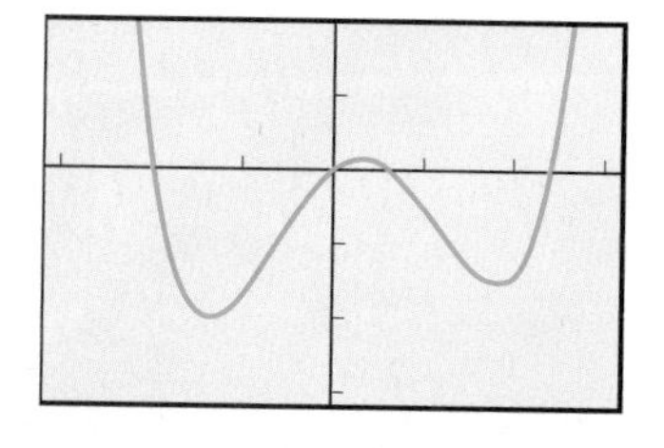

$-8 \le x \le 8$, x-scale = 2.5
$-800 \le y \le 500$, y-scale = 250

The relations between the standard forms of the polynomials and the zeros are subtle. However, when looking at the *factored* forms and the zeros a pattern emerges: each zero c of the polynomial appears to correspond with a linear factor $(x - c)$.

This result holds for all polynomials and can be proved using the Remainder Theorem from Lesson 9-4.

Factor Theorem

For a polynomial $f(x)$, a number c is a solution to $f(x) = 0$ if and only if $(x - c)$ is a factor of f.

Proof

The theorem says "if and only if," so two statements must be proved:

(1) If $(x - c)$ is a factor of f, then c is a solution to $f(x) = 0$.

(2) If c is a solution to $f(x) = 0$, then $(x - c)$ is a factor of f.

In (1), $(x - c)$ is given to be a factor of f. So $f(x) = (x - c)\,q(x)$, where $q(x)$ is a polynomial. In particular, when $x = c$, $f(x) = f(c) = (c - c)q(c) = 0$. So $f(c) = 0$; that is, c is a solution to $f(x) = 0$.

In (2), c is given to be a solution to $f(x) = 0$. Then, by the definition of a solution, $f(c) = 0$. From the Remainder Theorem, $f(x) = (x - c)q(x) + f(c)$, so here $f(x) = (x - c)q(x)$, thus making $(x - c)$ a factor of f.

Graphically, a solution to $f(x) = 0$ is an x-intercept of the graph. Putting this fact together with the Remainder and Factor Theorems produces the following result.

Factor-Solution-Intercept Equivalence Theorem

For any polynomial f, the following are logically equivalent statements.

(1) $(x - c)$ is a factor of f.

(2) $f(c) = 0$.

(3) c is an x-intercept of the graph of $y = f(x)$.

(4) c is a zero of f.

(5) The remainder when $f(x)$ is divided by $(x - c)$ is 0.

Using the Factor Theorem to Factor Polynomials

Example 1

Factor $g(x) = 6x^3 - 25x^2 - 31x + 30$.

Solution

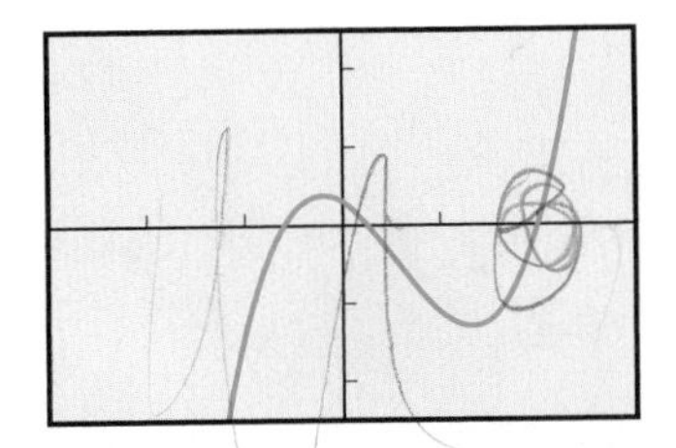

$-7.5 \le x \le 7.5$, x-scale = 2.5
$-250 \le y \le 250$, y-scale = 100

Begin with a graph to see if any zeros are obvious. On the graph at the left, there appears to be a zero at $x = 5$. Verify by substitution:

$$g(5) = 6(5)^3 - 25(5)^2 - 31(5) + 30 = 0.$$

Thus one linear factor is $(x - 5)$. Divide $6x^3 - 25x^2 - 31x + 30$ by this factor to find another factor.

$$\begin{array}{r|l} & 6x^2 + 5x - 6 \\ \hline x - 5 & 6x^3 - 25x^2 - 31x + 30 \\ & \underline{6x^3 - 30x^2} \\ & \quad 5x^2 - 31x + 30 \\ & \quad \underline{5x^2 - 25x} \\ & \qquad -6x + 30 \\ & \qquad \underline{-6x + 30} \\ & \qquad\qquad 0 \end{array}$$

The quotient $6x^2 + 5x - 6$ is a second factor. This polynomial can be factored into a product of binomials.

$$6x^2 + 5x - 6 = (2x + 3)(3x - 2)$$

So
$$\begin{aligned} g(x) &= (x - 5)(6x^2 + 5x - 6) \\ &= (x - 5)(2x + 3)(3x - 2). \end{aligned}$$

Check 1

Multiply the factors.

$$\begin{aligned} (x - 5)(2x + 3)(3x - 2) &= (2x^2 - 7x - 15)(3x - 2) \\ &= 6x^3 - 21x^2 - 45x - 4x^2 + 14x + 30 \\ &= 6x^3 - 25x^2 - 31x + 30 \\ &= g(x) \end{aligned}$$

Check 2

Check the zeros of g. In the solution above, $g(5)$ was shown to equal 0. By the Factor Theorem, the factor $(2x + 3)$ corresponds to a zero of $-\frac{3}{2}$, and the factor $(3x - 2)$ corresponds to a zero of $\frac{2}{3}$. These appear to be x-intercepts on the graph. Substitute to show that $g\left(\frac{2}{3}\right) = 0$ and $g\left(-\frac{3}{2}\right) = 0$.

Finding Polynomials When Their Zeros Are Known

The Factor Theorem can also be used to find equations of polynomials, given their zeros.

Example 2

Find an equation for a polynomial function with zeros -1, $\frac{4}{5}$, and $-\frac{8}{3}$.

Solution

Each zero indicates a factor of the polynomial. Call the polynomial $p(x)$. Then $p(x)$ has factors $(x + 1)$, $\left(x - \frac{4}{5}\right)$, and $\left(x + \frac{8}{3}\right)$. It may have other factors as well. Then $p(x) = k(x + 1)\left(x - \frac{4}{5}\right)\left(x + \frac{8}{3}\right)$ where k may be any nonzero constant or polynomial in x.

Check

Substitute -1 for x. Is $p(-1) = 0$?

$$p(-1) = k(-1 + 1)\left(-1 - \frac{4}{5}\right)\left(-1 + \frac{8}{3}\right)$$

The second factor is zero, so the product is zero.

Similarly, $p\left(\frac{4}{5}\right) = 0$ and $p\left(-\frac{8}{3}\right) = 0$.

Notice that the degree of $p(x)$ in Example 2 is at least 3. However, the degree of k is not known, so the degree of $p(x)$ cannot be determined, nor can the coefficients of its terms. Graphs of many polynomials go through the points (-1, 0), $\left(\frac{4}{5}, 0\right)$, and $\left(-\frac{8}{3}, 0\right)$. Below are graphs of three different polynomials, two of degree 3 and one of degree 4, all with zeros of $-1, \frac{4}{5}$, and $-\frac{8}{3}$.

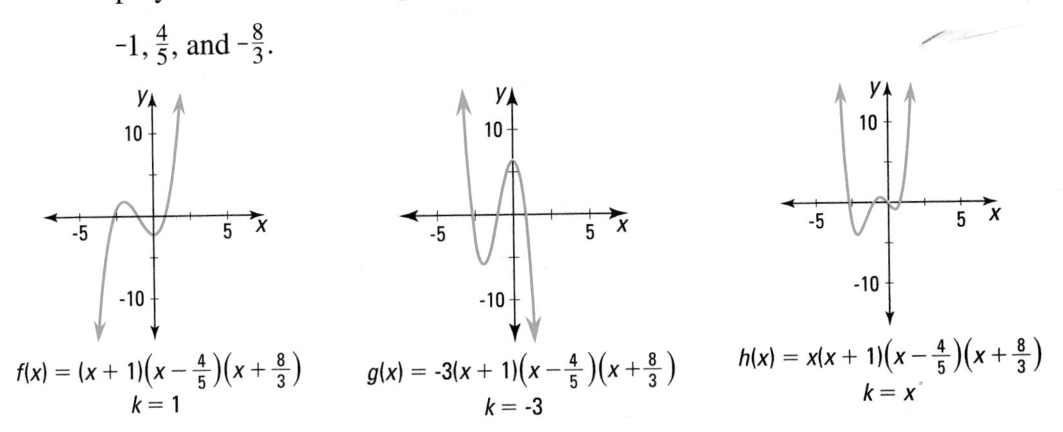

QUESTIONS

Covering the Reading

1. State the Factor Theorem.

2. If $f(x) = x^3 - 3x^2 + 6x - 18$ has a factor of $(x - 3)$, what must be true about $f(3)$?

In 3 and 4, one fact is stated about a polynomial. State at least two other conclusions you can draw.

3. -1 is a solution to $g(x) = x^4 - x^3 + 3x^2 + 3x - 2 = 0$.

4. The graph of $h(x) = x^6 + x^5 - 2x^4$ crosses the x-axis at $x = -2$.

In 5 and 6, find the zeros of the polynomial function by graphing. Use this information to factor the polynomial into linear factors.

5. $r(x) = 7x^3 - 22x^2 - 67x + 10$

6. $t(x) = 3x^3 + 20x^2 - 108x - 80$

7. Corina used a symbol manipulator to factor $g(x) = 3x^3 + 4x^2 - 17x - 6$ as shown below.

INPUT	OUTPUT
factor $(3x^3 + 4x^2 - 17x - 6)$	$(x - 2) \cdot (x + 3) \cdot (3x + 1)$

   a. Graph $y = g(x)$ and $f(x) = (x + 3)(x - 2)(3x + 1)$ on the same set of axes.

   b. Is Corina's factorization correct?

8. Find an equation for a polynomial function with zeros equal to $-5, \frac{9}{2}$, and $\frac{7}{3}$.

Applying the Mathematics

9. Consider the polynomial $x^3 + 6x^2 + 3x - 10$. Without dividing, which two of $(x + 2)$, $(x - 2)$, $(x + 1)$, and $(x - 1)$ must be factors of the polynomial?

In 10 and 11, an equation and some of its solutions are given. Find the other solutions.

10. $4x^3 + 20x^2 - 68x - 84 = 0$; -1 is one solution.

11. $2p^4 + 13p^3 + 12p^2 - 17p - 10 = 0$; 1 and $-\frac{1}{2}$ are solutions.

In 12 and 13, a graph of a polynomial function with integer zeros is given. Find an equation of the given degree for the graph.

12. degree 3

13. degree 4

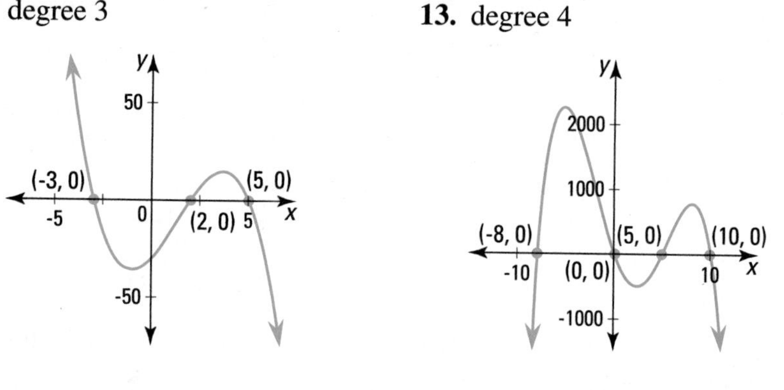

Review

14. If a polynomial $g(x)$ is divided by _?_, then the remainder is $g(a)$. *(Lesson 9-4)*

15. Suppose $m(x) = x^5 - x^3 + 3x$. Without dividing, find the remainder when $m(x)$ is divided by $x + 4$. *(Lesson 9-4)*

16. *Multiple choice.* A polynomial $q(x)$ is divided by $x + 3$ and the remainder is 7. Which of the following points must be on the graph of $q(x)$? *(Lesson 9-4)*

(a) (-3, 7)
(b) (7, -3)
(c) (-3, 0)
(d) (7, 0)
(e) none of these

In 17 and 18, find the quotient when the first polynomial is divided by the second. *(Lesson 9-4)*

17. $x^5 + 243$; $x + 3$

18. $y^5 + 2y^4 - 7y^3 - 14y^2$; $y^2 - 7$

19. **Pentagonal numbers** $p(n)$ are the numbers of dots in the sequence of figures beginning with those pictured below. *(Lessons 2-6, 9-3)*

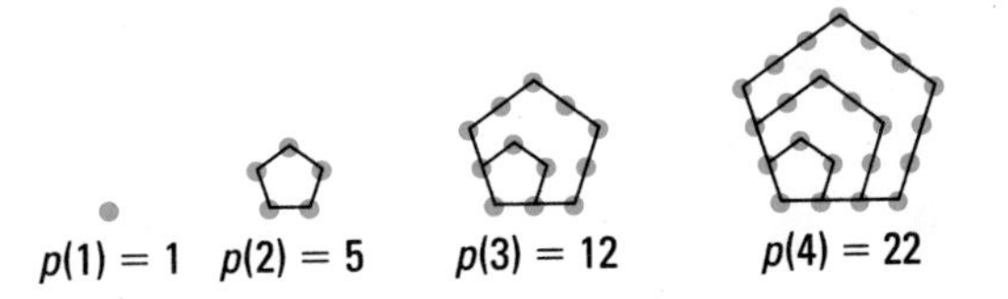

a. Show that there is a polynomial of degree 2 which generates these pentagonal numbers.
b. Determine the quadratic polynomial $p(n)$.
c. Use the polynomial of part **b** to calculate $p(5)$ and $p(6)$, and verify your answer geometrically.

20. At the right is a graph of a polynomial $y = f(x)$.
a. Identify the zeros of f.
b. Identify the relative extrema.
c. In what interval(s) is f increasing?
d. In what interval(s) is f decreasing?
e. In what interval(s) is f positive?
f. In what interval(s) is f negative?
(Lesson 9-2)

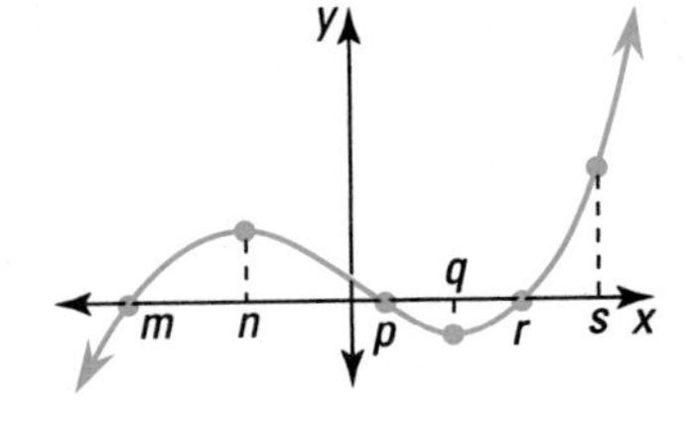

Pete Sampras

21. At some point during the men's final match in the 1996 U.S. Open tennis tournament, Pete Sampras had the following statistics.
First serve in: 54%
First serve points won: 84%
Second serve points won: 58%
Assuming that he had not double faulted (missed both serves) up to that point, what was the probability that, next time he served, Sampras did the following?
a. got his first serve in
b. got his first serve in and won the point
c. got his second serve in
d. got his second serve in and lost the point
e. lost the point *(Lesson 7-1)*

Exploration

22. **a.** Graph
$y = x + 2$
$y = x^2 + 4$
$y = x^3 + 8$
$y = x^4 + 16$
and $y = x^n + 2^n$ for two integer values of $n \geq 5$ of your choice.
b. For what values of n does $y = x^n + 2^n$ seem to have zeros? For these values of n, what binomial is a factor of $x^n + 2^n$?

LESSON

9-6

Complex Numbers

The Number i

Consider the polynomial $f(x) = x^2 + 1$. Its zeros are the solutions to $x^2 + 1 = 0$ or, more simply, $x^2 = -1$. Does this sentence have any solutions?

That depends on the domain of available numbers. If x is a real number, $x^2 = -1$ has no solution, since the square of any real number is either positive or zero. The graph at the right verifies that $f(x) = x^2 + 1$ has no real zeros, because its graph does not cross the x-axis.

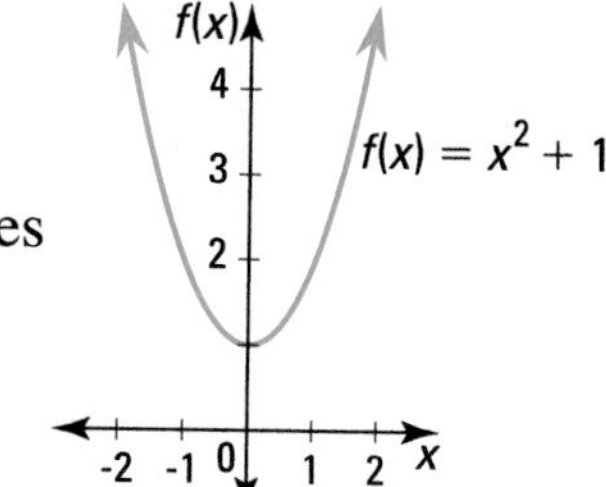

However, it is possible to define solutions to $x^2 + 1 = 0$ that are not real numbers. Because $x^2 = -1$, these solutions are called *the square roots of negative 1*. One of these solutions is denoted as $\sqrt{-1}$. It is customary also to call this number i.

Definition

$$i = \sqrt{-1}$$

The number i and its nonzero real number multiples bi are called **imaginary numbers** because when they were first used, mathematicians had no concrete way of representing them. They are, nevertheless, a reality in mathematics, and many important applications have been found for them.

Clearly, $i^2 = -1$. Note that if we assume that properties of real numbers can be extended to i, then it is also true that

$$(-i)^2 = (-i) \cdot (-i) = -1 \cdot i \cdot -1 \cdot i = -1 \cdot -1 \cdot i \cdot i = 1 \cdot i^2 = 1 \cdot -1 = -1.$$

Thus, in the domain of imaginary numbers, the polynomial $f(x) = x^2 + 1$ has two zeros, i and $-i$. You can verify this by applying the Quadratic Formula to the equation $x^2 + 1 = 0$.

Square Roots of Negative Numbers

If operations with imaginary numbers are assumed to satisfy the commutative and associative properties of multiplication, the square root of any negative number can be expressed as a multiple of i. Example 1 gives an instance.

Example 1

Show that a square root of -5 is $i\sqrt{5}$.

Solution

Multiply $i\sqrt{5}$ by itself.

$i\sqrt{5} \cdot i\sqrt{5} = i \cdot i \cdot \sqrt{5}\sqrt{5} = i^2 \cdot 5 = -1 \cdot 5 = -5$

In general, if k is a positive real number, then $\sqrt{-k} = i\sqrt{k}$, so the square root of any negative number is the product of i and a real number. This means that all equations of the form $x^2 + k = 0$, with $k > 0$, have two solutions, $i\sqrt{k}$ and $-i\sqrt{k}$.

Operations with Complex Numbers

When an imaginary number is added to a real number, the sum is a *complex number*.

Definitions

A **complex number** is a number of the form $a + bi$, where a and b are real numbers and $i = \sqrt{-1}$. The number a is the **real part** and b is the **imaginary part** of $a + bi$.

Complex numbers have many similarities to binomials. For instance, two complex numbers $a + bi$ and $c + di$ are **equal** if and only if their real parts are equal and their imaginary parts are equal. That is, $a + bi = c + di$ if and only if $a = c$ and $b = d$. Furthermore, the arithmetic of complex numbers is similar to the arithmetic of polynomials.

Example 2

Let $z = 4 + 5i$ and $w = 2 - 3i$. Express each of the following in $a + bi$ form.

a. $z + w$ **b.** $z - w$ **c.** zw **d.** $\frac{z}{2}$

Solution

a. $z + w = (4 + 5i) + (2 - 3i)$
$= (4 + 2) + (5i - 3i)$
$= 6 + 2i$

b. $z - w = (4 + 5i) - (2 - 3i)$
$= 4 + 5i - 2 + 3i$
$= (4 - 2) + (5i + 3i)$
$= 2 + 8i$

c. $zw = (4 + 5i)(2 - 3i)$
$= (4)(2) - (4)(3i) + (5i)(2) - (5i)(3i)$
$= 8 - 12i + 10i - 15i^2$
$= 8 - 2i - 15(i^2)$ Use $i^2 = -1$.
$= 8 - 2i - 15(-1)$
$= 23 - 2i$

d. $\frac{z}{2} = \frac{4 + 5i}{2} = \frac{4}{2} + \frac{5}{2}i = 2 + \frac{5}{2}i$

The example illustrates the following theorem:

Theorem
Given two complex numbers $a + bi$ and $c + di$ and real number r, then:

$(a + bi) + (c + di) = (a + c) + (b + d)i$	complex addition
$(a + bi)(c + di) = (ac - bd) + (ad + bc)i$	complex multiplication
$\frac{a + bi}{r} = \frac{a}{r} + \frac{b}{r}i.$	complex division by any real number r

It is not necessary to memorize this theorem. Simply remember to operate as you do with binomials: combine like terms when adding and use the distributive property when multiplying.

Conjugate Factors

Just as finding solutions to equations depends on the domain of allowable numbers, so does factoring. The binomial $x^2 - 9$ can be factored over the set of polynomials with integer coefficients: $x^2 - 9 = (x + 3)(x - 3)$. In contrast, $x^2 - 5$ cannot be factored over the set of polynomials with integer coefficients. But it can be factored over the set of polynomials with real coefficients into $\left(x - \sqrt{5}\right)\left(x + \sqrt{5}\right)$. Finally, $x^2 + 14$ cannot be factored over either of these sets; it is factorable over the set of polynomials with complex number coefficients, into $\left(x - i\sqrt{14}\right)\left(x + i\sqrt{14}\right)$. The factorization of $x^2 + 14$ suggests that with the introduction of complex numbers, the sum of two squares can be factored.

Theorem
If a and b are real numbers, then

$$a^2 + b^2 = (a + bi)(a - bi).$$

Proof
Multiply the factors, using the distributive property.

$$\begin{aligned}(a + bi)(a - bi) &= a^2 - abi + abi - (b^2i^2)\\ &= a^2 - b^2(-1)\\ &= a^2 + b^2\end{aligned}$$

If a and b are real numbers, the complex numbers $a + bi$ and $a - bi$ are called **complex conjugates** of each other. As the preceding proof confirms, the product of complex conjugates is a real number.

Complex conjugates are useful in performing division of complex numbers.

Example 3

Express $\frac{3 - 4i}{6 + i}$ in $a + bi$ form.

▶

Solution

When the denominator is multiplied by its complex conjugate, the result is a real number. So multiply numerator and denominator by the complex conjugate of the denominator.

$$\frac{3 - 4i}{6 + i} = \frac{3 - 4i}{6 + i} \cdot \frac{6 - i}{6 - i} = \frac{14 - 27i}{36 + 1} = \frac{14}{37} - \frac{27}{37}i$$

Check

Multiply the quotient by the divisor.

$$\left(\frac{14}{37} - \frac{27}{37}i\right)(6 + i) = \frac{1}{37}(14 - 27i)(6 + i)$$
$$= \frac{1}{37}(84 + 14i - 162i - 27i^2)$$
$$= \frac{1}{37}(111 - 148i) = 3 - 4i$$

Complex numbers make possible the solution of all quadratic equations.

Example 4

Solve $x^2 - 4x + 13 = 0$.

Solution

Use the quadratic formula.

$$x = \frac{4 \pm \sqrt{16 - 4(1)(13)}}{2(1)} = \frac{4 \pm \sqrt{-36}}{2}$$
$$= \frac{4 \pm 6i}{2} = 2 \pm 3i$$

Note that the two solutions are complex conjugates. Recall that $b^2 - 4ac$ is the *discriminant* of the quadratic $ax^2 + bx + c = 0$. In general, if a quadratic equation with real coefficients has a negative discriminant, then the two solutions are complex conjugates of each other.

Both the Factor and the Remainder Theorems hold for complex numbers. For instance, $-i$ is a solution to the equation $x^2 + 1 = 0$, and $x + i$ is a factor of $x^2 + 1$.

How Are Various Types of Numbers Related to Each Other?

For the complex number $a + bi$, if $a = 0$, then $a + bi = 0 + bi = bi$, so every imaginary number is also complex. Similarly, for any real number a, $a = a + 0i$. Thus, every real number is also complex. The diagram below shows the way that many types of numbers are related.

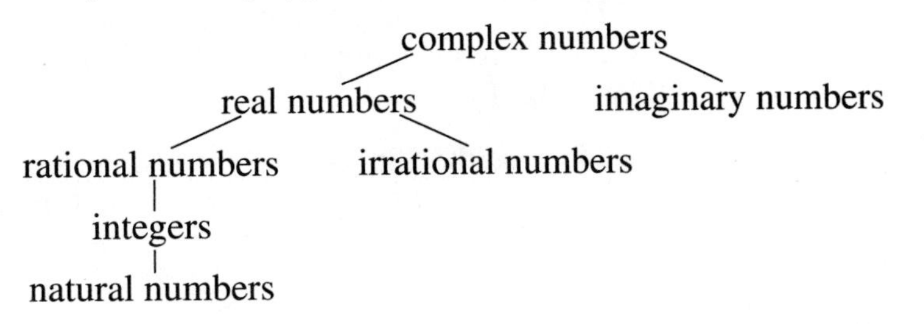

QUESTIONS

Covering the Reading

In 1–6, simplify.

1. $\sqrt{-25}$ **2.** $\sqrt{-8}$ **3.** $(7i)^2$

4. i^3 **5.** i^4 **6.** $(-i)^6$

7. Show that $i\sqrt{7}$ and $-i\sqrt{7}$ are each square roots of -7.

8. A complex number is a number of the form __a.__ where a and b are __b.__ numbers.

9. When are two complex numbers equal?

10. *True or false.* Every real number is a complex number.

11. Give the conjugate.
a. $2 - 3i$ **b.** $6i + 5$

12. Factor $x^2 - 3$ over each set.
a. the set of polynomials with rational coefficients
b. the set of polynomials with real coefficients

In 13–17, write in $a + bi$ form.

13. $(4 + 8i) + (-3 - 9i)$ **14.** $5(2 - 3i)$

15. $(2 - 3i)(4 + 7i)$ **16.** $\frac{3 + i}{2 - i}$ **17.** $\frac{5 - 3i}{1 + 2i}$

In 18 and 19, a binomial is given. **a.** Factor over the set of polynomials with complex coefficients. **b.** Check by multiplying.

18. $x^2 + 25$ **19.** $9z^2 + 18$

In 20 and 21, an equation is given. **a.** Calculate its discriminant. **b.** Solve and express the solutions in $a + bi$ form. **c.** What relation do the solutions have to one another?

20. $x^2 + -2x + 26 = 0$ **21.** $9x^2 + 229 = 12x$

22. Refer to Example 4. Graph $f(x) = x^2 - 4x + 13$. What can you say about the graph of a quadratic polynomial if its roots are complex?

Applying the Mathematics

23. a. According to the Factor Theorem, if $g(x)$ is a polynomial, a number b is a solution to $g(x) = 0$ if and only if __?__.
b. Does part **a** hold if b is a nonreal complex number?

24. Find the 20th term of the arithmetic sequence
$2, 5 + i, 8 + 2i, 11 + 3i, \ldots.$

25. Let $f(x) = x^2 - 4x + 5$.
   a. Evaluate $f(2 + i)$.
   b. Evaluate $f(2 - i)$.
   c. Use the results of parts **a** and **b** to factor f over the complex numbers.

26. Use the quadratic formula to factor $x^2 - 2x + 3$ over the complex numbers.

27. Let $z = \frac{1}{2} + \frac{\sqrt{3}}{2}i$.
   a. Calculate z^3 and write the result in $a + bi$ form.
   b. Let w be the complex conjugate of z. Calculate w^3.
   c. Both z and w are cube roots of __?__.
   d. Find another cube root of the answer to part **c**.

Review

28. Let $h(x)$ be a polynomial function whose graph intersects the x-axis at (-2, 0). State at least two conclusions you can make from this information. *(Lesson 9-5)*

29. Identify three different polynomial functions with zeros at 2, 4, and $-\frac{6}{5}$. *(Lesson 9-5)*

30. A wooden cube with edge of length 10 cm has a square hole with edge of length x cm bored through from top to bottom. Give the total surface area of the shape. *(Previous course, Lesson 9-1)*

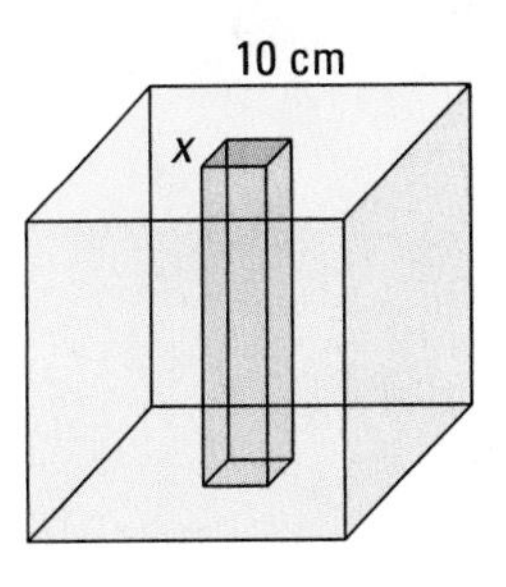

31. The following table gives the probability of a spinner landing on each of eight numbers.

Number x_i	1	2	3	4	5	6	7	8
$P(x_i)$	$\frac{1}{24}$	$\frac{1}{12}$	$\frac{1}{8}$	$\frac{1}{4}$	$\frac{5}{24}$	$\frac{1}{6}$	$\frac{1}{12}$	$\frac{1}{24}$

   a. Verify that P satisfies the two conditions for a probability distribution.
   b. Draw a histogram of the distribution.
   c. Calculate the mean of the distribution.
   d. Explain what the result in part **c** indicates in terms of the spinner. *(Lesson 7-6)*

Exploration

32. Explore patterns in powers of i.
   a. Predict the value of each of i^{1992}, i^{1993}, and i^{2000}.
   b. Describe in words or in symbols how to evaluate a large power of i.

LESSON

9-7

The Fundamental Theorem of Algebra

The Number of Zeros of a Quadratic Function

As you know, the solutions to any quadratic equation can be found using the quadratic formula. The graph of a quadratic function intersects the x-axis at two points when there are two real zeros, in exactly one point when there is a single real solution, and does not intersect the x-axis when its zeros are complex. As the table below indicates, the graph of a quadratic function, its discriminant, its zeros, and its factors are related.

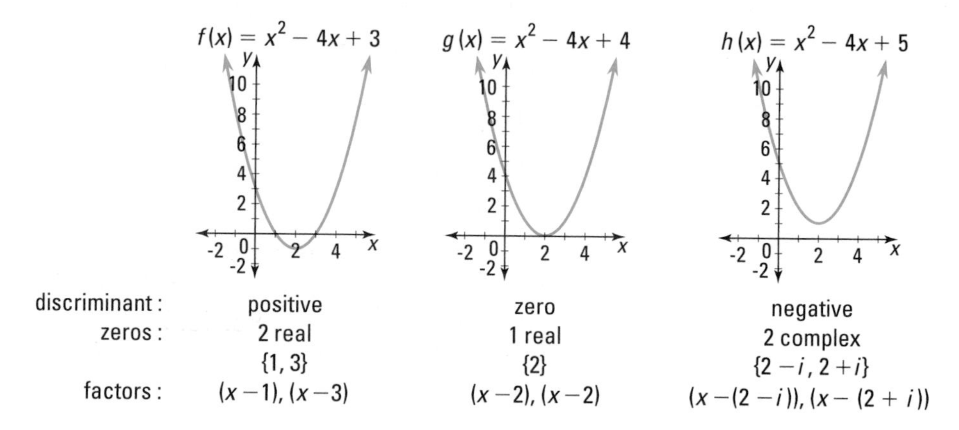

In general, consider the quadratic function $g(x) = ax^2 + bx + c$ with real coefficients. If the discriminant D is positive, g has two real zeros. If D is zero, g has one real zero, and if D is negative, g has two complex conjugate zeros.

The Number of Zeros of Higher-Degree Polynomial Functions

You may wonder how zeros and graphs of higher-degree polynomial functions are related. For example, are there formulas like the quadratic formula to provide zeros for all higher-degree polynomials? Can all polynomials be decomposed into linear factors as quadratics can? What is the greatest number of zeros a polynomial can have? These questions intrigued mathematicians for centuries.

The Arabian mathematician al'Khowarizmi (from whose name is derived the word "algorithm") is believed to have first discovered the quadratic formula in about 825 A.D. His use of the formula was limited to what are now called *real solutions*. Europeans first learned of his discovery in 1202 when it was translated into Latin by Fibonacci, the Italian mathematician also known for the sequence with his name.

For centuries mathematicians sought general formulas, like the quadratic formula, for finding zeros of higher-degree polynomials. Several Italian

Nicolo Tartaglia (woodcut, 1546)

mathematicians of the 16th century made progress with cubics. The works of Scipione dal Ferro (1465–1526) and of Nicolo Tartaglia (1500–1557) were published by Girolamo Cardano (1501–1576) in 1545 in his treatise on algebra, *Ars Magna* ("Great Art"). In that book, formulas for zeros for classes of cubics are given and complex numbers are recognized as legitimate solutions to equations. Shortly after, Ludovico Ferrari (1522–1565), a student of Cardano, found a method for finding exact zeros of any polynomial of degree 4. In all these discoveries, no new numbers were needed beyond the complex numbers. The search for a formula for zeros to all quintics and beyond continued.

In 1797, the following key result connecting previous investigations was discovered by Gauss when he was 18 years old. It made him famous among mathematicians.

Fundamental Theorem of Algebra
If $p(x)$ is any polynomial of degree $n \geq 1$ with complex coefficients, then $p(x) = 0$ has at least one complex zero.

This theorem, whose proof is beyond the scope of this book, is remarkable because:

It refers to all polynomials.
It tells the complex nature of at least one zero.
It leads to another simple, yet powerful result.

Theorem
A polynomial of degree n has at most n zeros.

Proof
Let $p(x)$ be a polynomial of degree n. By the Fundamental Theorem of Algebra, $p(x)$ has at least one complex zero, call it c. Then, by the Factor and Remainder Theorems, when $p(x)$ is divided by $(x - c)$ the quotient, $q(x)$, is a polynomial of degree $n - 1$. Now begin again. $q(x)$ has at least one complex zero, so divide $q(x)$ by the factor associated with that zero to get a quotient $r(x)$ of degree $n - 2$, and so on. Each division reduces the degree of the previous polynomial by 1, so the process of repeated division can have at most n steps, each providing one zero.

Thus another important consequence of the Fundamental Theorem of Algebra is that regardless of the degree of the polynomial, each of its zeros is a complex number; no new numbers are needed!

Multiplicities of Zeros

Of course, some of the zeros at the various divisions may be the same. For example, the quadratic $g(x) = x^2 - 4x + 4$, shown at the beginning of this lesson, factors into $(x - 2)^2$. It has a *double zero*. The **multiplicity of a zero** r is the highest power of $(x - r)$ that appears as a factor of that polynomial.

Example 1

Find the zeros of $p(x) = x^3 - 6x^2 + 9x$.

Solution

You can factor out an x immediately, to get

$$p(x) = x(x^2 - 6x + 9).$$

The quadratic factor is a perfect square trinomial. Thus

$$p(x) = x(x - 3)^2.$$

This means **$p(x)$ has three zeros: the zero 0 has multiplicity 1; the zero 3 has multiplicity 2.**

In Example 1, the polynomial p has degree 3. Notice that it has exactly 3 complex zeros. The zeros (all of which are real in this case) are indicated in the graph to the right. So there is no need to look at a larger domain to find other zeros.

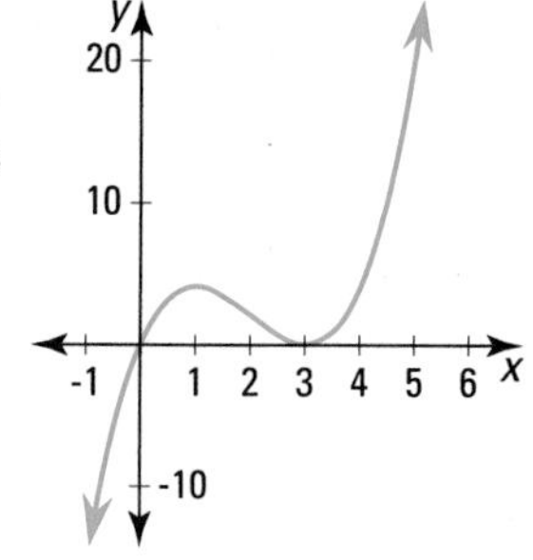

In general, the idea of multiplicities of zeros and the fact that no new numbers are needed to factor polynomials of any degree implies the following result.

Number of Zeros of a Polynomial Theorem
A polynomial of degree $n \geq 1$ with complex coefficients has exactly n complex zeros, if multiplicities are counted.

Determining the Possible Degrees of a Polynomial Function from Its Graph

From the graph of a polynomial function, you can determine information about its degree. Not only does the Number of Zeros Theorem dictate the maximum number of intersections of a polynomial graph and the x-axis, it also determines the number of intersections the graph may have with any horizontal line.

Theorem
Let $p(x)$ be a polynomial of degree $n \geq 1$ with real coefficients. The graph of $p(x)$ can cross any horizontal line $y = d$ at most n times.

Proof
Let $p(x)$ be a polynomial with degree $n \geq 1$ with real coefficients. The points of intersection of the graph of $y = p(x)$ and the horizontal line $y = d$ are the solutions of the equation $p(x) = d$. This equation is equivalent to $g(x) = p(x) - d = 0$. The degree of $g(x)$ is the same as the degree of $p(x)$ because the two polynomials differ only by a constant. Thus, $g(x)$ has at most n zeros. So the graph of $p(x)$ has at most n intersections with $y = d$.

Example 2

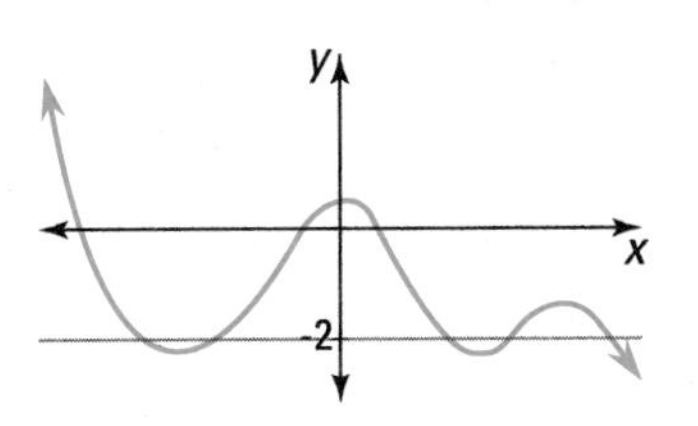

A polynomial $f(x)$ is graphed at the left. What is the lowest possible degree of $f(x)$?

Solution

The polynomial crosses the horizontal line $y = -2$ five times. So the degree of $f(x)$ must be at least 5.

When one (or more) of the coefficients of the polynomial is nonreal, the solutions cannot be pictured on a standard graph. However, the Number of Zeros of a Polynomial Theorem can still be applied. For instance, the polynomial $g(x) = -3x^5 - ix$ has degree 5, so it has 5 zeros.

When a polynomial has real coefficients, then its nonreal zeros always come in complex conjugate pairs. The proof of this theorem is long, so we omit it.

Conjugate Zeros Theorem
Let $p(x) = a_n x^n + a_{n-1}x^{n-1} + \ldots + a_1 x + a_0$ where $a_n, a_{n-1}, \ldots a_1, a_0$ are all real numbers, and $a_n \neq 0$. If $z = a + bi$ is a zero of $p(x)$, then the complex conjugate of z, $a - bi$, is also a zero of $p(x)$.

Example 3

Let $p(x) = 2x^3 - x^2 + 18x - 9$.

a. Verify that $3i$ is a zero of $p(x)$.

b. Find the remaining zeros of $p(x)$ and their multiplicities.

Solution

a.

$$\begin{aligned} p(3i) &= 2(3i)^3 - (3i)^2 + 18(3i) - 9 \\ &= 54i^3 - 9i^2 + 54i - 9 \\ &= -54i + 9 + 54i - 9 \\ &= 0 \end{aligned}$$

b. Because $3i$ is a zero, then, by the Conjugate Zeros Theorem, so is its conjugate $-3i$. The Factor Theorem implies that $(x - 3i)$ and $(x + 3i)$ are factors of $p(x)$. Thus their product $(x - 3i) \cdot (x + 3i) = x^2 + 9$ is a factor of $p(x)$. Divide $p(x)$ by $x^2 + 9$ to find another factor:

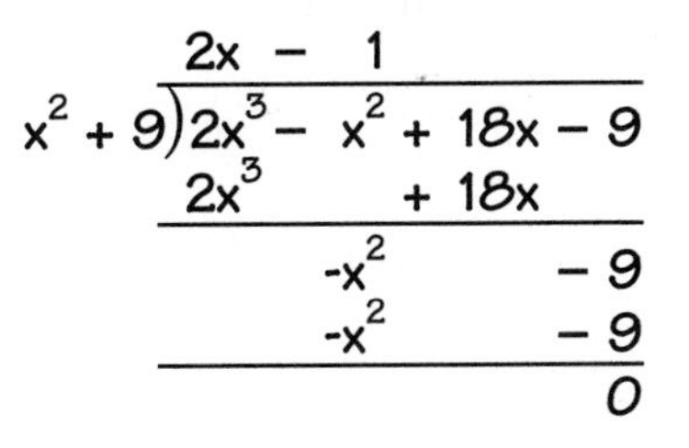

Thus $p(x) = (x^2 + 9)(2x - 1)$. So, the zeros of $p(x)$ are $3i$, $-3i$, and $\frac{1}{2}$.

Check

In part **a**, $p(3i)$ was shown to equal 0. Similarly,

$$p(-3i) = 2(-3i)^3 - (-3i)^2 + 18(-3i) - 9$$
$$= 54i + 9 - 54i - 9 = 0$$

Also,

$$p\left(\tfrac{1}{2}\right) = 2\left(\tfrac{1}{2}\right)^3 - \left(\tfrac{1}{2}\right)^2 + 18\left(\tfrac{1}{2}\right) - 9$$
$$= \tfrac{1}{4} - \tfrac{1}{4} + 9 - 9 = 0.$$

The question of finding a formula for exact zeros to all polynomials was not settled until the early 19th century. In 1824 Niels Abel (1802–1829), a Norwegian mathematician, wrote a conclusive proof that it is impossible to construct a general formula for zeros of any polynomial beyond degree 4. Abel's work had several effects. First, the theory he developed contributed to the foundation of another advanced branch of modern mathematics, *group theory*. Second, rather than searching for exact zeros to polynomials, mathematicians knew they had to rely on approximation techniques. These techniques are studied in another branch of advanced mathematics called *numerical analysis*.

QUESTIONS

Covering the Reading

1. When and by whom was the quadratic formula first discovered?

2. Name three mathematicians who contributed to the analysis of zeros of cubic or quartic polynomials.

3. State the Fundamental Theorem of Algebra.

In 4–9, *true or false*.

4. Every polynomial has at least one real zero.

5. A polynomial of degree n has at most n real zeros.

6. A cubic may have 4 zeros.

7. A polynomial with zeros 2, 3, and -1 could be of degree greater than three.

8. All polynomials with real coefficients have zeros that are complex numbers.

9. Suppose $p(x)$ is a polynomial with real coefficients. If $2 + 3i$ is a zero of $p(x)$, then $2 - 3i$ is a zero of $p(x)$.

10. Consider $q(x) = (x - 5)^2 (x + 2)^3$.
a. Identify the zeros of $q(x)$ and give their multiplicities.
b. Verify your solution to part **a** by graphing $y = q(x)$.

11. Find all zeros of $p(x) = x^5 - 16x$.

12. a. How many zeros does $r(x) = 3x^{11} - ix$ have?
b. How many of these zeros are real?

13. Consider the polynomial $p(x) = x^4 + 2x^3 + 11x^2 + 2x + 10$.

a. Verify that i is a zero of $p(x)$.

b. Find the remaining zeros of $p(x)$ and their multiplicities.

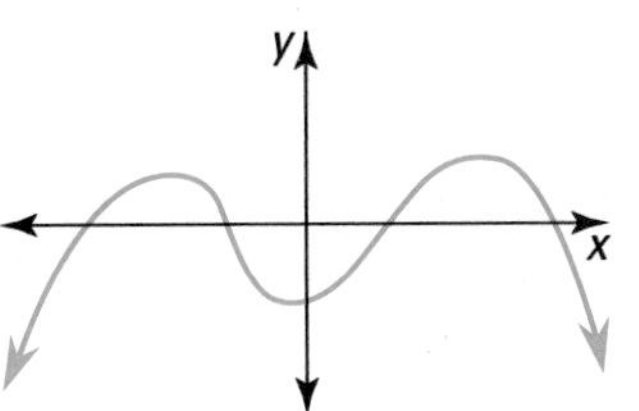

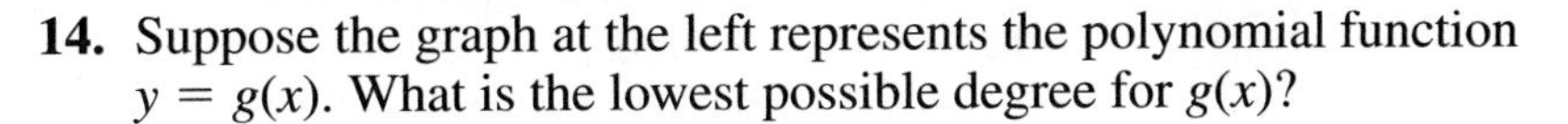

14. Suppose the graph at the left represents the polynomial function $y = g(x)$. What is the lowest possible degree for $g(x)$?

Applying the Mathematics

15. The zeros of $x^n - 1$ are called the ***n*th roots of unity**. Find the fourth roots of unity.

16. Suppose $p(x)$ is a polynomial with real coefficients and $p(4 + 9i) = 0$. What is $p(4 - 9i)$?

17. Find a polynomial $p(x)$ with real coefficients, leading coefficient 1, and of the lowest degree possible that has the two zeros 3 and $1 - 2i$.

18. **a.** Find the zeros of $t(x) = 2x^2 + ix + 3$.

b. The zeros are not complex conjugates. Explain why this does not contradict the Conjugate Zeros Theorem.

19. Tell whether each of the following could or could not be part of the graph of a fourth degree polynomial function. Explain your decision for each one.

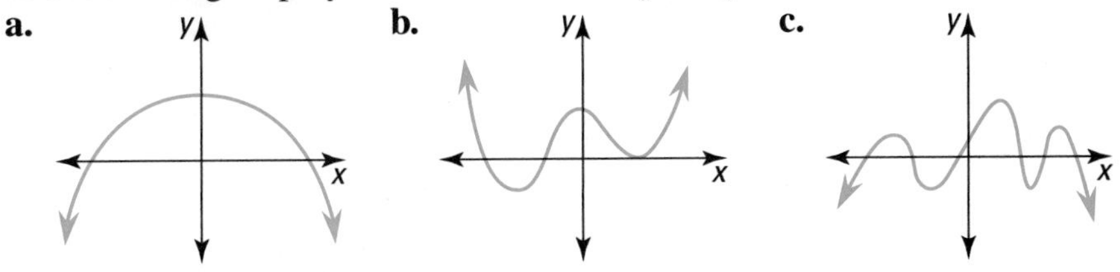

20. The curve pictured at the left is the graph of a polynomial function p of degree 5 with real coefficients. Copy the figure and insert a horizontal axis so that each condition is satisfied.

a. p has one real zero. **b.** p has five real zeros.

Review

21. Let $z = 3 - 8i$. Write in $a + bi$ form. *(Lesson 9-6)*

a. w, the complex conjugate of z.

b. $w + z$ **c.** $w - z$ **d.** wz **e.** $\frac{w}{z}$

In 22–24, factor the polynomial into linear factors. *(Lesson 9-6)*

22. $3p^2 - 4$ **23.** $4p^2 - 9$ **24.** $4p^2 + 9$

25. How can you check a polynomial division problem when the remainder is not zero? *(Lesson 9-4)*

26. Approximate, to the nearest tenth, all the real zeros of the polynomial $p(x) = x^5 - 4x^3 + 8x^2 - 12$. *(Lesson 9-2)*

27. A silo is in the shape of a cylinder with a hemispherical top. The height of the cylinder is 17 m. *(Lesson 9-1)*

a. Write a polynomial equation $V(r)$ which expresses the volume of the silo as a function of r, its radius.

b. What is the degree of $V(r)$?

c. What is the leading coefficient of $V(r)$?

d. Suppose the radius may be anywhere from 3 m to 5 m. What are the maximum and minimum capacities of the silo, assuming the entire space can be filled?

28. Expand $(x - 5)^3$. *(Lesson 8-8)*

29. The government of a certain country decides to increase the salaries of all government employees by 5%. Disregarding all other factors (such as promotions, resignations, or new hirings), how will this raise affect each statistic?

a. the average salary of government employees nationally

b. the standard deviation of salaries *(Lesson 3-6)*

In 30 and 31, *true or false*. *(Lesson 3-4)*

30. The graph of every odd function passes through the origin.

31. If z is a zero of an odd function f, then $-z$ is also a zero of $-f$.

Exploration

32. Write your nine-digit social security number. (Make up one if you do not have one.) Use the digits in order as the coefficients of a polynomial of degree 8 with alternating signs. For instance, if your social security number is 369-46-4564, your polynomial is

$$y = 3x^8 - 6x^7 + 9x^6 - 4x^5 + 6x^4 - 4x^3 + 5x^2 - 6x + 4.$$

a. Graph your social security number polynomial. Tell how many real zeros it has.

b. If the nine digits of a social security number may be any one of 0 through 9, and the system of alternating signs of coefficients is used to create a polynomial, what is the least number m of real zeros the polynomial can have? What is the greatest number M of real zeros it may have? Can a social security polynomial have any number of zeros between m and M? Why or why not?

LESSON

9-8

Factoring Sums and Differences of Powers

Finding All Cube Roots of a Real Number

We usually think of 5 as being *the* cube root of 125, but every solution to $x^3 = 125$ is a cube root of 125, and according to the Number of Zeros Theorem, $x^3 - 125 = 0$ has three complex roots. You might think 5 is the only root, with multiplicity three, but then $x^3 - 125$ would have to equal $(x - 5)^3$. The Binomial Theorem shows that these are not equal, so a different approach is needed.

Example 1

Find the cube roots of 125 other than 5.

Solution

The desired cube roots are the solutions to $P(x) = x^3 - 125 = 0$. Since $P(5) = 0$, $(x - 5)$ is a factor of $x^3 - 125$. Divide to obtain the other factor.

$$\begin{array}{r}
x^2 + 5x + 25 \\
x - 5\,\overline{)\,x^3 + 0x^2 + 0x - 125} \\
\underline{x^3 - 5x^2 } \\
5x^2 + 0x - 125 \\
\underline{5x^2 - 25x } \\
25x - 125 \\
\underline{25x - 125} \\
0
\end{array}$$

Thus $x^3 - 125 = (x - 5)(x^2 + 5x + 25)$. Now use the quadratic formula to find the zeros of the quadratic factor. If $x^2 + 5x + 25 = 0$, then

$$x = \frac{-5 \pm \sqrt{5^2 - 4 \cdot 25}}{2} = \frac{-5 \pm \sqrt{-75}}{2} = \frac{-5 \pm 5\sqrt{3}\,i}{2}.$$

The other cube roots of 125 are $-\frac{5}{2} + \frac{5\sqrt{3}}{2}i$ and $-\frac{5}{2} - \frac{5\sqrt{3}}{2}i$.

Check

$$\begin{aligned}
\left(-\tfrac{5}{2} + \tfrac{5\sqrt{3}}{2}i\right)^3 &= \left(-\tfrac{5}{2} + \tfrac{5\sqrt{3}}{2}i\right)\left(-\tfrac{5}{2} + \tfrac{5\sqrt{3}}{2}i\right)^2 \\
&= \left(-\tfrac{5}{2} + \tfrac{5\sqrt{3}}{2}i\right)\left(\tfrac{25}{4} - \tfrac{25\sqrt{3}}{2}i - \tfrac{75}{4}\right) \\
&= \left(-\tfrac{5}{2} + \tfrac{5\sqrt{3}}{2}i\right)\left(-\tfrac{25}{2} - \tfrac{25\sqrt{3}}{2}i\right) \\
&= \tfrac{125}{4} + \tfrac{125\sqrt{3}}{4}i - \tfrac{125\sqrt{3}}{4}i + \tfrac{375}{4} \\
&= \tfrac{500}{4} = 125
\end{aligned}$$

A check for $\left(-\frac{5}{2} - \frac{5\sqrt{3}}{2}i\right)$ is asked for in Question 1.

Factoring Sums and Differences of Cubes

In Example 1, the difference of two cubes $x^3 - 125$ was factored. More generally, consider the problem of factoring $x^3 - y^3$, the difference of any two cubes. Notice that $x = y$ is clearly a solution to $x^3 - y^3 = 0$, so $x - y$ is one factor. Divide $x^3 - y^3$ by $x - y$ to find the other factor.

$$\begin{array}{r|l} & x^2 + xy + y^2 \\ x - y & x^3 - 0x^2y - 0xy^2 - y^3 \\ & \underline{x^3 - x^2y} \\ & x^2y - 0xy^2 - y^3 \\ & \underline{x^2y - xy^2} \\ & xy^2 - y^3 \\ & \underline{xy^2 - y^3} \end{array}$$

Thus $x^3 - y^3 = (x - y)(x^2 + xy + y^2)$.

This proves the second part of the following theorem.

Sums and Differences of Cubes Theorem
For all x and y,

$$x^3 + y^3 = (x + y)(x^2 - xy + y^2)$$
$$x^3 - y^3 = (x - y)(x^2 + xy + y^2)$$

Activity

Prove the first part of the theorem.

Neither one of the quadratic factors in the Sums and Differences of Cubes Theorem can be factored further over the set of polynomials with real coefficients.

Example 2

Factor $8a^3 + 27b^6$.

Solution

This is an instance of the sum of two cubes $x^3 + y^3$ where $x = 2a$ and $y = 3b^2$. Apply the previous theorem.

$$\begin{aligned} 8a^3 + 27b^6 &= (2a)^3 + (3b^2)^3 \\ &= (2a + 3b^2)((2a)^2 - (2a)(3b^2) + (3b^2)^2) \\ &= (2a + 3b^2)(4a^2 - 6ab^2 + 9b^4) \end{aligned}$$

Factoring Sums and Differences of Odd Powers

The method used to find factors of sums and differences of cubes generalizes to all odd powers.

Sums and Differences of Odd Powers Theorem
For all x and y and for all odd positive integers n,
$$x^n + y^n = (x + y)(x^{n-1} - x^{n-2}y + x^{n-3}y^2 - \dots - xy^{n-2} + y^{n-1})$$
$$x^n - y^n = (x - y)(x^{n-1} + x^{n-2}y + x^{n-3}y^2 + \dots + xy^{n-2} + y^{n-1})$$

You are asked in the Questions to verify the theorem for specific values of n. Example 3 applies it to a sum of fifth powers.

Example 3

Factor $a^5 + b^5$.

Solution

Since $a^5 + b^5$ is a sum, $a + b$ is a factor, and in the other factor the signs alternate.

Thus, $$a^5 + b^5 = (a + b)(a^4 - a^3b + a^2b^2 - ab^3 + b^4).$$

A similar theorem for the factorization of sums and differences of even powers does not exist. If n is a positive even integer, then $x^n + y^n$ does not have a linear factor with real coefficients. To factor the difference of two powers, $x^n - y^n$ for n even, consider the even power as the square of some lower power, and reduce the problem to the difference of two squares. Example 4 illustrates a specific case.

Example 4

Factor $x^6 - 64$ completely over the set of polynomials with real coefficients.

Solution

$x^6 = (x^3)^2$, and $64 = 2^6 = (2^3)^2$.

So $$x^6 - 64 = (x^3)^2 - (2^3)^2$$
$$= (x^3 - 2^3)(x^3 + 2^3).$$

Each of the factors is a sum or difference of cubes, so they can be factored further. Hence,
$$x^6 - 64 = (x - 2)(x^2 + 2x + 4)(x + 2)(x^2 - 2x + 4).$$

Since $x^2 + 2x + 4$ and $x^2 - 2x + 4$ each has discriminant -12, they cannot be factored into polynomials with real coefficients. So this factorization is complete.

QUESTIONS

Covering the Reading

1. Show that $-\frac{5}{2} - \frac{5\sqrt{3}}{2}i$ is a cube root of 125.

In 2 and 3, a function is described. **a.** Find the zeros of the function by factoring. **b.** Verify your result by drawing a graph.

2. $f(x) = 2x^3 - 32x$

3. $g(x) = x^3 - 64$

4. **a.** Show that $x - 3$ is a factor of $x^3 - 27$ by using long division.
   b. Check your answer by multiplying $x - 3$ by the quotient.
   c. Show that the quotient is not factorable over the set of polynomials with real coefficients by calculating its discriminant.
   d. Determine the three cube roots of 27.

In 5–7, a binomial is given. **a.** Describe the polynomial as a difference of squares, sum of squares, difference of cubes, or sum of cubes. **b.** Factor the given polynomial.

5. $a^2 - 64x^2$ **6.** $125x^3 + 1$ **7.** $27 - 64a^3$

8. Give your answer to the Activity.

In 9 and 10, a binomial is given. **a.** Factor the expression using the Sums and Differences of Odd Powers Theorem. **b.** Justify your answer using either multiplication or division, or a graph.

9. $x^5 - 32$ **10.** $x^7 + 10{,}000{,}000$

In 11 and 12, *true or false.* Justify your answer.

11. $(x + y)$ is a factor of $x^4 + y^4$.

12. $(a - b)$ is a factor of $a^n - b^n$, if n is an odd integer.

In 13 and 14, a binomial is given. **a.** Factor the given binomial over integers using the Sums and Differences of Odd Powers Theorem. **b.** Verify the factorization by multiplying.

13. $t^9 - 512$ **14.** $x^7 + y^7$

Applying the Mathematics

In 15–17, factor completely over the set of polynomials with integer coefficients.

15. $28x^2y^2 - 7x^4$ **16.** $x^4 - y^4$ **17.** $8x^3y^3 + 343z^3$

18. Refer to Example 4.
   a. Factor $x^6 - 64$ as a difference of cubes.
   b. Verify that the result you get in part **a** can be factored further to get the solution shown in Example 4.

19. Let $p(x) = x^5 - 5x^3 + 4x$.
   a. Find the zeros of the polynomial function p by factoring.
   b. Verify your results to part **a** by graphing the function p.

Review

20. *True or false.* The Fundamental Theorem of Algebra guarantees that the equation $4x^4 + 16x^3 + 5x^2 + 25 = 0$ has at least one real solution. *(Lesson 9-7)*

21. *True or false.* The polynomial $c(x) = x^3 - 1271x^2 + 1273x - 1272$ has at least one real zero. *(Lesson 9-7)*

22. What is the minimum degree of the polynomial function graphed at the right? *(Lesson 9-7)*

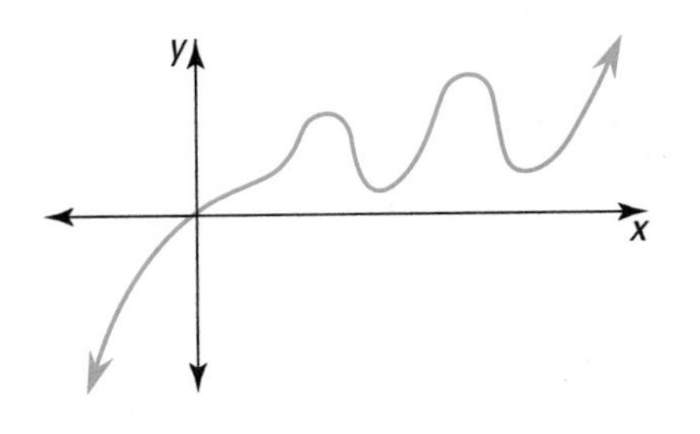

23. Suppose that $(x - 3)$ is a factor of the polynomial $f(x)$. *True or false.*
    a. 3 is a solution to the equation $f(x) = 0$.
    b. -3 is a solution to the equation $f(x) = 0$.
    c. The graph of $f(x)$ crosses the x-axis at (3, 0).
    d. When $f(x)$ is divided by $(x - 3)$, the remainder is zero.
    e. $f(3) = 0$. *(Lesson 9-5)*

24. Consider the functions f and g with $f(x) = x^3 - 27x$ and $g(x) = (x - 2)^3 - 27(x - 2)$. *(Lessons 3-3, 3-4, 9-2)*
    a. Find the x- and y-intercepts of f.
    b. State whether f is odd, even, or neither.
    c. Find x- and y-intercepts of g.
    d. State whether g is odd, even, or neither.

Aquaculture. *This woman is working in the hydroponics industry. Hydroponics is an alternative to growing vegetables in soil.*

25. Suppose that 36% of the available labor force of a certain country are women. A company hires twelve new workers.
    a. Determine the probability that exactly three of the new workers are women.
    b. What is the probability that fewer than four of the new workers are women? *(Lesson 8-9)*

Exploration

26. Consider the polynomial which when factored is $(3x - 5)(2x + 9)(2x + 7)$.
    a. When it is expanded, what will the leading coefficient be?
    b. When it is expanded, what will the constant term be?
    c. Write the zeros of the polynomial as simple fractions.
    d. Ignoring the sign, what is the relationship of the numerators of the zeros to the linear factors?
    e. Ignoring the sign, what is the relationship of the denominators of the zeros to the linear factors?
    f. Suppose a polynomial in factored form is $(ax + b)(cx + d)(ex + f)(gx + h)$.
    Tell what the constant term will be, what the leading coefficient will be, and give the relationship of these products to the coefficients in the original polynomial in expanded form.
    g. Generalize parts **a**-**f**.

LESSON

9-9

Advanced Factoring Techniques

In previous lessons, polynomials were factored by using graphs, recognizing special patterns (sums and differences), and using the quadratic formula. In this lesson, you will utilize chunking and another factoring technique called *grouping*. Grouping is used to factor polynomials which contain groups of terms with common factors, usually monomials. It involves only the repeated application of the distributive property. Example 1 gives an instance of this technique.

Example 1

Factor $x^3 + 2x^2 - 9x - 18$.

Solution

Observe that the first two terms have a common factor of x^2 and the last two terms are each divisible by -9. Factoring these pairs of terms yields

$$x^3 + 2x^2 - 9x - 18 = x^2(x + 2) - 9(x + 2).$$

This shows that another common factor is $(x + 2)$. Now apply the Distributive Property.

$$= (x^2 - 9)(x + 2)$$

Finally, factor the difference of squares.

$$= (x - 3)(x + 3)(x + 2)$$

Check 1

Multiply the factors. You are asked to do this in the Questions.

Check 2

Draw graphs of $y = x^3 + 2x^2 - 9x - 18$, and $y = (x - 3)(x + 3)(x + 2)$. If the factorization is correct, the two graphs will coincide. At the right is the output from an automatic grapher. The two graphs are identical. Also, the graphs have zeros at -3, -2, and 3, as predicted by the factored form.

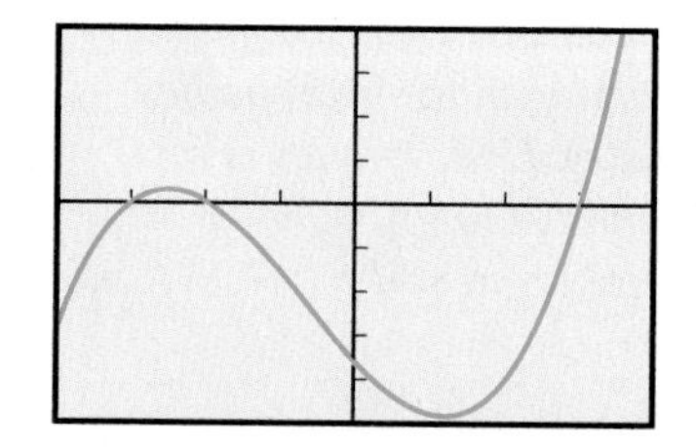

$-4 \le x \le 4$, x-scale = 1
$-25 \le y \le 20$, y-scale = 5

Grouping can be applied to factor the general trinomial $ax^2 + bx + c$. If there exist two numbers n_1 and n_2 such that $n_1n_2 = ac$ and $n_1 + n_2 = b$, then the middle term bx can be split up into $n_1x + n_2x$ (since $n_1 + n_2 = b$). This new polynomial, $ax^2 + n_1x + n_2x + c$, is always factorable by grouping. Example 2 illustrates this.

Example 2

Factor $6x^2 - 13x + 5$.

Solution

Here $a = 6$, $b = -13$, and $c = 5$. Are there two numbers whose product is 30 and whose sum is -13? Mentally you realize that the numbers are -3 and -10. So rewrite the given polynomial as

$$6x^2 - 3x - 10x + 5.$$

Now group:

$$\begin{aligned} 6x^2 - 3x - 10x + 5 &= (6x^2 - 3x) + (-10x + 5) \\ &= 3x(2x - 1) - 5(2x - 1) \\ &= (3x - 5)(2x - 1). \end{aligned}$$

Check

Multiply:

$$\begin{aligned} (3x - 5)(2x - 1) &= 6x^2 - 3x - 10x + 5 \\ &= 6x^2 - 13x + 5. \end{aligned}$$

Combining grouping and chunking can allow the factoring of polynomials with more than one variable. When a polynomial in two variables is equal to 0, as in Example 3, grouping terms may help you draw the graph of the relation.

Example 3

Draw a graph of $y^2 - xy + 5x - 5y = 0$.

Solution

The form of the equation makes it difficult to evaluate numbers and plot by hand; and many automatic graphers cannot accept an equation if it is not solved for y. Grouping with repeated applications of the Distributive Property yields the following.

$$\begin{aligned} 0 &= y^2 - xy + 5x - 5y \\ &= y(y - x) + 5(x - y) \\ &= y(y - x) - 5(y - x) \\ &= (y - 5)(y - x) \end{aligned}$$

So the original equation is true if and only if $y - 5 = 0$ or $y - x = 0$; that is, if $y = 5$ or $y = x$. The graphs of these equations are lines. Thus the graph of the original equation is the union of these two lines, as shown at the right.

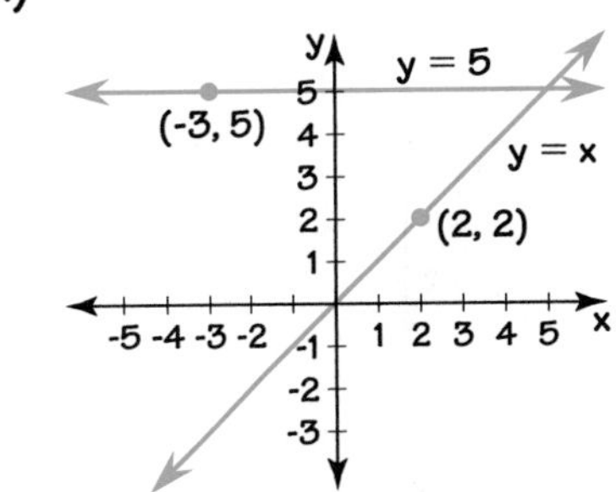

Check

Pick any point on the line $y = x$, say (2, 2). Substitute these coordinates in the original equation. Does $2^2 - 2 \cdot 2 + 5 \cdot 2 - 5 \cdot 2 = 0$? Yes. They check. Similarly, the coordinates of any point on the line $y = 5$, say (-3, 5), check:

$$5^2 - (-3)(5) + 5(-3) - 5 \cdot 5 = 0.$$

QUESTIONS

Covering the Reading

In 1 and 2, refer to Example 1.

1. Factor the polynomial by rewriting it as $(x^3 - 9x) + (2x^2 - 18)$ and then applying the Distributive Property twice.

2. Verify that the product $(x - 3)(x + 3)(x + 2)$ equals $x^3 + 2x^2 - 9x - 18$.

3. Factor the polynomial $x^3 + 3x^2 - 4x - 12$ by grouping the first and second terms and the third and fourth terms and then applying the Distributive Property twice.

In 4 and 5, use grouping to factor the following trinomials.

4. $12x^2 + 8x + 1$

5. $2n^2 - 9n - 5$

6. a. Graph the set of ordered pairs (x, y) satisfying

$$y^2x - x^3 - y^3 + x^2y = 0.$$

b. Describe the graph in words.

Applying the Mathematics

7. Find the zeros of the function $f(x) = 2x^3 - 5x^2 + 6x - 15$ using each method.

a. by grouping and factoring

b. by drawing a graph

In 8 and 9, factor.

8. $ax - bx - by + ay$

9. $2x^2 + xy - 2xz - yz$

10. Draw a graph of $\{(x, y): -x^2 + xy + 2y^2 = 0\}$.

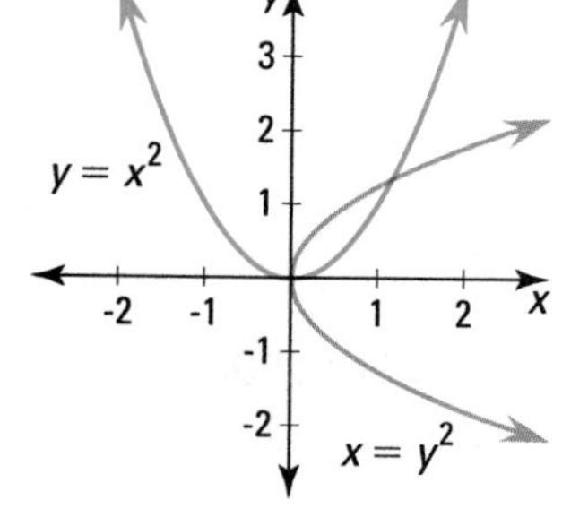

11. Find an equation describing the graph of the union of the two relations $y = x^2$ and $x = y^2$ shown at the left.

12. Let $f(x) = x^2 + 6x + 8$. Simplify $\frac{f(x) - f(b)}{x - b}$.

Review

In 13–16, factor over the set of polynomials with real coefficients. *(Lesson 9-8)*

13. $x^3 - 8$

14. $t^5 + u^5$

15. $36x^6 - y^2z^4$

16. $x^6y^3 - 27z^6$

17. Determine the three cube roots of 10. *(Lesson 9-8)*

18. a. Find the sum of the 6th roots of unity.

b. Find the product of the 6th roots of unity. *(Lessons 9-6, 9-7, 9-8)*

19. *Skill sequence.* Find all real solutions. *(Lessons 5-7, 9-6, 9-7)*

a. $2x^3 - x^2 = 0$

b. $2x^3 - x^2 - 2x + 1 = 0$

c. $2 \sin^3\theta - \sin^2\theta - 2 \sin \theta = -1$

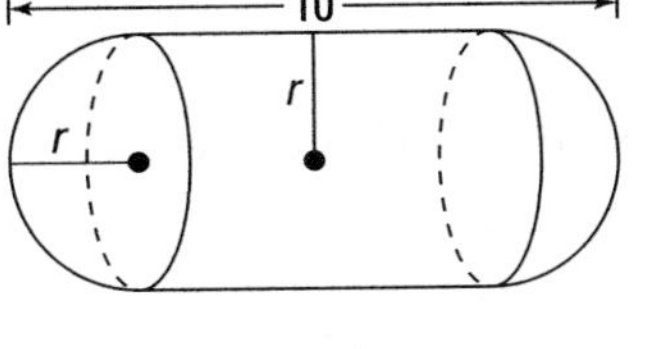

20. A propane gas tank is in the shape of a cylinder with hemispheres on each end as shown at the left. Suppose that the total length of the tank is 10 ft. *(Lessons 9-1, 9-2)*

a. Find the volume $V(r)$ of the tank in terms of its radius r.

b. Draw a graph of the equation $y = V(r)$ over the largest domain over which r is defined.

c. What is the largest volume such a tank can have?

21. Suppose a binomial probability is given by ${}_nC_r p^r q^{n-r} = 45p^r\left(\frac{1}{9}\right)^{10-r}$.

a. How many trials are there?

b. How many successes are there?

c. What is the probability of success for each trial? *(Lesson 8-9)*

Playing in the Rain. *Some sports are played rain or shine, and rain may affect the outcome.*

22. A meteorologist has predicted that the probability of rain in each of the two days of a weekend is 0.6. Explain how to code a set of random digits to simulate the weather on both days of the weekend. *(Lesson 7-7)*

23. **a.** How many permutations consisting of four letters each can be formed from the letters of FACTORING?

b. How many of the permutations in part **a** end in G? *(Lesson 7-4)*

Exploration

24. Consider the function f, with $f(x) = 12x^4 - 8x^3 - 27x^2 + 18x$.

a. Graph f on the domain $-4 \leq x \leq 4$. Use a range that allows you to see all four zeros and three relative extrema.

b. Estimate the zeros to the nearest tenth.

c. Use factoring to determine the zeros exactly.

LESSON

9-10

Roots and Coefficients of Polynomials

In mathematics, it is common to switch the given information with what is to be found and thus invent a new problem. For instance, instead of using the lengths of two sides of a rectangle to find its area, you could be given its area and search for possible lengths of sides. Or, instead of being given x and asked to find $\tan x$, you could know $\tan x$ and need to find x. As you saw in the previous lessons of this chapter, instead of multiplying binomials to obtain a polynomial, it is often helpful to be given the polynomial and asked to find its factors.

To reverse the process of solving equations, you could begin with the solutions and, from them, find the equation. Of course, more than one equation could have the same solution. For instance, if $x = 6$ is the only solution, any of the following could be an equation, and you could find many more.

$$\log x \approx .7782 \quad 2^x = 64 \quad 3x^2 - 6x + 8 = 80 \quad x - 6 = 0$$

However, if the equation must be a polynomial equation in standard form $a_n x^n + a_{n-1}x^{n-1} + \ldots + a_1 x + a_0 = 0$, then the choice is more restricted. Only the two rightmost equations above are polynomial equations, and only the rightmost is in standard form. If the multiplicities of solutions are to be considered as 1 unless otherwise indicated, then only the equations of the form $ax - 6a = 0$, where a is any nonzero complex number, would have the solution $x = 6$. Finally, if the leading coefficient must be 1, then only the equation $x - 6 = 0$ satisfies all these criteria and has only the solution $x = 6$. Thus, with certain constraints—standard form, multiplicities known, leading coefficient 1—the polynomial is uniquely determined.

Roots and Coefficients of Quadratic Equations

What polynomial equation in standard form, and with leading coefficient 1, has the solutions $\frac{2}{3}$ and -5? Using the Factor Theorem, the polynomial can be found by multiplying $\left(x - \frac{2}{3}\right)(x - -5)$ to obtain the left side of the desired equation $x^2 + \frac{13}{3}x - \frac{10}{3} = 0$.

In general, if a polynomial equation in standard form $P(x) = 0$ has leading coefficient 1 and two zeros or *roots* r_1 and r_2, then $P(x)$ is found by multiplying $(x - r_1)(x - r_2)$, and the equation is $x^2 - (r_1 + r_2)x + r_1 r_2 = 0$. This argument proves the following theorem.

Theorem
For the quadratic equation $x^2 + bx + c = 0$, the sum of the roots is $-b$ and the product of the roots is c.

Girolamo Cardano (woodcut, 1539)

For example, to find two numbers whose sum is 10 and whose product is 40, you need only solve the quadratic equation $x^2 - 10x + 40 = 0$. The solutions are the desired numbers. This exact problem was used by Girolamo Cardano in 1533 to introduce complex numbers for the first time.

Roots and Coefficients of Cubic Equations

If a polynomial equation $P(x) = 0$ has three roots (counting multiplicities), then you know $P(x)$ is of degree 3. If $a_n = 1$ and the roots are r_1, r_2, and r_3, then

$$P(x) = (x - r_1)(x - r_2)(x - r_3).$$

To write $P(x) = 0$ in standard form, multiply the three binomials. The result is the equation

$$x^3 - (r_1 + r_2 + r_3)x^2 + (r_1r_2 + r_1r_3 + r_2r_3)x - r_1r_2r_3 = 0.$$

Notice how the multiplication of the three binomials creates this polynomial. The coefficient of x^3 is 1 because there is only one way to multiply the three x's from the binomials. To explain the x^2 term, notice that there are three ways to choose two of the x's, and in each case one of the r_i must be the other factor. This creates the x^2 term. For the x term, there are three ways to choose the x, but the other two factors in each term must be pairs of r_i. And then, choosing r_i from each of the three binomials can be done in only one way. (You are asked to confirm this result in the Questions.) The alternating subtraction and addition occurs because each root is subtracted in its binomial, and so the sign of the product depends on whether there are an odd or even number of roots multiplied.

> **Theorem**
> For the cubic equation $x^3 + bx^2 + cx + d = 0$, the sum of the roots is $-b$, the sum of the products of the roots two at a time is c, and the product of the three roots is $-d$.

Roots and Coefficients of Any Polynomial Equation

The theorems for quadratic and cubic equations can be generalized to polynomial equations of any degree. If a polynomial equation $P(x) = 0$ has leading coefficient $a_n = 1$ and n roots $r_1, r_2, \ldots r_n$, then

$$P(x) = (x - r_1)(x - r_2)(x - r_3) \ldots (x - r_n).$$

The key to understanding the generalization is to see the multiplication of the binomials $(x - r_i)$ as a problem in combinations. Each term contributing to the coefficient of x^k is a result of choosing x from k of the binomial factors and the r_i from the other $n - k$ binomial factors. So there are ${}_nC_k$ terms with the factor x^k. The coefficient of x^k is the sum of the coefficients in all these terms—that is, the sum of the products of the roots taken $n - k$ at a time, multiplied by -1 if the number of roots chosen is odd.

Theorem
For the polynomial equation

$$x^n + a_1x^{n-1} + a_2x^{n-2} + \ldots + a_{n-1}x + a_n = 0,$$

the sum of the roots is $-a_1$, the sum of the products of the roots two at a time is a_2, the sum of the products of the roots three at a time is $-a_3, \ldots$, and the product of all the roots is $\begin{cases} a_n \text{ if } n \text{ is even,} \\ -a_n \text{ if } n \text{ is odd.} \end{cases}$

For instance, to find a polynomial equation with roots -8, 9, 2, and 5, you could multiply

$$(x + 8)(x - 9)(x - 2)(x - 5)$$

and set the product equal to zero. You could also determine the coefficients by taking the products of the roots one at a time, two at a time, three at a time, and four at a time. The coefficient of x^4 is 1. Products one at a time are just the terms, and the opposite of their sum is the coefficient of x^3.

$$-(-8 + 9 + 2 + 5) = -8$$

There are ${}_4C_2 = 6$ products two at a time. Their sum gives the coefficient of x^2.

$$-8 \cdot 9 + -8 \cdot 2 + -8 \cdot 5 + 9 \cdot 2 + 9 \cdot 5 + 2 \cdot 5 = -55$$

There are ${}_4C_3 = 4$ products three at a time. The opposite of their sum gives the coefficient of x.

$$-(-8 \cdot 9 \cdot 2 + -8 \cdot 9 \cdot 5 + -8 \cdot 2 \cdot 5 + 9 \cdot 2 \cdot 5) = 494$$

There is ${}_4C_4 = 1$ product four at a time. This is the product of the 4 roots, and it gives the constant term, the coefficient of x^0.

$$-8 \cdot 9 \cdot 2 \cdot 5 = -720$$

A polynomial equation with roots -8, 9, 2, and 5 is therefore

$$x^4 - 8x^3 - 55x^2 + 494x - 720 = 0.$$

An Application to Databases

Finding equations with given solutions sometimes arises when working with databases. In databases, people or other variables are typically categorized in various ways, and the categories are identified by numbers. For instance, in a database for students in a high school, one variable might be the section of the community in which a student lives. Name this variable SECT and suppose it has the 8 integer values 1 to 8, each identifying a particular section of the community. Suppose that a survey is to be done of how students get to school, and further suppose sections 3, 5, and 6 are very close to the school. To choose students from these sections, you could use the following instruction.

```
IF SECT = 3 OR SECT = 5 OR SECT = 6 THEN ...
```

The three equations and the two OR statements can be replaced by a single equation

IF (SECT – 3)*(SECT – 5)*(SECT – 6) = 0 THEN . . .

Multiplying the three binomials does not result in a shorter form of the line of the instruction. To see this, replace SECT by x and use the results of the previous theorem to rewrite the polynomial in standard form.

$$\begin{aligned}(x-3)(x-5)(x-6) &= x^3 - (3+5+6)x^2 + \\ &\quad (3\cdot 5 + 5\cdot 6 + 3\cdot 6)x - 3\cdot 5\cdot 6 \\ &= x^3 - 14x^2 + 63x - 90\end{aligned}$$

Since computers are often preprogrammed to use logarithms to calculate powers, and because that arithmetic involves approximations, it may be better to put the final polynomial in nested form.

$$= ((x-14)x + 63)x - 90$$

The replacement of x by SECT in the decision line gives the following.

IF ((SECT – 14)*SECT + 63)*SECT – 90 = 0 THEN . . .

In our tests, the OR statements ran faster. But for large programs, there might be a savings of computer time and memory to use the other statements.

QUESTIONS

Covering the Reading

1. Give four equations different from those in this lesson that have the solution $x = 1$. Try to make your equations unlike each other.

2. A quadratic equation has solutions $-\frac{3}{4}$ and 6. If the leading coefficient of the quadratic is 1, write the equation in standard form.

3. Solve Cardano's problem.

4. The sum of two numbers is 17 and their product is 100. What are the numbers?

5. Find a polynomial equation with the three solutions 1, 2, and 3.

6. A polynomial equation in x has the five solutions -10, -5, 0, 5, and 10. The leading coefficient of the polynomial is 1.
a. Give the coefficient of x^4. **b.** Give the coefficient of x^3.
c. Give a possible equation.

7. Consider the equation $x^5 - 3x^2 + 60 = 0$.
a. What is the sum of the roots of this equation?
b. What is the product of the roots of this equation?

8. In instructions to find a file in a database, how could the following OR statement be replaced by a statement with one equation and no OR?

IF SECT = 7 OR SECT = 2 OR SECT = 6 THEN . . .

Review

9. Find the zeros of $p(x) = x^5 - x^3 + x^2 - 1$ by grouping. Describe any multiple zeros. *(Lessons 9-7, 9-9)*

10. Factor the polynomial $t^3 - 1$ over each set of numbers.
a. integers **b.** reals **c.** complex numbers
(Lessons 9-6, 9-8)

11. Find the exact solutions of $\sin^4\theta - \cos^4\theta = 0$ in the interval $0 \le \theta \le 2\pi$. *(Lessons 4-4, 5-7, 9-8)*

12. Sketch the graph of a fourth degree polynomial satisfying the given condition.
a. four real roots, one of multiplicity two
b. no real roots *(Lesson 9-7)*

13. The first two terms of a geometric sequence are $6i$ and -12. Find each.
a. the common ratio **b.** the next two terms
c. the 100th term *(Lessons 8-1, 9-6)*

14. When a polynomial $g(x)$ is divided by $3x + 4$, the remainder is 0. Make a conclusion about the equation $g(x) = 0$. *(Lessons 9-4, 9-5)*

15. a. Find a general equation for a cubic function with zeros at -1, 0, and 2.
b. Use the result in part **a** to find an equation for the cubic function passing through the points $(-1, 0)$, $(0, 0)$, $(1, -1)$, and $(2, 0)$.
c. How are the answers to parts **a** and **b** related? *(Lessons 9-3, 9-5)*

16. When a polynomial $p(x)$ is divided by $x - 12$, the quotient is $x^3 + 5$ and the remainder is -1. Determine $p(x)$. *(Lesson 9-4)*

17. Consider a (closed) rectangular box with dimensions x, $x + 3$, and $x - 5$.
a. Write a polynomial in expanded form for $V(x)$, the volume of the box.
b. Write a polynomial in expanded form for $S(x)$, the surface area of the box.
c. If x is measured in cm, in what unit is each of $V(x)$ and $S(x)$ measured? *(Lesson 9-1)*

18. In 1995, about 24.5% of the U.S. population was aged 40 to 60. Determine the probability that the first four people called in a national telephone survey in 1995 were all aged 40 to 60. *(Lessons 7-3, 7-5)*

19. The 12-oz packages (in glass jars) of a certain brand of peanuts are found to weigh 24.5 ounces on the average and the weights have a standard deviation of 0.45 oz. The company decides to switch to plastic jars which weigh 8 ounces less than the glass ones. Determine the mean and standard deviation of the weights of the new packages. *(Lesson 3-3)*

Pea or Nut? *Peanuts are not true nuts; they are legumes like peas. A peg grows from the base of the peanut plant flower and digs as far as 10 cm into the ground where the peanuts grow.*

Exploration

20. Explore a database program and explain how it sets up files and how it enables the user to make choices from those files.

A project presents an opportunity for you to extend your knowledge of a topic related to the material of this chapter. You should allow more time for a project than you do for a typical homework question.

1 Completing the Pattern

On some tests you are asked to "complete the pattern," or to find the next term in a sequence such as

$$1, 4, 9, \ldots.$$

These are misleading questions, because there are always many justifiable answers to such problems. In fact, for any n points, if you add one more point of your own, you can find a polynomial of degree n to model the data. For example, below is a table of differences for the pattern begun above.

Only one second difference, 2, is known.

Now make up any value you like for the third difference, 6 for instance, and work backward from the third difference to the next y value.

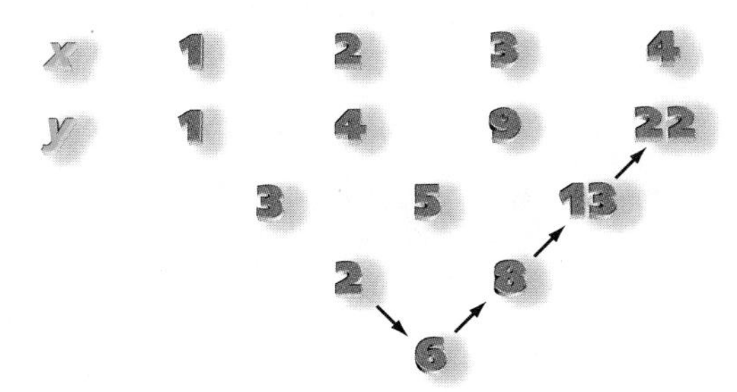

a. Use the method of finite differences to find a polynomial for these data. Check that the first four values fit the polynomial.

b. Now go back to the original data and choose a different value for the third difference, and work backwards to find the y value associated with $x = 4$. Use finite differences to find a polynomial different from that in part **a** that models the original data.

c. Find a value for y when $x = 4$ that could be justified by a quartic model.

d. If n data points are given, what is the degree of the polynomial needed to fit all of the data? What do the results of your investigation in parts **a–c** tell you about the number of polynomials of higher degree that might fit the data?

2 Pascal's Triangle Revisited

Examine each diagonal of Pascal's Triangle. These are the sequences of numbers indicated by the arrows in the figure at the right. Explain why the nth term of each diagonal can be represented by a polynomial. Find examples of diagonals in this triangle that can be described by linear, quadratic, cubic, quartic, and quintic polynomials, and find formulas for those polynomials.

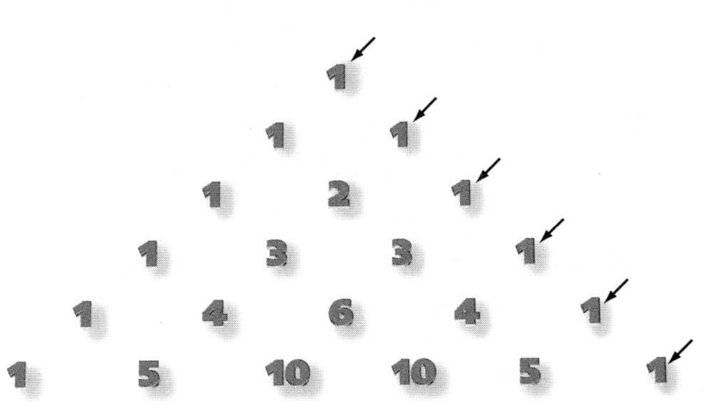

(continued)

3 Synthetic Division

Synthetic division is another way to perform long division of a polynomial by a linear factor. Find a book that explains this procedure. Teach yourself to do it. Prove why it works. Figure out how to use the Remainder Theorem in conjunction with it.

4 Properties of Cubics

Recall that the graph of every quadratic function $f(x) = ax^2 + bx + c$ is reflection-symmetric to the line $x = -\frac{b}{2a}$. The purpose of this project is to explore the symmetry of the graph of the general cubic function $f(x) = ax^3 + bx^2 + cx + d$.

a. Graph $y = x^3$ and four other cubic functions. Describe any line or point symmetry you observe.

b. Examine specifically several functions with equations of the form $f(x) = ax^3 + px$. Prove that each of these is an odd function, and explain how your proof shows that the origin is a center of symmetry for the graph of $f(x) = ax^3 + px$.

c. Now, examine graphs of equations of the form $y = ax^3 + px + q$. What is the center of symmetry for these curves?

d. Consider equations of the form
$$f(x) = a(x - h)^3 + p(x - h) + q.$$
What are the coordinates of the center of symmetry for these curves?

e. When an equation of the form
$$f(x) = a(x - h)^3 + p(x - h) + q$$
is expanded and like terms are combined, explain why it must be of the form
$$f(x) = ax^3 + bx^2 + cx + d.$$
By equating coefficients of terms of equal degree, prove that $h = -\frac{b}{3a}$. Use this result to find a center of symmetry for the graph of
$$f(x) = ax^3 + bx^2 + cx + d.$$

5 Algebraic and Transcendental Numbers

Algebraic numbers and *transcendental numbers* are two types of real numbers. Two transcendental numbers you have studied are π and e. What are the distinguishing characteristics of transcendental or algebraic numbers? How are they related to the rational and irrational numbers? Where are they used? What led to their discovery?

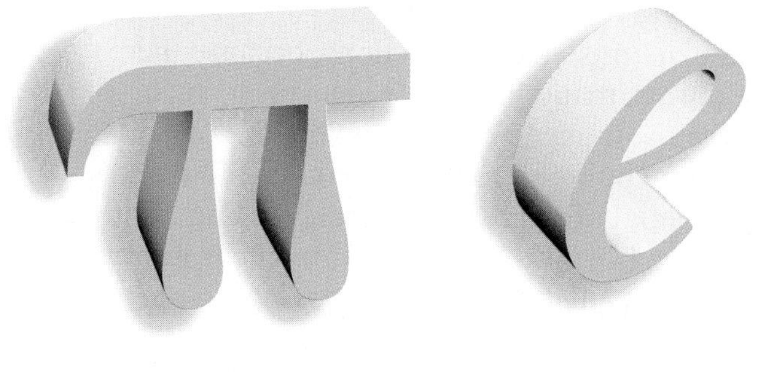

6 Tragedy Strikes Brilliant Young Mathematicians

Like Abel, Evariste Galois contributed important results to the study of polynomials at an early age. And also like Abel, Galois died at an early age. Find out more about the mathematical work of these two men and the tragic circumstances that led to their early deaths.

SUMMARY

A polynomial in x of degree n is an expression of the form $a_nx^n + a_{n-1}x^{n-1} + \ldots + a_1x + a_0$, where $a_n \neq 0$. Polynomials model situations such as long-term loan repayment, savings accounts with periodic installments, volumes and surface areas of three-dimensional figures, and so forth.

The graphs of polynomial functions of a given degree n share certain characteristics. To approximate or determine specific values for a given polynomial (such as relative extrema, zeros, or intercepts), automatic graphers or computer programs that tabulate values of the function over specified intervals can be used.

For any nth degree polynomial, the nth differences of y-values corresponding to any arithmetic sequence of x-values are equal and nonzero. If a polynomial of degree n fits a given set of data, then $n + 1$ points give rise to $n + 1$ equations that determine its coefficients.

The algorithm for dividing polynomials is very similar to that for dividing integers. If there is a remainder, its degree is always less than the degree of the dividend. Thus, when a polynomial $f(x)$ is divided by the linear factor $(x - c)$, the remainder is $f(c)$. Consequently, a number c is a solution to $f(x) = 0$ if and only if $(x - c)$ is a factor of $f(x)$. Thus, binomial factors of polynomial functions can be used to determine x-intercepts of their graphs or solutions to polynomial equations. Conversely, equations for polynomial functions can always be constructed if their zeros are known.

Imaginary numbers are nonzero real-number multiples of $i = \sqrt{-1}$. Complex numbers are sums of imaginary and real numbers. Operations with complex numbers are similar to those with polynomials. The Fundamental Theorem of Algebra and some of its consequences guarantee that every polynomial of degree $n \geq 1$ with complex coefficients has exactly n complex zeros, if multiplicities are counted.

No general formula exists for finding exact solutions for all polynomial equations. However, some polynomial equations can be solved by factoring. All sums and differences of the same odd power can be factored as can differences of even powers. Another technique is to group terms with common factors and then use the distributive property.

Coefficients of a polynomial are directly determined by its roots. If the leading coefficient is 1, the next coefficient is the opposite of the sum of the roots, the next one is the sum of the products of the roots taken two at a time, and so on.

CHAPTER NINE

VOCABULARY

Below are the most important terms and phrases for this chapter. You should be able to give a general description and a specific example of each and a precise definition for those marked with an asterisk (*).

Lesson 9-1
*polynomial in x
general form, standard form
degree of a polynomial
coefficient, leading coefficient
monomial, binomial, trinomial
degree of a polynomial in more than one variable
polynomial function
square numbers, triangular numbers

Lesson 9-2
extreme values
extrema of functions, extrema
maximum/minimum value of a function
relative maximum/minimum
zeros, roots of a polynomial function p
linear/quadratic polynomial function
positive/negative on an interval
increasing/decreasing on an interval

Lesson 9-3
tetrahedral numbers
Polynomial Difference Theorem

Lesson 9-4
dividend, divisor, quotient
remainder
Remainder Theorem

Lesson 9-5
Factor Theorem
Factor-Solution-Intercept Equivalence Theorem
pentagonal numbers

Lesson 9-6
*imaginary numbers, i
*complex numbers, $a + bi$
*real part, imaginary part (of a complex number)
equal (complex numbers)
factored over a set
*complex conjugates

Lesson 9-7
Fundamental Theorem of Algebra
multiplicity of a zero
Number of Zeros of a Polynomial Theorem
Conjugate Zeros Theorem
nth roots of unity

Lesson 9-8
Sums and Differences of Cubes Theorem
Sums and Differences of Odd Powers Theorem

CHAPTER NINE

PROGRESS SELF-TEST

Take this test as you would take a test in class. You will need an automatic grapher. Then check the test yourself using the solutions at the back of the book.

1. In the data given below, y is a polynomial function of x. Find an equation of least degree for the polynomial.

x	1	2	3	4	5	6	7
y	-4	-3	4	17	36	61	92

2. Approximate, to the nearest hundredth, the smallest positive x-intercept of the graph of $y = x^5 - x^3 + 3x^2 - 9$.

3. Determine the quotient and remainder when $3x^4 - 7x^3 + 8x^2 - 14x - 10$ is divided by $x + 2$.

4. Factor $9x^2 - 3x - 2$.

5. Factor $t^6 + 1000y^3$ over the set of polynomials with integer coefficients.

6. *Multiple choice.* For the polynomial $f(x) = x^8 - 7x^6 + 6x^3 - 4x^2 + 12x - 8$, $f(1) = 0$. Which is a factor of $f(x)$?

(a) $x - 1$ (b) $x + 1$

(c) $x - 2$ (d) $x + 2$

7. Let $z = 2 + 5i$ and $w = 3 - i$. Express each of the following in $a + bi$ form.

a. $2z + w$ **b.** $\frac{z}{w}$

In 8–10, consider the polynomial function g, with $g(x) = (x - 8)^3(2x + 3)^2(5x - 1)$.

8. Which zero of g has multiplicity two?

9. What is the degree of $g(x)$?

10. How many x-intercepts does the graph of g have?

11. Explain why a polynomial function of degree seven with real coefficients must have at least one real zero.

12. Solve $x^4 + 11x^2 + 10 = 0$ completely, given that one of the solutions is i.

13. The prices for a thin crust spinach pizza at Sophia's pizzeria are listed below.

10″	12″	14″
\$5.95	\$6.95	\$8.50

If pricing is based on a quadratic function containing these three points, what should a 16″ pizza cost (rounded to the nearest penny)?

14. In a right triangle the sides are as given at the right. Find x to the nearest hundredth.

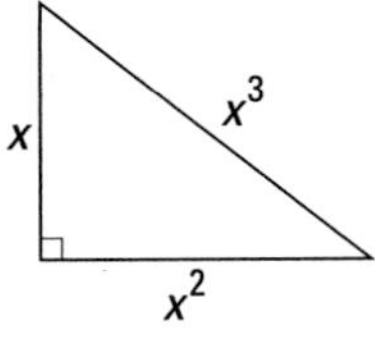

15. Part of the graph of a polynomial function t is graphed below.

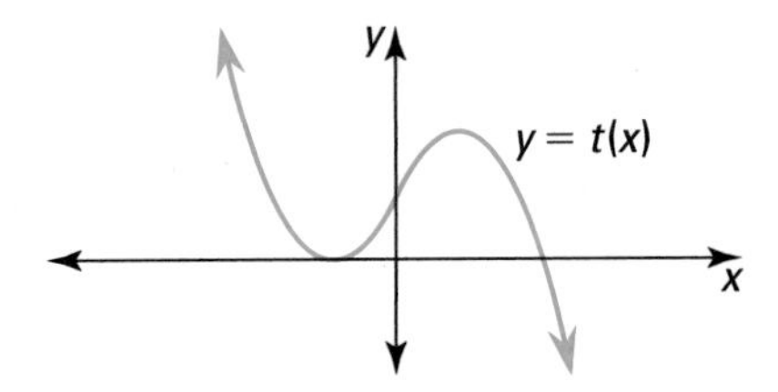

a. At least how many real zeros (including multiplicities) does t have?

b. What is the lowest degree the polynomial $t(x)$ must have?

16. A 25-meter high cylindrical grain silo is to have 35 cm of insulation between two layers of sheet metal, as shown below.

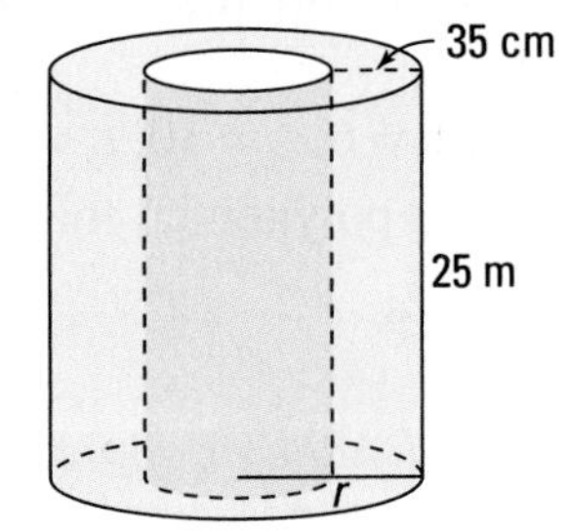

Express the volume V of insulation material as a polynomial function of r, the radius of the outer layer of the silo.

CHAPTER REVIEW

Questions on SPUR Objectives

SPUR stands for **S**kills, **P**roperties, **U**ses, and **R**epresentations. The Chapter Review questions are grouped according to the SPUR Objectives for this chapter.

SKILLS DEAL WITH THE PROCEDURES USED TO GET ANSWERS.

Objective A: *Use finite differences and systems of equations to determine an equation for a polynomial function from data points.* (Lesson 9-3)

1. In a set of data points, the x values form an arithmetic sequence, and the 5th differences of y-values for the consecutive x-values are the first set of differences equal to 0.

a. What is the degree of the polynomial function for y in terms of x?

b. How many data points are necessary to determine an equation for this polynomial?

In 2 and 3, use the data listed in the table. **a.** Determine if y is a polynomial function of x of degree less than 5. **b.** If so, find an equation for it.

2.

x	1	2	3	4	5	6	7
y	6	13	26	45	70	101	138

3.

x	2	4	6	8	10	12	14
y	4	16	64	256	1024	4096	16384

4. The following are the first six triangular numbers, t_n.

$t_1 = 1, t_2 = 3, t_3 = 6, t_4 = 10, t_5 = 15, t_6 = 21$

a. Determine a polynomial formula for t_n.

b. Calculate t_{100}.

Objective B: *Calculate or approximate zeros and relative extrema of polynomial functions.* (Lesson 9-2)

In 5–7, consider the function g, with $g(t) = t^3 - 2t^2 - 4t + 3$.

5. Determine, to the nearest hundredth, a negative zero of g.

6. Determine, to the nearest tenth, a relative maximum of g by graphing.

7. Explain why 3 must be a t-intercept of the graph of g.

8. Approximate, to the nearest hundredth, the largest x-intercept of the graph of $y = x^3 - x^2 - 10x + 10$.

Objective C: *Divide polynomials.* (Lesson 9-4)

In 9–12, determine the quotient and remainder when the first polynomial is divided by the second.

9. $2t^5 - 3t^3 + t^2 + 11, t^2 + 3$

10. $t^6, t^3 - 1$

11. $x^6 - 2x^5 + x^4 - 2x^3 + 2x^2 - x + 1, x^3 - 1$

12. $x^3 + 2x^2y - 2xy^2 - y^3, x - y$

Objective D: *Factor polynomials and solve polynomial equations using the Factor Theorem, sums or differences of powers, grouping terms, or trial and error.* (Lessons 9-5, 9-6, 9-8, 9-9)

13. True or false. Since $(x - \sqrt{5})$ is a factor of $x^4 - 2x^2 - 15$, then $\sqrt{5}$ is a solution to $x^4 - 2x^2 - 15 = 0$.

14. Solve $x^3 - x^2 - 4x + 4 = 0$.

In 15–20, factor over the set of polynomials with coefficients in the indicated domain.

15. $243t^5 - u^5$; integers

16. $x^5 + x^2 - 2x^3 - 2$; reals

17. $z^3 - 8$; complex numbers

18. $8x^2 + 10x + 3$; integers

19. $20x^2 - 8x - 1$; integers

20. $t^5 - t^4 - 16t + 16$; integers

Objective E: *Perform operations with complex numbers.* (*Lesson 9-6*)

21. Let $z = 3 + 2i$ and $w = 5 - 4i$. Express each of the following in $a + bi$ form.

a. $5z + w$ **b.** $z - w$

c. zw^2 **d.** $\frac{z}{4}$

22. Repeat Question 21 if $z = 1 + 6i$ and $w = -2 - 3i$.

23. Express $\frac{6 + i}{3 - 4i}$ in $a + bi$ form.

24. Express $\frac{2 + 2i}{-8 + 3i}$ in $a + bi$ form.

25. Determine the sum $\sum_{k=1}^{100} i^k$, where $i = \sqrt{-1}$.

26. Show that $-2 + 2\sqrt{3}\, i$ is a cube root of 64.

PROPERTIES DEAL WITH THE PRINCIPLES BEHIND THE MATHEMATICS.

Objective F: *Apply the vocabulary of polynomials.* (*Lessons 9-1, 9-2, 9-7*)

27. Given the polynomial function $P(x) = 3x^7 + x^5 - 2x^3 + 6x^2 - 127$, indicate each.

a. the degree of the polynomial

b. the leading coefficient

c. the coefficient of x^4

d. the constant term

e. the number of zeros P must have

28. Write a cubic polynomial with two terms and a leading coefficient of 4.

29. *True or false.* If a polynomial function p has a relative minimum at (5, 1), then the graph of $y = p(x)$ never crosses the x-axis.

30. Consider the polynomial function m with $m(z) = (z - 3)(z + 2)^2(z - 1)^3$. Determine the zero(s) of m with each multiplicity.

a. one **b.** two **c.** three

Objective G: *Apply the Remainder Theorem, Factor Theorem, and Factor-Solution-Intercept Equivalence Theorem.* (*Lessons 9-4, 9-5*)

In 31–33, $f(x)$ is a polynomial. *True or false.*

31. If the remainder is 6 when $f(x)$ is divided by $(x - 1)$, then $f(6) = 1$.

32. If the remainder is 0 when $f(x)$ is divided by $(x^2 - 9)$, then $f(3) = 0$.

33. If the remainder is 0 when $f(x)$ is divided by $(x^2 - 5)$, then $f(x) = (x^2 - 5)p(x)$, where $p(x)$ is another polynomial.

34. Given that $g(x) = (x + 2)^2(3x - 4)(5x + 1)$, how many x-intercepts does the graph of $y = g(x)$ have?

Objective H: *Apply the Fundamental Theorem of Algebra and Conjugate Zeros Theorem.* (*Lesson 9-7*)

35. Explain why every real number is equal to its complex conjugate.

36. *True or false.* Every odd-degree polynomial with real coefficients must have at least one real zero. Explain your answer.

37. If the graph of a fourth degree polynomial does not cross the horizontal axis, what conclusions can be made about its zeros?

38. Solve $x^4 + 5x^2 - 36 = 0$ completely, given that one of the solutions is $3i$.

39. *True or false.* If $2 + i$ is a zero of $z^3 + 3z^2 - 23z + 35$, then $1 + i$ cannot be another zero of it. Explain your answer.

USES DEAL WITH APPLICATIONS OF MATHEMATICS IN REAL SITUATIONS.

Objective I: *Construct and interpret polynomials that model real situations.* *(Lessons 9-1, 9-3)*

40. Each month Mehmet deposits $40 from his salary directly into a bank account where interest is calculated monthly. He keeps this account (and his job) for a whole year without any other transactions. Assume that he opened the account with an initial amount of $100, and deposits take effect on the last business day of each month. Let $x = 1 + r$, where r is the monthly interest rate for this account.

a. Write a polynomial $M(x)$ which gives the balance in Mehmet's account at the end of the year.

b. Calculate how much Mehmet's account would have at the end of the year if the monthly interest rate is .5625%.

41. A rectangular horse-training area is to be enclosed with 1000 ft of fencing, leaving a 20-ft opening for a gate, as shown below.

The area of the enclosed region is given by $w\ell$, and the amount of available fencing indicates that $2\ell + 2w - 20 = 1000$.

a. Express ℓ in terms of w and use this to write a polynomial $A(w)$ which gives the area of the training pen.

b. Use the polynomial $A(w)$ in part **a** to determine the area of the training pen when its width is each of the following.

i. 100 feet **ii.** 250 feet **iii.** 300 feet

c. Find the dimensions of the pen with the largest possible area.

42. The total daily revenue from a yogurt stand is given by the equation $R(c) = c \cdot p(c)$, where c is the number of cups of yogurt sold and $p(c)$ is the price of one cup of yogurt. The price of one cup is given by the equation $p(c) = 2.50 + .001c - .00002c^2$.

a. Find a polynomial in standard form equal to $R(c)$.

b. Use an automatic grapher to approximate the number of cups of yogurt that would produce the maximum daily revenue.

c. What is the maximum daily revenue possible?

In 43 and 44, a confectioner is designing a new fruit-bit-and-nut treat that looks like an ice cream cone with a hemisphere of goodies on top.

The height of the cone is h cm, and the radius is r cm. The entire shape is to be filled with bits of fruit and nuts.

43. Write a formula for the volume of the treat in terms of r and h.

44. a. If the height of the cone is fixed at 6 cm, write a polynomial in r for the volume of the bits of fruit and nuts needed.

b. Identify the degree of the polynomial and tell why it is a reasonable degree for the situation.

c. What is the leading coefficient of the polynomial?

REPRESENTATIONS DEAL WITH PICTURES, GRAPHS, OR OBJECTS THAT ILLUSTRATE CONCEPTS.

Objective J: *Represent two- or three-dimensional figures with polynomials.* *(Lesson 9-1)*

45. A cone is inscribed in a sphere of radius 5 inches, as shown below. Let x be the distance from the center of the sphere to the base of the cone.

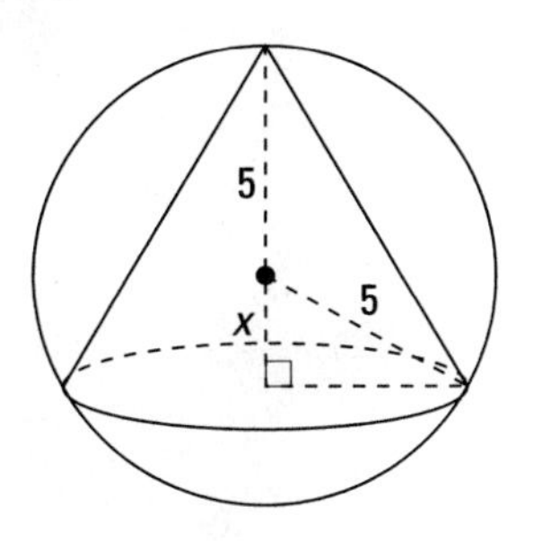

a. Express the volume of the cone as a polynomial function of x.

b. What is the degree of this polynomial?

c. Find the value of x which makes the volume of the cone 27π.

46. A cube with side s is expanded by adding h cm to each edge as shown.

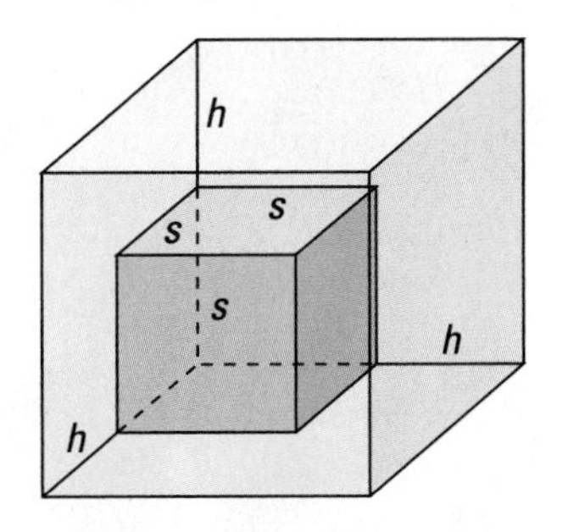

Write the volume of the new figure as a polynomial in expanded form.

47. The lengths of the sides (measured in cm) of a right triangle, shown below, form an arithmetic sequence. Determine the area of the triangle in cm^2.

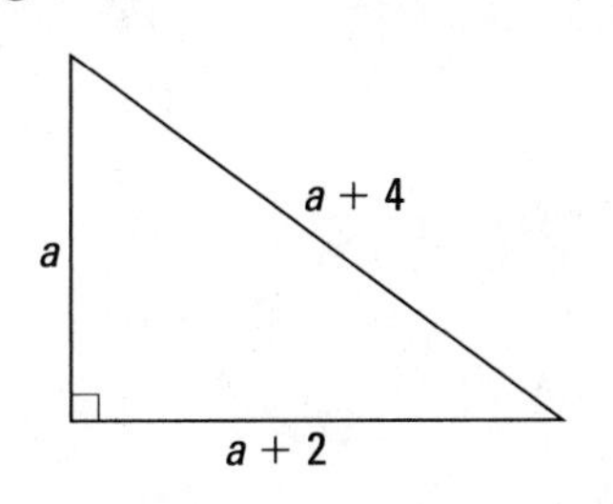

Objective K: *Relate properties of polynomial functions and their graphs.* *(Lesson 9-2, 9-5, 9-7)*

In 48–51, an equation for a polynomial function is given. **a.** Graph the function using an automatic grapher. **b.** Estimate any relative extrema. **c.** Estimate all real zeros.

48. $y = -2x^2 + 20x - 42$

49. $y = x^3 + 6x^2 + 11x + 6$

50. $y = 3x^4 + 25x^3 - 53x^2 - 54x + 72$

51. $y = x^5 - x^3 + x^2 - 1$

In 52–54, consider the part of the graph of $f(x) = 0.1x^5 - 2x^3 + x^2 - 27$ shown below.

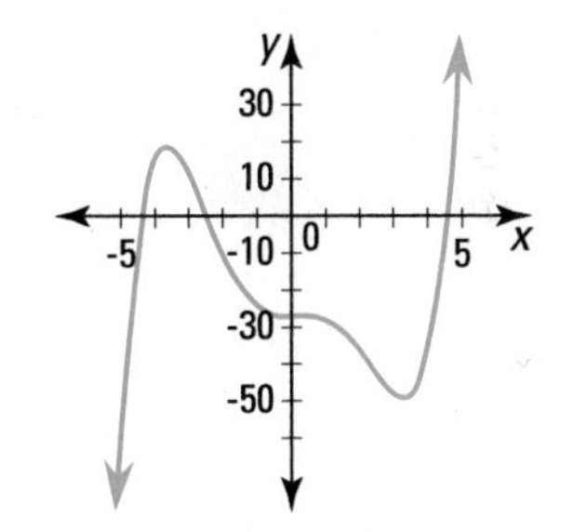

52. a. How many real zeros does f seem to have?

b. The number of real zeros and the degree of f do not match. Give a possible explanation.

53. *True or false.* The equation $0.1x^5 - 2x^3 + x^2 - 27 = 0$ has exactly three solutions. Explain your answer. If the statement is false, suggest a change to make it true.

54. Explain why the graph of f above probably contains all the essential information about the function.

CHAPTER 10

BINOMIAL AND NORMAL DISTRIBUTIONS

Below are two distributions of heights of people. The histogram on the left shows the distribution of heights (in inches) of the players in the National Basketball Association during the 1995–1996 season. It approximates the graph of a *binomial probability distribution*. Each bar indicates the number of players with heights in a 2" interval. The graphs on the right model distributions of heights of American adults. Each model is a bell-shaped curve called a *normal curve*, picturing a probability distribution called a *normal distribution*.

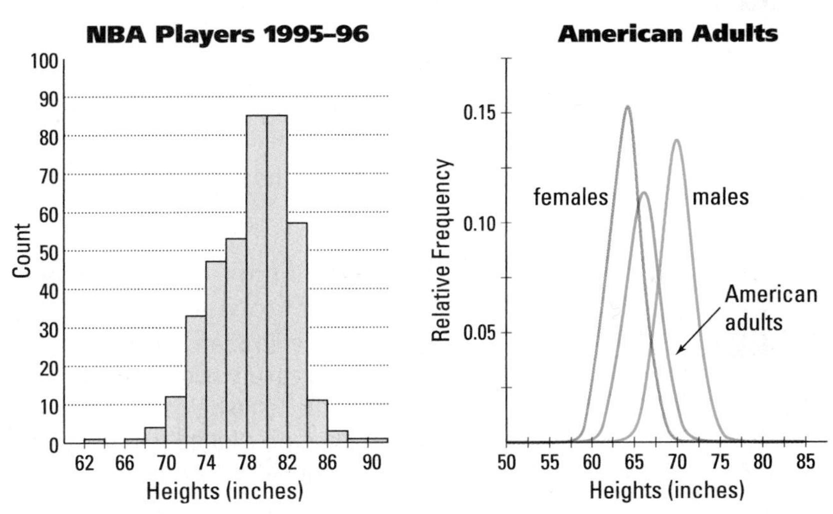

Binomial and normal distributions are very important functions in mathematics, and are often employed to make or to support decisions in situations involving uncertainty. In this chapter, you will see how these distributions are related to the testing of hypotheses, to standardized tests, and to the degree of confidence one can have in the results of random sampling.

LESSON

10-1

Binomial Probability Distributions

Recall that a binomial probability experiment is one in which there are a fixed number of independent trials, each with only two possible outcomes (with fixed probabilities), usually called *success* and *failure*. In Lesson 8-9, you studied the Binomial Probability Theorem, that in a binomial experiment with n trials in which the probability of success is p, the probability of exactly k successes is

$$_nC_k \cdot p^k(1-p)^{n-k}.$$

An Example of a Binomial Probability Distribution

Studies of long sequences of free throws by basketball players have found no evidence that successive shots are dependent. Thus, it is reasonable to consider successive free throw attempts as independent trials of a binomial experiment in which making a free throw is considered a success, and missing a free throw is considered a failure. Then, the distribution of the numbers k of free throws made in n attempts by a player with a known free throw success percentage p yields a binomial probability distribution.

Example 1

Assume a basketball player makes 75% of free throw attempts and that the attempts are independent of each other. Determine and graph the probability distribution for the number of free throws made in 8 attempts.

Solution

Let x be the number of successes in 8 trials. Then x can be any whole number from 0 to 8. The probability p of success is given here as 0.75. By the Binomial Probability Theorem, $P(x) = {}_8C_x \cdot (.75)^x(.25)^{8-x}$. Evaluating this expression for each possible value of x generates the numbers in the table below at the left. The data are graphed in the histogram below at the right. Notice that the bars of the histogram are centered on the value of the random variable.

x	P(x)
0	$1 \cdot (.75)^0 \cdot (.25)^8 \approx 0.0000153$
1	$8 \cdot (.75)^1 \cdot (.25)^7 \approx 0.0003662$
2	$28 \cdot (.75)^2 \cdot (.25)^6 \approx 0.0038452$
3	$56 \cdot (.75)^3 \cdot (.25)^5 \approx 0.0230713$
4	$70 \cdot (.75)^4 \cdot (.25)^4 \approx 0.0865173$
5	$56 \cdot (.75)^5 \cdot (.25)^3 \approx 0.2076416$
6	$28 \cdot (.75)^6 \cdot (.25)^2 \approx 0.3114624$
7	$8 \cdot (.75)^7 \cdot (.25)^1 \approx 0.2669678$
8	$1 \cdot (.75)^8 \cdot (.25)^0 \approx 0.1001129$

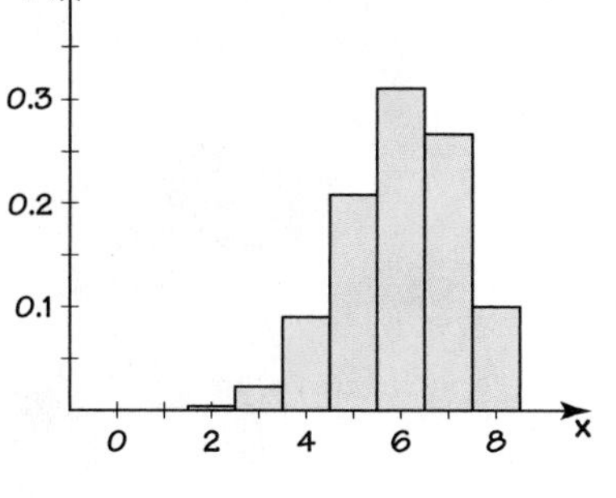

Check

The nine probabilities in the table should add to 1, which is the case.

The expression ${}_nC_k p^k(1-p)^{n-k}$ has three variables: k, n, and p. For given values of n and p, the function B with $B(k) = {}_nC_k p^k(1-p)^{n-k}$ is called a **binomial distribution function**. $B(k)$ is the probability of getting exactly k successes in n binomial trials, each of which has probability p of success. The numbers n and p are *parameters* of the binomial distribution.

Some calculators and statistical packages have built-in features to generate all values of a binomial probability distribution at once.

Activity 1

a. Determine if your technology has a binomial probability distribution generator. If it does, what variables does it use for what we call k, n, and p? Use your technology to check the values in the table in Example 1.

b. Will your technology draw graphs of binomial distributions? If yes, explain how to do this. Then draw the graph to check the histogram in Example 1.

Graphs of Binomial Distributions for a Fixed Number of Trials

Suppose that the number of trials in a binomial experiment is fixed at 8, and a particular value of p is chosen. The graph of B can be determined for the nine possible values of k. Below are graphs showing the distributions for the probability of success on six such binomial experiments with probabilities of success ranging from $p = 0.05$ to $p = 0.95$. For instance, the graph with $p = 0.75$ represents the situation in Example 1, showing the probability of k successes in 8 free throws from a player with a free throw success rate of 75%. The other graphs could represent similar situations with other success rates.

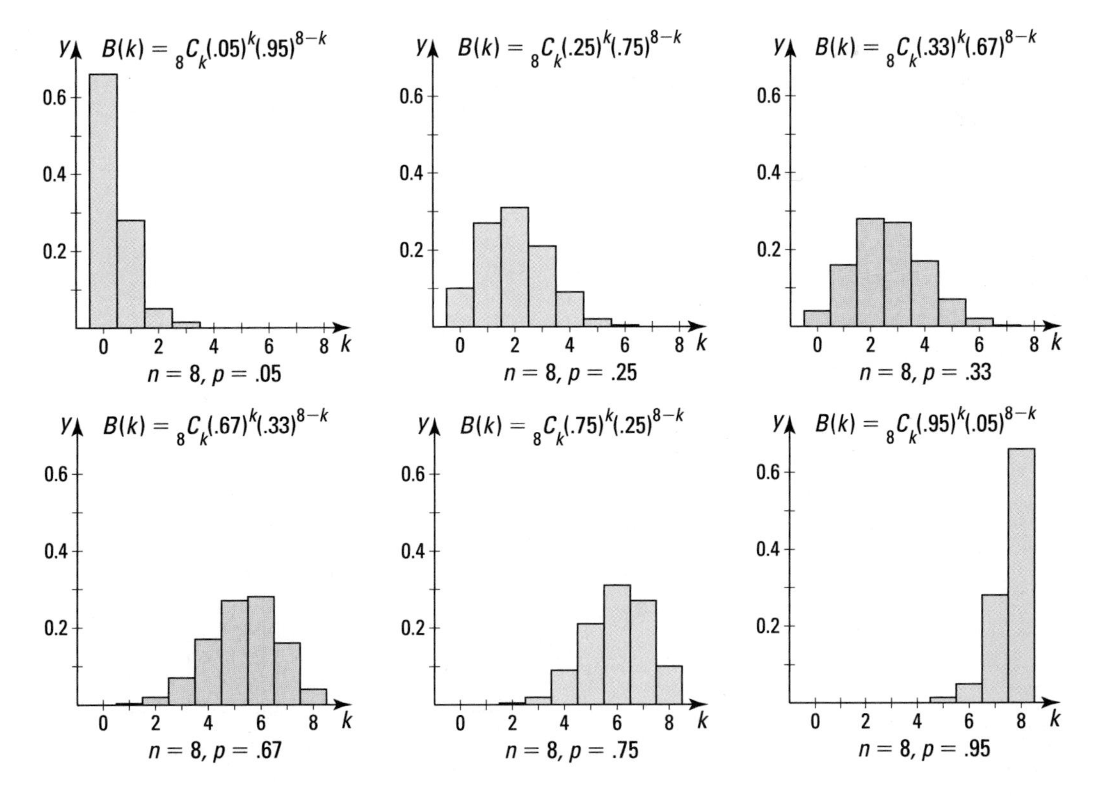

Activity 2

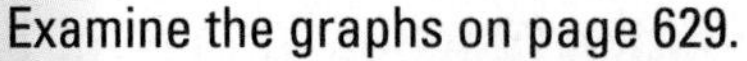

Examine the graphs on page 629.

a. Describe a free throw situation that would lead to the distribution in which $B(k) = {}_8C_k(.67)^k(.33)^{8-k}$.

b. When two values of p total 1, for instance $p = 0.05$ and $p = 0.95$, how are the two graphs related to each other? Explain why this happens.

c. As the value of p increases, what happens to the **mode** of the distribution (the domain value for which the probability function has its maximum value)?

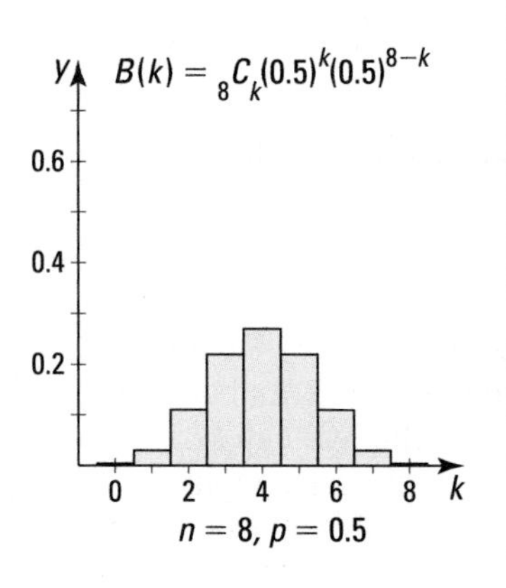

From the preceding graphs, you might expect that when $n = 8$ and $p = 0.5$, the binomial distribution is symmetric to the line $k = 4$, the mode of the distribution. As shown in the graph at the left, this is indeed the case.

The Graphs of Binomial Distributions for a Fixed Probability

It is also useful to study the graphs of binomial distributions for a fixed probability p and various values of n, the number of trials.

Example 2

a. Let $p = 0.5$. Draw graphs of the binomial probability distributions when $n = 2, 6, 10$, and 50.

b. Describe the effect of increasing n on the probability distribution B when $p = 0.5$.

Solution

a. The data for the graphs determined by $n = 2, 6$, and 10 can be generated by hand. But for the case of $n = 50$, we use a calculator or statistics utility with a built-in feature for generating binomial distributions.

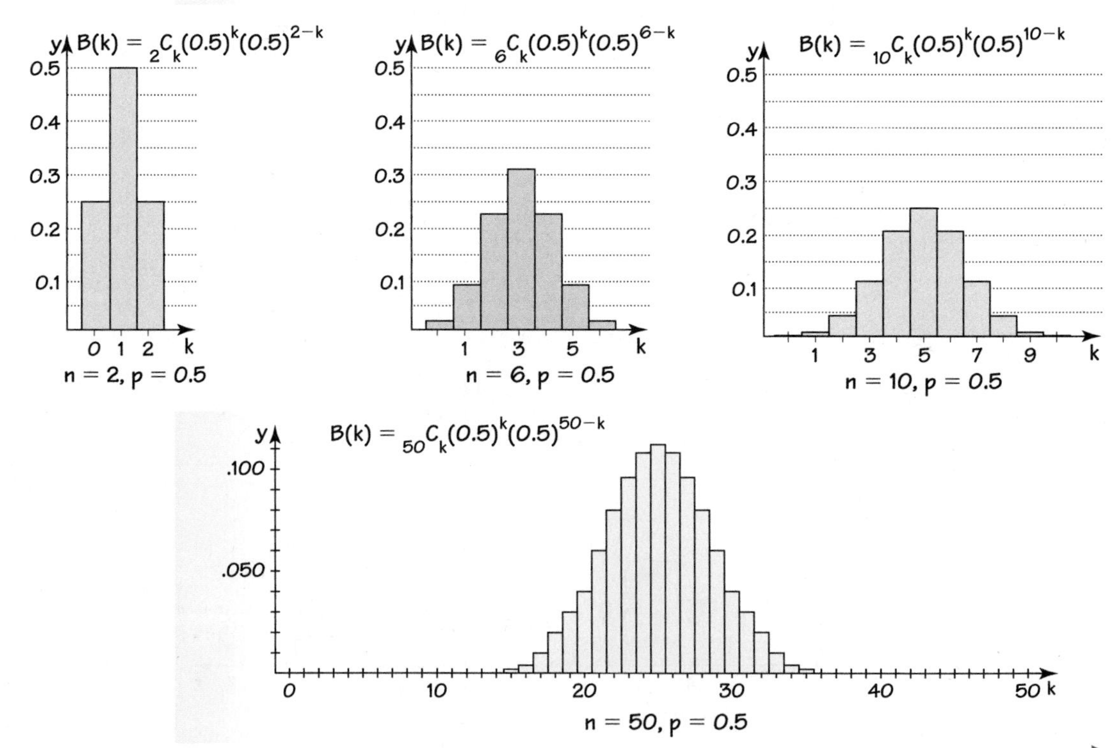

b. When $p = 0.5$, as n increases, the following patterns can be observed.

1. The mode of the distribution increases along the k-axis. That is, the more trials, the greater the most likely value.
2. The graph is symmetric to the bar at $\frac{n}{2}$.
3. The graph "spreads out."
4. The maximum value of the range, which is the maximum probability, decreases. That is, the distribution "flattens."

In the next lesson you will see theorems that justify the patterns observed in this lesson.

QUESTIONS

Covering the Reading

Sheryl Swoopes at the 1996 Olympic Games.

1. Assume a basketball player makes 40% of shots taken and that the attempts are independent.
   a. Determine and graph the probability distribution for the number of free throws made in 8 attempts.
   b. What is the probability that the player will make at least 6 of the next 8 shots?
   c. Compare and contrast the graph in part **a** to the one drawn in Example 1.

2. The expression ${}_nC_k p^k(1 - p)^{n-k}$ gives the probability of getting exactly __a.__ successes in __b.__ trials of a __c.__ experiment in which the probability of success on each trial is __d.__ .

3. If your calculator or statistics utility has a built-in feature for generating values of a binomial distribution, show what you found for Activity 1.

4. Indicate your answers to Activity 2.

In 5 and 6, consider a binomial probability distribution. *True or false.*

5. When $p = 0.5$, the graph is symmetric to the line $k = \frac{n}{p}$.

6. When $p = 0.5$, as n increases, the probability of getting the modal number of successes increases.

7. a. Graph the five probability distributions B with $n = 7$, and $p = 0.8, 0.6, 0.5, 0.4$, and 0.2.
   b. Which of the graphs are reflection images of each other?
   c. As p decreases, what is the effect on the graph of B?

8. a. Graph the probability distributions B when $p = 0.3$ and $n = 5, 10, 25$, and 100.
   b. Describe the effect on this distribution of fixing p and increasing n.

Applying the Mathematics

9. A multiple-choice test has 15 questions each with 5 alternatives. Assume that a student answers all questions by random guessing. Determine the following probabilities.

a. P(no more than 5 right answers)

b. P(exactly 5 right answers) **c.** P(more than 5 right answers)

10. The wheel used on a certain TV game show has 19 sections. Nine sections have big prizes, nine sections have small prizes, and one section throws the player out of the game. The scatterplot below shows the probability of winning k big prizes in 50 spins of this wheel.

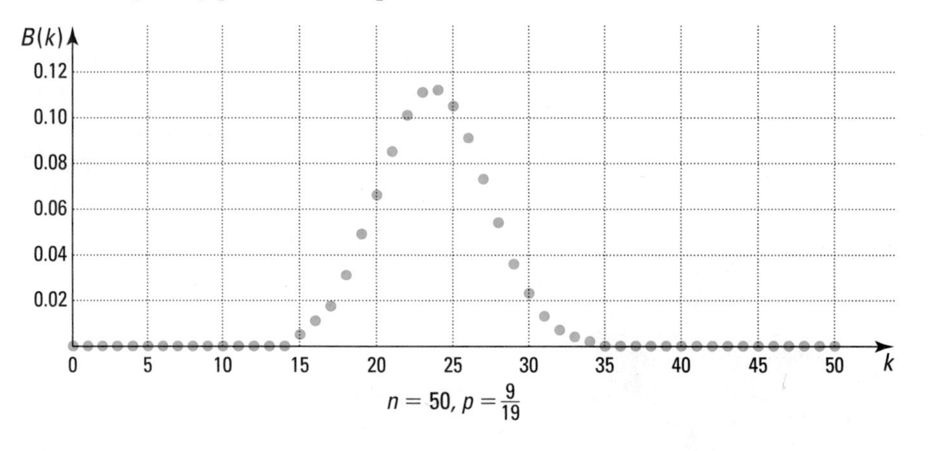

a. From the graph, estimate the probability of winning 30 or more big prizes.

b. The graph is nearly reflection-symmetric. Why?

c. If the wheel were spun more than 50 times, how would you expect the graph to change?

Review

In 11 and 12, determine whether the given situation is a binomial experiment. *(Lesson 8-9)*

11. At a highway weigh station, all trucks are stopped and weighed. Trucks over 40 tons are not allowed to continue traveling on that highway. Statistics at this weigh station show that about 2% of trucks are rerouted. It is desired to determine the probability that exactly 3 of the first 50 trucks weighed on a particular day will be rerouted.

12. Suppose that 100 watermelons are being emptied from a truck at a farmer's market. Each one is weighed and put into one of three piles (small, medium, and large). In the past years, this farm has produced about 35% small, 50% medium, and 15% large watermelons. It is desired to determine the probability that this will again be the distribution today.

13. Design a simulation using the RND function to model the situation in Question 12 for a selection of 20 watermelons. How many small, medium, and large watermelons do you end up with? *(Lesson 7-8)*

14. Three fair coins are tossed. Each head is assigned a value of 2, and each tail a value of 1. Let m be the product of the values of the three tossed coins.

a. Find the probability distribution for m.

b. What is the mean of the distribution? *(Lesson 7-6)*

In 15 and 16, find θ. *(Lessons 5-2, 5-4)*

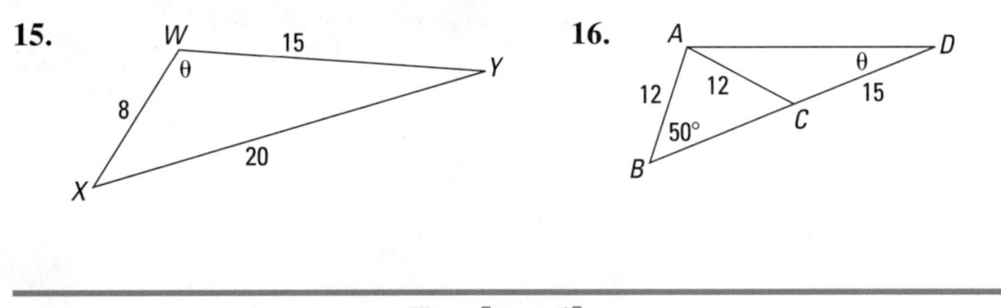

Exploration

17. A *cumulative binomial probability table* gives, for fixed n and p, the probabilities for k or fewer successes. Below is a table of cumulative binomial probabilities when $n = 7$. The number in row k and column p represents the probability of k or fewer successes in 7 binomial trials, each of which has probability p. For instance, the probability of no more than 2 successes in 7 binomial trials, each of which has probability of success equal to 0.8, is about 0.0047.

k \ p ($n = 7$)	0.01	0.05	0.1	0.2	0.3	0.4	0.5	0.6	0.7	0.8	0.9	0.95	0.99
0	.9321	.6983	.4783	.2097	.0824	.0280	.0078	.0016	.0002	.0000	.0000	.0000	.0000
1	.9980	.9556	.8503	.5767	.3294	.1586	.0625	.0188	.0038	.0004	.0000	.0000	.0000
2	1.0000	.9962	.9743	.8520	.6471	.4199	.2266	.0963	.0288	.0047	.0002	.0000	.0000
3	1.0000	.9998	.9973	.9667	.8740	.7102	.5000	.2898	.1260	.0333	.0027	.0002	.0000
4	1.0000	1.0000	.9998	.9953	.9712	.9037	.7734	.5801	.3529	.1480	.0257	.0038	.0000
5	1.0000	1.0000	1.0000	.9996	.9962	.9812	.9375	.8414	.6706	.4233	.1497	.0444	.0020
6	1.0000	1.0000	1.0000	1.0000	.9998	.9984	.9922	.9720	.9176	.7903	.5217	.3017	.0679

a. Use the table to determine the probability of five or fewer successes in a binomial experiment with 7 trials, if in each trial the probability of success is 0.8. Compare this answer to the one you get by applying the method learned in Chapter 8 directly.

b. Cumulative binomial probability tables can also be used to calculate probabilities for single events. Figure out how to use a cumulative binomial table to determine the probability of exactly two successes in seven trials, each with 0.4 probability of success. Verify your answer by direct calculation using the Binomial Probability Theorem.

c. Some statistics utilities have built-in features for generating cumulative binomial probabilities. Find out whether your calculator has such a feature. If it does, use it to check your work in part **a**.

LESSON

10-2

Mean and Standard Deviation of a Binomial Distribution

Conventional way. *President Clinton and Vice-President Gore greet attendees at the 1996 Democratic National Convention. On election day, they received 50% of the popular vote while the Republicans received 41% and others 9%.*

In the previous lesson, you studied the shapes of the graphs of binomial probability distributions produced under two conditions: (1) fixing the number n of trials, and allowing p, the probability of success on an individual trial, to vary; or (2) fixing the value of p, and allowing n to vary. In particular, you saw that if p is fixed, then as n increases, the mode of the distribution increases, and the distribution spreads out. In this lesson we examine the effect of n and p on two other measures of center and spread, the mean and standard deviation. You will see that despite the variety of shapes binomial distributions can have, each of these statistics can be calculated using a surprisingly simple formula.

The Mean of a Binomial Probability Distribution

Consider the binomial distribution P from Example 1 of Lesson 10-1. P gives the probability of x successes in 8 trials, when the probability of success in any one trial is .75. The graph of P is repeated at the right.

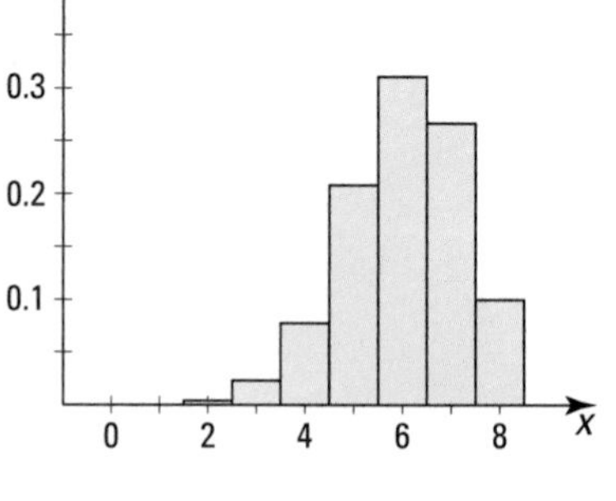

In Example 1 of Lesson 10-1, P referred to a situation in basketball. P is also the model for other situations with the same characteristics. Suppose candidate C for an election is thought to be preferred by 75% of the voters. When a sample poll is taken of 8 people from the population of voters, it is not always the case that 6 people will say they prefer C, even though 6 is 75% of 8. But the *mean* of the binomial probability distribution is 6. This can be verified by substituting the values from Example 1 into the formula for the mean of a general probability distribution, which you saw in Lesson 7-6.

$$\begin{aligned}\mu &= \sum_{x=0}^{8} x \cdot P(x)\\ &= 0 \cdot P(0) + 1 \cdot P(1) + 2 \cdot P(2) + 3 \cdot P(3) + 4 \cdot P(4) + 5 \cdot P(5) +\\ &\quad 6 \cdot P(6) + 7 \cdot P(7) + 8 \cdot P(8)\\ &\approx 0 \cdot 0.0000153 + 1 \cdot 0.0003662 + \ldots + 8 \cdot 0.1001129\\ &= 6\end{aligned}$$

Activity 1

Using the other values found in Example 1 of Lesson 10-1, check the arithmetic above.

This confirms that our intuition is correct.

The following example shows how the mean of a binomial distribution varies with the probability of success of a single event.

Example 1

Suppose a darts player has probability p of hitting the bull's-eye with a single dart, and all attempts are independent. Find the expected number of bull's-eyes the player will hit in three attempts.

Solution

This is a binomial experiment with $n = 3$ and probability of success p, and probability $q = 1 - p$ of failure. The probability distribution for the random variable, number of bull's-eyes, is shown below.

x = number of bull's-eyes	3	2	1	0
B(x) = probability	p^3	$3p^2q$	$3pq^2$	q^3

Let μ be the mean of this distribution. Then by the definition

$$\begin{aligned}\mu &= \sum_{x=0}^{3} x\, B(x)\\ \mu &= 3(p^3) + 2(3p^2q) + 1(3pq^2) + 0(q^3)\\ &= 3p^3 + 6p^2q + 3pq^2\\ &= 3p(p^2 + 2pq + q^2)\\ &= 3p(p + q)^2.\end{aligned}$$

Because $p + q = 1$,

$$\mu = 3p.$$

So the player can expect to hit $3p$ bull's-eyes with three shots.

Check

Substitute a value for p. If the probability of getting a bull's-eye is $\frac{2}{3}$, then in 3 shots the player will get, on average, 2 bull's-eyes. This agrees with intuition.

The results about the basketball player and the darts player generalize to a simple formula for the mean of any binomial distribution. Its proof is not so simple, but uses only properties you have studied.

Theorem (Mean of a Binomial Distribution)
The mean μ of a binomial distribution B with n trials and probability p of success on each trial is given by $\mu = np$.

Proof

$\mu = \sum_{x=0}^{n} xB(x) = \sum_{x=0}^{n} x\binom{n}{x}p^x(1-p)^{n-x}$	B is a binomial distribution.
$= \sum_{x=1}^{n} x\dfrac{n!}{x!(n-x)!}p^x(1-p)^{n-x}$	Formula for $\binom{n}{x}$ When $x = 0$, the term is 0.
$= \sum_{x=1}^{n} \dfrac{n\cdot(n-1)!}{(x-1)!(n-x)!}p\cdot p^{x-1}(1-p)^{n-x}$	Rewriting factorials and powers
$= np\sum_{x=1}^{n} \dfrac{(n-1)!}{(x-1)!(n-x)!}p^{x-1}(1-p)^{n-x}$	Since n and p do not depend on x, they distribute over the sum.
$= np\sum_{x=1}^{n} \binom{n-1}{x-1}p^{x-1}(1-p)^{n-x}$	Formula for $\binom{n-1}{x-1}$
$= np(p+(1-p))^{n-1}$	Binomial Theorem
$= np\cdot 1^{n-1}$	$p+(1-p)=1$
$= np$	

The Variance and Standard Deviation of a Binomial Distribution

The variance and standard deviation of a binomial probability distribution can also be calculated directly from n and p. Recall that the variance σ^2 of a population with n values $x_1, x_2, \ldots, x_n$ equals $\dfrac{\sum_{i=1}^{n}(x_i - \bar{x})^2}{n}$, where $\bar{x}$ is the mean of the numbers $x_1, x_2, \ldots, x_n$. This can be rewritten as

$$\sigma^2 = \frac{\sum_{i=1}^{n} x_i^2}{n} - \bar{x}^2.$$

The analogous formula for the **variance σ^2 of a probability distribution** P with n outcomes and mean μ is

$$\sigma^2 = \sum_{i=1}^{n}(x_i^2 \cdot P(x_i)) - \mu^2.$$

Example 2

Find the variance and standard deviation for the distribution generated by the darts player in Example 1.

Solution

Use the table of values of the probability distribution given in the solution of Example 1, and the result that $\mu = 3p$.

By definition,

$$\sigma^2 = \sum_{x=0}^{3} x^2 B(x) - \mu^2$$

$$\sigma^2 = (3^2p^3 + 2^2(3p^2q) + 1^2(3pq^2) + 0^2q^3) - (3p)^2.$$

Expand and rearrange terms to simplify.

$$\sigma^2 = 9p^3 + 12p^2q + 3pq^2 - 9p^2$$

Rewrite $12p^2q$ as $9p^2q + 3p^2q$.

$$\sigma^2 = 9p^3 + 9p^2q + 3p^2q + 3pq^2 - 9p^2$$

$$= 9p^2(p + q) + 3pq(p + q) - 9p^2$$

$$= 9p^2 + 3pq - 9p^2 \qquad \text{since } p + q = 1$$

Thus $\sigma^2 = 3pq$.

The standard deviation is the square root of the variance.

$$\sigma = \sqrt{3pq}$$

The result in Example 2 also generalizes. The proof is quite lengthy and is omitted here.

Theorem (Variance and Standard Deviation of a Binomial Distribution)

In a binomial distribution with n trials, probability p of success and probability q of failure on each trial, the variance $\sigma^2 = npq$, and the standard deviation $\sigma = \sqrt{npq}$.

Applying the Theorems about Means and Standard Deviations

Example 3

In the United States, the probability that a newborn child will be female is about $p = 0.48$. Suppose a large hospital has 2500 live births in a given year. Let $B(x)$ = the probability that x females are born.

a. What is the mean of the distribution B?

b. What is the standard deviation of the distribution B?

Solution

Let x be the number of female children in 2500 live births. If births are independent, then the probability distribution B is binomial with $n = 2500$ and $p = 0.48$. By the previous theorems,

a. the mean $\mu = 2500(0.48) = 1200$;

b. the standard deviation $\sigma = \sqrt{2500(0.48)(0.52)} = \sqrt{624} \approx 25$.

Check

It is very tedious to calculate by hand a table of values of the probability distribution. Below is the output generated by a statistics package.

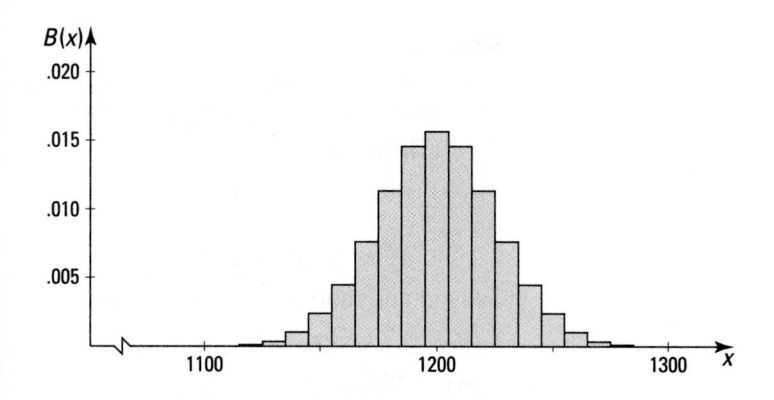

From the graph you can see that the mean appears to be about 1200, and that most of the other values are within 50 units, or two standard deviations, of the mean.

QUESTIONS

Covering the Reading

In 1 and 2, consider a basketball player with a 60% free throw average who attempts five consecutive free throws.

1. Let μ be the expected number of made free throws.
  a. Find μ by calculating a sum using the definition of the mean of a probability distribution.
  b. Find μ by using the theorem in this lesson.

2. **a.** Find the variance for the distribution of made free throws.
  b. Find the standard deviation for the distribution of made free throws.

3. Suppose a darts player has probability $p = \frac{2}{3}$ of hitting a bull's-eye on any toss of a single dart.
  a. Suppose the player throws 100 darts. Find the expected number of bull's-eyes.
  b. Let $P(x)$ be the probability of x bull's-eyes. Find the standard deviation for the distribution P.

In 4 and 5, characteristics of a binomial probability experiment are given. **a.** Find the mean of the probability distribution. **b.** Find the variance of the probability distribution. **c.** Find the standard deviation of the probability distribution.

4. $n = 10, p = .3$

5. $n = 50, p = 0.75$

6. Consider the same hospital and year referred to in Example 3. Let $P(x)$ = the probability that x males are born.
   a. What is the mean of the distribution?
   b. What is the standard deviation of P?

Applying the Mathematics

7. Suppose that both parents in a family with four children carry genes for blood types A and B. Then the blood types of their children are independent, and each child has probability $\frac{1}{4}$ of having blood type A. Let $P(x)$ = the probability that x of the four children in the family have type A blood.
   a. Construct a table for the probability distribution P.
   b. Draw a histogram of the distribution in part **a**.
   c. Find the mean number of children with type A blood, and mark the location of the mean on the histogram.
   d. Find the standard deviation of the distribution.

Cal Ripken, Jr.

8. A baseball player has a batting average a, where $0 \leq a \leq 1$. Let x = the number of hits made in the next 25 times at bat, and consider the probability distribution $P(x)$. For this distribution, find each statistic.
   a. the mean
   b. the variance

9. How many six-sided dice must be tossed if the expected number of 1's showing is to be 4?

10. If for some binomial probability distribution, $\mu = 45$ and $\sigma = 6$, find n and p.

11. *True or false.*
   a. The mean of a binomial distribution is directly proportional to n, the number of trials.
   b. The standard deviation of a binomial distribution is directly proportional to n, the number of trials.

12. According to a study by a federal agency, the probability is about 0.2 that a polygraph (lie detector) test given to a truthful person suggests that the person is deceptive. (That is, in about 20% of cases a truthful person will be labeled deceptive.) Suppose that a firm asks 20 job applicants about thefts from previous employers, and uses a polygraph to judge their truthfulness. Suppose also that all 20 answer truthfully.
   a. What is the probability that the polygraph tests show that at least one person is deceptive?
   b. What is the mean number among 20 truthful persons who will be classified as deceptive? What is the standard deviation of the number expected to be classified as deceptive?
   c. What is the probability that the number classified as deceptive is less than the mean?

Review

13. Customs officers have the following policy for accepting shipments of packaged dried fruit from another country: Select a sample of 8 boxes and check. If two or more are found substandard, reject the entire shipment. *(Lesson 10-1)*

a. Determine and graph the probability distribution of the number of shipments rejected out of the next 10 if 5% of the boxes of dried fruit produced by this country are defective.

b. What is the probability that at least 8 of the next 10 shipments of dried fruit will be accepted?

c. How would the graph of the probability distribution change if, instead of 5%, 10% of the boxes of dried fruit were defective?

d. How would the graph of the probability distribution change if, instead of sampling 8 boxes, customs officers sampled 20 boxes?

14. About 3% of a city's 327,000 water patrons have complaints about polluted water. Of these, 25% are from the residential area next to the chemical plant in town. There are 15,840 water patrons in this area.

a. Determine the probability that a water patron is from the area near the chemical plant.

b. Determine the probability that a water patron is from the area near the plant and has polluted water.

c. Show that living near the chemical plant and having polluted water are *not* independent events. *(Lessons 7-1, 7-5)*

15. a. Graph $f(x) = e^x$ and $g(x) = e^{-x}$ on the same set of axes.

b. What transformation maps f to g?

c. What is $\lim_{x \to \infty} g(x)$?

d. What is $\lim_{x \to -\infty} f(x)$? *(Lessons 2-4, 3-5, 6-4, 8-2)*

In 16 and 17, solve exactly. *(Lessons 6-5, 6-6)*

16. $e^y = 198$

17. $\log(m^2 + 10) = 3$

18. a. Draw a square whose sides are parallel to the x- and y-axes.

b. Apply the transformation $S: (x, y) \to \left(3x, \frac{y}{4}\right)$.

c. Describe the effect of this transformation on the shape, and on the area of the preimage. *(Lesson 3-5)*

19. a. What is the sum of the measures of the interior angles of a convex pentagon?

b. Use an indirect proof to explain why a convex pentagon cannot contain four acute angles. *(Previous course)*

Exploration

20. a. Find a dartboard, and, using area, compute the probability p that a dart that hits the target at random is a bull's-eye.

b. Compute answers for Examples 1 and 2 of this lesson using the value of p found in part **a**.

LESSON

10-3

Is That Coin Fair?

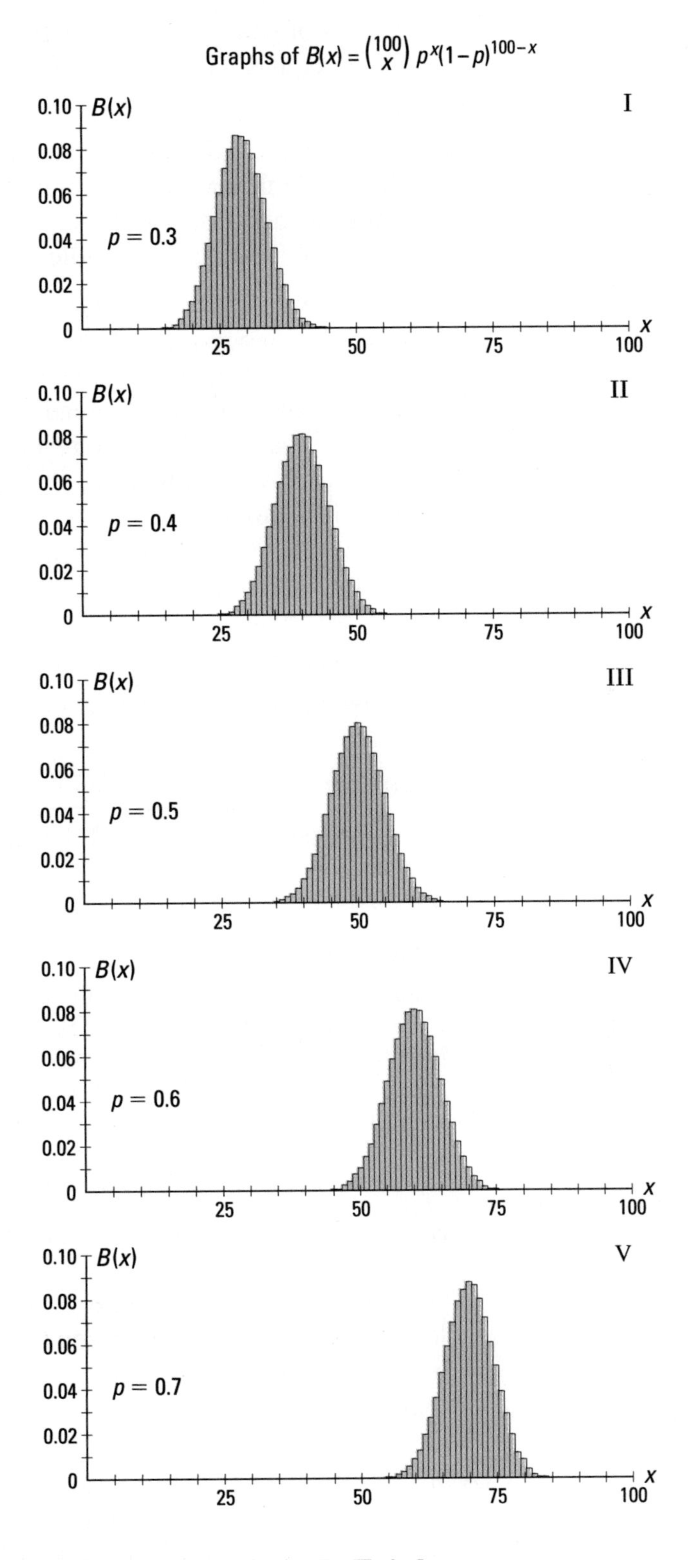

Can You Tell Whether a Coin Is Fair?

In questions involving probability, it is common to assume that a coin is fair. The question we consider in this lesson is: Is it possible to tell *for certain* whether an actual coin is fair? To answer this question, consider the five binomial probability distributions graphed above. They show the probabilities of getting x heads in 100 tosses when the probability of heads is .3, .4, .5, .6, and .7.

Suppose that you actually toss a coin 100 times in an attempt to determine whether it is fair. And suppose you get 50 heads and 50 tails. You might immediately think that the coin must be fair, but from examination of the binomial probability distributions above, you can see that many situations are possible. We call each possible situation a **hypothesis**.

One possible hypothesis is that the coin *is* fair. This certainly is reasonable; Distribution III shows that 50 heads and 50 tails can happen when the coin is fair. However, Distribution II shows that if the probability of heads is .4, it is also possible to obtain 50 heads in 100 tosses, though this is less likely. Distribution IV shows the same result if the probability of heads is .6. Even if the coin were so weighted that the probability of heads was .7 or .3, there is a possibility, though a remote one, that there could be 50 heads in 100 tosses. This argument holds regardless of how many times you toss the coin. It shows that you can never tell for certain if a coin is fair.

Can You Tell Whether a Coin Is Unfair?

Can a person tell for certain that a coin is *not* fair? Consider this example.

Example 1

A coin is tossed 100 times and 39 heads occur. Find the probability that outcomes as unusual as 39 or fewer heads occur in 100 tosses of a fair coin. Should the hypothesis that the coin is fair be rejected?

Solution

When tossing a coin 100 times, the probability of any particular outcome is quite small. So consider all the possible outcomes that are at least as far from the mean as 39 heads. Because the hypothesis is that the coin is fair, suppose the probability of heads were 0.5. Then, if x is the number of heads, using a calculator or statistics utility,

$$P(x \leq 39) = \sum_{x=0}^{39} \binom{100}{x}(0.5)^x(1 - 0.5)^{100-x} \approx 0.0176.$$

So 39 or fewer heads would occur about 2% of the time if the coin were fair. Also, 39 or more tails would occur about 2% of the time. Thus an outcome at least as unusual as 39 heads in 100 tosses would occur about 4% of the time even if the coin were fair. For us, this is not rare enough to reject the hypothesis that the coin is fair.

A probability distribution is a model for a situation of chance. Every situation of chance may be explained by more than one model. The word "hypothesis" is often used by researchers when they are considering various models. Example 1 demonstrates that as long as an outcome has a positive probability under a particular hypothesis, you cannot reject that hypothesis for certain. A rare event might have occurred. Thus you never can say for sure whether a coin is fair or not fair.

What Can You Say in a Situation of Uncertainty?

If you tossed a coin 100 times and only 10 heads occurred, then there is a great deal of evidence that the coin is not fair, *because the probability of an event as extreme as this is so low*. But how small must the probability of an event be before you reject the hypothesis that led to it? That depends on the situation. If the hypothesis is that a coin is fair, then you might choose 0.05 or 0.01 as the level below which you would reject it. If the hypothesis is that a person is innocent of a serious crime, you might choose 0.000001, or $\frac{1}{1{,}000{,}000}$, as the level that would cause a belief that the person is guilty.

The level chosen is called a **significance level** for a hypothesis. The most common significance levels are 0.05, 0.01, and 0.001. To reject a hypothesis for an experiment at the 0.05 significance level means that the event consisting of the experiment's outcome and all more extreme ones has a theoretical probability that is less than 0.05.

Significance levels are often set before an experiment to avoid debate after the fact. For instance, in Example 1, if the significance level 0.05 had been agreed to before testing the coin, and 39 heads appeared in 100 tosses, you would be obliged to reject the hypothesis that the coin is fair.

Hypothesis Testing

The logic of reasoning in Example 1 is an instance of statistical *hypothesis testing*. In this example, we hypothesized that the coin is unbiased. Such an assumption is called a *null hypothesis*, abbreviated H_0 and pronounced "*H*-naught." The word "null" suggests that the coin is not out of the ordinary. Usually, a **null hypothesis** is a statement of "no effect" or "no difference." A null hypothesis is usually contrasted with an **alternative hypothesis** H_1 which identifies an alternative conclusion from the same experiment. An alternative hypothesis is often the complement of the null hypothesis. For the coin flip, compare the null hypothesis and an alternative hypothesis.

Null	H_0: The probability that the coin lands heads is 0.5.
Alternative	H_1: The probability that the coin lands heads is not 0.5.

The choice of null and alternative hypotheses is subjective. Another alternative hypothesis is H_2: The probability that the coin lands heads is greater than 0.5. Once hypotheses are made, probability theory and statistical inference are used to determine whether a hypothesis should be accepted. The logic of hypothesis testing is similar in structure to that of indirect proof. In an indirect proof, there is a statement S you wish to prove.

Assume not-S.
Reason from not-S.

If you arrive at a false statement, or contradiction, reject not-S, which means accepting S.

In testing a hypothesis, the logic is quite similar.

Assume a null hypothesis H_0.
Reason from H_0.
If you arrive at a situation whose probability is less than your significance level, reject H_0, which means accepting an alternative hypothesis.

Here is another example of how statisticians use probability to test a hypothesis.

Example 2

A coin was tossed 10 times and 8 heads occurred.

a. At the .05 level, test the hypothesis that the coin is fair.

b. At the .05 level, test the hypothesis that the coin is weighted towards heads.

Solution

a. First state the null hypothesis H_0: The coin is fair.
Then state an alternative hypothesis H_1: The coin is not fair. Notice that H_1 is the opposite of H_0, so if H_0 is rejected, then H_1 must be accepted. Now determine the probability of the outcome that occurred or that outcomes like it occurred. In this case, we wish to include the possibility that 9 or more heads occurred, or that 8 or more tails occurred, because they are the same kind of event as what occurred. So we ask: What is the probability that when a fair coin is tossed 10 times, 8 or more heads or 8 or more tails occur? Pascal's triangle helps in determining the probabilities. In 10 tosses of a fair coin

$$P(\text{exactly 8 heads}) = \frac{45}{1024} = P(\text{exactly 8 tails}),$$

$$P(\text{exactly 9 heads}) = \frac{10}{1024} = P(\text{exactly 9 tails}), \text{ and}$$

$$P(\text{10 heads}) = \frac{1}{1024} = P(\text{10 tails}).$$

Since these six outcomes are mutually exclusive, the total probability is $\frac{112}{1024}$. Since the probability of the event is greater than .05, we cannot reject the hypothesis H_0. So we cannot accept the hypothesis H_1.

b. Although one might take as a null hypothesis that the coin is not weighted towards heads, this does not make it easy to calculate probabilities. So we again take as the null hypothesis H_0: The coin is fair. But the alternate hypothesis now is H_2: the coin is weighted towards heads. So we calculate only the probability that 8 or more heads might occur in the tossing of a coin 10 times. This probability is half that found in part **a**.

$$P(\text{8 or more heads in 10 tosses of a fair coin}) = \frac{56}{1024}$$

Again the probability is greater than .05, so we cannot reject the hypothesis that the coin is fair. Thus the data do not lead us to accept the hypothesis that the coin is weighted towards heads.

In Example 2, notice that the probability of the outcome "8 heads in 10 tosses" is less than .05. That particular outcome is unusual. But we are testing whether the coin is fair or weighted, not whether the outcome is unusual. So we must consider all possible similarly unusual outcomes. It is not always easy to determine what outcomes are similar to a given outcome.

The use of probability to test hypotheses has applications well beyond coins and games of chance. In medicine it is very unusual for all patients to react the same way to a new treatment. For some the treatment may be helpful, while for others it is not. We can never be certain that a new treatment is better than an old one, so we are forced into hypothesis testing. In elections, seldom do all people favor the same candidate. So a sample poll can never tell for certain whether one candidate will win. Instead, hypothesis testing is used. A typical null hypothesis is that the candidates are equally popular. Then, when the poll's results are found, pollsters ask: If the candidates were equally popular, how unusual would it be to get poll results like these?

In medicine, polling, and coin flips, and almost all other places where this type of testing is done, the samples are larger than the ones we have used here. Calculations of individual probabilities, as in Example 2, are tedious. Fortunately, when the number of trials increases, binomial distributions become closer and closer to a distribution whose characteristics are given in statistical tables. That distribution is the subject of the next lesson.

QUESTIONS

Covering the Reading

1. Suppose a coin is tossed 100 times, and 30 heads occur.
   a. Under the hypothesis that the coin is fair, use a calculator to estimate the following probabilities.
   i. $P(H = 30)$ **ii.** $P(H \leq 30)$
   b. If a 0.05 significance level is used to test the hypothesis that the coin is fair, should the hypothesis be accepted?

2. What does it mean to test a hypothesis for an experiment at the 0.01 level?

In 3 and 4, state an appropriate null hypothesis H_0, and an alternative hypothesis H_1.

3. A new car averages 30 miles per gallon on the highway. The owner switches to a new motor oil that claims to increase gas mileage. After driving 2000 miles with the new oil, the owner wants to determine if gas mileage has actually increased.

4. A bag of kitty litter is supposed to contain 10 lb. A consumer group thinks that the manufacturer is consistently filling the bags with less than the labeled amount. They weigh some bags.

5. A coin is tossed 12 times and 10 tails occur.
   a. To test H_0: the coin is fair, against H_1: $P(\text{heads}) \neq .5$, what outcomes should be considered along with this outcome?
   b. At the .05 level, test the hypothesis that the coin is fair.
   c. At the .01 level, test the hypothesis that the coin is fair.
   d. At the .01 level, test the hypothesis that the coin is weighted in favor of tails.

Applying the Mathematics

Scott Blanton (16) and Gus Frerotte (12) of the Washington Redskins

6. A pollster taking an exit poll in a particular precinct after an election polls 6 voters and finds that all of them voted for candidate A. At the .01 significance level, test the hypothesis that this precinct went for candidate B.

7. A coin is tossed 10 times and 5 heads occur. At the .05 significance level, test the hypothesis that the probability of heads is $\frac{1}{3}$.

8. A field-goal kicker in football is thought to be able to make 90% of field-goal attempts from within 20 yards. On the first 5 attempts of the season from within 20 yards, the kicker makes only 2 field goals. Is the coach justified in saying that the kicker seems no longer able to make 90% of field-goal attempts from within 20 yards? Answer the question by using hypothesis testing.

9. Determine the mean and standard deviation of the binomial distribution of the null hypothesis in Question 7.

Review

10. Consider a multiple-choice test of 20 questions, each of which has four choices.
    a. Find the expected number of questions a student guessing on all answers will get right.
    b. Find the standard deviation for the corresponding binomial distribution. *(Lessons 10-1, 10-2)*

11. *True or false.* The graph of a binomial distribution with a fixed probability of success "spreads out" as the number of trials is increased. *(Lessons 10-1, 10-2)*

12. Suppose that a certain disease has a 50% recovery rate.
    a. What is the probability that in a study of five people all five will recover?
    b. In one experiment, a drug is tested on five people and all five recover. Consider your answer to part **a**; comment on the drug's effectiveness.
    c. In a second experiment, 25 people get the drug. Find the probability that 18 or more people recover even if the drug has no effect on the illness.
    d. Consider your answers to parts **b** and **c**. Does the drug appear to be effective? Which experiment might be considered more conclusive and why? *(Lesson 10-1)*

13. Factor $2a^5 + 486a^5b^5c^{10}$ over the set of polynomials with integer coefficients. *(Lesson 9-8)*

14. There are eleven girls in Carla's Girl Scout troop and thirteen in her second grade class. Altogether, there are twenty girls in the two groups. How many girls are in both the Girl Scout troop and the class? *(Lesson 7-2)*

grade equivalent	percent
2.0 – 2.9	0.5
3.0 – 3.9	3.5
4.0 – 4.9	5.2
5.0 – 5.9	18.4
6.0 – 6.9	23.8
7.0 – 7.9	22.8
8.0 – 8.9	16.4
9.0 – 9.9	7.3
10.0 – 10.9	1.5
11.0 – 11.9	0.5
12.0 – 12.9	0.1

15. The table at the left summarizes the mathematics achievement scores (as grade equivalents) of a large group of seventh graders.
   a. Draw a histogram of these data.
   b. If a student is selected at random from this group of seventh graders, what is the probability that the student's mathematics achievement is at least one year above grade level?
   c. Shade the region of the histogram corresponding to part **b**.
   (Lessons 1-5, 7-2)

16. The graph below represents an EKG reading of the electrical impulses from the heart, abnormal in this case. Each large square represents 0.2 seconds. Find the period of this heartbeat pattern. *(Lesson 4-6)*

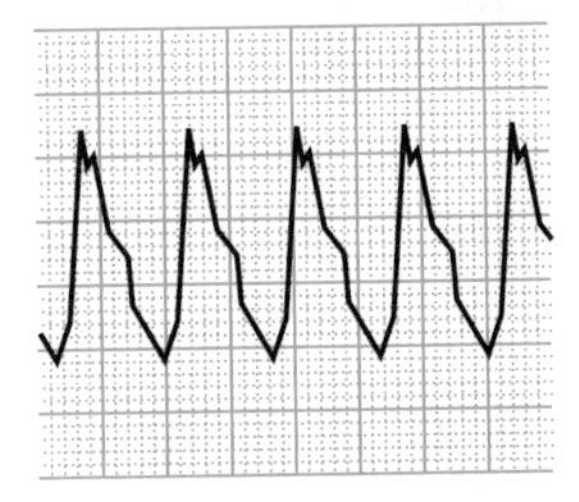

17. A circular archery target is 122 cm in diameter and consists of a bull's-eye of diameter 12.2 cm, surrounded by nine evenly spaced concentric circles. Assume that an arrow that hits a target from 90 meters away is equally likely to land anywhere on the target. Find the probability that the arrow hits within the given region.
   a. the bull's-eye
   b. somewhere in the outermost 4 circles
   c. within the fifth ring counting from the outer edge *(Lesson 7-1)*

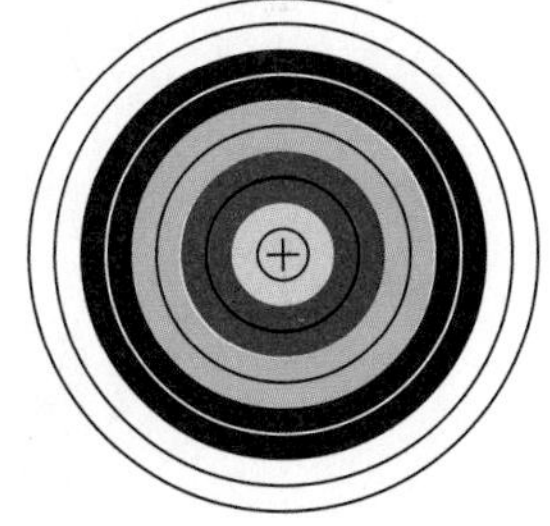

Exploration

18. What combinations of horizontal and vertical scale changes can be applied to the semicircular region at the right so that the area of the image is 1?

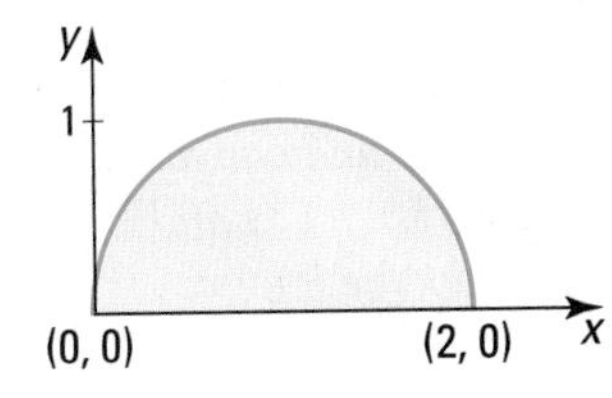

Introducing
Lesson 10-4

The Graph of $y = e^{-x^2}$

IN-CLASS ACTIVITY

The function with equation $y = e^{-x^2}$ is the parent of many probability distributions. Its graph is sometimes called the **parent normal curve**.

1 **a.** Graph $f(x) = e^{-x^2}$ on the window $-2.5 \leq x \leq 2.5$ and $-0.5 \leq y \leq 1.5$.
b. Describe the shape of the curve.

2 What kind of symmetry does f have? Justify your response with an algebraic argument.

3 **a.** Evaluate $\lim_{x \to \infty} f(x)$.
b. Describe what happens to the values of $f(x)$ as $x \to -\infty$.

4 Does the graph of $y = f(x)$ have any asymptotes? If yes, give equations for all asymptotes. If no, explain why not.

5 Notice that near the y-intercept the graph is curved downward, called **concave down**. Farther away from the y-axis, the graph is curved upward, called **concave up**.

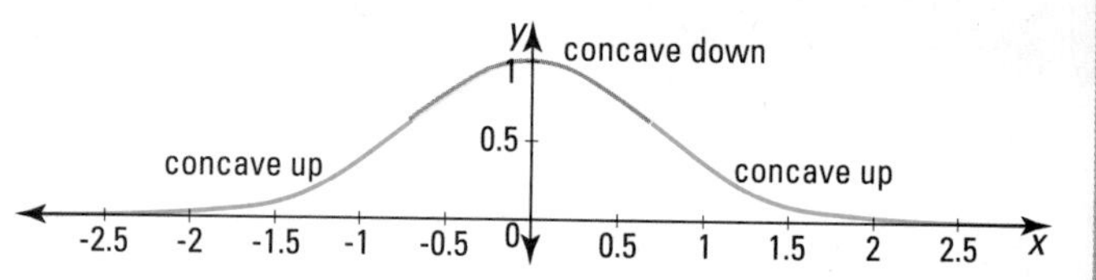

At two points, the graph changes concavity. These points are called **inflection points**. Estimate the coordinates of the inflection points as closely as you can.

This mirror is both concave and convex, which stretches and shrinks the image.

LESSON

10-4

Normal Curves

You have seen that when the probability p of success is fixed, then as the number n of trials increases, the graph of a binomial probability distribution approaches a bell-shaped curve. For instance, below is a set of binomial probability distributions for $p = .8$ showing the change in the shape of the distribution as n takes on the values of 5, 20, 50, and 100.

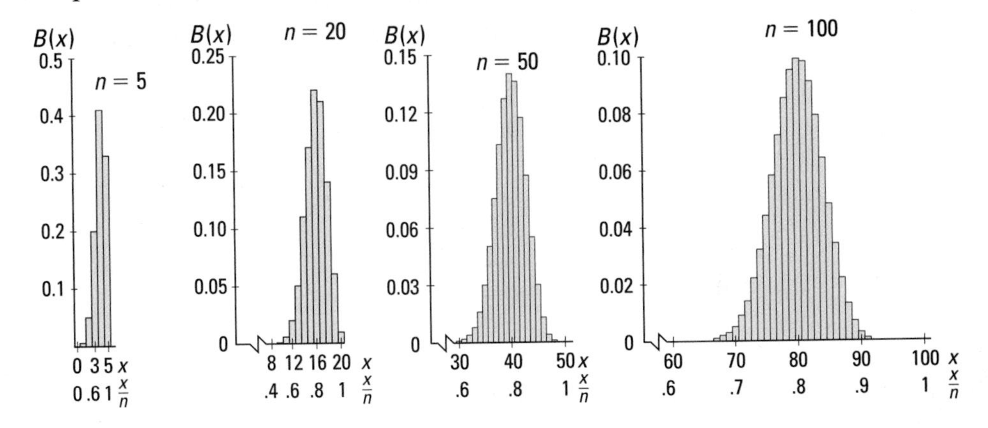

As n increases, the values of the binomial distribution approach those of a continuous function called a *normal distribution.*

The Parent Normal Curve

The graph of a normal distribution is called a **normal curve**. Normal curves were first studied by Gauss and Pierre Simon de Laplace in the early part of the 19th century. The **parent normal curve** is the graph of $f(x) = e^{-x^2}$, which you studied in the preceding In-class Activity.

Many everyday data sets or natural phenomena have approximately normal distributions. For instance, the heights of people from the same population can usually be modeled closely by an image of the parent normal curve under a rubberband transformation. Other data which have approximately normal distributions are the amounts of annual rainfall in a city over a long period of time, and the weights of individual fruits from a particular orchard in a year.

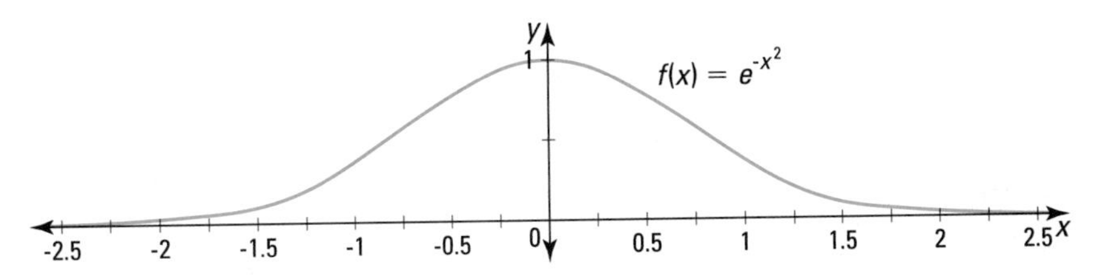

The following are some properties of the function f with $f(x) = e^{-x^2}$.

1. Its domain is the set of real numbers; the range is $\{y: 0 < y \leq 1\}$.
2. The maximum value of the function is 1. This value occurs when $x = 0$.
3. f is an even function, so the y-axis is an axis of symmetry.
4. $\lim_{x \to \infty} f(x) = 0$ and $\lim_{x \to -\infty} f(x) = 0$, so the x-axis is an asymptote of the function.
5. The graph changes concavity when $x = \pm\frac{1}{\sqrt{2}} = \pm\frac{\sqrt{2}}{2}$.

Even though the graph of $f(x) = e^{-x^2}$ never touches the x-axis, it can be shown that the area under the parent of the normal curve is finite. Finding the area exactly requires calculus, but it can be approximated using Monte Carlo methods.

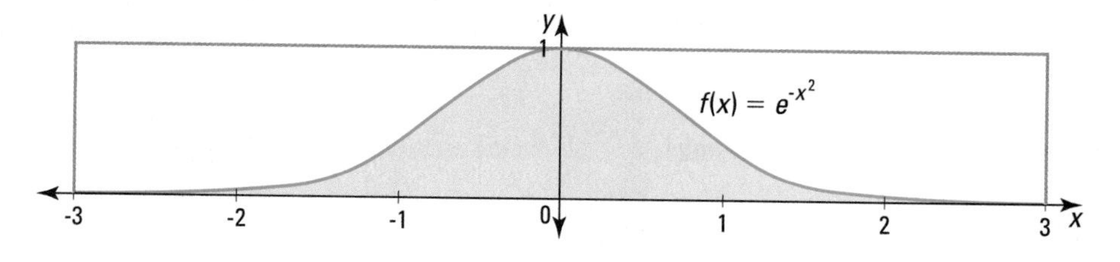

Imagine a rectangle containing the part of $f(x) = e^{-x^2}$ between $x = -3$ and $x = 3$ and between $y = 0$ and $y = 1$, as shown above. Randomly pick n points in the rectangle and count the number m which are under the curve. Then an approximation to the area under the curve is $\frac{m}{n}$ times the area of the rectangle. We used the technique described in Lesson 7-8 ten times, each time picking $n = 3000$ points from the rectangle with $-3 \leq x \leq 3$ and $0 \leq y \leq 1$. The number of points under f generated by a computer in the ten runs were 908, 928, 914, 843, 891, 879, 885, 897, 900, and 842. The mean of these ten numbers is 888.7. So $\frac{m}{n} = \frac{888.7}{3000} \approx 0.296$, giving an area under the curve of about $6 \cdot 0.296 = 1.776$. This value is very close to 1.772, the approximate value for the area under $f(x) = e^{-x^2}$ from $x = -3$ to $x = 3$ that can be found using calculus.

Using calculus, it can be shown that the area between the complete graph of $f(x) = e^{-x^2}$ and the x-axis is $\sqrt{\pi} \approx 1.7725$. Clearly, not much area is added to the region under $f(x) = e^{-x^2}$ when $|x| > 3$. In fact, because $\frac{1.772}{\sqrt{\pi}} \approx 0.9997$, about 99.97% of the area under $f(x) = e^{-x^2}$ is between $x = -3$ and $x = 3$.

The shape rings a bell. *The shape of a bell depends on cultural environment, intended use, and material of construction. Normal curves are shaped somewhat like the Liberty Bell pictured here.*

The Standard Normal Curve

An important offspring of the function $y = e^{-x^2}$ is $y = f(z)$, the bell-shaped curve shown below. This curve has two important properties. The inflection points are when $x = 1$ and $x = -1$. And the area between the curve and the x-axis is 1. Now we find its equation.

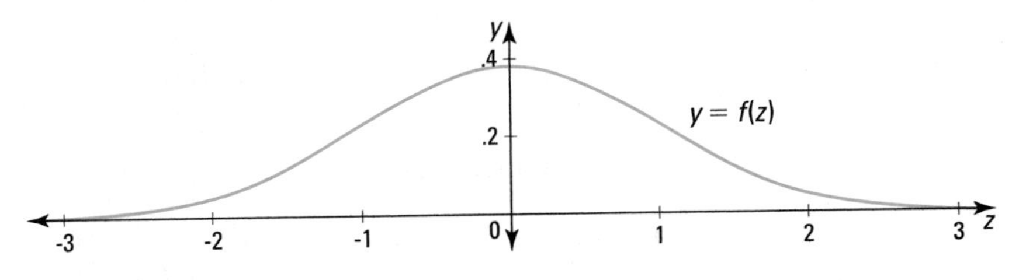

Since the inflection points of $y = e^{-x^2}$ are where $x = \pm\frac{1}{\sqrt{2}}$, to make the points of inflection of the image curve occur at $x = \pm 1$, apply the scale change S_1: $(x, y) \to (\sqrt{2}\,x, y)$. The image is $y = e^{-(x/\sqrt{2})^2}$, which simplifies to $y = e^{-x^2/2}$.

The parent (blue) and image (orange) under S_1 are graphed below. Notice that under the transformation S_1: $(x, y) \to (\sqrt{2}\,x, y)$, the maximum point stays at (0, 1).

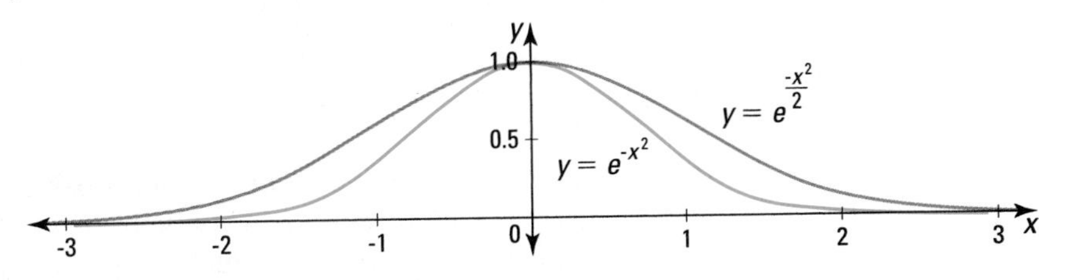

The area between the graph of $y = e^{-x^2}$ and the x-axis is $\sqrt{\pi}$. The scale change S_1 multiplies area by $\sqrt{2}$, so the area between the graph of $y = e^{-x^2/2}$ and the x-axis is $\sqrt{\pi} \cdot \sqrt{2} = \sqrt{2\pi}$. When a second scale change S_2: $(x, y) \to \left(x, \frac{y}{\sqrt{2\pi}}\right)$ is applied to $y = e^{-x^2/2}$, the area under the image is 1.

Specifically, an equation of the image of $y = e^{-x^2/2}$ under S_2 is

$$\sqrt{2\pi}\, y = e^{-x^2/2}.$$

Solving for y gives an equation of this curve.

$$y = \frac{1}{\sqrt{2\pi}} e^{-x^2/2}$$

This graph is known as the **standard normal curve**. It represents a probability distribution called the **standard normal distribution**. It is the most important of all probability distributions.

Shown on page 652 is a graph of the standard normal distribution and its relation to the parent curve. We have labeled the horizontal axis as the z-axis. This is customary for the standard normal curve because of the relation between the standard normal curve and z-scores.

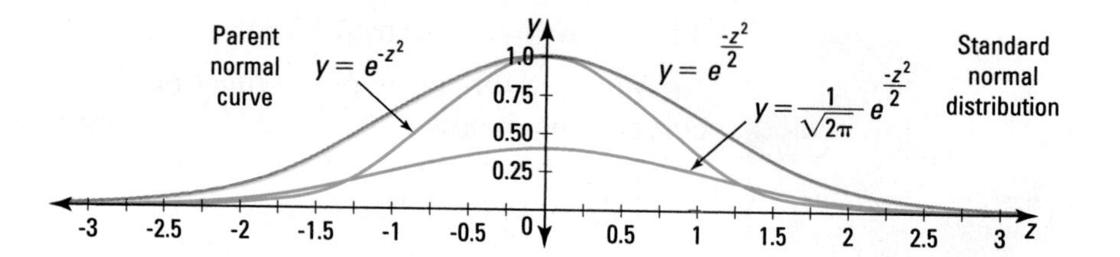

Using z for the horizontal axis, the standard normal distribution has the following properties.

(1) Its domain is the set of all real numbers; its range is $\{y: 0 < y \leq \frac{1}{\sqrt{2\pi}}\}$.

(2) Its maximum value is $f(0) = \frac{1}{\sqrt{2\pi}} \approx 0.3989$.

(3) It is an even function, and so is symmetric to the y-axis.

(4) As $z \to \infty$ or $z \to -\infty$, $f(z) \to 0$; the z-axis is an asymptote of the function.

(5) It is concave down where $-1 < z < 1$, and concave up where $|z| > 1$; its inflection points occur when $z = 1$ or $z = -1$.

(6) The area between the curve and the z-axis is 1.

QUESTIONS

Covering the Reading

1. *True or false.* Given a binomial probability distribution where the probability of success on a single trial is 0.8, then as the number of trials increases, the graph of the distribution approaches a bell-shaped curve.

In 2 and 3, give an equation of the indicated feature of the graph of $y = e^{-x^2}$.

2. line of symmetry

3. asymptote(s)

In 4 and 5, for the graph of $y = e^{-x^2}$, give the coordinates of the indicated points.

4. all inflection points

5. all relative extrema

In 6 and 7, give an equation for the curve.

6. parent normal curve

7. standard normal curve

8. What type of transformation maps the parent normal curve to the standard normal curve?

9. **a.** Use an automatic grapher to graph the parent normal curve and the standard normal curve on the same set of axes.
b. Describe two ways the graphs are alike, and two ways the graphs are different.

In 10 and 11, give an equation of the indicated feature of the standard normal curve.

10. line of symmetry

11. asymptotes

In 12 and 13, for the standard normal curve, give coordinates of the indicated points.

12. all inflection points

13. all relative extrema

Applying the Mathematics

14. The distribution of heights of junior girls is nearly normal. It has been found that the median height of junior girls is 163 cm, and 22% of them have a height greater than 169 cm. Estimate the probability that a randomly chosen junior girl will have height h in cm as follows.

a. $h > 163$ **b.** $h < 169$ **c.** $163 < h < 169$

15. Use a Monte Carlo technique to approximate the area under the standard normal curve from $x = -2$ to $x = 2$.

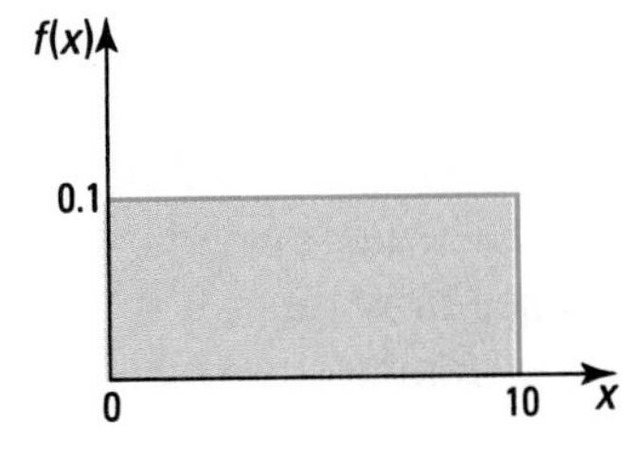

16. The figure at the left represents a uniform (constant) probability distribution in which $f(x) = 0.1$ for $0 \le x \le 10$ and $f(x) = 0$, elsewhere.

a. Suppose a point is selected randomly from the rectangular region. What is the probability that its x-coordinate is between 1.5 and 8.5?

b. If five points are selected randomly from the rectangular region, what is the probability that all five will have x-coordinates between 1.5 and 8.5?

Review

17. A coin is tossed 11 times and 8 tails appear. Is this ample evidence to reject the hypothesis that the coin is fair at the .01 level? *(Lesson 10-3)*

18. A spinner with 5 equal sections lands on the same section 4 times in a row at the beginning of the game. Would you replace the spinner? Why or why not? *(Lesson 10-3)*

19. Express the quotient $\frac{x^5 - 32}{x - 2}$ as a polynomial. *(Lesson 9-4)*

20. Expand $(3x - 5)^4$ using the Binomial Theorem. *(Lesson 8-8)*

21. Consider two events, A and B. *True or false.* Justify your answer.

a. If $P(A) + P(B) = 1$, then A and B must be complementary events.

b. If A and B are complementary events, then $P(A) + P(B) = 1$. *(Lesson 7-2)*

22. A school compares its students' performance on a college-entrance examination to the performance of students in the nation.

a. What is the population?

b. What is the sample? *(Lesson 1-1)*

Exploration

23. Find out some things about the mathematician Pierre Simon de Laplace.

LESSON

10-5

Finding Probabilities Using the Standard Normal Distribution

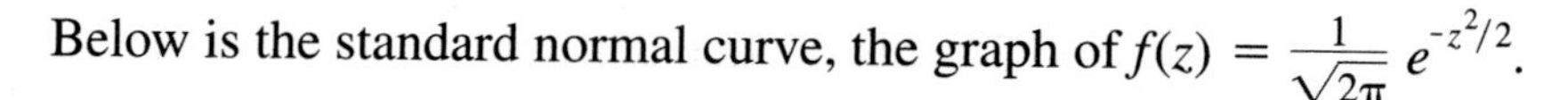

Below is the standard normal curve, the graph of $f(z) = \frac{1}{\sqrt{2\pi}} e^{-z^2/2}$.

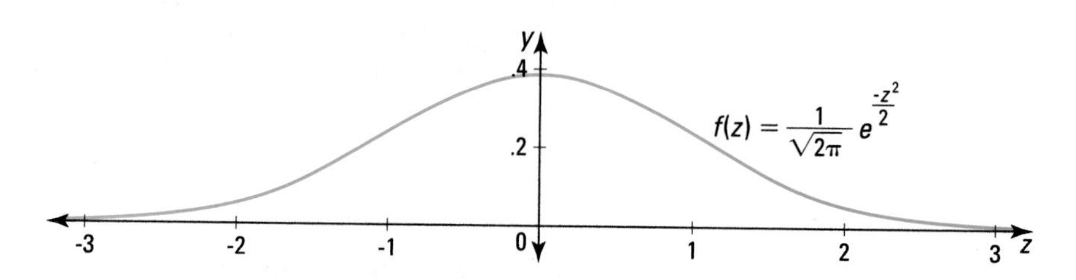

In the last lesson, the standard normal distribution was called the most important probability distribution of all. It is important among all normal distributions because any other normal distribution can be transformed into it by the use of z-scores. In Lesson 10-6, you will see how this transformation is accomplished. Here we work with the standard normal distribution to prepare for that lesson.

This curve can represent a probability distribution because the area between it and the z-axis is 1. It is called the standard normal distribution because its mean and standard deviation are 0 and 1, respectively. Recall from Lesson 3-9 that these are exactly the mean and standard deviation of a set of data that has been transformed into z-scores. *The standard normal probability distribution is a distribution of z-scores.*

From Area to Probability

The calculation of probabilities using the standard normal distribution is different in a major way from the calculation of binomial probabilities. With a binomial distribution, we can calculate the probability that there are 12 heads in 20 tosses of a fair coin. The probability is the area of the histogram bar above 12 in the graph at the right.

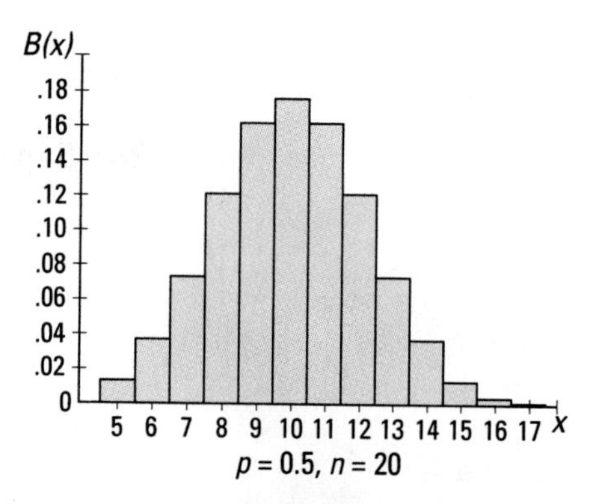

$p = 0.5$, $n = 20$

However, a normal distribution is continuous. The area above 12 in its graph on page 655 is 0. So when we approximate the binomial distribution by a normal distribution, we calculate the probability that there are between 11.5 heads and 12.5 heads (even though exactly 12 heads is the only possibility). The answer is given by the area between the vertical lines for the z-scores corresponding to $x = 11.5$ and $x = 12.5$. That is, using a normal distribution, we can only calculate the probability that x (or its corresponding z-score) lies in a particular interval.

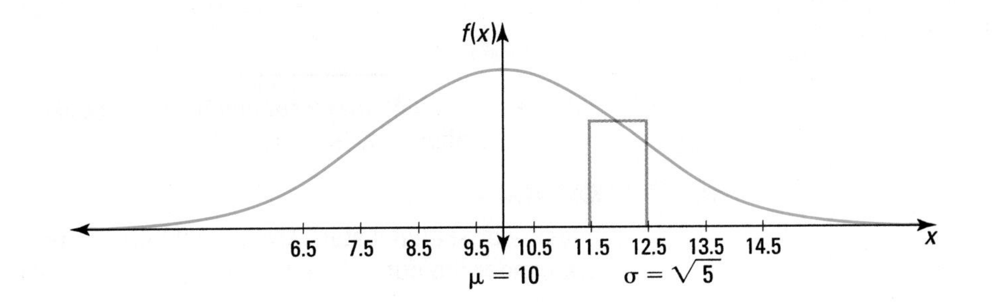

Calculating Specific Probabilities

Consider first the probability that a normally distributed value is less than the mean. That means the corresponding z-score is less than 0. This is represented by the shaded area below. Because of the symmetry of the standard normal curve and the fact that the area between the curve and the z-axis is 1, $P(z < 0) = 0.5$. This is what you would expect. Also $P(z > 0)$ is $1 - 0.5$, which is also 0.5.

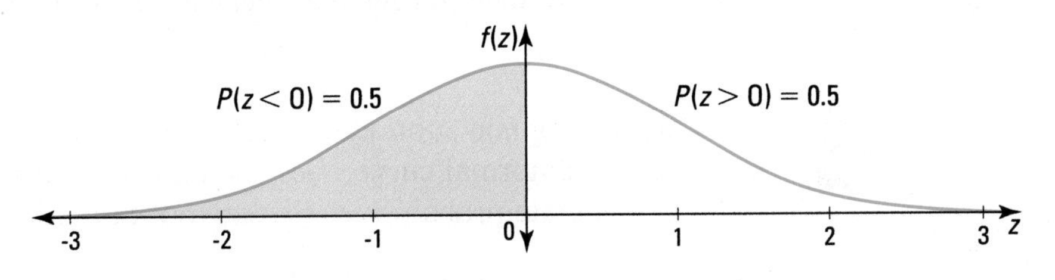

The standard normal distribution is so important that probabilities derived from it have been calculated and recorded in tables. Below is part of the **Standard Normal Distribution Table** given in Appendix D. It gives the area under the standard normal curve to the left of a given positive number a. The table does not give values for $a > 3.09$ because there is very little area under the standard normal curve to the right of $z = 3.09$.

Standard Normal Distribution Table
$P(z < a)$ for $a \geq 0$

a	0	1	2	3	4	5	6	7	8	9
0.0	.5000	.5040	.5080	.5120	.5160	.5199	.5239	.5279	.5319	.5359
⋮										
0.6	.7257	.7291	.7324	.7357	.7389	.7422	.7454	.7486	.7517	.7549
0.7	.7580	.7611	.7642	.7673	.7704	.7734	.7764	.7794	.7823	.7852
0.8	.7881	.7910	.7939	.7967	.7995	.8023	.8051	.8078	.8106	.8133
0.9	.8159	.8186	.8212	.8238	.8264	.8289	.8315	.8340	.8365	.8389
1.0	.8413	.8438	.8461	.8485	.8508	.8531	.8554	.8577	.8599	.8621
⋮										
1.7	.9554	.9564	.9573	.9582	.9591	.9599	.9608	.9616	.9625	.9633
⋮										
2.9	.9981	.9982	.9982	.9983	.9984	.9984	.9985	.9985	.9986	.9986
3.0	.9987	.9987	.9987	.9988	.9988	.9989	.9989	.9989	.9990	.9990

Example 1 considers the probability that a value in a normal distribution is less than 0.85 standard deviations above the mean. Since all values below the mean are included, you should expect a probability greater than 0.5.

Example 1

Find the probability that a randomly chosen observation from a standard normal distribution is less than 0.85.

Solution

Imagine or sketch a standard normal curve. The desired probability is the area under the curve to the left of the line $z = 0.85$.

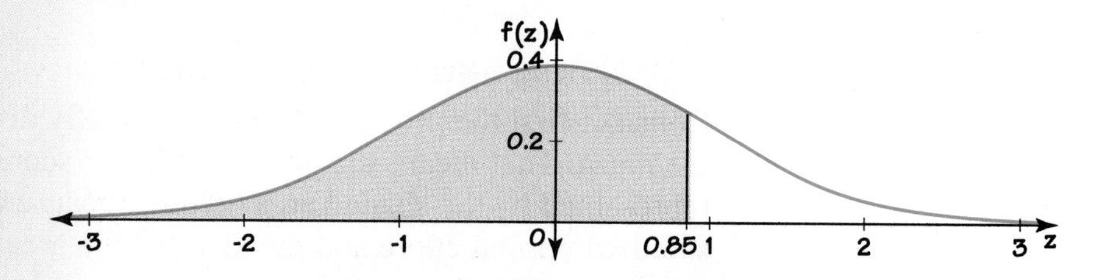

Use the table directly. Read down the *a*-column until you get to 0.8. Go across this row until you get to the column headed by 5. The entry there is .8023. So

$$P(z < 0.85) \approx 0.8023.$$

By adding and subtracting areas and using symmetry properties of the standard normal curve, the Standard Normal Distribution Table can be used to calculate probabilities that are not of the form $P(z < a)$ with $a \geq 0$.

Example 2

Find the probability that a randomly chosen observation from a standard normal distribution is in the given interval.

a. between 0 and 0.85

b. greater than 0.85

c. less than -1.73

d. greater than -1.73

Solution

a. We wish $P(0 < z < 0.85)$. This is the area under the normal curve between $z = 0$ and $z = 0.85$. It can be found by subtracting $P(z \leq 0)$ from $P(z < 0.85)$.

$$P(0 < z < 0.85) = P(z < 0.85) - P(z \leq 0).$$

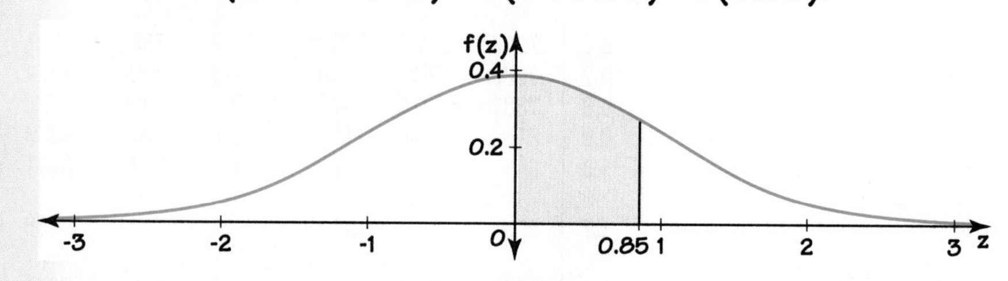

From Example 1, $P(z < 0.85) \approx 0.8023$. From the symmetry of f, $P(z \leq 0) = 0.5$. So

$$P(0 < z < 0.85) \approx 0.8023 - 0.5000 = 0.3023.$$

b. We wish $P(z > 0.85)$. It is the area of the shaded region below.

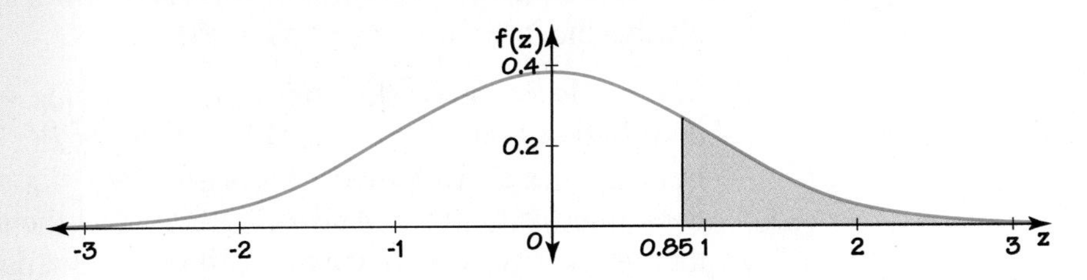

To find the area under the standard normal curve to the *right* of a given value, subtract the area to its *left* from the total area under the curve, which is 1.

$$\begin{aligned} P(z > 0.85) &= 1 - P(z < 0.85) \\ &\approx 1 - 0.8023 \\ &= 0.1977 \end{aligned}$$

c. The table does not show values of $P(z < a)$ when a is negative. To find $P(z < -1.73)$, the user is expected to apply the symmetry of the graph.

$$P(z < -1.73) = P(z > 1.73)$$

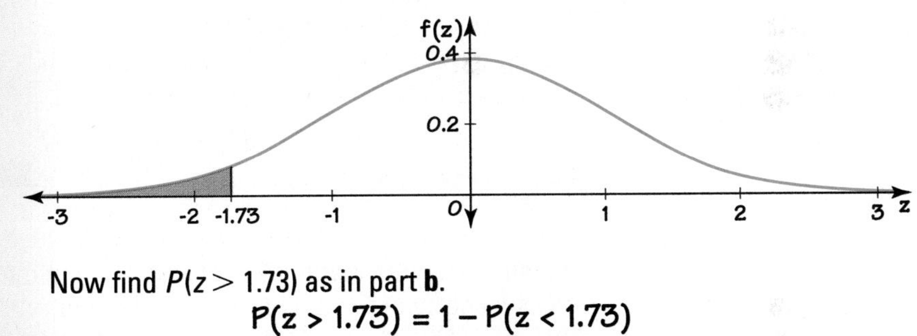

Now find $P(z > 1.73)$ as in part **b**.

$$\begin{aligned} P(z > 1.73) &= 1 - P(z < 1.73) \\ &\approx 1 - .9582 \\ &= 0.0418 \end{aligned}$$

So $\quad P(z < -1.73) \approx 0.0418.$

d. Here we wish to find $P(z > -1.73)$. It is the area of the shaded region below.

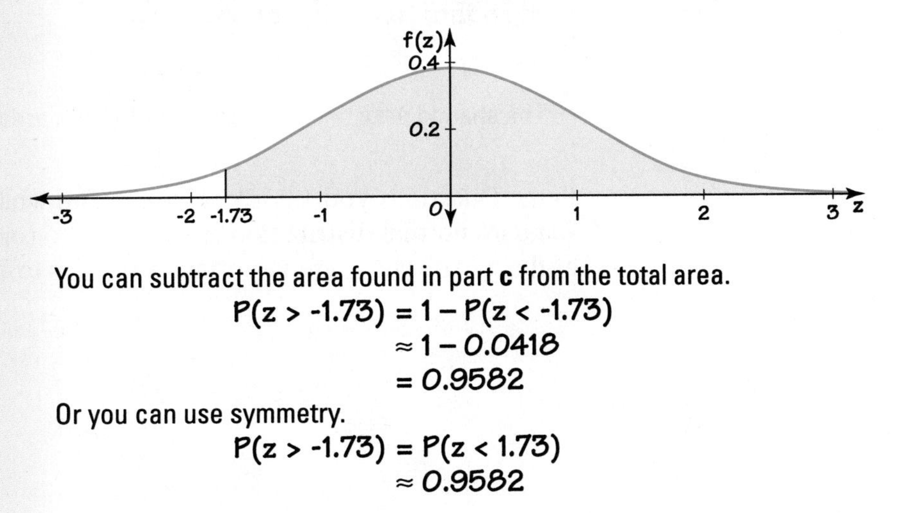

You can subtract the area found in part **c** from the total area.

$$\begin{aligned} P(z > -1.73) &= 1 - P(z < -1.73) \\ &\approx 1 - 0.0418 \\ &= 0.9582 \end{aligned}$$

Or you can use symmetry.

$$\begin{aligned} P(z > -1.73) &= P(z < 1.73) \\ &\approx 0.9582 \end{aligned}$$

Note that the probability for any particular value, such as $P(z = a)$, is zero by the area interpretation. For this reason, if z is normally distributed, it is always the case that $P(z < a) = P(z \leq a)$.

Many calculators or statistics utilities provide values from the normal distribution table. Some provide values for $P(z < a)$ as we do in the table in Appendix D. However, others give $P(0 < z < a)$, that is, the area under the curve from 0 to a. And still others give the area to the right of a. Check that you know how to use the technology available to you.

Example 3 derives another important property of the standard normal distribution.

Example 3

About what percent of the data in a standard normal distribution are within one standard deviation of the mean?

Solution

Sketch the standard normal curve.

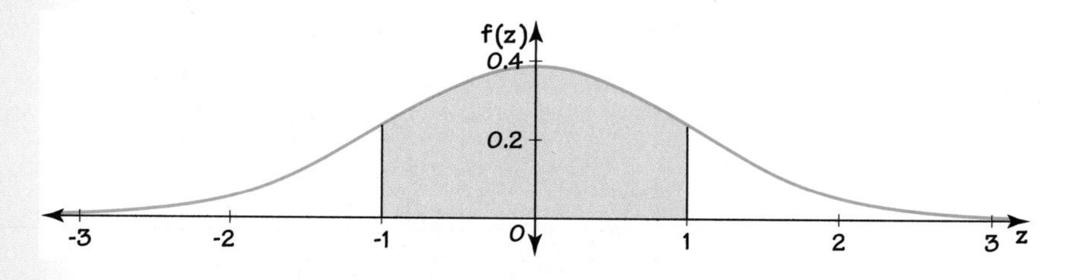

Being within one standard deviation of the mean means that $-1 < z < 1$. From the symmetry of the standard normal curve,

$$\begin{aligned} P(-1 < z < 1) &= 2 \cdot P(0 < z < 1) \\ &= 2(P(z < 1) - P(z < 0)) \\ &\approx 2(0.8413 - 0.5) \\ &= 0.6826. \end{aligned}$$

Thus, about 68% of normally distributed data are within one standard deviation of the mean.

Check

The shaded area seems to be about $\frac{2}{3}$ of the area under the curve.

In the Questions you are asked to estimate what percent of the data in a standard normal distribution are within two (or three) standard deviations of the mean. These are important estimates to know.

QUESTIONS

Covering the Reading

In 1 and 2, use the fact that in a standard normal distribution, $P(z < 1.6) \approx .9452$.

1. The graph below shows a standard normal curve.

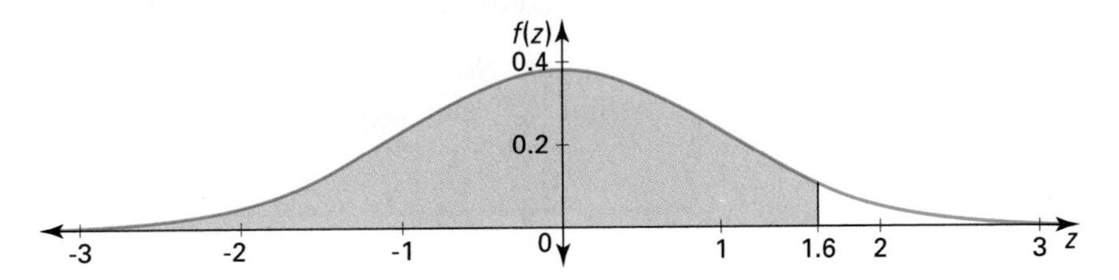

a. What is the area of the shaded region?
b. What is the area of the unshaded region between the curve and the z-axis?

2. Calculate the following probabilities.
a. $P(0 < z < 1.6)$ **b.** $P(|z| < 1.6)$ **c.** $P(z > -1.6)$

In 3–6, evaluate using the Normal Distribution Table in Appendix D.

3. $P(z < 1.88)$

4. $P(z > 0.07)$

5. $P(-1.5 < z < 1.3)$

6. $P(z > -2)$

7. Find the area of the shaded region shown under the standard normal distribution curve below.

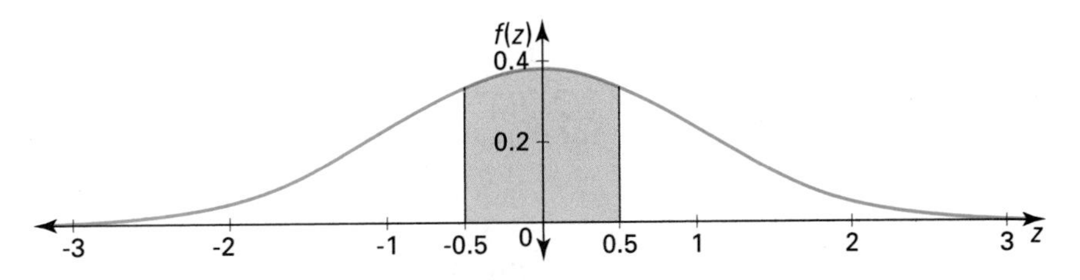

8. State each for the standard normal distribution.
a. the mean **b.** the standard deviation

9. *True or false.* About two-thirds of the observations from a standard normal distribution are within one standard deviation of the mean.

10. Explain why about 95% of the values in the standard normal distribution are within two standard deviations of the mean.

11. About what percent of the data in a standard normal distribution are within three standard deviations of the mean?

12. Give a reason why the Normal Distribution Table does not list probabilities for z larger than 3.09.

Applying the Mathematics

In 13 and 14, find the value of c satisfying the equation.

13. $P(z < c) = 0.975$

14. $P(z \geq c) = 0.4522$

15. Which value of the random variable in a standard normal distribution is exceeded by about 75% of the distribution?

16. Complete: 90% of the observations of a standard normal distribution fall within __?__ standard deviations of the mean.

Review

17. How do the areas under the parent $y = e^{-x^2}$ and the standard normal curve compare? *(Lesson 10-4)*

18. If for some binomial probability distribution $\mu = 20$ and $\sigma = 2.3$, find n and p. *(Lesson 10-2)*

19. Let $f(x) = 2x^2 + 3x + 4$. Evaluate $\frac{f(x) - f(h)}{x - h}$. *(Lesson 9-9)*

In 20 and 21, an equation for a function is given. **a.** Find the exact zeros of the function. **b.** Check your answer by graphing the function and locating zeros correct to the nearest hundredth. *(Lessons 6-4, 9-5)*

20. $s(x) = 3 \ln x - 5$

21. $p(x) = x^3 - 3x^2 + x$

22. A box has length 4 inches, width 3 inches, and height 2 inches. Another box with twice the volume has dimensions $4 + x$, $3 + x$, and $2 + x$ inches. Approximate the value of x to the nearest 0.1 inch. *(Lessons 9-1, 9-2)*

23. In a certain city, 60% of the citizens are in favor of a school bond rate increase. A sample of ten citizens is taken at random. What is the probability that fewer than half of them will be in favor of the increase? *(Lesson 8-9)*

score	percent
750–800	8
700–740	22
650–690	21
600–640	17
550–590	8
500–540	13
450–490	5
400–440	4
350–390	2

24. The table at the left summarizes the SAT-Math scores of a large group of students.

a. Construct a histogram of these data.

b. Find a scale change that can be applied to the histogram in part **a** so that the area of the histogram is 1.

c. If a student is selected at random from this group, what is the probability that the student's SAT-Math score is over 600?

d. Shade the region of the histogram corresponding to part **c**.

(Lessons 1-5, 7-2)

25. Consider $f(x) = -x^2 + 9$.

a. Find an equation for g, the image of f under the transformation $T: x \rightarrow \frac{x-2}{3}$.

b. Predict how the axes of symmetry of $y = f(x)$ and $y = g(x)$ are related.

c. Check your prediction in part **b** by graphing the two functions.
(Lesson 4-9)

26. The number of calories in one ounce of each of five different kinds of cereal is: 145, 90, 110, 110, 100.

a. Find the mean and standard deviation of these data.

b. Let x_i = the number of calories in the ith cereal. Let $z_i = \frac{x_i - m}{s}$, where m is the mean and s the standard deviation found in part **a**. Find the mean and standard deviation of the transformed data. *(Lesson 3-9)*

Exploration

27. a. Examine the differences between successive values in the first row of the Standard Normal Distribution Table. Estimate the following values.

i. $P(z < 0.035)$ **ii.** $P(z < 0.068)$

b. Why are the differences referred to in part **a** almost constant?

c. Why are differences between successive values in other rows of the table not constant?

LESSON

10-6

Other Normal Distributions

Transforming Any Normal Curve into the Standard Normal Curve

Recall that if each number in a data set is translated by a constant, the mean of the distribution is also translated by that constant, but the standard deviation remains unchanged. For instance, consider the fact that the heights of adult men in the United States are approximately normally distributed with a mean of 70 inches and a standard deviation of 3 inches. If $m = 70$ is subtracted from each height, the mean of the resulting distribution is $70 - 70 = 0$. This translation has no effect on the standard deviation of the resulting distribution.

If each translated height is multiplied by $\frac{1}{3}$, the standard deviation of the resulting distribution is $\frac{1}{3} \cdot 3 = 1$. Thus, the rubberband transformation $x \to \frac{x - 70}{3}$ maps the distribution of heights with $m = 70$ and $s = 3$, shown below at the left, onto a distribution with mean 0 and standard deviation 1. With the Graph-Standardization Theorem you can show that this distribution can be transformed into the standard normal curve shown below at the right.

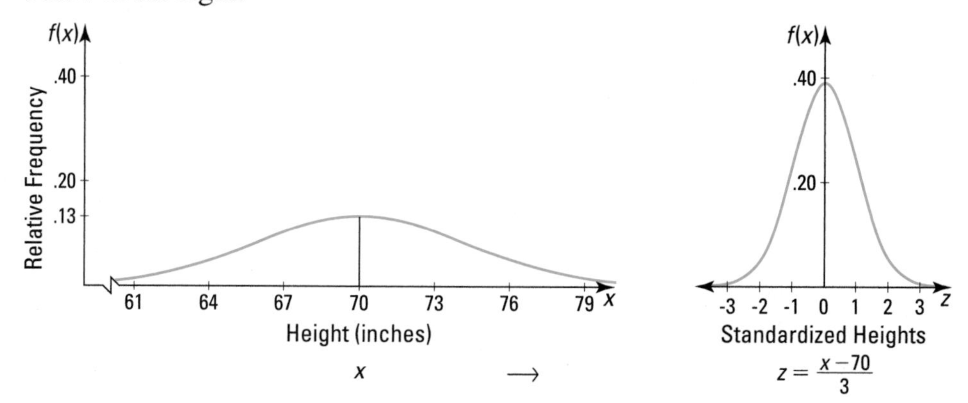

The preceding analysis generalizes to the following theorem.

Theorem
If a variable x has a normal distribution with mean m and standard deviation s, then the transformed variable

$$z = \frac{x - m}{s}$$

has the standard normal distribution.

As is the case with finite data sets, the value of the transformed variable z is called the **standard score** or **z-score** for the value x. The process of getting z-values from an original data set by applying the transformation

$$x \rightarrow \frac{x - m}{s}$$

is often referred to as **standardizing** the variable. By standardizing the values of normal distributions, you can determine many probabilities.

Standardizing Variables to Find Probabilities

Example 1

An adult American male is selected randomly. What is the probability that the man is less than 6 feet tall?

Solution

Because the height x of adult American males has approximately a normal distribution with a mean of 70 inches and standard deviation of 3 inches, the variable $z = \frac{x - 70}{3}$ **has a standard normal distribution.** The z-score associated with $x = 72$ is $z = \frac{72 - 70}{3} = \frac{2}{3} \approx 0.67$. This means that a height of 72 inches is $\frac{2}{3}$ of a standard deviation above the mean of 70 inches. As illustrated by the graphs of the normal distribution and standard normal distribution below, the two shaded areas are equal. Because each area represents a probability, the two probabilities are equal.

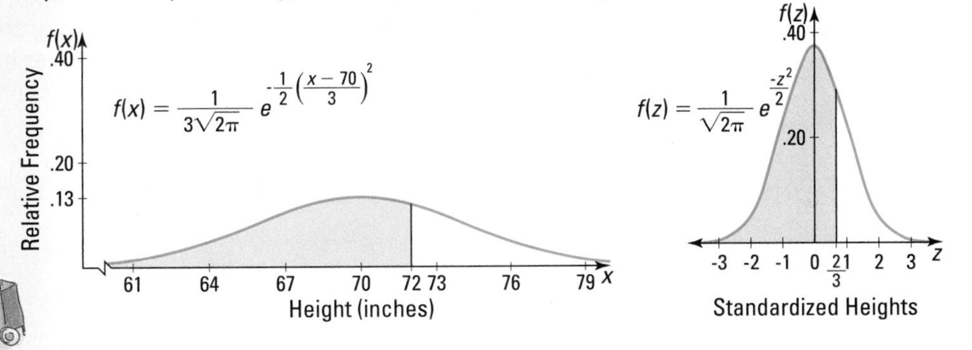

From the table of values for the standard normal distribution,

$$P(x < 72) \approx P(z < 0.67)$$
$$\approx 0.7486.$$

The probability of a randomly selected adult American male being less than 6 feet tall is about 0.75. In other words, about $\frac{3}{4}$ of all adult males in the United States are less than 6 feet tall.

In Example 2, we want the probability that the width of a pencil lead lies in a particular interval.

Example 2

The refills for a particular mechanical pencil are supposed to be 0.5 mm in diameter. Refills of 0.485 mm or less in diameter do not stay in the pencil, while those of 0.520 mm or more do not fit in the pencil at all. If a firm makes refills with diameters whose differences from the correct size are normally distributed with a standard deviation of .01 mm, find the probability that a randomly chosen refill will fit.

Solution

Let x = the diameter of the refill in mm. The task is to find $P(0.485 < x < 0.520)$, where x is normally distributed with $m = 0.5$ and $s = 0.01$. Change to standard scores using

$$z = \frac{x - 0.5}{0.01}.$$

The z-score z_1 associated with $x = 0.485$ is

$$z_1 = \frac{0.485 - 0.5}{0.01} = -1.5.$$

The z-score z_2 associated with $x = 0.520$ is

$$z_2 = \frac{0.520 - 0.5}{0.01} = 2.$$

According to the preceding theorem, z_1 and z_2 are on the standard normal distribution. Thus, the probability of a diameter between 0.485 mm and 0.52 mm equals the probability of having a z-score between $z_1 = -1.5$ and $z_2 = 2$.

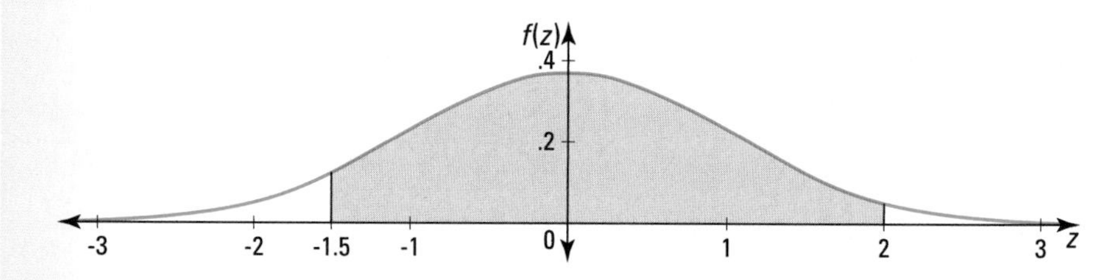

Use the table of values for the standard normal distribution.

$$\begin{aligned} P(0.485 < x < 0.520) = P(-1.5 < z < 2.0) &= P(z < 2.0) - P(z < -1.5) \\ &= P(z < 2.0) - (1 - P(z < 1.5)) \\ &\approx 0.9772 - (1 - 0.9332) \\ &= 0.9104 \end{aligned}$$

The probability that a refill will fit is about 0.91. That is, about 91% of the refills will fit the pencil, 9% will not.

The answer to Example 2 is too far from 100%; the manufacturer should probably adjust the machinery and the procedures used in order to get more accurate thicknesses.

Approximating a Binomial Distribution with a Normal Distribution

The normal distribution is related to many other probability distributions. In particular, as you have seen earlier in this chapter, some binomial distributions are approximately bell-shaped.

For instance, the binomial probability distribution B with $n = 100$ and $p = 0.2$ has mean $\mu = 100(0.2) = 20$ and standard deviation $\sigma = \sqrt{npq} = \sqrt{100(0.2)(0.8)} = \sqrt{16} = 4$. Below is the probability histogram for this binomial distribution with the curve for the normal distribution with mean 20 and standard deviation 4 superimposed.

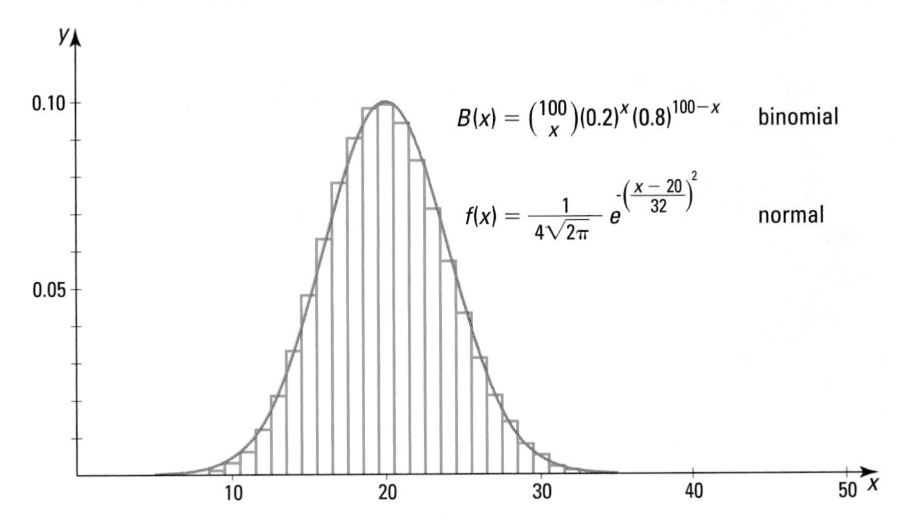

For these values of n and p, the normal distribution appears to approximate the binomial distribution quite well.

In general, if n is quite large, or when p is close to 0.5, a normal curve approximates a binomial distribution quite well. If n is small and p is near 0 or 1, the binomial distribution is not well approximated by a normal distribution. With $q = 1 - p$, a rule of thumb is that a binomial distribution can be approximated by a normal distribution with mean np and standard deviation $\sqrt{npq}$ provided np and nq are each ≥ 5.

The graphs of binomial distributions in Lessons 10-1 and 10-2 provide evidence for this approximation. Example 3 shows how to apply it.

O'Hare International Airport, Chicago

Example 3

In the past, about 85% of ticketed passengers have shown up for the regularly scheduled Chicago-New York flights with a capacity of 240. The airline company proposes to accept 270 reservations. What is the probability that with this policy, the Chicago-New York flight will be overbooked?

Solution

Because each passenger either arrives or doesn't arrive, and all passengers are assumed to act independently, the number of passengers arriving is binomially distributed. The distribution has $n = 270$, $p = 0.85$, and $q = 0.15$. Because each of $np = 229.5$ and $nq = 40.5$ is greater than 5, the normal approximation to the binomial distribution can be used. The appropriate normal distribution has mean $np = 229.5$ and standard deviation $\sqrt{npq} \approx 5.87$. The flight is overbooked when the number n of passengers is greater than 240. The binomial distribution interval is (239.5, 240.5). Since the number of passengers cannot exceed 240, you should calculate $p(n > 240.5)$, which is represented by the area shaded below.

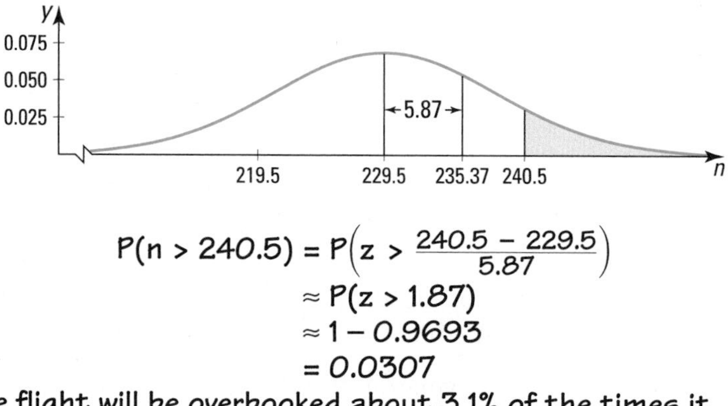

$$P(n > 240.5) = P\left(z > \frac{240.5 - 229.5}{5.87}\right)$$
$$\approx P(z > 1.87)$$
$$\approx 1 - 0.9693$$
$$= 0.0307$$

So the flight will be overbooked about 3.1% of the times it departs. If the flight operates once a day except on Sundays, company officials should expect it to be overbooked about once a month.

Note how much simpler the calculation is for the normal approximation than is the calculation for the exact answer using the binomial distribution. The exact answer would require calculating a sum of 30 terms:

$$_{270}C_{241}(.85)^{241}(.15)^{29} + {}_{270}C_{242}(.85)^{242}(.15)^{28} + \ldots + {}_{270}C_{270}(.85)^{270}(.15)^{0}.$$

As a final example, we return to the situation of testing whether a coin is fair or not. Notice how the use of the normal approximation to the binomial allows us to deal with the large numbers that are more realistic in real tests.

Example 4

A coin is tossed 1000 times and 530 heads result. Using the .01 significance level, test the hypothesis that the coin is fair.

Solution

The number of heads is binomially distributed. Assuming the coin is fair, $p = 0.5$, and in this case $n = 1000$. So the binomial distribution and the approximating normal distribution have mean $np = 500$ and standard deviation

$$\sqrt{npq} = \sqrt{1000 \cdot 0.5 \cdot 0.5} = \sqrt{250} \approx 15.81.$$

The z-score equivalent of 530 is thus $\frac{530 - 500}{15.81}$, which is about 1.898. (That is, 530 is about 1.898 standard deviations away from the mean.) Consequently, you must find the probability of an outcome at least as far from the mean as 530. That is, find $P(z \geq 1.898 \text{ or } z < -1.898)$. To use the Standard Normal Distribution Table, you must round these values to the nearest hundredth, to 1.90 and -1.90.

The table indicates that $P(z < 1.90) \approx 0.9713.$

So $P(z \geq 1.90) \approx 1 - 0.9713 = 0.0287.$

Thus $P(z \geq 1.898 \text{ or } z < -1.898) \approx 2(.0287) = 0.0574.$

This probability is higher than 0.01, so the hypothesis cannot be rejected. Even a fair coin would result in 530 or more heads or 530 or more tails in 1000 tosses over 5% of the time.

QUESTIONS

Covering the Reading

In 1–4, use the fact that the heights of adult men in the United States are normally distributed with mean 70" and standard deviation 3".

1. Suppose a variable x is normally distributed with mean 70 and standard deviation 3. If the transformation $x \rightarrow \frac{x - 70}{3}$ is applied to each data point, what type of distribution results?

2. What is the median height?

3. What proportion of men are less than five feet, nine inches tall?

4. How many of a group of 1200 male employees of a company can the basketball coach of the company team expect to be taller than six feet, six inches?

5. Refer to the distribution of mechanical pencil refill sizes in Example 2.
   a. What is the probability a randomly chosen refill will be too large?
   b. What is the probability a randomly chosen refill will be too small?

6. Under what conditions may a binomial distribution be approximated by a normal distribution?

7. Refer to Example 3. Find the probability that the flight will be overbooked if 280 bookings are accepted.

8. A binomial distribution with $p = 0.15$ and $n = 80$ can be approximated by the normal distribution with mean __a.__ and standard deviation __b.__.

9. A coin is tossed 500 times, resulting in 273 heads and 227 tails. Test the hypothesis that the coin is fair using each significance level.
   a. .05 **b.** .01 **c.** .001

10. State one advantage of using a normal approximation for a binomial distribution.

Applying the Mathematics

11. Suppose that the lifetime t of a flashlight battery is normally distributed with mean 100 hours and standard deviation 4 hours.
    a. Identify a transformation that can be used to transform t to z, the argument in the standard normal distribution.
    b. What are the mean and standard deviation of the distribution of z-scores?

In 12 and 13, assume that the time for a certain surgical incision to heal is normally distributed with a mean of 150 hours and a standard deviation of 20 hours.

12. What proportion of incisions should heal within a week?

13. If a patient must stay in the hospital until his or her wound heals, what is the probability that a randomly chosen patient will stay ten days or more?

14. In 1996, the scaled scores on the SAT verbal section had mean 505 and standard deviation 110. Assume that the scaled scores are normally distributed. What is the probability that a randomly selected student in 1996 had an SAT verbal score between 500 and 600?

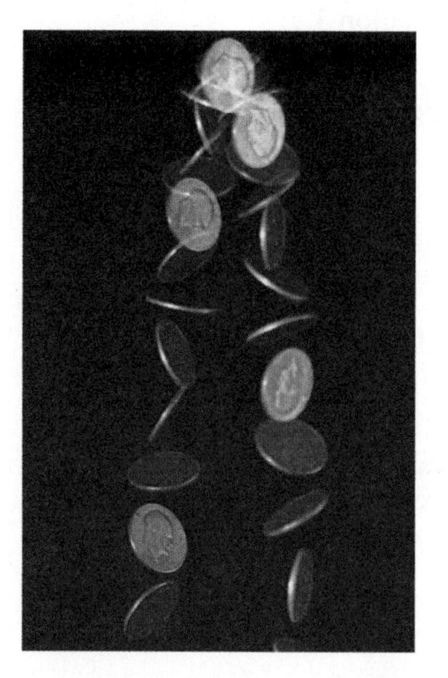

15. Officials in Lawrence, Pennsylvania, needed to select a bank that would lend the town $450,000 at the lowest rate. When they opened the sealed bids from the banks, they found that National City Bank and National Bank of the Commonwealth had submitted identical bids. They decided the bid by a coin toss. Suppose that you were entrusted with the job of ensuring that the coin used was a fair coin.
    a. How many times would you flip the coin to test it?
    b. What significance level would you use?
    c. For your number of tosses, how many heads could appear and still not cause you to think the coin was unfair?

Review

In 16 and 17, suppose the variable z has a standard normal distribution.

16. Find the area of the shaded region below.

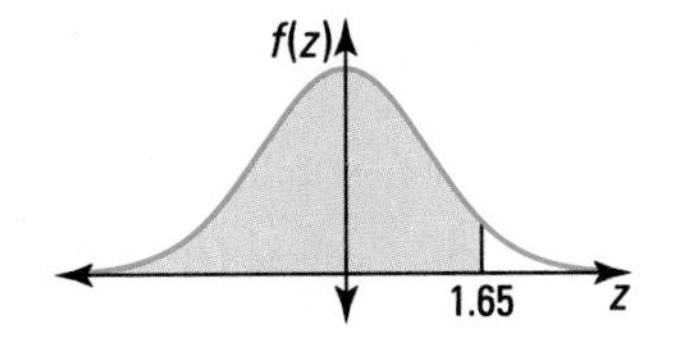

17. Determine $P(z \geq 2.67)$. *(Lesson 10-5)*

18. Complete: In a standard normal distribution 99% of the observations are within _?_ standard deviations of the mean. *(Lesson 10-5)*

19. How many ways are there of selecting a committee of five faculty and two students from a group of 20 faculty and 300 students? *(Lesson 8-6)*

In 20 and 21, suppose that a system on a spacecraft is composed of three independent subsystems, X, Y, and Z. The probability that these will fail during a mission is 0.002, 0.006, and 0.003, respectively. *(Lessons 7-2, 7-3, 7-4)*

20. If the three are connected in series, as below, a failure in any one of the three will lead to a failure in the whole system.

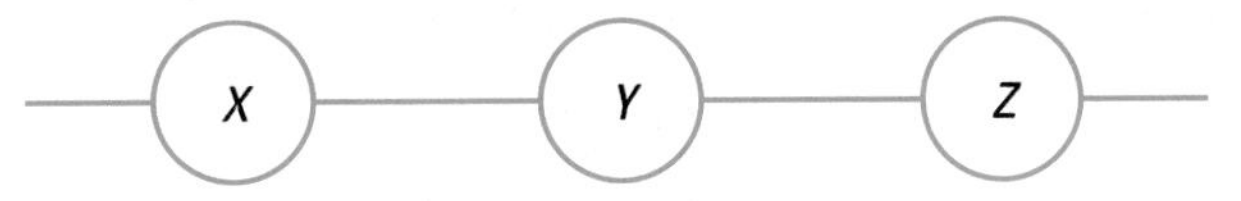

What is the probability that the system will be reliable—that is, it will *not* fail?

21. Suppose the subsystems are connected as shown at the right. In this case, both X and either Y or Z must be reliable for the whole system to be reliable. What is the probability that this whole system will not fail?

22. Consider the set {0, 1, 2, 3, 4, 5, 6, 7, 8, 9}.
a. Find the mean of the numbers in the set.
b. Find the standard deviation of the numbers in the set. *(Lessons 1-3, 1-7)*

Exploration

23. Some books give the following rule of thumb for finding the standard deviation of a normally distributed variable:

$$s \approx \frac{\text{range}}{6}.$$

Explain why this rule of thumb works.

Introducing Lesson 10-7

The Sampling Distribution of the Mean

You will need something to generate random digits—a calculator or a table of random digits. Work with a partner.

To understand how measures of a sample are related to the corresponding measures of the population from which it was taken, it is helpful to study how various samples drawn from the same population vary. In this activity, you will investigate how random samples from a uniform distribution vary.

1 Consider the uniform distribution of random digits from 0 through 9. A histogram of this probability distribution is shown at the right. Use the formulas from Lesson 10-2 to determine the mean and standard deviation of this distribution.

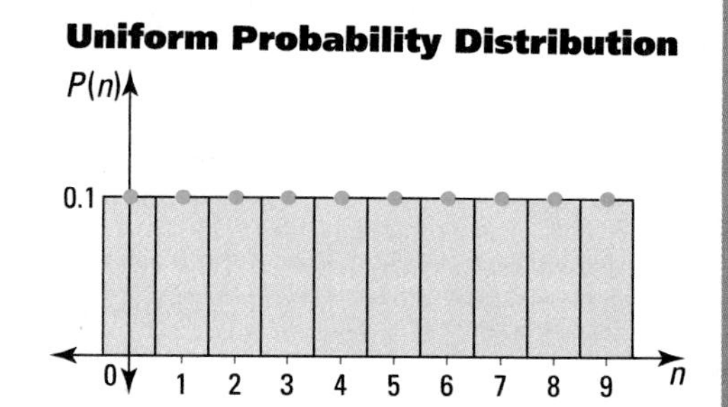

2 **a.** Design a simulation to choose a random sample of size four from the uniform distribution of digits from 0 to 9. Run the simulation and calculate the mean of the four numbers that occur.
b. Run the simulation in part **a** 24 more times. After each run, record the mean of the sample of size four.
c. Draw a histogram to illustrate the distribution of your 25 sample means.
d. Calculate the mean and standard deviation of the distribution of sample means in part **c**.

3 **a.** Choose a random sample of size 15 from the uniform distribution of digits from 0 to 9. Run the simulation and calculate the mean of the 15 numbers.
b. Repeat part **a** 4 more times.
c. Combine your data from part **b** with that of four other people to obtain 25 sample means.
d. Calculate the mean and standard deviation of the distribution in part **c**.

4 Make a conjecture about the mean and standard deviation of the distribution of sample means, if 1000 random samples, each of size four, were taken from the uniform distribution of digits from 0 to 9.

LESSON

10-7

Sampling Distributions and the Central Limit Theorem

As you know, it is often too costly, too difficult, or impossible to study an entire population. Usually a sample is taken. Then inferences about the population are made from the sample data. However, even if a random sample is taken, the characteristics of the sample are not likely to be identical to the corresponding characteristics of the population. For instance, the means of various samples from the same population are likely to differ somewhat from each other, and from the population mean.

What Is a Sampling Distribution?

In the preceding In-class Activity, three types of means were calculated—the mean of the probability distribution, the means of individual samples, and the mean of a set of sample means. We will assume that the digits you generated from a table or calculator are indeed random. With this assumption, the statistics of the population (all possible random digits that could be generated) are the same as the statistics for the model (the uniform distribution). It is customary to use $\bar{x}$ to stand for the mean of a sample, and μ to indicate the population mean. We shall use $\mu_{\bar{x}}$ to stand for the mean of a set of sample means. Similarly, we use s for the sample standard deviation, σ for the population standard deviation, and $\sigma_{\bar{x}}$ for the standard deviation of the set of sample means.

Activity 1

Refer to your data from the preceding In-class Activity.

a. What are the values of μ and σ for the population studied?
b. What is the first value of $\bar{x}$ you calculated?
c. For the means of the samples of size 4, give the values for $\mu_{\bar{x}}$ and $\sigma_{\bar{x}}$.
d. For the means of the samples of size 15, give the values of $\mu_{\bar{x}}$ and $\sigma_{\bar{x}}$.

When the samples are all the same size, as they were in the In-class Activity, a distribution of their means is called a **sample distribution** or a **sampling distribution**. Note that although the distribution of the original population (the digits) used in the In-class Activity is a uniform distribution, the distribution of sample means is not. However, you should have found that the mean of the distribution of sample means is almost equal to the population mean.

You should have also found that the standard deviation of the distribution of sample means is much less than the standard deviation σ of the population. That is, averages are less variable than individual observations.

Finally, you may have noted that as the number of samples increases, say from 25 to 1000, that the distribution of $\bar{x}$, the sampling distribution, becomes nearly bell-shaped.

We did this experiment, taking 1000 random samples of size four from the digits from 0 to 9. Pictured below is the sampling distribution, that is, the distribution of sample means. Note that this sampling distribution is clearly not uniform. It can be modeled by a normal distribution with mean 4.5.

Sampling Distribution of $\overline{x}$ from a Uniform Distribution Based on 1000 Samples Each of Size 4

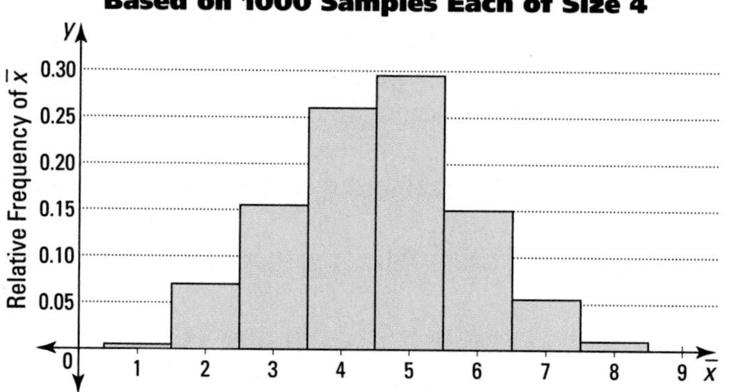

Is This Batch Tasty? *A sample of size 30, as shown here, is about the smallest size for which means are normally distributed.*

The Effect of Sample Size on the Sampling Distribution

The work with samples drawn from a uniform distribution can be generalized to populations with other distributions. If a large number of random samples of sufficient and equal size are drawn from *any* population, the distribution of sample means approaches a normal distribution, and the mean $\mu_{\overline{x}}$ of the sample means approaches the mean μ of the population.

As the size n of the individual samples increases, another pattern emerges.

Example 1

Simulate drawing the following samples from the uniform distribution of digits from 0 to 9. Find the mean of each sample, and the mean and standard deviation of each distribution of sample means.

a. 1000 samples of size 15 **b.** 1000 samples of size 100

Solution

Simulations of this size are best done by computer or calculator, not by using a table of random digits. Below is output we obtained from a statistics utility.

a. 1000 sample means, each the mean of a sample of 15 random digits, gave $\mu_{\overline{x}} = 4.494$ and $\sigma_{\overline{x}} = 0.758$.

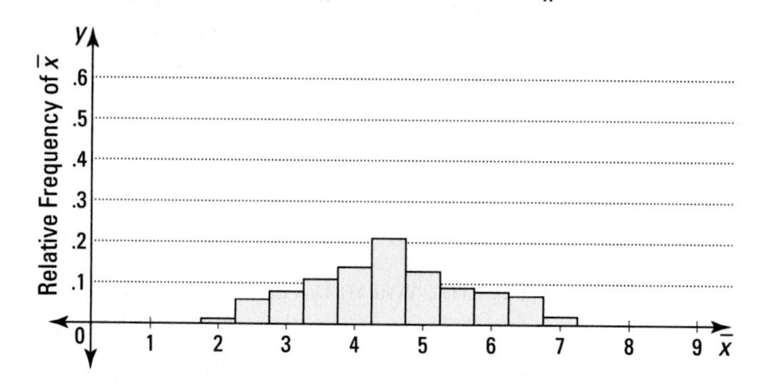

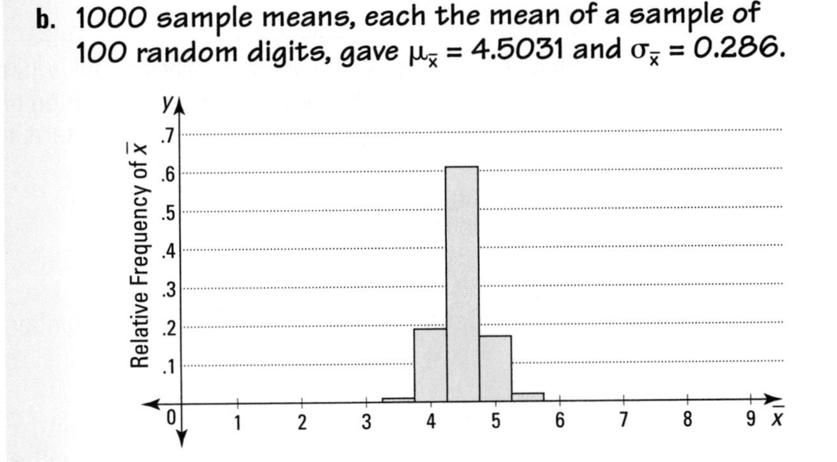

Note that as the size of the sample n increases, the mean $\mu_{\bar{x}}$ of the sampling distribution does not vary very much, but the standard deviation $\sigma_{\bar{x}}$ decreases. Surprisingly, the relations between the sample size n, the means of the population and of the sampling distribution, and the standard deviations of the population and the sampling distribution are quite simple. They were first proved by Pierre Simon Laplace (1749–1827), and are summarized in the *Central Limit Theorem*. The proof of this theorem is well beyond the scope of this course.

The Central Limit Theorem (CLT)
Suppose random samples of size n are selected from a population with mean μ and standard deviation σ. Then, as n increases, the following occur.

1. The mean $\mu_{\bar{x}}$ of the distribution of sample means approaches μ.
2. The standard deviation $\sigma_{\bar{x}}$ of the distribution of sample means approaches $\frac{\sigma}{\sqrt{n}}$.
3. The distribution of sample means approaches a normal distribution with mean μ and standard deviation $\frac{\sigma}{\sqrt{n}}$.

Activity 2

In the In-class Activity, you used samples of size $n = 4$. For the population consisting of the digits from 0 to 9, calculate the value of $\frac{\sigma}{\sqrt{n}}$. This should be approximately equal to the value you found for $\sigma_{\bar{x}}$ in Activity 1.

Making Inferences Using the Central Limit Theorem

The Central Limit Theorem allows you to make predictions about samples if characteristics of the population are known.

Example 2

In a certain country, the mean family income (when converted to U.S. dollars) is known to be $13,500 with a standard deviation of $2000. Suppose random samples of 100 families are to be chosen. Determine each of the following.

a. the mean of $\overline{x}$

b. the standard deviation of $\overline{x}$

c. the distribution of $\overline{x}$

Solution

Use the Central Limit Theorem. For a large number of samples,

a. $\mu_{\overline{x}} \approx \mu = \$13{,}500;$

b. $\sigma_{\overline{x}} \approx \frac{\sigma}{\sqrt{n}} = \frac{\$2000}{\sqrt{100}} = \frac{\$2000}{10} = 200;$

c. The distribution of sample means will approach a normal distribution with mean $13,500 and standard deviation $200.

The Central Limit Theorem is *central* because it deals with a mean of a population, a measure of its *center*. It is a *limit* theorem because it deals with what can be expected as samples of larger and larger size are involved.

Note that the Central Limit Theorem states that even if the underlying population distribution is not normal, the means of samples of sufficient size will be normally distributed. However, the Central Limit Theorem does not specify exactly what that sufficient size is. Fortunately, a corollary to the Central Limit Theorem provides a rule of thumb for determining how large the samples should be so that the distribution of sample means is close enough to normal. The proof of this corollary is also beyond the scope of this course.

Corollary

Consider a population with mean μ and standard deviation σ from which random samples of size n are taken. Then the distribution of sample means is approximately normal with mean $\mu_{\overline{x}} \approx \mu$ and standard deviation $\sigma_{\overline{x}}$ approximately equal to $\frac{\sigma}{\sqrt{n}}$ whenever one of the following occurs:

a. the population itself is normally distributed, or

b. the sample size $n \geq 30$.

Calculating Probabilities Using the Central Limit Theorem

The Central Limit Theorem and its corollary allow you to test hypotheses about the sample means for "large" samples, whether or not the population is normal.

Example 3

A manufacturer of copy machines claims that the relative frequency distribution of x, the amount of time needed by a technician to perform routine maintenance on a copy machine, is modeled by the distribution graphed at the right, with $\mu = 1$ hour and $\sigma = 1$ hour. A local supplier finds that the average maintenance time for a random sample of 50 machines is 75 minutes, and believes that the manufacturer is underestimating the maintenance time for the machines. Test the manufacturer's hypothesis at the 0.01 level.

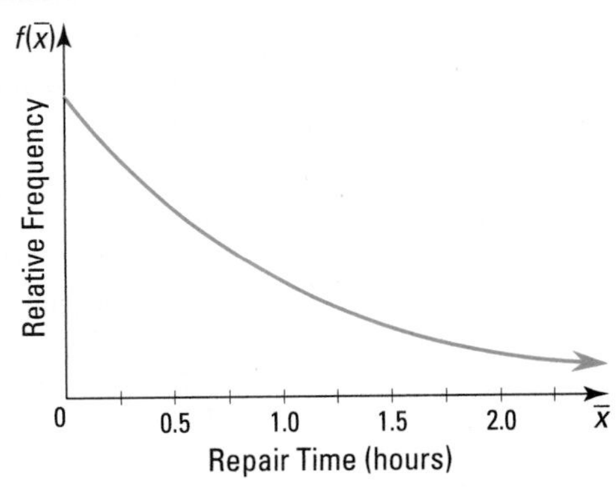

Solution

First, state the hypothesis to be tested. **The null hypothesis H_0 is: The mean maintenance time for this brand of copy machine is 1 hour.** Now, using the manufacturer's model, compute the probability that the average maintenance time for a sample of 50 machines is greater than 75 minutes. Since the sample size $n \geq 30$, **use the Central Limit Theorem and its corollary on the manufacturer's model. They imply that $\bar{x}$, the mean maintenance time for a sample of 50 machines, is approximately normally distributed, with mean $\mu_{\bar{x}} \approx \mu = 1$ hour and standard deviation $\sigma_{\bar{x}} \approx \frac{\sigma}{\sqrt{50}} = \frac{1}{\sqrt{50}} \approx 0.14$ hours. Thus, the variable $z = \frac{\bar{x} - 1}{0.14}$ has a standard normal distribution.** Because 75 minutes is 1.25 hours, the probability that the average maintenance time is greater than 75 minutes is

$$P(\bar{x} > 1.25) \approx P\left(\frac{\bar{x} - 1}{0.14} > \frac{1.25 - 1}{0.14}\right)$$
$$\approx P(z > 1.79).$$
$$P(z > 1.79) = 1 - P(z < 1.79)$$
$$\approx 0.0367$$

Thus, assuming the manufacturer's model, in 3.67% of all samples of 50 machines, the mean maintenance time would be greater than 75 minutes. Because 0.0367 is not less than 0.01, the null hypothesis cannot be rejected. The supplier is not justified in claiming that the manufacturer is underestimating the maintenance time for the machines.

Check

The standard deviation $\sigma_{\bar{x}}$ is about 0.14 hours, or 8.4 minutes. The local supplier's mean was 75 minutes. So the supplier's mean was within 2 standard deviations of the manufacturer's claim. In a standard normal distribution about 95% of the area under the curve is within 2 standard deviations of the mean 0. Thus it seems reasonable that over 2.5% of the time this could happen.

Notice that in Examples 2 and 3 the mean μ and standard deviation σ of the population were known, and from them questions about the sample mean $\bar{x}$ and its probability distribution were answered. In Lesson 10-8 we consider the converse problem, that of predicting population statistics μ and σ when the sample statistics $\bar{x}$ and s are known.

QUESTIONS

Covering the Reading

1. Explain the difference between a sample and a sampling distribution.

2. Write your answers to Activity 1. **3.** Write your answer to Activity 2.

In 4 and 5, consider the uniform distribution of integers from 0 to 9. Suppose two simulations A and B are conducted where A has 100 random samples each of size 50, and B has 10 random samples each of size 500.

4. *True or false.* The means of the sample means from the two experiments will be approximately equal.

5. Which experiment is likely to yield the sampling distribution with the larger standard deviation?

In 6–8, consider a population from which a very large number of random samples of equal size are taken. *True or false.*

6. The mean of the sample means approximates the population mean.

7. The standard deviation of the sample means approximates the standard deviation of the population.

8. The shape of the distribution of the sample means approximates the shape of the population.

9. To what populations does the Central Limit Theorem apply?

10. To what kinds of samples do the Central Limit Theorem and its corollary apply?

11. The distribution of heights of young adult women in the United States can be modeled by a normal distribution with $\mu = 63.7$ inches and $\sigma = 2.6$ inches. A medical study is conducted in which women are randomly selected from this population in sample sizes of 100 and the mean height of the women in each sample is recorded.
a. Estimate the mean and standard deviation of the numbers recorded.
b. Describe the distribution of sample means.

In 12 and 13, refer to Example 3. Assume the manufacturer's claim is correct.

12. Consider the distribution of the average amount of time needed by a technician to perform maintenance on a random sample of 50 copy machines.
a. Give the mean.
b. Give the standard deviation.
c. Describe the distribution.

13. Suppose another supplier maintains a random sample of 100 such machines. Find the probability that the average maintenance time for these machines exceeds 45 minutes.

Applying the Mathematics

In 14 and 15, use the graphs below, showing the relative frequency distributions of 100 sample means from the same population. The scales on the y-axes are not the same.

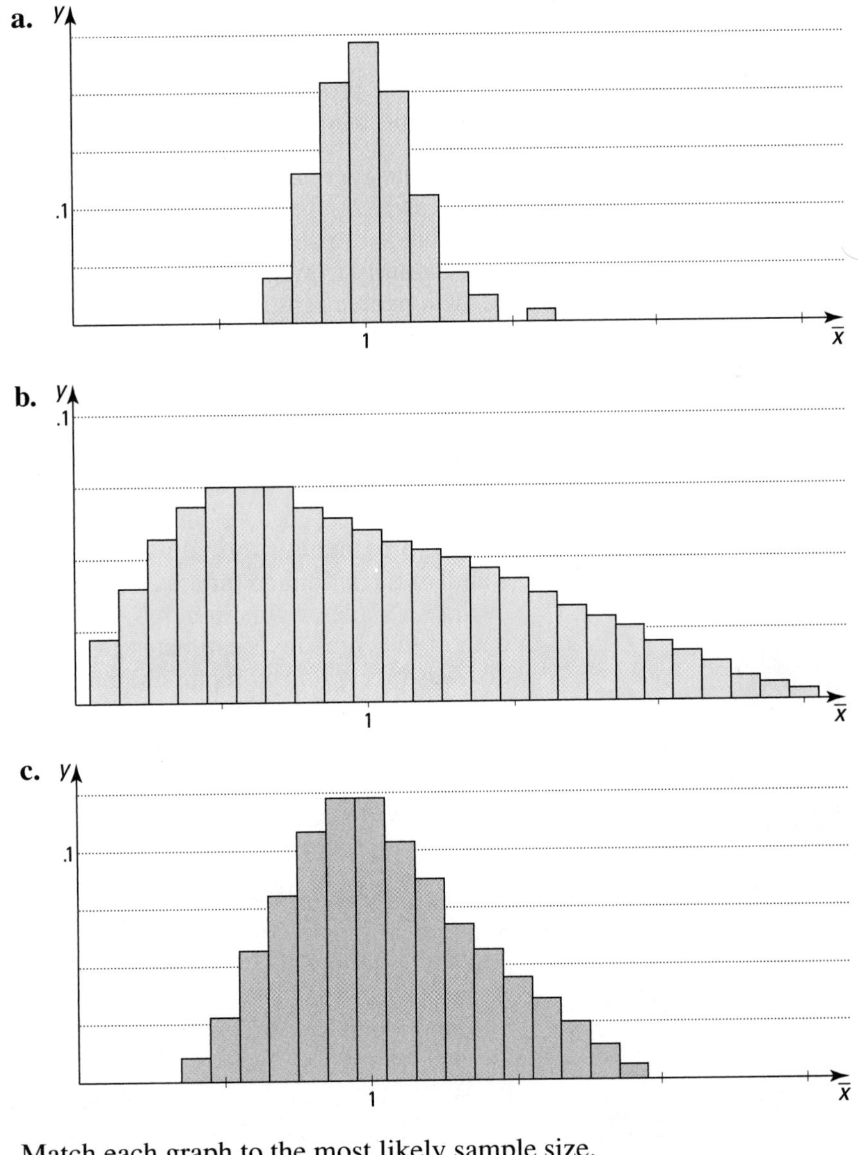

14. Match each graph to the most likely sample size.

(i) 2 (ii) 15 (iii) 40

15. Was the population from which the samples were drawn normal? How can you tell?

16. What advantage do larger sample sizes give in estimating population means?

17. Consider a bowler in a league who keeps track of individual games, as well as average scores for three games played each time the league meets. The league meets once a week for 15 weeks during a season.
   a. How is the mean of the 45 games bowled related to the mean of the 15 weekly averages?
   b. Which will have the larger spread, the scores of the 45 games or the 15 weekly averages? Explain why.

In 18 and 19, in a recent year the scores of students on the ACT college entrance exam were modeled by a normal distribution with $\mu = 20.9$ and $\sigma = 4.7$.

18. What is the probability that a randomly chosen student from the population who took the exam has a score of 24 or higher?

19. The mean score of the 84 students at Acme High who took the ACT that year was 22.9.
   a. What is the probability that the mean score for 84 students selected randomly from all who took the test nationally is 22.9 or higher?
   b. The people at Acme believe they scored significantly higher than the nation as a whole. Test this hypothesis at the .01 level.

Review

20. An electrical company estimates the maintenance-free life of a dishwasher to be approximately normally distributed with mean ten years and standard deviation ten months and guarantees to make spare parts available to the original purchaser within twelve years of the purchase date. If the company's estimates are correct, what proportion of dishwashers will need repairs before the guarantee expires? *(Lesson 10-6)*

21. Consider the standard normal curve for variable z. Determine the probability that z is between -1.65 and 1.65. *(Lesson 10-5)*

22. *True or false.* Given any normally distributed variable, its mean, median, and mode are equal. *(Lesson 10-4)*

23. A researcher is testing for color preference of babies. There are ten balls of identical size in a box; five are red, five are green. A baby is observed picking up four balls from the box. She chooses three red balls and a green one.
   a. State a null hypothesis H_0 and an alternative hypothesis H_1 for this experiment.
   b. What outcomes should be considered in deciding whether the null hypothesis should be rejected?
   c. Determine which hypothesis should be accepted at the .05 significance level. *(Lessons 8-6, 10-3)*

24. Factor $6a^2 - 10a + 3ab - 5b$, if possible. *(Lesson 9-9)*

25. Refer to the cartoon above.

a. If the person on the left is 5'6" tall and has a shadow 15' long, what is the angle of elevation of the sun?

b. Why does the person on the right want the person on the left to come back around noon?

26. The following are the average monthly temperatures in °F for Nashville, Tennessee.

Jan.	Feb.	Mar.	Apr.	May	June	July	Aug.	Sept.	Oct.	Nov.	Dec.
36	40	50	59	68	76	79	78	72	60	50	41

a. Draw a scatterplot of these data, using x = number of the month of the year.

b. Pick three points and determine a quadratic function to model the data.

c. Graph the function you found in part **b** on the same axes with the scatterplot.

d. Explain why a quadratic function is probably not the best choice for modeling data on weather. *(Lessons 1-1, 2-6, 4-10)*

27. Solve for x: $z = \frac{x - m}{s}$. *(Previous course)*

Exploration

28. Begin on a randomly chosen page of text in this book. Choose 30 consecutive sentences (continue to successive page(s) of text if necessary). Count the number of words in each sentence. Then calculate the mean of these counts. Repeat this process with different pages ten times.

a. Determine the mean $\mu_{\bar{x}}$ and standard deviation $\sigma_{\bar{x}}$ of the ten means.

b. Based on the Central Limit Theorem, what can you predict about the mean and standard deviation of the distribution of the number of words in all the sentences in this book?

c. State one assumption which allows the use of the Central Limit Theorem in making the prediction in part **b**.

d. Discuss how different (if at all) the results would be for parts **a** and **b** if you used each of the following.

i. a physics textbook

ii. a novel

iii. a computer software manual

LESSON

10-8

Confidence and Cautions in Statistical Reasoning

Estimating the Population Mean from a Sample Mean

Consider the following situation. In Ohio in 1995–1996 the scores of the seniors taking the mathematics section of the Scholastic Aptitude Test (the SAT-M) had a mean of 535 and a standard deviation of 104. This group is clearly not a random sample of all seniors. Students choose to take the test, and virtually all are college-bound. In fact, only about 24% of seniors in Ohio took the SAT-M in 1995–1996.

Suppose that you want to know how *all* high school seniors in Ohio might do on the SAT-M. After considerable effort and expense, you give the SAT-M to a random sample of 400 high school seniors and find that the mean of this sample is 440 and the standard deviation is 119. What can you say about the mean on the SAT-M if all seniors in Ohio took this test? That is, what does your sample mean predict about the population mean?

Clearly, another sample of 400 students would be likely not to yield a mean of 440 again. By the Central Limit Theorem, in repeated samples of size 400, the sample means are normally distributed with mean $\mu_{\bar{x}} = \mu$ and standard deviation $\sigma_{\bar{x}} \approx \frac{\sigma}{\sqrt{n}}$, where μ and σ are the mean and standard deviation of the population you are trying to describe.

With no other information available, it is natural to assume that the population mean is the sample mean and that the variation among the SAT-M scores of the entire population of seniors in the state of Ohio is equal to the variation among the SAT-M scores of the seniors who took the test in 1995–1996 (an unrealistic assumption, but one that you make, because without some value for σ the mathematics is a bit more complicated). That is, assume $\sigma = 119$. Thus, in repeated samples of 400 randomly chosen students, the distribution should be approximately normal with $\mu_{\bar{x}} \approx \mu \approx 440$ and $\sigma_{\bar{x}} \approx \frac{\sigma}{\sqrt{n}} = \frac{119}{\sqrt{400}} = \frac{119}{20} \approx 6$.

With this information and these assumptions, you can make inferences about μ, the mean of the population. The reasoning goes as follows. You know that in a normal distribution, about 68% of the data fall within one standard deviation of the mean. Thus, the probability is about 0.68 that a sample mean $\bar{x}$ will be within 6 points of the population mean 440. So you can say that in about 68% of random samples of size 400 from the population of seniors the mean will fall between $440 - 6$ and $440 + 6$, that is, between 434 and 446.

Confidence Intervals

The interval $434 \leq \mu \leq 446$ is called the *68% confidence interval* for the population mean μ. The quantity ± 6 is called the *margin of error* for the confidence interval.

Jerzy Neyman

Confidence intervals were invented in 1937 by Jerzy Neyman (1884–1981), a Polish mathematician who moved to the United States where he was professor of mathematics for many years at the University of California at Berkeley. Statisticians have invented techniques for finding confidence intervals for many different parameters based on various assumptions. But all confidence intervals share two properties: There is an interval of possible values constructed from the sample data, and a confidence level which gives the probability that the method produces an interval which contains the true value of the parameter.

The user chooses the confidence level, a percent near 1. Usually it is at least 90%, and 95% and 99% are commonly used. A 95% level for μ indicates that 95% of the sample means fall within about two standard deviations of the population mean; for this situation, between $440 - 2(6) = 428$ and $440 + 2(6) = 452$. You can report with 95% confidence that the mean score of the population of seniors in Ohio on the SAT-M is between 428 and 452.

Compare this result with the one found earlier: a 68% confidence interval for the mean is $434 \leq \mu \leq 446$. Notice that, except for rounding, each interval is centered on $\bar{x} = 440$, the sample mean.

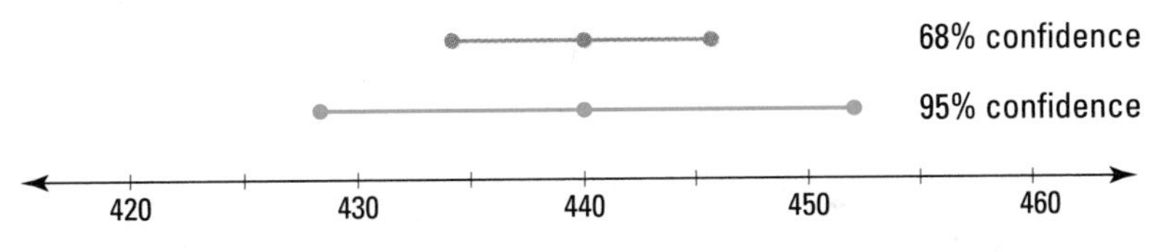

Also, as the level of confidence increases, so does the width of the confidence interval. This is because, if you want to place a higher probability on your estimate, you need a wider estimate to "cover your bases."

What does this mean if you would like a "finer tuning" or closer estimate of the mean? You have two choices: choose a lower confidence level or use a larger sample. Generally, people who use statistics do not want to use a confidence level below 90%, so in order to get within a desired margin of error, they must increase the sample size.

How Large a Sample Is Necessary?

Surprisingly, it is relatively simple to figure out how large a sample size is needed to ensure a certain margin of error at a desired confidence level.

Example

Suppose you want to estimate the mean score of all seniors in Ohio on the SAT-M with 99% confidence to within 10 points. How large a sample size is necessary?

Solution

You know that the standard score for the sample mean is

$$z = \frac{\bar{x} - \mu_{\bar{x}}}{\sigma_{\bar{x}}} = \frac{\bar{x} - \mu}{\frac{\sigma}{\sqrt{n}}}.$$

From the table of the Standard Normal Distribution, in order for the confidence level to be 99%, z must equal 2.57. Suppose you want $|\bar{x} - \mu| = 10$. If you assume as we did earlier that $\sigma = 119$, you must find n so that

$$2.57 = \frac{10}{\frac{119}{\sqrt{n}}}.$$

$$2.57 = \frac{10\sqrt{n}}{119}$$ Rewrite the right side.

$$\frac{(2.57)(119)}{10} = \sqrt{n}$$ Multiply each side by 119, and divide each side by 10.

$$935.32 \approx n$$ Square each side.

or $$n \approx 935.$$

That is, to estimate the population mean to within 10 points at the 99% confidence level, you would have to select a random sample of nearly 1000 students. You would have to decide whether the increase in precision of measurement is worth the increased cost of selecting and testing this much larger sample.

In general, to find the sample size needed so that you can estimate a mean μ for a population with known standard deviation σ at a given confidence level and accuracy A, where $A = |\bar{x} - \mu|$, you must first find the z-score corresponding to that confidence level. Then you must solve the following equation for n:

$$z = \frac{A}{\frac{\sigma}{\sqrt{n}}}.$$

Repeating the steps used in the Example gives

$$n = \left(\frac{z\sigma}{A}\right)^2.$$

Notice that n varies directly with the square of z and inversely with the square of A. Thus, as the desired accuracy gets smaller, the needed sample size increases quite rapidly. Consequently, getting a high level of confidence and small margin of error simultaneously can result in the need for very large sample sizes, and these, in turn, can be very costly. Even in statistics, there is no such thing as a free lunch!

Cautions about Statistical Inferences

You should note that just as medications carry warnings about their potential harmful effects, the techniques described in this lesson to make inferences about populations must be applied with caution. First, the data collected must be from a random sample of the population. The methods used here to determine a confidence interval for μ do not apply to other types of samples such as volunteers or similar "convenient" samples. Second, as a practical matter, if the sample size is relatively small, outliers can have a large effect on the confidence interval. You should always look for outliers in a sample, and try to correct them or justify their removal before computing a sample mean.

Third, the techniques developed here require that you know the standard deviation σ of the population. In most surveys this is unrealistic. There are ways to estimate σ from the sample standard deviation s, and to construct confidence intervals based on s, but they require distributions other than the binomial or normal. Fourth, the margin of error in a confidence interval covers only random sampling errors. That is, the margin of error describes typical error expected because of chance variation in random selection. It does not describe errors arising from sloppy data collection or data entry. Fancy formulas can never compensate for sloppy data.

QUESTIONS

Covering the Reading

In 1 and 2, refer to the SAT-M data in the text with samples of size 400. A confidence level is given. **a.** Find the confidence interval. **b.** Find the margin of error.

1. 68% level

2. 95% level

3. Find a 90% confidence interval for the SAT-M scores of the seniors in the state of Ohio. Assume, as in the lesson, that $\bar{x} = 440$, $\sigma = 119$, and $n = 400$.

In 4 and 5, *true or false*.

4. In most statistical applications a confidence level of at least 90% is used.

5. As the confidence level increases, the width of the confidence interval increases.

6. Below are shown 90% and 95% confidence intervals for a population with mean μ.

a. Estimate μ.

b. Which is the 95% confidence interval? How can you tell?

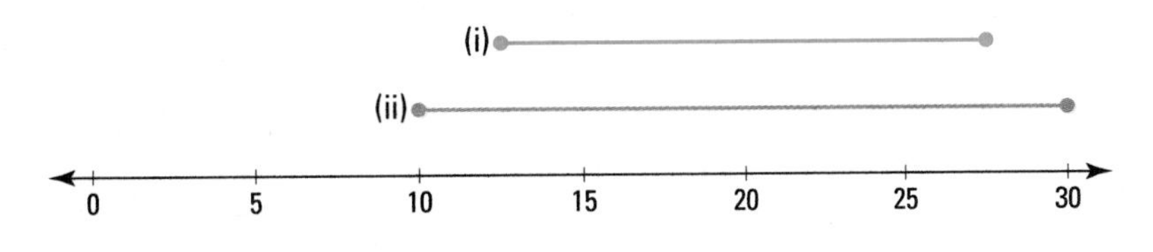

7. Identify two ways to decrease the range of a confidence interval.

8. Refer again to the SAT-M data in the lesson. Suppose you wanted to estimate μ with 95% confidence to within 10 points. How large a sample would be needed?

Applying the Mathematics

9. When opinion polls are conducted, the results are often reported as a percent in favor of something $\pm$ a margin of error as a percent. In most polls it is standard practice to report the margin of error for a 95% confidence interval unless stated otherwise.
   a. Suppose you read that 28% of Americans surveyed recently felt that homelessness was the most serious problem in the United States, and that the poll has a margin of error of $\pm 3\%$. What is the 95% confidence interval for the percent of adults who think that homelessness is the most serious problem in the United States?
   b. Can you be certain that the true population percent falls within the interval in part **a**?

10. A pollster wants accuracy to within 2% in a close election between candidates A and B, with a 95% confidence interval. Assuming a 50% probability of a person preferring candidate A, then $\sigma = \frac{1}{2}$. How many people need to be polled?

11. The test for cholesterol level is not perfectly precise. Moreover, level of blood cholesterol varies from day to day. Suppose that repeated measurements for an individual on different days vary normally with $\sigma = 5$ mg/dl. On a single test Alisa's cholesterol level is reported to be 180 mg/dl.
    a. Find a 95% confidence level for her mean cholesterol level.
    b. A person with a cholesterol level of about 200 mg/dl is considered moderately at risk for a stroke or heart attack, and if the person is either overweight or smokes the risks are even higher. Should Alisa be concerned about the results of her cholesterol test?

Review

In 12 and 13, refer to the Central Limit Theorem. *True or false.* *(Lesson 10-7)*

12. As more and more samples are selected, the mean of the sample means approaches the population mean.

13. As more and more samples are selected, the standard deviation of the sample means approaches the standard deviation of the population.

14. Suppose that in the past year the monthly cost of residential customers' long-distance phone calls in a particular city had a mean of \$28.25 and a standard deviation of \$7.20.
   a. If 100 telephone bills from the past year are randomly selected, what is the probability that the mean charge for long-distance calls on these bills is greater than \$29.00?
   b. Suppose that in the past few months random samples of 100 bills have shown a mean charge of \$29.90 for long-distance charges. Test at the 0.01 level the hypothesis that the average monthly cost has not increased. *(Lesson 10-7)*

In 15 and 16, consider the set of two-digit numbers from 10 to 99. *(Lessons 7-6, 10-7)*

15. Suppose one number is chosen at random.
   a. Name the type of probability distribution that best models this situation.
   b. Find the mean of this distribution.

16. Suppose random samples of size 40 are selected, and their means calculated.
   a. What type of distribution models the distribution of sample means?
   b. How does the mean of the distribution in part **a** compare to the mean of the distribution in Question 15?

17. The height of a certain species of plant is known to be normally distributed with mean 61 cm and standard deviation 5 cm. If a nursery grows 3000 plants of this species in preparation for Mother's Day, how many should they expect to be less than 48 cm tall (and consequently, too short to sell as top-quality)? *(Lesson 10-6)*

18. Consider a standard normal distribution of a variable z. Suppose it is known that the probability that z is less than a is p. Express each of the following probabilities in terms of p. *(Lesson 10-5)*

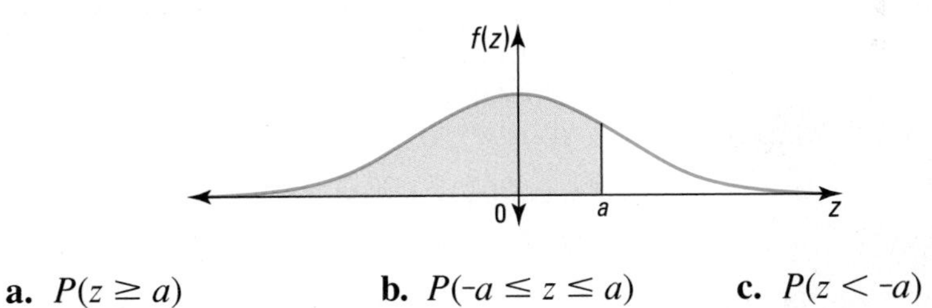

   a. $P(z \geq a)$
   b. $P(-a \leq z \leq a)$
   c. $P(z < -a)$

19. *Multiple choice.* Which of the following questions does a hypothesis test answer?
   (a) Is the sample random?
   (b) Is the experiment properly designed?
   (c) Is the result due to chance?
   (d) Is the result important? *(Lesson 10-3)*

In 20–23, *multiple choice.* What equation corresponds to the graph? *(Lessons 6-4, 10-4, 10-5, 10-6)*

(a) $y = e^{-x}, x > 0$ (b) $y = e^{-x^2}$

(c) $y = \frac{1}{\sqrt{2\pi}} e^{-x^2/2}$ (d) $y = \frac{1}{\sqrt{2\pi}} e^{-\frac{1}{2}(x-1)^2}$

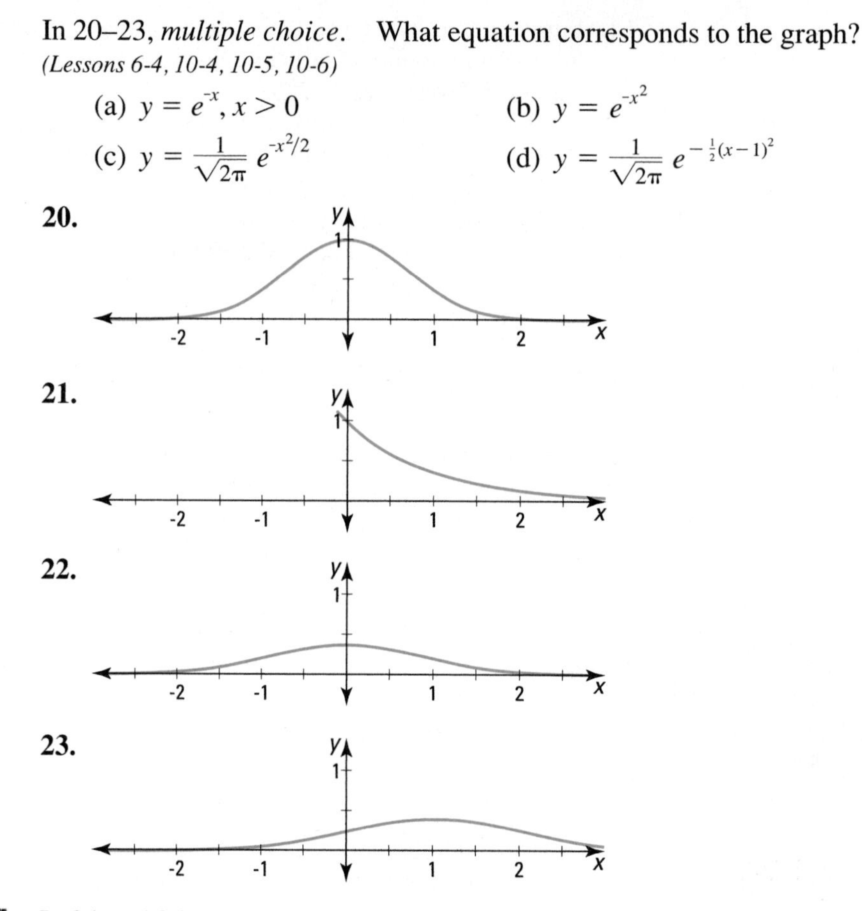

In 24 and 25, a series is given. **a.** Evaluate. **b.** Identify the series as arithmetic, geometric, or neither. *(Lessons 8-3, 8-4)*

24. $\sum_{i=1}^{7} (2i - 1)$

25. $\sum_{k=4}^{6} 2^k$

26. a. How many permutations consisting of four letters each can be formed from the letters of the word CONFIDE?

b. How many of the permutations in part **a** begin with a vowel? *(Lesson 7-4)*

27. The land area of the United States is about 3,717,796 square miles. The area of Colorado is about 104,100 square miles. What is the probability that a randomly chosen point of land in the United States is in each area?

a. in Colorado **b.** not in Colorado *(Lesson 7-1)*

Engineer Mountain, Durango, Colorado

Exploration

28. What size sample is used to determine the number of viewers of TV programs? What is the accuracy of these ratings? What is the confidence level?

A project presents an opportunity for you to extend your knowledge of a topic related to the material of this chapter. You should allow more time for a project than you do for a typical homework question.

1 The Quincunx

In the early 1870s the English physician, explorer, and scientist, Sir Francis Galton, designed an apparatus he called a *quincunx* to illustrate binomial experiments. Sometimes the quincunx is called a Galton board. The original quincunx had a glass face and a funnel at the top. Small balls were poured through the funnel and cascaded through an array of pins. Each ball struck on a pin at each level; theoretically, it had an equal probability of falling to the right or left. The balls collected in compartments at the bottom. Turning the quincunx upside down sent all the balls back to their original position. Galton's original quincunx still survives in England (see photo below); large replicas exist in many science museums, and smaller ones can be purchased from science suppliers.

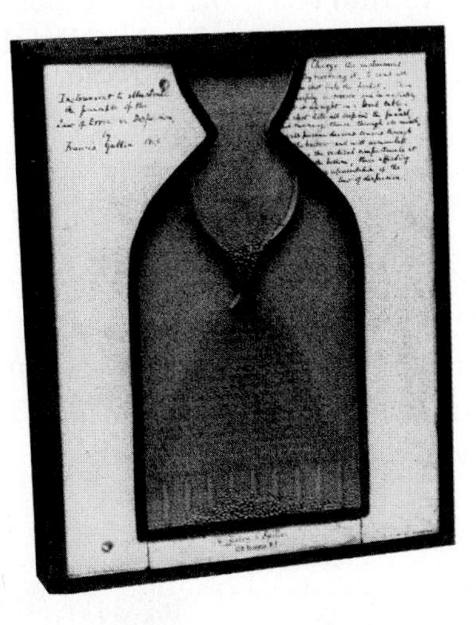

a. Obtain an example, or build your own Galton board with at least ten rows of pins. Release the balls and observe the distribution. Repeat this experiment 20–30 times and describe any trends.

b. What binomial probability distribution does your quincunx represent? Discuss the relation between your observations in part **a** and this probability distribution.

2 Cumulative Percentile Curves

The curves in the graph below are called *percentile curves* or *cumulative percentage curves*. Each ordered pair (x, y) represents the percent y of the data in the set that are less than x. For instance, in the data set pictured by these curves, about 60% of the girls and about 18% of the boys had scores less than 35 on a test of coordination.

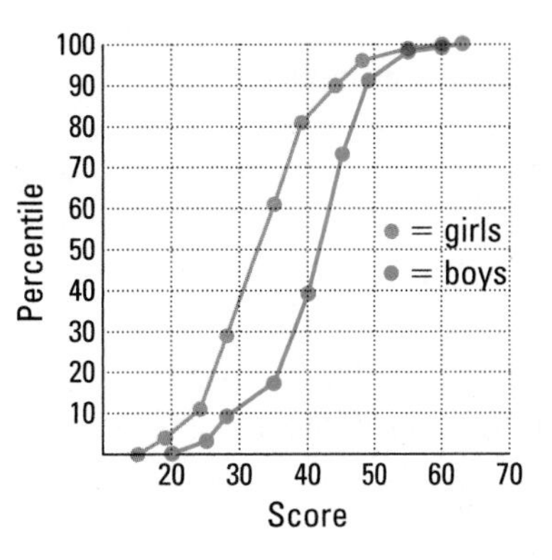

a. Obtain examples of data sets each with at least 25 numbers, but different distributions. For instance, collect examples of data sets that are approximately uniform, binomial, and normal. Calculate percentile ranks for the scores in each data set and plot the corresponding percentile curve. If you have software that can draw percentile curves, draw some graphs using it. Compare and contrast the shapes of the percentile curves.

b. Galton (see Project 1) called such a percentile curve an ogive (pronounced "oh′-jive") based on an architectural term. Find pictures of ogives in architecture books and compare and contrast them to the curves you drew in part **a**.

(continued)

3 Is Your Class Typical?

Refer to Project 6 of Chapter 1 (p. 69) and the related projects in Chapters 2 and 3.

a. Determine a way to choose a random sample of at least 30 students in your school. Conduct a survey of that sample with the same variables.

b. Use displays and descriptive statistics to describe a typical student in the random sample.

c. Make inferences to describe a typical student in your school.

d. Compare your results from part **b** above to the results you obtained in earlier chapters. How typical is your class of the school as a whole?

4 How Common Is the Letter *e*?

a. Describe a way to pick letters at random from this chapter, and pick 30 such letters. Calculate the relative frequency of occurrence of the letter *e*.

b. Repeat part **a** at least 9 times and use your collected data to determine a 95% confidence interval for the percentage of *e*'s in the English language.

c. Repeat parts **a** and **b** with another book.

d. Compare your answers to parts **b** and **c**.

5 Sums of Random Digits

a. Use a computer, calculator, or table of random numbers to choose two random *digits* from 0 to 9. Then calculate their sum. Repeat this until you have 50 such random sums. For instance, your first ten sums might be

14 10 5 3 15 3 6 7 7 12.

Let s = the sum of the two random digits. Then s can be any integer from 0 to 18. Find $P(s \leq 5)$, $P(s \leq 12)$, and $P(s \leq n)$ for any $n \in \{0, 1, 2, \ldots, 18\}$. Express your answer as a table of values and as a graph.

b. Modify part **a** to choose two random *numbers* from 0 to 9. That is, consider the analogous *continuous* random variable s. To calculate $P(s \leq 5)$ in this case it will help to think geometrically. For instance, to calculate $P(s \leq 5)$ and $P(s \leq 12)$ you will need to consider the areas of the figures below.

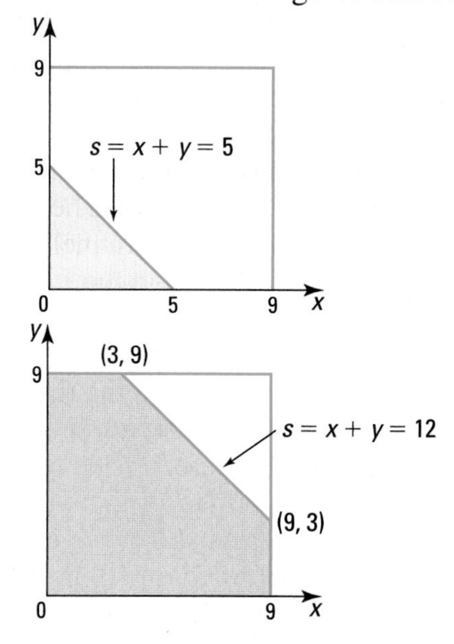

Use areas to find $P(s \leq n)$ for all integers n between 0 and 18. Again, describe the probability distribution with a table and with a graph.

c. Compare and contrast the functions $(n, P(s \leq n))$ in parts **a** and **b**.

6 Design a Study

Consider a problem that concerns you: crime, drug abuse, air pollution, poverty, etc. Design a study to investigate some aspect of the problem. Use descriptive and inferential statistics, as appropriate, to report the results of your study.

 CHAPTER TEN

SUMMARY

Binomial probabilities are used to analyze events with repeated independent trials. A binomial distribution function gives the probability of getting exactly k successes in n binomial trials, each of which has probability p of success. Usually computers or calculators are used to calculate the necessary binomial probabilities.

The mean μ and standard deviation σ of a binomial probability distribution are given by $\mu = np$ and $\sigma = \sqrt{npq}$, respectively. For large n, graphs of binomial probability distributions resemble a bell-shaped curve.

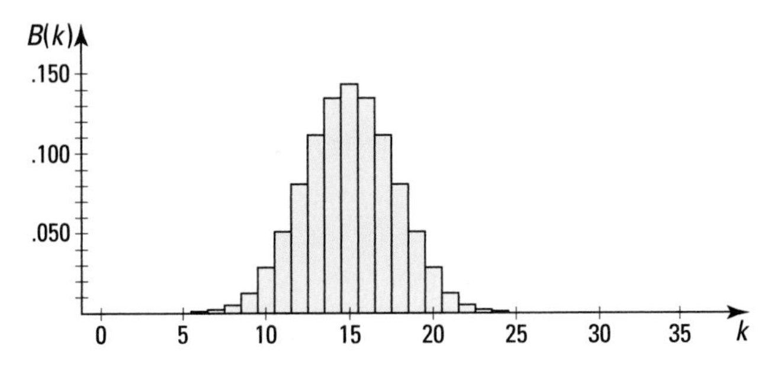

A commonly observed continuous distribution is the normal distribution, characterized by bell-shaped distribution curves. Many naturally occurring phenomena can be approximated by normal distributions. The parent of all these curves is given by $f(x) = e^{-x^2}$. The standard normal distribution has a mean of 0 and a standard deviation of 1; its equation is $f(z) = \frac{1}{\sqrt{2\pi}} e^{-z^2/2}$.

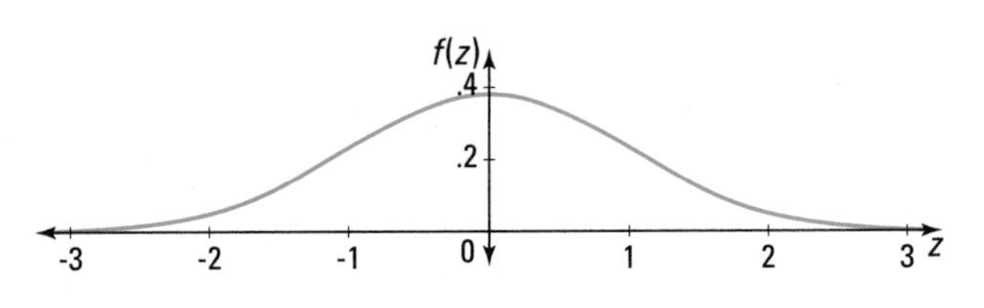

Areas under any normal curve can be calculated using calculus or closely approximated using computer programs, tables, or some calculators. The area between this curve and the x-axis is 1. Probabilities of events in any normal distribution can be estimated by first standardizing the variable with z-scores, where $z = \frac{x - m}{s}$, and then using the tabulated values for the standard normal distribution.

Binomial and normal distributions are often used to make judgments or inferences about issues. Assuming a binomial or normal distribution, one can determine how probable a certain observed event is. Then, based on predefined significance levels, one can decide whether the calculated probability supports the null hypothesis that the event *is* a reasonable result given the assumed distribution, or it supports the alternative hypothesis that the assumed distribution is *not* a proper one.

The Central Limit Theorem states that if a large number of random samples of size n are selected from any population with mean μ and standard deviation σ, then as n increases, the distribution of sample means has the following properties:

(1) its mean approaches μ; (2) its standard deviation approaches $\frac{\sigma}{\sqrt{n}}$; and (3) it approaches a normal distribution.

The theorem can be applied if the original population is itself normally distributed, or if the sample size $n \geq 30$.

Based on the Central Limit Theorem, confidence interval estimates can be determined for the mean of a population using sample results. The intervals may be narrow or wide, depending on the preset confidence level.

CHAPTER TEN

VOCABULARY

Below are the most important terms and phrases for this chapter. You should be able to give a general description and a specific example of each and a precise definition for those marked with an asterisk (*).

Lesson 10-1
*binomial distribution function, $B(k)$
parameters of the binomial distribution
mode (of a probability distribution)
cumulative binomial probability table

Lesson 10-2
Mean of a Binomial Distribution Theorem
variance of a probability distribution
Variance and Standard Deviation of a Binomial Distribution Theorem

Lesson 10-3
hypothesis
significance level
hypothesis testing
null hypothesis, H_0
alternative hypothesis, H_1

Lesson 10-4
concave down, concave up
inflection points
*normal distribution
normal curve
parent normal curve
*standard normal curve
*standard normal distribution

Lesson 10-5
Standard Normal Distribution Table

Lesson 10-6
standard score
standardizing (a variable)

Lesson 10-7
sample/sampling distribution
mean of a sampling distribution, $\mu_{\bar{x}}$
standard deviation of a sampling distribution, $\sigma_{\bar{x}}$
Central Limit Theorem

Lesson 10-8
confidence interval
margin of error

CHAPTER TEN

PROGRESS SELF-TEST

Take this test as you would take a test in class. You will need Appendix D and a calculator or computer that generates binomial probabilities. Then check the test yourself using the solutions at the back of the book.

1. Suppose the probability is 0.89 that a randomly selected patient with a particular heart condition will survive more than one year. Draw a histogram of the binomial probability distribution that x of 10 heart patients will survive a year or more.
2. Describe how the domain, range, and the shape of the binomial distribution in Question 1 would change if 100 patients are studied.
3. A binomial probability distribution has $p = 0.2$ and $n = 60$. What are the mean μ and standard deviation σ of the distribution?
4. In the product specification sheet for their 1.5 kΩ resistors, a manufacturer reports the 99% confidence interval as 1500 ohms $\pm$ 5%. Assuming their data are normally distributed, what are the mean and standard deviation of the resistances for these resistors?

In 5 and 6, consider the function f with equation $f(x) = \frac{1}{2} e^{-x^2}$.

5. Is the graph of f reflection-symmetric? If yes, give an equation for the line of symmetry. If not, explain why not.
6. *True or false.* The equation for f is an equation for the standard normal curve.

In 7 and 8, find the probability that a randomly chosen observation z from a standard normal distribution is in the given interval.

7. less than 1.3
8. between -1.5 and 1.5
9. It is commonly thought that average "normal" body temperature is 98.6°F. A study of the temperatures of 130 healthy adults revealed a normal distribution of temperatures with an average of 98.2°F and a standard deviation of 0.7°F.
   a. State a null hypothesis H_0 and an alternative hypothesis H_1 that could be used to test whether average "normal" body temperature is 98.6°F.
   b. Test the null hypothesis at the 0.01 level. (Assume that the standard deviations of the sample and the entire population are the same.)
10. The heights of all 946 girls in one high school are measured and the girls are found to have a mean height of 170 cm with a standard deviation of 7.2 cm. Would it be unusual for a sample of 40 girls from this high school to have a mean height of over 180 cm? Explain your answer.
11. Complete: 95% of all observations on a normal distribution fall within __?__ standard deviations of the mean.
12. If a variable x has a normal distribution with mean m and standard deviation s, then the transformed variable $z = \frac{x - m}{s}$ has what distribution?
13. A survey of the students at Peaks High School shows that they travel an average of 2.15 miles to school every day with a standard deviation of 0.36 miles. Assuming a normal distribution, determine the probability that a randomly chosen student at Peaks High travels over 3 miles to school.
14. The area shaded below, which lies between the standard normal curve and the z-axis, is about 0.8212. Determine $P(|z| < 0.92)$.

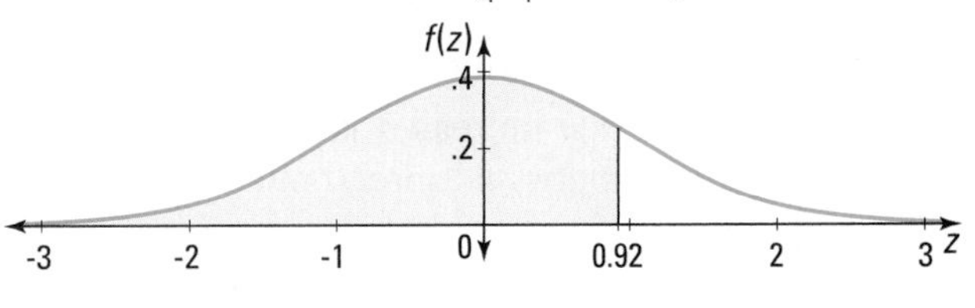

CHAPTER REVIEW

Questions on SPUR Objectives

SPUR stands for **S**kills, **P**roperties, **U**ses, and **R**epresentations. The Chapter Review questions are grouped according to the SPUR Objectives for this chapter.

SKILLS DEAL WITH THE PROCEDURES USED TO GET ANSWERS.

Objective A: *Calculate the mean and standard deviation of a binomial probability distribution.* *(Lesson 10-2)*

In 1 and 2, find the mean and standard deviation for the distribution.

1. a binomial distribution with $p = .6, n = 60$

2. a binomial distribution with $q = .3, n = 100$

In 3 and 4, consider a test with 20 items.

3. If all items are True-False and students guess randomly, what is the expected mean and standard deviation?

4. If all items are multiple choice with four options and students guess randomly, what is the expected mean and standard deviation?

5. How many questions with five options should there be on a multiple-choice test to have an expected mean of 20 when students guess randomly?

6. If $\mu = 158$ and $\sigma = 5$ for a binomial probability distribution, determine n and p (with three-digit accuracy).

Objective B: *Use the Standard Normal Distribution to find probabilities.* *(Lesson 10-5)*

In Questions 7–11, use the table in Appendix D.

7. a. What is the probability that a random variable z with the standard normal distribution takes on a value between -1.28 and 1.28?

b. Determine the area under the standard normal curve from $z = -1.28$ to $z = 1.28$.

In 8–11, evaluate the given probability.

8. $P(z < 2)$ **9.** $P(1 < z < 2)$

10. $P(z < -2.34)$ **11.** $P(z > 3.01)$

12. Verify the statement that 99.7% of the area under the standard normal curve is between $z = -3$ and $z = 3$.

PROPERTIES DEAL WITH THE PRINCIPLES BEHIND THE MATHEMATICS.

Objective C: *Compare and contrast characteristics of different binomial probability distribution graphs.* *(Lesson 10-1)*

In 13–15, consider binomial probability distributions with n trials and a probability p of success of any trial. *True or false.*

13. The graph of any binomial distribution is symmetric to the line $x = m$, where m is the mode of the distribution.

14. With fixed p, as n increases, the graphs of binomial distributions "spread out."

15. With fixed n, as p increases, the mode of a binomial distribution moves to the right along the x-axis.

16. Give an equation for $B(x)$, the probability of exactly x successes.

Objective D: *Use properties of normal distributions and their parent function.* *(Lessons 10-4, 10-5, 10-6)*

17. a. Show that $f(x) = e^{-x^2}$ is an even function.

b. What kind of symmetry does this imply for the graph of any normal distribution with mean μ and standard deviation σ?

CHAPTER TEN

In 18–20, *true or false*.

18. The graph of $y = e^{-x^2}$ never intersects the x-axis.

19. The area between the graph of $y = e^{-x^2}$ and the x-axis is infinite.

20. The area between the standard normal curve and the x-axis is 1.

USES DEAL WITH APPLICATIONS OF MATHEMATICS IN REAL SITUATIONS.

Objective E: *Solve probability problems using binomial or normal distributions.* *(Lessons 10-1, 10-2, 10-6)*

21. 20% of the deer in a wildlife preservation park are believed to have a certain antler infection. A zoologist randomly captures 15 deer and checks their antlers. Assuming the prediction is accurate, determine the probability that more than three of the deer will have infected antlers.

22. An allergy test requires that small samples of chemicals be injected under the skin of the patient. Individuals sensitive to any one of the chemicals have a reaction time that is approximately normally distributed with a mean of 11 hours and a standard deviation of 3 hours. How often can one expect a reaction time of more than 18 hours with such individuals?

23. A new test of extroversion-introversion was administered to a large group of adults, and found to yield scores that were approximately normally distributed with a mean of 35 and a standard deviation of 8. For the instruction manual, various scores are to be interpreted as in the table below. Determine the highest and the lowest scores for each of these five groups.

highly extroverted	top 5%
extroverted	next to top 15%
average	middle 60%
introverted	next to bottom 15%
highly introverted	bottom 5%

24. Based on factory and field tests, a car company determines that the trouble-free mileage for their new model is normally distributed with a mean of 31,600 miles and a standard deviation of 16,200 miles. The car is marketed with a 60,000-mile guarantee. Determine the percentage of cars of this make the company should expect to repair due to malfunctioning before 60,000 miles.

Objective F: *Use binomial and normal distributions to test hypotheses.* *(Lessons 10-3, 10-7)*

In 25 and 26, a certain disease has a recovery rate of 70%. A researcher has developed a new treatment for the disease and tests it on 120 patients. She finds that 97 of the 120 patients recovered from the disease. The researcher claims that her new treatment is effective against the disease.

25. *Multiple choice.* To test this claim, what is the most appropriate set of hypotheses?

(a) H_0: The new treatment is effective against the disease.
H_1: The new treatment is not effective against the disease.

(b) H_0: The recovery rate for patients receiving the new treatment is greater than 70%.
H_1: The recovery rate for patients receiving the new treatment is not greater than 70%.

(c) H_0: The new treatment has no effect on the disease.
H_1: The new treatment is effective against the disease.

26. Test the researcher's claim at the 0.05 significance level.

27. The average weight of checked luggage allowed per person on a domestic flight must be 20 kg. For flight safety purposes, one airline randomly samples 450 of its customers and studies the weight of their checked luggage. The mean weight is found to be 27.8 kg and the sample standard deviation to be 5.3 kg. Can the airline officers claim that the average weight of checked luggage is heavier than 20 kilograms? Use a 0.01 significance level. (Because the sample size is large, assume that the standard deviation of the sample and the standard deviation of the population are approximately the same.)

28. A highway patrol group decides to check the results they have read in a report which claimed that the speed of cars in their region of the highway has a mean of 63 and standard deviation of 15 miles per hour. They track 100 cars every day for a month and record the average speed observed at the end of each day. Suppose that, based on the total of 3000 cars they track in a month, they calculate an average speed of 58.75 mph. Can they claim that the results in the report are wrong using a 0.05 significance level?

Objective G: *Apply the Central Limit Theorem.* *(Lesson 10-7)*

In 29 and 30, *true or false*.

29. If the distribution of population data is not known to be normal, one needs to pick large samples ($n \geq 30$) to apply the Central Limit Theorem.

30. Given a population with mean μ and standard deviation σ, the standard deviation of the means of k samples of size n from this population is approximately $\frac{\sigma}{\sqrt{k}}$.

31. Suppose that the weights of full-grown oranges in a citrus grove are normally distributed with mean 7.3 ounces and standard deviation 2.1 ounces. Determine the probability that 50 oranges randomly picked from this grove have a mean weight greater than 10.5 ounces.

32. A vitamin manufacturer reports that the average weight of their vitamin C tablets is 500 mg with a standard deviation of 2 mg. To check the veracity of this claim, a consumer protection group randomly samples 100 tablets from each lot produced and records the mean weight of each sample. If the numbers reported by the manufacturer are correct, describe the distribution of the data collected by this group.

CHAPTER TEN

Objective H: *Apply confidence intervals to real-world problems.* *(Lesson 10-8)*

33. Otto is traveling down the highway when the gas indicator of his car goes on, warning him that he has only 1 gallon of gas left. The manufacturer of Otto's car reports that the 95% confidence interval for the car's highway fuel efficiency is 36 ± 5 mpg. If Otto knows he is 41 miles from the next gas station, what is the probability of his making it?

34. Dr. Al Kali, an environmental chemist, measures the pH of numerous samples of water collected from a polluted lake. His data are normally distributed with a mean pH of 8.25 and a standard deviation of 0.35. What should Dr. Kali report as the margin of error for the 90% confidence interval for his data?

35. A manufacturer of contact lenses measures the radius of 225 randomly sampled lenses from their inventory of a certain size lens. The mean and standard deviation of this sample are 0.625 cm and 0.015 cm, respectively. Because the sample size is large, the manufacturer assumes the standard deviation of the sampled lenses is the same as the standard deviation for the entire inventory.
    a. What would the manufacturer report as a 68% confidence interval for the mean radius of its lenses?
    b. Suppose the manufacturer wants to change its sampling procedure so that it can estimate the mean radius of its lenses with 95% confidence to within 0.001 cm. How many lenses would they need to sample?

REPRESENTATIONS DEAL WITH PICTURES, GRAPHS, OR OBJECTS THAT ILLUSTRATE CONCEPTS.

Objective I: *Graph and interpret a binomial probability distribution.* *(Lesson 10-1)*

36. Tell why this table does *not* show a probability distribution.

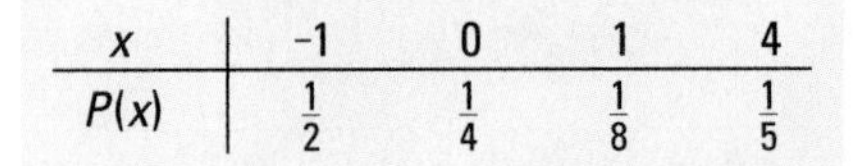

x	-1	0	1	4
$P(x)$	$\frac{1}{2}$	$\frac{1}{4}$	$\frac{1}{8}$	$\frac{1}{5}$

37. Assuming that the births of boys and girls are equally likely, the probability of x boys in a family with 4 children is given below.

x = number of boys	0	1	2	3	4
$P(x)$	$\frac{1}{16}$	$\frac{1}{4}$	$\frac{3}{8}$		

a. Finish the table of probabilities.

b. Graph the distribution as a histogram.

38. Let x be the number of items a person gets right (by guessing) on a 3-item multiple-choice test. If each question has three possible choices, then the probability $P(x)$ of getting x items correct is $P(x) = {}_3C_x\left(\frac{1}{3}\right)^x\left(\frac{2}{3}\right)^{3-x}$.

a. Construct a table of probabilities for $x = 0, 1, 2, 3$.

b. Graph the probability distribution as a scatterplot.

39. Construct a graph of the probability distribution for the function P where $P(x)$ is the probability of getting k heads in 5 tosses of a coin that is biased with $p(\text{heads}) = .6$.

40. The graph of a binomial probability distribution is given below.

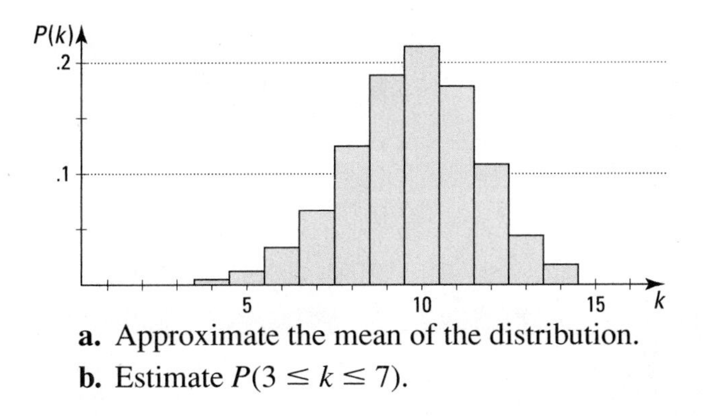

a. Approximate the mean of the distribution.

b. Estimate $P(3 \le k \le 7)$.

41. Give two reasons why the graph below *cannot* represent a binomial probability distribution.

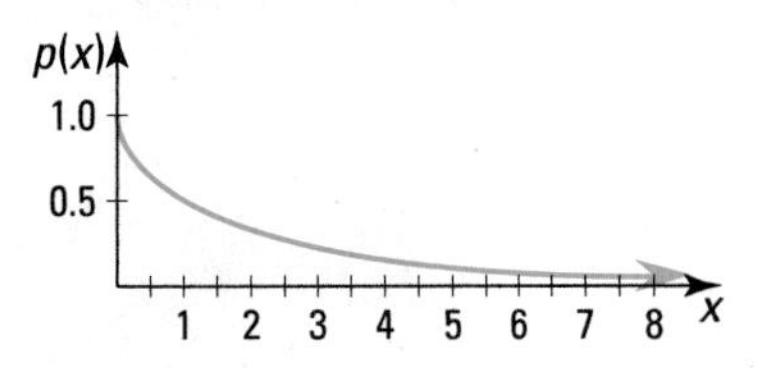

Objective J: *Graph and interpret normal distributions.* *(Lessons 10-5, 10-6)*

42. Below are the graphs of three normal distributions. Identify each.

a. the standard normal distribution

b. the distribution with $\sigma = 2$

c. the distribution with $\sigma = \frac{1}{2}$

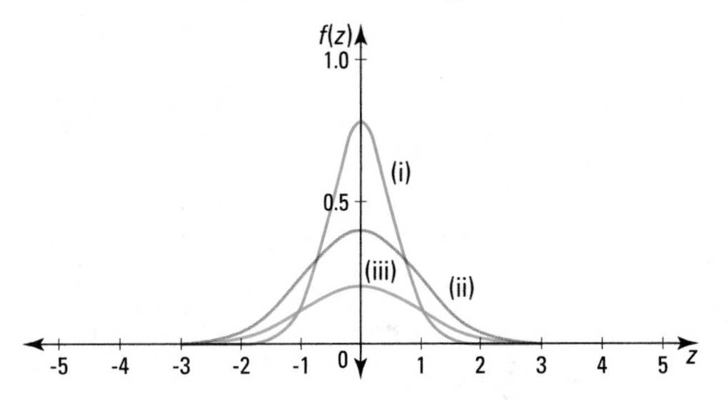

In 43–45, the area shaded below, between the standard normal curve and the z-axis, is about .9544. Determine the following probabilities.

43. $P(z \le 2)$ **44.** $P(0 < z < 2)$ **45.** $P(-2 < z < 2)$

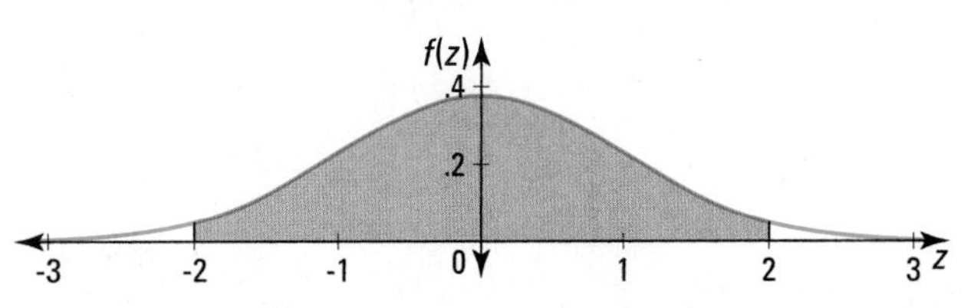

In 46–48, suppose that the variable z is normally distributed with a mean of 0 and standard deviation 1, and that the probability that z is between $-a$ and a is r. Express each of the following in terms of r.

46. $P(z \ge a)$

47. $P(0 < z < a)$

48. $P(|z| > a)$

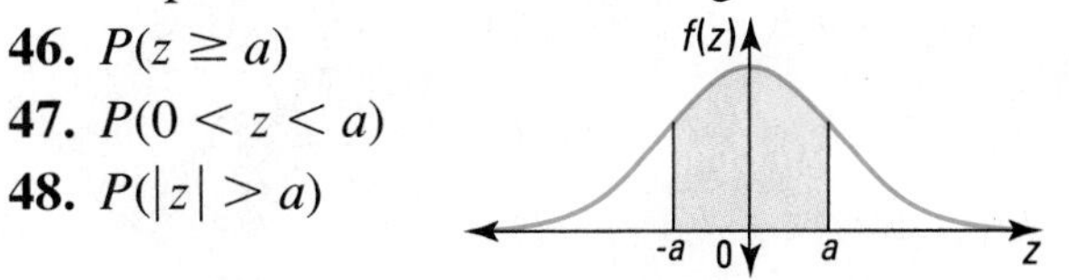

CHAPTER

Matrices and Trigonometry

Have you ever wondered how computer games produce animated images? A standard programming technique uses matrices and trigonometry. A *matrix* (plural *matrices*) is a rectangular arrangement of objects.

For instance, to generate an animation with frogs, a single frog might be described by a set of points. These data are stored in a matrix in which each column represents a key point on the frog. Then the figure is changed by transformations such as scale changes, translations, or rotations. These transformations can also be stored as matrices. Multiplying the matrix representing a figure by a matrix representing a transformation gives a matrix for the image of the original figure. For example, the following matrix represents a transformation that translates the figure and rotates it 22.5° clockwise.

$$\begin{bmatrix} .9239 & .3827 & 82.016 \\ -.3827 & .9239 & 37.462 \\ 0 & 0 & 1 \end{bmatrix}$$

In this chapter you will study matrices for many transformations, including rotations of any magnitude around the origin. You will also apply matrices to derive some trigonometric identities, and to illustrate some elementary computer graphics techniques.

LESSON

11-1

Matrix Multiplication

What Is a Matrix?

The Math Team holds an autumn and a spring fund raiser. Below are the numbers of each item sold at each sale last year.

	Trail Treats	Carob Chews	Fruit Clusters	Nut Bars
Autumn	40	100	0	40
Spring	75	108	80	65

The numbers are presented in a **matrix**, a rectangular array. We identify a matrix by enclosing the array in square brackets. Each object in a matrix is called an **element**. The matrix above has 2 rows (labeled autumn and spring) and 4 columns (one for each item). The labels are not part of the matrix. Each element may be identified by giving its row and column. For instance, the element in row 2, column 1 is 75. This matrix is said to have *dimensions* 2 by 4, written 2×4. In general, a matrix with m rows and n columns has **dimensions** $\boldsymbol{m \times n}$. It is sometimes called an $m \times n$ matrix.

Example 1

The prices for trail treats, carob chews, fruit clusters, and nut bars are 1.00, 1.00, .50, and 1.50 dollars, respectively. Present these values in a matrix.

Solution

There are two possible matrices. One is a 4×1 matrix. It has 4 rows and 1 column, and is shown below.

$$\begin{bmatrix} 1.00 \\ 1.00 \\ 0.50 \\ 1.50 \end{bmatrix}$$

The other is the 1×4 matrix shown below.

$$\begin{bmatrix} 1.00 & 1.00 & 0.50 & 1.50 \end{bmatrix}$$

Multiplying a Row and a Column

To calculate the total amount of money (*the revenue*) received from each fund raiser, the club treasurer multiplies the cost of each item by the quantity sold, and then adds the results. For the autumn sale the revenue is $200 because

$$40(1.00) + 100(1.00) + 0(0.50) + 40(1.50) = 200.$$

This can be considered as the product of a matrix of quantities and a matrix of prices. The first matrix, the quantity matrix, is called a **row matrix**, because it consists of a single row. The second matrix, the price matrix, is a **column matrix**, because it consists of a single column.

$$\begin{bmatrix} 40 & 100 & 0 & 40 \end{bmatrix} \cdot \begin{bmatrix} 1.00 \\ 1.00 \\ 0.50 \\ 1.50 \end{bmatrix} = \begin{bmatrix} 200.00 \end{bmatrix}$$

The product of a row matrix and a column matrix is a matrix with a single element.

Similarly, the revenue received in the spring sale is \$320.50 .

$$75(1.00) + 108(1.00) + 80(.50) + 65(1.50) = 320.50$$

This can be represented as the following product of matrices.

$$\begin{bmatrix} 75 & 108 & 80 & 65 \end{bmatrix} \cdot \begin{bmatrix} 1.00 \\ 1.00 \\ 0.50 \\ 1.50 \end{bmatrix} = \begin{bmatrix} 320.50 \end{bmatrix}$$

Multiplying Entire Matrices

The two sets of products can be written as a single product by multiplying the 4×1 cost matrix from Example 1 by the original 2×4 matrix for quantities. If Q is the matrix with quantities sold, and U is the matrix with the unit prices, then $Q \cdot U = R$ represents the revenue.

$$\begin{array}{l} \\ \\ \text{Autumn} \\ \text{Spring} \end{array} \begin{array}{cccc} \text{Trail} & \text{Carob} & \text{Fruit} & \text{Nut} \\ \text{Treats} & \text{Chews} & \text{Clusters} & \text{Bars} \\ \left[40 \right. & 100 & 0 & \left. 40 \right] \\ \left[75 \right. & 108 & 80 & \left. 65 \right] \end{array} \cdot \begin{bmatrix} 1.00 \\ 1.00 \\ 0.50 \\ 1.50 \end{bmatrix} \begin{array}{l} \text{Trail Treats} \\ \text{Carob Chews} \\ \text{Fruit Clusters} \\ \text{Nut Bars} \end{array}$$

$$Q \cdot U$$

In general, *matrix multiplication* is done using rows from the left matrix and columns from the right matrix. Multiply the first element in the row by the first element in the column, the second element in the row by the second element in the column, and so on. Finally, add the resulting products. The shading below shows the first row times the column, which gave a total of \$200.00. Similarly, the second row times the column gives \$320.50. These results may be represented in a 2×1 matrix.

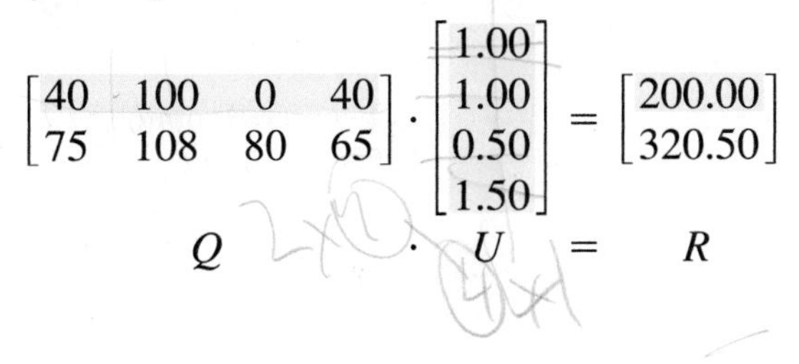

$$\begin{bmatrix} 40 & 100 & 0 & 40 \\ 75 & 108 & 80 & 65 \end{bmatrix} \cdot \begin{bmatrix} 1.00 \\ 1.00 \\ 0.50 \\ 1.50 \end{bmatrix} = \begin{bmatrix} 200.00 \\ 320.50 \end{bmatrix}$$

$$Q \cdot U = R$$

Notice how the dimensions of the original matrices relate to the product matrix: The product of a 2×4 matrix and a 4×1 matrix is a 2×1 matrix.

(must be equal)

In general, the product, $A \cdot B$, of two matrices A and B exists if and only if the number of columns of A equals the number of rows of B.

Definition

Suppose A is an $m \times n$ matrix and B is an $n \times p$ matrix. Then the **product matrix** $A \cdot B$ is an $m \times p$ matrix whose element in row i and column j is the sum of the products of elements in row i of A and corresponding elements in column j of B.

As usual, often we write AB for the product $A \cdot B$.

Example 2

Consider $A = \begin{bmatrix} 3 & 0 \\ 1 & 2 \end{bmatrix}$ and $B = \begin{bmatrix} 4 & 3 & 2 \\ 1 & 0 & 5 \end{bmatrix}$. Find the product matrix, if it exists.

a. AB

b. BA

Solution

a. By definition, the product of a 2×2 and a 2×3 matrix is a 2×3 matrix. This means you should expect to find 6 elements. The product of row 1 of A and column 1 of B is

$$3 \cdot 4 + 0 \cdot 1 = 12.$$

Write this in the 1st row and 1st column of the product matrix.

$$\begin{bmatrix} 3 & 0 \\ 1 & 2 \end{bmatrix} \cdot \begin{bmatrix} 4 & 3 & 2 \\ 1 & 0 & 5 \end{bmatrix} = \begin{bmatrix} 12 & - & - \\ - & - & - \end{bmatrix}$$

The product of row 1 of A and column 2 of B is $3 \cdot 3 + 0 \cdot 0 = 9$. This is the element in row 1 and column 2 of the product.

$$\begin{bmatrix} 3 & 0 \\ 1 & 2 \end{bmatrix} \cdot \begin{bmatrix} 4 & 3 & 2 \\ 1 & 0 & 5 \end{bmatrix} = \begin{bmatrix} 12 & 9 & - \\ - & - & - \end{bmatrix}$$

The other four elements of the product matrix are found by using the

same row by column pattern. For instance, the element in the 2nd row, 3rd column of the product is found by multiplying the 2nd row of A by the 3rd column of B, shown here along with the final result.

$$\begin{bmatrix} 3 & 0 \\ 1 & 2 \end{bmatrix} \cdot \begin{bmatrix} 4 & 3 & 2 \\ 1 & 0 & 5 \end{bmatrix} = \begin{bmatrix} 12 & 9 & 6 \\ 6 & 3 & 12 \end{bmatrix}$$

b. To calculate the element in the 1st row, 1st column of BA you would have to multiply the shaded numbers.

$$\begin{bmatrix} 4 & 3 & 2 \\ 1 & 0 & 5 \end{bmatrix} \cdot \begin{bmatrix} 3 & 0 \\ 1 & 2 \end{bmatrix}$$

The row by column multiplication cannot be done. The product BA does not exist.

Properties of Matrix Multiplication

As Example 2 illustrates, matrix multiplication is not commutative. However, matrix multiplication is associative. That is, for matrices A, B, C where multiplication exists, $(AB)C = A(BC)$. In Example 3 one product of three matrices is calculated. In the Questions you will verify associativity for this case.

Example 3

Suppose that the Math Team mentioned earlier is permitted to keep 40% of its sales in the autumn and 50% in the spring. Let $P = [.4\ .5]$ represent the percents kept. Calculate $P(QU)$, and describe what this product represents.

Solution

Earlier we calculated

$$QU = \begin{bmatrix} 40 & 100 & 0 & 40 \\ 75 & 108 & 80 & 65 \end{bmatrix} \cdot \begin{bmatrix} 1.00 \\ 1.00 \\ 0.50 \\ 1.50 \end{bmatrix} = \begin{bmatrix} 200.00 \\ 320.50 \end{bmatrix}.$$

Thus

$$\begin{aligned} P(QU) &= \begin{bmatrix} .4 & .5 \end{bmatrix} \cdot \begin{bmatrix} 200.00 \\ 320.50 \end{bmatrix} \\ &= \begin{bmatrix} 80 + 160.25 \end{bmatrix} \\ &= \begin{bmatrix} 240.25 \end{bmatrix}. \end{aligned}$$

The product represents the total amount of profit earned by the Math Team on its two fund raisers.

QUESTIONS

Covering the Reading

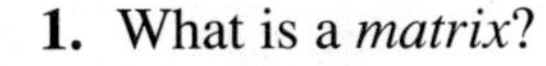

1. What is a *matrix*?

In 2–5, use the matrix at the right below which shows the numbers of members of the House of Representatives of each gender for the 102nd–105th Congresses.

	male	female
1991	407	28
1993	388	47
1995	388	47
1997	384	51

2. What are the dimensions of this matrix?
3. What is the element in row 3, column 2?
4. If a_{ij} represents the element in row i and column j, what is a_{21}?
5. What does the sum of the elements in each row represent?
6. If A and B are matrices, under what circumstances does the product AB exist ?

In 7 and 8, give the dimensions of AB.

7. A is 3×2, B is 2×4
8. A is 5×1, B is 1×7

In Congressional hearing rooms, Senatorial or House committees listen to testimony covering topics such as human rights, the budget, farming, or education.

In 9–12, multiply.

9. $\begin{bmatrix} 8 & 2 \end{bmatrix} \cdot \begin{bmatrix} 9 \\ 1 \end{bmatrix}$

10. $\begin{bmatrix} 7 & 3 & 1 \\ 0 & 4 & 2 \end{bmatrix} \cdot \begin{bmatrix} -1 \\ 1 \\ -2 \end{bmatrix}$

11. $\begin{bmatrix} a & b \\ c & d \end{bmatrix} \cdot \begin{bmatrix} x \\ y \end{bmatrix}$

12. $\begin{bmatrix} 1 & 0 \\ 2 & 3 \end{bmatrix} \cdot \begin{bmatrix} -2 & 3 \\ 1 & 4 \end{bmatrix}$

13. Give the dimensions of two matrices which cannot be multiplied.

14. Refer to the Math Team fund raiser described in the Lesson. In Example 3, the matrix $P(QU)$ was calculated. Calculate $(PQ)U$. That is, find the product matrix PQ, then multiply this result by U. Does $P(QU) = (PQ)U$?

Applying the Mathematics

In 15 and 16, solve for the variables.

15. $\begin{bmatrix} 3 & 4 \\ 1 & 2 \end{bmatrix} \cdot \begin{bmatrix} x \\ 1 \end{bmatrix} = \begin{bmatrix} -2 \\ 0 \end{bmatrix}$

16. $\begin{bmatrix} 2 & a \\ 3 & b \end{bmatrix} \cdot \begin{bmatrix} 5 \\ 6 \end{bmatrix} = \begin{bmatrix} 7 \\ 8 \end{bmatrix}$

17. For square matrices, $M^2 = M \cdot M$. Let $M = \begin{bmatrix} 0 & -2 \\ -2 & 0 \end{bmatrix}$.

a. Calculate M^2. **b.** Calculate M^3.

18. The diagram below shows the major highways connecting four cities.

a. Write the number of direct routes (not through any other city on the diagram) between each pair of cities into a matrix as begun below. (Note that U.S. 41–U.S. 52 is considered to be one road.)

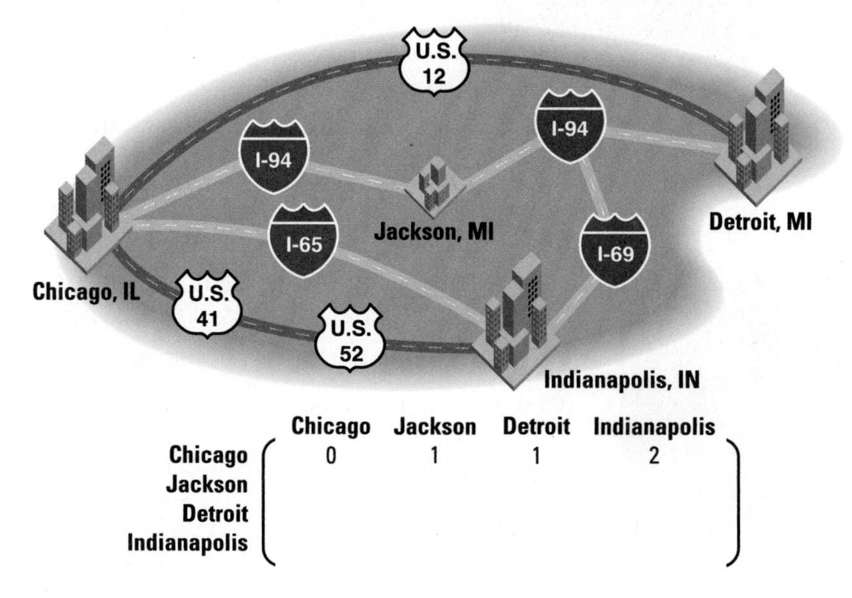

	Chicago	Jackson	Detroit	Indianapolis
Chicago	0	1	1	2
Jackson				
Detroit				
Indianapolis				

b. Multiply the matrix from part **a** by itself and interpret what it signifies.

Beauty and the Beast

In 19 and 20, the matrix N gives the number of tickets sold for a Children's Theater performance. The matrix C gives the unit cost in dollars for each ticket.

$$N = \begin{array}{r} \text{Weekday matinee} \\ \text{Weekend matinee} \\ \text{Weekend evening} \end{array} \overset{\begin{array}{cc} \text{Adults} & \text{Children} \end{array}}{\begin{bmatrix} 250 & 340 \\ 273 & 320 \\ 170 & 405 \end{bmatrix}} \qquad C = \begin{bmatrix} 6.00 \\ 4.00 \end{bmatrix} \begin{array}{l} \text{Adults} \\ \text{Children} \end{array}$$

19. **a.** Find NC.

b. What was the theater's total revenue for the weekday performance?

20. A portion of the receipts for each performance goes to a children's health charity: 50% for the weekday performance and 40% for each of the weekend performances. Let $P = \begin{bmatrix} .50 & .40 & .40 \end{bmatrix}$. Find the total contribution to charity for all three performances.

Review

21. Five pairs each of red, blue, yellow, and green socks are in a drawer. Four pairs are selected randomly. Let b = number of blue pairs selected. *(Lesson 7-6)*

a. List all possible values of b.

b. Make a probability distribution table for the random variable b.

c. Construct a histogram of the probability distribution.

22. Let (x, y) be the image of the point $(1, 0)$ under a rotation of magnitude θ about the origin. Then x = __?__ and y = __?__. *(Lesson 4-3)*

23. Let f and g be functions whose equations are given by $f(x) = x^2 + 2$ and $g(x) = 3x - 1$. Find a rule for $f(g(x))$. *(Lesson 3-7)*

24. **a.** Draw $\triangle SAD$, where $S = (3, 7)$, $A = (0, 5)$, and $D = (2, -3)$.

b. Draw $\triangle S'A'D'$, the reflection image of $\triangle SAD$ over the y-axis.

c. If r_y represents reflection over the y-axis, then r_y: $(x, y) \rightarrow$ __?__. *(Lesson 3-4)*

25. Match each transformation with the *best* description. *(Lessons 3-2, 3-4, 3-5)*

a. $M(x, y) = (x + 3, y - 2)$ (i) reflection over the x-axis

b. $N(x, y) = (x, -y)$ (ii) reflection over the line $y = x$

c. $P(x, y) = (y, x)$ (iii) scale change

d. $Q(x, y) = \left(\frac{x}{3}, \frac{y}{3}\right)$ (iv) size change

e. $V(x, y) = (0.1x, 10y)$ (v) translation

Exploration

26. Matrices frequently appear in the business and sports sections of newspapers, though they are not usually identified with brackets.

a. Find an example of a matrix in a newspaper.

b. State its dimensions.

c. Describe what each row and column represents.

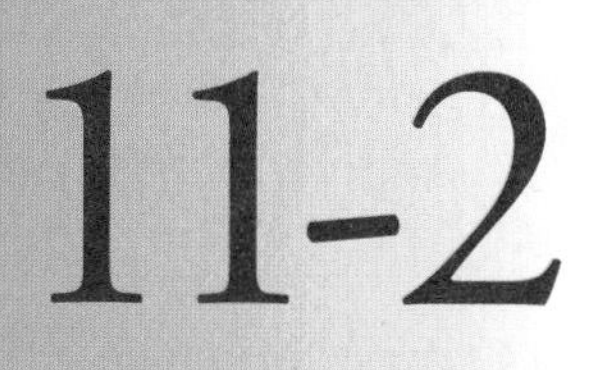

Matrices for Transformations

Representing a Geometric Figure by a Matrix

Matrices can represent geometric figures as well as numerical data. To do so, let the point (a, b) be written as the matrix $\begin{bmatrix} a \\ b \end{bmatrix}$. Such a matrix is sometimes called a **point matrix**. Then a polygon with n sides can be represented by a $2 \times n$ matrix in which the columns are the coordinates of consecutive vertices. For instance, $\triangle QRS$ below can be represented by the matrix $\begin{bmatrix} -1 & 3 & 3 \\ -1 & -1 & 2 \end{bmatrix}$. If named $\triangle SRQ$, the triangle is represented by $\begin{bmatrix} 3 & 3 & -1 \\ 2 & -1 & -1 \end{bmatrix}$.

$Q \quad R \quad S$

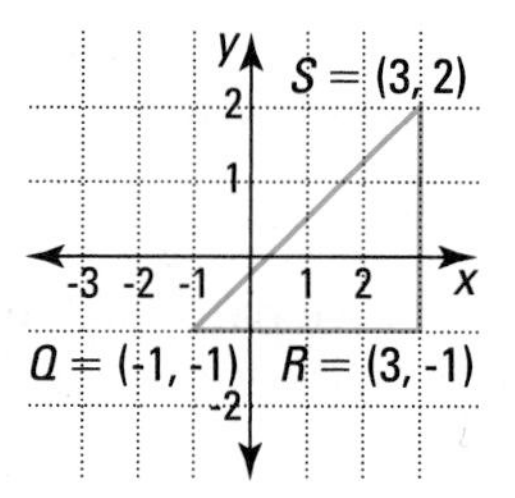

Representing a Transformation by a Matrix

Matrices may also represent transformations.

Example 1

a. Multiply the matrix for $\triangle QRS$ above by the matrix $\begin{bmatrix} 1 & 0 \\ 0 & -1 \end{bmatrix}$ and graph the resulting image, $\triangle Q'R'S'$.

b. Describe the transformation represented by the matrix.

Solution

a. $\begin{bmatrix} 1 & 0 \\ 0 & -1 \end{bmatrix} \cdot \begin{bmatrix} -1 & 3 & 3 \\ -1 & -1 & 2 \end{bmatrix} = \begin{bmatrix} -1 & 3 & 3 \\ 1 & 1 & -2 \end{bmatrix}$

$Q \quad R \quad S \qquad Q' \quad R' \quad S'$

b. $\triangle Q'R'S'$ is the reflection image of $\triangle QRS$ over the x-axis.

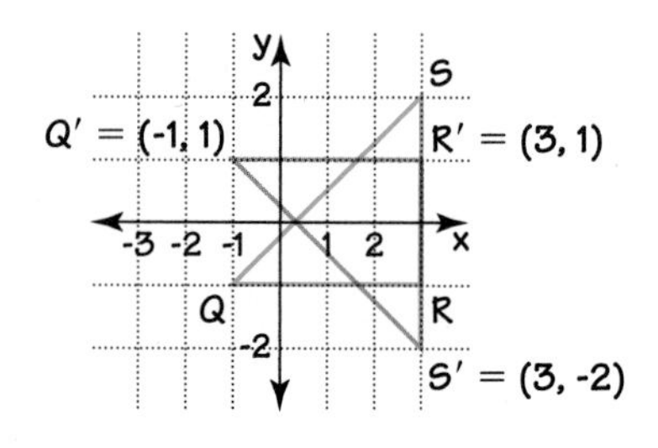

In general, multiplying any point matrix $\begin{bmatrix} x \\ y \end{bmatrix}$ by $\begin{bmatrix} 1 & 0 \\ 0 & -1 \end{bmatrix}$ gives

$$\begin{bmatrix} 1 & 0 \\ 0 & -1 \end{bmatrix} \cdot \begin{bmatrix} x \\ y \end{bmatrix} = \begin{bmatrix} x \\ -y \end{bmatrix}.$$

This means that multiplication by $\begin{bmatrix} 1 & 0 \\ 0 & -1 \end{bmatrix}$ maps (x, y) to $(x, -y)$. You should recognize this transformation as r_x, the reflection over the x-axis.

The above result can be generalized. Let F be a matrix for a geometric figure. Whenever multiplication of F by matrix M produces a matrix for the image of F under a transformation T, then M is called the **matrix representing the transformation *T***, or the matrix for T.

Matrices for Reflections

Below are matrices for r_x and other reflections.

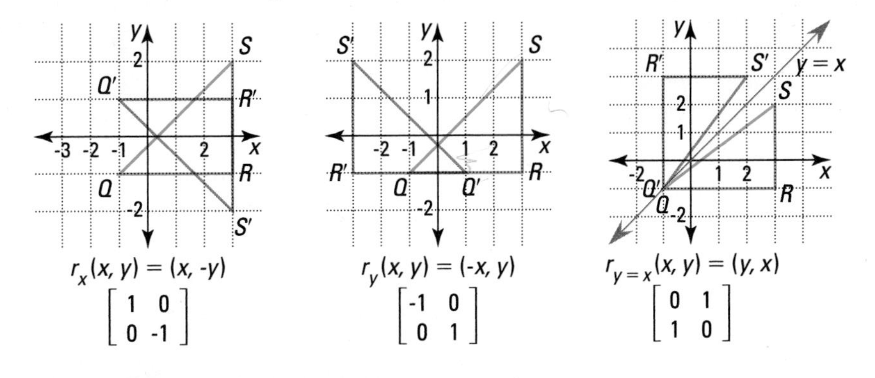

$r_x(x, y) = (x, -y)$ $\begin{bmatrix} 1 & 0 \\ 0 & -1 \end{bmatrix}$

$r_y(x, y) = (-x, y)$ $\begin{bmatrix} -1 & 0 \\ 0 & 1 \end{bmatrix}$

$r_{y=x}(x, y) = (y, x)$ $\begin{bmatrix} 0 & 1 \\ 1 & 0 \end{bmatrix}$

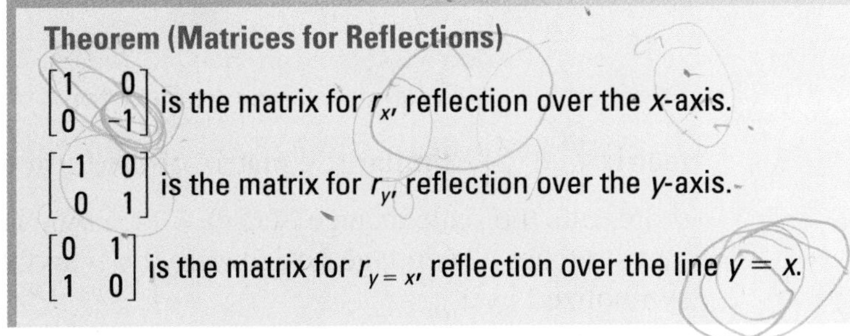

Theorem (Matrices for Reflections)

$\begin{bmatrix} 1 & 0 \\ 0 & -1 \end{bmatrix}$ is the matrix for r_x, reflection over the x-axis.

$\begin{bmatrix} -1 & 0 \\ 0 & 1 \end{bmatrix}$ is the matrix for r_y, reflection over the y-axis.

$\begin{bmatrix} 0 & 1 \\ 1 & 0 \end{bmatrix}$ is the matrix for $r_{y=x}$, reflection over the line $y = x$.

Matrices for Certain Other Transformations

What transformation does the matrix $\begin{bmatrix} 1 & 0 \\ 0 & 1 \end{bmatrix}$ represent? Since $\begin{bmatrix} 1 & 0 \\ 0 & 1 \end{bmatrix} \cdot \begin{bmatrix} x \\ y \end{bmatrix} = \begin{bmatrix} x \\ y \end{bmatrix}$, the transformation represented by this matrix maps any point (x, y) to itself, and is the identity transformation. Futhermore, since $\begin{bmatrix} 1 & 0 \\ 0 & 1 \end{bmatrix} \cdot \begin{bmatrix} a & b \\ c & d \end{bmatrix} = \begin{bmatrix} a & b \\ c & d \end{bmatrix} \cdot \begin{bmatrix} 1 & 0 \\ 0 & 1 \end{bmatrix} = \begin{bmatrix} a & b \\ c & d \end{bmatrix}$ for all a, b, c, and d, $\begin{bmatrix} 1 & 0 \\ 0 & 1 \end{bmatrix}$ is an identity for the set of 2×2 matrices under multiplication. There is no other 2×2 matrix with this property. Thus, the matrix $\begin{bmatrix} 1 & 0 \\ 0 & 1 \end{bmatrix}$ is called the **2 × 2 identity matrix**.

Transformations other than reflections or the identity transformation can be represented by matrices.

Is It Really Larger?
The full moon nearest the autumnal equinox is called the Harvest Moon. Near the horizon, the moon appears enlarged by a scale change, but it is an illusion.

Example 2

a. Multiply the matrix for $\triangle JKL$ with $J = (-1, 2)$, $K = (1, 3)$, and $L = (1, -1)$ by $\begin{bmatrix} 3 & 0 \\ 0 & 3 \end{bmatrix}$.

b. Graph the preimage and image.

c. What transformation does $\begin{bmatrix} 3 & 0 \\ 0 & 3 \end{bmatrix}$ represent?

Solution

a. Write the matrix for $\triangle JKL$ and multiply it by the given matrix.

$$\begin{bmatrix} 3 & 0 \\ 0 & 3 \end{bmatrix} \cdot \begin{bmatrix} -1 & 1 & 1 \\ 2 & 3 & -1 \end{bmatrix} = \begin{bmatrix} -3 & 3 & 3 \\ 6 & 9 & -3 \end{bmatrix}$$

b.

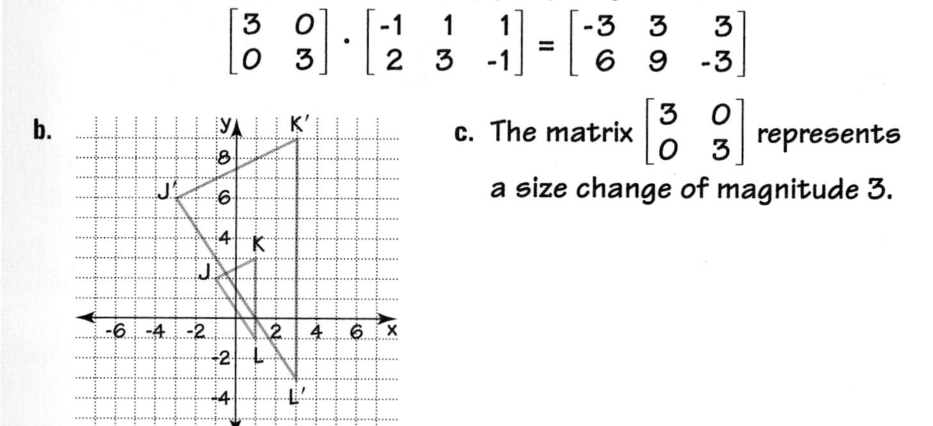

c. The matrix $\begin{bmatrix} 3 & 0 \\ 0 & 3 \end{bmatrix}$ represents a size change of magnitude 3.

In general, a size change of magnitude k for $k \neq 0$ is represented by the matrix $\begin{bmatrix} k & 0 \\ 0 & k \end{bmatrix}$. Similarly, a matrix of the form $\begin{bmatrix} a & 0 \\ 0 & b \end{bmatrix}$ with $a \neq 0$, $b \neq 0$ represents the scale change $S(x, y) = (ax, by)$. This is the transformation that stretches a preimage horizontally by a and vertically by b and is symbolized by $S_{a,b}$.

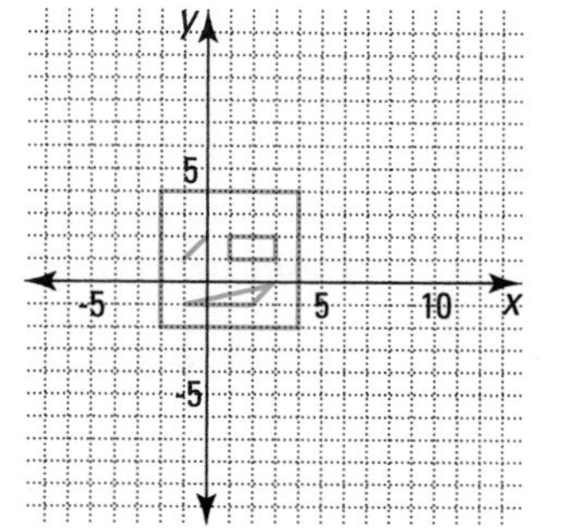

Example 3

a. Apply $\begin{bmatrix} 3 & 0 \\ 0 & 2 \end{bmatrix}$ to the figure at the left.

b. Identify the transformation.

Solution

a. Here is the product that represents the image of the square.

$$\begin{bmatrix} 3 & 0 \\ 0 & 2 \end{bmatrix} \cdot \begin{bmatrix} 4 & 4 & -2 & -2 \\ 4 & -2 & -2 & 4 \end{bmatrix} = \begin{bmatrix} 12 & 12 & -6 & -6 \\ 8 & -4 & -4 & 8 \end{bmatrix}$$

The images of the interior figures are found with the following products.

segment $$\begin{bmatrix} 3 & 0 \\ 0 & 2 \end{bmatrix} \cdot \begin{bmatrix} -1 & 0 \\ 1 & 2 \end{bmatrix} = \begin{bmatrix} -3 & 0 \\ 2 & 4 \end{bmatrix}$$

rectangle $$\begin{bmatrix} 3 & 0 \\ 0 & 2 \end{bmatrix} \cdot \begin{bmatrix} 1 & 1 & 3 & 3 \\ 1 & 2 & 2 & 1 \end{bmatrix} = \begin{bmatrix} 3 & 3 & 9 & 9 \\ 2 & 4 & 4 & 2 \end{bmatrix}$$

triangle $$\begin{bmatrix} 3 & 0 \\ 0 & 2 \end{bmatrix} \cdot \begin{bmatrix} -1 & 3 & 2 \\ -1 & 0 & -1 \end{bmatrix} = \begin{bmatrix} -3 & 9 & 6 \\ -2 & 0 & -2 \end{bmatrix}$$

b. Graph the image.

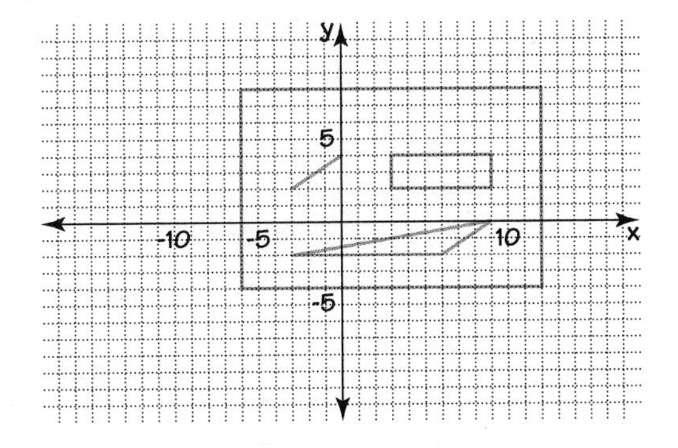

Notice that the image is a distortion, not a simple enlargement of the original figure. **Every part of the original figure is stretched 3 times horizontally and twice vertically. The transformation is the scale change $S_{3,2}$.**

QUESTIONS

Covering the Reading

1. *Multiple choice.* Which matrix represents the point (5, -2)?

(a) $\begin{bmatrix} 5 & -2 \end{bmatrix}$ (b) $\begin{bmatrix} -2 & 5 \end{bmatrix}$ (c) $\begin{bmatrix} 5 \\ -2 \end{bmatrix}$ (d) $\begin{bmatrix} -2 \\ 5 \end{bmatrix}$

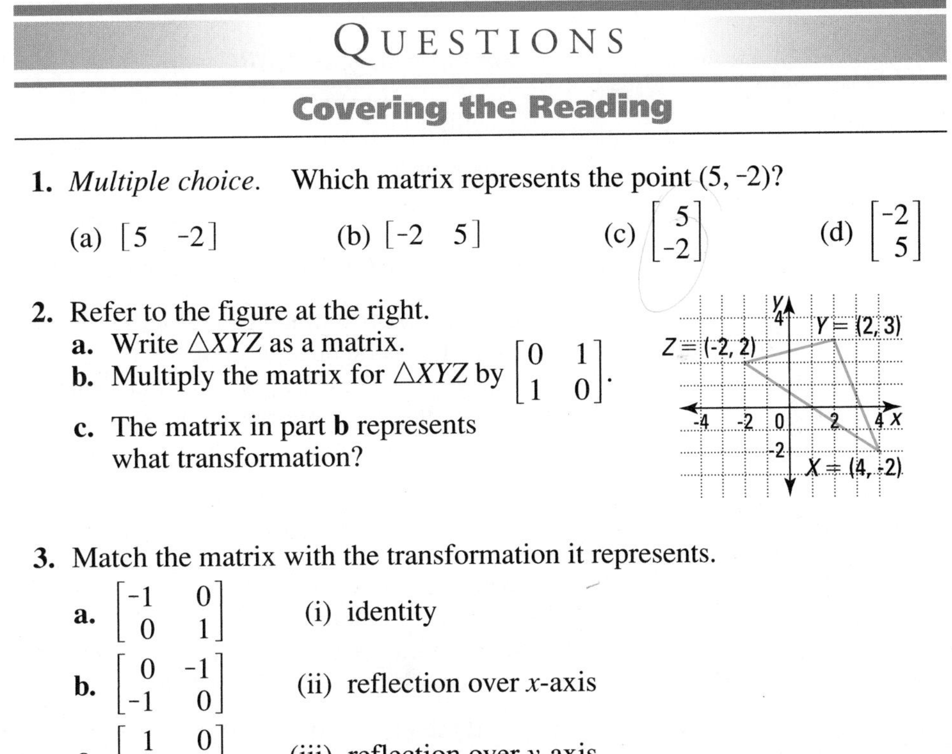

2. Refer to the figure at the right.

a. Write $\triangle XYZ$ as a matrix.

b. Multiply the matrix for $\triangle XYZ$ by $\begin{bmatrix} 0 & 1 \\ 1 & 0 \end{bmatrix}$.

c. The matrix in part **b** represents what transformation?

3. Match the matrix with the transformation it represents.

a. $\begin{bmatrix} -1 & 0 \\ 0 & 1 \end{bmatrix}$ (i) identity

b. $\begin{bmatrix} 0 & -1 \\ -1 & 0 \end{bmatrix}$ (ii) reflection over x-axis

c. $\begin{bmatrix} 1 & 0 \\ 0 & -1 \end{bmatrix}$ (iii) reflection over y-axis

d. $\begin{bmatrix} 1 & 0 \\ 0 & 1 \end{bmatrix}$ (iv) reflection over $y = x$

e. $\begin{bmatrix} 0 & 1 \\ 1 & 0 \end{bmatrix}$ (v) none of these

In 4 and 5, use the trapezoid *TRZD* at the right.

a. Find the image of *TRZD* under the transformation with the given matrix.

b. Describe the transformation.

4. $\begin{bmatrix} 1.5 & 0 \\ 0 & 1.5 \end{bmatrix}$ **5.** $\begin{bmatrix} 2 & 0 \\ 0 & 3 \end{bmatrix}$

In 6 and 7, state a matrix for the transformation.

6. size change of magnitude a

7. scale change $S_{a,b}$

Applying the Mathematics

8. Prove that $\begin{bmatrix} -1 & 0 \\ 0 & 1 \end{bmatrix}$ is the matrix for r_y, reflection over the y-axis.

9. a. Write the matrix for $r_{y=x}$.

b. Square the matrix.

c. What transformation does the matrix in part **b** represent?

10. a. Find the image of $\triangle ABC = \begin{bmatrix} 2 & 3 & 0 \\ -1 & 2 & 4 \end{bmatrix}$ under the transformation T with matrix $\begin{bmatrix} -1 & 0 \\ 0 & -1 \end{bmatrix}$.

b. Describe T.

In 11 and 12, consider the drawing of the cat Felix at the right.

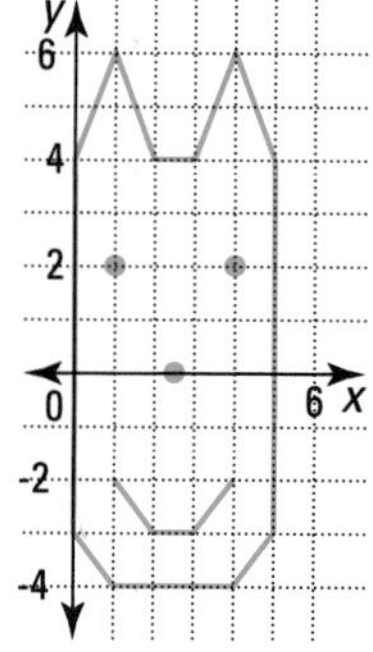

11. Write a matrix F to represent the outline of Felix's face.

12. Find a matrix for a transformation that when multiplied by F produces the desired image.

a. a face similar to Felix's with four times the area

b. a face that is shorter and wider than Felix's

c. a face that is longer and thinner than Felix's

13. Here are matrices for three collinear points A, B, and C, and a matrix T for a transformation:

$$A = \begin{bmatrix} 1 \\ 4 \end{bmatrix}, B = \begin{bmatrix} 0 \\ 2 \end{bmatrix}, C = \begin{bmatrix} -2 \\ -2 \end{bmatrix}; T = \begin{bmatrix} 2 & 7 \\ -1 & -4 \end{bmatrix}.$$

a. Find the images of the points under the transformation.

b. Are the images collinear?

c. Does this transformation preserve distance?

14. The matrix $\begin{bmatrix} \frac{\sqrt{3}}{2} & \frac{1}{2} \\ \frac{1}{2} & -\frac{\sqrt{3}}{2} \end{bmatrix}$ is associated with the reflection over a line ℓ which contains the origin. What is the measure of the acute angle formed by ℓ and the x-axis? You may need to experiment with graph paper and a protractor.

Review

15. Matrix X has dimensions 3×5 and matrix Y has dimensions 5×4.
   a. What are the dimensions of XY?
   b. How many elements are in XY? *(Lesson 11-1)*

In 16 and 17, multiply, if the product exists. *(Lesson 11-1)*

16. $\begin{bmatrix} 2 & 3 \\ 0 & 4 \end{bmatrix} \begin{bmatrix} x \\ y \end{bmatrix}$

17. $\begin{bmatrix} 3 & 0 & 1 \\ 2 & -1 & -2 \end{bmatrix} \cdot \begin{bmatrix} 4 & 0 \\ 1 & -3 \end{bmatrix}$

18. A clothing manufacturer has factories in Oakland, CA, and Charleston, SC. The quantities (in thousands) of each of three products manufactured are given in the production matrix P below. The costs in dollars for producing each item during three years are given in the cost matrix C below.

$$\begin{array}{l} \\ \text{Oakland} \\ \text{Charleston} \end{array} \begin{array}{c} \begin{array}{ccc} \text{Coats} & \text{Pants} & \text{Shirts} \end{array} \\ \begin{bmatrix} 10 & 10 & 22 \\ 20 & 15 & 0 \end{bmatrix} \end{array} = P, \quad \begin{array}{l} \\ \text{Coats} \\ \text{Pants} \\ \text{Shirts} \end{array} \begin{array}{c} \begin{array}{ccc} 1994 & 1995 & 1996 \end{array} \\ \begin{bmatrix} 30 & 30 & 32 \\ 5 & 7 & 8 \\ 2 & 3 & 3.5 \end{bmatrix} \end{array} = C$$

   a. Calculate PC.
   b. Interpret PC by telling what each element represents.
   c. Does CP exist? Why or why not? *(Lesson 11-1)*

19. Consider $X = \begin{bmatrix} 1 & 2 \\ 3 & -1 \end{bmatrix}$, $Y = \begin{bmatrix} 4 & 3 \\ 0 & -1 \end{bmatrix}$, and $Z = \begin{bmatrix} -2 & 0 \\ 1 & -1 \end{bmatrix}$.
   a. Find $(XY)Z$.
   b. Find $X(YZ)$.
   c. What property of matrix multiplication do the results of parts **a** and **b** illustrate? *(Lesson 11-1)*

In 20 and 21, solve for θ. *(Lesson 4-4)*

20. $\cos(-\theta) = -\cos\theta$

21. $\tan\theta = \sin\theta$

22. Let $k(x) = \sqrt{x}$ and $n(x) = 3x + 1$. *True or false.* $(k \circ n)(x) = (n \circ k)(x)$. Justify your answer. *(Lesson 3-7)*

Exploration

23. A cube in a three-dimensional coordinate system can be represented by the matrix C below.

$$C = \begin{bmatrix} 1 & 1 & 1 & 1 & -1 & -1 & -1 & -1 \\ 1 & 1 & -1 & -1 & -1 & 1 & 1 & -1 \\ 1 & -1 & -1 & 1 & 1 & 1 & -1 & -1 \end{bmatrix}$$

   a. Graph the cube.
   b. Let T be the transformation represented by the matrix $M = \begin{bmatrix} 2 & 0 & 0 \\ 0 & 2 & 0 \\ 0 & 0 & 2 \end{bmatrix}$. Calculate and graph MC.
   c. Describe the transformation T.

LESSON

11-3

Matrices for Composites of Transformations

Using Matrices to Find the Image of a Figure Under a Composite of Transformations

As you know, when two transformations are composed, the result is another transformation. In this lesson, composites of transformations are represented using matrices.

Example 1

Let $\triangle ABC = \begin{bmatrix} 2 & 6 & 6 \\ 1 & 1 & 3 \end{bmatrix}$.

a. Find $\triangle A'B'C'$, the image of $\triangle ABC$ under a reflection over the x-axis.

b. Reflect the image over $y = x$ to obtain $\triangle A''B''C''$.

Solution

a. The matrix for r_x is $\begin{bmatrix} 1 & 0 \\ 0 & -1 \end{bmatrix}$. So $\triangle A'B'C'$ is represented by the matrix

$$\begin{bmatrix} 1 & 0 \\ 0 & -1 \end{bmatrix} \cdot \begin{bmatrix} 2 & 6 & 6 \\ 1 & 1 & 3 \end{bmatrix} = \begin{bmatrix} 2 & 6 & 6 \\ -1 & -1 & -3 \end{bmatrix}.$$

b. The matrix for $r_{y=x}$ is $\begin{bmatrix} 0 & 1 \\ 1 & 0 \end{bmatrix}$. Apply this matrix to the matrix for $\triangle A'B'C'$ to get a matrix for $\triangle A''B''C''$.

$$\begin{bmatrix} 0 & 1 \\ 1 & 0 \end{bmatrix} \cdot \begin{bmatrix} 2 & 6 & 6 \\ -1 & -1 & -3 \end{bmatrix} = \begin{bmatrix} -1 & -1 & -3 \\ 2 & 6 & 6 \end{bmatrix}$$

At the right is a graph of the three triangles.

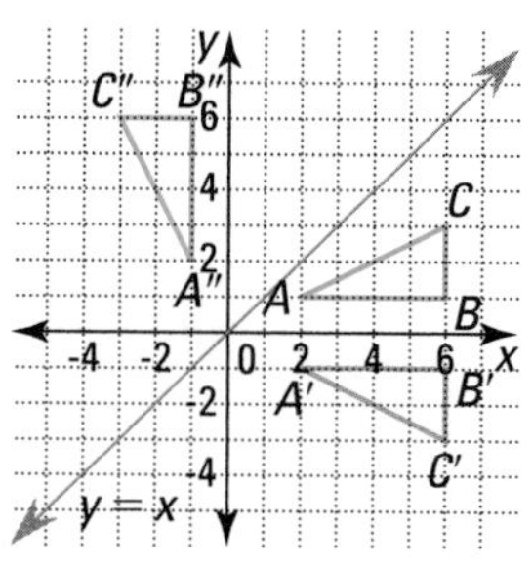

In Example 1, $\triangle A''B''C''$ is the image of $\triangle ABC$ under the *composite* of the reflections $r_{y=x}$ and r_x. That is, $\triangle A''B''C'' = r_{y=x}(r_x(\triangle ABC))$. To find a single matrix for the composite $r_{y=x} \circ r_x$, notice that the matrix for $\triangle A''B''C''$ came from the product

$$\begin{bmatrix} 0 & 1 \\ 1 & 0 \end{bmatrix} \cdot \left(\begin{bmatrix} 1 & 0 \\ 0 & -1 \end{bmatrix} \begin{bmatrix} 2 & 6 & 6 \\ 1 & 1 & 3 \end{bmatrix} \right).$$

Because matrix multiplication is associative, the preceding expression may be rewritten as

$$\left(\begin{bmatrix} 0 & 1 \\ 1 & 0 \end{bmatrix} \cdot \begin{bmatrix} 1 & 0 \\ 0 & -1 \end{bmatrix} \right) \cdot \begin{bmatrix} 2 & 6 & 6 \\ 1 & 1 & 3 \end{bmatrix}.$$

Thus, multiplying the matrices for $r_{y=x}$ and r_x gives the matrix for the composite $r_{y=x} \circ r_x$.

$$\begin{bmatrix} 0 & 1 \\ 1 & 0 \end{bmatrix} \cdot \begin{bmatrix} 1 & 0 \\ 0 & -1 \end{bmatrix} = \begin{bmatrix} 0 & -1 \\ 1 & 0 \end{bmatrix}$$

Compare the preimage and the final image in Example 1. The transformation that maps $\triangle ABC$ to $\triangle A''B''C''$ is R_{90}, the *rotation* of 90° counterclockwise with the origin as its center. (Note: We usually omit the degree symbol in the subscript for rotations.) So $R_{90} = r_{y=x} \circ r_x$.

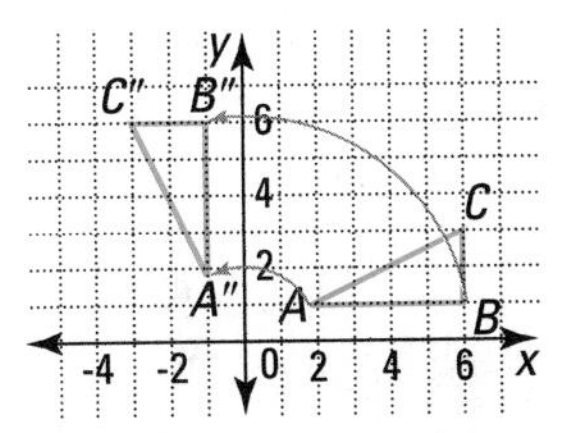

The results of Example 1 can be generalized:

A Good Turn. *This wheel has 90° rotation symmetry.*

Theorem
If M is the matrix associated with a transformation t, and N is the matrix associated with a transformation u, then NM is the matrix associated with the transformation $u \circ t$.

How to Find the Matrix for a Composite of Transformations

Example 2

Use the fact that a rotation of 180° is the composite of a 90° rotation with a 90° rotation to find a matrix for R_{180}.

Solution

$R_{180} = R_{90} \circ R_{90}$. Thus, the product of the matrix for R_{90} with itself equals the matrix for R_{180}.

$$\begin{bmatrix} 0 & -1 \\ 1 & 0 \end{bmatrix} \cdot \begin{bmatrix} 0 & -1 \\ 1 & 0 \end{bmatrix} = \begin{bmatrix} -1 & 0 \\ 0 & -1 \end{bmatrix}$$

So $\begin{bmatrix} -1 & 0 \\ 0 & -1 \end{bmatrix}$ is a matrix for R_{180}.

Check

Apply this matrix to $\triangle ABC$ of Example 1.

$$\begin{bmatrix} -1 & 0 \\ 0 & -1 \end{bmatrix} \cdot \begin{bmatrix} 2 & 6 & 6 \\ 1 & 1 & 3 \end{bmatrix} = \begin{bmatrix} -2 & -6 & -6 \\ -1 & -1 & -3 \end{bmatrix}$$

The product should represent the image of $\triangle ABC$ under a rotation of 180° around the origin. The graph below illustrates that it does.

Similarly, a matrix for R_{270} can be found by using $R_{270} = R_{180} \circ R_{90}$. In the Questions you are asked to prove that R_{270} is represented by $\begin{bmatrix} 0 & 1 \\ -1 & 0 \end{bmatrix}$.

The following theorem summarizes these results.

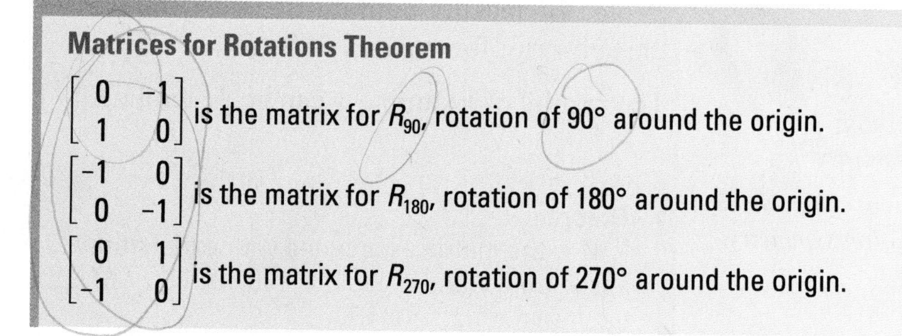

Matrices for Rotations Theorem

$\begin{bmatrix} 0 & -1 \\ 1 & 0 \end{bmatrix}$ is the matrix for R_{90}, rotation of 90° around the origin.

$\begin{bmatrix} -1 & 0 \\ 0 & -1 \end{bmatrix}$ is the matrix for R_{180}, rotation of 180° around the origin.

$\begin{bmatrix} 0 & 1 \\ -1 & 0 \end{bmatrix}$ is the matrix for R_{270}, rotation of 270° around the origin.

Remembering Matrices for Transformations

You may wonder how you will ever remember matrices for each of the transformations you have studied. The key is a simple but beautiful result: if a transformation can be represented by a 2×2 matrix, then the first column of the matrix is the image of (1, 0), and the second column of the matrix is the image of (0, 1).

For instance, suppose you forget the matrix for R_{90}. Visualize the 90° rotation of (1, 0) and (0, 1). Note that $R_{90}(1, 0) = (0, 1)$ and $R_{90}(0, 1) = (-1, 0)$. So the matrix for R_{90} is

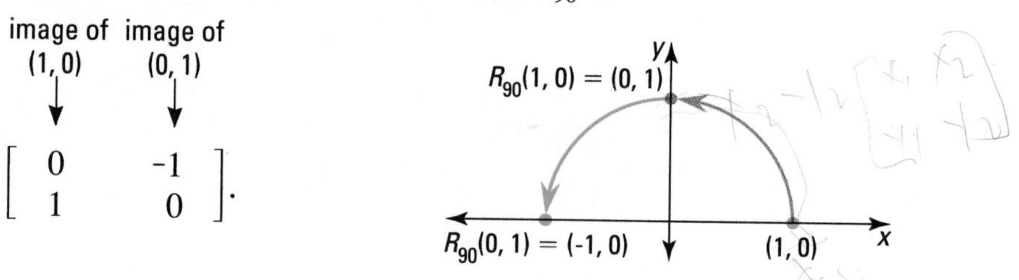

This relation is called the Matrix Basis Theorem because the matrix is *based* on the images of the points (1, 0) and (0, 1).

Matrix Basis Theorem

Suppose T is a transformation represented by a 2×2 matrix.

If $T(1, 0) = (x_1, y_1)$ and $T(0, 1) = (x_2, y_2)$, then T has the matrix $\begin{bmatrix} x_1 & x_2 \\ y_1 & y_2 \end{bmatrix}$.

Proof

Let M be the 2×2 matrix for T. Because $T(1, 0) = (x_1, y_1)$ and $T(0, 1) = (x_2, y_2)$,

$$M \cdot \begin{bmatrix} 1 & 0 \\ 0 & 1 \end{bmatrix} = \begin{bmatrix} x_1 & x_2 \\ y_1 & y_2 \end{bmatrix}.$$

(1st point, 2nd point; image of 1st point, image of 2nd point)

But $\begin{bmatrix} 1 & 0 \\ 0 & 1 \end{bmatrix}$ is the 2×2 identity matrix for multiplication, so $M = \begin{bmatrix} x_1 & x_2 \\ y_1 & y_2 \end{bmatrix}$.

Example 3

Use the Matrix Basis Theorem to verify that $\begin{bmatrix} -1 & 0 \\ 0 & -1 \end{bmatrix}$ represents the transformation R_{180}.

Solution

Under a 180° rotation, the image of (1, 0) is (-1, 0) and the image of (0, 1) is (0, -1). Thus, by the Matrix Basis Theorem,

$$R_{180} = \begin{bmatrix} -1 & 0 \\ 0 & -1 \end{bmatrix}.$$

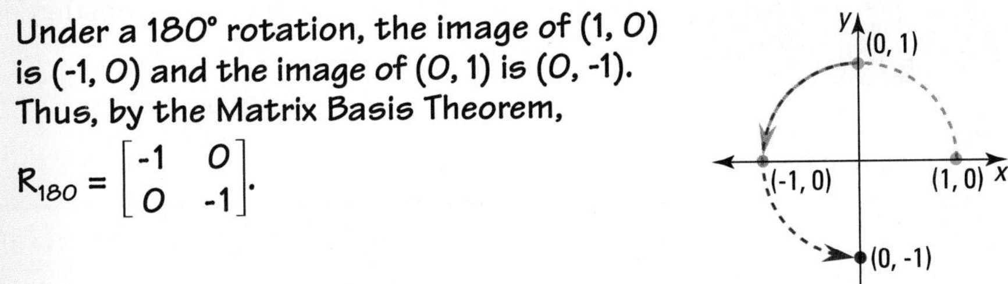

QUESTIONS

Covering the Reading

1. In the composite $r_{y=x} \circ r_x$, which reflection is done first?

2. What is a single transformation for $r_{y=x} \circ r_x$?

3. What is a matrix for R_{90}?

4. Refer to Example 1.
   a. Reflect $\triangle ABC$ over the x-axis. Then reflect its image $\triangle A'B'C'$ over the y-axis to get a second image $\triangle A''B''C''$.
   b. What transformation can take you directly from $\triangle ABC$ to $\triangle A''B''C''$?
   c. The composite $r_y \circ r_x$ is represented by $\begin{bmatrix} -1 & 0 \\ 0 & 1 \end{bmatrix} \cdot \begin{bmatrix} 1 & 0 \\ 0 & -1 \end{bmatrix}$. Find this product.
   d. What transformation is represented by the product in part **c**?

5. Refer to the figures graphed at the right.
   a. What transformation you have studied maps $\triangle RQS$ to $\triangle R'Q'S'$?
   b. Write a matrix for that transformation.

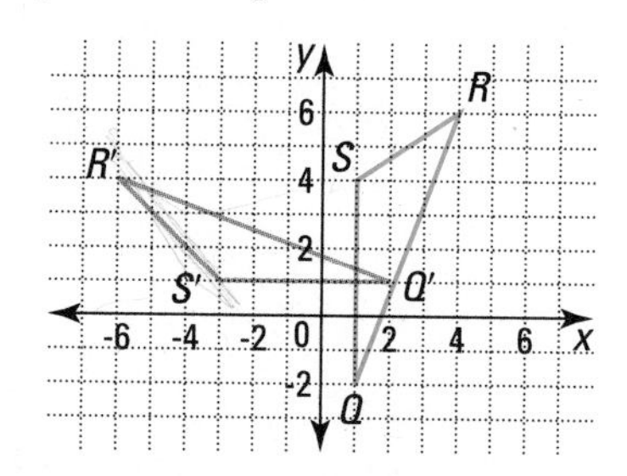

6. **a.** Derive the matrix for R_{270} by multiplying matrices for R_{90} and R_{180}.
   b. Does the order in which you multiply the matrices matter? Why or why not?

Which Way is Up?
This photograph of beach bungalows in Bali, Indonesia, has been rotated 90°. Which side is the preimage?

7. Let $\triangle DEF$ be represented by the matrix $\begin{bmatrix} 0 & 6 & 6 \\ 0 & 0 & 2 \end{bmatrix}$.
   a. Find the reflection image of $\triangle DEF$ over the line with equation $y = x$.
   b. Transform the image in part **a** by the scale change $S_{2,\,0.6}$.
   c. Give a matrix for the composite $S_{2,\,0.6} \circ r_{y=x}$.

8. Solve for a, b, c, and d. $\begin{bmatrix} a & b \\ c & d \end{bmatrix} \cdot \begin{bmatrix} 1 & 0 \\ 0 & 1 \end{bmatrix} = \begin{bmatrix} w & x \\ y & z \end{bmatrix}$

In 9–11, a transformation is given. **a.** Find the image of (1, 0) under the transformation. **b.** Find the image of (0, 1) under the transformation. **c.** Find the 2×2 matrix for the transformation derived from the Matrix Basis Theorem.

9. R_{-90}

10. $r_{x=-y}$

11. $S_{4,\,3}$

Applying the Mathematics

In 12 and 13, a transformation t has matrix $\begin{bmatrix} 2 & 5 \\ 1 & 3 \end{bmatrix}$ and a transformation u has matrix $\begin{bmatrix} 4 & 2 \\ -1 & 3 \end{bmatrix}$. Let $\triangle ABC$ be represented by $\begin{bmatrix} 8 & 3 & 2 \\ -2 & 0 & -5 \end{bmatrix}$. Calculate and graph $\triangle ABC$ and the indicated image.

12. $t \circ u\ (\triangle ABC)$

13. $u \circ t\ (\triangle ABC)$

14. Use matrices to verify that $R_{90} \circ R_{270}$ is the identity transformation.

15. **a.** Calculate a matrix for $r_x \circ r_{y=x}$.
   b. Describe the composite transformation.

16. **a.** Find the image of (3, 4) under each of R_{90}, R_{180}, and R_{270}.
b. Graph (3, 4) and its three images.
c. The four points are vertices of what kind of polygon?
d. Find the center and radius of a circle that passes through these four points.

17. Find a 2 × 2 matrix for T if $T(x, y) = (3x - y, x + y)$.

Review

18. Write a matrix for the size change of magnitude 6. *(Lesson 11-2)*

19. Find x and y so that the following is true. *(Lesson 11-1)*

$$\begin{bmatrix} 1 & -1 \\ x & 3 \end{bmatrix} \cdot \begin{bmatrix} 2 & y \\ 0 & 1 \end{bmatrix} = \begin{bmatrix} 2 & 6 \\ -4 & -11 \end{bmatrix}$$

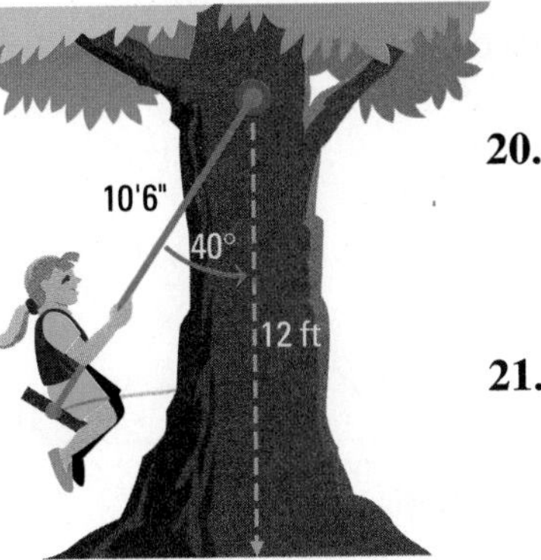

20. A child's swing is mounted 12 ft off the ground.If the ropes supporting the swing are 10'6" long, and the swing rotates through a vertical angle of 40°, as shown at the left, how high off the ground is the bottom of the swing in the position shown? *(Lesson 5-1)*

21. *Multiple choice.* The point (1, 0) is rotated 30° counterclockwise around the origin. Which statement is false? *(Lessons 4-2, 4-3, 4-5)*
(a) Its image is (cos 30°, sin 30°).
(b) Its image is $\left(\frac{\sqrt{3}}{2}, \frac{1}{2}\right)$.
(c) The arc length from (1, 0) to the image is $\frac{\pi}{6}$.
(d) The arc length from (1, 0) to the image is tan 30°.

22. The point $(x, 0.8)$ is in the second quadrant and on the unit circle. Find x. *(Lesson 4-3)*

23. **a.** Graph $f(\theta) = 2 \cos \theta$.
b. On the same set of axes, graph $g(\theta) = \cos 2\theta$.
c. Identify a scale change S which maps the graph of f onto the graph of g. *(Lessons 3-5, 4-7)*

In 24 and 25, simplify. *(Previous course)*

24. $\frac{\sqrt{2}}{2}\left(-\frac{\sqrt{2}}{2}\right)$

25. $\frac{3}{2} \cdot \frac{\sqrt{3}}{2} + \frac{\sqrt{3}}{2}$

Exploration

26. Write a Matrix Basis Theorem for three dimensions. Verify your theorem with an example.

LESSON

11-4

The General Rotation Matrix

You have seen that size changes with center at (0, 0), scale changes, reflections over the x- and y-axes and the line $y = x$, rotations of 90°, 180°, and 270°, and several other transformations can all be represented by 2×2 matrices. For what other transformations do 2×2 matrices exist?

Finding the Matrix for R_θ

Perhaps surprisingly, all rotations around (0, 0) can be represented by 2×2 matrices. To develop a general rotation matrix requires only the Matrix Basis Theorem and a little trigonometry.

Let θ be the magnitude of a rotation around the origin. In this discussion, we assume θ is in degrees. First, note that composition of rotations with the same center is commutative, so $R_\theta \circ R_{90} = R_{90} \circ R_\theta$.

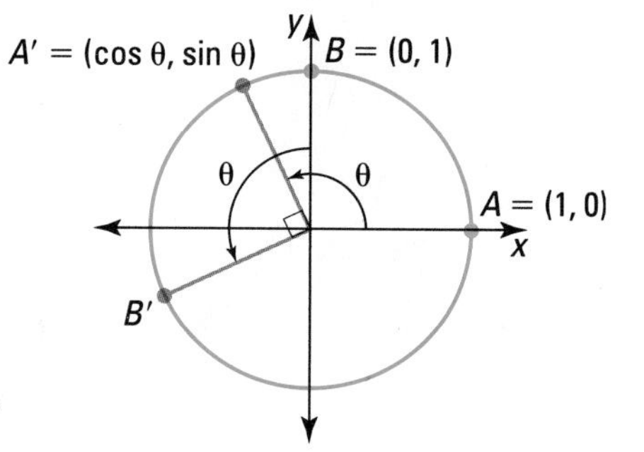

Consider the images A' and B' of the points $A = (1, 0)$ and $B = (0, 1)$ under R_θ. By definition of the cosine and sine, $A' = R_\theta(1, 0) = (\cos\theta, \sin\theta)$. Since $B' = R_{90}(B)$ and $B = R_{90}(A)$, then $B' = (R_\theta \circ R_{90})(A) = (R_{90} \circ R_\theta)(A) = R_{90}(A')$. Thus, if $B' = (x, y)$, then

$$\begin{bmatrix} x \\ y \end{bmatrix} = \begin{bmatrix} 0 & -1 \\ 1 & 0 \end{bmatrix} \cdot \begin{bmatrix} \cos\theta \\ \sin\theta \end{bmatrix} = \begin{bmatrix} -\sin\theta \\ \cos\theta \end{bmatrix}.$$

$$B' \quad = \quad R_{90} \quad \cdot \quad A'$$

Thus, $R_\theta(0, 1) = (-\sin\theta, \cos\theta)$.

From the images of (1, 0) and (0, 1) and the Matrix Basis Theorem, the matrix for R_θ follows.

Rotation Matrix Theorem
The matrix for R_θ, the rotation of magnitude θ about the origin, is

$$\begin{bmatrix} \cos\theta & -\sin\theta \\ \sin\theta & \cos\theta \end{bmatrix}.$$

Proof
The first column is $R_\theta(1, 0)$. The second column is $R_\theta(0, 1)$.

In the Questions you are asked to verify that the matrices for R_{90}, R_{180}, and R_{270} are special cases of this theorem.

Example 1

Find a 2×2 rotation matrix for R_{30}.

Solution

Use the Rotation Matrix Theorem.

$$R_{30} = \begin{bmatrix} \cos 30° & -\sin 30° \\ \sin 30° & \cos 30° \end{bmatrix} = \begin{bmatrix} \frac{\sqrt{3}}{2} & -\frac{1}{2} \\ \frac{1}{2} & \frac{\sqrt{3}}{2} \end{bmatrix}$$

Check

Triangle ABC below is represented by $\begin{bmatrix} 1 & 2 & 2 \\ 3 & 3 & 6 \end{bmatrix}$. Its image, $\triangle A'B'C'$, is represented by the product

$$\begin{bmatrix} \frac{\sqrt{3}}{2} & -\frac{1}{2} \\ \frac{1}{2} & \frac{\sqrt{3}}{2} \end{bmatrix} \cdot \begin{bmatrix} 1 & 2 & 2 \\ 3 & 3 & 6 \end{bmatrix} = \begin{bmatrix} \frac{\sqrt{3}}{2} - \frac{3}{2} & \sqrt{3} - \frac{3}{2} & \sqrt{3} - 3 \\ \frac{1}{2} + \frac{3\sqrt{3}}{2} & 1 + \frac{3\sqrt{3}}{2} & 1 + 3\sqrt{3} \end{bmatrix}$$

You are asked to verify that $AO = A'O$ and $m\angle AOA' = 30°$ in the Questions.

Computer animators use matrices to produce rotation images. Points are identified as ordered pairs on a coordinate grid. To rotate a set of points around the origin, a matrix for the points is multiplied by a matrix for the rotation.

An Application to Animation

Example 2

In a computer game, the wheel at the right (pictured on a coordinate grid) spins counterclockwise around the origin at the rate of π radians per second. The T (in the word TO) has endpoints at (1.7, 4.8), (1.8, 8), and (4, 7). Approximate the coordinates of the endpoints of T if someone playing the game hits a key to stop the wheel in 5.43 seconds.

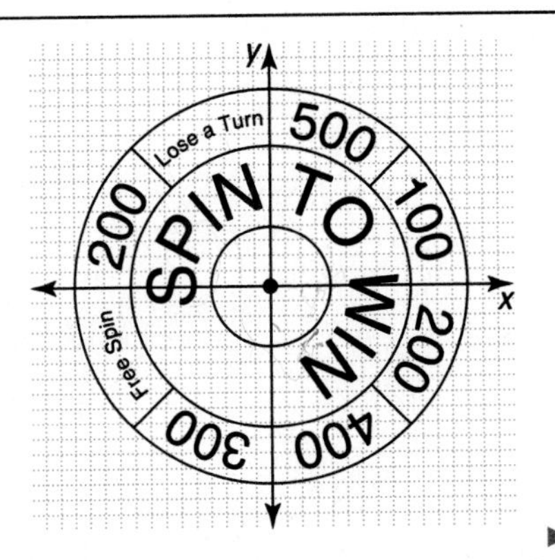

Solution

Here we consider everything in radians. In 5.43 seconds, the wheel covers 5.43π radians. As any multiple of 2π revolutions preserves the image, it is the last 1.43π of a revolution that should be considered.

The matrix for $R_{1.43\pi}$ is

$$\begin{bmatrix} \cos 1.43\pi & -\sin 1.43\pi \\ \sin 1.43\pi & \cos 1.43\pi \end{bmatrix} \approx \begin{bmatrix} -.218 & .976 \\ -.976 & -.218 \end{bmatrix}$$

Multiply the matrix for the preimage by this matrix.

$$\begin{bmatrix} -.218 & .976 \\ -.976 & -.218 \end{bmatrix} \cdot \begin{bmatrix} 1.7 & 1.8 & 4 \\ 4.8 & 8 & 7 \end{bmatrix} = \begin{bmatrix} 4.3 & 7.4 & 6.0 \\ -2.7 & -3.5 & -5.4 \end{bmatrix}$$

Thus, the coordinates of the endpoints of T in its new position are (4.3, -2.7), (7.4, -3.5), and (6.0, -5.4).

Check

1.43π radians is about $\frac{7}{10}$ of a full revolution, or about 260°. The image is shown at the right.

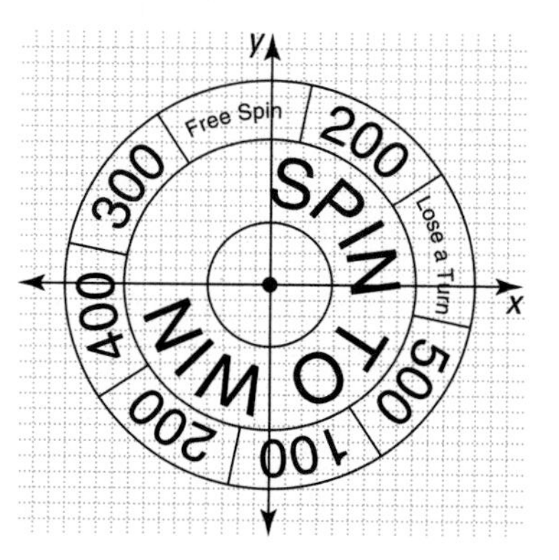

QUESTIONS

Covering the Reading

1. What is the matrix for R_t, the rotation of magnitude t about the origin?

2. a. Give the 2×2 matrix for R_{45}.
   b. Check your result by multiplying the matrix for the triangle in Example 1 by the matrix for R_{45}, and plotting the preimage and image on the same set of axes.

3. If $\sin 27° \approx 0.454$ and $\cos 27° \approx 0.891$, what is an approximate matrix for R_{27}?

4. If $\sin(-12°) \approx -0.208$ and $\cos(-12°) \approx 0.978$, what is an approximate matrix for R_{-12}?

In 5–7, verify the Rotation Matrix Theorem for these special cases.

5. R_{90}

6. R_{180}

7. R_{270}

8. For Example 1, verify the following.
   a. $AO = A'O$
   b. $m\angle AOA' = 30°$

9. Refer to Example 2. The endpoints of the I in "SPIN" are given by the matrix $\begin{bmatrix} -4.2 & -6.8 \\ 3.4 & 5 \end{bmatrix}$. Approximate the coordinates of the I after it is turned 3.2π radians counterclockwise.

Applying the Mathematics

10. a. Use the Rotation Matrix Theorem to find a matrix for R_{60}.

b. Verify your result in part **a** by showing that the cube of the matrix for R_{60} is the matrix for R_{180}.

11. The 30°-60°-90° triangle shown at the right may be represented by the matrix $\begin{bmatrix} 0 & 8 & 6 \\ 0 & 0 & 2\sqrt{3} \end{bmatrix}$.

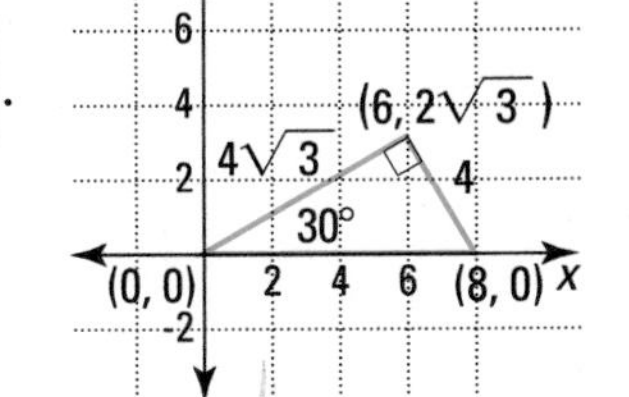

a. Find a matrix for its image under R_{210}. (Use exact values.)

b. Graph the image.

12. A student is designing a club logo to be produced on a computer screen. The outline is a regular pentagon inscribed in a circle with radius 10. One vertex is at (0, 10). Find (to the nearest thousandth) the coordinates of the other vertices.

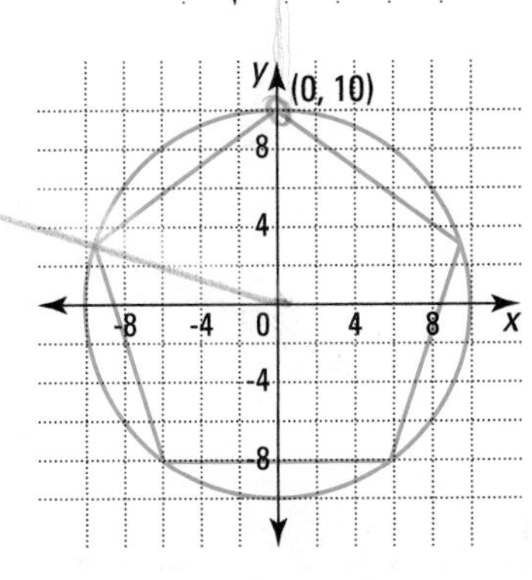

13. a. Show that a matrix for $R_{-\theta}$, a clockwise rotation of θ around the origin, is $\begin{bmatrix} \cos\theta & \sin\theta \\ -\sin\theta & \cos\theta \end{bmatrix}$.

b. Use part **a** to determine the matrix for a clockwise rotation of 90° around the origin.

Review

14. Use the Matrix Basis Theorem to determine the matrix for the reflection over the line $y = -x$. *(Lesson 11-3)*

15. Is the given transformation the identity transformation; that is, does it map a figure to itself? *(Lesson 11-2)*

a. rotation of 360°
b. reflection over the y-axis
c. size change of magnitude 1
d. size change of magnitude -1

16. For a standard normal distribution, find each of the following. *(Lesson 10-5)*

a. the mean
b. the standard deviation
c. the area between the curve and the x-axis

17. Consider the points (1, 0), (-1, 4), and (-3, 16). *(Lessons 2-6, 9-2, 9-3)*
   a. Find an equation for the quadratic function that passes through these points.
   b. Find an equation for a cubic function that passes through these points.

18. a. Determine an equation for a sine curve s which has an amplitude of 3 and a phase shift of $\frac{\pi}{4}$ from the parent sine curve.
   b. Explain why the point $\left(\frac{\pi}{2}, \frac{3\sqrt{2}}{2}\right)$ should be on s. *(Lesson 4-8)*

In 19–21, *true or false*. *(Lessons 4-4, 4-5, 5-1)*

19. $\cos(30° + 60°) = \cos 30° + \cos 60°$.

20. $\sin 90° = 2 \sin 45°$.

21. $\cos\frac{\pi}{3} + \sin\frac{\pi}{3} = 1$.

In 22–24, *multiple choice*. For the graph of the given data set, determine which of the following best describes the correlation coefficient r of the line of best fit.

(a) strongly positive (b) strongly negative
(c) approximately zero *(Lesson 2-2)*

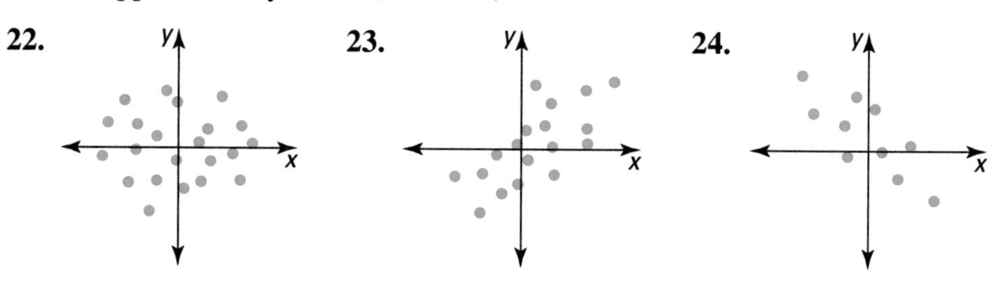

Many people collect posters such as this classic.

25. Suppose a print shop states that it costs \$65 to print 500 posters and \$125 to print 1000 posters. Assume that the cost c is linearly related to the number n of copies made.
   a. Find an equation relating c to n.
   b. How much should the print shop charge to print 2000 posters? *(Lesson 2-2)*

Exploration

26. The *determinant* of the matrix $M = \begin{bmatrix} a & b \\ c & d \end{bmatrix}$ is $ad - bc$. Apply the matrix M to the square $S = \begin{bmatrix} 0 & 1 & 1 & 0 \\ 0 & 0 & 1 & 1 \end{bmatrix}$. How is the area of the figure MS related to the determinant of M?

LESSON

11-5

Formulas for cos (α + β) and sin (α + β)

Image Rotation. *Images created by a CAD/CAM program can be rotated on screen to simulate the movements of parts of the car or passengers. Engineers use this in designing automobiles and their safety features.*

The Point (cos (α + β), sin (α + β))

Suppose that a computer animator wishes to rotate the point $P = (\cos \alpha, \sin \alpha)$ counterclockwise $\beta°$ around the origin. The image of P will be Q, where $Q = R_{\alpha + \beta}(1, 0)$. Thus, $Q = (\cos (\alpha + \beta), \sin (\alpha + \beta))$, as illustrated here.

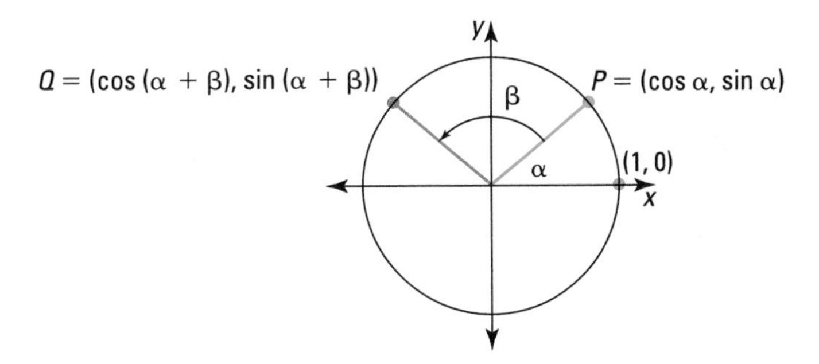

As you know, in general, $\cos (\alpha + \beta) \neq \cos \alpha + \cos \beta$ and $\sin (\alpha + \beta) \neq \sin \alpha + \sin \beta$. For instance, when $\alpha = 45°$ and $\beta = 30°$,

$$\sin (45° + 30°) = \sin 75° \approx 0.966 \quad \text{but} \quad \sin 45° + \sin 30° \approx 0.707 + 0.5 = 1.207.$$

Still, the coordinates of Q can be stated in terms of cosines and sines of α and β. Formulas for these coordinates can be found by using rotation matrices to compute $(R_\alpha \circ R_\beta)(1, 0)$.

Theorem (Addition Formulas for the Cosine and Sine)
For all real numbers α and β,

$$\cos(\alpha + \beta) = \cos\alpha\cos\beta - \sin\alpha\sin\beta$$
$$\sin(\alpha + \beta) = \sin\alpha\cos\beta + \cos\alpha\sin\beta.$$

Proof
By definition of the sine and cosine functions,

$$(\cos(\alpha + \beta), \sin(\alpha + \beta)) = R_{\alpha+\beta}(1, 0).$$

But it is also true that $R_{\alpha+\beta} = R_\alpha \circ R_\beta$.

Thus,

$$\begin{aligned}(\cos(\alpha + \beta), \sin(\alpha + \beta)) &= R_\alpha \circ R_\beta(1, 0)\\ &= R_\alpha(R_\beta(1, 0))\\ &= R_\alpha(\cos\beta, \sin\beta).\end{aligned}$$

Now translate this last sentence into matrices.

$$\begin{bmatrix}\cos(\alpha + \beta)\\ \sin(\alpha + \beta)\end{bmatrix} = \begin{bmatrix}\cos\alpha & -\sin\alpha\\ \sin\alpha & \cos\alpha\end{bmatrix}\begin{bmatrix}\cos\beta\\ \sin\beta\end{bmatrix}$$
$$= \begin{bmatrix}\cos\alpha\cos\beta - \sin\alpha\sin\beta\\ \sin\alpha\cos\beta + \cos\alpha\sin\beta\end{bmatrix}$$

Two matrices are equal if and only if their corresponding elements are equal, so

$$\cos(\alpha + \beta) = \cos\alpha\cos\beta - \sin\alpha\sin\beta$$

and

$$\sin(\alpha + \beta) = \sin\alpha\cos\beta + \cos\alpha\sin\beta.$$

The Addition Formulas for the Cosine and Sine are very useful in mathematics. You should either memorize them or be able to reconstruct them.

Activity

Verify the formula for $\cos(\alpha + \beta)$ by letting $\alpha = 84°$ and $\beta = 17°$.

Using the exact values of cosine and sine of 30°, 45°, 60°, and 90°, these formulas lead to the exact values for the sine and cosine of many other angles.

Example 1

Find an exact value for sin 75°.

Solution

Let $\alpha = 45°$ and $\beta = 30°$. Then

$$\begin{aligned}\sin 75° &= \sin(45° + 30°)\\ &= \sin 45°\cos 30° + \cos 45°\sin 30°\\ &= \frac{\sqrt{2}}{2}\cdot\frac{\sqrt{3}}{2} + \frac{\sqrt{2}}{2}\cdot\frac{1}{2}\\ &= \frac{\sqrt{6} + \sqrt{2}}{4}.\end{aligned}$$

Check

Evaluate $\frac{\sqrt{6} + \sqrt{2}}{4}$ and sin 75° on your calculator. You should get approximately 0.966 for each value.

There are also formulas for sin ($\alpha - \beta$) and cos ($\alpha - \beta$). Example 2 shows how to derive a formula for sin ($\alpha - \beta$). You are asked to verify that cos ($\alpha - \beta$) = cos α cos β + sin α sin β in the Questions.

Example 2

Derive a formula for sin ($\alpha - \beta$) in terms of sines and cosines of α and β.

Solution

Rewrite $\alpha - \beta$ as $\alpha + (-\beta)$. Then for all α and β,

$\sin(\alpha - \beta) = \sin(\alpha + (-\beta))$	Algebraic definition of subtraction
$= \sin\alpha\cos(-\beta) + \cos\alpha\sin(-\beta)$	Addition Formula for the Sine
$= \sin\alpha\cos\beta + \cos\alpha(-\sin\beta)$	Opposites Theorem
$= \sin\alpha\cos\beta - \cos\alpha\sin\beta.$	Simplify

The formulas for cos ($\alpha + \beta$) and sin ($\alpha + \beta$) provide another way to prove some theorems about circular functions, such as the Supplements and Complements Theorems in Lesson 4-4.

Example 3

Prove the Supplements Theorem for the sine function:

$$\sin(\pi - \theta) = \sin\theta \text{ for all real numbers } \theta.$$

Solution

From the formula derived in Example 2, for all real numbers θ,

$$\begin{aligned}\sin(\pi - \theta) &= \sin\pi\cos\theta - \cos\pi\sin\theta\\ &= 0 \cdot \cos\theta - (-1)\sin\theta\\ &= \sin\theta.\end{aligned}$$

QUESTIONS

Covering the Reading

1. In the proof of the theorem in the lesson it is stated that $R_\alpha \circ R_\beta(1, 0) = R_\alpha(\cos\beta, \sin\beta)$. Explain why this is true.

2. Consider the statement: *For all α and β, cos ($\alpha + \beta$) = cos α + cos β.*
  a. Give one pair of values for α and β for which the statement is true.
  b. Give a counterexample to the statement.

In 3 and 4, simplify without using a calculator.

3. $\sin 75° \cos 15° + \cos 75° \sin 15°$

4. $\cos\left(\frac{11\pi}{12}\right)\cos\left(\frac{7\pi}{12}\right) - \sin\left(\frac{11\pi}{12}\right)\sin\left(\frac{7\pi}{12}\right)$

In 5 and 6, give an exact value.

5. $\cos 75°$

6. $\sin 15°$

In 7–9, use the formula for $\cos(\alpha + \beta)$ to prove the stated theorem.

7. $\cos(\alpha - \beta) = \cos\alpha\cos\beta + \sin\alpha\sin\beta$

8. Supplements Theorem for the cosine function

9. Complements Theorem for the cosine function

Applying the Mathematics

In 10–12, give exact values.

10. $\sin 255°$ **11.** $\cos\left(-\frac{13\pi}{12}\right)$ **12.** $\tan 75°$

13. Give an exact matrix for $R_{5\pi/12}$. (Hint: $\frac{5\pi}{12} = \frac{3\pi}{12} + \frac{2\pi}{12}$.)

14. *True or false.* Exact values of $\sin\theta$ and $\cos\theta$ can be found for all integral multiples of $\frac{\pi}{12}$ between 0 and 2π. Justify your answer.

15. a. Without graphing the equations, tell which graph will be different from the others.

$f(x) = 2\sin\left(x + \frac{\pi}{6}\right)$

$g(x) = 2\sin x + 2\sin\left(\frac{\pi}{6}\right)$

$h(x) = \sqrt{3}\sin x + \cos x$

b. Check your prediction by graphing $y = f(x)$, $y = g(x)$, and $y = h(x)$ on the same set of axes.

c. Explain your results using a theorem in this lesson.

16. Use the formula for $\sin(\alpha + \beta)$ to show that $\sin(x + 2\pi n) = \sin x$ for all integers n.

17. Prove: For all x, $\sin\left(x - \frac{\pi}{2}\right) = -\cos x$.

18. Give the elements of the matrix for $R_{\alpha + \beta}$ in terms of sines and cosines of α and β.

19. $\triangle PQR$ has acute angles P and Q with $\cos P = \frac{1}{2}$ and $\cos Q = \frac{1}{3}$.

a. Find $\cos(P + Q)$.

b. Find $\cos R$.

c. Draw a possible $\triangle PQR$.

Review

20. Determine the coordinates of the image of point (2, 5) under a counterclockwise rotation about the origin of 42°. *(Lesson 11-4)*

In 21 and 22, consider the polygon represented by the matrix

$$P = \begin{bmatrix} 1 & 6 & 8 & 3 \\ 1 & 1 & 4 & 4 \end{bmatrix}.$$

21. **a.** Calculate $P' = \begin{bmatrix} 2 & 0 \\ 0 & -1 \end{bmatrix} \cdot P$.

b. Describe the transformation mapping P onto P'. *(Lessons 11-2, 11-3)*

22. **a.** Calculate $P'' = \begin{bmatrix} \cos 45° & -\sin 45° \\ \sin 45° & \cos 45° \end{bmatrix} \cdot P$.

b. Describe the transformation mapping P onto P''. *(Lessons 11-2, 11-4)*

23. Kevin, Laura, and Sergio work part-time after school. The matrix R below gives the hourly payment each one earns. The matrix H shows the number of hours each worked on the days of a certain week. *(Lesson 11-1)*

$$R = \begin{bmatrix} 5.25 \\ 4.90 \\ 5.50 \end{bmatrix}$$

	Kevin	Laura	Sergio
Monday	3	4	4
Tuesday	5	5	4
Wednesday	2	4	4
Thursday	4	2	4
Friday	3	0	4

$= H$

a. How many hours did Laura work in this week?
b. On which day was the combined time of the three the least?
c. Which matrix, HR or RH, gives the total earnings of Kevin, Laura, and Sergio for each day of this week?
d. How much did the three of them earn on Thursday?

24. Solve $x^4 - 2x^3 - 13x^2 - 4x - 30 = 0$ completely, given that one of the solutions is $\sqrt{2}\, i$. *(Lessons 9-6, 9-7)*

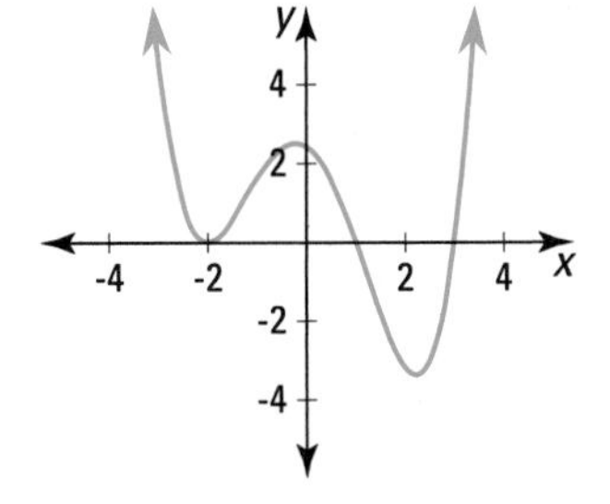

25. Consider the graph of a polynomial function g pictured at the left.
a. How many real zeros does g seem to have?
b. What is the smallest possible degree g can have?
c. *True or false.* The factorization of g over the set of polynomials with real number coefficients has at least four factors. Explain your answer. *(Lessons 9-5, 9-6, 9-7)*

26. Give an exact value.
a. $\log 1000$ **b.** $\log_2 8 - \log_8 2$ **c.** $\log 2 \cdot \log_2(.1)$
(Lessons 6-3, 6-5)

27. *Multiple choice.* Which correlation coefficient indicates the strongest linear relationship? *(Lesson 2-2)*
(a) 0.43 (b) 0.16 (c) -0.79 (d) 0.1

Exploration

28. **a.** Use the fact that $\tan(\alpha + \beta) = \frac{\sin(\alpha + \beta)}{\cos(\alpha + \beta)}$ to derive a formula for $\tan(\alpha + \beta)$ in terms of tangents of α and β. (Hint: divide both numerator and denominator of the fraction by $\cos \alpha \cos \beta$.)
b. Check your answer to part **a** by using some values of tangents known to you.

LESSON

11-6

Formulas for cos 2θ and sin 2θ

A Use for sin 2θ

Ignoring air resistance and wind, the path of an object thrown or kicked into the air from ground level will be part of a parabolic trajectory. Specifically, if a golf ball is driven off the ground with velocity v m/sec at an angle of θ degrees to the ground, the horizontal distance d that the ball travels is given by $d = \frac{v^2 \sin 2\theta}{g}$, where g is the acceleration due to gravity.

Thus, a golf ball leaving a tee at 45 meters per second at an angle of 30° to the ground will travel about

$$\frac{\left(45\ \frac{\text{m}}{\text{sec}}\right)^2 \cdot \sin(2 \cdot 30°)}{9.81\ \frac{\text{m}}{\text{sec}^2}} \approx 179\text{m}.$$

Proving the Double Angle Formulas

Expressions like sin 2θ and cos 2θ occur often in mathematics and science. Formulas expressing sin 2θ and cos 2θ as functions of θ are often called Double Angle or Double Argument Formulas. They can be derived using the Addition Formulas for the sine and cosine functions.

Theorem (Double Angle Formulas)
For all real numbers θ,

$$\sin 2\theta = 2 \sin \theta \cos \theta;$$

and

$$\begin{aligned}\cos 2\theta &= \cos^2\theta - \sin^2\theta \\ &= 2\cos^2\theta - 1 \\ &= 1 - 2\sin^2\theta.\end{aligned}$$

Proof
Set $\alpha = \theta$ and $\beta = \theta$ in the formulas for $\sin(\alpha + \beta)$ and $\cos(\alpha + \beta)$.
Then

$$\begin{aligned}\sin 2\theta &= \sin(\theta + \theta) \\ &= \sin\theta\cos\theta + \cos\theta\sin\theta \\ &= 2\sin\theta\cos\theta.\end{aligned}$$

Similarly,

$$\begin{aligned}\cos 2\theta &= \cos(\theta + \theta) \\ &= \cos\theta\cos\theta - \sin\theta\sin\theta \\ &= \cos^2\theta - \sin^2\theta.\end{aligned}$$

Substituting $\sin^2\theta = 1 - \cos^2\theta$ from the Pythagorean Identity yields the second form of the Double Angle Formula for the cosine function.

$$\begin{aligned}\cos 2\theta &= \cos^2\theta - (1 - \cos^2\theta) \\ &= \cos^2\theta - 1 + \cos^2\theta \\ &= 2\cos^2\theta - 1\end{aligned}$$

You are asked to derive the third form of the Double Angle Formula for the cosine function in the Questions.

Picturing the Double Angle Formula

Graphically, the first Double Angle Formula means that the graphs of $y = \sin 2x$ and $y = 2 \sin x \cos x$ coincide. The graphs of these functions are shown below. You are asked to verify the formulas for $\cos 2x$ graphically in the Questions.

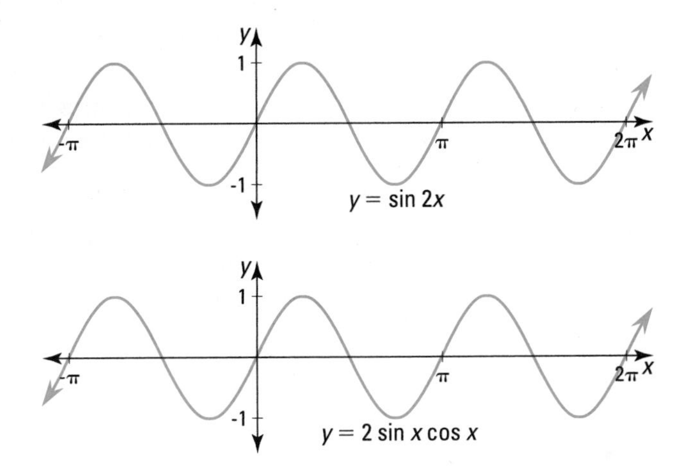

Verifying the Double Angle Formulas

Since the Double Angle Formulas are true for all θ, you can use a specific value of θ to check them.

Example 1

For $\theta = \frac{\pi}{6}$, verify the formula for $\sin 2\theta$.

Solution

When $\theta = \frac{\pi}{6}$, $\sin 2\theta = 2 \sin \theta \cos \theta$ becomes

$\sin\left(2 \cdot \frac{\pi}{6}\right) = 2 \sin \frac{\pi}{6} \cos \frac{\pi}{6}$. Is this true?

$$\sin\left(2 \cdot \frac{\pi}{6}\right) = \sin \frac{\pi}{3} = \frac{\sqrt{3}}{2} \quad \text{and} \quad 2 \sin \frac{\pi}{6} \cos \frac{\pi}{6} = 2 \cdot \frac{1}{2} \cdot \frac{\sqrt{3}}{2} = \frac{\sqrt{3}}{2}$$

The identity is verified.

Extending the Double Angle Formulas

From the identities for $\cos 2\theta$ and $\sin 2\theta$, identities for the cosine and sine of other multiples of θ can be found.

Example 2

Express $\cos 4\theta$ as a function of $\cos \theta$ only.

Solution

First, express $\cos 4\theta$ as a function of $\cos 2\theta$.

$$\begin{aligned}\cos 4\theta &= \cos 2(2\theta)\\ &= 2\cos^2(2\theta) - 1\end{aligned}$$

Now use the Double Angle Formula again.

$$\begin{aligned}\cos 4\theta &= 2(2\cos^2\theta - 1)^2 - 1\\ &= 2(4\cos^4\theta - 4\cos^2\theta + 1) - 1\\ &= 8\cos^4\theta - 8\cos^2\theta + 2 - 1\\ &= 8\cos^4\theta - 8\cos^2\theta + 1\end{aligned}$$

Check

Substitute a value for θ for which the values of $\cos \theta$ and $\cos 4\theta$ are known. We use $\theta = 45°$. Then

$\cos 4\theta = \cos(4 \cdot 45°)$ and $8\cos^4\theta - 8\cos^2\theta + 1 = 8\left(\frac{\sqrt{2}}{2}\right)^4 - 8\left(\frac{\sqrt{2}}{2}\right)^2 + 1$

$= \cos 180°$ $\qquad = 8\left(\frac{4}{16}\right) - 8\left(\frac{2}{4}\right) + 1$

$= -1$ $\qquad = -1.$

QUESTIONS

Covering the Reading

In 1 and 2, use the formula $d = \frac{v^2 \sin 2\theta}{g}$.

1. About how far will a soccer ball travel with respect to the ground if you kick it at $34 \frac{\text{m}}{\text{sec}}$ at an initial angle of 45° to the ground?

2. How far will a tennis ball travel horizontally if it leaves the ground at $25 \frac{\text{m}}{\text{sec}}$ at an angle of 90°?

3. Prove that $\cos 2\theta = 1 - 2\sin^2\theta$.

4. Find a value of θ for which $\cos 2\theta \neq 2\cos\theta$.

5. a. Graph the functions f, g, and h on the same set of axes.

$f(x) = \cos^2 x - \sin^2 x$

$g(x) = 2\cos^2 x - 1$

$h(x) = 1 - 2\sin^2 x$

b. Find another equation whose graph coincides with those of f, g, and h.

6. Use $\theta = 60°$ and a formula for $\cos 2\theta$ to find an exact value for $\cos 120°$.

In 7–10, simplify each expression using the appropriate Double Angle Formula.

7. $2\cos^2 25° - 1$

8. $2\sin 35° \cos 35°$

9. $1 - 2\sin^2\left(\frac{3\pi}{8}\right)$

10. $\cos^2\left(\frac{4\pi}{9}\right) - \sin^2\left(\frac{4\pi}{9}\right)$

11. Express $\sin 4\theta$ as a function of $\cos\theta$ and $\sin\theta$.

Applying the Mathematics

Tiger Woods's long drives are due to the great speed of his club head as it hits the ball.

12. Suppose a golf ball can be hit at an initial speed of 60 $\frac{\text{m}}{\text{sec}}$. Use the formula $d = \frac{v^2 \sin 2\theta}{g}$.

a. At what angle should the ball leave the tee in order to have it go the maximum horizontal distance?

b. What horizontal distance will the ball then travel?

13. If $\angle A$ is acute and $\sin A = \frac{4}{5}$, find exact values for each of the following.

a. $\cos A$ **b.** $\sin 2A$

14. Suppose $\cos A = \frac{1}{4}$. Find $\cos 2A$, if A is in the given interval.

a. $0° < A < 90°$ **b.** $270° < A < 360°$

In 15–17, consider the line L which passes through the origin at an angle θ with the positive x-axis. It can be shown that the matrix $\begin{bmatrix} \cos 2\theta & \sin 2\theta \\ \sin 2\theta & -\cos 2\theta \end{bmatrix}$ represents r_L, reflection over L.

15. Suppose that L is the x-axis. Verify that the matrix for r_L equals the matrix already studied for r_x.

16. Suppose that L is the line $y = x$.

a. What is θ in this case?

b. Verify that the matrix for r_L equals the matrix already studied for $r_{y=x}$.

17. a. If L is the line $y = \frac{1}{\sqrt{3}}x$, find a matrix of exact values for r_L.

b. Use your matrix from part **a** to find the image of (1, 0) when reflected over $y = \frac{1}{\sqrt{3}}x$. Check your answer with a drawing.

In 18 and 19, the double angle formulas are employed to derive **Half Angle** formulas.

18. Consider the system of equations

$$\cos 2\theta = \cos^2\theta - \sin^2\theta$$
$$1 = \cos^2\theta + \sin^2\theta.$$

a. Prove: For all θ, $\cos\theta = \pm\sqrt{\frac{1 + \cos 2\theta}{2}}$. (The sign used is determined by the quadrant in which θ lies.) Hint: As a first step, add the equations.

b. Use the formula in part **a** to show that $\cos\frac{\pi}{8} = \frac{\sqrt{2 + \sqrt{2}}}{2}$.

19. a. Prove: For all θ, $\sin\theta = \pm\sqrt{\frac{1 - \cos 2\theta}{2}}$. (The sign used is determined by the quadrant in which θ lies.)

b. Find an exact value for $\sin\frac{\pi}{8}$.

20. Write $\cos 3\theta$ as a function of $\sin\theta$ and $\cos\theta$.

Review

21. Find an exact value for sin 195°. *(Lesson 11-5)*

22. *Multiple choice.* For all real numbers α and β, the expression $\cos \alpha \cos \beta - \sin \alpha \sin \beta$ equals which of the following?
(a) $\cos(\alpha + \beta)$ (b) $\sin(\alpha + \beta)$
(c) $\cos(\alpha - \beta)$ (d) $\sin(\alpha - \beta)$ *(Lesson 11-5)*

23. A transformation which can be represented by a matrix maps a square with vertices at (0, 0), (0, 1), (1, 1), and (1, 0) to a parallelogram with corresponding vertices at (0, 0), (2, 3), (-2, 4), and (-4, 1). What is the matrix? *(Lesson 11-4)*

24. If $\begin{bmatrix} a & -4 \\ -7 & b \end{bmatrix}\begin{bmatrix} 3 & 4 \\ 7 & 9 \end{bmatrix} = \begin{bmatrix} -1 & 0 \\ 0 & -1 \end{bmatrix}$, find a and b. *(Lesson 11-1)*

25. Suppose the gestation period (time from conception to birth) in humans has an approximately normal distribution with a mean of 266 days and a standard deviation of 16 days. Determine an interval for the number of days after conception when 90% of births occur. *(Lesson 10-6)*

26. Given that $a = 2 + i$ and $b = 1 - 2i$, calculate each.
a. $a^2 - b^2$ **b.** $\frac{a}{b}$ *(Lesson 9-6)*

27. Suppose that a test of anxiety is given to representative samples of people of ages 10, 15, 20, 40, and 60, and that the respective means of anxiety levels on the test are 40, 70, 65, 60, and 50.
a. Draw a scatterplot of these data using age as the independent variable.
b. *Multiple choice.* Which of the following best describes the correlation between age and anxiety level?
(i) strongly positive
(ii) strongly negative
(iii) nearly zero *(Lessons 1-1, 3-6)*

Exploration

28. You have seen derivations of the following identities:

$$\cos 2\theta = \cos^2\theta - 1$$
$$\cos 4\theta = 8\cos^4\theta - 8\cos^2\theta + 1.$$

Can $\cos n\theta$, where n is a positive integer, always be expressed as a polynomial in $\cos \theta$? If it can be, what can you say about the degree and coefficients of the polynomial? Justify your answers.

LESSON

11-7

Inverses of 2 × 2 Matrices

The Identity Transformation and Identity Matrix

You have seen that the function I with $I(x) = x$ and some particular domain is called an *identity function* under composition because for all functions f with that domain,

$$I \circ f = f \circ I = f.$$

Transformations are functions, so the transformation I with $I(P) = P$ for all points P is the *identity transformation*. Why is this so? Because if $I(P) = P$ for all P, then $I \circ T(P) = I(T(P)) = T(P)$, so $I \circ T = T$, and $T \circ I(P) = T(I(P)) = T(P)$, so $T \circ I = T$. If the points have coordinates (x, y) in the plane, then $I(x, y) = (x, y)$. Because R_0, the rotation of magnitude 0, maps each point onto itself, $R_0 = I$. Also, because the translation T: $(x, y) \rightarrow (x + h, y + k)$ maps each point onto itself when $h = 0$ and $k = 0$, the identity transformation can be thought of as a translation that slides a point nowhere. It can also be thought of as a size change with magnitude 1.

Also recall from Lesson 11-2 that $\begin{bmatrix} 1 & 0 \\ 0 & 1 \end{bmatrix}$ is the *identity matrix* for multiplication of 2 × 2 matrices.

Inverse Transformations

When two elements combine under some operation to give an identity for that operation, then they are *inverses*. For instance, $3 + -3 = -3 + 3 = 0$, so 3 and -3 are additive inverses.

As with functions, you can find the inverse of a transformation by switching the domain (preimage) and range elements (image). That is, if P is a point and $T(P) = Q$, then the **inverse transformation** T^{-1} is such that $T^{-1}(Q) = P$. This means that for all P, $T^{-1} \circ T(P) = T^{-1}(Q) = P$, which means that $T^{-1} \circ T$ is the identity transformation. $T \circ T^{-1} = T^{-1} \circ T = I$.

Inverses of the basic transformations you have studied in this course can be found from their geometric or algebraic definitions.

Type of Transformation	Name	Inverse
reflection	r_m	r_m
translation	$T(x, y) = (x + h, y + k)$	$T^{-1}(x, y) = (x - h, y - k)$
rotation	R_θ	$R_{-\theta}$
size change	S_k	$S_{1/k}$
scale change	$S_{a, b}$	$S_{1/a, 1/b}$

Inverses are of more than just passing importance. In algebra, you used inverses to solve linear equations. In this course, you have used inverses of trigonometric functions and exponential and logarithm functions in the solution of many problems. So it is natural to examine inverses of matrices and expect them to have applications to solving equations and to solving certain problems. You will see that all the inverses above, except for inverses of translations, can be found using 2×2 matrices.

Examples of Inverse 2 × 2 Matrices

R_θ, the rotation of magnitude θ around the origin, can be represented by the matrix $\begin{bmatrix} \cos\theta & -\sin\theta \\ \sin\theta & \cos\theta \end{bmatrix}$. Consequently, a matrix for $R_{-\theta}$ is $\begin{bmatrix} \cos(-\theta) & -\sin(-\theta) \\ \sin(-\theta) & \cos(-\theta) \end{bmatrix}$. Using the Opposites Theorem of Lesson 4-4, the matrix for $R_{-\theta}$ is $\begin{bmatrix} \cos\theta & \sin\theta \\ -\sin\theta & \cos\theta \end{bmatrix}$.

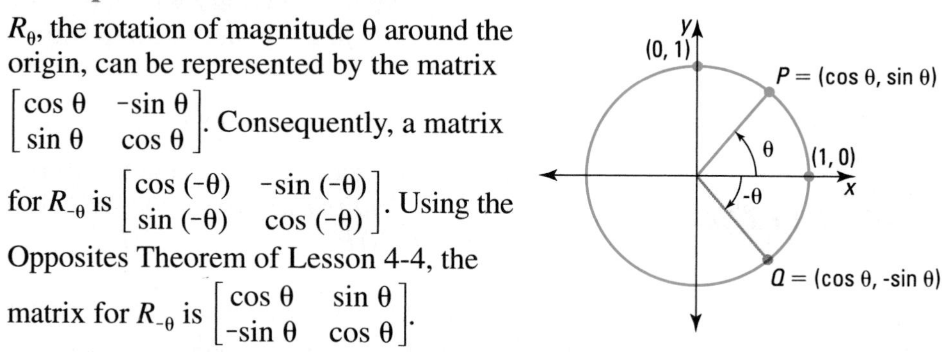

The composite transformation $R_{-\theta} \circ R_\theta$ can be represented by the product

$$\begin{bmatrix} \cos\theta & \sin\theta \\ -\sin\theta & \cos\theta \end{bmatrix} \cdot \begin{bmatrix} \cos\theta & -\sin\theta \\ \sin\theta & \cos\theta \end{bmatrix}$$

$$= \begin{bmatrix} \cos^2\theta + \sin^2\theta & -\cos\theta\sin\theta + \sin\theta\cos\theta \\ -\sin\theta\cos\theta + \cos\theta\sin\theta & \sin^2\theta + \cos^2\theta \end{bmatrix}$$

$$= \begin{bmatrix} 1 & 0 \\ 0 & 1 \end{bmatrix},$$

the identity matrix. This verifies that R_θ and $R_{-\theta}$ are inverse transformations. We say that their associated matrices are *inverse matrices*. In symbols, if M and N are both 2×2 matrices, then M and N are inverses if and only if $MN = NM = \begin{bmatrix} 1 & 0 \\ 0 & 1 \end{bmatrix}$.

Some inverses are easy to find. Recall that $\begin{bmatrix} 3 & 0 \\ 0 & 5 \end{bmatrix}$ is the matrix for the scale change $S: (x, y) \rightarrow (3x, 5y)$. The inverse of this scale change is the scale change $S^{-1}: (x, y) \rightarrow \left(\frac{1}{3}x, \frac{1}{5}y\right)$, whose associated matrix is $\begin{bmatrix} \frac{1}{3} & 0 \\ 0 & \frac{1}{5} \end{bmatrix}$.

This suggests that the inverse of the matrix $\begin{bmatrix} 3 & 0 \\ 0 & 5 \end{bmatrix}$ is $\begin{bmatrix} \frac{1}{3} & 0 \\ 0 & \frac{1}{5} \end{bmatrix}$. This can be proved.

Example 1

Show that $\begin{bmatrix} 3 & 0 \\ 0 & 5 \end{bmatrix}$ and $\begin{bmatrix} \frac{1}{3} & 0 \\ 0 & \frac{1}{5} \end{bmatrix}$ are inverses.

Solution

Because 2×2 matrix multiplication is not commutative, you should check the multiplications in both orders.

$$\begin{bmatrix} 3 & 0 \\ 0 & 5 \end{bmatrix}\begin{bmatrix} \frac{1}{3} & 0 \\ 0 & \frac{1}{5} \end{bmatrix} = \begin{bmatrix} 1 & 0 \\ 0 & 1 \end{bmatrix}, \qquad \begin{bmatrix} \frac{1}{3} & 0 \\ 0 & \frac{1}{5} \end{bmatrix}\begin{bmatrix} 3 & 0 \\ 0 & 5 \end{bmatrix} = \begin{bmatrix} 1 & 0 \\ 0 & 1 \end{bmatrix}$$

Finding the Inverse of a 2 × 2 Matrix

If the transformation for a matrix is not known, you can find its inverse using algebra.

Example 2

Find the inverse of $\begin{bmatrix} 3 & 7 \\ 2 & 5 \end{bmatrix}$.

Solution

The task is to find a matrix $\begin{bmatrix} w & x \\ y & z \end{bmatrix}$ such that

$$\begin{bmatrix} 3 & 7 \\ 2 & 5 \end{bmatrix}\begin{bmatrix} w & x \\ y & z \end{bmatrix} = \begin{bmatrix} w & x \\ y & z \end{bmatrix}\begin{bmatrix} 3 & 7 \\ 2 & 5 \end{bmatrix} = \begin{bmatrix} 1 & 0 \\ 0 & 1 \end{bmatrix}.$$

Multiply the left two matrices.

$$\begin{bmatrix} 3 & 7 \\ 2 & 5 \end{bmatrix}\begin{bmatrix} w & x \\ y & z \end{bmatrix} = \begin{bmatrix} 3w + 7y & 3x + 7z \\ 2w + 5y & 2x + 5z \end{bmatrix}.$$

So
$$3w + 7y = 1,$$
$$3x + 7z = 0,$$
$$2w + 5y = 0,$$
and
$$2x + 5z = 1.$$

To solve this system, note that the first and third equations have the same two variables. Multiply the first equation by 2 and the third by -3 and add the resulting sentences. This yields $y = -2$. Substituting this value into the first equation gives $w = 5$. Similarly, multiplying the second equation by 2 and the fourth by -3 and adding the results yields $z = 3$. Substituting this value into the second equation gives $x = -7$. So the inverse of $\begin{bmatrix} 3 & 7 \\ 2 & 5 \end{bmatrix}$ is $\begin{bmatrix} 5 & -7 \\ -2 & 3 \end{bmatrix}$.

Check

$$\begin{bmatrix} 3 & 7 \\ 2 & 5 \end{bmatrix} \cdot \begin{bmatrix} 5 & -7 \\ -2 & 3 \end{bmatrix} = \begin{bmatrix} 15 - 14 & -21 + 21 \\ 10 - 10 & -14 + 15 \end{bmatrix} = \begin{bmatrix} 1 & 0 \\ 0 & 1 \end{bmatrix}$$

$$\begin{bmatrix} 5 & -7 \\ -2 & 3 \end{bmatrix} \cdot \begin{bmatrix} 3 & 7 \\ 2 & 5 \end{bmatrix} = \begin{bmatrix} 15 - 14 & 35 - 35 \\ -6 + 6 & -14 + 15 \end{bmatrix} = \begin{bmatrix} 1 & 0 \\ 0 & 1 \end{bmatrix}$$

If the inverse of a 2×2 matrix exists, you can generalize the procedure used in Example 2, or you can use the following theorem. Here we use the symbol M^{-1} to stand for the inverse of M.

Theorem (Inverse of a 2 × 2 Matrix)
If $ad - bc \neq 0$, then

$$\begin{bmatrix} a & b \\ c & d \end{bmatrix}^{-1} = \begin{bmatrix} \frac{d}{ad - bc} & \frac{-b}{ad - bc} \\ \frac{-c}{ad - bc} & \frac{a}{ad - bc} \end{bmatrix}.$$

Proof

It must be shown that the product of the matrix $\begin{bmatrix} a & b \\ c & d \end{bmatrix}$ with its inverse in either order is the identity matrix. Here is one order.

$$\begin{bmatrix} a & b \\ c & d \end{bmatrix}\begin{bmatrix} \frac{d}{ad - bc} & \frac{-b}{ad - bc} \\ \frac{-c}{ad - bc} & \frac{a}{ad - bc} \end{bmatrix} = \begin{bmatrix} \frac{ad}{ad - bc} - \frac{bc}{ad - bc} & \frac{-ab}{ad - bc} + \frac{ab}{ad - bc} \\ \frac{cd}{ad - bc} - \frac{cd}{ad - bc} & \frac{-bc}{ad - bc} + \frac{ad}{ad - bc} \end{bmatrix}$$

$$= \begin{bmatrix} \frac{ad - bc}{ad - bc} & \frac{0}{ad - bc} \\ \frac{0}{ad - bc} & \frac{ad - bc}{ad - bc} \end{bmatrix}$$

$$= \begin{bmatrix} 1 & 0 \\ 0 & 1 \end{bmatrix}$$

You are asked to verify multiplication in the other order in the Questions.

Example 3

Use the Inverse of a 2×2 Matrix Theorem to find $\begin{bmatrix} 2 & -3 \\ 6 & -1 \end{bmatrix}^{-1}$.

Solution

In $\begin{bmatrix} 2 & -3 \\ 6 & -1 \end{bmatrix}$, $a = 2$, $b = -3$, $c = 6$, and $d = -1$. So,

$ad - bc = (2)(-1) - (-3)(6) = 16$.

Therefore, $\begin{bmatrix} 2 & -3 \\ 6 & -1 \end{bmatrix}^{-1} = \begin{bmatrix} -\frac{1}{16} & \frac{3}{16} \\ -\frac{6}{16} & \frac{2}{16} \end{bmatrix}$.

Check

$$\begin{bmatrix} 2 & -3 \\ 6 & -1 \end{bmatrix}\begin{bmatrix} -\frac{1}{16} & \frac{3}{16} \\ -\frac{6}{16} & \frac{2}{16} \end{bmatrix} = \begin{bmatrix} -\frac{2}{16} + \frac{18}{16} & \frac{6}{16} - \frac{6}{16} \\ -\frac{6}{16} + \frac{6}{16} & \frac{18}{16} - \frac{2}{16} \end{bmatrix} = \begin{bmatrix} 1 & 0 \\ 0 & 1 \end{bmatrix}$$

$$\begin{bmatrix} -\frac{1}{16} & \frac{3}{16} \\ -\frac{6}{16} & \frac{2}{16} \end{bmatrix}\begin{bmatrix} 2 & -3 \\ 6 & -1 \end{bmatrix} = \begin{bmatrix} -\frac{2}{16} + \frac{18}{16} & \frac{3}{16} - \frac{3}{16} \\ -\frac{12}{16} + \frac{12}{16} & \frac{18}{16} - \frac{2}{16} \end{bmatrix} = \begin{bmatrix} 1 & 0 \\ 0 & 1 \end{bmatrix}$$

Not all 2×2 matrices have inverses. If $M = \begin{bmatrix} a & b \\ c & d \end{bmatrix}$ and $ad - bc = 0$, then $\frac{1}{ad - bc}$ is undefined, so M^{-1} cannot exist. The expression $ad - bc$ is called the **determinant** of the matrix because it can be used to determine whether the matrix has an inverse. The word *determinant* is abbreviated as **det**, and we write

$$\det \begin{bmatrix} a & b \\ c & d \end{bmatrix} = ad - bc.$$

Thus, if $M = \begin{bmatrix} a & b \\ c & d \end{bmatrix}$, and $ad - bc \neq 0$, another way to write the formula for M^{-1} is $M^{-1} = \begin{bmatrix} \frac{d}{\det M} & \frac{-b}{\det M} \\ \frac{-c}{\det M} & \frac{a}{\det M} \end{bmatrix}$.

In general, only square ($n \times n$) matrices can have inverses, because both products MM^{-1} and $M^{-1}M$ must exist. For matrices where $n > 2$, inverses also exist, but are not always easy to calculate by hand. However, some calculators and computer software packages will find them easily.

QUESTIONS

Covering the Reading

In 1–4, give the identity for each set under the indicated operation.

1. $+$, set of real numbers

2. $\circ$, set of real functions

3. $\circ$, set of transformations of the plane

4. $\bullet$, set of 2×2 matrices

5. In the set of real numbers, what is the sum of the additive and multiplicative inverses of 12?

6. Complete this statement. Two transformations S and T are inverses if and only if __?__.

7. a. Use the Inverse of a 2×2 Matrix Theorem to find

$$\begin{bmatrix} \cos\theta & -\sin\theta \\ \sin\theta & \cos\theta \end{bmatrix}^{-1}.$$

b. *True or false.* $R_\theta^{-1} = R_{-\theta}$.

8. a. What is the matrix for the scale change $S_{3,0.5}$?

b. Find the matrix for the inverse of this scale change and prove that your answer is correct.

9. a. Write a matrix for the size change $S(x, y) = (4x, 4y)$.

b. What transformation T undoes S?

c. Write a matrix for T.

d. *True or false.* The matrices for S and T are inverses. Justify your answer.

10. Complete the proof of the Inverse of a 2 × 2 Matrix Theorem.

11. Find det $\begin{bmatrix} 3 & -12 \\ 6 & 5 \end{bmatrix}$.

12. In order for the inverse of a 2 × 2 matrix to exist, what must be true about its determinant?

In 13 and 14, find the inverse of the matrix.

13. $\begin{bmatrix} -3 & 7 \\ 6 & -14 \end{bmatrix}$

14. $\begin{bmatrix} 8 & 3 \\ 2 & 7 \end{bmatrix}$

In 15 and 16, explain why the matrix does not have an inverse.

15. $\begin{bmatrix} 4 & 2 \\ 2 & 1 \end{bmatrix}$

16. $\begin{bmatrix} 1 & 2 & 3 \\ 4 & 5 & 6 \end{bmatrix}$

Applying the Mathematics

17. a. *True or false.* det $\begin{bmatrix} 90 & -75 \\ 63 & 112 \end{bmatrix} = -\det \begin{bmatrix} 63 & 112 \\ 90 & -75 \end{bmatrix}$.

b. Generalize the result of part **a**: det $\begin{bmatrix} W & X \\ Y & Z \end{bmatrix} = \underline{\ ?\ }$.

c. Prove the generalization in part **b**.

18. Find the determinant for the matrix representing R_θ.

19. Consider the following system.

$$\begin{cases} x + 2y = 11 \\ 3x - y = 12 \end{cases}$$

a. Multiply $\begin{bmatrix} 1 & 2 \\ 3 & -1 \end{bmatrix}\begin{bmatrix} x \\ y \end{bmatrix}$. (The answer means that it is possible to represent the left side of the system by a matrix product.)

b. Find $\begin{bmatrix} 1 & 2 \\ 3 & -1 \end{bmatrix}^{-1}$.

c. Multiply both sides of the equation $\begin{bmatrix} 1 & 2 \\ 3 & -1 \end{bmatrix}\begin{bmatrix} x \\ y \end{bmatrix} = \begin{bmatrix} 11 \\ 12 \end{bmatrix}$ on the left by the answer to part **b**.

d. What is the solution to the system of equations?

e. Use the method of parts **a-d** to solve the following system.

$$\begin{cases} -8x + 3y = 11 \\ 4x + 3y = 5 \end{cases}$$

20. Let $A = \begin{bmatrix} 2 & 5 \\ 1 & 4 \end{bmatrix}$ and $B = \begin{bmatrix} -1 & -2 \\ 3 & 4 \end{bmatrix}$.

a. Find AB.

b. Find $(AB)^{-1}$.

c. Find A^{-1}.

d. Find B^{-1}.

e. Find $A^{-1}B^{-1}$ and $B^{-1}A^{-1}$.

f. Generalize from the results of parts **b** and **e**.

Review

21. Consider the graph of the function $y = 6 \sin x \cos x$.

a. What is its amplitude? **b.** What is its period?

c. Use parts **a** and **b** to write another equation for the function.

d. Use a Double Angle Formula to rewrite the formula for the function and verify your answers in parts **a** and **b**. *(Lessons 4-7, 11-6)*

In 22 and 23, rewrite each expression as the cosine or sine of a single argument. *(Lessons 11-5, 11-6)*

22. $\cos^2 \frac{\pi}{30} - \sin^2 \frac{\pi}{30}$

23. $\cos 2\theta \cos \theta - \sin 2\theta \sin \theta$

24. Simplify $\sin (a + b) + \sin (a - b)$. *(Lesson 11-5)*

In 25 and 26, let $M_1 = \begin{bmatrix} \cos a & -\sin a \\ \sin a & \cos a \end{bmatrix}$ and $M_2 = \begin{bmatrix} 1 & 0 \\ 0 & -1 \end{bmatrix}$.

25. What transformation is represented by each matrix?

a. M_1 **b.** M_2 *(Lessons 11-2, 11-4)*

26. *True or false.* $M_1M_2 = M_2M_1$. Justify your answer. *(Lessons 11-1, 11-2)*

27. Let $A = (2, -1)$, $B = (5, -1)$, and $C = (5, -5)$.

a. Write a matrix M representing $\triangle ABC$.

b. Draw $r_x \circ R_{90}(\triangle ABC)$.

c. Write a matrix M' representing $r_x \circ R_{90}(\triangle ABC)$.

d. Draw $R_{90} \circ r_x(\triangle ABC)$.

e. Write a matrix representing $R_{90} \circ r_x(\triangle ABC)$.

(Previous course, Lessons 11-2, 11-3)

28. Find all three solutions to the equation $x^3 = 343$. *(Lesson 9-8)*

In 29 and 30, an equation is given.

a. Give all real solution(s) exactly.

b. Estimate all real solution(s) to the nearest hundredth. *(Lessons 6-1, 6-6)*

29. $x^{2/3} = 81$

30. $3^x = 20$

Exploration

31. The matrix $\begin{bmatrix} 1 & 0 & 0 \\ 0 & 1 & 0 \\ 0 & 0 & 1 \end{bmatrix}$ is the identity for multiplication of 3×3 matrices.

Solve systems of equations to find the inverse of $\begin{bmatrix} 10 & 3 & 4 \\ -2 & 1 & 5 \\ 0 & 2 & -4 \end{bmatrix}$ in the set of 3×3 matrices.

LESSON

11-8

Matrices in Computer Graphics

computer simulation of a space shuttle landing (Courtesy Evans & Sutherland)

The four pictures of the space shuttle above are a small part of a computer simulation of take-offs and landings. To make the shuttle appear to the human eye to be in smooth motion, at least 15 pictures must appear each second, each one showing the new position of the shuttle, its shadow, and any changes in background. The screen that produced this simulation has about 1024×1024 pixels. Thus, to change every pixel 15 times a second requires $15 \times 1024 \times 1024 \approx 15{,}700{,}000$ computations of images of points.

How do computer graphics terminals perform these operations fast enough to fool the human eye? One way is to make sure the hardware operates as fast as possible. Another is to use mathematics to make the computations for each picture as efficient as possible. Matrices play a role in accomplishing both. This lesson shows how ideas from this chapter form the foundation of computer graphics.

An Example of Animation

On page 697, you saw various images of a frog. Suppose you want to change the frog from the position on the left to the position on the right.

Every point of the frog, his eyes, nose, hands, feet, etc., must be transformed in a consistent manner. To produce such an image, graphics programmers generate a point matrix for the frog, just as you have done for simple geometric figures in this chapter, and then multiply that matrix by a matrix representing the transformation.

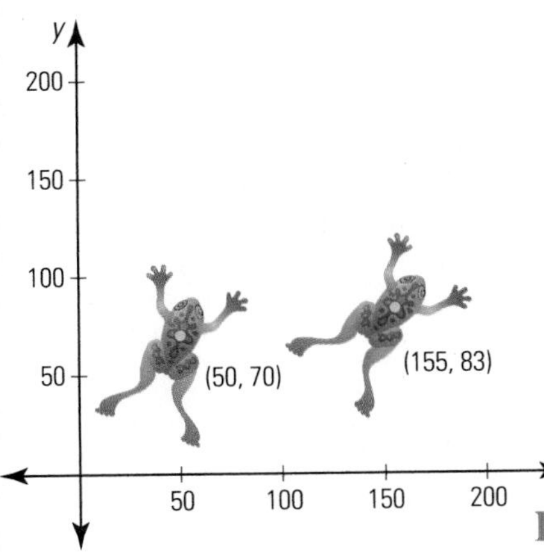

Three steps describe the transformation of the frog. Take any point of the picture, say the spot on the frog at (50, 70).

1. Translate the spot from (50, 70) to the origin. Call this transformation T_1.
2. Rotate the image about the origin 22.5° clockwise. This is $R_{-22.5}$.
3. Translate the rotated frog so that the spot is at (155, 83). Call this second translation T_2.

If you can write each transformation as a matrix, then you can find a single matrix which represents the composite $T_2 \circ R_{-22.5} \circ T_1$. (Note: multiplication of matrices is associative, so grouping parentheses are not needed.)

Representing Translations by Matrices

Unfortunately, a translation cannot be represented by a 2×2 matrix. This is because any 2×2 matrix maps the origin onto the origin,

$$\begin{bmatrix} a & b \\ c & d \end{bmatrix} \begin{bmatrix} 0 \\ 0 \end{bmatrix} = \begin{bmatrix} 0 \\ 0 \end{bmatrix},$$

whereas under a translation with nonzero magnitude, the image of the origin is not the origin.

Computer graphics programs get around this dilemma by expressing matrices for points, translations, and rotations in *homogeneous form.* The **homogeneous form** for any point (x, y) is $(x, y, 1)$. Thus, the origin is (0, 0, 1) in homogeneous form. The spot on the frog has homogeneous coordinates (50, 70, 1), and the tip of the frog's right foot is (59, 14, 1).

You may think that appending a 1 to the coordinates of every point doesn't gain much information. However, it allows you to write every translation of the plane as a 3×3 matrix. Consider the translation h units horizontally and k units vertically. This translation has the rule $T: (x, y) \rightarrow (x + h, y + k)$. In matrix form

$$T: \begin{bmatrix} x \\ y \end{bmatrix} \rightarrow \begin{bmatrix} x + h \\ y + k \end{bmatrix}.$$

T can be expressed using homogeneous coordinates with the matrix

$\begin{bmatrix} 1 & 0 & h \\ 0 & 1 & k \\ 0 & 0 & 1 \end{bmatrix}$, because $\begin{bmatrix} 1 & 0 & h \\ 0 & 1 & k \\ 0 & 0 & 1 \end{bmatrix} \begin{bmatrix} x \\ y \\ 1 \end{bmatrix} = \begin{bmatrix} x + h \\ y + k \\ 1 \end{bmatrix}$. In particular, the image of the origin is $\begin{bmatrix} 1 & 0 & h \\ 0 & 1 & k \\ 0 & 0 & 1 \end{bmatrix} \begin{bmatrix} 0 \\ 0 \\ 1 \end{bmatrix} = \begin{bmatrix} h \\ k \\ 1 \end{bmatrix}$, as needed.

Now you can find matrices for the translations applied to the frog. The translation to the origin, T_1, requires a shift of 50 left and 70 down. Thus,

$$T_1 = \begin{bmatrix} 1 & 0 & -50 \\ 0 & 1 & -70 \\ 0 & 0 & 1 \end{bmatrix}.$$

T_2 translates 155 right and 83 up. So

$$T_2 = \begin{bmatrix} 1 & 0 & 155 \\ 0 & 1 & 83 \\ 0 & 0 & 1 \end{bmatrix}.$$

Now the rotation matrix must be made into a 3 × 3 matrix. In general, the 2 × 2 transformation matrix $\begin{bmatrix} a & b \\ c & d \end{bmatrix}$ has homogeneous form $\begin{bmatrix} a & b & 0 \\ c & d & 0 \\ 0 & 0 & 1 \end{bmatrix}$. So, the rotation matrix for the frog is

$$R_{-22.5°} = \begin{bmatrix} \cos(-22.5°) & -\sin(-22.5°) & 0 \\ \sin(-22.5°) & \cos(-22.5°) & 0 \\ 0 & 0 & 1 \end{bmatrix}.$$

The composite transformation which moves the frog all at one time is

$$T_2 \quad \circ \quad R_{-22.5°} \quad \circ \quad T_1.$$

Its matrix is $\begin{bmatrix} 1 & 0 & 155 \\ 0 & 1 & 83 \\ 0 & 0 & 1 \end{bmatrix} \begin{bmatrix} \cos(-22.5°) & -\sin(-22.5°) & 0 \\ \sin(-22.5°) & \cos(-22.5°) & 0 \\ 0 & 0 & 1 \end{bmatrix} \begin{bmatrix} 1 & 0 & -50 \\ 0 & 1 & -70 \\ 0 & 0 & 1 \end{bmatrix}$

$$\approx \left(\begin{bmatrix} 1 & 0 & 155 \\ 0 & 1 & 83 \\ 0 & 0 & 1 \end{bmatrix} \begin{bmatrix} .9239 & .3827 & 0 \\ -.3827 & .9239 & 0 \\ 0 & 0 & 1 \end{bmatrix} \right) \begin{bmatrix} 1 & 0 & -50 \\ 0 & 1 & -70 \\ 0 & 0 & 1 \end{bmatrix}$$

$$= \begin{bmatrix} .9239 & .3827 & 155 \\ -.3827 & .9239 & 83 \\ 0 & 0 & 1 \end{bmatrix} \begin{bmatrix} 1 & 0 & -50 \\ 0 & 1 & -70 \\ 0 & 0 & 1 \end{bmatrix}$$

$$= \begin{bmatrix} .9239 & .3827 & 82.016 \\ -.3827 & .9239 & 37.462 \\ 0 & 0 & 1 \end{bmatrix}.$$

The calculations can be checked by considering the spot, which moves from (50, 70) to (155, 83).

$$\begin{bmatrix} .9239 & .3827 & 82.016 \\ -.3827 & .9239 & 37.462 \\ 0 & 0 & 1 \end{bmatrix} \begin{bmatrix} 50 \\ 70 \\ 1 \end{bmatrix} = \begin{bmatrix} 155 \\ 83 \\ 1 \end{bmatrix}$$

To find the image of any point (x, y) on the frog, then, you would multiply the 3 × 3 matrix for $T_2 \circ R_{-22.5} \circ T_1$ by $\begin{bmatrix} x \\ y \\ 1 \end{bmatrix}$. Notice that the difficulty of the multiplication is not greatly increased by going from 2 × 2 form to homogeneous form. The last row of all 3 × 3 homogeneous form matrices is [0 0 1], so that row contributes very little to the complexity of calculations.

Representing Three-Dimensional Transformations by Matrices

A generalization of this idea is used to picture three-dimensional objects on a two-dimensional computer screen. Just as 3×3 matrices are used for homogeneous coordinates of 2×2 matrices, 4×4 matrices can be used to transform the position and orientation of any 3-D object. The point (x, y, z) in 3-space has homogeneous coordinates $(x, y, z, 1)$, and a translation of 5 units in x, -3 units in y, and 2.5 units in z is represented by the matrix

$$\begin{bmatrix} 1 & 0 & 0 & 5 \\ 0 & 1 & 0 & -3 \\ 0 & 0 & 1 & 2.5 \\ 0 & 0 & 0 & 1 \end{bmatrix}.$$

Coordinate systems which are used for representing 3-D objects are called **world coordinates**. Modeling an object's change in position can be achieved by multiplying its world coordinates by a 4×4 transformation matrix. In this way, world coordinates for an object maintain a record of where the object is in space.

When viewing a 3-D object, someone must choose the viewing point. Where should the viewer be stationed? This is a separate issue from computing world coordinates. A viewer on the right side of the classroom has a different view of your teacher than a person on the left side. But the teacher's world coordinates are the same for both viewing positions. Once the viewing position is determined, then the view must be restricted, or clipped, to fit into the boundary of a computer screen, as though the computer screen were a window. Finally, the projection of coordinates must be accomplished, to determine where on the 2-D screen the 3-D points are to appear.

All of these steps can be performed with 4×4 matrices. Here is a summary.

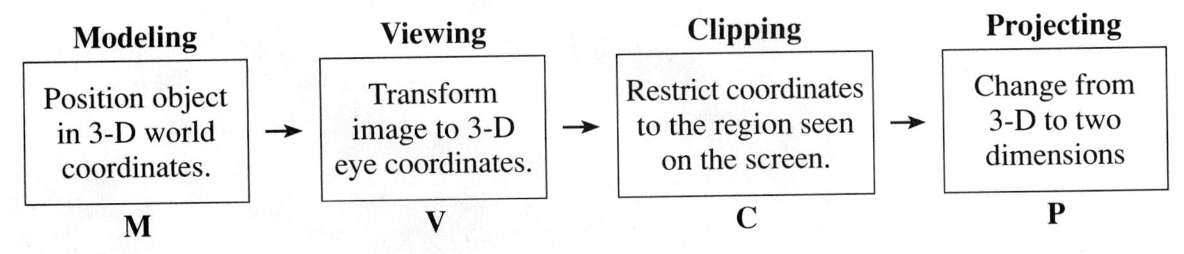

The matrix product $P \cdot C \cdot V \cdot M$ is applied to the world coordinates to give points on the screen. (Note the order of the matrices—M represents the first-applied transformation.) Each frame of an animated sequence has a different product matrix.

The Role of High-Speed Computers

The complexity of three-dimensional graphics makes it difficult to do high-quality work on personal computers. The multiplications needed to perform the transformations take a long time. However, supercomputers and high-quality graphics workstations do matrix operations with great speed. *Vector processors* are designed to multiply a row times a column in one step. On supercomputers these vector processors vastly shorten the time needed for each 4-matrix product. On graphics workstations, more than one processor might be devoted to the matrix multiplications. Here is how the work can be shared among processors. Consider the following multiplication.

$$\begin{bmatrix} 3 & -1 & 2 & 7 \\ 5 & 8 & 4 & 3 \\ 2 & 9 & -6 & 4 \\ 0 & 0 & 0 & 1 \end{bmatrix} \begin{bmatrix} 33 \\ 27 \\ 11 \\ 1 \end{bmatrix} = \begin{bmatrix} x' \\ y' \\ z' \\ 1 \end{bmatrix}$$

A human or microcomputer would have to perform 12 multiplications and 9 additions to find x', y', and z'. If there were three processors sharing the task, each could have 4 multiplications and 3 additions. For example, the first processor could find $x' = 3 \cdot 33 + -1 \cdot 27 + 2 \cdot 11 + 7 \cdot 1$. The second processor could find y', and the third, z'. So three processors would cut the computational time to $\frac{1}{3}$ that of a single processor. If the processors are vector processors, they can further reduce the time to that of a single multiplication step.

High-powered computers for graphics are organized to perform matrix multiplications quickly so that the motion they represent appears smooth and natural. When combined with shadows and light reflections, also computable with matrices, you can get the realism which fascinates viewers, as in the picture below.

scene from the Star Wars *trilogy*

QUESTIONS

Covering the Reading

1. A commercial film has 24 frames a second; a computer simulation has 5000 × 5000 pixels for each frame. How many point calculations must be performed per second for computer simulation of the commercial film?

2. Write the homogeneous form of (3, -7).

3. Write the nonhomogeneous form of (2, 0, -1, 1).

4. Write the homogeneous form of the matrix for R_{30}, using exact values.

5. Give the 2×2 matrix which has homogeneous form $\begin{bmatrix} -1 & 0 & 0 \\ 0 & -1 & 0 \\ 0 & 0 & 1 \end{bmatrix}$.

6. What is the homogeneous form of the 2×2 identity matrix?

7. Find the image of the tip of the frog's right foot under the composite transformation in the lesson.

8. Give a 4×4 matrix which represents a translation of -4 units in x, 0.3 units in y, and 0 units in z.

9. Why are 3 processors, not 4, used to speed the multiplication of 4×4 matrices representing 3-D graphics?

10. Prove that if A and B are 3×3 matrices in homogeneous form, then so is the product AB.

11. A microcomputer with a single processor runs a 3-D computer game with 10 frames per second. In an analysis of the computation steps, the designers found that the processor was doing computations involved in the matrix operations of 3-D graphics 60% of the time and running the video display 40% of the time. If they replace the single processor with a graphics "engine" that has three processors to handle matrix multiplications and if they don't change the speed of the video display, how many frames per second can they expect? (Assume that the three processors can do real-number multiplications and additions no faster than a single processor.)

Review

12. a. Give the entries of the matrix for R_{-10}, rounded to the nearest thousandth.

b. What matrix is the inverse of the matrix in part **a**? *(Lessons 11-4, 11-7)*

13. Let $A = \begin{bmatrix} 1 & 0 \\ 0 & -1 \end{bmatrix}$.

a. What transformation does A represent?

b. Find A^{-1}.

c. What transformation does A^{-1} represent? *(Lessons 11-2, 11-7)*

14. Give an example of a 2×2 matrix with a zero determinant. *(Lesson 11-7)*

15. State a corresponding sentence involving transformations.

$\begin{bmatrix} 3 & 0 \\ 0 & \frac{1}{2} \end{bmatrix} \cdot \begin{bmatrix} \frac{1}{3} & 0 \\ 0 & 2 \end{bmatrix} = \begin{bmatrix} 1 & 0 \\ 0 & 1 \end{bmatrix}$ *(Lessons 11-2, 11-7)*

16. Use matrices to solve the system $\begin{cases} 4x + y = 11 \\ -5x + 2y = 7 \end{cases}$. *(Lesson 11-7)*

17. Give a formula for sin 3θ in terms of sin θ. *(Lesson 11-6)*

18. Use a Double Angle Formula to show that the graph of the function $f(x) = 10\cos^2 x - 5$ has amplitude 5. *(Lesson 11-6)*

19. Give an exact value. *(Lessons 4-7, 11-5)*

a. cos 255° **b.** $\sin \frac{29\pi}{2}$

20. Suppose that a triangle is represented by the matrix $\begin{bmatrix} a & c & e \\ b & d & f \end{bmatrix}$. Tell what the following product represents.

$$\begin{bmatrix} \cos 25° & -\sin 25° \\ \sin 25° & \cos 25° \end{bmatrix} \cdot \begin{bmatrix} a & c & e \\ b & d & f \end{bmatrix}$$ *(Lesson 11-4)*

21. Suppose a 2 × 2 matrix is used to transform a figure. (1, 0) has image (3, -1), and (0, 1) has image (5, 4).
a. What is the 2 × 2 matrix?
b. What is the image of (0, 0)?
c. What is the image of (1, 1)? *(Lesson 11-3)*

22. Consider two thin lenses with focal lengths f_1 and f_2 at a distance d apart in the air. Physicists and engineers studying optics have shown that the product

$$\begin{bmatrix} 1 & 0 \\ -\frac{1}{f_1} & 1 \end{bmatrix}\begin{bmatrix} 1 & d \\ 0 & 1 \end{bmatrix}\begin{bmatrix} 1 & 0 \\ -\frac{1}{f_2} & 1 \end{bmatrix}$$

describes the image of light passing through this system. *(Lesson 11-1)*

d

a. Calculate this product for the special case when the lenses touch each other, that is, when $d = 0$.
b. Calculate this product for the general case given above.

Exploration

23. Estimate your world coordinates in your math class with relation to the front door of where you live. Let x be feet north; y be feet east; and z be feet up. (If you are 2 miles west of your house, for instance, you would have a y-coordinate of $-2 \cdot 5280 = -10560$. If you are on the third floor of your school and your front door is at the level of the school entrance, $z \approx 24$ for you.)

24. One kind of projection matrix is $\begin{bmatrix} 1 & 0 & 0 & 0 \\ 0 & 1 & 0 & 0 \\ 0 & 0 & 0 & 0 \\ 0 & 0 & 0 & 1 \end{bmatrix}$. In what way does this matrix transform a 3-D object?

A project presents an opportunity for you to extend your knowledge of a topic related to the material of this chapter. You should allow more time for a project than you do for a typical homework question.

PROJECTS 11

CHAPTER ELEVEN

1 Programming 2-D Graphics

Write a program to display a figure and its images under some of the transformations described in this chapter. Include the images under a reflection, rotation, translation, and scale change.

2 Maximizing Shot-Put Distance

The formula $d = \frac{v^2 \sin 2\theta}{9.8}$, for the distance d in meters at which an object projected from ground level with an initial velocity v (in meters per second) at an angle θ to the horizontal will land, only applies if the points of release and landing are at the same horizontal level. This assumption is often not satisfied. For instance, in the shot put an athlete propels a shot, a heavy metal sphere, and tries to maximize the horizontal distance it travels. But a shot-putter releases the shot at about shoulder level, not at ground level. It can be shown that when the shot is released at a height h meters above the ground with a velocity of v meters per second at an angle θ with the horizontal, its horizontal displacement d is given by

$$d = \frac{v^2 \sin 2\theta}{19.6} + \frac{v^2 \cos \theta}{9.58}\sqrt{\sin^2 \theta + \frac{19.6\,h}{v^2}}.$$

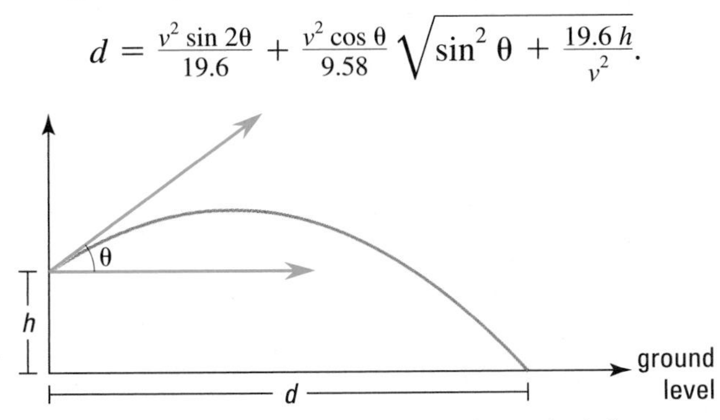

When the release velocity and release height are given, d is solely a function of θ.

a. World-class shot-putters can achieve a release velocity of 13 meters per second. Suppose for such a shot-putter $h = 1.90$ m. Construct a table of values for d as a function of θ for angles between 20° and 50°, in increments of 5°. Then, using smaller increments, find the angle θ to the nearest degree at which the shot should be released so as to achieve the maximum value of d. According to this model, what is the maximum distance possible for this shot-putter?

b. Consider a shorter athlete who releases the shot from a height of 1.7 m at the same velocity. What is the maximum distance this shot-putter can attain?

c. How do the data in parts **a** and **b** above compare to all-time records in the shot put for your school or local area? for the Olympics?

3 Inverse 3 × 3 Matrices

a. Two 3 × 3 matrices M and N are inverse matrices if and only if their product MN is the 3 × 3 identity matrix. Verify that

$$\begin{bmatrix} 2 & 1 & 1 \\ 1 & 4 & -3 \\ -1 & -3 & 3 \end{bmatrix}^{-1} = \begin{bmatrix} 3/7 & -6/7 & -1 \\ 0 & 1 & 1 \\ 1/7 & 5/7 & 1 \end{bmatrix}$$

b. Consider the system

$$\begin{aligned} 2x + y + z &= 0 \\ x + 4y - 3z &= 5 \\ -x - 3y + 3z &= 7. \end{aligned}$$

Verify that you can represent this system with the matrix equation

(continued)

ZIVOGQWSCSLV

$$\begin{bmatrix} 2 & 1 & 1 \\ 1 & 4 & -3 \\ -1 & -3 & 3 \end{bmatrix} \cdot \begin{bmatrix} x \\ y \\ z \end{bmatrix} = \begin{bmatrix} 0 \\ 5 \\ 7 \end{bmatrix}.$$

c. Multiply both sides of the matrix representation for the system by the inverse matrix in part **a**. What is the solution to the system?

d. Use a calculator to compute the inverse of $\begin{bmatrix} 2 & 1 & 1 \\ 1 & 4 & -3 \\ -1 & -3 & 3 \end{bmatrix}$, and verify that it is equal to the matrix in part **a**.

e. Solve the system

$$\begin{aligned} 3x + y + z &= 4 \\ 2x - 2y - z &= 2 \\ 3x - y - z &= 1 \end{aligned}$$

using a calculator. Check your results by solving the system through adding or subtracting equations.

---

4 Matrix Codes

An application of matrices to codes was found in 1929–31 by the mathematician Lester Hill. To encode a message, put its letters into 2×2 matrices four at a time. For instance, to encode the message HELP ME PLEASE, use the matrices $\begin{bmatrix} H & E \\ L & P \end{bmatrix}$, $\begin{bmatrix} M & E \\ P & L \end{bmatrix}$, and $\begin{bmatrix} E & A \\ S & E \end{bmatrix}$. Now assign an integer to each letter using A = 1, B = 2, C = 3, … , Z = 26. This yields the matrices $\begin{bmatrix} 8 & 5 \\ 12 & 16 \end{bmatrix}$, $\begin{bmatrix} 13 & 5 \\ 16 & 12 \end{bmatrix}$, and $\begin{bmatrix} 5 & 1 \\ 19 & 5 \end{bmatrix}$. Next, multiply each matrix on the left by an *encoding matrix*, one whose determinant is 1 or -1. We choose the matrix $\begin{bmatrix} 3 & -2 \\ 1 & -1 \end{bmatrix}$. The product of this encoding matrix with the first matrix of the message is $\begin{bmatrix} 0 & -17 \\ -4 & -11 \end{bmatrix}$. Now translate the numbers back to letters, adding or subtracting multiples of 26 to each number if it is not from 1 to 26. For instance, the first coded matrix becomes $\begin{bmatrix} 26 & 9 \\ 22 & 15 \end{bmatrix}$, which is $\begin{bmatrix} Z & I \\ V & O \end{bmatrix}$.

a. Multiply matrices to verify that the second and third coded matrices are $\begin{bmatrix} G & Q \\ W & S \end{bmatrix}$ and $\begin{bmatrix} C & S \\ L & V \end{bmatrix}$. So the coded message is ZIVOGQWSCSLV.

b. Notice that, by using matrices, the same letter in the original message HELPMEPLEASE is replaced by different letters in the coded message. This is what makes the matrix coding more difficult to decipher. But, if you know the encoding matrix, you can decipher the message using its inverse, the *decoding matrix*. In this case, the decoding matrix is $\begin{bmatrix} 3 & -2 \\ 1 & -1 \end{bmatrix}^{-1}$, or $\begin{bmatrix} 1 & -2 \\ 1 & -3 \end{bmatrix}$. Multiplying each of the coded matrices by this inverse gets you back to the original message. For instance, $\begin{bmatrix} 1 & -2 \\ 1 & -3 \end{bmatrix} \cdot \begin{bmatrix} 26 & 9 \\ 22 & 15 \end{bmatrix} = \begin{bmatrix} -18 & -21 \\ -40 & -36 \end{bmatrix}$ which becomes (after adding multiples of 26) $\begin{bmatrix} 8 & 5 \\ 12 & 16 \end{bmatrix} = \begin{bmatrix} H & E \\ L & P \end{bmatrix}$. Verify that multiplication of the second and third coded matrices by the decoding matrix retrieves the rest of the message.

c. Make up your own message of at least 24 letters in length and encode it using a different coding matrix than the one shown here.

d. Show that your message can be decoded by using the inverse of your encoding matrix.

e. Why is it important that the determinant of the coding matrix be 1 or -1?

SUMMARY

An $m \times n$ matrix is a rectangular array of elements arranged in m rows and n columns. If $m = n$, the matrix is a square matrix.

If A and B are matrices, the product $C = AB$ exists if the number of columns of A equals the number of rows of B. The element in the ith row and jth column of C is the sum of the term-by-term products of the ith row of A and the jth row of B. Matrix multiplication has many applications. If the elements of A represent coefficients, the elements of B are variables, and C is a column matrix of constants, then $AB = C$ represents a linear system of equations. If A contains numbers of items and B represents corresponding unit values of the items, then AB gives total values of the items.

Some geometric figures and some transformations can be represented by 2×2 matrices. Any n-gon can be represented by a $2 \times n$ matrix whose columns are its vertices. If M represents a transformation T and P represents a polygon, then the product MP represents $T(P)$. This enables transformations to be performed by using matrices. If M_1 and M_2 are matrices for transformations T_1 and T_2, then M_1M_2 represents $T_1 \circ T_2$. Thus composites of transformations can also be represented by matrices. Lifelike computer animations can be performed by multiplying a large number of points by successive matrices representing the transformations desired of the animated figure.

Some of the transformations for which 2×2 matrices exist are: reflections over the x-axis, y-axis, and line $x = y$; all rotations with center at the origin; all size changes with center $(0, 0)$; all scale changes of the form $(x, y) \rightarrow (ax, by)$. The Matrix Basis Theorem provides an easy way to recall the matrix for a given transformation; you need only know the images of $(1, 0)$ and $(0, 1)$ under that transformation.

If a matrix with a non-zero determinant exists for a transformation, then the multiplicative inverse of that matrix is the matrix for the inverse of the transformation. Matrices and their inverses are useful for solving systems of equations. Any 2×2 matrix will have an inverse if its determinant is not equal to zero.

From the matrix for a rotation, formulas for $\cos(x + y)$ and $\sin(x + y)$ can be rather quickly derived. From these formulas, formulas for $\cos(x - y)$, $\sin(x - y)$, $\cos 2x$, and $\sin 2x$ follow. These formulas enable exact values for certain cosines and sines to be determined.

VOCABULARY

Below are the most important terms and phrases for this chapter. You should be able to give a general description and a specific example of each and a precise definition for those marked with an asterisk (*).

Lesson 11-1
matrix
element
*dimensions of a matrix
row matrix
column matrix
matrix multiplication
product matrix

Lesson 11-2
point matrix
matrix representing a transformation
2×2 Identity Matrix

Lesson 11-3
Matrices for Rotations Theorem
Matrix Basis Theorem

Lesson 11-4
Rotation Matrix Theorem

Lesson 11-5
Addition Identities for the Cosine and Sine

Lesson 11-6
Double Angle Formulas
Half Angle Formulas

Lesson 11-7
*inverse transformations
*inverse matrices
Inverse of a 2×2 Matrix Theorem
determinant, det

PROGRESS SELF-TEST

Take this test as you would take a test in class. You will need graph paper and a calculator. Then check the test yourself using the solutions at the back of the book.

In 1–3, use the following matrices. P gives the number of registered voters (in millions) in each part of a state. V represents the percent of registered voters in those areas telling how they would expect to vote in an election.

$$\begin{matrix}\text{Urban}\\ \text{Rural}\\ \text{Suburban}\end{matrix}\begin{bmatrix}3.4\\0.6\\2.1\end{bmatrix} = P$$

$$\begin{matrix} & \text{Urban} & \text{Rural} & \text{Suburban}\\ \text{Democrat} & .50 & .47 & .29\\ \text{Republican} & .29 & .41 & .58\\ \text{Independent} & .21 & .12 & .13\end{matrix} = V$$

1. How many people in the state are expected to vote Republican?
2. Find VP.
3. What does the matrix VP represent?
4. Find the product $\begin{bmatrix}5 & -1\\2 & 0\end{bmatrix}\begin{bmatrix}3 & 8\\-1 & 1\end{bmatrix}$.
5. Suppose M is a 3×4 matrix, N is a $4 \times t$ matrix, and Z is a 3×5 matrix. If $MN = Z$, find the value of t.

In 6–8 use the figure below.

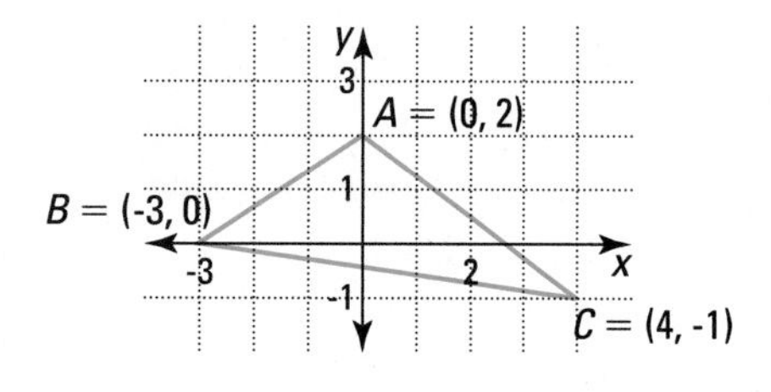

6. Write a matrix M for $\triangle ABC$.
7. Find XM, where $X = \begin{bmatrix}-1 & 0\\0 & 2\end{bmatrix}$.
8. Graph the image represented by XM.

9. **a.** Give a matrix representing the transformation for the reflection over the line $y = x$.

   b. Use the matrix in part **a** to show that the transformation $r_{y=x}$ is its own inverse.

10. *Multiple choice.* Which matrix represents R_{30}?

    (a) $\begin{bmatrix}\sqrt{3}/2 & 1/2\\1/2 & \sqrt{3}/2\end{bmatrix}$ (b) $\begin{bmatrix}\sqrt{3}/2 & -1/2\\1/2 & \sqrt{3}/2\end{bmatrix}$

    (c) $\begin{bmatrix}-\sqrt{3}/2 & -1/2\\1/2 & -\sqrt{3}/2\end{bmatrix}$ (d) $\begin{bmatrix}1/2 & -\sqrt{3}/2\\\sqrt{3}/2 & 1/2\end{bmatrix}$

    (e) $\begin{bmatrix}1/2 & \sqrt{3}/2\\-\sqrt{3}/2 & 1/2\end{bmatrix}$

11. A figure is transformed by $R_{180} \circ r_x$.

    a. What transformation is done first?

    b. What single matrix represents the composite?

12. Let $P = (0, 0)$, $Q = (1, 0)$ and $R = (0, 1)$. What is the image of $\triangle PQR$ under a rotation of magnitude θ?
13. Write the following expression as the sine or cosine of a single argument:

    $\sin 83° \cos 42° - \cos 83° \sin 42°$

14. Using a formula for $\cos(\alpha + \beta)$, simplify $\cos(\pi + \theta)$.
15. If $\sin A = 0.40$ and A is acute, find $\sin 2A$.
16. Find the inverse of $C = \begin{bmatrix}1 & -1\\3 & 5\end{bmatrix}$.
17. Show that $G = \begin{bmatrix}3x & 6\\5x & 10\end{bmatrix}$ has no inverse.
18. **a.** Write a matrix equation to represent the system.

    $$\begin{cases}3x - y = 6\\5x - 2y = 11\end{cases}$$

    b. Solve the system in part **a**.

CHAPTER REVIEW

Questions on SPUR Objectives

SPUR stands for **S**kills, **P**roperties, **U**ses, and **R**epresentations. The Chapter Review questions are grouped according to the SPUR Objectives for this chapter.

SKILLS DEAL WITH THE PROCEDURES USED TO GET ANSWERS.

Objective A: *Multiply matrices, when possible.* *(Lesson 11-1)*

In 1–4, use the following matrices.

$A = \begin{bmatrix} 1/2 & 3 \\ 5 & -1 \end{bmatrix}$ $B = \begin{bmatrix} 1 & 5 & -1 \\ -1 & 0 & 1 \end{bmatrix}$

$C = \begin{bmatrix} x \\ 3 \end{bmatrix}$ $D = \begin{bmatrix} 1 & -7 \end{bmatrix}$

1. *Multiple choice.* Which of the following products is not possible?
   (a) AC (b) CD
   (c) BA (d) A^2C
2. Find AB.
3. Find DC.
4. Find A^2.

Objective B: *Use matrices to solve systems of equations.* *(Lesson 11-7)*

5. Solve for x: $\begin{bmatrix} 1 & 2 \\ -1 & 1 \end{bmatrix}\begin{bmatrix} x \\ 1 \end{bmatrix} = \begin{bmatrix} 7 \\ -4 \end{bmatrix}$.
6. Consider the system $\begin{cases} x + 3y = 11 \\ 2x - y = 8 \end{cases}$.
   a. Represent the system by a matrix equation.
   b. Find the inverse of the coefficient matrix in part **a**.
   c. Multiply on the left both sides of the matrix equation by the answer in part **b**.
   d. What is the solution to the system of equations?

In 7 and 8, solve the given system of equations using matrices.

7. $\begin{cases} 5x + 2y = 6 \\ 10x - 10y = -9 \end{cases}$
8. $\begin{cases} 8x + 3y = 10 \\ x + 8y = -14 \end{cases}$
9. Solve the system $\begin{cases} x + 2y + 3z = 10 \\ 3x + y + 2z = 13, \\ 2x + 3y + z = 13 \end{cases}$

   given that

   $$\begin{bmatrix} 1 & 2 & 3 \\ 3 & 1 & 2 \\ 2 & 3 & 1 \end{bmatrix}^{-1} = \begin{bmatrix} -\frac{5}{18} & \frac{7}{18} & \frac{1}{18} \\ \frac{1}{18} & -\frac{5}{18} & \frac{7}{18} \\ \frac{7}{18} & \frac{1}{18} & -\frac{5}{18} \end{bmatrix}.$$

Objective C: *Find the inverse of a 2 × 2 matrix.* *(Lesson 11-7)*

In 10 and 11, find the inverse of the given matrix.

10. $\begin{bmatrix} 2 & 1 \\ -5 & 4 \end{bmatrix}$
11. $\begin{bmatrix} \cos 40° & -\sin 40° \\ \sin 40° & \cos 40° \end{bmatrix}$
12. Find $\begin{bmatrix} \frac{2}{9} & \frac{1}{9} \\ -\frac{1}{3} & \frac{4}{3} \end{bmatrix}^{-1}$.
13. *Multiple choice.* Tell which two of the following matrices have no inverses.
    (a) $\begin{bmatrix} 0 & 0 \\ 0 & 0 \end{bmatrix}$ (b) $\begin{bmatrix} 1 & 0 \\ 0 & 1 \end{bmatrix}$
    (c) $\begin{bmatrix} 0 & 1 \\ 1 & 0 \end{bmatrix}$ (d) $\begin{bmatrix} -2 & 4 \\ -6 & 8 \end{bmatrix}$
    (e) $\begin{bmatrix} -2 & 4 \\ -1 & 2 \end{bmatrix}$

PROPERTIES DEAL WITH THE PRINCIPLES BEHIND THE MATHEMATICS.

Objective D: *Apply properties of matrices and matrix multiplication.* *(Lessons 11-1, 11-3, 11-7)*

In 14 and 15, an equation relating the matrices M, N, and P is given. The matrix M has dimensions 4×2, and the matrix P has dimensions 4×5. Give the dimensions of N.

14. $MN = P$

15. $PN = M$

16. *Multiple choice.* Which of the following statements about 2×2 matrices R, S, and T is false?

(a) RS is also a 2×2 matrix.

(b) $(RS)T = R(ST)$

(c) There is a matrix I such that $RI = IR = R$

(d) $RS = SR$

17. Name three types of transformations that can be represented by 2×2 matrices.

Objective E: *Apply the Addition and Double Angle Formulas.* *(Lessons 11-5, 11-6)*

In 18 and 19, state the exact value.

18. $\sin 105°$ **19.** $\cos \frac{5\pi}{12}$

In 20 and 21, A and B are acute angles with $\sin A = .8$ and $\cos B = .5$. Find each.

20. $\cos (A - B)$ **21.** $\sin 2A$

In 22 and 23, simplify.

22. $\cos (\pi - \theta)$ **23.** $\sin \left(\theta - \frac{\pi}{2}\right)$

24. Give a formula for $\cos 4\theta$ in terms of $\cos \theta$ only.

In 25–27, write as the sine or cosine of a single argument.

25. $2 \sin A \cos A$ **26.** $\cos\frac{\pi}{5} \cos\frac{\pi}{3} + \sin\frac{\pi}{5} \sin\frac{\pi}{3}$

27. $2 \cos^2 25° - 1$

In 28–29, explain how the formula was derived.

28. $\sin (\alpha + \beta)$ **29.** $\cos 2\theta$

USES DEAL WITH APPLICATIONS OF MATHEMATICS IN REAL SITUATIONS.

Objective F: *Use a matrix to organize information.* *(Lessons 11-1)*

In 30 and 31, use the production matrix P and the cost matrix C shown here.

P =	Melons	Lettuce (heads)
Farm A	1000	10,000
Farm B	2000	10,000
Farm C	500	20,000
Farm D	500	5,000

C =	Cost to Produce	Cost to Consumer
Melons	.45	.90
Lettuce	.65	1.00

30. a. Calculate PC. **b.** What does PC represent?

c. Find the total cost of producing melons and lettuce on Farm C.

d. What element of PC contains this cost?

31. Find the total cost to the consumer of the melons and lettuce produced on Farm A.

In 32 and 33, use the following matrix of Foreign Exchange rates.

F =	United Kingdom (pound)	Canada (dollar)	Japan (yen)	United States (dollar)
1975	2.22	0.98	0.0034	1.00
1980	2.32	0.86	0.0044	1.00
1985	1.30	0.73	0.0042	1.00
1990	1.78	0.86	0.0069	1.00
1995	1.58	0.73	0.0106	1.00

32. a. Describe the data given by each row of F.

b. How many U.S. dollars were 1000 Japanese yen worth in 1995?

33. a. If a tourist entered the U.S. in 1995 with 150 pounds U.K., 212 dollars Canadian, and 100 dollars U.S., what is the U.S. equivalent of that cash?

b. *True or false.* To compare the total cash value of the tourist in part **a** at five-year intervals between 1975 and 1995, one would look at the product matrix FC. (C is shown at the right.)

$$C = \begin{bmatrix} 150 \\ 212 \\ 0 \\ 100 \end{bmatrix}$$

REPRESENTATIONS DEAL WITH PICTURES, GRAPHS, OR OBJECTS THAT ILLUSTRATE CONCEPTS.

Objective G: *Represent reflections, rotations, scale changes, and size changes as matrices.* *(Lesson 11-2, 11-3, 11-4)*

34. Write the matrix representing r_x, reflection over the x-axis.

35. Write the matrix for the scale change $T: (x, y) \rightarrow \left(x, \frac{1}{3}y\right)$.

36. Write the matrix which represents a 90° rotation counterclockwise about the origin.

In 37 and 38, describe the transformation represented by the matrix.

37. $\begin{bmatrix} 11 & 0 \\ 0 & 11 \end{bmatrix}$

38. $\begin{bmatrix} 0 & 1 \\ 1 & 0 \end{bmatrix}$

39. Tell what rotation is represented by $\begin{bmatrix} -1 & 0 \\ 0 & -1 \end{bmatrix}$.

40. Give the rotation matrix for R_{32}.

41. Give exact values of the matrix for R_{120}.

42. If $T(1, 0) = (q, t)$, $T(0, 1) = (e, z)$, and T can be represented by a 2 × 2 matrix, what is this matrix?

43. A transformation which can be represented by a matrix takes (0, 0) to (0, 0), (1, 0) to (5, 0), and (0, 1) to (0, -1).

a. What is the matrix for the transformation?

b. What is the image of (1, 1)?

Objective H: *Represent composites of transformations as matrix products.* *(Lessons 11-3, 11-4)*

44. A figure is rotated 90° clockwise, then reflected over the y-axis.

a. Write a matrix product for the composite transformation.

b. Compute the matrix product from part **a**.

45. Tell, in words, what composition of transformations is represented by

$$\begin{bmatrix} \cos 32° & -\sin 32° \\ \sin 32° & \cos 32° \end{bmatrix} \cdot \begin{bmatrix} 0 & 1 \\ 1 & 0 \end{bmatrix} \cdot \begin{bmatrix} 0 & -1 \\ 1 & 0 \end{bmatrix}.$$

46. The matrix representing R_{135} is

$$A = \begin{bmatrix} -\sqrt{2}/2 & -\sqrt{2}/2 \\ \sqrt{2}/2 & -\sqrt{2}/2 \end{bmatrix}.$$

a. Compute A^2.

b. What transformation does A^2 represent?

47. Let Y be the matrix representing r_y.

a. Compute Y^3.

b. What transformation does Y^3 represent?

Objective I: *Use matrices to find the image of a figure under a transformation.* *(Lessons 11-2, 11-3, 11-4)*

48. Refer to $\triangle ABC$ below.

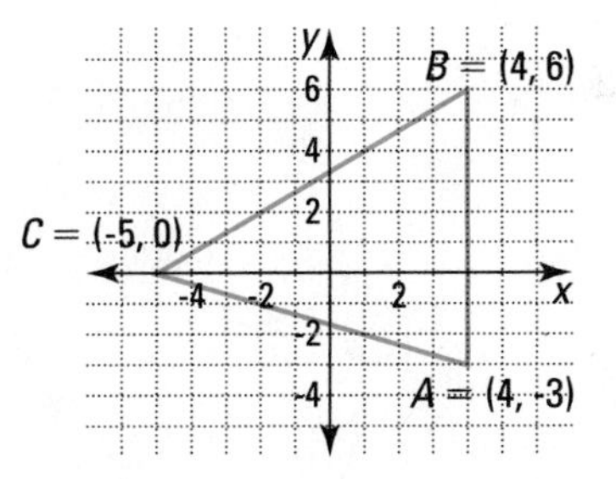

a. Find a matrix for the image $\triangle A'B'C'$ under the transformation represented by $\begin{bmatrix} 1 & 1 \\ 0 & -1 \end{bmatrix}$.

b. Draw the image.

49. a. Find a matrix for the vertices of the image of the square having opposite vertices (0, 0) and (1, 1) under the transformation with matrix $\begin{bmatrix} 7 & 0 \\ -1 & 1 \end{bmatrix}$.

b. Draw the square and its image on the same axes.

50. Let $A = (7, 0)$, $B = (0, 2)$, and $C = (-1, -1)$.

a. Describe $(r_x \circ R_{90})(\triangle ABC)$ as the product of three matrices.

b. Find a single matrix for the image triangle.

51. A two-dimensional figure has been rotated counterclockwise around the origin by 75°. Write the matrix for the transformation which returns the figure to its original orientation.

CHAPTER 12

QUADRATIC RELATIONS

In the 3rd century B.C., only about 25 years after the appearance of Euclid's *Elements*, another Greek mathematician, Appollonius, wrote a set of books entitled *Conics*, dealing with the curves formed by intersecting a cone with a plane: ellipses, parabolas, and hyperbolas.

Apollonius did not consider any applications of these curves, but 1800 years later, in the 10-year period from 1609 to 1619, the German scholar Johannes Kepler performed one of the greatest examples of mathematical modeling of all time. Until Kepler, almost all people thought that the planets moved in circles (either around the earth or the sun) and the stars were fixed on a celestial sphere. Using the measurements of the positions of the planets obtained by his teacher, the Danish astronomer Tycho Brahe, Kepler found that the orbits of the planets around the sun were ellipses and that these ellipses satisfied several simple but not obvious properties.

At about the same time, Descartes applied his new coordinates (the rectangular coordinates you know very well) to the geometry of the *conic sections* and found that all conics could be described by equations of the form $Ax^2 + Bxy + Cy^2 + Dx + Ey + F = 0$. Because the greatest degree of any term in this equation is 2, the sets of ordered pairs (x, y) satisfying it are called *quadratic relations*.

This chapter explores the relationships between the graphs of conic sections and equations of quadratic relations. Along the way, you will encounter a variety of applications of these curves.

LESSON

12-1

The Geometry of the Ellipse

The Three Conic Sections

The "cone" that gives rise to a conic section is not the same as the cones studied in geometry. The conic section cone is formed by rotating one of two intersecting, non-perpendicular lines about the other. The fixed line is called the **axis** of the cone; the point of intersection of these lines is the cone's **vertex**. Any position of the rotating line is an **edge** of the cone. The conic section cone has two parts, called **nappes**, one on each side of its vertex, as shown in the figure below at the left.

In general, a **cross section** or **section** of a three-dimensional figure is the intersection of a plane with that figure. The three figures below are the sections of a cone formed when a plane intersects the cone but does not contain the cone's vertex.

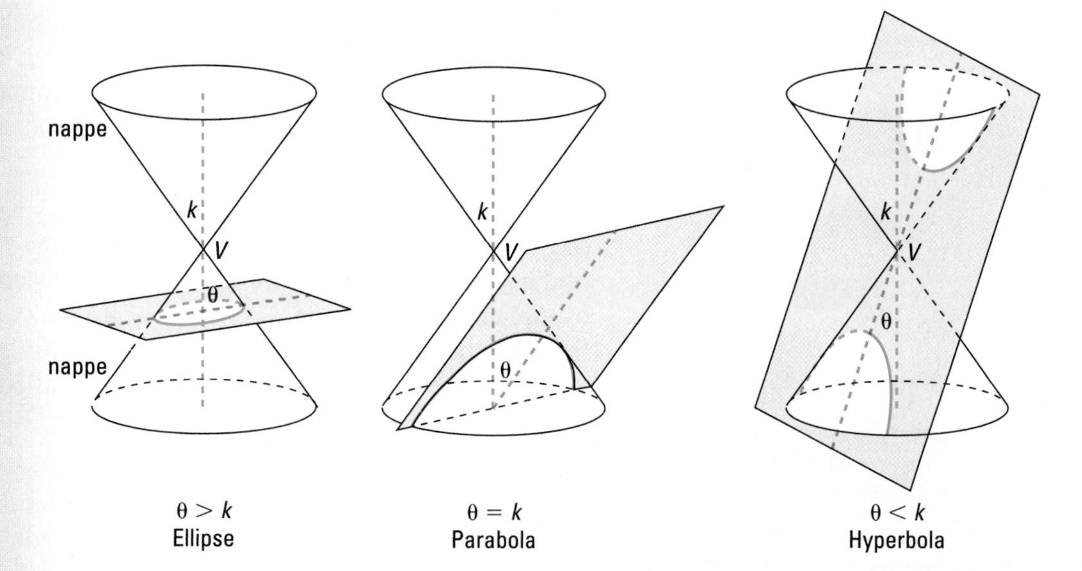

Because drawings can only show a part of a cone, it may not be obvious that every cone intersects every plane in space. Let k be the measure of the angle between the lines that formed the cone (that is, between its axis and the rotating line). Let θ be the measure of the smallest angle between the cone's axis and the plane. (This angle cannot be obtuse, so $\theta \le 90°$.) If $\theta > k$, the plane intersects only one nappe of the cone and the section is an *ellipse*. If $\theta = k$, the plane is parallel to an edge of the cone, the conic section is unbounded, and the section is a *parabola*. If $\theta < k$ or if the axis and plane are parallel, the plane intersects both nappes of the cone, the conic section is unbounded in opposite directions, and a *hyperbola* is formed.

Dandelin Spheres and the Ellipse

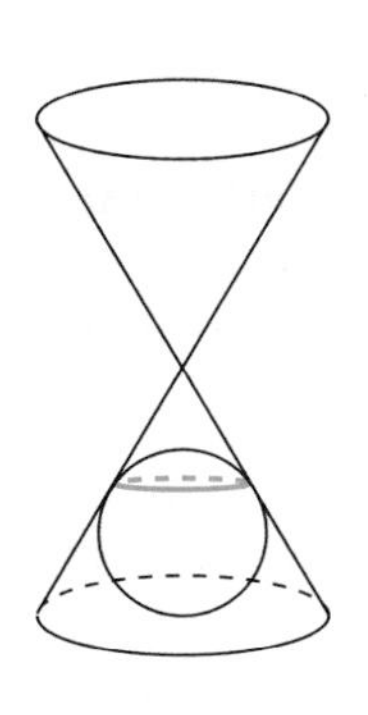

The three-dimensional descriptions of conic sections in the previous paragraph are like those used by Apollonius to define the three types of conic sections. The French mathematician Germinal Pierre Dandelin (1794–1847) gave an elegant way to obtain a two-dimensional algebraic characterization for one of the conic sections, the ellipse, from the above three-dimensional description. Dandelin's method involves spheres that are nested inside the cone and applies the following properties.

1. The intersection of a cone and a sphere nested in the cone is a circle (in blue at the left) whose points are all the same distance from the vertex of the cone.
2. The intersection of a sphere and a plane tangent to the sphere is a single point. (Think of a hard ball resting on a flat surface; there is, in theory, one point in common.)
3. The lengths of all tangents from a given point to a given sphere are equal.

Now consider the ellipse formed by a plane M intersecting a cone as drawn at the right. There are only two spheres that can be nested in the cone and that are tangent to the plane M. One sphere S_1 is between the plane and the vertex. A larger sphere S_2 is on the other side of M. Let F_1 and F_2 be the points of tangency of the spheres with the plane, and let C_1 and C_2 be the circles of intersection of the spheres and the cone. Notice that the cone and the plane determine an ellipse; then, all of these named spheres, circles, and points are determined by the ellipse and are fixed.

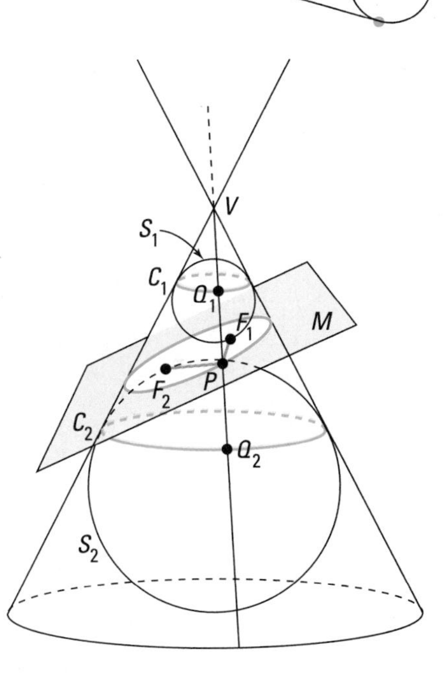

To describe the ellipse, we will find a property that relates any point on the ellipse to the fixed points F_1 and F_2. Let P be any point on the ellipse. P is on an edge $\overleftrightarrow{PV}$ of the cone and that edge intersects the circles C_1 and C_2 at Q_1 and Q_2, respectively. Notice that Q_1Q_2 is the distance along the cone between the circles, and since VQ_2 and VQ_1 are constant distances (property 3 above),

$$Q_1Q_2 = VQ_2 - VQ_1 = \text{a constant.}$$

So the distance between circles C_1 and C_2 along any edge of the cone is the same.

Now notice that both $\overline{PF_1}$ and $\overline{PQ_1}$ are tangents to sphere S_1, so $PF_1 = PQ_1$. Similarly, both $\overline{PF_2}$ and $\overline{PQ_2}$ are tangents to sphere S_2, so $PF_2 = PQ_2$. Thus $PF_1 + PF_2 = PQ_1 + PQ_2 = Q_1Q_2$, (since P is on Q_1Q_2), which is a constant. That means that the sum of the distances from any point P on the ellipse to the points F_1 and F_2 is constant. In this way, Dandelin proved that the three-dimensional definition of an ellipse is the same as the normal two-dimensional definition of an ellipse with *foci* F_1 and F_2 and a given focal constant. (The word *foci* [pronounced "foe sigh"] is the plural of the word *focus*.)

A Two-dimensional Definition of the Ellipse

Definition

Let F_1 and F_2 be two given points in a plane and k be a positive real number with $k > F_1F_2$. Then the **ellipse with foci F_1 and F_2 and focal constant k** is the set of all points in the plane which satisfy

$$PF_1 + PF_2 = k.$$

This definition of an ellipse can be used to draw an ellipse.

Activity

a. Mark two points on a sheet of paper, put pins (or tacks) at each of the foci. Tie string to the pins so that the string is not tight. Then, keeping the string taut, trace out the ellipse with a pencil.

b. Move the two pins closer together, and draw a new ellipse. How is this ellipse different than the one you drew in part **a**?

c. Describe what happens to the ellipse when the foci F_1 and F_2 are the same point.

Some people call an ellipse an oval, and the word "oval" comes from the Latin word for egg, "ovum," so they think of an ellipse as egg-shaped. But the cross sections of many eggs have only one symmetry line. Eggs are often more pointed at one end than the other, while every ellipse has two symmetry lines.

Theorem

An ellipse with foci F_1 and F_2 is reflection-symmetric to $\overleftrightarrow{F_1F_2}$ and to the perpendicular bisector of F_1F_2.

Proof

Let F_1 and F_2 be the foci of an ellipse with focal constant k and let $m = \overleftrightarrow{F_1F_2}$. Then, by definition, for any point P on the ellipse, $PF_1 + PF_2 = k$. To show that the ellipse is reflection-symmetric to m, it must be shown that the ellipse coincides with its reflection image over that line. Let $P' = r_m(P)$. Because F_1 and F_2 are on the reflecting line, $r_m(F_1) = F_1$ and $r_m(F_2) = F_2$. Because reflections preserve distance, $P'F_1 = PF_1$ and $P'F_2 = PF_2$. So for all P, $P'F_1 + P'F_2 = PF_1 + PF_2 = k$. Thus P' is on the ellipse. So the image of each point on the ellipse is also on the ellipse.

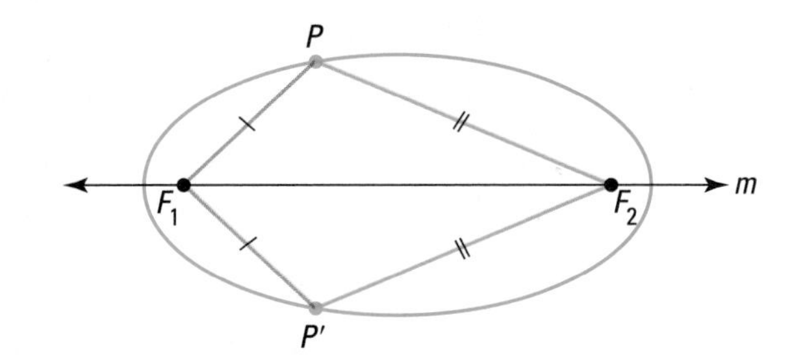

To show that the image is the entire ellipse, let Q be any point on the original ellipse. Then its image, $r_m(Q)$, is on the original ellipse (using the argument above). But $r_m(r_m(Q)) = Q$. So Q is also on the image, and thus all points of the ellipse are on the image.

A similar argument can be written to show that the perpendicular bisector of F_1F_2 is also a symmetry line for the ellipse.

Ellipses in Astronomy

One discovery by Kepler about planetary orbits, known as his first law, was that the orbit of each planet is an ellipse with the sun at one focus. Another discovery was that a planet does not go around the sun at a constant speed, but that a segment from the sun to the planet sweeps out equal areas in equal times. This is now known as Kepler's second law. His third discovery, called his third law, related the distance of the planet from the sun to its period, the length of time it takes to make one revolution. You are asked to investigate Kepler's third law in the Questions.

Johannes Kepler discussing planetary motion with his sponsor Emperor Rudolph II

QUESTIONS

Covering the Reading

1. What is the difference between the cones studied in geometry and the cones that give rise to the conic sections?

2. Refer to the figures on page 754. Use k and θ to describe how a plane intersects a given cone to result in the given figure.

a. parabola **b.** ellipse **c.** hyperbola
d. exactly one point **e.** no points

3. **a.** If a sphere is *nested* in a cone, how are these figures related?
   b. Draw a picture of a sphere nested in a cone.

4. **a.** Draw a cone and a plane whose intersection is an ellipse.
   b. Describe the location of the Dandelin spheres for this ellipse.
   c. How are the foci of the ellipse related to the location of the Dandelin spheres?

5. State the two-dimensional definition for *ellipse*.

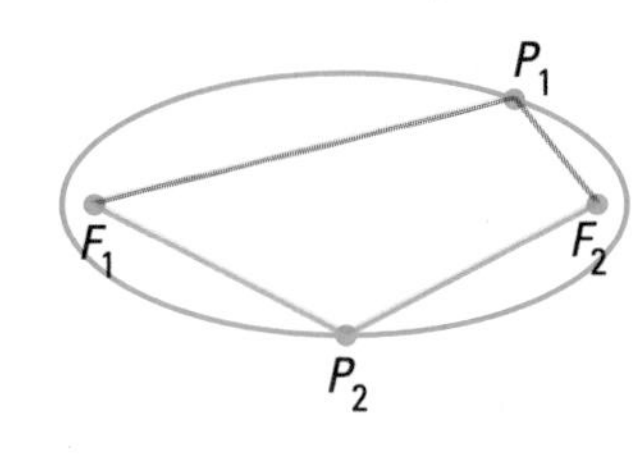

6. Consider P_1 and P_2 on the ellipse at the left, $F_1F_2 = 4$ and $P_1F_1 + P_1F_2 = 5$. Find $P_2F_1 + P_2F_2$.

7. Answer the questions in parts **b** and **c** of the Activity in the lesson.

8. **a.** At least how many symmetry lines does every ellipse have?
   b. How are they related to the foci of the ellipse?

9. Apply Kepler's second law to describe the orbit of Earth.

10. Prove that the perpendicular bisector of the segment joining the foci of an ellipse is a symmetry line for the ellipse.

Applying the Mathematics

11. *True or false.* A circle is a special type of ellipse. Explain your thinking.

12. In Kepler's day, the orbits of the six known planets around the sun were thought to be circular, and the radii of these circles were calculated in **astronomical units (a.u.)**, where 1 astronomical unit was the radius of the Earth's orbit. Here are the values that Kepler had for these radii and for the periods of the planets.

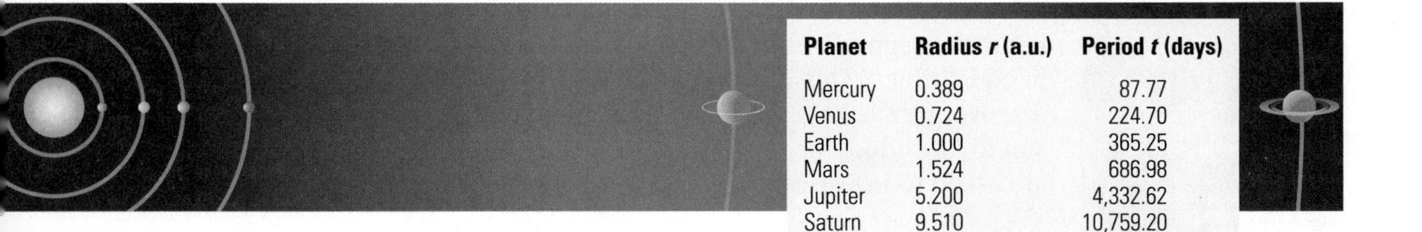

Planet	Radius r (a.u.)	Period t (days)
Mercury	0.389	87.77
Venus	0.724	224.70
Earth	1.000	365.25
Mars	1.524	686.98
Jupiter	5.200	4,332.62
Saturn	9.510	10,759.20

   a. Kepler discovered that $\frac{r^3}{t^2}$ is nearly a constant. Verify Kepler's calculations. What is the mean value that you get for $\frac{r^3}{t^2}$?
   b. Graph the points $(\log_{10} r, \log_{10} t)$ for the six planets. What property of this scatterplot verifies that $\frac{r^3}{t^2}$ is nearly a constant?

13. Suppose the two foci of an ellipse are 1 meter apart.
   a. What is the smallest possible focal constant for this ellipse?
   b. As the focal constant gets larger, what happens to the shape of the ellipse?
   c. Is there a largest possible focal constant for this ellipse? If so, what is it?

Review

14. Suppose a and c are real numbers and $a^2 - b^2 = c^2$. How must a and c be related in order for b to be a real number? *(Lesson 9-6)*

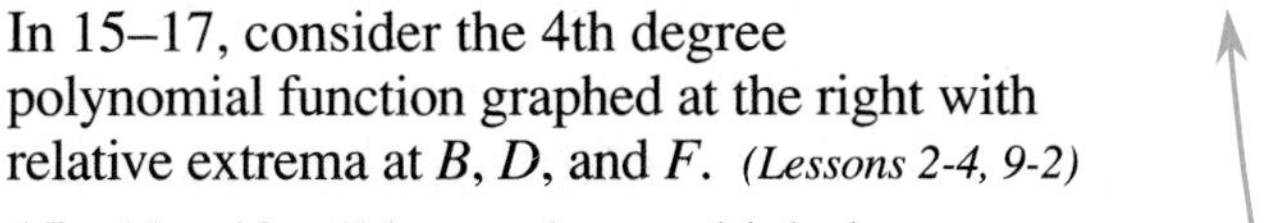

In 15–17, consider the 4th degree polynomial function graphed at the right with relative extrema at B, D, and F. *(Lessons 2-4, 9-2)*

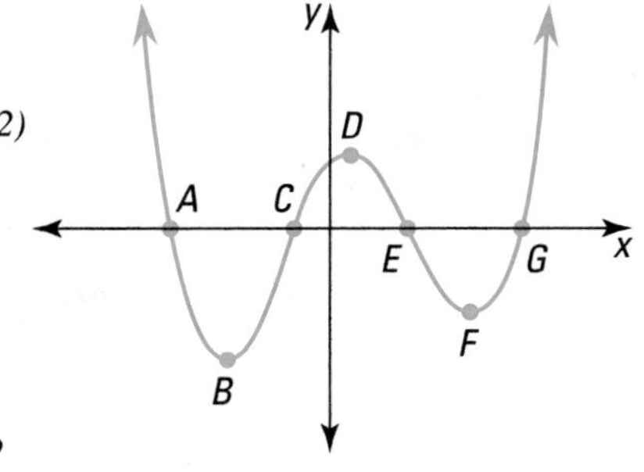

15. Identify all intervals on which the function is increasing.

16. Identify all intervals on which the function is positive.

17. Does the function have any asymptotes? If yes, identify them.

18. Determine the sum of the first 100 multiples of 3. *(Lesson 8-3)*

19. Let $f(x) = x^6$ and $g(x) = x^{1/6}$. *True or false.* $f(g(x)) = g(f(x))$ for all real numbers x. Justify your answer. *(Lesson 6-1)*

20. The following are the average monthly temperatures in °F for Huron, South Dakota.

Jan	Feb	Mar	Apr	May	June	July	Aug	Sep	Oct	Nov	Dec
13	19	32	46	58	68	74	72	61	49	32	18

a. Draw a scatterplot of the data.
b. Sketch a sine curve to fit the data.
c. Determine an equation for the curve in part **b** to model the data. *(Lessons 1-2, 4-10)*

In 21 and 22, expand the binomials and combine like terms. *(Previous course)*

21. $(a + b)^2 - (a - b)^2$

22. $(2p - \sqrt{d})^2 - d^2$

23. Find the distance between the points (a, b) and (x, y). *(Previous course)*

Exploration

24. The mathematician Hypatia wrote a book, *On the Conics of Apollonius*, around 400 A.D. Find out something else about Hypatia.

This small statuette of Hypatia is in the Greco-Roman Museum of Alexandria in Egypt.

LESSON

12-2

The Algebra of the Ellipse

From the two-dimensional definition of an ellipse in Lesson 12-1, an equation for any ellipse in the plane can be found. If the foci are $F_1 = (a, b)$ and $F_2 = (c, d)$ and the focal constant is k, then, by definition, any point $P = (x, y)$ on the ellipse must satisfy the equation

$$PF_1 \quad + \quad PF_2 \quad = k.$$

Applying the distance formula gives

$$\sqrt{(x - a)^2 + (y - b)^2} + \sqrt{(x - c)^2 + (y - d)^2} = k.$$

This is an equation for the ellipse. But this equation is rather unwieldy and it does not lend itself to graphing, even with an automatic grapher. A more common approach is to begin with an ellipse that is symmetric to the x- and y-axes, find its equation, and then transform the ellipse as needed to find equations for other ellipses. This is the approach we take.

Developing an Equation for an Ellipse

To simplify the algebraic manipulations, the focal constant is called $2a$, and the foci are on the x-axis, symmetric to the origin. So let $F_1 = (\text{-}c, 0)$, $F_2 = (c, 0)$, and $P = (x, y)$. The following eleven steps are numbered for reference.

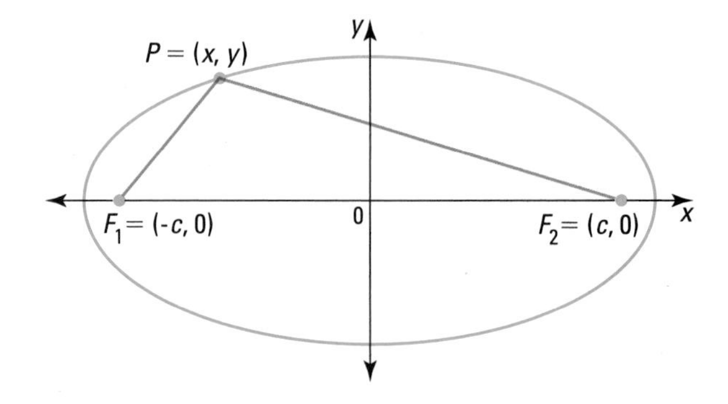

1. By the definition of an ellipse

$$PF_1 + PF_2 = 2a.$$

Using the Distance Formula, this becomes

$$\sqrt{(x + c)^2 + y^2} + \sqrt{(x - c)^2 + y^2} = 2a.$$

2. Subtract one of the square roots from both sides.

$$\sqrt{(x - c)^2 + y^2} = 2a - \sqrt{(x + c)^2 + y^2}$$

3. Square both sides (the right side is like a binomial) to eliminate one radical.

$$(x - c)^2 + y^2 = 4a^2 - 4a\sqrt{(x + c)^2 + y^2} + (x + c)^2 + y^2$$

4. Expand the binomials and do appropriate subtractions.

$$-2cx = 4a^2 - 4a\sqrt{(x + c)^2 + y^2} + 2cx$$

5. Use the Addition Property of Equality and rearrange terms.

$$4a\sqrt{(x + c)^2 + y^2} = 4a^2 + 4cx$$

6. Multiply both sides by $\frac{1}{4}$.

$$a\sqrt{(x + c)^2 + y^2} = a^2 + cx$$

7. Square both sides again to eliminate the radical.

$$a^2((x + c)^2 + y^2) = a^4 + 2a^2cx + c^2x^2$$

8. Expand $(x + c)^2$ and subtract $2a^2cx$ from both sides.

$$a^2x^2 + a^2c^2 + a^2y^2 = a^4 + c^2x^2$$

9. Subtract a^2c^2 and c^2x^2 from both sides, then factor.

$$(a^2 - c^2)x^2 + a^2y^2 = a^2(a^2 - c^2)$$

10. Since $c > 0$, $F_1F_2 = 2c$; and since $2a > F_1F_2$, $2a > 2c$. So $a > c > 0$. Thus $a^2 > c^2$ and $a^2 - c^2$ is positive. So $a^2 - c^2$ can be considered as the square of some real number, say b. Now let $b^2 = a^2 - c^2$ and substitute.

$$b^2x^2 + a^2y^2 = a^2b^2$$

11. Dividing both sides by a^2b^2 gives

$$\frac{x^2}{a^2} + \frac{y^2}{b^2} = 1.$$

This argument yields the **standard form** for an equation of this ellipse.

Theorem (Equation for an Ellipse)
The ellipse with foci $(c, 0)$ and $(-c, 0)$ and focal constant $2a$ has equation $\frac{x^2}{a^2} + \frac{y^2}{b^2} = 1$, where $b^2 = a^2 - c^2$.

Properties of an Ellipse

By substitution into the equation, it is easy to verify that the points $A_1 = (a, 0)$, $A_2 = (-a, 0)$, $B_1 = (0, b)$, and $B_2 = (0, -b)$ are on this ellipse. Notice that in the equation for an ellipse $|x|$ cannot be greater than a, nor can $|y|$ be greater than b; otherwise the left side would be greater than 1. This shows that those four points are extreme points for the ellipse. These points help to sketch a graph of the ellipse.

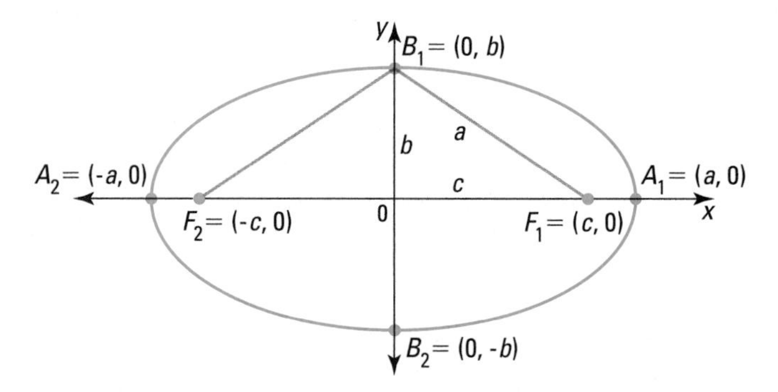

This figure illustrates the following theorem.

Theorem

In the ellipse with equation $\frac{x^2}{a^2} + \frac{y^2}{b^2} = 1$,
$2a$ is the length of the horizontal axis,
$2b$ is the length of the vertical axis, and
$2c$ is the distance between the foci, where $c^2 = a^2 - b^2$.

Because $2a$ is the focal constant, $B_1F_1 + B_1F_2 = 2a$. Also, $B_1F_1 = B_1F_2$, so each of these distances is a. You can also see in the drawing that $b^2 + c^2 = a^2$, as was used in step 10 of the argument yielding the equation. Thus $a > b$.

The segments $\overline{A_1A_2}$ and $\overline{B_1B_2}$ and their lengths are called, respectively, the **major axis** and **minor axis** of the ellipse. The major axis contains the foci and is never shorter than the minor axis. (If $a = b$, the ellipse becomes a circle.) The two axes lie on the symmetry lines and intersect at the **center** of the ellipse.

If $a \geq b$, as in the proof of the equation for an ellipse, then $(c, 0)$ and $(-c, 0)$ are the foci, the focal constant is $2a$, and $c^2 = a^2 - b^2$. However, if $a < b$, then the major axis of the ellipse is vertical. In this case, the foci are $(0, c)$ and $(0, -c)$, the focal constant is $2b$, and $c^2 = b^2 - a^2$.

Using Properties of the Ellipse

Example 1 illustrates both cases.

Example 1

Determine the foci of the ellipse with the given equation and sketch its graph.

a. $\frac{x^2}{36} + \frac{y^2}{9} = 1$ **b.** $\frac{x^2}{9} + \frac{y^2}{36} = 1$

Solution

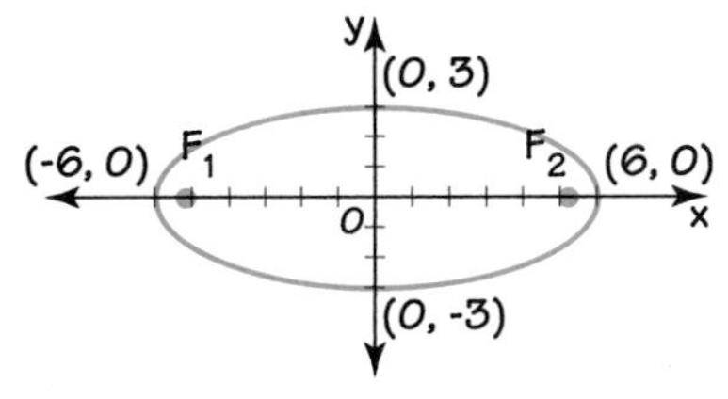

a. The equation is in standard form $\frac{x^2}{a^2} + \frac{y^2}{b^2} = 1$ with $a = 6$ and $b = 3$. Because $a > b$, the foci are on the horizontal axis. So let the foci be $(c, 0)$ and $(-c, 0)$, where $c^2 = a^2 - b^2 = 36 - 9 = 27$. So $c = \sqrt{27}$. Thus, $(\sqrt{27}, 0) \approx (5.2, 0)$ and $(-\sqrt{27}, 0) \approx (-5.2, 0)$ are the foci. The extreme points for this ellipse are (6, 0), (–6, 0), (0, 3), and (0, –3). This enables the ellipse to be sketched rather easily.

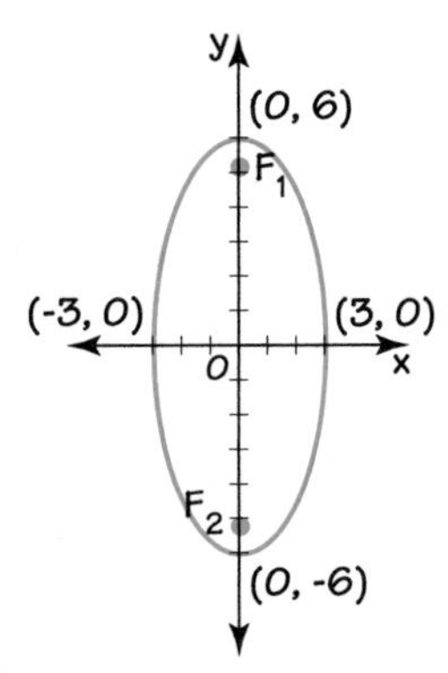

b. The ellipse in part **b** is the reflection image of the ellipse in part **a** over the line $y = x$. So its foci are $(0, \sqrt{27})$ and $(0, -\sqrt{27})$. The extreme points are (3, 0), (–3, 0), (0, 6), and (0, –6). Its graph is sketched at the left.

Activity

a. Check the graph in part **b** of Example 1 by finding a fifth pair of numbers x and y satisfying the equation and showing that (x, y) is on the graph.

b. Check the foci by showing that the sum of the distances from this point to the two foci is 12.

The theorems about ellipses can be used to answer questions about the orbits of planets.

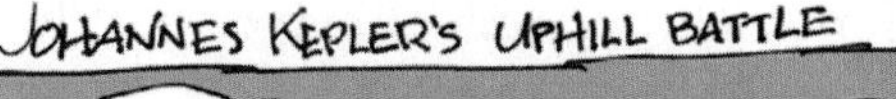

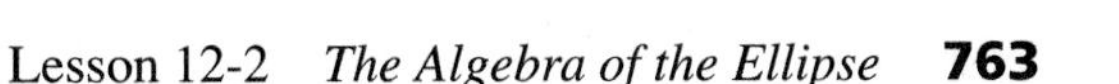

Example 2

The closest Earth gets to the sun is approximately 91.4 million miles and the farthest is 94.6 million miles. Given that the orbit is an ellipse with the sun at one focus, how far from the sun is the other focus?

Solution

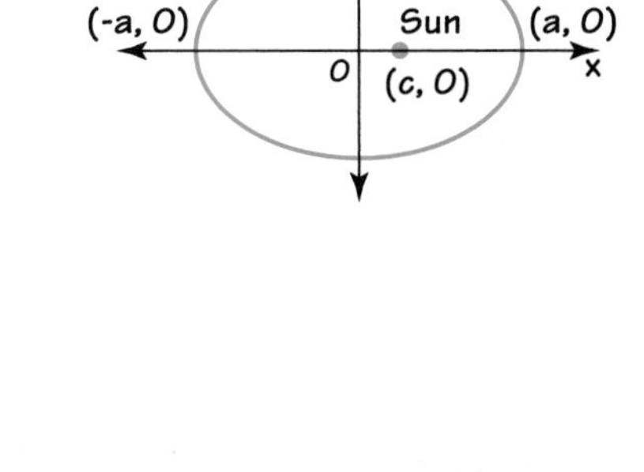

A picture, even as exaggerated as the one at the left, helps. Think of the center of the orbit as being the origin and place the sun at $(c, 0)$, where the unit is one million miles. The maximum and minimum distances from the sun occur when Earth's orbit intersects the x-axis. **From the given information, $a - c = 91.4$ and $c - (-a) = 94.6$.** This is a system of two linear equations in two variables and is easily solved. Adding these equations **$2a = 186.0$, so $a = 93.0$. Thus $c = 1.6$. So the second focus is $(-1.6, 0)$ and is 3.2 million miles from the sun.**

The sun itself has a radius of about 433,000 miles, so the second focus is about 2.8 million miles from the surface of the sun.

Hail! Hale-Bopp. *The comet Hale-Bopp, shown here in 1997, was for a time one of the brightest objects in the sky. It has a very eccentric elliptical orbit and will make its next appearance in about 2400 years.*

Not long after Kepler, Isaac Newton (1642–1727) *deduced* that the orbits of the planets were ellipses from assumed principles of force and mass. Newton worked backwards from Kepler's third law to discover these principles, and then worked forward to apply them to explain how the planets moved. The mathematics of his time was insufficient to deal with these ideas, so Newton developed calculus to solve the problem. This is another one of the greatest mathematical achievements of all time. Newton understood the generality of his results, that any body moves around any other body in an elliptical orbit. The orbits of the moon or artificial satellites around Earth, of comets around the sun, and even of particles around the centers of atoms obey these laws; they are ellipses.

Using Technology to Graph an Ellipse

An ellipse is not the graph of a function in the xy-plane, so automatic graphers need special routines to graph ellipses. Some graphers allow you to plot ellipses centered at the origin and their translation images. On some of these graphers you must enter the constants a and b in the standard form of the equation for an ellipse.

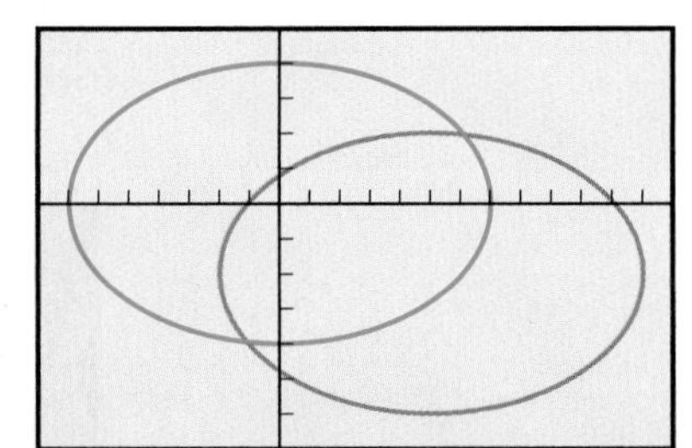

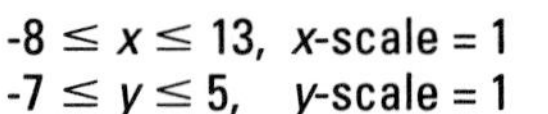

$-8 \le x \le 13$, x-scale = 1
$-7 \le y \le 5$, y-scale = 1

At the right are the graphs of $\frac{x^2}{49} + \frac{y^2}{16} = 1$ and $\frac{(x-5)^2}{49} + \frac{(y+2)^2}{16} = 1$ as produced by an automatic grapher. Notice that each has major axis of length $2 \cdot 7 = 14$ and minor axis of $2 \cdot 4 = 8$.

In general, because translations preserve distance, the graph of the ellipse with equation

$$\frac{(x - h)^2}{a^2} + \frac{(y - k)^2}{b^2} = 1$$

has center (h, k), horizontal axis of length $2a$, and vertical axis of length $2b$.

When an automatic grapher does not have a special program to graph an ellipse, you can solve the equation of the ellipse for y. This is explored in Question 16.

QUESTIONS

Covering the Reading

1. Use the distance formula to write an equation for the ellipse with foci (11, 6) and (-2, 7) and focal constant 15. (The equation does not have to be in standard form.)

2. a. Find an equation in standard form for the ellipse with foci (5, 0) and (-5, 0) and focal constant 26 by going through the steps that led to the first theorem of this lesson.

b. Give the distance between foci, length of major axis, and length of minor axis for this ellipse.

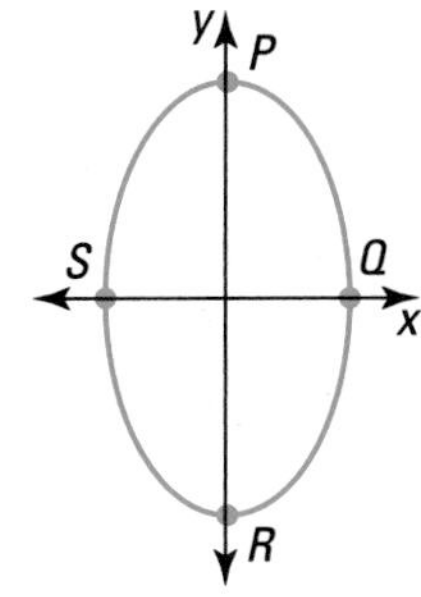

3. Consider the ellipse drawn at the left. Identify each of the following.

a. the major axis

b. the minor axis

c. the axis which contains the foci

In 4 and 5, consider the ellipse with equation $\frac{x^2}{a^2} + \frac{y^2}{b^2} = 1$.

4. Identify each of the following.

a. the center

b. the endpoints of the horizontal axis

c. the length of the horizontal axis

5. If the horizontal axis is the major axis, what is true about a and b?

In 6 and 7, an equation for an ellipse is given. **a.** Sketch a graph of the ellipse. **b.** Determine its foci. **c.** Determine the length of the major axis.

6. $\frac{x^2}{25} + \frac{y^2}{16} = 1$

7. $\frac{x^2}{16} + \frac{y^2}{25} = 1$

8. Give your work for the Activity in this lesson.

9. Consider the ellipse with equation $\frac{(x - 1)^2}{36} + \frac{(y + 7)^2}{9} = 1$.

a. Explain how its graph is related to the graph of one of the ellipses in Example 1.

b. Graph this ellipse.

The planet Neptune was named after Neptune, the Roman god of the sea, well before its blue color was revealed by the Hubble Space Telescope.

10. The closest distance the planet Pluto comes to the sun is about 2759 million miles, and its farthest distance from the sun is about 4599 million miles. In fact, it was "inside" Neptune's orbit for most of the 1990s and only in 1999 will again become farther from the sun than Neptune. Is the second focus of Pluto's orbit nearer or farther from the sun than Earth?

11. Consider the ellipse with equation $\frac{(x-h)^2}{a^2} + \frac{(y-k)^2}{b^2} = 1$.
a. What are the coordinates of its center?
b. What is the length of the vertical axis?
c. How is this ellipse related to the ellipse with equation $\frac{x^2}{a^2} + \frac{y^2}{b^2} = 1$?

Applying the Mathematics

12. Find an equation for the ellipse pictured below.

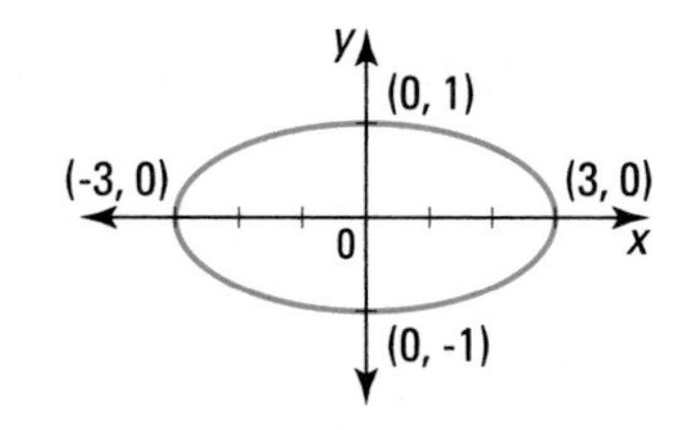

13. Explain why the set of points (x, y) satisfying $2x^2 + 3y^2 = 12$ is an ellipse.

14. Consider the curve with equation $\frac{x^2}{25} + \frac{y^2}{25} = 1$ as an ellipse. State the length of the major and minor axes, and the focal constant.

15. a. Give an equation for the ellipse whose center is the origin, whose horizontal axis has length 20, and whose vertical axis has length 14.
b. Give an equation for the image of the ellipse in part **a** under the translation $(x, y) \rightarrow (x + 3, y - 6)$.

16. Even if an automatic grapher does not have a special feature for graphing conics, you can still graph an ellipse by following these steps.

Step 1: Solve $\frac{x^2}{a^2} + \frac{y^2}{b^2} = 1$ for y.
Step 2: Graph one of the solutions.
Step 3: Graph the other solution. The union of the graphs is the ellipse.

a. Graph the ellipse with equation $\frac{x^2}{4} + \frac{y^2}{9} = 1$ on an automatic grapher.
b. Give the coordinates of four points on the ellipse other than the endpoints of the axes.

In 17–19, the **eccentricity** of an ellipse is the ratio of the distance between the foci to the length of its major axis.

17. a. What is the eccentricity of the ellipse with equation $\frac{x^2}{a^2} + \frac{y^2}{b^2} = 1$? (Assume $a \geq b$; give a formula in terms of a, b, and/or c.)
b. Is the eccentricity of a long thin ellipse greater or less than the eccentricity of an ellipse that is more like a circle?

18. a. What is the eccentricity of a circle?
b. What are the largest and smallest possible values of the eccentricity?

19. Refer to Question 10. Pluto has the most eccentric orbit of the planets. What is the eccentricity of Pluto's orbit?

Review

20. Draw an ellipse in which the distance between the foci is 2 inches and the focal constant is 4 inches. *(Lesson 12-1)*

21. If a cone with two nappes is cut by a plane which is parallel to its axis, and does not contain the axis, what kind of figure can the intersection be? *(Lesson 12-1)*

22. Consider the equation $\cos 2\theta = \sin^2\theta - \cos^2\theta$.
a. Show that the equation is true when $\theta = \frac{\pi}{4}$.
b. Give an example to show that the equation is *not true* for all values of θ.
c. Sketch the graphs of $f(\theta) = \cos 2\theta$ and $g(\theta) = \sin^2\theta - \cos^2\theta$ on the same set of axes to explain the results in parts **a** and **b**.
d. Replace one side of the equation with another expression so that the resulting sentence is an identity. *(Lessons 4-5, 4-6, 11-6)*

23. Given that $R_\theta = \begin{bmatrix} -.5736 & -.8192 \\ .8192 & -.5736 \end{bmatrix}$, estimate θ if $0° < \theta < 360°$. *(Lesson 11-4)*

24. Write a matrix which represents a similarity transformation that results in an image whose area is five times the area of the preimage. *(Previous course, Lesson 11-2)*

Overachiever. *Pioneer 10, completed and launched in 1972, was still transmitting signals in 1997 when it was over 10 billion kilometers from Earth. At that distance, radio signals, traveling at the speed of light, took almost ten hours to reach Earth.*

25. A certain space probe can transmit 500 megabytes (1 megabyte = 10^6 bytes) of electronic information during the first year of its mission. Due to decrease in energy sources and increasing distance, the transmission drops by $\frac{1}{10}$ every year. Determine how many megabytes of information this probe will transmit in the given time period.
a. in 15 years
b. if it operates "forever" *(Lessons 8-4, 8-5)*

Exploration

26. Although Earth is closer to the sun at some times than others, it is not this aspect of Earth's orbit that determines whether it is winter or summer. (It could not be, for when it is winter in one hemisphere, it is summer in the other.) What aspect of Earth's orbit causes the seasons?

LESSON

12-3

The Hyperbola

It is not known for certain how or why the dinosaurs became extinct, but about 65 million years ago, after nearly 140 million years of roaming the earth, they suddenly disappeared. One theory is that a large asteroid hit Earth, raising so much dust that sunlight was blocked out for a time. Another theory is that a star came close to the sun and spewed dangerous radiation, and the dinosaurs, being so large, could not avoid it. If that star swerved past the sun, not to return, then its orbit would not be an ellipse. In the neighborhood of the sun, its orbit would be one branch of a hyperbola.

Because both hyperbolas and ellipses are conic sections, the hyperbola is a relative of the ellipse. That certain orbits are hyperbolas suggests other similarities between these two quite different-looking figures. In fact, much of what you have seen in the previous two lessons can be adapted to the hyperbola.

Dandelin Spheres and the Hyperbola

Here is Dandelin's way of relating the three-dimensional definition of a hyperbola as a conic section to a two-dimensional definition in terms of foci and a focal constant.

Consider a hyperbola formed by a plane M intersecting both nappes of a cone, as shown at the right. As with the ellipse, two spheres are tangent to the cone and to the plane M, but now one is in each nappe. Let F_1 and F_2 be the points of tangency of the spheres with the plane and let C_1 and C_2 be the circles of intersection of the spheres and the cone.

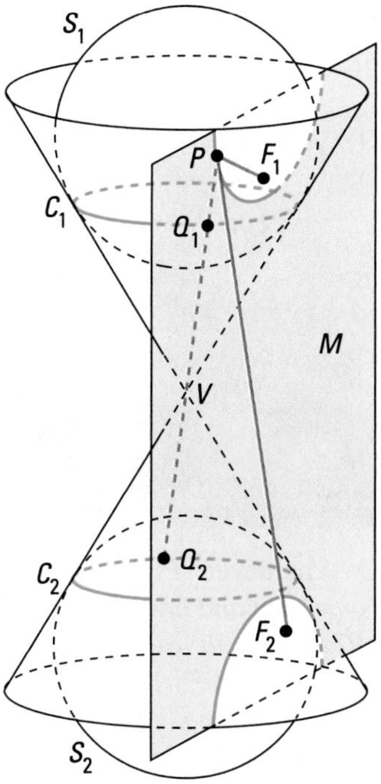

There is a property that relates any point P on the hyperbola to the fixed points F_1 and F_2. Suppose P is on the nappe of the cone containing sphere S_1. P is on an edge $\overleftrightarrow{PV}$ of the cone and that edge intersects the circles at Q_1 and Q_2. Since Q_1Q_2 is the distance along the edge between the circles, and the circles lie in parallel planes, Q_1Q_2 is a constant, regardless of the position of P.

Now notice that $\overline{PF_1}$ and $\overline{PQ_1}$ are tangents to sphere S_1 from point P, and $\overline{PF_2}$ and $\overline{PQ_2}$ are tangents from P to sphere S_2, so $PF_1 = PQ_1$ and $PF_2 = PQ_2$. So $PF_2 - PF_1 = PQ_2 - PQ_1 = Q_1Q_2$, a constant. That means that the difference $PF_2 - PF_1$ is a constant.

If P were located on the other nappe of the cone, then the argument on page 768 would result in the difference $PF_1 - PF_2 = PQ_1 - PQ_2 = Q_1Q_2$, the same constant.

Thus either $PF_2 - PF_1 = Q_1Q_2$ or $PF_1 - PF_2 = Q_1Q_2$. These two equations are equivalent to the single equation $|PF_2 - PF_1| = Q_1Q_2$. That is, the absolute value of the difference of the distances from any point P on the hyperbola to the foci is a constant. This property is normally taken as the two-dimensional definition of a hyperbola.

A Two-dimensional Definition of the Hyperbola

Definition

Let F_1 and F_2 be two given points in a plane and k be a positive real number with $k < F_1F_2$. Then the **hyperbola with foci F_1 and F_2 and focal constant k** is the set of all points in the plane which satisfy $|PF_1 - PF_2| = k$.

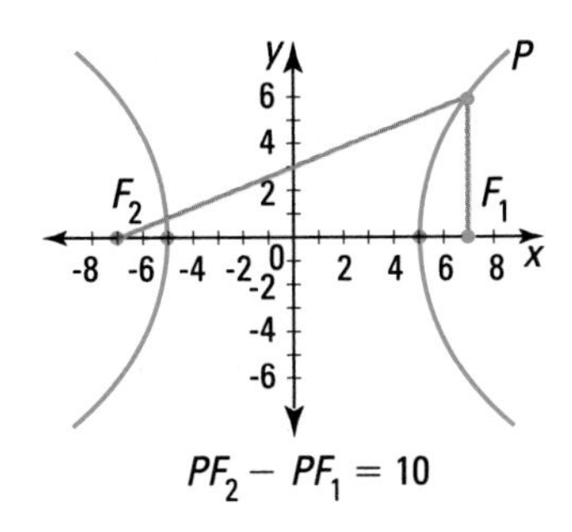

$PF_2 - PF_1 = 10$

For instance, here is a hyperbola with foci F_1 and F_2 that are 14 units apart and $k = 10$. Notice that, unlike the ellipse, this hyperbola is unbounded. A point can be farther than any specified distance from either focus and still be 10 units closer to one focus than to the other.

Activity

a. Draw two points F_1 and F_2, 2 units apart.
b. Draw six points that are 1 unit closer to F_1 than to F_2.
c. *True or false.* All six points must lie on the same branch of a hyperbola with foci F_1 and F_2.
d. Sketch the set of all points P such that $|PF_1 - PF_2| = 1$.
e. Draw all lines of symmetry of the curve in part **d**.

Hyperbolas possess the same symmetries as ellipses.

Theorem

A hyperbola with foci F_1 and F_2 is reflection-symmetric to $\overleftrightarrow{F_1F_2}$ and to the perpendicular bisector of the segment $\overline{F_1F_2}$.

Proof

The proof follows the ideas of the corresponding proof for the ellipse found in Lesson 12-1 and is left to you.

Developing an Equation for a Hyperbola

From the two-dimensional definition of a hyperbola, an equation for any hyperbola in the plane can be found, again by a method similar to that used for the ellipse. If the foci are $F_1 = (a, b)$ and $F_2 = (c, d)$ and the focal constant is k, then any point $P = (x, y)$ on the hyperbola must satisfy the equation

$$|PF_1 - PF_2| = k$$

or $$\sqrt{(x-a)^2 + (y-b)^2} - \sqrt{(x-c)^2 + (y-d)^2} = \pm k.$$

This is an equation for the hyperbola. Again, it is unwieldy and it does not lend itself to graphing even with an automatic grapher. What we will do is to begin with a hyperbola whose foci are particularly well-chosen and find an equation for that hyperbola. Then we will apply transformations to generate equations for other hyperbolas.

Theorem (Equation for a Hyperbola)
The hyperbola with foci $(c, 0)$ and $(-c, 0)$ and focal constant $2a$ has equation $\frac{x^2}{a^2} - \frac{y^2}{b^2} = 1$, where $b^2 = c^2 - a^2$.

Proof
The proof is identical to the proof of the equation for an ellipse in standard form, with two exceptions. In Step 1, by the definition of hyperbola,

$$|PF_1 - PF_2| = 2a.$$

Now if $P = (x, y)$, $F_1 = (c, 0)$, and $F_2 = (-c, 0)$, then using the Distance Formula,

$$\sqrt{(x-c)^2 + y^2} - \sqrt{(x - -c)^2 + y^2} = \pm 2a.$$

Steps 2–9 are identical to those in the proof of the theorem for the ellipse. A difference comes in Step 10. Because for the hyperbola $c > a > 0$, then $c^2 > a^2$, so we let $b^2 = c^2 - a^2$. This accounts for the minus sign in the equation for the hyperbola (see Step 11), where there is a plus sign for the ellipse.

The equation $\frac{x^2}{a^2} - \frac{y^2}{b^2} = 1$ is said to be the **standard form** for an equation of a hyperbola.

The Hyperbola $x^2 - y^2 = 1$

The simplest equation in standard form is $x^2 - y^2 = 1$, which occurs when $a = b = 1$. Then, since $b^2 = c^2 - a^2$, $1 = c^2 - 1$, so $c = \pm\sqrt{2}$. Thus the hyperbola with foci $(\sqrt{2}, 0)$ and $(-\sqrt{2}, 0)$ and focal constant 2 is the set of points (x, y) that satisfy the equation $x^2 - y^2 = 1$. Every other hyperbola with an equation of the form $\frac{x^2}{a^2} - \frac{y^2}{b^2} = 1$ is a scale-change image of this hyperbola. So it helps to study the hyperbola $x^2 - y^2 = 1$ in some detail.

Here is a table of some values. Notice that it contains the points $(1, 0)$ and $(-1, 0)$. Other points can be found by solving for y. Since $y^2 = x^2 - 1$, $y = \pm\sqrt{x^2 - 1}$. The two lines of symmetry of the hyperbola enable points to be found in all four quadrants. This hyperbola is graphed on page 771.

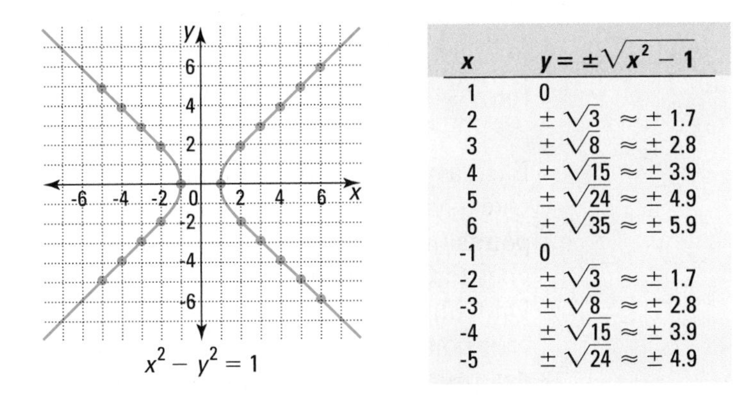

$x^2 - y^2 = 1$

x	$y = \pm\sqrt{x^2 - 1}$
1	0
2	$\pm\sqrt{3} \approx \pm 1.7$
3	$\pm\sqrt{8} \approx \pm 2.8$
4	$\pm\sqrt{15} \approx \pm 3.9$
5	$\pm\sqrt{24} \approx \pm 4.9$
6	$\pm\sqrt{35} \approx \pm 5.9$
-1	0
-2	$\pm\sqrt{3} \approx \pm 1.7$
-3	$\pm\sqrt{8} \approx \pm 2.8$
-4	$\pm\sqrt{15} \approx \pm 3.9$
-5	$\pm\sqrt{24} \approx \pm 4.9$

Unique among the conic sections, every hyperbola has asymptotes, lines it approaches as x gets farther from the foci. The asymptotes for the hyperbola $x^2 - y^2 = 1$ are $y = x$ and $y = -x$. This is because as x gets larger, $\sqrt{x^2 - 1}$ becomes closer and closer to $\sqrt{x^2}$, which is $|x|$. So y gets closer and closer to $\pm x$. You can verify this by examining the above table. Even for as small a value as $x = 6$, $y \approx \pm 5.92$, which is close to $\pm x$. Alternately, you can also use an automatic grapher to investigate the asymptotes of this hyperbola. Below are two views of the hyperbola $x^2 - y^2 = 1$ and its asymptotes in two different windows.

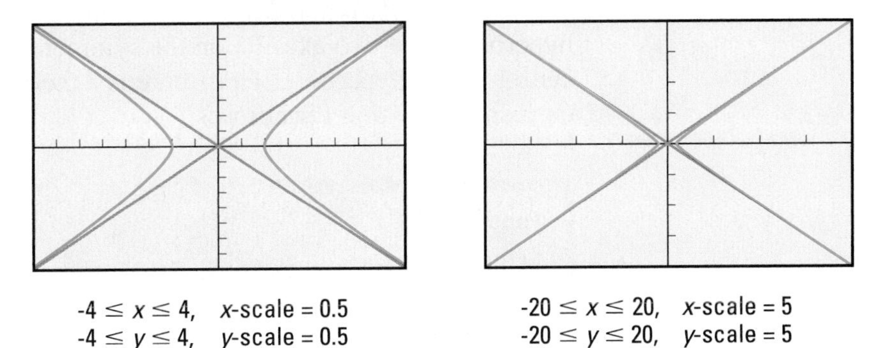

$-4 \le x \le 4$, x-scale = 0.5
$-4 \le y \le 4$, y-scale = 0.5

$-20 \le x \le 20$, x-scale = 5
$-20 \le y \le 20$, y-scale = 5

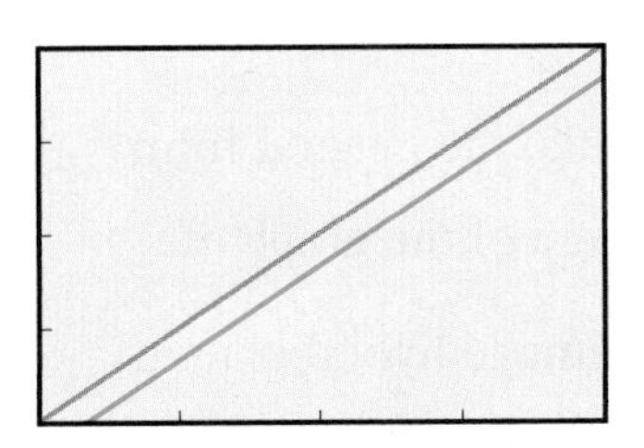

$14.8 \le x \le 15.2$, x-scale = 0.1
$14.8 \le y \le 15.2$, y-scale = 0.1

Note that as you look at larger values of $|x|$ in each window, the hyperbola gets closer to its asymptote.

It is important to realize, however, that the hyperbola never reaches its asymptotes. If you zoom or rescale around a point that appears to be on $y = \pm x$, you will see that there is always some distance between the graphs. For instance, at the left is a view of the graphs of $x^2 - y^2 = 1$ and $y = x$ near the point (15, 15). The graph of $y = x$ (in orange) does not intersect the graph of $x^2 - y^2 = 1$ (in blue).

The Hyperbola $\frac{x^2}{a^2} - \frac{y^2}{b^2} = 1$

Other hyperbolas are scale-change images of the parent $x^2 - y^2 = 1$. The scale change $(x, y) \to (ax, by)$ maps $x^2 - y^2 = 1$ onto $\frac{x^2}{a^2} - \frac{y^2}{b^2} = 1$. The asymptotes $y = \pm x$ are mapped onto the lines $\frac{y}{b} = \pm\frac{x}{a}$ or, solving for y,

$y = \pm\frac{b}{a}x$. With this information, the hyperbola with equation in standard form $\frac{x^2}{a^2} - \frac{y^2}{b^2} = 1$ can be sketched easily.

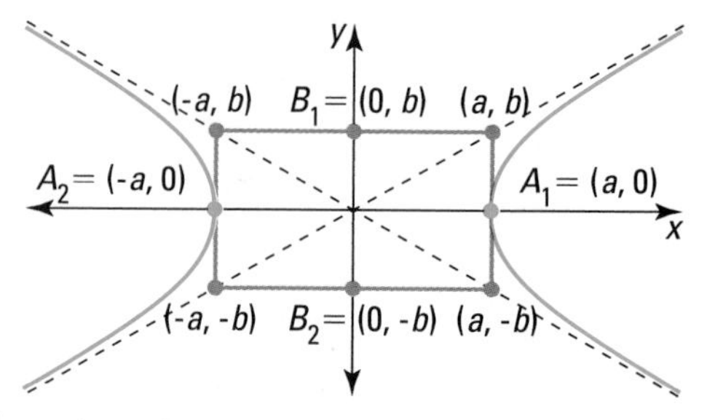

Each asymptote contains the origin. One asymptote goes through the points (a, b) and $(-a, -b)$; the other goes through $(a, -b)$ and $(-a, b)$. Drawing the rectangle with these four points as vertices, and the lines determined by its diagonals, helps to position the hyperbola. Notice that since $b^2 = c^2 - a^2$, then $a^2 + b^2 = c^2$, and so the sides and diagonals of the guiding rectangle have lengths $2a$, $2b$, and $2c$.

By substitution, you can verify that $(a, 0)$ and $(-a, 0)$ are on this hyperbola. These points are the **vertices** of the hyperbola. Now sketch the hyperbola with vertices at $(\pm a, 0)$ and the diagonals of the rectangle as asymptotes.

Notice that when $|x| < a$, y is not a real number. Thus the hyperbola $\frac{x^2}{a^2} - \frac{y^2}{b^2} = 1$ contains no points with x-coordinates between $-a$ and a.

The segments $\overline{A_1A_2}$ and $\overline{B_1B_2}$ of the guiding rectangle are the **axes** of the hyperbola. The two axes lie on the symmetry lines and intersect at the **center** of the hyperbola. Thus there is a theorem for hyperbolas that corresponds to that for ellipses.

Theorem

In the hyperbola with equation $\frac{x^2}{a^2} - \frac{y^2}{b^2} = 1$,
$2a$ is the length of the horizontal axis,
$2b$ is the length of the vertical axis, and
$2c$ is the distance between the foci, where $c^2 = a^2 + b^2$.

If x and y are switched in the equation for a hyperbola, the general form becomes $\frac{y^2}{a^2} - \frac{x^2}{b^2} = 1$. Its graph is the reflection image of the graph of $\frac{x^2}{a^2} - \frac{y^2}{b^2} = 1$ over the line $y = x$, and the foci of the image hyperbola are on the y-axis. In this case, $2a$ is the length of the vertical axis, and $2b$ is the length of the horizontal axis.

Example

Sketch a graph of the hyperbola, and determine equations of its asymptotes.

a. $\frac{x^2}{9} - \frac{y^2}{16} = 1$

b. $\frac{y^2}{9} - \frac{x^2}{16} = 1$

Solution

a. In this hyperbola the foci are on the x-axis, and $a = 3$ and $b = 4$. Thus the vertices of the hyperbola are (3, 0) and (–3, 0). To sketch the hyperbola, draw a rectangle centered at the origin with horizontal axis of length $2 \cdot 3 = 6$, and vertical axis of length $2 \cdot 4 = 8$. The diagonals of this rectangle are the asymptotes. They have equations $\frac{y}{4} = \pm\frac{x}{3}$ or, equivalently $y = \pm\frac{4}{3}x$. The hyperbola has vertices $(\pm 3, 0)$ and is bounded by these asymptotes. A sketch is at the left below.

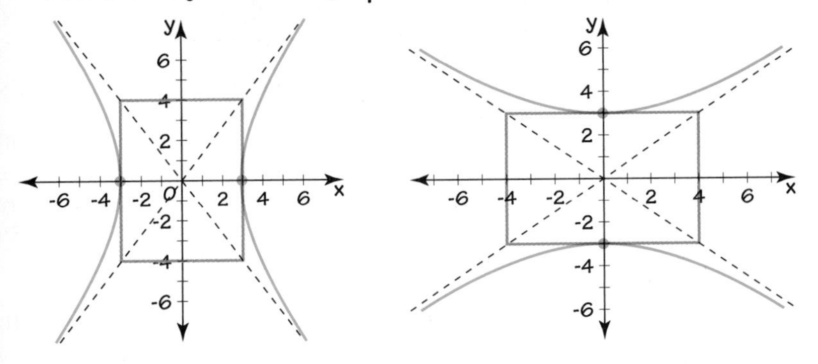

b. In this hyperbola, $a = 3$ and $b = 4$. However, the foci and vertices are on the y-axis. The vertices of this hyperbola are (0, 3) and (0, -3). The asymptotes have equations $\frac{y}{3} = \pm\frac{x}{4}$ or equivalently, $y = \pm\frac{3x}{4}$. A graph is at the right above.

Check

a. Analyze the equation for values excluded from the domain or range. In part **a**, $\frac{x^2}{9} - 1 = \frac{y^2}{16}$ or $y = \pm\sqrt{16\left(\frac{x^2}{9} - 1\right)}$. The expression under the radical sign is a real number if and only if $\frac{x^2}{9} - 1 \geq 0$ or $x^2 \geq 9$. That is, all points on the hyperbola must have $|x| \geq 3$. This agrees with the sketch we drew.

b. You are asked to check the work for part **b** in the Questions.

Using Hyperbolas to Locate Objects

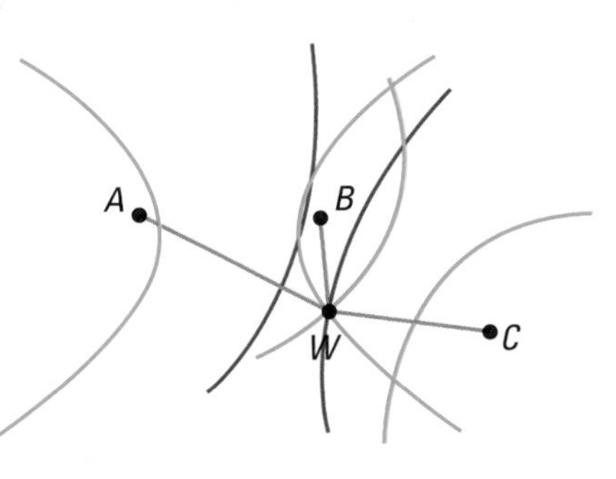

Hyperbolas can be and are used to locate objects that emit sound waves. The idea comes directly from the definition of hyperbola. Suppose a whale at an unknown point W emits a sound. Let A and B be locations of two underwater devices that can receive the sound, and suppose A and B are 10,000 feet apart. Suppose a sound from the whale is received 0.5 seconds later at point A than at point B. The speed of sound in water is known to be about 5000 feet per second. So the difference of the distances WA and WB is 2500 feet. Thus the position of the whale must be on a hyperbola with foci A and B and with focal constant 2500 feet.

If another device receives the same sound at point C and the time is recorded, then the position of the whale can be located on two other hyperbolas (one with foci A and C, the other with foci B and C). The whale's position at the time of emitting the sound, which is the solution of two equations in two variables, can be located quite precisely.

QUESTIONS

Covering the Reading

1. *True or false.* The path of an object in space may be hyperbolic in shape.

2. Suppose ℓ and m are intersecting lines and m is rotated around ℓ to form a cone. Now a plane P intersects the cone. Which position of P gives a hyperbola, which an ellipse, which a parabola?
a. P is parallel to m. **b.** P is perpendicular to ℓ.
c. P is parallel to ℓ.

3. **a.** Draw a plane intersecting a cone to form a hyperbola.
b. Draw the Dandelin spheres for this hyperbola.
c. How are the Dandelin spheres related to the foci of the hyperbola?

4. If $|m - n| = k > 0$, what are the possible values of $m - n$?

5. Show your work from the Activity in the lesson.

6. **a.** Graph $x^2 - y^2 = 1$. **b.** Graph $y^2 - x^2 = 1$.
c. Write several sentences comparing and contrasting the graphs in parts **a** and **b**.

7. Consider the hyperbola $\frac{x^2}{25} - \frac{y^2}{49} = 1$.
a. Find the coordinates of six points on the graph.
b. Give equations for its asymptotes.
c. Use the results of parts **a** and **b** to sketch a graph of the hyperbola.

8. **a.** Graph the hyperbola with equation $\frac{x^2}{64} - \frac{y^2}{9} = 1$.
b. Graph the hyperbola with equation $\frac{y^2}{64} - \frac{x^2}{9} = 1$.
c. How are the graphs of parts **a** and **b** related?

9. Check part **b** of the Example of this lesson.

Applying the Mathematics

10. Prove that every hyperbola is symmetric to the line containing its foci.

11. Use the definition of hyperbola to verify that $(1, 0)$ is on the hyperbola with foci $(\sqrt{2}, 0)$ and $(-\sqrt{2}, 0)$ and focal constant 2.

12. Let A and B be points on the x-axis 10,000 units apart. Find an equation for a hyperbola on which the whale of this lesson lies.

13. **a.** Explain why the graph of $x^2 - 2y^2 = 2$ is a hyperbola.
b. Find the foci and focal constant of this hyperbola.

14. Consider the hyperbola with equation $(x + 2)^2 - (y + 3)^2 = 1$.
a. Name its vertices.
b. Give equations for its asymptotes.
c. Sketch a graph of the hyperbola.

15. Consider the hyperbola with equation $\frac{(x - h)^2}{a^2} - \frac{(y - k)^2}{b^2} = 1$. Identify each of the following.
a. its center
b. its vertices
c. its foci
d. its asymptotes

Review

16. **a.** What is an equation for the ellipse shown at the right?
b. Where are its foci? *(Lesson 12-2)*

17. Consider the ellipse with equation
$\frac{(x + 2)^2}{25} + \frac{(y - 5)^2}{4} = 1$.
a. Determine the center and the foci of this ellipse.
b. How long are its major and minor axes?
c. Graph this ellipse. *(Lesson 12-2)*

18. Give the matrix for the rotation of the given magnitude around the origin. *(Lesson 11-4)*
a. $\frac{3\pi}{2}$
b. θ
c. $-\theta$

19. The operational life span of a certain brand of toner for laser printers is known to be normally distributed with mean 4500 pages of text and standard deviation 500 pages. If a printing office is buying 50 of these toners, how many of them should they expect to last for less than 4000 pages? *(Lesson 10-6)*

20. **a.** Use the Binomial Theorem to write out the terms of the following powers of $(1 + 1)$.
i. $(1 + 1)^0$
ii. $(1 + 1)^1$
iii. $(1 + 1)^2$
iv. $(1 + 1)^3$
b. *True or false.* The binomial expansion of $(1 + 1)^n$ for any n gives the elements in the nth row of Pascal's Triangle. Justify your answer. *(Lessons 8-6, 8-7, 8-8)*

21. Simplify $(\sqrt{2}\,a + b)^2 + (\sqrt{2}\,a - b)^2$. *(Previous course)*

Exploration

22. **a.** Describe the graph of the set of points (x, y) satisfying $x^2 - y^2 < 1$.
b. Describe the graph of the set of points (x, y) satisfying $x^2 - y^2 > 1$.
c. Generalize parts **a** and **b** to apply to any hyperbola in standard form.

LESSON

12-4

Rotating Relations

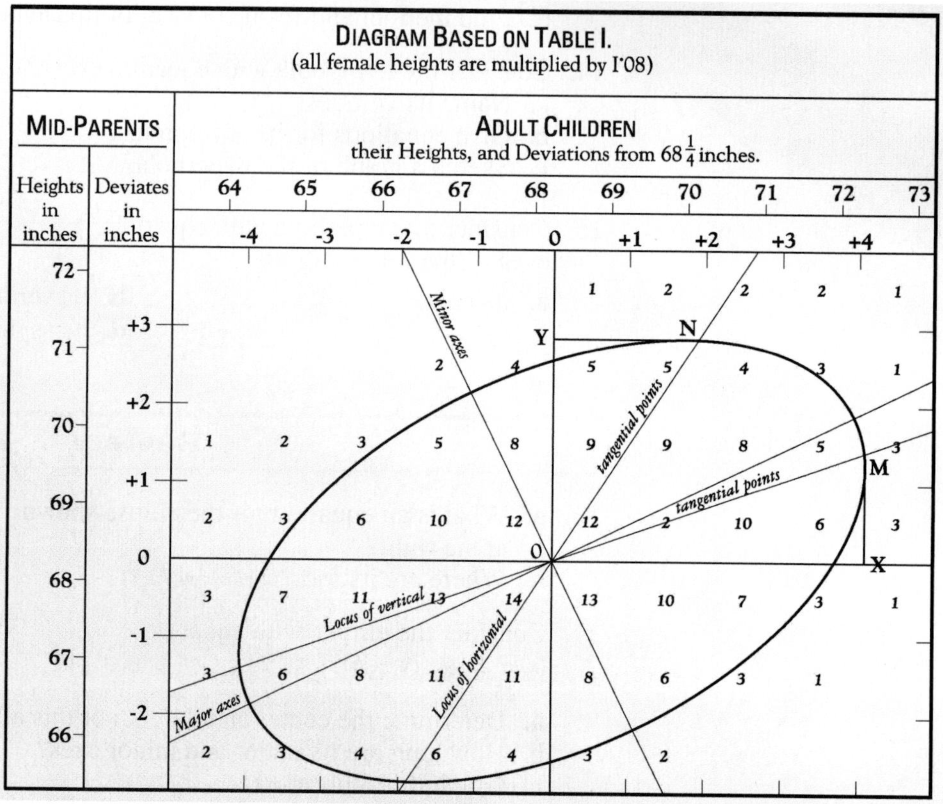

DIAGRAM BASED ON TABLE I.
(all female heights are multiplied by 1·08)

MID-PARENTS: Heights in inches (72, 71, 70, 69, 68, 67, 66); Deviates in inches (+3, +2, +1, 0, -1, -2)

ADULT CHILDREN: their Heights, and Deviations from $68\frac{1}{4}$ inches.

64 (-4)	65 (-3)	66 (-2)	67 (-1)	68 (0)	69 (+1)	70 (+2)	71 (+3)	72 (+4)	73
					1	2	2	2	1
			2	4	5	5	4	3	1
1	2	3	5	8	9	9	8	5	3
2	3	6	10	12	12	2	10	6	3
3	7	11	13	14	13	10	7	3	1
3	6	8	11	11	8	6	3	1	
2	3	4	6	4	3	2			

Minor axes; Major axes; tangential points; Locus of vertical; Locus of horizontal; Y; N; M; X; O

In Lesson 12-1, it was noted that Kepler's discovery that the planets go around the sun in elliptical orbits is one of the great examples of mathematical modeling of all time. Another brilliant example of mathematical modeling, which also involved ellipses, occurred only a little over a century ago, in 1886. It came as the result of the work of Francis Galton (1822–1911), an English scientist and statistician.

Galton was attempting to show the influences of heredity on height. He tabulated the heights of 928 adult children from 205 families against the mean heights of their parents (which he called the *mid-parent height*). He then grouped the data to plot frequencies as shown in the graph above. He discovered that, in this grouped data, the frequencies with the same values lay roughly on a series of similar ellipses with the same center and whose axes were at the same angle of inclination. For instance, the eleven points with frequency 3 lie on an ellipse slightly larger than the one drawn.

He showed his findings to a mathematician, J. Hamilton Dickson, who proved that Galton's discovery was the result of these heights being related by a *bivariate normal distribution*, that is, a three-dimensional curve with two planes of symmetry in which each cross section parallel to a plane of symmetry is a normal curve. The ellipses are the contour lines of equal probabilities, as shown on page 777.

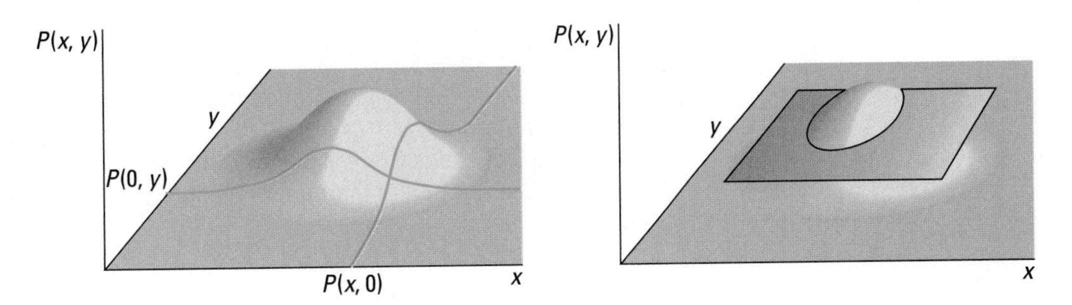

This work of Galton led to the development of the ideas of correlation and variance and their connection with regression and the line of best fit. While those details are beyond the scope of this course, you can determine the equations of ellipses that are rotated so that their axes are no longer horizontal or vertical, like Galton's ellipse pictured on page 776. The techniques for finding rotation images of graphs are developed in this lesson.

The Graph-Rotation Theorem

Recall that if the point (x, y) is rotated through magnitude θ about the origin, then its image (x', y') can be found by matrix multiplication.

$$\begin{bmatrix} x' \\ y' \end{bmatrix} = \begin{bmatrix} \cos\theta & -\sin\theta \\ \sin\theta & \cos\theta \end{bmatrix} \begin{bmatrix} x \\ y \end{bmatrix}$$

The inverse of the matrix for R_θ is the matrix for $R_{-\theta}$. To obtain an equation for (x, y) in terms of (x', y'), multiply each side of the preceding matrix equation by that inverse.

$$\begin{bmatrix} \cos\theta & \sin\theta \\ -\sin\theta & \cos\theta \end{bmatrix} \begin{bmatrix} x' \\ y' \end{bmatrix} = \begin{bmatrix} \cos\theta & \sin\theta \\ -\sin\theta & \cos\theta \end{bmatrix} \begin{bmatrix} \cos\theta & -\sin\theta \\ \sin\theta & \cos\theta \end{bmatrix} \begin{bmatrix} x \\ y \end{bmatrix}$$

$$= \begin{bmatrix} 1 & 0 \\ 0 & 1 \end{bmatrix} \begin{bmatrix} x \\ y \end{bmatrix}$$

So $$\begin{bmatrix} \cos\theta & \sin\theta \\ -\sin\theta & \cos\theta \end{bmatrix} \begin{bmatrix} x' \\ y' \end{bmatrix} = \begin{bmatrix} x \\ y \end{bmatrix}.$$

Now multiply the two matrices on the left side to get the following equation.

$$\begin{bmatrix} x'\cos\theta + y'\sin\theta \\ -x'\sin\theta + y'\cos\theta \end{bmatrix} = \begin{bmatrix} x \\ y \end{bmatrix}$$

Equating the two matrices above gives the following.

$$x = x'\cos\theta + y'\sin\theta$$
$$y = -x'\sin\theta + y'\cos\theta$$

Now, if a sentence involving x and y is known, then the above expressions can be substituted for x and y and the result will be a sentence involving x' and y'. The new sentence describes the rotation image. Once the sentence for the rotation image is found, the primes in x' and y' are removed so that the resulting sentence is in the variables x and y. The result is the following theorem on page 778.

Graph-Rotation Theorem

In a relation described by a sentence in x and y, the following two processes yield the same graph:

1. replacing x by $x \cos \theta + y \sin \theta$ and y by $-x \sin \theta + y \cos \theta$;
2. applying the rotation of magnitude θ about the origin to the graph of the original equation.

Using the Graph-Rotation Theorem

Example 1

Find an equation for the image of the ellipse $\frac{x^2}{4} + \frac{y^2}{9} = 1$ under a rotation of 30° about the origin.

Solution

To simplify computation, first multiply each side of the given equation by 36. The equation becomes $9x^2 + 4y^2 = 36$. Now, to find an equation for the image, use part (1) of the Graph-Rotation Theorem.

Replace x by $x \cos 30° + y \sin 30°$, or $\frac{\sqrt{3}}{2}x + \frac{1}{2}y$. Replace y by $-x \sin 30° + y \cos 30°$, or $-\frac{1}{2}x + \frac{\sqrt{3}}{2}y$.

$$9\left(\frac{\sqrt{3}}{2}x + \frac{1}{2}y\right)^2 + 4\left(-\frac{1}{2}x + \frac{\sqrt{3}}{2}y\right)^2 = 36$$

$$\frac{9}{4}\left(\sqrt{3}x + y\right)^2 + \left(-x + \sqrt{3}y\right)^2 = 36$$

$$\frac{9}{4}\left(3x^2 + 2\sqrt{3}\,xy + y^2\right) + \left(x^2 - 2\sqrt{3}\,xy + 3y^2\right) = 36$$

$$\frac{31}{4}x^2 + \frac{5}{2}\sqrt{3}\,xy + \frac{21}{4}y^2 = 36$$

For a simpler expression, multiply each side by 4.

$$31x^2 + 10\sqrt{3}xy + 21y^2 = 144$$

Check

Find a point on the preimage. Check that the coordinates of its image under R_{30} satisfy the equation. We take (2, 0). Its image under a rotation of 30° is

$$\begin{bmatrix} \cos 30° & -\sin 30° \\ \sin 30° & \cos 30° \end{bmatrix}\begin{bmatrix} 2 \\ 0 \end{bmatrix} = \begin{bmatrix} \frac{\sqrt{3}}{2} & -\frac{1}{2} \\ \frac{1}{2} & \frac{\sqrt{3}}{2} \end{bmatrix}\begin{bmatrix} 2 \\ 0 \end{bmatrix} = \begin{bmatrix} \sqrt{3} \\ 1 \end{bmatrix}$$

Is $\left(\sqrt{3}, 1\right)$ a solution to the equation found for the image? Substitute $\sqrt{3}$ for x and 1 for y.

$$31x^2 + 10\sqrt{3}\,xy + 21y^2 = 144$$

Does $31(\sqrt{3})^2 + 10\sqrt{3}(\sqrt{3})(1) + 21(1)^2 = 144$?

Does $93 + 30 + 21 = 144$?

Yes, it checks.

Some automatic graphers allow you to graph any equation of the form $Ax^2 + Bxy + Cy^2 + Dx + Ey + F = 0$. If you have access to such a grapher, you can also check the solution to Example 1 by graphing. Below are the graphs of $9x^2 + 4y^2 - 36 = 0$ and $31x^2 + 10\sqrt{3}\,xy + 21y^2 - 144 = 0$ produced by such a grapher.

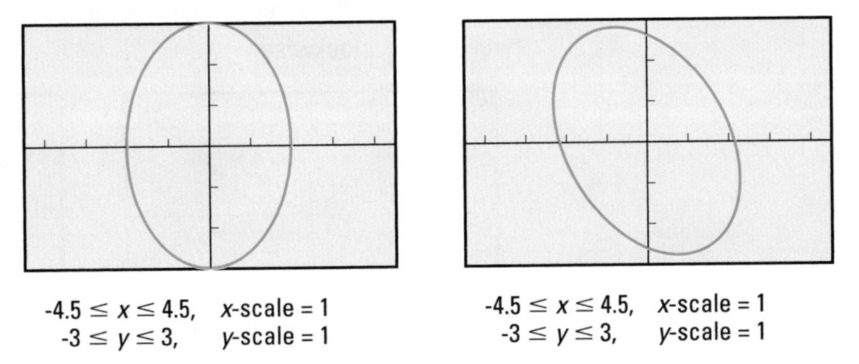

$-4.5 \le x \le 4.5$, x-scale = 1
$-3 \le y \le 3$, y-scale = 1

$-4.5 \le x \le 4.5$, x-scale = 1
$-3 \le y \le 3$, y-scale = 1

The second appears to be the image of the first under a rotation of 30° around the origin.

In the solution of Example 1 notice that an xy term appears. This is typical of quadratic relations that are not symmetric to the coordinate axes. Example 2 shows that rotation of the parent hyperbola can result in a hyperbola whose equation contains *only* an xy term.

Example 2

Rotate the hyperbola $x^2 - y^2 = 1$ a magnitude $-\frac{\pi}{4}$ about the origin.

Solution

Use the Graph-Rotation Theorem.

Replace x by $x\cos\left(-\frac{\pi}{4}\right) + y\sin\left(-\frac{\pi}{4}\right)$ and replace y by $-x\sin\left(-\frac{\pi}{4}\right) + y\cos\left(-\frac{\pi}{4}\right)$. Note that $\sin\left(-\frac{\pi}{4}\right) = -\frac{\sqrt{2}}{2}$ and $\cos\left(-\frac{\pi}{4}\right) = \frac{\sqrt{2}}{2}$. Thus an equation for the image is

$$\left(\frac{\sqrt{2}}{2}x - \frac{\sqrt{2}}{2}y\right)^2 - \left(\frac{\sqrt{2}}{2}x + \frac{\sqrt{2}}{2}y\right)^2 = 1.$$

Since $\left(\frac{\sqrt{2}}{2}\right)^2 = \frac{1}{2}$, the computation is easier than in Example 1.

$$\frac{1}{2}x^2 - xy + \frac{1}{2}y^2 - \left(\frac{1}{2}x^2 + xy + \frac{1}{2}y^2\right) = 1$$
$$-2xy = 1$$
$$xy = -\frac{1}{2}$$

Check

Draw graphs of the preimage and image. The graph of $xy = -\frac{1}{2}$, on the right below, is known to be a hyperbola whose graph lies entirely in the 2nd and 4th quadrants and whose asymptotes are the x- and y-axes. This is what would be expected from rotating the hyperbola $x^2 - y^2 = 1$, on the left below, a magnitude $\frac{\pi}{4}$ clockwise.

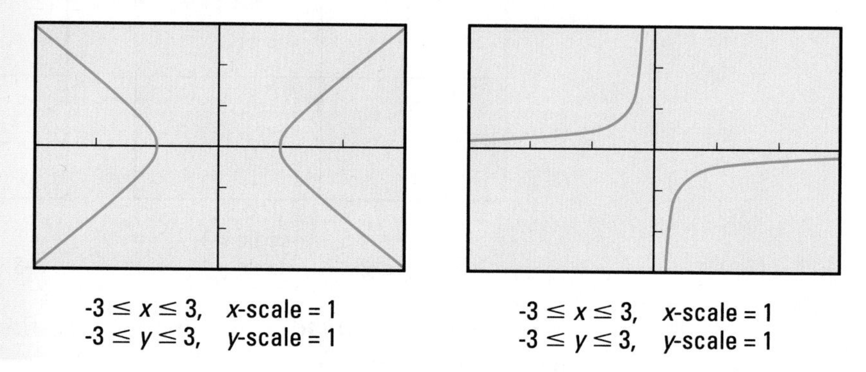

$-3 \le x \le 3$, x-scale = 1
$-3 \le y \le 3$, y-scale = 1

$-3 \le x \le 3$, x-scale = 1
$-3 \le y \le 3$, y-scale = 1

When the asymptotes of a hyperbola are perpendicular, as in Example 2, the hyperbola is called a **rectangular hyperbola**. Also, each is a rotation image of the other, so they are congruent. Now if a size change of magnitude $\sqrt{2}$ is applied to the hyperbola $xy = -\frac{1}{2}$, the result is a third hyperbola $\frac{x}{\sqrt{2}} \cdot \frac{y}{\sqrt{2}} = -\frac{1}{2}$, which simplifies to $xy = -1$. When this hyperbola is reflected over the x-axis, its image is a fourth hyperbola $xy = 1$. All of these transformations give rise to similar figures, so this reasoning shows that the hyperbolas $x^2 - y^2 = 1$ and $xy = 1$ are similar. More generally, all rectangular hyperbolas are similar. Still more generally, two hyperbolas are similar if and only if the angles between their asymptotes are congruent.

Composites of Rotations and Translations

Recall that an **isometry** is a composite of translations, rotations, and reflections. Some isometries need no reflections; for example, rotations of magnitude θ around a point (a, b) can be accomplished by translating the figure using $T_{-a,-b}$, rotating θ about the origin, then translating back using $T_{a,b}$. It can be proved that if all translations and rotations are possible, then any isometry needs a maximum of one reflection. Specifically, only the reflection over the line $y = x$ is needed. Thus the Graph-Translation Theorem and the Graph-Rotation Theorem, together with reflection over the line $y = x$, give the means to perform any isometry in the plane on any relation.

Example 3 illustrates a composite of transformations applied to a parabola.

Example 3

Find an equation for the image of the parabola $y = x^2$ when rotated 20° about the point (5, 8).

Solution

Following the discussion above, first translate the parabola using $T_{-5,-8}$. (This maps (5, 8) onto the origin.)

The image of $y = x^2$ under $T_{-5,-8}$ is

$$y + 8 = (x + 5)^2.$$

Then, rotate this curve 20° about the origin.

Replace x by $x \cos 20° + y \sin 20° \approx .94x + .34y$, and

y by $-x \sin 20° + y \cos 20° \approx -.34x + .94y$.

Then $y + 8 = (x + 5)^2$ becomes

$$-.34x + .94y + 8 \approx (.94x + .34y + 5)^2$$

Now, translate back using $T_{5,8}$. That is, replace x by $x - 5$ and y by $y - 8$.

$$-.34(x - 5) + .94(y - 8) + 8 \approx (.94(x - 5) + .34(y - 8) + 5)^2$$

This simplifies to

$$.88x^2 + .64xy + .12y^2 - 4.21x - 2.59y + 3.68 \approx 0.$$

Check

The images of the original parabola after each of the three transformations are graphed below.

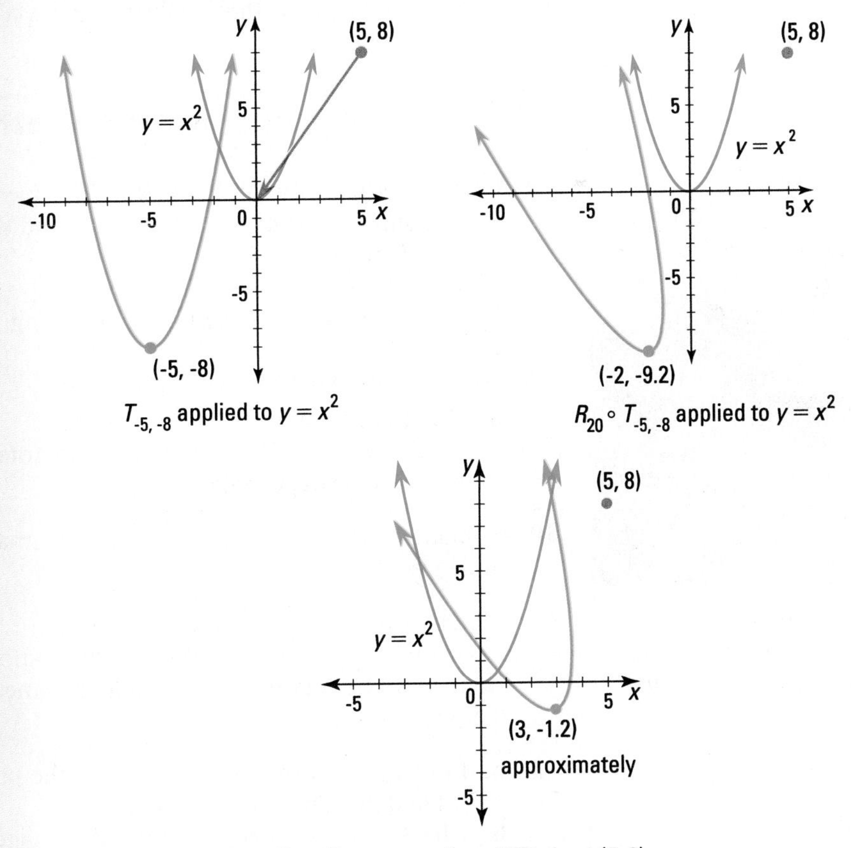

$T_{-5,-8}$ applied to $y = x^2$

$R_{20} \circ T_{-5,-8}$ applied to $y = x^2$

$T_{5,8} \circ R_{20} \circ T_{-5,-8}$ = rotation of 20° about (5, 8)

QUESTIONS

Covering the Reading

1. What situation was Galton trying to model when he found that ellipses described the points with equal probability of occurrence?

2. If a figure F is the image of a figure G under R_θ, then G is the image of F under what transformation?

In 3 and 4, find an equation for the image of the given figure under the given rotation.

3. $\frac{x^2}{25} + \frac{y^2}{16} = 1$; R_{60}

4. $y = x^2 + 4$; $R_{\pi/4}$

5. Tell whether or not the hyperbola is a rectangular hyperbola.

a. $xy = -2$

b. $x^2 - y^2 = 8$

c. $y^2 - x^2 = 8$

d. $\frac{x^2}{4} - \frac{y^2}{9} = 1$

6. *Multiple choice.* The hyperbolas $x^2 - y^2 = 1$ and $xy = 1$ are which of the following?

(a) congruent

(b) similar but not congruent

(c) neither similar nor congruent

7. Find an equation for the image of $x^2 + y^2 = 10$ under a rotation of 40° around the origin without using the Graph-Rotation Theorem.

Applying the Mathematics

Sir Francis Galton, the subject of an oil painting by Charles Wellington Furse

8. Galton's ellipse, pictured on page 776, has a major axis with length about 8 and a minor axis of length about 5, and the major axis makes an angle of about 30° with the x-axis.

a. Find an equation for this ellipse.

b. Find equations for the lines containing its major and minor axes.

9. Suppose the hyperbola $xy = k$ is rotated $\frac{\pi}{4}$ about the origin.

a. What is an equation for its image?

b. *True or false.* Both $xy = k$ and its rotation image in part **a** are rectangular hyperbolas.

10. Explain why, if an ellipse is rotated, its image must have an equation of degree 2.

11. Suppose the x-axis is rotated θ about the origin. Prove that an equation for its image is $y = x \tan \theta$. (This provides another way of showing that the slope of a line that makes an angle of θ measured counterclockwise from the positive x-axis is $\tan \theta$.)

12. a. Find an equation for the image of the parabola $y = (x - 2)^2 + 3$ when rotated 30° about the point (2, 3).

b. Check your work by graphing the image and preimage with an automatic grapher.

Review

13. Consider the hyperbola with equation $\frac{x^2}{36} - y^2 = 1$.

a. Sketch its graph.

b. Give equations for its asymptotes.

c. State an equation for the image of this curve under reflection over the line $y = x$. *(Lesson 12-3)*

14. Find an equation for the ellipse with foci (0, 3) and (0, -3) and focal constant 7. *(Lesson 12-2)*

15. a. What is an identity?

b. Give an example of a statement that is an identity.

c. Give an example of a statement that is not an identity. *(Lesson 4-4)*

In 16–19, *multiple choice.* Which expression below equals the given expression? *(Lessons 4-4, 11-6)*

(a) 1 (b) $\sin \theta$ (c) $\sin 2\theta$ (d) $\cos 2\theta$

16. $\cos^2\theta - \sin^2\theta$

17. $\cos^2\theta + \sin^2\theta$

18. $2 \sin \theta \cos \theta$

19. $1 - 2 \sin^2\theta$

20. *Skill sequence.* Complete the square. *(Previous course)*

a. $x^2 + 10x +$ _?_

b. $x^2 + bx +$ _?_

c. $2x^2 + 7x +$ _?_

d. $ax^2 + bx +$ _?_

Exploration

21. Ask each of about 25 students for the height of his or her biological parents. Graph the ordered pairs of the form (height of student, mid-parent height). As Galton did, multiply heights of mothers by 1.08.

a. Find the center of gravity (mean student height, mean mid-parent height) of this bivariate distribution.

b. Find an equation for the line of best fit.

c. The line from part **b** estimates the major axis of the ellipse which contain points of equal probability in the distribution. Derive an equation for an ellipse that seems to contain about $\frac{2}{3}$ of the data points.

LESSON

12-5

The General Quadratic Equation

You have learned that any conic section has an equation that is a polynomial of degree 2. That is, every conic section has an equation of the form

$$Ax^2 + Bxy + Cy^2 + Dx + Ey + F = 0,$$

where at least one of A, B, and C is not zero. This is the **general form of a quadratic relation in two variables**. Thus every conic section is a quadratic relation.

In this lesson, the converse question is discussed. Is every quadratic relation a conic? The answer, which is developed in this lesson, is "Usually, but not always." We separate our analysis into two cases: When $B = 0$ and $B \neq 0$.

The General Quadratic Equation When B = 0

If $B = 0$, the equation $Ax^2 + Bxy + Cy^2 + Dx + Ey + F = 0$ has the form

$$Ax^2 + Cy^2 + Dx + Ey + F = 0$$

We say it has no xy term. By reordering the terms, this equation can be rewritten as

$$Ax^2 + Dx + Cy^2 + Ey + F = 0.$$

In this form, the equation is set up for completing the square. First factor out A and C from the x and y terms, respectively.

$$A\left(x^2 + \frac{D}{A}x + \quad\right) + C\left(y^2 + \frac{E}{C}y + \quad\right) + F = 0$$

Then add the appropriate constants $\frac{D^2}{4A^2}$ and $\frac{E^2}{4C^2}$ to each side and simplify. Example 1 applies this technique to show that a certain quadratic equation represents a hyperbola.

Example 1

Show that the equation $3x^2 - y^2 + 6x + 7y - 12 = 0$ represents a hyperbola.

Solution

Rewrite the given equation in the standard form of a hyperbola. First, reorder the terms to group the terms in x and the terms in y.

$$3x^2 + 6x - y^2 + 7y - 12 = 0$$

Factor out the coefficients of x^2 and y^2 from the terms in x and y.

$$3(x^2 + 2x + \quad) - (y^2 - 7y + \quad) - 12 = 0$$

Complete the square. Be careful to add the same amount to each side, and to watch out for the numbers that have been factored out.

$$3(x^2 + 2x + 1) - (y^2 - 7y + 12.25) - 12 = 0 + 3 - 12.25$$

Rewrite the binomials as squares and simplify the constant.

$$3(x + 1)^2 - (y - 3.5)^2 = 2.75$$

This is actually far enough to see what is going on. By dividing both sides by 2.75, an equation of the form

$$\frac{(x + 1)^2}{a^2} - \frac{(y - 3.5)^2}{b^2} = 1$$

is obtained. This is an equation for a hyperbola with center at (-1, 3.5).

Check

Use an automatic grapher that graphs equations of the form $Ax^2 + Bxy + Cy^2 + Dx + Ey + F = 0$. Input $A = 3$, $B = 0$, $C = -1$, $D = 6$, $E = 7$, and $F = -12$. At the right is the output from such a grapher. The graph is a hyperbola with $x = -1$ and $y = 3.5$ as axes of symmetry.

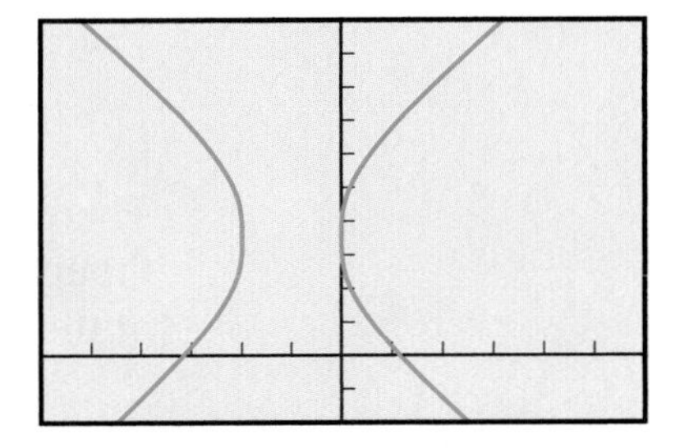

$-6 \le x \le 6$, x-scale = 1
$-2 \le y \le 10$, y-scale = 1

Example 1 illustrates the graph of a quadratic relation $Ax^2 + Bxy + Cy^2 + Dx + Ey + F = 0$ where $B = 0$ and A and C have opposite signs. In such a case $AC < 0$. For such values of A, B, and C, the graph is typically a hyperbola. If A and C have the same sign, that is, if $AC > 0$, then it is possible that no points may satisfy the equation. But if more than one point satisfies the equation, then the graph of the quadratic relation is an ellipse. (The special case of a circle occurs when $A = C$.)

Activity 1

Explain why there are no ordered pairs of real numbers (x, y) which satisfy $3x^2 + 4y^2 + 5 = 0$.

If one of A or C is zero, that is, if $AC = 0$, and there are points which satisfy the equation, then the graph of $Ax^2 + Cy^2 + Dx + Ey + F = 0$ is typically a parabola.

Notice the word "typically" occurs in the preceding discussion twice. The reason is that, on occasion, the graph of

$$Ax^2 + Cy^2 + Dx + Ey + F = 0$$

is not an ellipse, parabola, or hyperbola. When this happens, the graph is called a *degenerate conic section.* For instance, the left side of

$$9x^2 - 4y^2 + 3x + 22y - 30 = 0$$

can be factored by grouping, leading to

$$(3x + 2y - 5)(3x - 2y + 6) = 0.$$

But if the product of two numbers is zero, then one or the other (or both) is zero. So

$$3x + 2y - 5 = 0 \text{ or } 3x - 2y + 6 = 0.$$

These are equations of lines. So a point satisfies the first quadratic relation if and only if it is on one or both of the two lines. These two intersecting lines form a *degenerate hyperbola.*

Activity 2

a. Graph the lines $3x + 2y - 5 = 0$ and $3x - 2y + 6 = 0$ on the same set of axes.
b. Describe some ways that the graph is like a hyperbola. How is this graph different from a hyperbola?

There are five possible degenerate conic sections. Three of them may be thought of as the intersection of a cone and a plane containing the vertex of the cone.

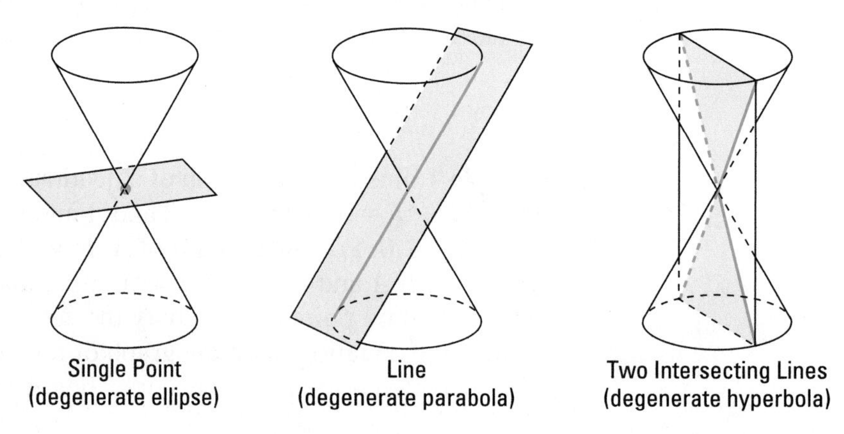
Single Point (degenerate ellipse) Line (degenerate parabola) Two Intersecting Lines (degenerate hyperbola)

The other possibilities are two parallel lines (which is sometimes considered a degenerate parabola), and the null set (which is sometimes considered a degenerate ellipse). This information is summarized in the following theorem.

Theorem
If A and C are not both zero, the graph of
$Ax^2 + Cy^2 + Dx + Ey + F = 0$ is
1. an ellipse, a point, or the null set, if $AC > 0$;
2. a hyperbola or a pair of intersecting lines, if $AC < 0$;
3. a parabola, a single line, two parallel lines, or the null set, if $AC = 0$.

Now do you see why we wrote "Usually, but not always" to answer the question of whether the graph of a quadratic relation is always a conic section?

The General Quadratic Equation When $B \neq 0$

When B is not zero, the equation $Ax^2 + Bxy + Cy^2 + Dx + Ey + F = 0$ has an xy term. In the last lesson, you saw that such equations occur by rotating a conic section so that its axes are no longer horizontal or vertical. Consequently, one way to classify such a conic section is to rotate it back in order to eliminate the xy term and then apply the above theorem. The argument is long, so read carefully.

Begin with the general quadratic relation

$$Ax^2 + Bxy + Cy^2 + Dx + Ey + F = 0.$$

We need to find θ so that under a rotation of θ about the origin, the image has no xy term, so we substitute $x \cos \theta + y \sin \theta$ for x, and $-x \sin \theta + y \cos \theta$ for y. The expressions become rather complicated, but you do not have to worry about the substitutions for x and y in Dx and Ey because they do not yield a term in xy.

$$A(x \cos \theta + y \sin \theta)^2 + B(x \cos \theta + y \sin \theta)(-x \sin \theta + y \cos \theta) + C(-x \sin \theta + y \cos \theta)^2 + \ldots + F = 0$$

We are looking for the xy-coefficient of the image, so consider only the terms in xy that will result from the squaring and multiplication of the binomials.

$$A(2xy \cos \theta \sin \theta) + B(xy \cos^2\theta - xy \sin^2\theta) + C(-2xy \sin \theta \cos \theta) + \ldots + F = 0$$

Factoring out xy from each of these terms gives

$$xy\,[2A \cos \theta \sin \theta + B(\cos^2\theta - \sin^2\theta) - 2C \sin \theta \cos \theta] + \ldots + F = 0.$$

Thus the coefficient of the xy term in the rotation image is

$$B' = 2A \cos \theta \sin \theta + B(\cos^2\theta - \sin^2\theta) - 2C \sin \theta \cos \theta.$$

Notice that each expression in θ is related to a double angle formula.

$$B' = A \sin 2\theta + B \cos 2\theta - C \sin 2\theta$$

So $$B' = (A - C) \sin 2\theta + B \cos 2\theta.$$

Remember that you want a value of θ so that there is no xy term. That means $B' = 0$. So consider this equation.

$$0 = (A - C)\sin 2\theta + B\cos 2\theta$$

This is equivalent to

$$B\cos 2\theta = (C - A)\sin 2\theta.$$

There are now two possibilities. If $C = A$, then solve $B\cos 2\theta = 0$ to find the magnitude of the rotation θ under which the image of the original quadratic has no xy term. That equation always has the solution $2\theta = \frac{\pi}{2}$, or $\theta = \frac{\pi}{4}$. If $C \neq A$, then neither B nor $C - A$ is 0 and so neither $\sin 2\theta$ nor $\cos 2\theta$ is 0. Then divide by $(C - A)\cos 2\theta$ to get

$$\frac{B}{C - A} = \frac{\sin 2\theta}{\cos 2\theta}$$

That is, $$\frac{B}{C - A} = \tan 2\theta.$$

This can be solved for 2θ to find the value of θ that will rotate the quadratic relation into one that has no xy term.

Example 2

What rotation will cause the image of the graph of

$$x^2 - 3xy + 4y^2 + 2x - y + 5 = 0$$

to have an equation with no xy term?

Solution

Here A = 1, B = -3, and C = 4. So $\tan 2\theta = \frac{-3}{4 - 1} = -1$, and thus $2\theta = \tan^{-1}(-1) = -\frac{\pi}{4}$ and so $\theta = -\frac{\pi}{8}$. A rotation of magnitude $-\frac{\pi}{8}$ will cause the image to have no xy term.

To find an equation in standard form for the image in Example 2, values for $\cos\theta$ and $\sin\theta$ must be found and then substitutions made as in Lesson 12-4. This can require a great deal of algebraic manipulation. Fortunately, if all that is desired is to know whether the quadratic relation is a parabola, ellipse, or hyperbola, there is a criterion that does not require finding this equation. It is based on the following theorem: under a rotation, the value of the **discriminant** $B^2 - 4AC$ does not change.

Theorem

Let S be the set of ordered pairs (x, y) satisfying

$$Ax^2 + Bxy + Cy^2 + Dx + Ey + F = 0,$$

and let $S' = R_\theta(S)$. Furthermore, suppose that

$$A'x^2 + B'xy + C'y^2 + D'x + E'y + F' = 0$$

is an equation for S'. Then $B^2 - 4AC = (B')^2 - 4A'C'$.

Proof

The proof requires quite a bit of algebraic manipulation. It is begun here, and you are asked to fill in some other details as one of the questions. To perform the rotation R_θ, $x\cos\theta + y\sin\theta$ is substituted for x in the equation for S, and $-x\sin\theta + y\cos\theta$ is substituted for y. After some algebraic manipulation, the result is the equation for S', and you should verify that

$$A' = A\cos^2\theta - B\cos\theta\sin\theta + C\sin^2\theta,$$

$$B' = 2(A - C)\sin\theta\cos\theta + B(\cos^2\theta - \sin^2\theta) \text{ (as stated on page 787),}$$

and

$$C' = A\sin^2\theta + B\cos\theta\sin\theta + C\cos^2\theta.$$

Now we have to find $(B')^2 - 4A'C'$. This too requires quite a bit of manipulation. To shorten the writing, let $s = \sin\theta$ and $t = \cos\theta$. Then

$$A' = At^2 - Bts + Cs^2,$$

$$B' = 2(A - C)ts + B(t^2 - s^2),$$

and

$$C' = As^2 + Bts + Ct^2.$$

Now calculate $B'^2 - 4A'C'$ and use the fact that $s^2 + t^2 = 1$ to finish the proof.

The above theorem holds for *any* rotation, so it certainly holds for the rotation for which $B' = 0$. Thus for the equation of the rotation image that has no xy term, $B^2 - 4AC = (B')^2 - 4A'C' = -4A'C'$. But, from the first theorem of this lesson, the type of conic section is determined by the sign of $A'C'$. The sign of $-4A'C'$ is just the opposite of the sign of $A'C'$. Putting this all together, the following theorem is obtained.

Theorem

Let S be the set of ordered pairs (x, y) satisfying

$$Ax^2 + Bxy + Cy^2 + Dx + Ey + F = 0.$$

Then:

if $B^2 - 4AC < 0$, then S is an ellipse, a single point, or the null set;
if $B^2 - 4AC > 0$, then S is a hyperbola or a pair of intersecting lines;
if $B^2 - 4AC = 0$, then S is a parabola, two parallel lines, a line, or the null set.

Example 3

What kind of conic section is the graph of the quadratic relation

$$2x^2 + 3xy - y^2 + 2x - 2y - 5 = 0?$$

Solution

Use the theorem above with $A = 2$, $B = 3$, and $C = -1$.
$B^2 - 4AC = 9 + 8 = 17 > 0$. Thus the conic is either a hyperbola or a pair of intersecting lines. To determine which, try to find some points on the graph. Begin with the given equation

$$2x^2 + 3xy - y^2 + 2x - 2y - 5 = 0.$$

If $x = 0$, then $-y^2 - 2y - 5 = 0$ or $y^2 + 2y + 5 = 0$, for which there is no real solution. This tells us that the graph does not cross the y-axis. This is impossible if the lines are intersecting, so the graph of $2x^2 + 3xy - y^2 + 2x - 2y - 5 = 0$ must be a hyperbola.

If in Example 3 we found points on the graph, then we would have had to find a total of at least three points. The reasoning is as follows: If the graph is a pair of intersecting lines, then at least two of these points must be on one of the lines. If all three points are on the same line, then the graph must be a pair of intersecting lines. If all three points are not on the same line, then try some other point (perhaps the midpoint) on each of the three lines connecting them. If the graph contains a straight line, then one of these lines must be one of the intersecting lines. If none of the midpoints satisfies the equation, then the graph does not contain any lines; the only possibility is that it is a hyperbola. Similar reasoning can be used to distinguish ellipses and parabolas from their degenerate forms.

QUESTIONS

Covering the Reading

In 1–3, an equation for a quadratic relation is given.

a. Rewrite the equation in the general form of a quadratic relation in two variables.
b. Give values for A, B, C, D, E, and F in that form.
c. Identify the conic section.

1. $\frac{x^2}{4} + \frac{y^2}{9} = 1$ **2.** $(x - 5)^2 + (y - 2)^2 = 6$ **3.** $xy = 1$

4. **a.** Rewrite the equation $3x^2 + y^2 + 6x + 7y - 12 = 0$ in the standard form of an ellipse.
b. Find the center of the ellipse.

5. What is a degenerate conic section?

6. **a.** Write your answer to Activity 1.
b. Which type of degenerate conic section is this equation?

7. Write your answers to Activity 2.

In 8–11, without graphing, name the conic section whose equation is given. Whenever possible, check by graphing.

8. $3x^2 + 5y^2 - 6x + 2y - 9 = 0$

9. $x^2 - 14x + y^2 + 2y + 50 = 0$

10. $x + y + xy = 8$

11. $3x^2 - 6xy + 3y^2 - 7x + 2y + 5 = 0$

In 12 and 13, what is the magnitude of the rotation which will cause an equation for the image of the graph of the given equation to have no term in xy?

12. $x^2 + 3xy + y^2 = 8$

13. $-2x^2 - 4xy - 5y^2 + 4x - 3y + 27 = 0$.

Applying the Mathematics

14. Explain why $(2x + 5y - 7)(3x - 7y + 11) = 0$ is an equation for a degenerate conic.

15. Examine the proof of the theorem on page 789. Do the algebraic manipulation to show that $(B')^2 - 4A'C' = B^2 - 4AC$.

16. Consider the graph of $x^2 - xy = 6$.

a. Use the $B^2 - 4AC$ criterion to determine the type of conic this is.
b. Solve for y and graph this conic.
c. At what angle are the axes of this conic inclined to the x-axis?

Review

17. Find an equation for the image of $x^2 - y^2 = 1$ under the rotation R_{-30}. *(Lesson 12-4)*

18. What makes a hyperbola a rectangular hyperbola? *(Lesson 12-4)*

In 19 and 20, conditions for a quadratic relation are given. **a.** Sketch the curve satisfying the conditions. **b.** Find an equation for the curve. *(Lessons 12-2, 12-3)*

19. ellipse with vertices $(\pm 5, 0)$ and minor axis of length 4

20. hyperbola with vertices $(0, \pm 6)$ and asymptotes $y = \pm 4x$

In 21 and 22 simplify each expression. *(Lessons 4-4, 11-5)*

21. $\cos(\pi - \theta)$

22. $\cos\left(\frac{\pi}{2} + \theta\right)$

23. *True or false.* For all real numbers x, $\sin\left(\frac{\pi}{2} - x\right) = \sin\left(x - \frac{\pi}{2}\right)$. Justify your answer. *(Lessons 4-4, 11-5)*

24. Given $z = 3 + 2i$ and $w = 5 - i$, find each. *(Lesson 9-6)*

a. $z + 4w$ **b.** zw **c.** $\frac{z}{w}$

Exploration

25. Explore the graph of the equation $x^2 + 2xy + Cy^2 - 12 = 0$ for various values of C. How many different types of conics are possible? What values of C lead to degenerate conics? Are there any properties that all members of this family of quadratic relations satisfy?

LESSON

12-6

It's All Done With Mirrors

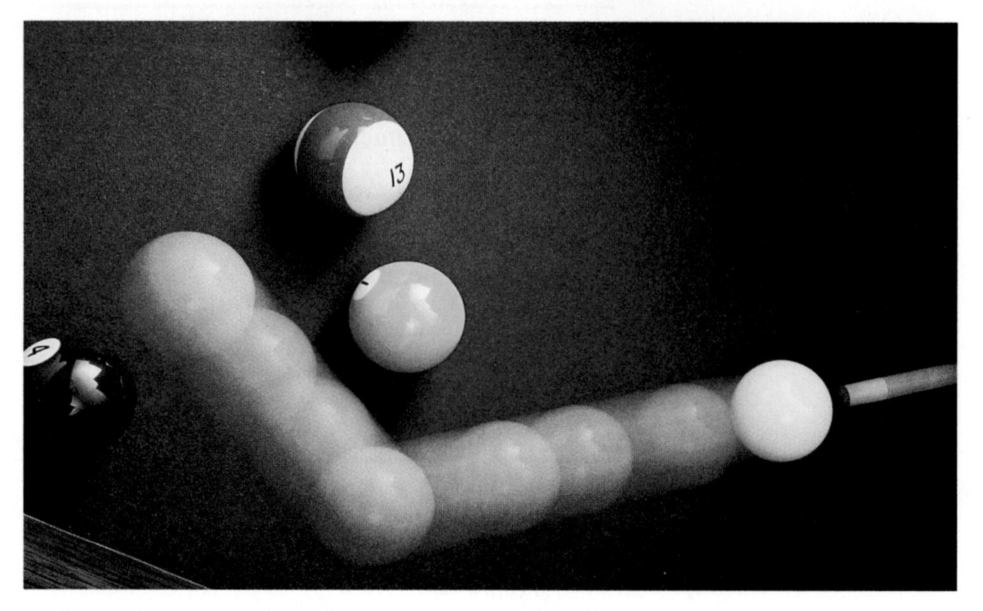

Follow the Bouncing Ball. *A typical shot in billiards involves banking the ball off at least one cushion. Knowing where the ball will carom is the key to winning.*

Reflecting Properties of a Plane

An object that hits a flat hard surface without spin will bounce off that surface in a path that is the reflection image of what its path would have been if the wall were not there. This reflection principle is often seen in handball, tennis, basketball, baseball, hockey, and many other sports.

In physics this principle is stated as *the angle of incidence equals the angle of reflection*, where the two angles in question are measured from the ray perpendicular to the surface at the point of contact. Furthermore, the two rays of the path of the object and the third perpendicular ray all lie in the same plane, so that the mathematics of this situation can be analyzed using plane geometry.

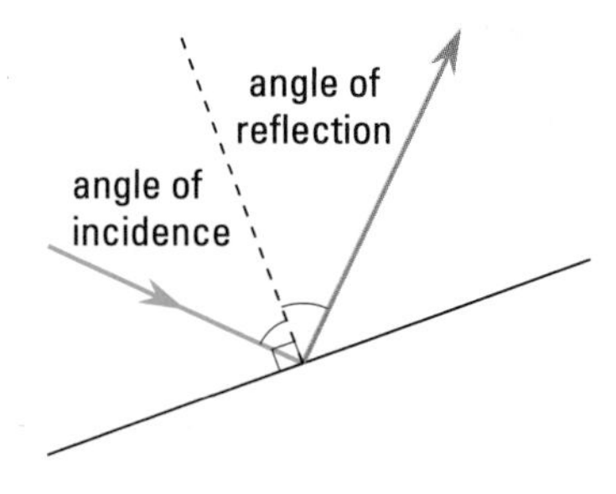

These reflection principles apply also to electromagnetic radiation (such as light waves and radio waves) and sound waves. When you look in a mirror and see the image of an object, the actual object is located in the position of the reflection image of the image you see. Acoustical engineers use these principles to design concert halls so that the sounds from the stage are not distorted as they bounce off the walls, ceiling, seats, and floor.

The reflection principles apply even when surfaces are curved, as long as the curvature of the surface is smooth, that is, as long as there is a plane tangent to the surface at the point of contact. Think of it this way: when the object hits such a surface, it does not know anything about the surface except at the exact point where it touches, so it bounces off the surface as if the surface is flat at that point. This is equivalent to saying that the object bounces off in a direction determined by the tangent plane to the surface at the point, as pictured below. The two rays of the path are coplanar, and they form equal angles with the perpendicular to the tangent plane at the point of contact, just as if the surface were flat there.

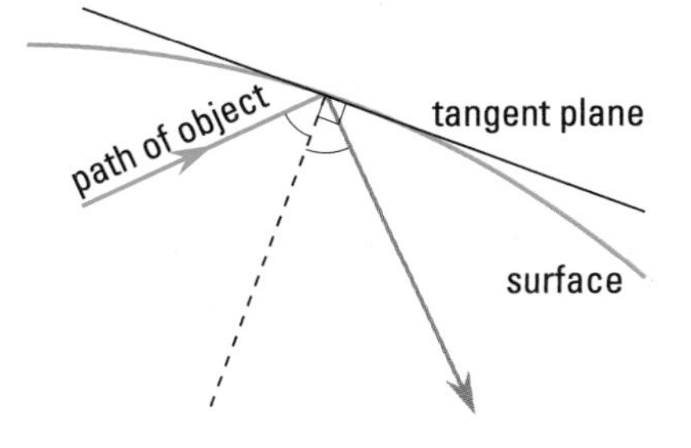

Reflecting Properties of an Ellipse

The conic sections possess reflection properties that are even more special. If an ellipse is rotated about its major axis, the surface formed is called an **ellipsoid.**

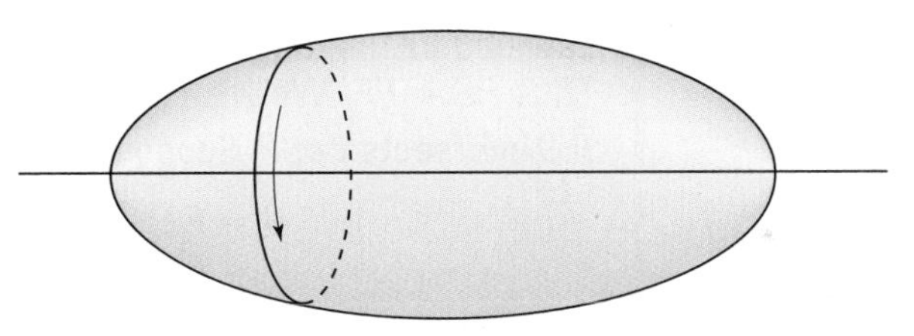

Shhh. . . *Noise from others does not disturb a quiet conversation between people standing at the two foci of this Whispering Gallery at the Museum of Science and Industry in Chicago.*

In a number of museums and other buildings (the U.S. Senate is one), one of the rooms is designed so that its walls (from head level up) and ceiling make up half of an ellipsoid.

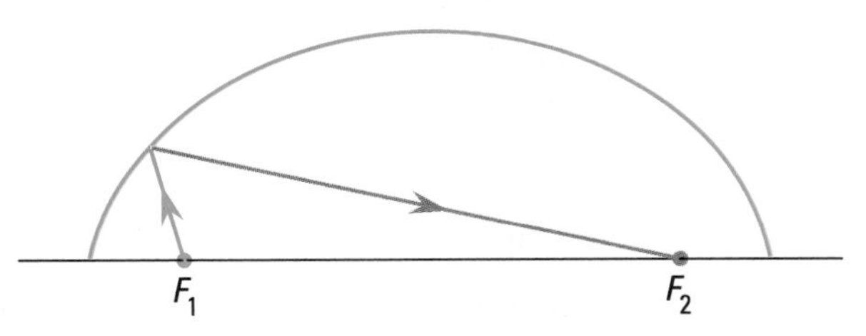
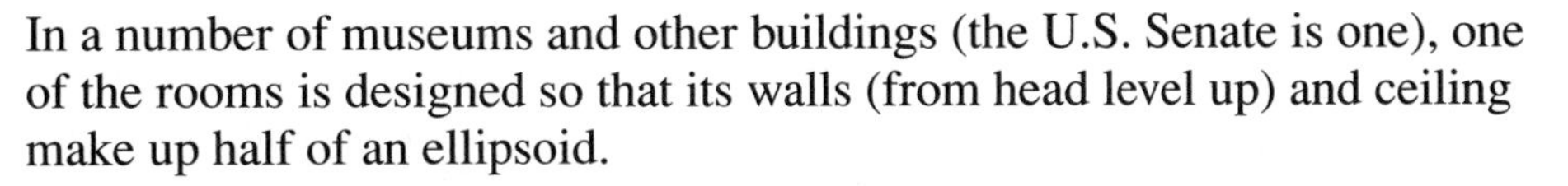

If a person speaks at one focus of the ellipsoidal room, the sound will bounce off of the walls and ceiling of the room and travel to the other focus. The sound is so "focused" that even if the two foci are quite far apart, whispers from one focus are heard at the other focus. For this reason, a room with this property is called a **whispering gallery**.

This property of ellipses is due to the following theorem.

Theorem (Reflecting Property of an Ellipse)
If P is a point on an ellipse with foci F_1 and F_2, then $\overrightarrow{PF_1}$ and $\overrightarrow{PF_2}$ form equal angles with the line tangent to the ellipse at P.

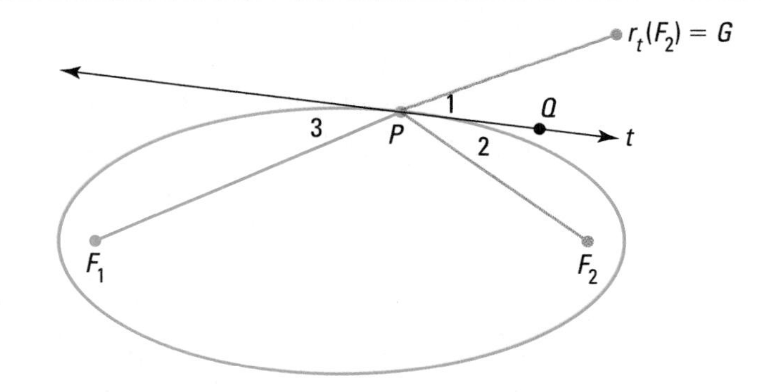

The proof of the Reflecting Property of an Ellipse Theorem requires one property of ellipses we have not discussed: namely, that if k is the focal constant, then a point Q is outside the ellipse if and only if $QF_1 + QF_2 > k$. The tangent to the ellipse at P, because it only intersects the ellipse at one point, consists of such points Q that satisfy $QF_1 + QF_2 > k$ and the single point P satisfying the defining property $PF_1 + PF_2 = k$.

Proof
Let line t be the tangent to the ellipse at P, and let $G = r_t(F_2)$, as pictured above. Thus $PG = PF_2$. We wish to show that G, P, and F_1 are collinear. This will occur if $\overline{F_1G}$ intersects t at P. Suppose $\overline{F_1G}$ intersected t at some other point Q on t. Then,

$$\begin{aligned} F_1G &= F_1Q + QG && \text{betweenness} \\ &= F_1Q + QF_2 && \text{reflections preserve distance} \\ &> k && \text{Q is outside the ellipse.} \end{aligned}$$

But $F_1P + PF_2 = k$ from the definition of the ellipse. Substituting PG for PF_2 gives $F_1P + PG = k$. So the shortest path from F_1 to G is through P, the point of tangency, and so P is on $\overline{F_1G}$. As a result, $\angle 1$ and $\angle 3$ are vertical angles, so $m\angle 1 = m\angle 3$. Because reflections preserve angle measure, $m\angle 1 = m\angle 2$. Consequently, $m\angle 2 = m\angle 3$ and so $\overrightarrow{PF_1}$ and $\overrightarrow{PF_2}$ make equal angles with the tangent to the ellipse.

Reflecting Properties of a Parabola

When a parabola is rotated about its axis, the three-dimensional surface formed is called a **paraboloid.** Any cross section of this paraboloid formed by a plane containing the axis is a parabola whose focus is the same as the focus of the original parabola; that point is also the focus of the paraboloid. If an object traveling parallel to the axis hits the "inside" of the paraboloid, then the object will be reflected through the focus of the parabola. A proof of this property of the parabola is not easy. You are asked only to apply the property in the Questions.

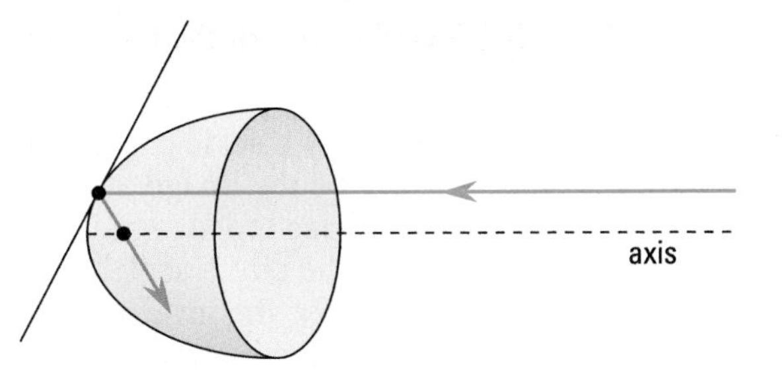

This property makes the paraboloid a particularly appropriate surface for collecting light or radio waves that come from a far distance; the waves are close to parallel, so after reflection they concentrate together at the focus where they can be collected. For this reason, satellite dishes to receive television or radio transmissions, and most telescope mirrors to collect light from stars, are parts of paraboloids.

Beaming. *The inner reflector of the headlights of many automobiles, such as this one from a 1940 LaSalle, are paraboloids.*

Automobile headlights use this property in reverse. The light bulb is placed at the focus of a parabolic (actually, *paraboloidal*) mirror. Most of the light from the bulb that hits the surface of the mirror bounces off in a direction parallel to the axis of the paraboloid. Usually the only difference between "brights" and normal headlights in a car is that the paraboloidal mirror is turned so that its axis is parallel to the ground, and so the light travels without hitting the ground.

QUESTIONS

Covering the Reading

In 1–3, suppose a laser beam hits the mirror at point *P*. Trace the picture and draw the path of the beam after it hits the mirror.

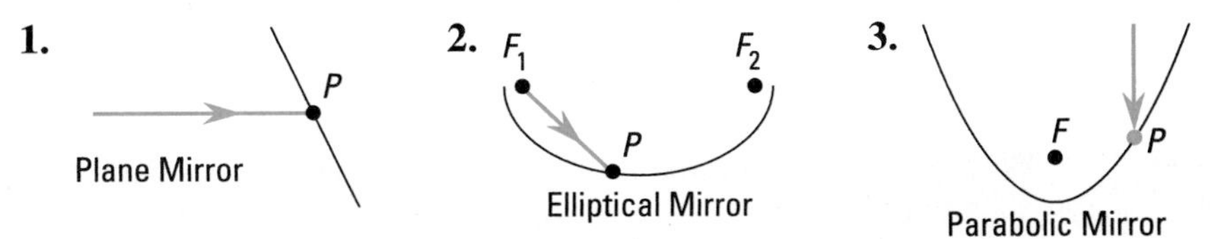

In 4 and 5, sketch and identify the three-dimensional figure obtained by each of the following.

4. rotating an ellipse 360° around the major axis

5. rotating a parabola around its axis of symmetry

6. a. State a reflecting property of an ellipsoid.
b. Give a practical application of this property.

7. a. State a reflecting property of a paraboloid.
b. Give a practical application of this property.

8. Find an equation for the line tangent to the circle $x^2 + y^2 = 25$ at the point (3, 4). (*Hint:* The tangent is perpendicular to the radius at the point of tangency.)

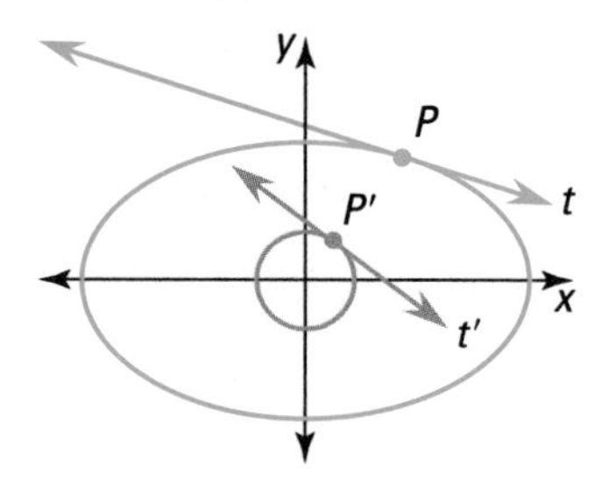

9. An equation for the tangent line t to a parent ellipse $\frac{x^2}{a^2} + \frac{y^2}{b^2} = 1$ at any point P on it can be found using the following procedure.

Step 1: By a scale change, map the ellipse onto the unit circle, and let P' be the image of P under this scale change.

Step 2: Use the idea of Question 8 to find an equation for t', the tangent to the circle at P'.

Step 3: Use the inverse of the transformation used in Step 1 to find an equation for the original tangent.

Use this procedure to find an equation for the tangent line t to the ellipse $\frac{x^2}{200} + \frac{y^2}{450} = 1$ at the point (14, 3).

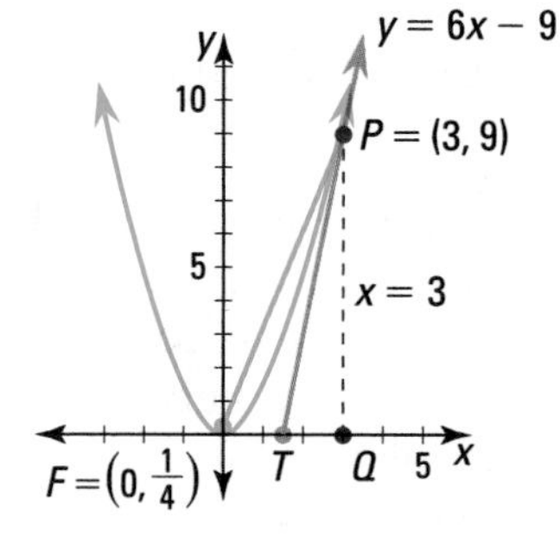

10. The focus F of the parabola $y = x^2$ is at the point $\left(0, \frac{1}{4}\right)$. It can be shown that the tangent to this parabola at the point $P = (3, 9)$ has equation $y = 6x - 9$. By drawing triangles and using trigonometry, show that $\overline{FP}$ and the vertical line $x = 3$ make equal angles with the tangent.

Review

In 11 and 12, name the conic section whose equation is given.

11. $4x^2 + 5xy - 6y^2 + 12x + 36 = 0$

12. $x^2 + xy + y^2 + x + y - 5 = 0$ *(Lesson 12-5)*

13. Suppose the curve with equation $xy = -6$ is rotated $\frac{\pi}{4}$ about the origin.

a. What is an equation for the image?

b. *True or false.* Both the preimage and image are rectangular hyperbolas. *(Lesson 12-4)*

In 14 and 15, an equation for a quadratic relation is given. **a.** Sketch a graph. **b.** Identify the foci. **c.** Identify the focal constant. *(Lessons 12-2, 12-3)*

14. $\frac{x^2}{25} + \frac{y^2}{8} = 1$

15. $\frac{x^2}{25} - \frac{y^2}{8} = 1$

16. Name the conic section(s) with the following symmetry. *(Lessons 12-1, 12-3)*

a. exactly one line of symmetry

b. at least two lines of symmetry

c. 90° rotation symmetry

Earthrise photographed from Apollo 17 as it orbited the Moon in 1972

17. The elliptical orbit of the moon has the center of Earth as one focus. If the closest distance from the center of the moon to the center of Earth is 216,000 miles and the largest distance to the center of Earth is 248,000 miles, how far from the center of Earth is the second focus? *(Lesson 12-2)*

18. Find all complex solutions to $x^3 - 1000 = 0$. *(Lesson 9-8)*

Exploration

19. There is a reflection property for the hyperbola. Find out what this is.

A project presents an opportunity for you to extend your knowledge of a topic related to the material of this chapter. You should allow more time for a project than you do for a typical homework question.

1 Orbits of Celestial Bodies

a. Collect data on the elliptical orbits of the planets. Arrange the eccentricities (see Project 4) of the orbits of the planets from smallest to largest.

b. Find data on the elliptical orbits of comets or other celestial bodies. Does there appear to be any relation between the period of the comet (i.e., how long it takes to complete one trip) and the eccentricity of its path? If so, what is it?

c. Can a heavenly body travel in a path that is parabolic? hyperbolic? Why or why not?

2 Using Paper-folding to Make Conic Sections

Using wax paper, determine the curve that results from each of the following.

a. Draw a line ℓ and a point P not on the line. Fold and crease the paper so a point Q on the line coincides with P. Repeat at least a dozen times for different points Q. How does the distance between P and ℓ affect the resulting curve?

b. Draw a circle and a point P in the interior of the circle (but not the center of it). Make different folds where a point on the circle coincides with P. How does the distance between P and the center of the circle affect the resulting curve?

c. Draw a circle and a point P in the exterior of the circle. Make different folds where a point on the circle coincides with P. Discuss the effect of the distance between P and the center of the circle on the resulting curve.

3 Using Drawing to Make Conic Sections

The following methods always generate conic sections. For each of the following methods below, draw the curve, name the curve, and explain why the method always produces a certain conic section.

a. Tie a pencil near the middle of a piece of string and pass the string around two pins inserted on a piece of paper. Using the pencil to keep the string taut, hold the two ends of the string together and draw them toward you around one of the pins, as shown below. Repeat by interchanging the roles of the two pins.

b. Place a piece of string of length AB as shown below on a T-square. Place the T-square perpendicular to a line ℓ on the paper and place the ends of the string at B and at a point C on the paper. As the T-square slides on ℓ, draw the curve by keeping the pencil firmly on the edge of the T-square.

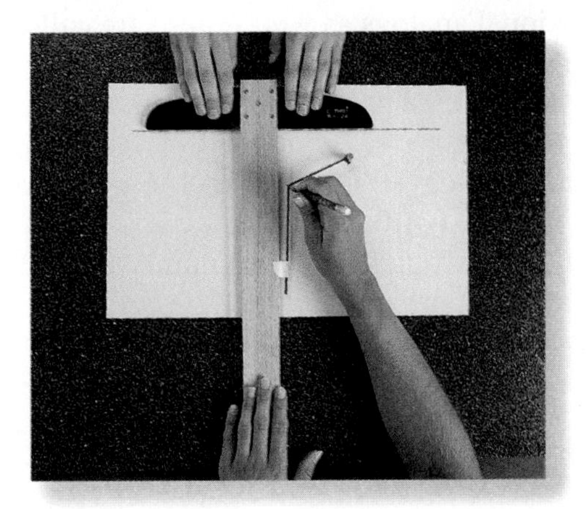

4 Eccentricity

It is possible to define a conic section in terms of distances from a fixed point and a fixed line. If the curve has its major axis along the x-axis, then the distance from a point on the curve to the focus $(c, 0)$ divided by the distance from a point on the curve to the directrix line with equation $x = \frac{a^2}{c}$ is $\frac{c}{a}$. The ratio $\frac{c}{a}$ is called the **eccentricity** of the conic and is denoted as e.

a. Calculate the value of the eccentricity e for some conic sections you have drawn before.

b. Both the ellipse and hyperbola have two foci and two *directrices*. Give equations for both directrices of ellipses and hyperbolas in standard form.

c. Draw curves with increasing eccentricities such as .25, .5, .75, .9, 1.0, 1.5, 2, 2.5, 3, 4, 5, and 10. *Multiple choice.* Match the following equations with their curves.

i. $0 < e < 1$	(I) ellipse
ii. $e = 1$	(II) hyperbola
iii. $e > 1$	(III) parabola

d. What is the eccentricity of the ellipse most pleasing to your eye? Some people believe it to be the reciprocal of the golden ratio or the reciprocal of the number e. Do you agree?

5 Quadric Sections

As the circle has three-dimensional analogs in the sphere and cylinder, the other conic sections have three-dimensional analogs as well. These are called **quadric surfaces** and can be expressed by the following general second degree equation in three variables:

$$Ax^2 + By^2 + Cz^2 + Dxy + Exz + Fyz + Gx + Hy + Iz + J = 0,$$

where the coefficients are real numbers. Do either parts **a** and **b**, or part **c**.

a. For instance, an **ellipsoid** has as its general equation

$$\frac{x^2}{a^2} + \frac{y^2}{b^2} + \frac{z^2}{c^2} = 1.$$

If two of a, b, and c in the above equation are equal, then the surface is a **spheroid.** A *prolate spheroid*, somewhat like a football, is created by rotating an ellipse about its major axis. An *oblate spheroid*, somewhat like a doorknob, is created by rotating an ellipse about its minor axis. Draw some ellipsoids and spheroids.

b. Other quadric surfaces have the following general equations.

hyperboloid of one sheet: $\frac{x^2}{a^2} + \frac{y^2}{b^2} - \frac{z^2}{c^2} = 1$

hyperboloid of two sheets: $-\frac{x^2}{a^2} - \frac{y^2}{b^2} + \frac{z^2}{c^2} = 1$

elliptic paraboloid: $z = \frac{x^2}{a^2} + \frac{y^2}{b^2}$

hyperbolic paraboloid (the "saddle-shaped" surface): $z = \frac{y^2}{b^2} - \frac{x^2}{a^2}$

Graph examples of each of these curves.

c. Many quadric surfaces can be approximated by string models.

Use string to build a quadric surface such as the one pictured here.

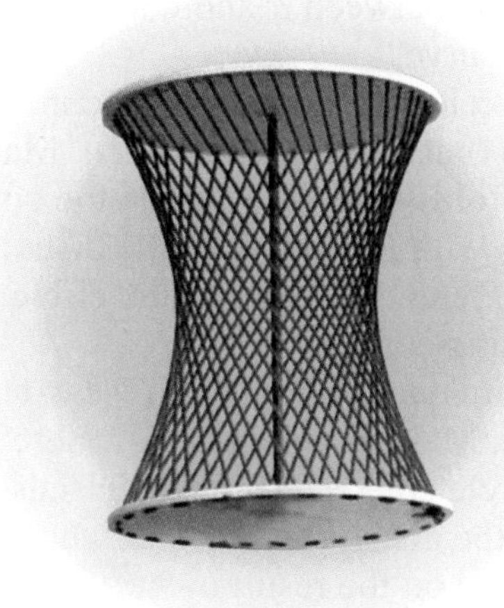

SUMMARY

When one of two intersecting lines is rotated about the other, an unbounded cone of two nappes is formed. The sections of this cone lead to the three primary conic sections: the parabola (which was studied earlier), the ellipse, and the hyperbola.

Both the ellipse and the hyperbola have two foci. An ellipse is the set of all points where the sum of the distances to each of the foci is constant. A hyperbola is the set of all points where the absolute value of the difference of the distances to the foci is constant. Relating these definitions to the description of the conic sections as intersections can be done elegantly by the use of Dandelin spheres.

Both the ellipse and hyperbola have two symmetry lines which contain the major axis and the minor axis of the curves. The major axis is the one containing the foci. If these symmetry lines are the x- and y-axes, then the ellipse can be described by the standard form equation $\frac{x^2}{a^2} + \frac{y^2}{b^2} = 1$, and the hyperbola can be described by the standard form equation $\frac{x^2}{a^2} - \frac{y^2}{b^2} = 1$ or $\frac{y^2}{a^2} - \frac{x^2}{b^2} = 1$.

When the asymptotes of a hyperbola are perpendicular, the hyperbola is called rectangular. Translation images can be described by applying the theorems studied earlier in this course.

When one symmetry line of an ellipse or hyperbola is not horizontal, the conic is a rotation image of an ellipse or hyperbola in standard form. If the center of the rotation is the origin, then the Graph-Rotation Theorem can be applied to find an equation for the conic. For instance, $xy = 1$ is an equation for the image of the rectangular hyperbola with equation $x^2 - y^2 = 1$ under R_{45}.

Graphs of the general quadratic equation

$$Ax^2 + Bxy + Cy^2 + Dx + Ey + F = 0$$

include all conic sections and the degenerate conic sections. The discriminant $B^2 - 4AC$ tells you the possible shapes of the curve. If $B^2 - 4AC < 0$, the curve is an ellipse, a single point, or the null set. If $B^2 - 4AC > 0$, the curve is a hyperbola or a pair of intersecting lines. If $B^2 - 4AC = 0$, the curve is a parabola, two parallel lines, a line, or the null set. By using the identity $\frac{B}{C - A} = \tan 2\theta$ or $B\cos\theta = 0$, you can determine the magnitude of rotation needed to map the curve onto a conic with a horizontal line of symmetry.

The reflection property of an ellipse—that a path through one focus will reflect off the ellipse through the other focus—is used in constructing whispering galleries. The reflection property of a parabola—that a path parallel to the axis will reflect off the parabola through the focus—is used in constructing satellite dishes and headlights. Systems of hyperbolas are used in locating and tracking objects that emit sound waves.

VOCABULARY

Below are the most important terms and phrases for this chapter. You should be able to give a general description and a specific example of each and a precise definition for those marked with an asterisk (*).

Lesson 12-1
*conic section
quadratic relation
axis, vertex, nappes of cone
cross section, section
edge (of a cone)
*ellipse
focus, foci of an ellipse
focal constant for an ellipse
astronomical units (a.u.)

Lesson 12-2
*standard form equation for an ellipse
center of an ellipse
horizontal axis, vertical axis
major axis, minor axis
eccentricity (of an ellipse)

Lesson 12-3
*hyperbola
focus, foci, focal constant of a hyperbola
*standard form equation for a hyperbola
vertices
axes, center of a hyperbola

Lesson 12-4
Graph-Rotation Theorem
rectangular hyperbola
isometry

Lesson 12-5
general form of a quadratic relation in two variables
degenerate conic sections
discriminant

PROGRESS SELF-TEST

Take this test as you would take a test in class. You will need an automatic grapher. Then, check the test yourself using the solutions at the back of the book.

1. a. Explain how to obtain an ellipse from a cone.

b. Draw a figure to illustrate your description.

In 2–4, graph.

2. $\frac{x^2}{25} + \frac{y^2}{81} = 1$

3. $x^2 - 9y^2 = 9$

4. $\frac{(x-2)^2}{36} + \frac{(y+1)^2}{20} = 1$

5. Find an equation for the hyperbola with foci (7, 0) and (-7, 0) and focal constant 10.

6. Draw an ellipse for which the distance between the foci is 8 cm and the focal constant is 10 cm.

7. a. Consider the hyperbola $\frac{x^2}{81} - \frac{y^2}{100} = 1$. Give equations for its asymptotes.

b. Give equations for its symmetry lines.

8. Find an equation for the image of $y = x^2 - 3x - 4$ under $R_{\pi/3}$.

9. Tell whether or not $\frac{y^2}{30} - \frac{x^2}{4} = 1$ is a rectangular hyperbola. Justify your answer.

10. Rewrite $\frac{x^2}{9} - \frac{y^2}{64} = 1$ in the general quadratic form, and give values of A, B, C, D, E, and F in that form.

In 11 and 12, describe the graph of the relation represented by the given equation.

11. $2x^2 - 6xy + 18y^2 - 14x + 6y - 110 = 0$

12. $9x^2 - 2xy + y^2 - 4x + 22 = 0$

13. The elliptical orbit of the planet Jupiter has the center of the sun as one focus. If the closest distance to the center of the sun is 460 million miles and the farthest distance is 508 million miles, how far from the center of the sun is the second focus?

The planet Jupiter was named after the Roman king of the gods before it was known to be the largest planet.

CHAPTER REVIEW

Questions on SPUR Objectives

SPUR stands for **S**kills, **P**roperties, **U**ses, and **R**epresentations. The Chapter Review questions are grouped according to the SPUR Objectives for this chapter.

SKILLS DEAL WITH THE PROCEDURES USED TO GET ANSWERS.

Objective A: *Use properties of ellipses and hyperbolas to write equations describing them. (Lessons 12-2, 12-3)*

1. Find an equation for the ellipse with foci (0, 15) and (0, -15) and focal constant 34.

2. Find an equation for the hyperbola with foci (4, 0) and (-4, 0) and focal constant 6.

3. Give an equation for the ellipse whose center is the origin, whose horizontal axis has length 18, and whose vertical axis has length 7.

4. Give equations for the asymptotes of the hyperbola $\frac{x^2}{16} - \frac{y^2}{4} = 1$.

Objective B: *Find equations for rotation images of figures. (Lesson 12-4)*

In 5–8, find an equation for the image of the given figure under the given rotation.

5. $\frac{x^2}{9} + \frac{y^2}{36} = 1; R_{45}$

6. $9x^2 - y^2 = 1; R_{\pi/3}$

7. $y = x^2 - 8; R_{\pi/6}$

8. $x^2 + y^2 = 20; R_{55}$

9. Suppose the hyperbola $xy = 120$ is rotated $\frac{\pi}{4}$ about the origin. What is an equation for the image hyperbola?

10. Find an equation for the image of the parabola $y = (x + 4)^2 + 5$ when rotated 60° about the point (-4, 5).

Objective C: *Rewrite equations of conic sections in the general form of a quadratic relation in two variables. (Lesson 12-5)*

In 11–14, rewrite the equation in the general form of a quadratic relation in two variables and give values of A, B, C, D, E, and F in that form.

11. $\frac{x^2}{25} + \frac{y^2}{49} = 1$

12. $(x + 3)^2 + (y - 8)^2 = 35$

13. $7xy = 8$

14. $\frac{(x - 2)^2}{4} - y^2 = 1$

PROPERTIES DEAL WITH THE PRINCIPLES BEHIND THE MATHEMATICS.

Objective D: *State and apply properties of ellipses and hyperbolas to draw or describe them. (Lessons 12-1, 12-3, 12-4)*

15. Draw an ellipse in which the distance between the foci is 6 cm and the focal constant is 8 cm.

16. Draw a hyperbola in which the distance between the foci is 2 inches and the focal constant is 1 inch.

17. At least how many symmetry lines does every ellipse have?

18. At most how many symmetry lines does every hyperbola have?

In 19 and 20, tell whether or not the hyperbola is a rectangular hyperbola. Justify your answer.

19. $\frac{x^2}{6} - \frac{y^2}{12} = 1$

20. $5xy = 80$

 CHAPTER TWELVE

Objective E: *Describe the intersections of a plane and a cone of 2 nappes.* *(Lessons 12-1, 12-5)*

21. How is the "cone" in conic sections generated?

22. Name the three degenerate conic sections.

23. Draw a plane intersecting a cone in a hyperbola.

24. *True or false.* Justify your thinking. Any given plane must intersect a given cone.

USES DEAL WITH APPLICATIONS OF MATHEMATICS IN REAL SITUATIONS.

Objective F: *Determine information about elliptical orbits.* *(Lesson 12-2)*

25. The elliptical orbit of the planet Mercury has the center of the sun as one focus. If the closest distance to the center of the sun is 28,440,000 miles and the farthest distance is 43,560,000 miles, how far from the center of the sun is the second focus?

26. The closest distance the planet Mars gets to the sun is 129 million miles and the farthest distance is 154 million miles. Is the second focus of Mars's orbit nearer or farther from the sun than the planet Mercury (use the information of Question 25)?

REPRESENTATIONS DEAL WITH PICTURES, GRAPHS, OR OBJECTS THAT ILLUSTRATE CONCEPTS.

Objective G: *Graph or identify graphs of ellipses and hyperbolas given their equations.* *(Lessons 12-2, 12-3)*

In 27–32, graph.

27. $x^2 + \frac{y^2}{16} = 1$

28. $16x^2 - y^2 = 16$

29. $\frac{y^2}{40} - \frac{x^2}{9} = 1$

30. $20x^2 + 49y^2 = 980$

31. $y^2 - x^2 = 1$

32. $\frac{x^2}{100} - \frac{y^2}{9} = 1$

In 33 and 34, give an equation for the ellipse.

33.

34.

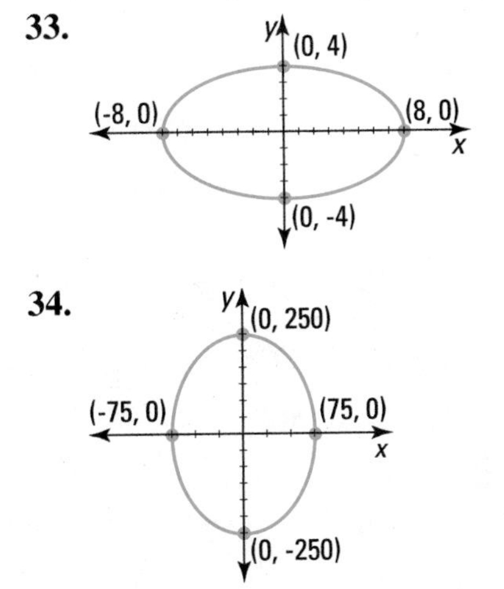

Objective H: *Graph transformation images of parent ellipses and hyperbolas.* *(Lessons 12-2, 12-3, 12-5)*

In 35 and 36, graph.

35. $\frac{(x - 4)^2}{25} + \frac{(y + 2)^2}{4} = 1$

36. $\frac{(x + 8)^2}{16} - (y - 3)^2 = 1$

37. Graph $xy = 20$.

38. Graph $x^2 - xy = 8$ by solving for y.

Objective I: *Describe graphs of quadratic equations.* *(Lesson 12-5)*

In 39–42, describe the graph of the relation represented by the given equation.

39. $8x^2 + 3y^2 - 12x + 6y + 18 = 0$

40. $8x + 8y - 4xy = -12$

41. $x^2 + 4xy + 4y^2 + 8x + 2y + 9 = 0$

42. $3y^2 - 4y = 2x^2 + 9x - 3$

CHAPTER 13

FURTHER WORK WITH TRIGONOMETRY

This chapter covers three topics in trigonometry. First, three more trigonometric functions are introduced—the *secant*, *cosecant*, and *cotangent*—and identities involving them and the original three trigonometric functions are proved.

The second topic is an introduction to a coordinate system different from rectangular coordinates, the *polar coordinate system*. When plotted with polar coordinates, the graphs of trigonometric functions often are quite beautiful. Patterns like those below are examples.

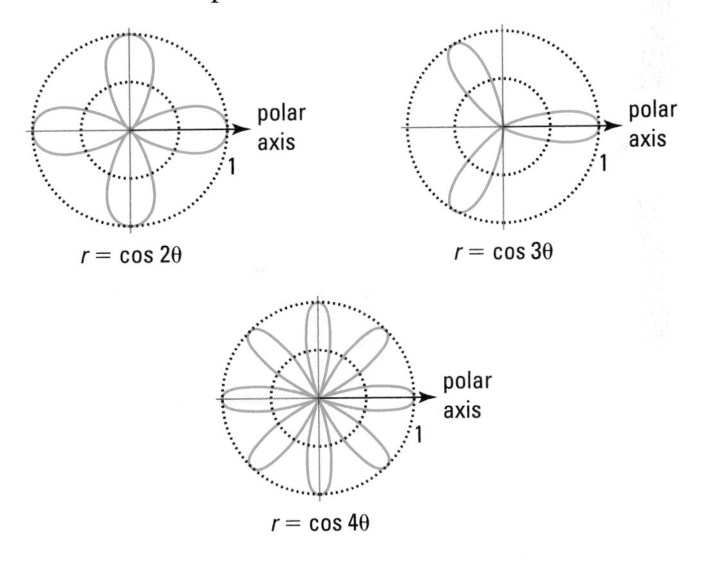

Lastly, complex numbers are graphed in both the rectangular and polar coordinate systems. Operations with complex numbers can be expressed simply and elegantly in these systems, and the trigonometric functions play a major role.

LESSON

13-1

The Secant, Cosecant, and Cotangent Functions

Three More Trigonometric Functions

The definition of tan θ is in terms of sin θ and cos θ, namely $\tan\theta = \frac{\sin\theta}{\cos\theta}$. Three other common circular functions, *secant*, *cosecant*, and *cotangent*, can also be defined in terms of the sine and cosine. As with the definition of tangent, division by zero must be avoided.

Definitions

Let θ be any real number. Then

secant of θ = **sec** $\theta = \frac{1}{\cos\theta}$, for $\cos\theta \neq 0$;

cosecant of θ = **csc** $\theta = \frac{1}{\sin\theta}$, for $\sin\theta \neq 0$;

cotangent of θ = **cot** $\theta = \frac{\cos\theta}{\sin\theta}$, for $\sin\theta \neq 0$.

Notice that $\frac{\cos\theta}{\sin\theta} = \frac{1}{\frac{\sin\theta}{\cos\theta}}$, except when $\sin\theta = 0$ or $\cos\theta = 0$. So $\cot\theta = \frac{1}{\tan\theta}$ except when $\cos\theta = 0$ or $\tan\theta = 0$. Because each of the secant, cosecant, and cotangent functions can be expressed as the reciprocal of a parent trigonometric function, these functions are sometimes called **reciprocal trigonometric functions**.

Example 1

a. Find $\sec\frac{7\pi}{6}$ exactly.

b. Find $\sec\frac{7\pi}{6}$ approximately, using a calculator.

Solution

a. By definition of secant,

$$\sec\frac{7\pi}{6} = \frac{1}{\cos\frac{7\pi}{6}} = \frac{1}{-\frac{\sqrt{3}}{2}} = \frac{-2}{\sqrt{3}} = \frac{-2\sqrt{3}}{3}.$$

b. There is no [sec] key on most calculators. So you need to use the reciprocal key, [1/x]. On some calculators you may use the key sequence (in radian mode) 7 [×] [π] [÷] 6 [=] [cos] [1/x]. On others, use [cos] 7 [×] [π] [÷] 6 [ENTER] [x^{-1}] [ENTER]. Either sequence leads to the display ≈ **-1.1547005 ...** .

Check

$\frac{-2\sqrt{3}}{3} \approx -1.1547005...$, so it checks.

Using the Reciprocal Functions in Right Triangles

For values of θ between 0 and $\frac{\pi}{2}$, values of the reciprocal trigonometric functions can be expressed in terms of the sides of a right triangle.

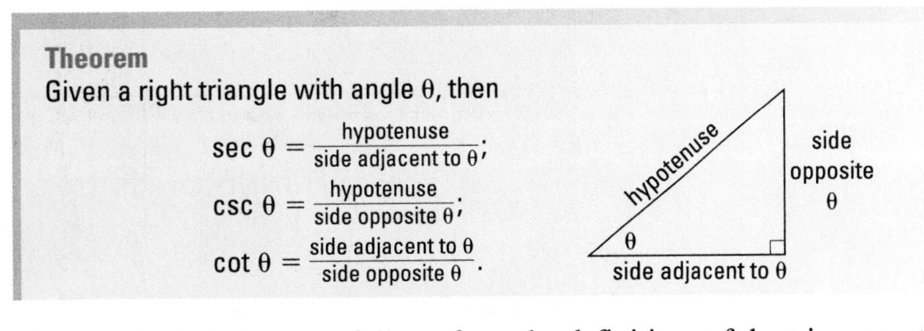

Theorem

Given a right triangle with angle θ, then

$$\sec \theta = \frac{\text{hypotenuse}}{\text{side adjacent to } \theta};$$

$$\csc \theta = \frac{\text{hypotenuse}}{\text{side opposite } \theta};$$

$$\cot \theta = \frac{\text{side adjacent to } \theta}{\text{side opposite } \theta}.$$

The proof of this theorem follows from the definitions of the trigonometric ratios given in Lesson 5-1 and the property that $\frac{1}{\frac{a}{b}} = \frac{b}{a}$.

Example 2

A safe angle for a fire ladder is 65° to the ground. To the nearest foot, how long must the ladder be to reach 19 feet up the side of a building?

Solution

In the diagram, the side opposite the 65° angle is known and the hypotenuse is unknown. Use the cosecant ratio.

$$\csc 65° = \frac{d}{19}$$

$$d = 19 \csc 65°$$

Set a calculator to degree mode. On some calculators you may use the key sequence 19 [×] [(] 65 [sin] [1/x] [)] [=], which displays 20.9642. The ladder needs to be about 21 feet long.

Check

Check using the sine ratio. Is $\frac{19}{21} \approx \sin 65°$? Yes, because $\frac{19}{21} \approx .905$ and $\sin 65° \approx .906$.

Graphs of the Reciprocal Functions

Because the expressions $\sec \theta$ and $\cos \theta$ are reciprocals, you can use the properties of the cosine function to determine characteristics of the secant function. These characteristics enable you to graph the function $y = \sec x$.

Function Properties	Graph Properties
When $\cos x$ is positive, $\sec x$ is positive. When $\cos x$ is negative, $\sec x$ is negative.	For a given value of x, the graphs of $y = \cos x$ and $y = \sec x$ are on the same side of the x-axis.
When $\cos x = 0$, $\sec x$ is undefined.	If $\cos k = 0$, then there is a vertical asymptote of $y = \sec x$ at $x = k$.
Because $\|\cos x\| \le 1$ for all x, $\|\sec x\| \ge 1$ for all x. The smaller $\|\cos x\|$ is, the larger $\|\sec x\|$ is.	The closer the graph of $y = \cos x$ is to the x-axis, the farther the graph of $y = \sec x$ is.
$\sec x = \cos x$ when $\cos x = \pm 1$.	The graphs intersect when $\cos x = \pm 1$.

These properties are exhibited in the graphs below. The graph of $y = \cos x$ is in blue; the graph of $y = \sec x$ is in orange.

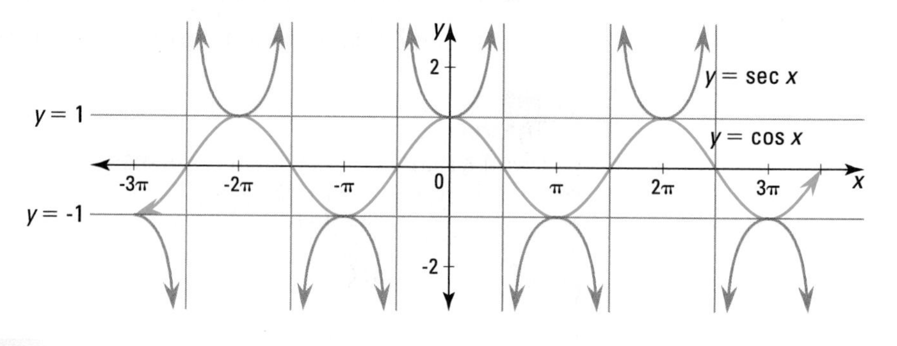

Example 3

Consider the function with equation $y = \sec x$.

a. Identify its domain and range.

b. Find its period.

c. Identify any minimum or maximum values.

Solution

a. The domain consists of all real numbers except $x = \frac{\pi}{2} + n\pi$, for any integer n. From both the definition and the graph above, you can see that the range is $\{y: y \leq -1 \text{ or } y \geq 1\}$.

b. The period of $y = \cos x$ is 2π. The graph of $y = \sec x$ also has period 2π.

c. There are no maximum or minimum values of $\sec x$. However, 1 is a relative minimum and -1 is a relative maximum of the secant function.

In the Questions, you are asked to analyze the graph of $y = \csc x$ in relation to the graph of $y = \sin x$.

The graph of $y = \cot x$ is shown below in orange. It is a reflection image, over any vertical line with equation $x = \frac{\pi}{4} + n\pi$ where n is an integer, of the graph of $y = \tan x$, which is drawn in blue.

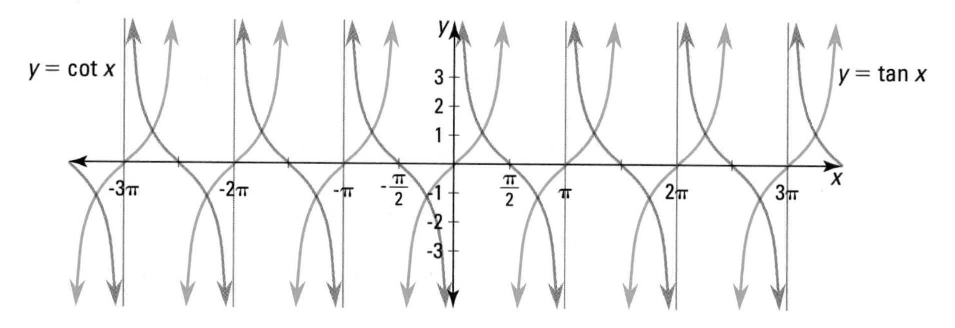

QUESTIONS

Covering the Reading

1. Find the exact value of each.
a. csc 45° **b.** sec 45° **c.** cot 45°

In 2–7, evaluate without using a calculator.

2. csc 90° **3.** sec 150° **4.** cot (-135°)

5. $\sec\left(-\frac{11\pi}{6}\right)$ **6.** $\cot \frac{17\pi}{3}$ **7.** $\csc\left(-\frac{5\pi}{2}\right)$

In 8 and 9, find x to the nearest tenth in two ways. **a.** Use a reciprocal trigonometric function. **b.** Use a parent trigonometric function.

8. **9.**

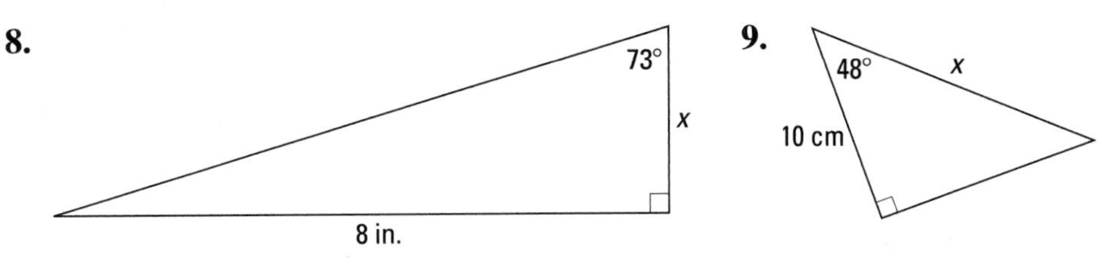

10. *Multiple choice.* The base of a ladder is placed so that it makes an angle of 56° with the ground. If it reaches 40 ft up the side of a building, how long must the ladder be?
(a) 40 sin 56° (b) 40 cos 56° (c) 40 sec 56° (d) 40 csc 56°

In 11 and 12, consider the function defined by the given equation on the interval $0 \le x < 2\pi$. **a.** Identify all values at which the function is undefined. **b.** Identify all x-intercepts.

11. $y = \sec x$ **12.** $y = \cot x$

Applying the Mathematics

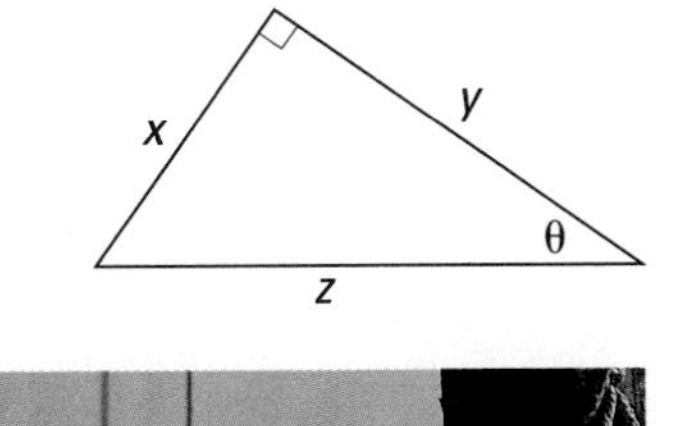

In 13–16, consider the triangle at the left. Evaluate the function in terms of x, y, and z.

13. csc θ **14.** cot θ

15. sec (90° − θ) **16.** cot (90° − θ)

17. A guy wire is attached to an electrical pole 5 feet from the top of the pole. The wire makes a 28° angle with the pole and is anchored to the ground 14 feet from the base of the pole. How tall is the pole?

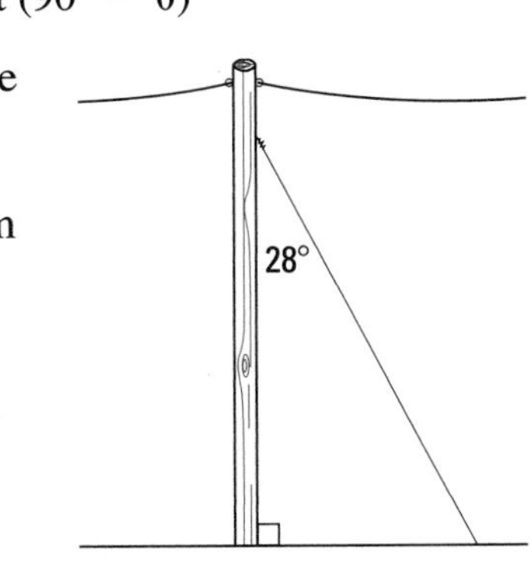

18. Let $f(x) = \sin x$ and $g(x) = \csc x$.
a. Graph both functions on the same set of axes on the interval $-2\pi \le x \le 2\pi$.
b. *True or false.* For a given value of x, the graphs of $y = f(x)$ and $y = g(x)$ are on the same side of the x-axis.
c. Give the domain and range of g.
d. State equations of all asymptotes of $y = g(x)$.
e. For what values of x between 0 and 2π does $f(x) = g(x)$?

In 19 and 20, an equation for a function is given. **a.** Sketch the graph of the function. **b.** Give the period of the function.

19. $y = \sec 6x$

20. $y = 3 \csc 2x$

21. Prove that $y = \cot x$ is an odd function.

Review

In 22 and 23, let $\cos \alpha = 0.8$ and $\sin \beta = -0.6$, where $0 < \alpha < \frac{\pi}{2}$ and $\pi < \beta < \frac{3\pi}{2}$. Evaluate. *(Lessons 4-4, 11-5, 11-6)*

22. $\cos 2\alpha$

23. $\sin (\alpha + \beta)$

24. Let $A = \begin{bmatrix} 2 & 6 & -8 \\ 4 & 0 & 1 \end{bmatrix}$ and $B = \begin{bmatrix} -3 & 2 \\ 10 & 2 \\ 1 & 1 \end{bmatrix}$. Find the product, if it exists. *(Lesson 11-1)*
a. AB
b. BA

25. What is the 99% confidence interval for a normally distributed set of data with a mean of 23.9 and a standard deviation of 2.3? *(Lesson 10-8)*

26. Tell whether the infinite series $\sum_{k=0}^{\infty} (-.25)^k 6$ is convergent or divergent. If it is convergent, give its sum. *(Lesson 8-5)*

27. Consider the equation $2 \sin^2 \theta - \sin \theta - 3 = 0$.
a. Find the solution(s) between 0 and 2π.
b. Find the general solution. *(Lesson 5-7)*

In 28 and 29, evaluate in degrees. *(Lessons 5-3, 5-6)*

28. $\tan^{-1} 1$

29. $\cos^{-1} (-0.5)$

30. a. *True or false.* The graphs of $f(x) = 6^x$ and $p(x) = x^6$ are reflection images of each other over the y-axis.
b. Use an automatic grapher to justify your answer to part **a.** *(Lesson 2-4)*

Exploration

31. Analyze the graph of $\frac{y - k}{b} = \sec \left(\frac{x - h}{a}\right)$.

LESSON

13-2

Proving Trigonometric Identities

In this lesson you will see various ways to derive and prove trigonometric identities. Although the proof techniques are illustrated using only trigonometric functions, they are applicable to any function.

Testing Whether an Equation Might Be an Identity

You have seen many instances where graphs are used to decide whether or not a particular statement is true. In particular, if you want to see whether an equation in one variable is an identity, you can consider each side of the equation as a separate function of x, and graph the two functions. If the graphs coincide, the original equation is likely to be an identity.

As an example, consider the Pythagorean Identity,

$$\cos^2 x + \sin^2 x = 1.$$

If each side of this equation is considered as a separate function of x, specifically if $f(x) = \cos^2 x + \sin^2 x$ and $g(x) = 1$, the following graphs result.

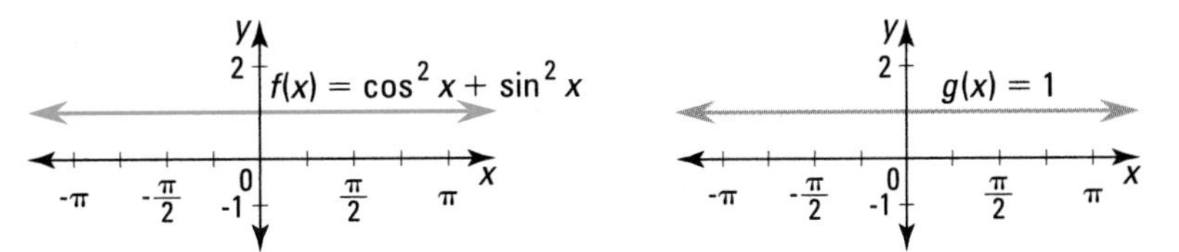

As expected, the graphs are identical. Had they been plotted on the same set of axes, the graphs would have coincided.

In contrast, the equation $(\cos x - \sin x)^2 = \cos^2 x - \sin^2 x$ is not an identity. The graphs of $f(x) = (\cos x - \sin x)^2$ and $g(x) = \cos^2 x - \sin^2 x$ are shown below. It is apparent that f and g are not the same function.

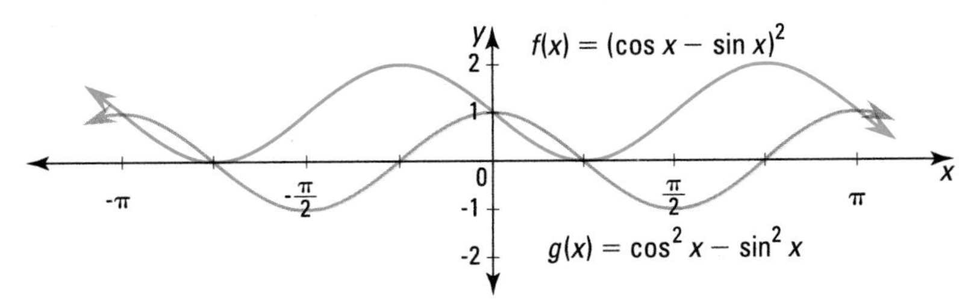

Notice that the graph of g appears to be a cosine function with amplitude 1 and period π. This suggests that an expression identically equal to $\cos^2 x - \sin^2 x$ is $\cos 2x$. This agrees with what was proved in Lesson 11-6: $\cos 2x = \cos^2 x - \sin^2 x$ for all x.

Deducing New Identities by Manipulating Expressions

Using identities you already know, you can derive new identities.

Example 1

Find an identity involving $(\cos x - \sin x)^2$.

Solution

Expand the expression.

$$(\cos x - \sin x)^2 = \cos^2 x - 2\cos x \sin x + \sin^2 x$$
$$= \cos^2 x + \sin^2 x - 2\cos x \sin x$$

Recall two identities: for all x, $\cos^2 x + \sin^2 x = 1$ and $2\cos x \sin x = \sin 2x$.

So, $(\cos x - \sin x)^2 = 1 - \sin 2x$.

Check

Graph $f(x) = (\cos x - \sin x)^2$ and $g(x) = 1 - \sin 2x$. Check that the graphs coincide. As shown below, they do.

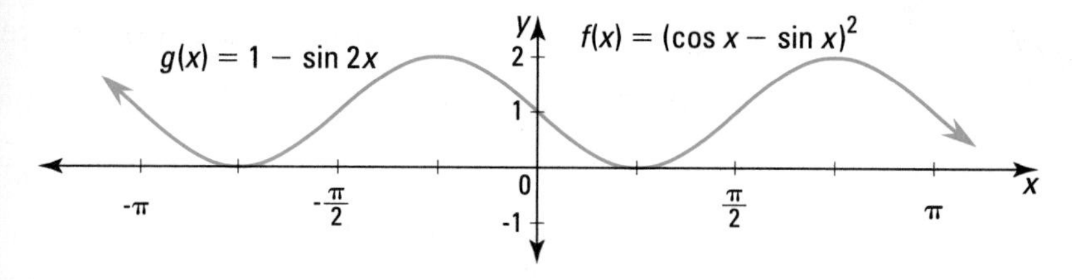

Proving Identities by Working with One Side

In Example 1, one expression was manipulated to equal a second expression. This technique can often be employed to prove that an equation is an identity. Start with one side of a proposed identity, and rewrite it using definitions, known identities, or algebraic properties, until it equals the other side.

$f(x) = 1 + \tan^2 x$

$-\frac{5\pi}{2} \le x \le \frac{5\pi}{2}$, x-scale $= \frac{\pi}{2}$
$-1 \le y \le 8$, y-scale $= 1$

$g(x) = \sec^2 x$

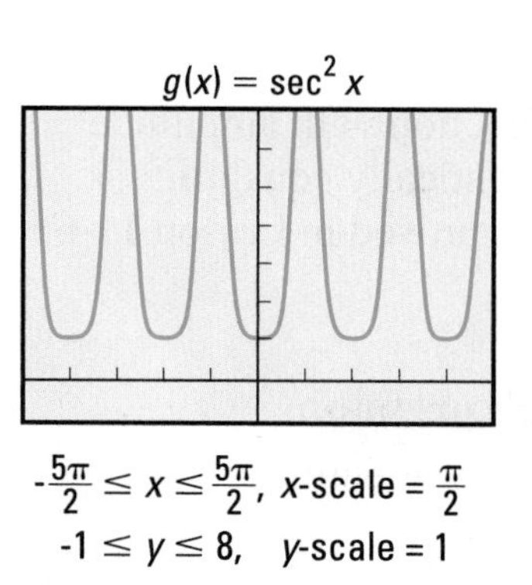

$-\frac{5\pi}{2} \le x \le \frac{5\pi}{2}$, x-scale $= \frac{\pi}{2}$
$-1 \le y \le 8$, y-scale $= 1$

Example 2

Prove that $1 + \tan^2 x = \sec^2 x$, for all x in the domains of these expressions.

Solution

Substitute into the left expression and rewrite until you get the right. For all x with $\cos x \neq 0$,

$1 + \tan^2 x = 1 + \frac{\sin^2 x}{\cos^2 x}$	Definition of tangent
$= \frac{\cos^2 x}{\cos^2 x} + \frac{\sin^2 x}{\cos^2 x}$	Forming a common denominator
$= \frac{\cos^2 x + \sin^2 x}{\cos^2 x}$	Adding fractions with a common denominator
$= \frac{1}{\cos^2 x}$	Pythagorean Identity
$= \sec^2 x.$	Definition of secant

So, $1 + \tan^2 x = \sec^2 x$ for all x in the domain of $\tan x$ and $\sec x$.

Check

Let $f(x) = 1 + \tan^2 x$ and $g(x) = \sec^2 x$. At the left, each function is shown on a separate set of axes. In practice, you should graph both on the same set of axes. Because the graphs appear to be identical, it checks.

Proving Identities by Working with Both Sides

A second proof technique is to rewrite each side of a proposed identity independently until equal expressions are obtained. When using this technique, because you cannot be sure that the proposed identity is true until you have finished, you should not write an equal sign between the two sides until the end. We draw a vertical line between the two sides as a reminder of this restriction. Thus, a proof that $A = B$ is an identity based on this technique has the following form.

$$\begin{array}{c|c} A & B \\ = \dots & = \dots \\ = \dots & = \dots \\ = E & = E \end{array}$$

So $\quad A = B.$

Example 3

Prove: For all x, $\sin\left(x + \frac{\pi}{4}\right) = \cos\left(x - \frac{\pi}{4}\right)$.

Solution

Use the Addition Identities for the sine and cosine.

$$\begin{array}{r|l} \sin\left(x + \frac{\pi}{4}\right) & \cos\left(x - \frac{\pi}{4}\right) \\ = \sin x \cos\frac{\pi}{4} + \cos x \sin\frac{\pi}{4} & = \cos x \cos\frac{\pi}{4} + \sin x \sin\frac{\pi}{4} \\ = \sin x \cdot \frac{\sqrt{2}}{2} + \cos x \cdot \frac{\sqrt{2}}{2} & = \cos x \cdot \frac{\sqrt{2}}{2} + \sin x \cdot \frac{\sqrt{2}}{2} \end{array}$$

So $\quad \sin\left(x + \frac{\pi}{4}\right) = \cos\left(x - \frac{\pi}{4}\right)$.

Deducing New Identities from Known Identities

A third proof technique is to begin with a known identity and derive statements equivalent to it until the proposed identity appears.

Example 4

Prove that $1 + \cot^2 x = \csc^2 x$ for $x \neq n\pi$, n an integer.

Solution

Begin with the Pythagorean Identity.

For all real numbers x,

$$\cos^2 x + \sin^2 x = 1.$$

$$\frac{\cos^2 x}{\sin^2 x} + \frac{\sin^2 x}{\sin^2 x} = \frac{1}{\sin^2 x}$$ Divide both sides by $\sin^2 x$. (Note that $\sin^2 x \neq 0$ when $x \neq n\pi$.)

$$\cot^2 x + 1 = \csc^2 x$$ Definitions of $\cot x$ and $\csc x$

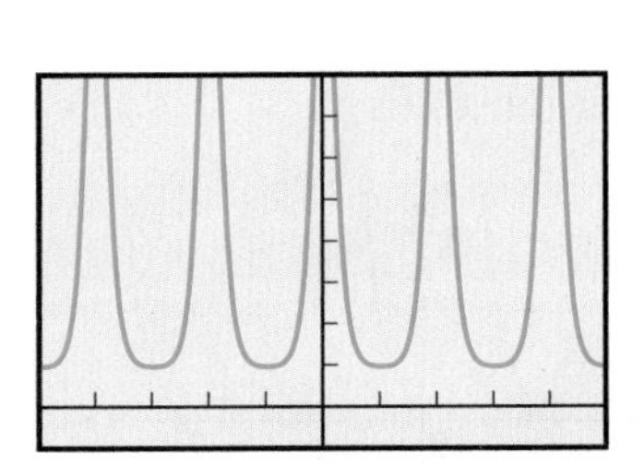

$-\frac{5\pi}{2} \leq x \leq \frac{5\pi}{2}$, x-scale $= \frac{\pi}{2}$
$-1 \leq y \leq 8$, y-scale $= 1$

Check

At the left is a graph of both $f(x) = 1 + \cot^2 x$ and $g(x) = \csc^2 x$. They appear to coincide.

As shown in the solution to Example 4, the identity $1 + \cot^2 x = \csc^2 x$ can be derived quickly from the Pythagorean Identity. Hence, it is sometimes called a *corollary* to the Pythagorean Identity. In the Questions you are asked to use this technique to show that $1 + \tan^2 x = \sec^2 x$ is also a corollary to the Pythagorean Identity.

QUESTIONS

Covering the Reading

1. *True or false.* $(\cos x - \sin x)^2 = \cos^2 x - \sin^2 x$.

2. a. Is the sentence $(\cos x + \sin x)^2 = \cos^2 x + \sin^2 x$ an identity? Justify your answer with a graph.
b. Find an expression involving a single circular function equal to $(\cos x + \sin x)^2$.

3. State three different techniques for proving that an equation is an identity.

In 4 and 5, prove the following statement using the specified technique: For all x such that $x \neq n\pi$, $1 + \cot^2 x = \csc^2 x$.

4. Use the technique of Example 2.

5. Use the technique of Example 3.

6. Show that $1 + \tan^2 x = \sec^2 x$ is a corollary to the Pythagorean Identity. That is, prove the identity $1 + \tan^2 x = \sec^2 x$, for all x such that $x \neq \frac{\pi}{2} + n\pi$, using the technique of Example 4.

Applying the Mathematics

7. Prove: For all x for which all the functions are defined, $\sin x \cdot \cos x \cdot \tan x = \frac{1}{\csc^2 x}$.

In 8 and 9, the graph of a product of trigonometric functions is drawn.
a. What identity is suggested by the graph? (Hint: The answer involves one of the six parent trigonometric functions.)
b. Prove your answer to part **a**.
c. Over what domain is the identity true?

8. $y = \cot x \sec x$

9. $y = \sec x \tan x \cos x$

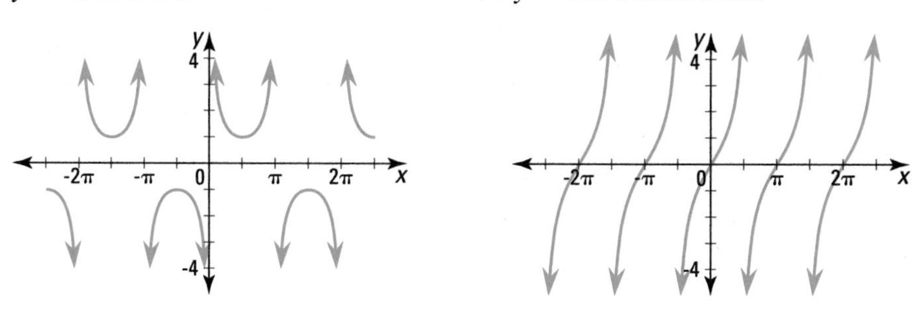

In 10–13, a trigonometric equation is given. **a.** Use an automatic grapher to test whether the equation may be an identity. **b.** Prove the identity or give a counterexample.

10. $\cos x = -\cos(\pi - x)$

11. $\sin 3x = 3 \sin x \cos x$

12. $\frac{\csc x}{\sec x} = \cot x.$

13. $\tan^2 x \cos^2 x = 1 - \cos^2 x$

14. Let θ be in the interval $270° < \theta < 360°$, and $\tan \theta = -\frac{3}{8}$. Use the Pythagorean Identity or one of its corollaries to find the following.
a. $\cot \theta$ **b.** $\sec \theta$ **c.** $\sin \theta$

15. Prove: For all x, $\cos^4 x + \sin^2 x = \sin^4 x + \cos^2 x$.

In 16 and 17, use the techniques in this lesson to test whether the statement is or is not an identity. Justify your answer.

16. $x^3 + x^4 = x^7$

17. $\log x^3 + \log x^4 = \log x^7$

Review

In 18 and 19, let $\triangle ABC$ be a right triangle with right angle C. Express each function in terms of the side a, b, or c. *(Lesson 13-1)*

18. $\csc A$

19. $\cot B$

20. a. Write the first six terms of the sequence *(Lesson 8-1)*

$$\begin{cases} a_1 = 1 \\ a_n = 2a_{n-1} + 1. \end{cases}$$

b. Tell whether the sequence is arithmetic, geometric, or neither.

In 21 and 22, evaluate in radians. *(Lessons 5-5, 5-6)*

21. $\sin^{-1}(-1)$

22. $\tan^{-1}(\sqrt{3})$

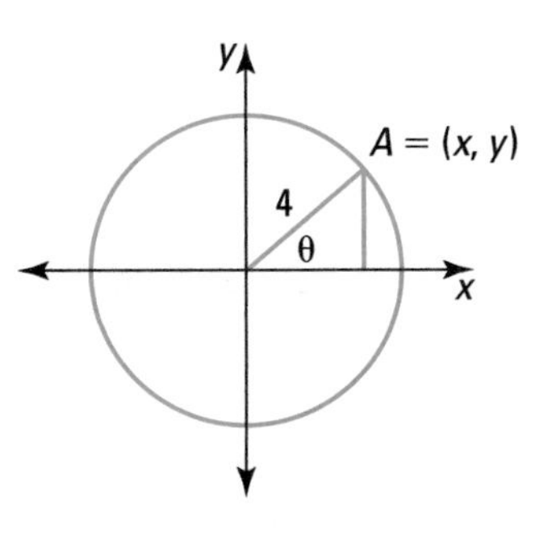

23. A is a point on a circle of radius 4, as shown at the left. Give the coordinates of A in terms of θ. *(Lesson 4-3)*

24. If a sector of a circle has a central angle of $\frac{\pi}{8}$ and an area of 5π square inches, what is the radius of the circle? *(Lesson 4-2)*

Exploration

25. Refer to Questions 8 and 9.
a. Find another pair of parent functions whose product seems to be a parent function, and prove the identity.
b. Find another set of three parent functions whose product seems to be another parent function, and prove the identity.

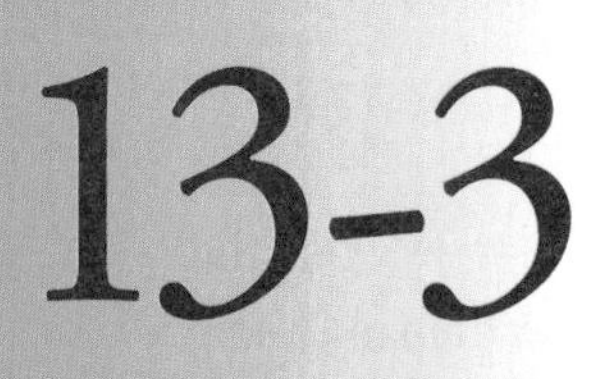

LESSON 13-3

Restrictions on Identities

Restrictions on the Domains of the Trigonometric Functions

Only two of the parent trigonometric functions—the sine and cosine—are defined for all real numbers. The others have the following restrictions on their domains.

Function	Not defined when $x =$	
tan	$\frac{\pi}{2} + n\pi$	n an integer
cot	$n\pi$	
sec	$\frac{\pi}{2} + n\pi$	
csc	$n\pi$	

Recall that an identity is a statement that is true for *all* values of a variable in a particular domain. In general, when trying to prove an identity you should consider the largest domain on which all the relevant functions are defined. Thus, the identity $1 + \cot^2 x = \csc^2 x$ is true for all real numbers x except where $\cot x$ and $\csc x$ are not defined. That is, $1 + \cot^2 x = \csc^2 x$ for all real numbers x except when $x = n\pi$, where n is an integer.

What Is a Singularity?

An isolated value for which a function is undefined is called a **singularity**. The singularities of the parent tangent, cotangent, secant, and cosecant functions are signaled graphically by vertical asymptotes. For instance, when n is an integer and $x = n\pi$, x is a singularity of $f(x) = \cot x$ and the lines with equations $x = n\pi$ are vertical asymptotes of the graph of $\cot x$. Singularities of other functions may not be represented by asymptotes, and may not be obvious on a graph. Thus, when using an automatic grapher to test a potential identity, you need to consider the restrictions on the domain.

Example 1

Consider the equation $\cos x \tan x = \sin x$. Use an automatic grapher to test whether or not the equation seems to be an identity. If it seems to be, prove the identity over the largest possible domain.

Solution

The graphs of $f(x) = \cos x \tan x$ and $g(x) = \sin x$, as they appear on one automatic grapher, are shown at the right. It appears that the graphs coincide, so an algebraic proof of the identity is worth pursuing. Rewrite the left side.

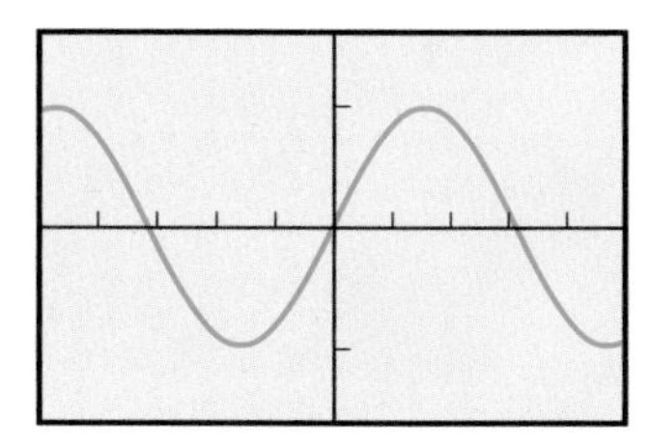

$-5 \le x \le 5$, x-scale = 1
$-2 \le y \le 2$, y-scale = 1

$$\cos x \tan x = \cos x \cdot \frac{\sin x}{\cos x} = \sin x$$

Notice that the tangent function is defined only when $\cos x \neq 0$.

So $\cos x \tan x = \sin x$ for all x except when $x = \frac{\pi}{2} + n\pi$, n an integer.

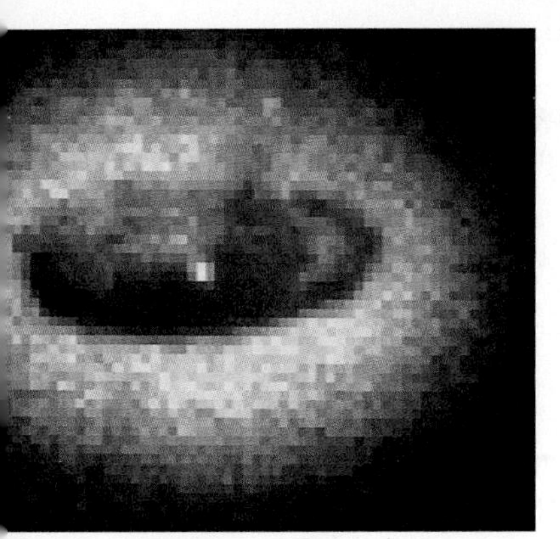

Nonremovable Singularity. *Because of its special properties, the center of a black hole is called a singularity. The bright point at the center of this image of a galaxy is theorized to be the final flare of heated matter as it disappears into a black hole.*

Removable Singularities

Notice that although the graph in Example 1 suggested that $\cos x \tan x = \sin x$ is an identity for all x, it is an identity only when $\tan x$ is defined. Geometrically, you can think of the singularities of the function $f(x) = \cos x \tan x$ as signaling "holes" in the graph of $f(x) = \sin x$ at the points where x is an odd multiple of $\frac{\pi}{2}$. A singularity of this type, where the break in the graph can be "removed" by adding a single point, is called a **removable singularity**. On some automatic graphers, if you plot $f(x) = \cos x \tan x$ and repeatedly zoom in around the point $\left(\frac{\pi}{2}, 1\right)$, you may eventually see a small hole in the graph. Try this with your technology.

Example 2 also involves an identity on a restricted domain.

Example 2

Consider the statement $\sin 2\theta = \frac{2 \cot \theta}{1 + \cot^2 \theta}$.

a. Determine any restrictions on the domain.

b. Prove the statement over the restricted domain in part **a**.

Solution

a. Singularities occur where $\cot \theta$ is undefined, so $\theta \neq n\pi$, for n an integer. Since $1 + \cot^2 \theta > 0$ for all θ, there are no other restrictions due to the denominator of the fraction.

b. Rewrite both sides of the equation until equivalent expressions remain. (In the Questions, you are asked to give justifications for each step, so they are numbered here.)

	$\sin 2\theta$	$\frac{2 \cot \theta}{1 + \cot^2 \theta}$	
1.	$= 2 \sin \theta \cos \theta$	$= \frac{2 \cot \theta}{\csc^2 \theta}$	2.
		$= \frac{\frac{2 \cos \theta}{\sin \theta}}{\frac{1}{\sin^2 \theta}}$	3.
		$= 2 \sin \theta \cos \theta$	4.

So $\sin 2\theta = \frac{2 \cot \theta}{1 + \cot^2 \theta}$ for all $\theta \neq n\pi$.

QUESTIONS

Covering the Reading

1. What is a *singularity* of a function?

In 2 and 3, identify any singularities of the function described.

2. $f(x) = \cot x$

3. $g(x) = \cos x \tan x$

4. *True or false.* All singularities of functions are signaled by asymptotes.

5. Give a justification for each numbered step in Example 2.

In 6–9, a trigonometric equation is given. **a.** Use an automatic grapher to test whether the equation may be an identity. **b.** If the equation is an identity, prove it and give its domain.

6. $\sin x \cot x = \cos x$

7. $\sec x = \tan x \csc x$

8. $\csc x = \frac{\tan x}{\sec x}$

9. $\sin 2x = \frac{2 \tan x}{1 + \tan^2 x}$

Applying the Mathematics

In 10 and 11, an equation for a function is given. **a.** Graph the function. **b.** Identify its domain. **c.** Propose an identity based on this graph. **d.** Prove the identity.

10. $f(x) = \frac{1 - \tan^2 x}{1 + \tan^2 x}$

11. $g(x) = \frac{1 + \cos 2x}{\sin 2x}$

In 12 and 13, a trigonometric equation is given. **a.** State any restrictions on the domain of the proposed identity. **b.** Prove or disprove the proposed identity over the domain you state in part **a**.

12. $\tan x + \cot x = \sec x \csc x$

13. $\csc^2 x \sin x = \frac{\sec^2 x - \tan^2 x}{\sin x}$

14. **a.** Graph $f(x) = \frac{x^2 - x - 12}{x - 4}$ and $g(x) = x + 3$ on the same set of axes.
   b. Find the singularity in the graph of $y = f(x)$.
   c. What is the domain for the identity $\frac{x^2 - x - 12}{x - 4} = x + 3$?
   d. Prove the identity.

Review

15. Suppose α is in the interval $\frac{\pi}{2} < \alpha < \pi$, and $\cot \alpha = -4$. Determine each of the following. *(Lessons 11-6, 13-1, 13-2)*
   a. $\csc \alpha$ **b.** $\sin \alpha$ **c.** $\sin 2\alpha$

16. Suppose $\frac{x^2}{16} - \frac{y^2}{9} = 1$ and $\frac{x^2}{16} + \frac{y^2}{9} = 1$.
   a. Solve this system graphically.
   b. Solve this system algebraically. *(Lessons 12-2, 12-3)*

17. *True or false.* The matrix $\begin{bmatrix} 1 & 0 \\ 0 & 1 \end{bmatrix}$ does not have an inverse. *(Lesson 11-7)*

18. Find the number z such that 75% of the area under the standard normal curve lies between $-z$ and z. *(Lesson 10-5)*

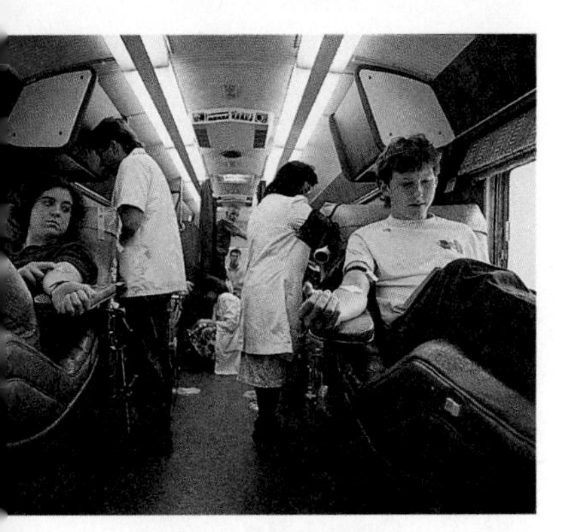

Gift of Life. *About 14 million pints of blood are donated each year in the U.S. These college students are donating blood in a bloodmobile.*

In 19 and 20, consider the ELISA test, which was introduced in the mid-1980s to screen donated blood for the presence of antibodies to the AIDS virus. *(Lessons 10-1, 10-2, 10-6)*

19. When presented with AIDS-contaminated blood, ELISA gives a positive response in about 98% of all cases. Suppose that among the blood that passes through a blood bank in a year there are 25 units containing AIDS antibodies.
a. What is the probability that ELISA will detect all 25 of these units?
b. What is the probability that more than 2 of the 25 contaminated units will escape detection?
c. What is the mean number of units among the 25 that will be detected by ELISA?
d. What is the standard deviation of the number detected?

20. ELISA claims that AIDS antibodies are present in uncontaminated blood about 7% of the time. Such a result is called a *false positive*. Suppose a blood bank contains 20,000 units of blood.
a. What is the expected number of false positives among this group?
b. What is the standard deviation of the number of false positives?

21. Consider the row of Pascal's Triangle that begins with 1, 12, ...
a. What is the next entry in the row?
b. What is the sum of all the numbers in the row? *(Lesson 8-7)*

In 22 and 23, solve to the nearest tenth. *(Lessons 6-6, 6-7)*

22. $2 = (1.07)^{y/100}$

23. $100 = 12.2 \ln t + 4.8$

24. Solve the equation $\tan \theta = 2.5$ on the given domain. *(Lesson 5-7)*
a. $\{\theta: -\frac{\pi}{2} \leq \theta \leq \frac{\pi}{2}\}$
b. $\{\theta: 0 \leq \theta \leq 2\pi\}$
c. the set of all real numbers

Exploration

25. The sentence $\sqrt{x^2 - 1} = x - \frac{1}{2x}$ is not an identity for $x \geq 1$. In fact, the expressions on the two sides never have the same value.
a. Evaluate the two expressions in the sentence at $x = 1$, $x = 5$, $x = 9$, and $x = 10$ to support the preceding claims.
b. Notice that the two expressions $\sqrt{x^2 - 1}$ and $x - \frac{1}{2x}$ have closer and closer values as x gets bigger. Use an automatic grapher to determine the values of x for which $\sqrt{x^2 - 1}$ is within .01 of $x - \frac{1}{2x}$.

LESSON

13-4

Polar Coordinates

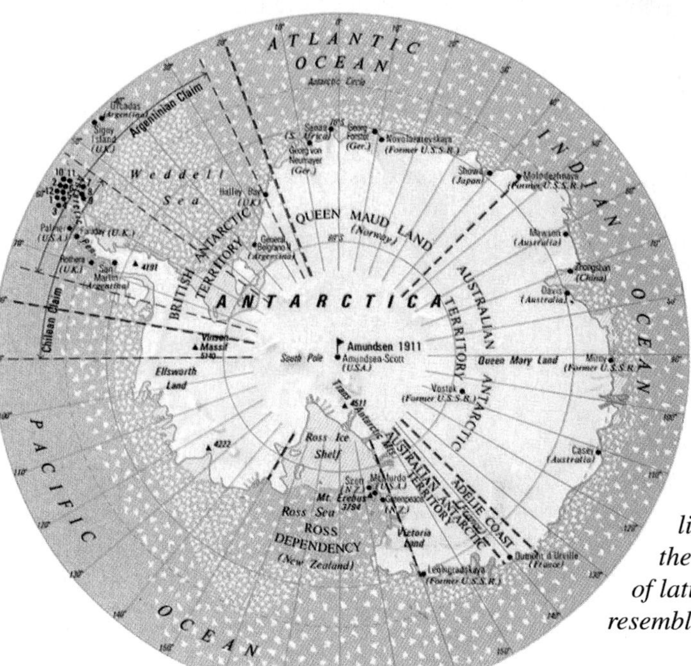

Don't Be Square. *On this map of Antarctica, the rays emanating from the pole are lines of longitude; the circles are lines of latitude. The grid resembles a polar grid.*

The rectangular coordinate system that you have been using for many years dates back to the early 1600s, when René Descartes and Pierre de Fermat worked to develop analytic geometry. Later in that same century, other mathematicians, notably Isaac Newton and Jakob Bernoulli, introduced other coordinate systems. This lesson introduces you to the system of *polar coordinates*.

The Polar Coordinate System

Recall that in a rectangular coordinate system, every point in the plane can be identified by a unique ordered pair of numbers (x, y) representing the point's distances and direction from two perpendicular axes. In a **polar coordinate system**, a pair of numbers $[r, \theta]$ again represent a unique point. Square brackets [,] are used to distinguish polar coordinates from rectangular coordinates. Here r or $-r$ is a distance, but θ is a magnitude of rotation measured in degrees or radians.

To construct a polar coordinate system, first select a point O as the **pole** of the system. Then select any line through O as the **polar axis**. Usually the polar axis is drawn horizontally as shown below. Coordinatize this line so O has coordinate 0. Any point P has **polar coordinates $[r, \theta]$** if and only if P is the image, under a rotation θ about the pole O, of the point on the polar axis with coordinate r. Below it seems as if $P = [4, 40°]$.

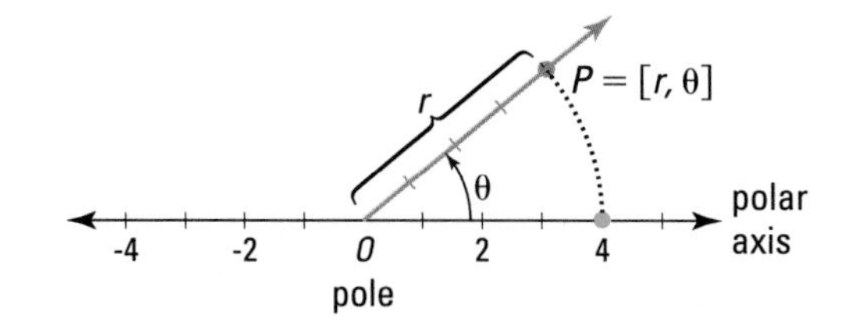

Example 1

Plot each point $[r, \theta]$, where θ is in radians.

a. $\left[2, \frac{\pi}{3}\right]$ **b.** $\left[1.4, -\frac{\pi}{2}\right]$ **c.** $\left[-2, \frac{7\pi}{5}\right]$

Solution

a. Rotate the point on the polar axis with coordinate 2 counterclockwise by $\frac{\pi}{3}$ radians.

b. Rotate the point on the polar axis with coordinate 1.4 clockwise by $\frac{\pi}{2}$ radians.

c. Rotate the point on the polar axis with coordinate -2 counterclockwise by $\frac{7\pi}{5}$ radians.

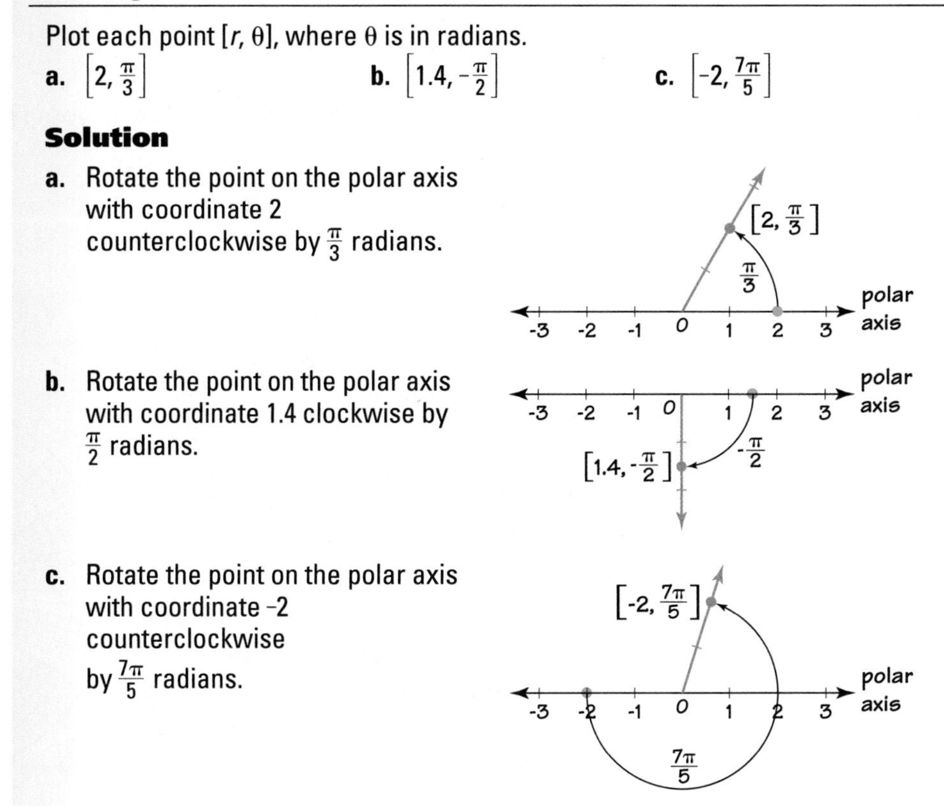

Every Point Has Many Polar Coordinates

A particular ordered pair $[r, \theta]$ identifies a unique point in the polar plane. However, there are an infinite number of polar coordinates for any given point. Example 2 illustrates how some of those pairs of coordinates can be found.

Example 2

Give four different polar coordinate pairs for the point *A* graphed at the right.

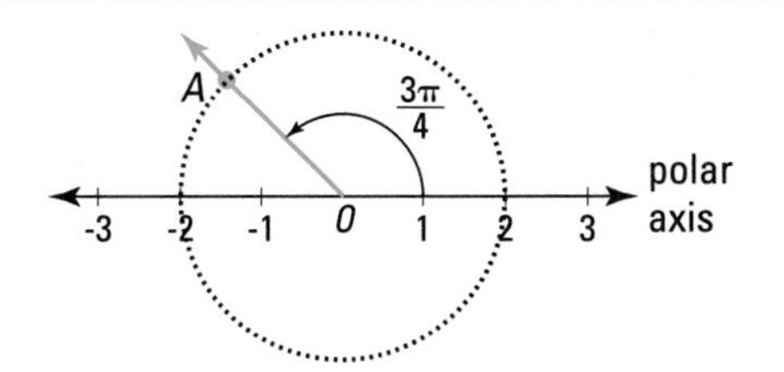

Solution

There are an infinite number of answers. One of them is $\left[2, \frac{3\pi}{4}\right]$ because *A* is the image of the point on the polar axis with coordinate 2 under a rotation of $\frac{3\pi}{4}$ radians. Rotating *A* another 2π yields $\left[2, \frac{11\pi}{4}\right]$. Point *A* can also be considered as the image of the point -2 on the polar axis under a rotation of either $-\frac{\pi}{4}$ or $\frac{7\pi}{4}$, so $\left[-2, -\frac{\pi}{4}\right]$ and $\left[-2, \frac{7\pi}{4}\right]$ also are polar coordinates for it.

The following theorem summarizes the possible polar coordinates for a point in the plane.

Theorem

For any particular values of r and θ, the following polar coordinate pairs name the same point.

a. $[r, \theta]$

b. $[r, \theta + 2\pi n]$, for all integers n

c. $[-r, \theta + (2n + 1)\pi]$, for all integers n

The Polar Grid

Polar coordinate graph paper, with grids like the *polar grid* pictured at the right, is very helpful for plotting points and sketching curves in the polar plane. Each of the concentric circles in the grid represents a value of r, and each ray from the pole represents a value of θ.

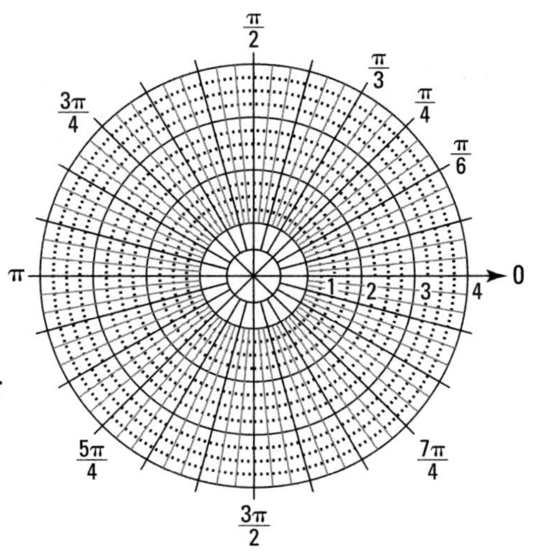

When plotting polar coordinates, you should identify the positive polar axis with an arrow and put a scale on it to indicate values of r.

Example 3

a. Sketch all solutions $[r, \theta]$ to the equation $r = 3$;

b. Sketch all solutions $[r, \theta]$ to the equation $\theta = -\frac{\pi}{3}$.

Solution

a. The equation $r = 3$ describes all points 3 units from the pole. The graph is a circle of radius 3 centered at the pole. This circle is drawn in blue at the right.

b. $\theta = -\frac{\pi}{3}$ is the line obtained by rotating the polar axis by $-\frac{\pi}{3}$. This line is drawn in orange at the right.

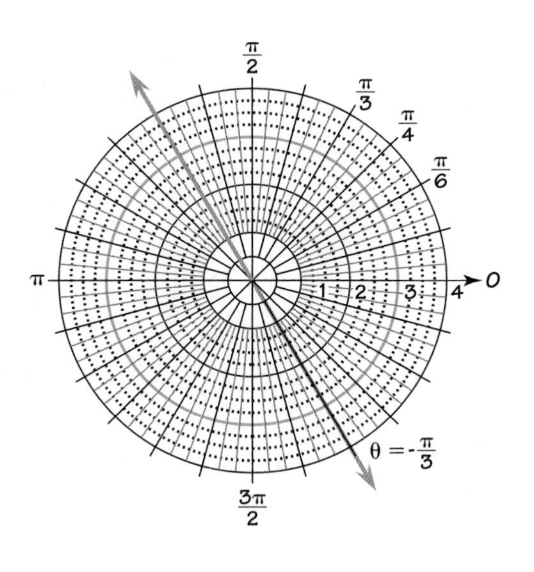

Converting from Polar to Rectangular Coordinates

Often polar and rectangular coordinate systems are superimposed on the same plane. Then the polar axis coincides with the x-axis and the pole is the origin. When this is done, you can use trigonometry to find the unique rectangular coordinate representation for any point for which polar coordinates are known.

Consider the diagram at the right. When the point on the polar axis with coordinate 1 is rotated θ about the origin, the rectangular coordinates of its image are $(\cos\theta, \sin\theta)$. A size change of magnitude r maps this image onto $(r\cos\theta, r\sin\theta)$. But this final image has polar coordinates $[r, \theta]$.

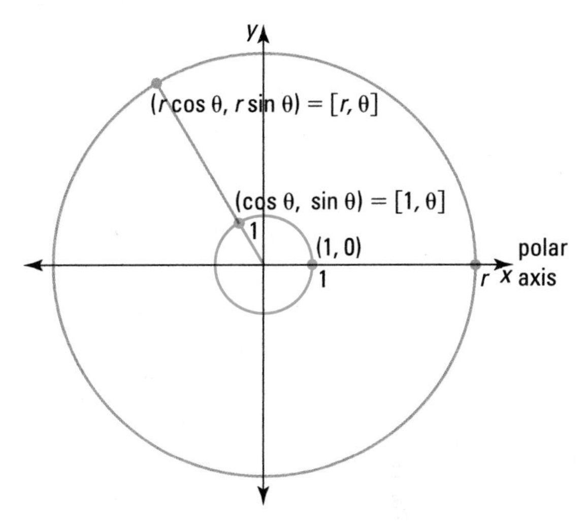

This proves the following theorem, which is true even when $r = 0$.

> **Theorem**
> If P has polar coordinates $[r, \theta]$, then the rectangular coordinates (x, y) of P are given by $x = r\cos\theta$ and $y = r\sin\theta$.

Example 4

Find the rectangular coordinates for the point with polar coordinates [4, 300°].

Solution

By the preceding theorem, the coordinates are $x = 4\cos 300°$ and $y = 4\sin 300°$. So

$$(x, y) = \left(4 \cdot \frac{1}{2}, 4 \cdot -\frac{\sqrt{3}}{2}\right)$$
$$= (2, -2\sqrt{3}).$$

Check

Use a graph. Both [4, 300°] and $(2, -2\sqrt{3})$ are in the 4th quadrant, and the points agree.

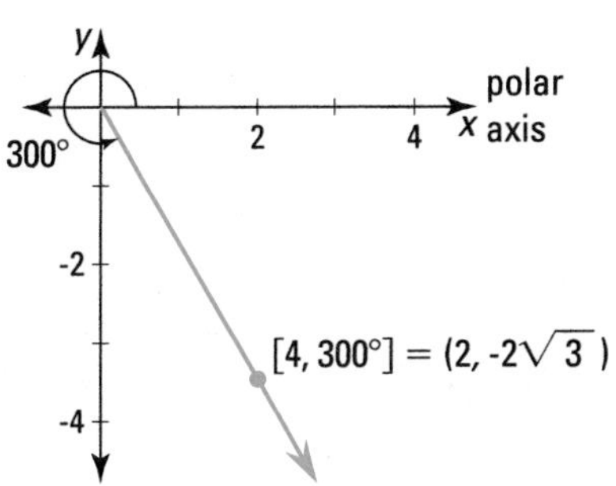

Converting from Rectangular to Polar Coordinates

Converting from rectangular coordinates to polar coordinates is a little trickier. Suppose a point has polar coordinates $[r, \theta]$ and rectangular coordinates (x, y). Squaring and adding the equations in the theorem on page 823,

$$\begin{aligned} x^2 + y^2 &= r^2\cos^2\theta + r^2\sin^2\theta \\ &= r^2(\cos^2\theta + \sin^2\theta) \\ &= r^2. \end{aligned}$$

So $$|r| = \sqrt{x^2 + y^2},$$

or $$r = \pm\sqrt{x^2 + y^2}.$$

To find θ, again use the theorem on page 823. Start with $x = r\cos\theta$ and $y = r\sin\theta$. If $x \neq 0$, then you can divide the second equation by the first.

$$\frac{y}{x} = \frac{r\sin\theta}{r\cos\theta} = \tan\theta.$$

Notice that r may be positive or negative and that there are infinitely many values of θ for which $\tan\theta = \frac{y}{x}$. These correspond to the infinitely many polar coordinates which exist for any given point.

If $x = 0$, then $r\cos\theta = 0$ and the point (x, y) lies on the y-axis. If $(x, y) = (0, 0)$, so that (x, y) is the origin, then $r = \sqrt{0^2 + 0^2} = 0$. In this case, θ can have any value. Otherwise when $(x, y) = (0, y)$ with $y \neq 0$, then $r = \sqrt{0^2 + y^2} = \pm y$ and it must be that $\cos\theta = 0$. So $\theta = \pm\frac{\pi}{2}$. In this case you can pick either the positive or negative value for r and then determine whether θ is positive or negative.

Example 5

Find two different sets of polar coordinates for the point whose rectangular coordinates are (-2, -5).

Solution

Plot the point and draw a triangle.

$$r^2 = 5^2 + 2^2$$

So $$r = \pm\sqrt{5^2 + 2^2}$$
$$= \pm\sqrt{29}.$$

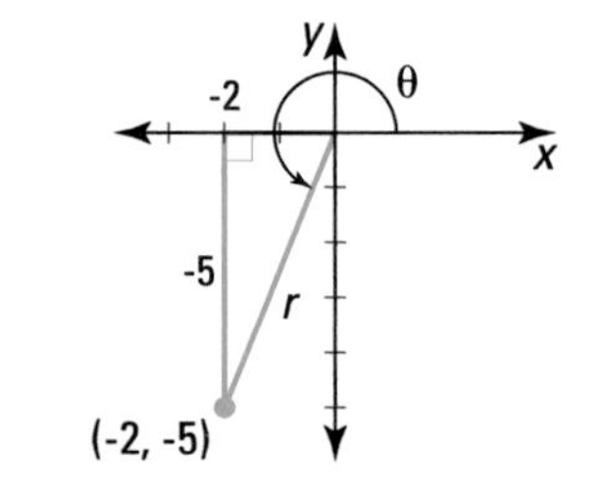

Also $\tan\theta = \frac{-5}{-2} = 2.5$. So one value of θ is $\tan^{-1} 2.5 \approx 68°$.

Thus $\theta \approx 68° \pm n \cdot 180°$. Now the choice of particular values of θ and r depend on matching the angle to the quadrant. If you use $r = \sqrt{29}$, then because (-2, -5) is in the third quadrant, a value of θ that can be used is $68° + 180° = 248°$. So one set of polar coordinates for (-2, -5) is about $[\sqrt{29}, 248°]$. If the value $-\sqrt{29}$ for r is used, the pair $[-\sqrt{29}, 68°]$ is another set of polar coordinates for this point.

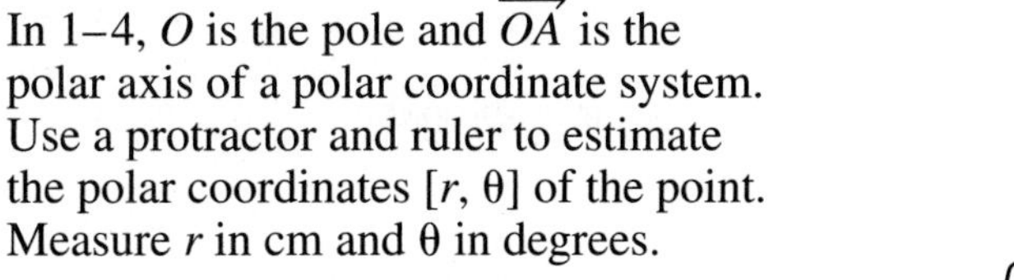

QUESTIONS

Covering the Reading

In 1–4, O is the pole and $\overrightarrow{OA}$ is the polar axis of a polar coordinate system. Use a protractor and ruler to estimate the polar coordinates $[r, \theta]$ of the point. Measure r in cm and θ in degrees.

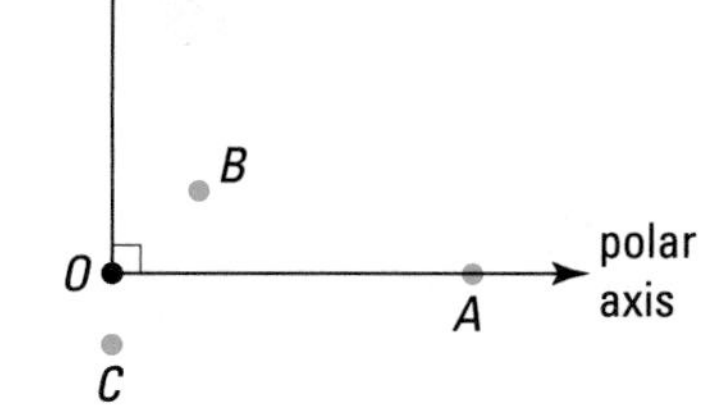

1. A **2.** B

3. C **4.** D

5. Plot all the points on the same polar grid.

a. $P = \left[1, \frac{\pi}{2}\right]$ **b.** $Q = \left[-1, \frac{\pi}{4}\right]$ **c.** $R = \left[3.25, -\frac{5\pi}{6}\right]$ **d.** $S = [-4, -75°]$

6. Suppose $P = \left[4, \frac{5\pi}{6}\right]$.

a. Give another set of polar coordinates for P with $r = 4$, $\theta \neq \frac{5\pi}{6}$.
b. Give another set of polar coordinates for P with $r = -4$.

7. *Multiple choice.* Which polar coordinates do not identify the same point as $[6, -40°]$?
(a) $[6, 320°]$ (b) $[6, -400°]$ (c) $[-6, 40°]$ (d) $[-6, 140°]$

8. On the same polar grid sketch all solutions to the following equations.

a. $r = 5$ **b.** $\theta = \frac{5\pi}{6}$

In 9 and 10, suppose (x, y) in a rectangular coordinate system names the same point as $[r, \theta]$ in a polar coordinate system. *True or false.*

9. $x = r \cos \theta$ **10.** $|r| = \sqrt{x^2 + y^2}$

In 11 and 12, find the rectangular coordinates for the point P whose polar coordinates are given.

11. $\left[10, \frac{3\pi}{2}\right]$ **12.** $[8, -60°]$

In 13 and 14, give one pair of polar coordinates for the (x, y) pair.

13. $(5, 5\sqrt{3})$ **14.** $(-6, -8)$

Applying the Mathematics

15. The point $[r, \theta]$ has $r = 8$. On what geometric figure must this point lie?

16. The point $[r, \theta]$ has $\theta = \frac{3\pi}{4}$ radians. On what geometric figure must this point lie?

In 17 and 18, consider the point $P = \left[6, \frac{\pi}{3}\right]$. State one pair of polar coordinates for the image of P under the given transformation.

17. reflection over the polar axis **18.** reflection over the line $\theta = \frac{\pi}{2}$

19. Airport runways are often numbered in a way that is related to polar coordinates. If you land from the north, you see a runway numbered 0. If you land from the west, you see a runway numbered 9. Each additional unit corresponds to 10° counterclockwise, the highest being 35. From what direction do you land on a runway with the given number?
a. 18 **b.** 1 **c.** 22 **d.** 16

20. a. Plot on polar graph paper.

r	0	$\frac{1}{2}(\sqrt{6}-\sqrt{2})$	1	$\sqrt{2}$	$\sqrt{3}$	$\frac{1}{2}(\sqrt{2}+\sqrt{6})$	2
$\theta°$	0	15	30	45	60	75	90

b. The points above all satisfy the equation $r = 2 \sin \theta$. Let $\theta = 105°, 120°, \ldots$, and find six more points satisfying this equation. Plot these points.
c. Make a conjecture about the graph of all points $[r, \theta]$ satisfying $r = 2 \sin \theta$.

Review

In 21 and 22, if the equation is an identity, give a proof and state the domain on which it is true. If the equation is not an identity, provide a counterexample. *(Lessons 11-5, 13-3)*

21. $\sin\left(\frac{\pi}{2} + x\right) = \cos x$ **22.** $\sec x + \cot x \csc x = \sec x \csc x$

In 23 and 24, simplify using trigonometric identities. *(Lessons 4-4, 13-2)*

23. a. $\sin^2 \theta + \cos^2 \theta$ **b.** $25 \sin^2 \theta + 25 \cos^2 \theta$

24. a. $1 + \tan^2 \theta$ **b.** $r^2 + r^2 \tan^2 \theta$

25. Give the center and radius of the circle with equation $x^2 + 2x + y^2 + 8y = 8$. *(Lesson 12-5)*

In 26 and 27, graph the two equations on the same set of axes. *(Lessons 4-7, 12-2)*

26. a. $x^2 + y^2 = 1$ **b.** $x^2 + y^2 = 9$

27. a. $y = \cos 2x$ **b.** $y = \cos 3x$

28. a. Prove that the quadrilateral with consecutive vertices $(0, 0)$, (m, n), (p, q), and $(p - m, q - n)$ is a parallelogram.
b. Draw such a parallelogram. *(Previous course)*

Exploration

29. How might points be described in three-dimensional space using polar coordinates?

LESSON

13-5

Polar Graphs

Any equation which involves only the variables r and θ can be graphed using polar coordinates. For instance, in the previous lesson the equations $r = 3$ and $\theta = -\frac{\pi}{3}$ were graphed. Some automatic graphers allow you to graph polar relations. The relation is usually entered in the form $r = f(\theta)$ or $r = f(t)$.

You should be able to draw by hand graphs of relatively simple equations of the form $r = f(\theta)$. In particular, you should study the patterns that emerge when graphs of the parent circular functions are made.

The Graph of the Cosine Function in Polar Coordinates

Example 1

Sketch a graph of the polar equation $r = \cos\theta$.

Solution

Make a table of values for $[r, \theta]$ for $0 \le \theta \le 2\pi$, and plot the points. A table for some values of θ between 0 and π is below, and the corresponding graph is below. When making the table it is usual to consider θ to be the independent variable and r to be the dependent variable.

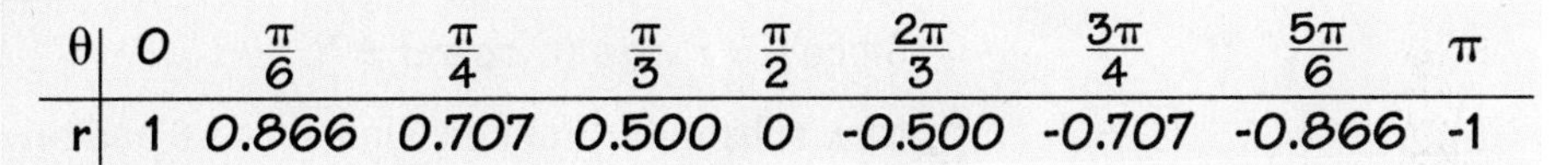

θ	0	$\frac{\pi}{6}$	$\frac{\pi}{4}$	$\frac{\pi}{3}$	$\frac{\pi}{2}$	$\frac{2\pi}{3}$	$\frac{3\pi}{4}$	$\frac{5\pi}{6}$	π
r	1	0.866	0.707	0.500	0	-0.500	-0.707	-0.866	-1

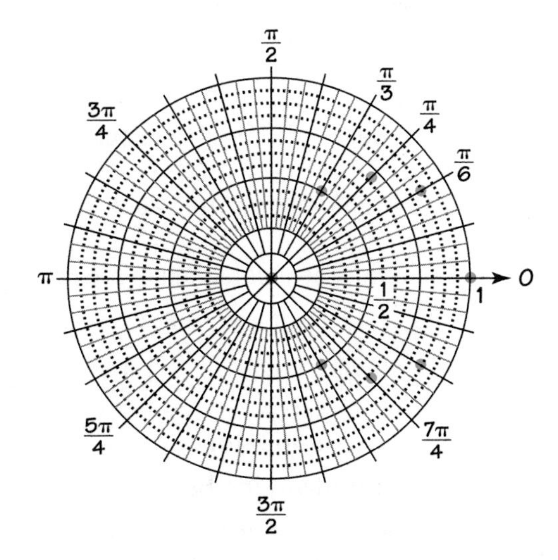

Notice that as θ increases from 0 to $\frac{\pi}{2}$, r decreases from 1 to 0, and points above the polar axis are generated. As θ increases from $\frac{\pi}{2}$ to π, r decreases from 0 to -1, which produces points below the polar axis.

When θ is between π and $\frac{3\pi}{2}$, $r = \cos\theta$ is negative. All such points are in the first quadrant, and coincide with the points generated when $0 \le \theta \le \frac{\pi}{2}$. For instance, if $\theta = \frac{5\pi}{4}$, $r = \cos\frac{5\pi}{4} \approx -0.707$. The point $\left[-0.707, \frac{5\pi}{4}\right]$ coincides with the point $\left[0.707, \frac{\pi}{4}\right]$, which has already been plotted.

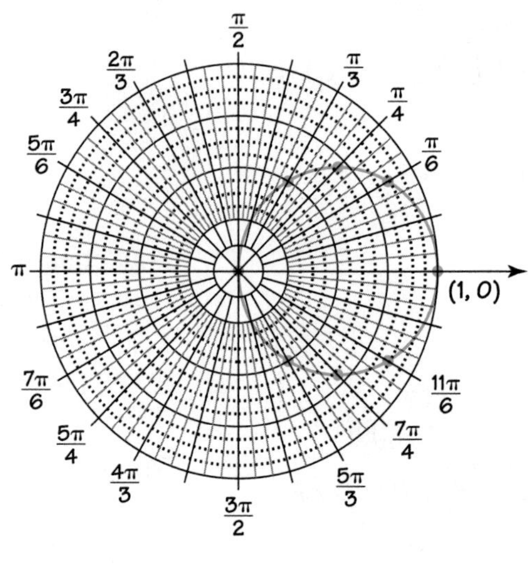

Similarly, when $\frac{3\pi}{2} \le \theta \le 2\pi$, the points generated coincide with those generated by $\frac{\pi}{2} \le \theta \le \pi$. The complete graph is drawn above. The graph appears to be a circle.

By converting from polar to rectangular coordinates, the graph of $r = \cos\theta$ can be proved to be a circle. The idea is to derive a rectangular equation for $r = \cos\theta$, and show that it is of the form $(x - h)^2 + (y - k)^2 = r^2$.

Example 2

Prove that the graph of $r = \cos\theta$ is a circle.

Solution

Since $x = r\cos\theta$, $\cos\theta = \frac{x}{r}$.

Now substitute $\frac{x}{r}$ for $\cos\theta$ in $r = \cos\theta$ and rewrite.

If $\quad r = \cos\theta$,

then $\quad r = \frac{x}{r}$.

So $\quad r^2 = x$.

But $r^2 = x^2 + y^2$, and substituting for r^2 in the preceding equation gives

$$x^2 + y^2 = x.$$

Subtracting x from each side of the equation gives

$$x^2 - x + y^2 = 0.$$

Now complete the square in x.

$$\left(x^2 - x + \frac{1}{4}\right) + y^2 = \frac{1}{4}$$

$$\left(x - \frac{1}{2}\right)^2 + y^2 = \frac{1}{4}$$

This equation, $\left(x - \frac{1}{2}\right)^2 + y^2 = \frac{1}{4}$, is an equation in the rectangular coordinate system for the circle with center at $\left(\frac{1}{2}, 0\right)$ and radius $\frac{1}{2}$. It is the same circle as graphed in Example 1 (shown here smaller).

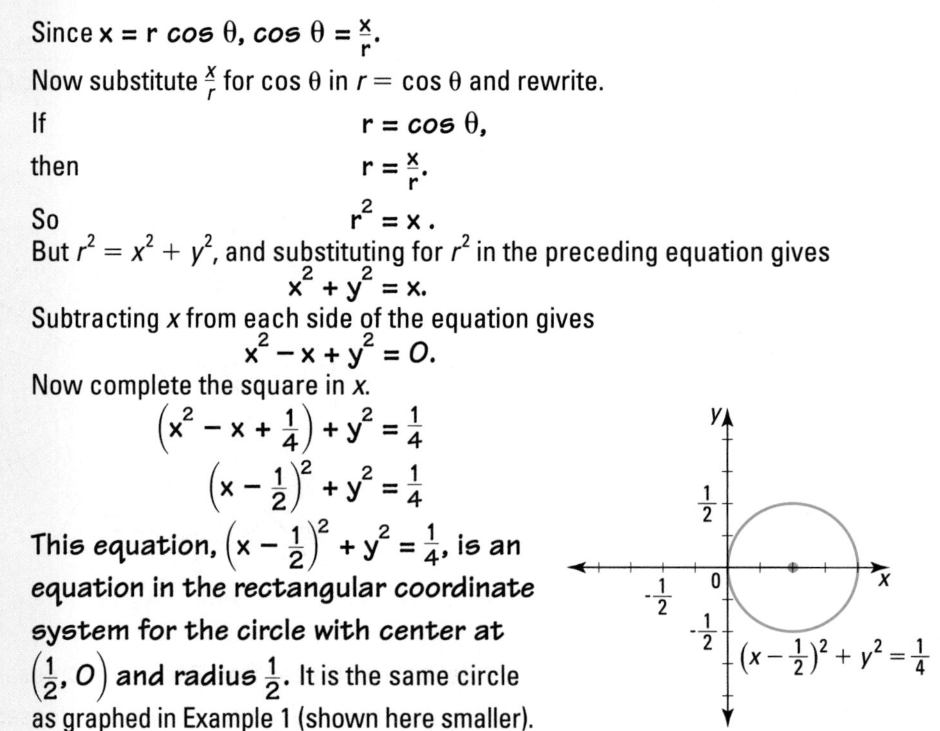

In the Questions you are asked to show that any equation of the form $r = a \cos \theta$, where $a \neq 0$, is a circle.

Rose Curves

Recall that in the rectangular coordinate system, graphs of functions of the form $y = \cos b\theta$, where b is a positive integer, are sine waves with amplitude 1 and period $\frac{2\pi}{b}$. The graphs of polar equations in the form $r = \cos b\theta$, where b is a positive integer, are quite different and beautiful. Below are graphs for $b = 2$, 3, and 4 made by an automatic grapher.

$r = \cos 2\theta$

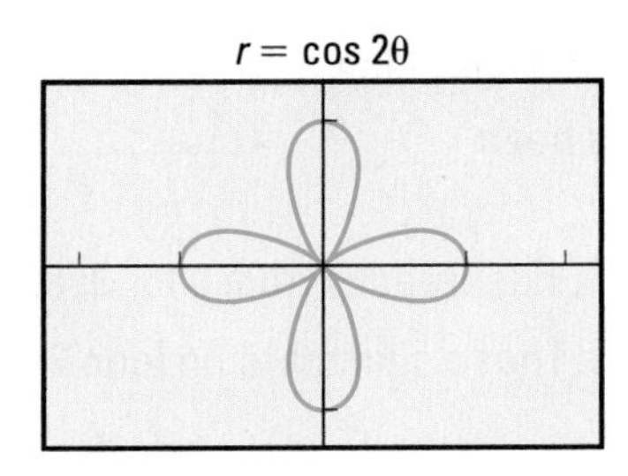

$0 \leq \theta \leq 360$, θ step = 7.5
$-2.25 \leq x \leq 2.25$, x-scale = 1
$-1.5 \leq y \leq 1.5$, y-scale = 1

$r = \cos 3\theta$

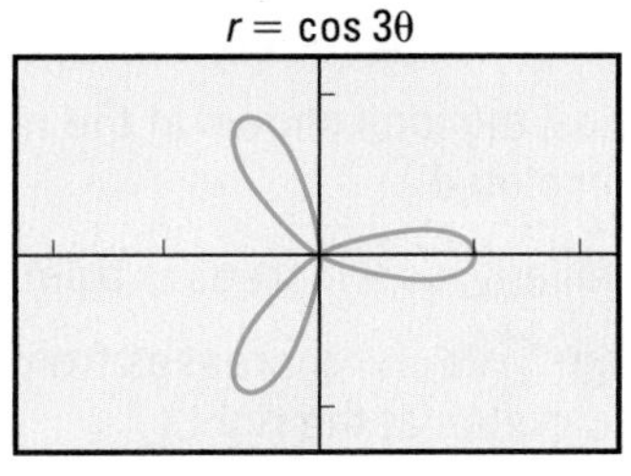

$0 \leq \theta \leq 180$, θ step = 7.5
$-2.25 \leq x \leq 2.25$, x-scale = 1
$-1.5 \leq y \leq 1.5$, y-scale = 1

$r = \cos 4\theta$

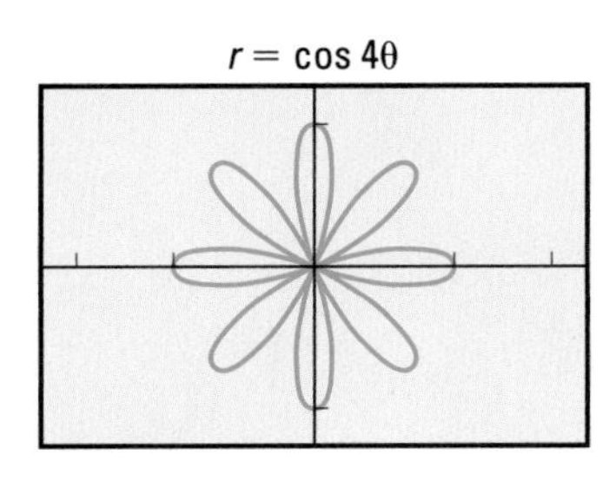

$0 \leq \theta \leq 360$, θ step = 7.5
$-2.25 \leq x \leq 2.25$, x-scale = 1
$-1.5 \leq y \leq 1.5$, y-scale = 1

dogwood

trillium

clematis

These graphs are part of a family of polar graphs called *rose curves* or *petal curves*. The following example shows how to draw a rose curve by hand without having to plot too many points.

Example 3

Sketch a graph of all $[r, \theta]$ with $r = 3 \sin 2\theta$.

Solution

First sketch a graph of $y = 3 \sin 2x$ for $0 \leq x \leq 2\pi$ in rectangular coordinates. As shown at the right, it has amplitude 3 and period $\frac{2\pi}{2} = \pi$.

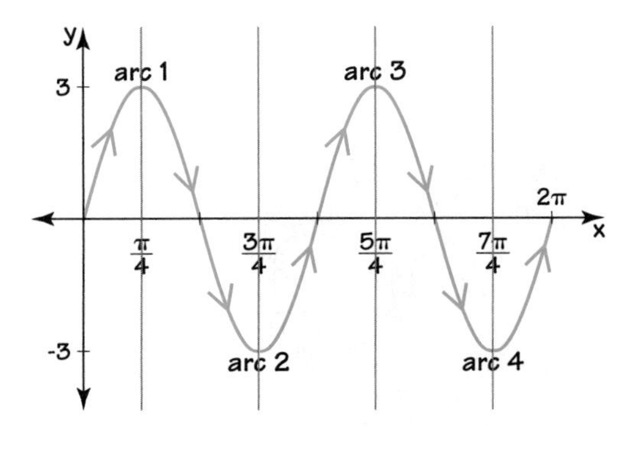

Since $y = 3 \sin 2x$ and $r = 3 \sin 2\theta$, the possible y values of the function on the rectangular coordinate graph are the possible values of r in the polar coordinate graph. Thus, $-3 \leq r \leq 3$.

The x-intercepts of the rectangular graph indicate when $r = 0$, that is, when the polar graph passes through the pole. Notice also that when $0 \leq x \leq 2\pi$, the rectangular coordinate graph has 4 congruent arcs, each symmetric to a vertical line where x is an odd multiple of $\frac{\pi}{4}$. In the polar graph, this reflection symmetry gives rise to symmetry in the "petals."

▸

To sketch the polar graph, begin with the point $[0, \theta]$. As θ increases from 0 to $\frac{\pi}{4}$, r increases from 0 to 3. This part of the graph of $r = 3 \sin 2\theta$ is pictured at the right.

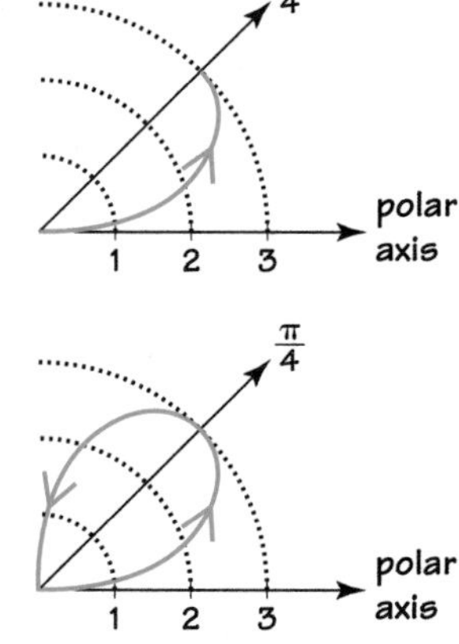

As θ continues to increase from $\frac{\pi}{4}$ to $\frac{\pi}{2}$, the value of r decreases from 3 to 0. The reflection symmetry in arc 1 above results in symmetry over the line $\theta = \frac{\pi}{4}$ for the corresponding arc in the polar plane. Thus, the loop shown at the right has been completed.

Similarly, as θ increases from $\frac{\pi}{2}$ to $\frac{3\pi}{4}$, r decreases from 0 to -3; and as θ goes from $\frac{3\pi}{4}$ to π, r increases from -3 to 0. These points are on loop 2, as noted on the sketch at the right.

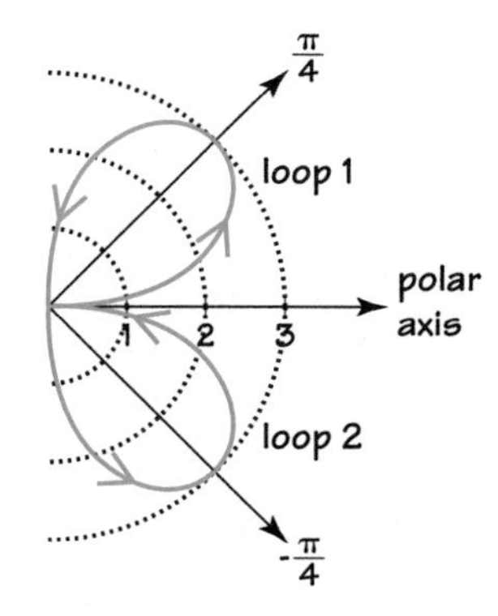

A similar analysis of arcs 3 and 4 indicates that there are two more loops in the polar graph. A complete graph of $r = 3 \sin 2\theta$ is sketched below. It is a 4-petaled rose.

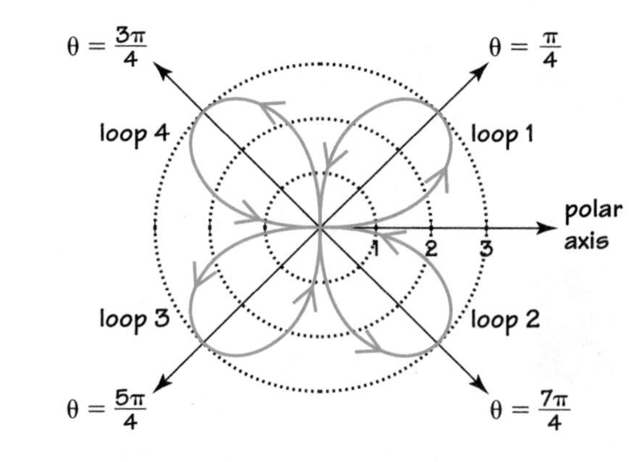

stained-glass rose window in Notre Dame Cathedral, Chartres, France

In general, polar graphs of trigonometric functions with equations of the form $r = c + a \sin b\theta$ or $r = c + a \cos b\theta$, where b is a positive integer and $a \neq 0$, are beautiful curves. You are asked to draw some of these in the Questions.

QUESTIONS

Covering the Reading

1. Consider the polar equation $r = 2$.
  a. Sketch a graph of the equation.
  b. Give an equation in rectangular coordinates x and y for this graph.

2. Describe the graph of $r = a$, where a is a constant nonzero real number.

3. Consider the equation $r = 2 \cos \theta$ in the polar plane.
  a. Find and plot at least six points on its graph.
  b. Prove that the graph is a circle.

4. Consider $r = \sin \theta$.
  a. Sketch a graph of this function in a polar coordinate system.
  b. Derive an equation for this curve in rectangular coordinates.

In 5 and 6, refer to the rose curves on page 829. *True or false.*

5. The point $[4, \pi]$ is on the graph of $r = \cos 4\theta$.

6. The point $[0, 0]$ is on the graph of $r = \cos 2\theta$.

7. Consider the equation $r = 3 \cos 2\theta$.
  a. Sketch a graph of this equation in the rectangular plane.
  b. What are the maximum and minimum values of r?
  c. Find r when $\theta = 0, \frac{\pi}{6}$, and $\frac{\pi}{2}$, and plot these points in the polar plane.
  d. Use the technique described in Example 3 to sketch a complete graph of this equation in polar coordinates.

Applying the Mathematics

8. At the right is a graph of $r = \sin 2\theta$. Give the coordinates of four points on the graph.

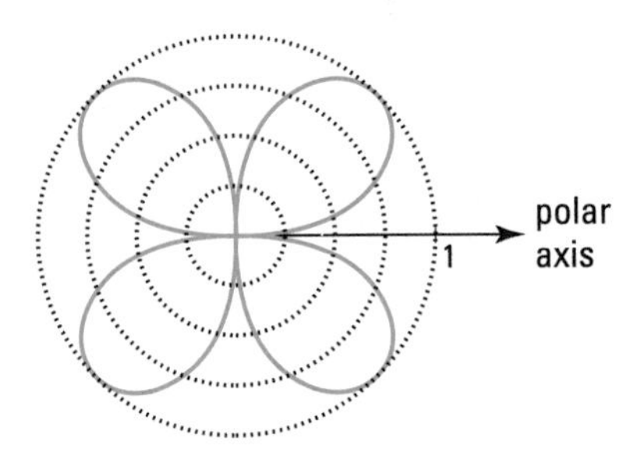

9. Sketch a graph in polar coordinates of $r = a \sin 2\theta$, where a is a positive real number.

10. Refer to the graphs of $r = \cos 2\theta$, $r = \cos 3\theta$, and $r = \cos 4\theta$ in the reading.
  a. Make a conjecture regarding the number of petals on the polar curve $r = \cos n\theta$, where n is a positive integer.
  b. Test your conjecture by drawing polar graphs of $r = \cos 5\theta$ and $r = \cos 6\theta$ with an automatic grapher.

With All My Cardioid. *Hearts are a traditional decoration for Valentine's Day cards. This Victorian valentine dates from about 1900.*

11. The graph of $r = \theta$, for $\theta > 0$, in the polar plane is called an *Archimedean spiral*, named after Archimedes. Graph this curve.

12. The graph of $r = a(\cos\theta - 1)$ in the polar plane is called a *cardioid.*
 a. Graph this curve for $a = 1$.
 b. Why is *cardioid* an appropriate name for this curve?

13. The graph of $r = a^{\theta}$, where $a > 0$, is called a *logarithmic spiral.*
 a. For $r = 2^{\theta}$, find the coordinates of the points in the interval $0 \le \theta < 2\pi$ where θ is a multiple of $\frac{\pi}{4}$.
 b. Graph the curve.

14. Consider the equation $r = \sec\theta$.
 a. Graph the equation in polar coordinates.
 b. Give an equation of the graph in rectangular coordinates.

Review

15. Which polar pairs describe the same point? *(Lesson 13-4)*
 (a) $\left[0.5, \frac{5\pi}{6}\right]$ (b) $\left[-\frac{1}{2}, -\frac{\pi}{6}\right]$ (c) $\left[\frac{1}{2}, -\frac{7\pi}{6}\right]$ (d) $\left[-0.5, -\frac{5\pi}{6}\right]$

In 16 and 17, a trigonometric equation is given. **a.** Use an automatic grapher to test whether the equation seems to be an identity. **b.** Prove your conclusion in part **a.** *(Lessons 13-2, 13-3)*

16. $\sin^2 x = \frac{1}{2}(1 - \cos 2x)$ **17.** $\tan 2x = 2\tan x$

18. Show that multiplication of 2×2 matrices is not always commutative. *(Lesson 11-1)*

19. Suppose $f(x) = x^3 - 729$. Find all complex numbers such that $f(x) = 0$. *(Lesson 9-8)*

20. Let $u = 3 - 4i$ and $v = 5 + i$. Write each of the following in $a + bi$ form. *(Lesson 9-6)*
 a. $u + v$ **b.** uv **c.** $\frac{u}{v}$

Exploration

21. Consider equations of the form $r = a + b\sin\theta$, where $a > 0$ and $b > 0$. Experiment with an automatic grapher using various values of a and b.
 a. Find an equation whose graph looks like the one at the right.
 b. In general, what is true about a and b if the graph of $r = a + b\sin\theta$ has a loop as above?

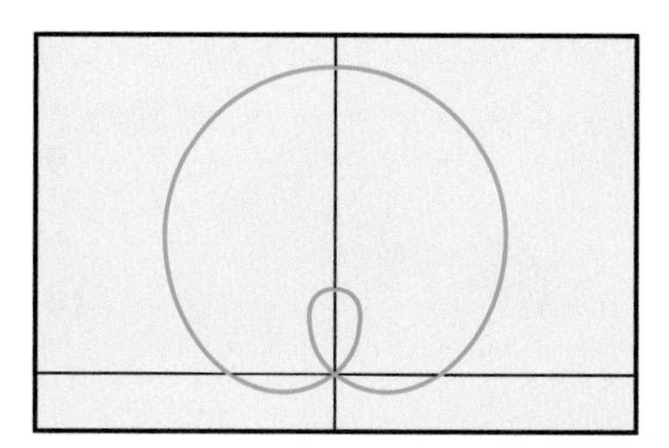

LESSON

13-6

The Geometry of Complex Numbers

Graphing Complex Numbers in the Rectangular Coordinate Plane

About 1800, Caspar Wessel, a Norwegian surveyor, and Jean Robert Argand, a Swiss mathematician, independently invented a geometric representation of complex numbers. Their diagrams, sometimes called *Argand diagrams*, involve graphs in a *complex plane*. As you will see in the remainder of this chapter, these graphs can be useful, illuminating, and beautiful.

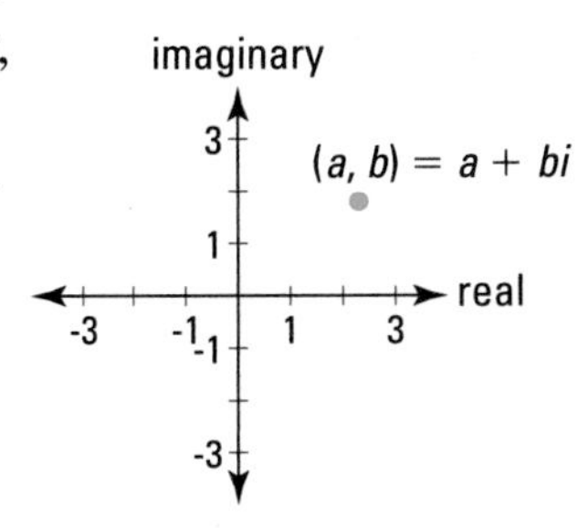

In a complex plane, the horizontal axis is called the **real axis** and the vertical axis is called the **imaginary axis**. To graph the complex number $a + bi$ in the complex plane, first write it as the ordered pair (a, b). Then plot (a, b) as you normally would in a rectangular coordinate system.

Each real number is of the form $a + 0i$, so it equals $(a, 0)$ and is plotted on the real axis in the complex plane. Similarly, every imaginary number is of the form $0 + bi$ and $(0, b)$ is plotted on the imaginary axis. The complex number $0 = 0 + 0i = (0, 0)$, and is graphed at the origin.

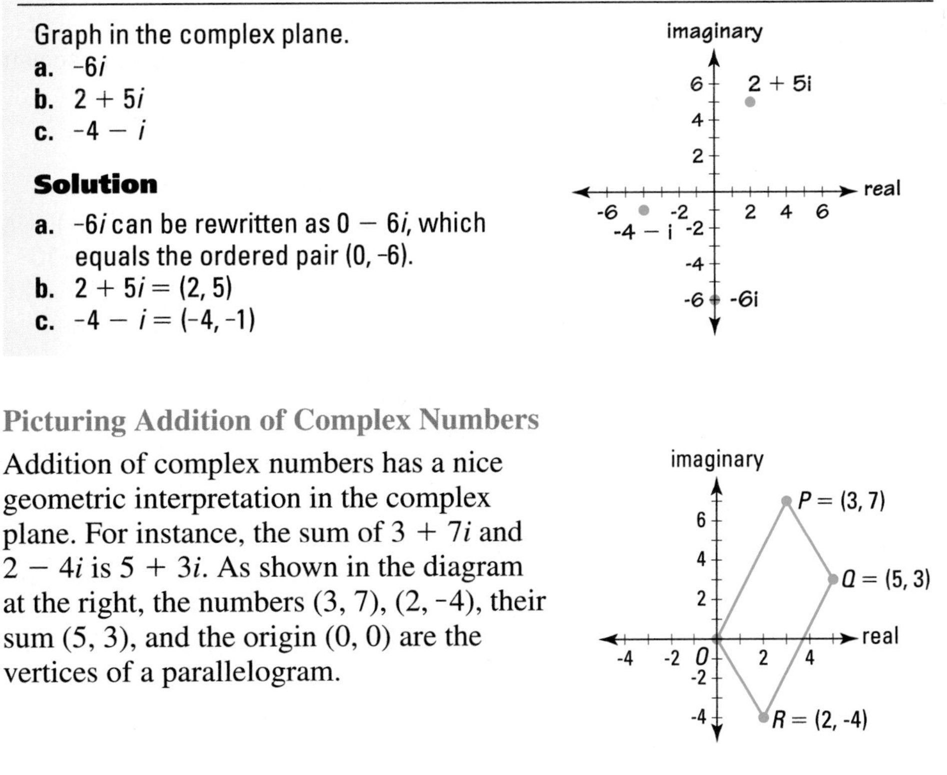

Example 1

Graph in the complex plane.

a. $-6i$

b. $2 + 5i$

c. $-4 - i$

Solution

a. $-6i$ can be rewritten as $0 - 6i$, which equals the ordered pair $(0, -6)$.

b. $2 + 5i = (2, 5)$

c. $-4 - i = (-4, -1)$

Picturing Addition of Complex Numbers

Addition of complex numbers has a nice geometric interpretation in the complex plane. For instance, the sum of $3 + 7i$ and $2 - 4i$ is $5 + 3i$. As shown in the diagram at the right, the numbers $(3, 7)$, $(2, -4)$, their sum $(5, 3)$, and the origin $(0, 0)$ are the vertices of a parallelogram.

This is easy to verify. Because the slopes of the opposite sides of *OPQR* are equal, the opposite sides are parallel and the quadrilateral is a parallelogram.

$$\text{slope of } \overline{OP} = \frac{7-0}{3-0} = \frac{7}{3}$$
$$\text{slope of } \overline{PQ} = \frac{3-7}{5-3} = \frac{-4}{2} = -2$$
$$\text{slope of } \overline{QR} = \frac{-4-3}{2-5} = \frac{-7}{-3} = \frac{7}{3}$$
$$\text{slope of } \overline{OR} = \frac{-4-0}{2-0} = \frac{-4}{2} = -2$$

This proves one instance of the following theorem. You are asked to prove the general case in the Questions.

Geometric Addition Theorem

If the complex numbers $a + bi$ and $c + di$ are not collinear with the origin in the complex plane, then their sum $(a + c) + (b + d)i$ is the fourth vertex of a parallelogram with consecutive vertices $a + bi$, 0, and $c + di$.

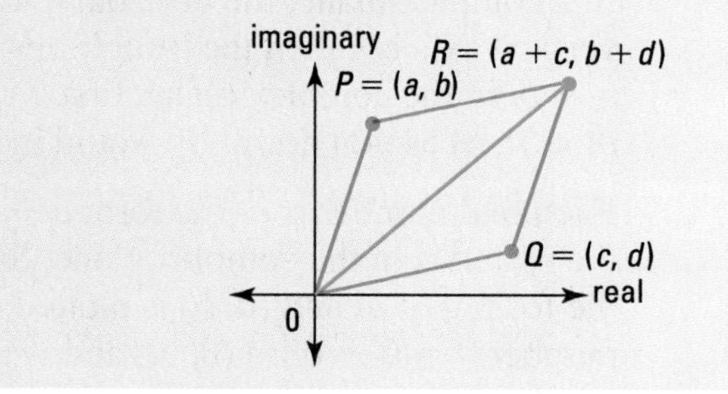

Example 2

Let $z = 8 + 6i$ and $w = 2 - 4i$. Represent geometrically the quantities $z + w$, $z - w$, $w - z$, and $-(z + w)$.

Solution

First perform the operations:
$$z + w = 10 + 2i$$
$$z - w = 6 + 10i$$
$$w - z = -6 - 10i$$
and
$$-(z + w) = -(10 + 2i).$$

Notice that $z - w$ is the opposite of $w - z$ and $-(z + w)$ is the opposite of $z + w$, as you would expect.

These complex numbers are graphed in the complex plane at the right. We have also graphed $-w$ and $-z$ to show how all these points are related.

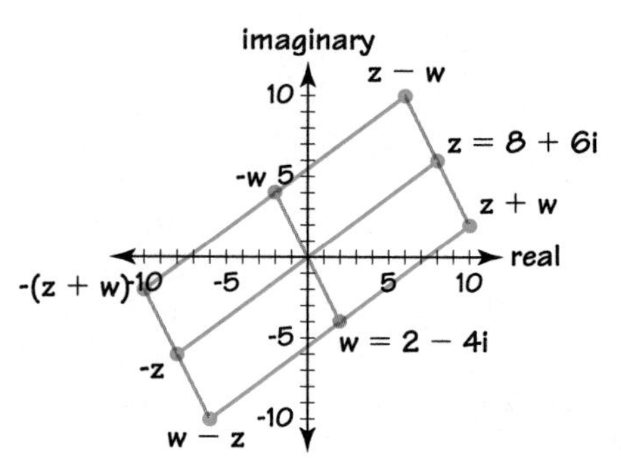

Graphing Complex Numbers in the Polar Coordinate Plane

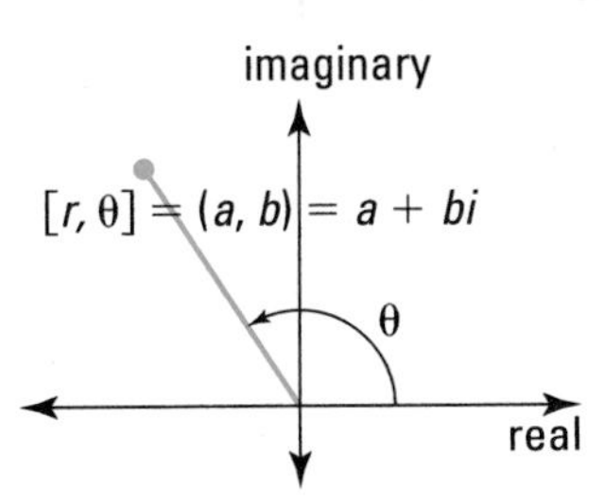

Complex numbers can also be represented with polar coordinates. Let $[r, \theta]$ with $r \geq 0$ be the polar coordinates for (a, b). Then from Lesson 13-4 you know that $r = \sqrt{a^2 + b^2}$ (because r is not negative) and $\tan \theta = \frac{b}{a}$. There are usually two values of θ between 0 and 2π which satisfy $\tan \theta = \frac{b}{a}$. The correct value can be determined by examining the quadrant in which (a, b) is located.

Example 3

Find polar coordinates for the complex number $3 - 5i$.

Solution

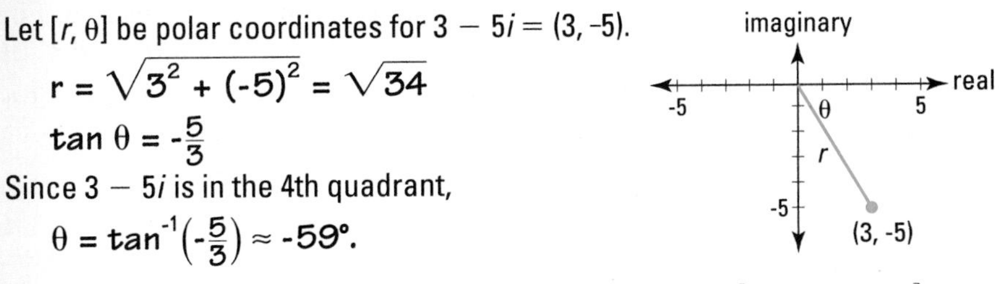

Let $[r, \theta]$ be polar coordinates for $3 - 5i = (3, -5)$.

$$r = \sqrt{3^2 + (-5)^2} = \sqrt{34}$$

$$\tan \theta = -\frac{5}{3}$$

Since $3 - 5i$ is in the 4th quadrant,

$$\theta = \tan^{-1}\left(-\frac{5}{3}\right) \approx -59°.$$

Thus one pair of polar coordinates for $(3, -5)$ is $[\sqrt{34}, -59°]$.

For any complex number $z = [r, \theta]$ with $r \geq 0$, r is its distance from the origin. That distance is also called the **absolute value** or **modulus** of the complex number and is written $|z|$. If $z = a + bi$, then $|z| = |a + bi| = \sqrt{a^2 + b^2}$. The direction θ is called an **argument** of the complex number and can be found using trigonometry: $\tan \theta = \frac{b}{a}$. An argument may be measured in degrees or radians. Because of periodicity, more than one argument exists for each complex number. In Example 3 the modulus of the complex number is $\sqrt{34}$, and an argument is -59°. Other arguments are of the form $-59° + 360°n$, where n is an integer.

The form $[r, \theta]$ for a complex number is called **polar form**. In the next lesson you will see that the polar form of complex numbers is very useful for describing the product or quotient of two complex numbers.

QUESTIONS

Covering the Reading

1. In a complex plane the horizontal axis is called the __**a.**__ axis, and the vertical axis is called the __**b.**__ axis.

In 2 and 3, a complex number is given. **a.** Rewrite each number as an ordered pair (a, b). **b.** Graph the number in the complex plane.

2. $4 - 6i$

3. $-5 + 4i$

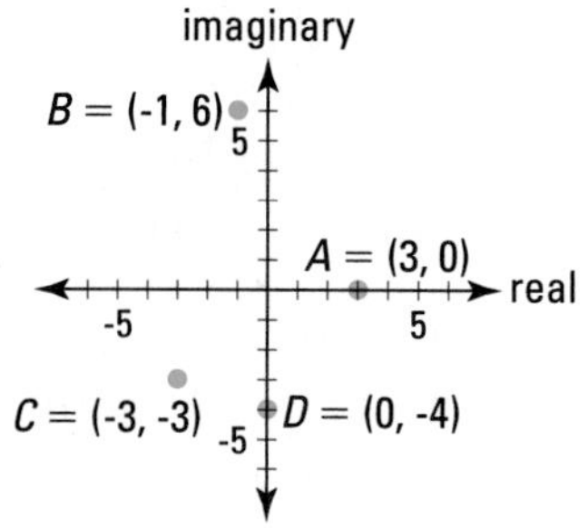

imaginary

B = (-1, 6)

A = (3, 0)

real

C = (-3, -3)

D = (0, -4)

-5 5 5 -5

4. Write each complex number pictured at the left in $a + bi$ form.

5. Let $U = 3 - 2i$, $V = -5 + 6i$, and $O = 0 + 0i$.
  a. Find $U + V$.
  b. Graph U, V, and $U + V$ in the same coordinate plane.
  c. Verify that U, O, V, and $U + V$ are vertices of a parallelogram.

6. Prove the Geometric Addition Theorem.

In 7 and 8, give polar coordinates $[r, \theta]$ for each complex number, assuming $r \geq 0$ and $0 \leq \theta \leq 2\pi$.

7. $4 - 3i$

8. $\frac{1}{2} + \frac{\sqrt{3}}{2}i$

9. How is the absolute value of the complex number $a + bi$ calculated?

In 10 and 11, a complex number is given. **a.** Find its absolute value. **b.** Find its argument θ, if $r \geq 0$ and $0° \leq \theta < 360°$.

10. $7i$

11. $-3 + 6i$

Applying the Mathematics

12. Name and graph four complex numbers with modulus 1.

13. Refer to Example 2.
  a. Prove that the largest quadrilateral pictured is a parallelogram.
  b. How many other parallelograms are determined by the complex numbers pictured?

14. a. Draw the quadrilateral with vertices $P = 6 + i$, $Q = 6 - i$, $P + Q$, and (0, 0).
  b. What special type of parallelogram is this?
  c. Determine the length of the longer diagonal of the quadrilateral.

15. On the real number line, the distance between points with coordinates u and v is $|u - v|$. Determine whether the distance from $u = a + bi$ to $v = c + di$ in the complex plane is $|u - v|$. Justify your answer.

16. Consider $u = -3 + 4i$ and $v = -12i$. Evaluate.
  a. $|u| + |v|$
  b. $|u + v|$
  c. Use the Triangle Inequality to explain why $|u + v| < |u| + |v|$ in general.

Review

In 17–20, graph each equation in the polar plane. *(Lesson 13-5)*

17. $\theta = \frac{3\pi}{4}$

18. $r = 3\theta, 0 \leq \theta \leq 4\pi$

19. $r = 2 \sin \theta$

20. $r = \sin 5\theta$

21. Give an equation in a rectangular coordinate system for the polar equation in Question 19. *(Lesson 13-4)*

22. Find three other pairs of polar coordinates for the point $\left[-4, \frac{\pi}{6}\right]$. *(Lesson 13-4)*

23. Give the coordinates of the image of (11, 6) under a rotation of θ about the origin. *(Lesson 11-4)*

Tamera and Tia Mowry are identical twins.

24. Seven pairs of 16-year-old African American female twins took part in a study of the heights (in inches) and weights (in pounds) of identical twins. Here are the (height, weight) data and a scatterplot of the data for each twin in each pair.

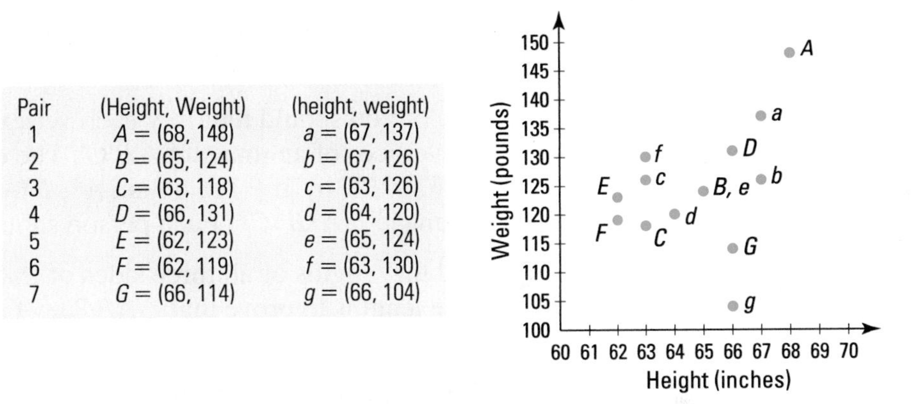

Pair	(Height, Weight)	(height, weight)
1	$A = (68, 148)$	$a = (67, 137)$
2	$B = (65, 124)$	$b = (67, 126)$
3	$C = (63, 118)$	$c = (63, 126)$
4	$D = (66, 131)$	$d = (64, 120)$
5	$E = (62, 123)$	$e = (65, 124)$
6	$F = (62, 119)$	$f = (63, 130)$
7	$G = (66, 114)$	$g = (66, 104)$

By calculating various statistics from the data, respond to the following questions.

a. Which pair do you think is most different on these variables?
b. Which pair do you think is most alike on these variables?
c. Defend your answers to parts **a** and **b**. *(Lessons 1-3, 1-7, 10-6)*

25. Give the complex conjugate. *(Lesson 9-6)*

a. $-1 + 5i$ **b.** $5i$ **c.** -1

26. Given $z_1 = 2 + i$ and $z_2 = 3 + 2i$, put in $a + bi$ form. *(Lesson 9-6)*

a. $z_1 z_2$ **b.** $\frac{z_1}{z_2}$

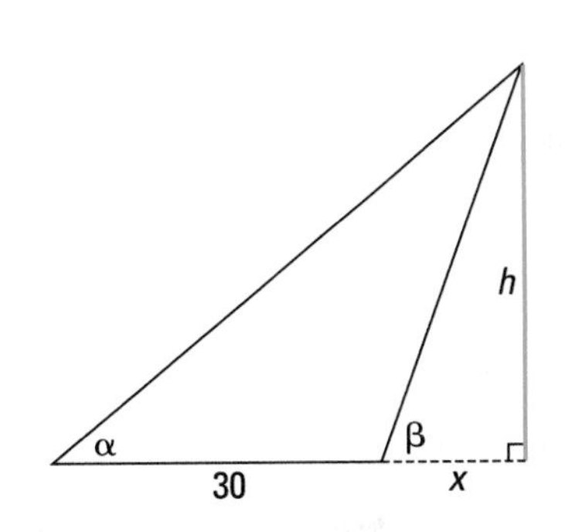

27. Two tracking stations are 30 miles apart. They measure the elevation angle of a weather balloon to be α and β, respectively. How high is a balloon sighted with $\alpha = 40°$ and $\beta = 70°$? *(Lesson 5-1)*

Exploration

28. Let $w = 1 + i$.

a. Write w^0, w^2, w^3, and w^4 in $a + bi$ form.
b. Graph w^0, w, w^2, w^3, and w^4 in the complex plane.
c. Describe the pattern that emerges in the graph of $(1 + i)^n$ for positive integers n.

Introducing Lesson 13-7

Geometric Transformations Using Complex Multiplication

Work in pairs. Graph paper will make this easier.

1 Graph $\triangle ABC$ in the complex plane with vertices $A = 3i$, $B = 4 - 3i$, and $C = 5$.

2 One of you should multiply each vertex by $2i$ to obtain A', B', and C', the vertices of an image $\triangle A'B'C'$. The other should multiply each vertex of $\triangle ABC$ by $1 + i$ to obtain A^*, B^*, and C^*, the vertices of a second image $\triangle A^*B^*C^*$. Each person should graph one of the images.

3 Find the lengths of all three sides of $\triangle ABC$ and of your image. Use these lengths to prove that $\triangle ABC$, $\triangle A'B'C'$, and $\triangle A^*B^*C^*$ are similar triangles.

4 Determine the ratio of similitude between $\triangle A'B'C'$ and $\triangle ABC$. Determine the ratio of similitude between $\triangle A^*B^*C^*$ and $\triangle ABC$. Try to determine how these ratios are related to the two complex numbers $2i$ and $1 + i$ that you used as multipliers.

LESSON

13-7

Trigonometric Form of Complex Numbers

You have now seen many ways of representing complex numbers.

z	single letter
$a + bi$	$a + bi$ form
(a, b)	rectangular coordinate form
$[r, \theta]$	polar coordinate form

You can convert from $a + bi$ or rectangular coordinate form to polar coordinate form using the relationships $r = \sqrt{a^2 + b^2}$ and $\tan \theta = \frac{b}{a}$. You can convert back using the relationships $a = r \cos \theta$ and $b = r \sin \theta$.

These conversions are useful because each form has advantages. The single letter form z is the shortest and helps shorten formulas such as the distance $|w - z|$ between two complex numbers w and z. In $a + bi$ form, operations with complex numbers can be performed as if the complex numbers are polynomials in i. In rectangular form, addition of complex numbers can be seen graphically as in finding the fourth vertex of a parallelogram.

In this lesson, we introduce the *trigonometric form* of a complex number. This form is related to the polar coordinate form and is quite useful for picturing multiplication, powers, and roots of complex numbers.

What Is the Trigonometric Form of a Complex Number?

Consider the complex number $z = a + bi$ with polar coordinates $[r, \theta]$, and with $r \geq 0$.

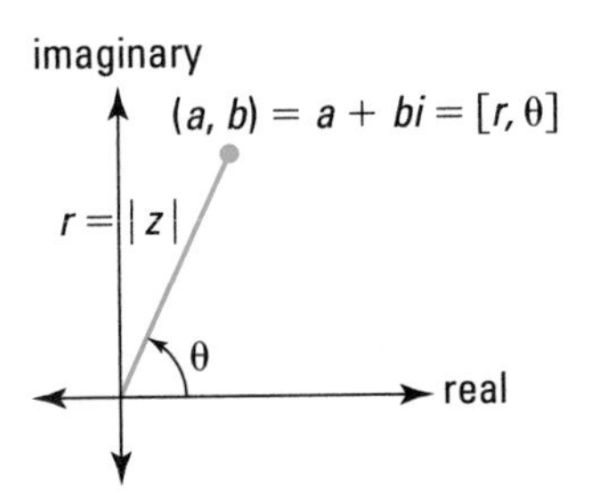

By a theorem of Lesson 13-4, $a = r \cos \theta$ and $b = r \sin \theta$. So

$$\begin{aligned} z &= a + bi \\ &= r \cos \theta + (r \sin \theta)i \\ &= r(\cos \theta + i \sin \theta). \end{aligned}$$

The expression $r(\cos \theta + i \sin \theta)$ is called the **trigonometric form of the complex number $a + bi$** because it uses the cosine and sine of the argument θ. Like polar form, the trigonometric form denotes a complex number in terms of r and θ, its absolute value and argument. But unlike polar form, a complex number in trigonometric form is still in the rectangular coordinate form $a + bi$. Because of this link between polar and rectangular coordinates, the trigonometric form of complex numbers is quite useful.

Converting from $a + bi$ Form to Trigonometric Form

Example 1

Write the complex number $-2 - 2\sqrt{3}i$ in trigonometric form. Use a value of θ in the interval $0 \le \theta < 2\pi$.

Solution

The process is quite similar to that used in finding polar coordinates for a point. First sketch a graph.

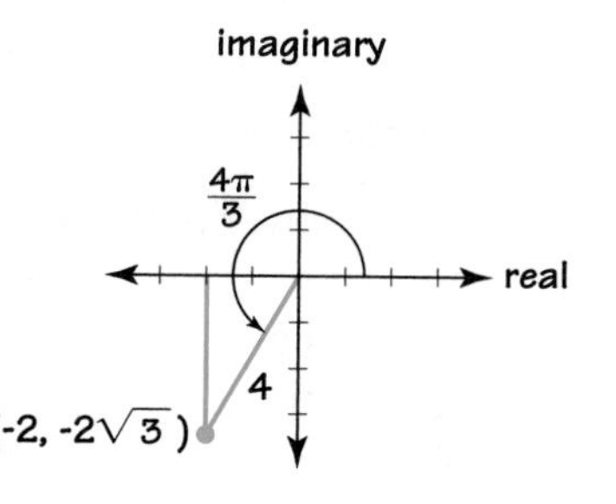

Let $-2 - 2\sqrt{3}i = a + bi$. Then $a = -2$ and $b = -2\sqrt{3}$.

$$r = \sqrt{a^2 + b^2} = \sqrt{(-2)^2 + (-2\sqrt{3})^2} = \sqrt{4 + 12} = 4$$

$$\tan\theta = \frac{b}{a} = \frac{-2\sqrt{3}}{-2} = \sqrt{3}$$

Since $-2 - 2\sqrt{3}i$ is in the third quadrant, $\theta = \pi + \frac{\pi}{3} = \frac{4\pi}{3}$.

So in polar coordinate form, $-2 - 2\sqrt{3}i = \left[4, \frac{4\pi}{3}\right]$.

Therefore, in trigonometric form, $-2 - 2\sqrt{3}i = 4\left(\cos\frac{4\pi}{3} + i\sin\frac{4\pi}{3}\right)$.

Consider again the number of Example 1. Since the sine and cosine have period 2π, $-2 - 2\sqrt{3}i = 4\left(\cos\left(\frac{4\pi}{3} + 2n\pi\right) + i\sin\left(\frac{4\pi}{3} + 2n\pi\right)\right)$, where n is an integer. In general, every complex number has infinitely many trigonometric forms.

Converting From Trigonometric Form to $a + bi$ Form

Example 2

Write the complex number $5\left(\cos\frac{2\pi}{3} + i\sin\frac{2\pi}{3}\right)$ in $a + bi$ form.

Solution

Distribute the 5 and simplify.

$$5\left(\cos\frac{2\pi}{3} + i\sin\frac{2\pi}{3}\right) = 5\cos\frac{2\pi}{3} + i\left(5\sin\frac{2\pi}{3}\right)$$

$$= -\frac{5}{2} + \frac{5\sqrt{3}}{2}i$$

Picturing Multiplication of Complex Numbers

The trigonometric form of complex numbers explains a nice geometrical property of complex number multiplication. Two instances were given in the In-class Activity on page 838, where three complex numbers A, B, and C were each multiplied by $2i$ and also by $1 + i$. Let us consider the multiplication by $2i$.

The graphs of $\triangle ABC$ and $\triangle A'B'C'$ are shown at the right. It appears that $\triangle A'B'C'$ is the image of $\triangle ABC$ under the composite of a size change of magnitude 2 and a rotation of 90°.

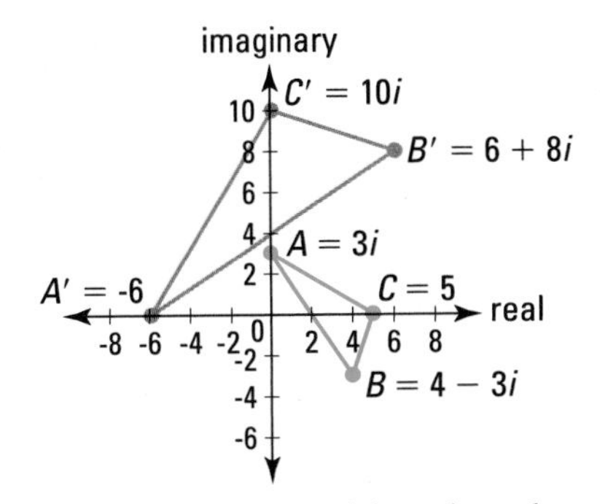

In trigonometric form, $2i = 2(\cos 90° + i \sin 90°)$. Thus the magnitudes of the transformations are the absolute value and argument of $2i$, respectively. That is, multiplication by $2i$ can be considered as the composite of a size change of magnitude 2 (its absolute value) and a rotation through 90° (its argument) around the origin.

In general, multiplying a complex number z_1 by the complex number $z_2 = [r_2, \theta_2] = r_2(\cos \theta_2 + i \sin \theta_2)$ applies to the graph of z_1 the composite of a size change of magnitude $|z_2|$ and a rotation θ_2 about the origin.

Product of Complex Numbers Theorem (Trigonometric Form)

If $z_1 = r_1(\cos \theta_1 + i \sin \theta_1)$ and
$z_2 = r_2(\cos \theta_2 + i \sin \theta_2)$,
then $z_1 z_2 = r_1 r_2(\cos (\theta_1 + \theta_2) + i \sin (\theta_1 + \theta_2))$.

Proof

The proof applies, perhaps surprisingly, the sum formulas for the cosine and sine.

$$\begin{aligned}
z_1 z_2 &= (r_1(\cos \theta_1 + i \sin \theta_1))\,(r_2(\cos \theta_2 + i \sin \theta_2)) \\
&= r_1 r_2(\cos \theta_1 + i \sin \theta_1)(\cos \theta_2 + i \sin \theta_2) \\
&= r_1 r_2(\cos \theta_1 \cos \theta_2 + i \cos \theta_1 \sin \theta_2 + i \sin \theta_1 \cos \theta_2 + i^2 \sin \theta_1 \sin \theta_2) \\
&= r_1 r_2((\cos \theta_1 \cos \theta_2 + i^2 \sin \theta_1 \sin \theta_2) + i(\cos \theta_1 \sin \theta_2 + \sin \theta_1 \cos \theta_2)) \\
&= r_1 r_2((\cos \theta_1 \cos \theta_2 - \sin \theta_1 \sin \theta_2) + i(\sin \theta_1 \cos \theta_2 + \cos \theta_1 \sin \theta_2)] \\
&= r_1 r_2(\cos (\theta_1 + \theta_2) + i \sin (\theta_1 + \theta_2))
\end{aligned}$$

This is the trigonometric form for a complex number with absolute value $r_1 r_2$ and argument $\theta_1 + \theta_2$.

In polar coordinate form, the above theorem states that the product of the complex numbers $[r_1, \theta_1]$ and $[r_2, \theta_2]$ is $[r_1 r_2, \theta_1 + \theta_2]$.

Example 3

If $z_1 = 10i$ and $z_2 = 3(\cos 75° + i \sin 75°)$, find the product z_1z_2 in trigonometric form.

Solution

In trigonometric form, $z_1 = 10(\cos 90° + i \sin 90°)$.
Now use the Product of Complex Numbers Theorem.

$$z_1z_2 = 10 \cdot 3 (\cos (90° + 75°) + i \sin (90° + 75°))$$
$$= 30(\cos 165° + i \sin 165°)$$

Check

Multiplying by $z_2 = 3 (\cos 75° + i \sin 75°)$ should apply the composite of a size change of magnitude 3 and a rotation of 75° to the graph of the complex number $z_1 = 10 (\cos 90° + i \sin 90°)$. The graph below illustrates that this is so.

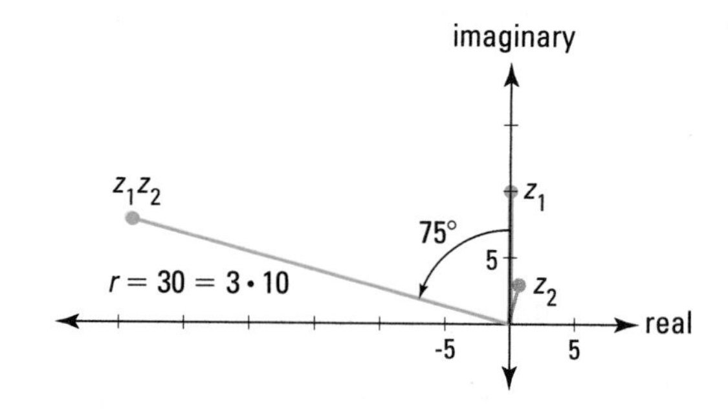

Picturing Division of Complex Numbers

Recall that to perform division of a number z by a complex number in $a + bi$ form, it was useful to multiply numerator and denominator of $\frac{z}{a + bi}$ by the complex conjugate $a - bi$. In trigonometric form, the conjugate of $r (\cos \theta + i \sin \theta)$ is $r (\cos \theta - i \sin \theta)$.

This result is needed to prove the following theorem, which you are asked to do in the Questions.

Division of Complex Numbers Theorem (Trigonometric Form)

If $z_1 = r_1(\cos \theta_1 + i \sin \theta_1)$ and
$z_2 = r_2(\cos \theta_2 + i \sin \theta_2)$,
then $\frac{z_1}{z_2} = \frac{r_1}{r_2}(\cos (\theta_1 - \theta_2) + i \sin (\theta_1 - \theta_2))$.

Geometrically, division of the complex number $z_1 = [r_1, \theta_1]$ by the complex number $z_2 = [r_2, \theta_2]$ applies to z_1 the composite of a size change of magnitude $\frac{1}{|z_2|}$ and a rotation of $-\theta_2$ about the origin. So, in polar coordinate form, the above theorem states that the quotient $\frac{[r_1, \theta_2]}{[r_2, \theta_2]}$ is $\left[\frac{r_1}{r_2}, \theta_1 - \theta_2\right]$.

Example 4

If $z_1 = 10\left(\cos\frac{\pi}{2} + i\sin\frac{\pi}{2}\right)$ and $z_2 = 2\left(\cos\frac{\pi}{3} + i\sin\frac{\pi}{3}\right)$, write $\frac{z_1}{z_2}$ in trigonometric form.

Solution

From the Division of Complex Numbers Theorem,

$$\frac{z_1}{z_2} = \frac{10}{2}\left(\cos\left(\frac{\pi}{2} - \frac{\pi}{3}\right) + i\sin\left(\frac{\pi}{2} - \frac{\pi}{3}\right)\right)$$
$$= 5\left(\cos\frac{\pi}{6} + i\sin\frac{\pi}{6}\right).$$

Check

Convert to $a + bi$ form.

$$z_1 = 10\,(0 + i(1)) = 10i$$
$$z_2 = 2\left(\frac{1}{2} + i\frac{\sqrt{3}}{2}\right) = 1 + \sqrt{3}i$$

Now compute the quotient by multiplying the numerator and denominator of $\frac{z_1}{z_2}$ by the conjugate of $1 + \sqrt{3}\,i$.

$$\frac{z_1}{z_2} = \frac{10i}{1 + \sqrt{3}i}$$
$$= \frac{10i(1 - \sqrt{3}i)}{(1 + \sqrt{3}i)(1 - \sqrt{3}i)}$$
$$= \frac{10i + 10\sqrt{3}}{4}$$
$$= \frac{5\sqrt{3} + 5i}{2}$$
$$= 5\left(\frac{\sqrt{3}}{2} + \frac{1}{2}i\right)$$
$$= 5\left(\cos\frac{\pi}{6} + i\sin\frac{\pi}{6}\right) \qquad \text{It checks.}$$

Note in Example 4 how using the trigonometric form greatly simplifies division of complex numbers. In the next lesson you will see how using the trigonometric form leads to beautifully simple ways to calculate powers and roots of complex numbers.

In 1–4, a complex number is given. **a.** Graph each number on the complex plane. **b.** Convert it to trigonometric form with $0° \le \theta < 360°$.

1. $3 + 3i$ **2.** $4\sqrt{3} - 4i$ **3.** -5 **4.** $-2 - 5i$

In 5 and 6, a complex number in trigonometric form is given. **a.** Graph each number on the complex plane. **b.** Convert to $a + bi$ form.

5. $3\left(\cos\frac{3\pi}{2} + i\sin\frac{3\pi}{2}\right)$

6. $2\left(\cos\left(-\frac{2\pi}{3}\right) + i\sin\left(-\frac{2\pi}{3}\right)\right)$

7. a. Multiply $z_1 = 2(\cos 65° + i \sin 65°)$ by $z_2 = 4(\cos 40° + i \sin 40°)$, and express the result in trigonometric form.

b. The composite of which two transformations maps z_1 to z_1z_2?

c. Illustrate the multiplication with a diagram showing the appropriate size transformation and rotation.

In 8–10, two complex numbers z_1 and z_2 are given. **a.** Find z_1z_2. **b.** Give the absolute value of the product. **c.** Give an argument of the product. Use exact values if possible.

8. $z_1 = 3(\cos 150° + i \sin 150°)$, $z_2 = 2(\cos 60° + i \sin 60°)$

9. $z_1 = 10\left(\cos \frac{11\pi}{4} + i \sin \frac{11\pi}{4}\right)$, $z_2 = 5\left(\cos \frac{\pi}{2} + i \sin \frac{\pi}{2}\right)$

10. $z_1 = 2 + 3i$, $z_2 = -4 + i$

In 11 and 12, write the conjugate of the complex number in the form given.

11. $3\left(\cos \frac{\pi}{6} + i \sin \frac{\pi}{6}\right)$

12. $[5, 175°]$

13. a. Divide $z_1 = 12(\cos 220° + i \sin 220°)$ by $z_2 = 5(\cos 100° + i \sin 100°)$ and express the result in trigonometric form.

b. The composite of which two transformations maps z_1 to $\frac{z_1}{z_2}$?

In 14 and 15, two complex numbers z_1 and z_2 are given. **a.** Find the quotient $\frac{z_1}{z_2}$ and express the result in trigonometric form. **b.** Check your result by converting to $a + bi$ form.

14. $z_1 = 18(\cos \pi + i \sin \pi)$, $z_2 = 3\left(\cos \frac{\pi}{6} + i \sin \frac{\pi}{6}\right)$

15. $z_1 = [20, 300°]$, $z_2 = [5, 60°]$

Applying the Mathematics

16. A complex number z has absolute value 7 and argument $\frac{2\pi}{3}$.

a. Express z in polar coordinate form.

b. Express z in $a + bi$ form.

17. Prove the Division of Complex Numbers Theorem. (Hint: $r(\cos \theta - i \sin \theta) = r \cos \theta - i(r \sin \theta) = r \cos(-\theta) + ir \sin(-\theta) = r(\cos(-\theta) + i \sin(-\theta))$.

18. The complex number $z = 3(\cos 40° + i \sin 40°)$ undergoes a transformation that multiplies its absolute value by 5 and rotates it 75° about the origin.

a. What is the image of z under the transformation?

b. Identify the mathematical operation and the complex number that will accomplish the transformation.

19. Let $z = 2(\cos 15° + i \sin 15°)$.

a. Calculate z^2, z^3, z^4, and z^5. (Hint: Use the fact that $z^2 = z \cdot z$, $z^3 = z^2 \cdot z$, etc.)

b. Look for a pattern in the results of part **a**. Use the pattern to predict what z^{10} should be.

Review

20. What is the length of the diagonal $\overline{OT}$ of the parallelogram formed in the complex plane by the origin, $F = 3 - i$, $R = -1 - 2i$, and T? *(Lesson 13-6)*

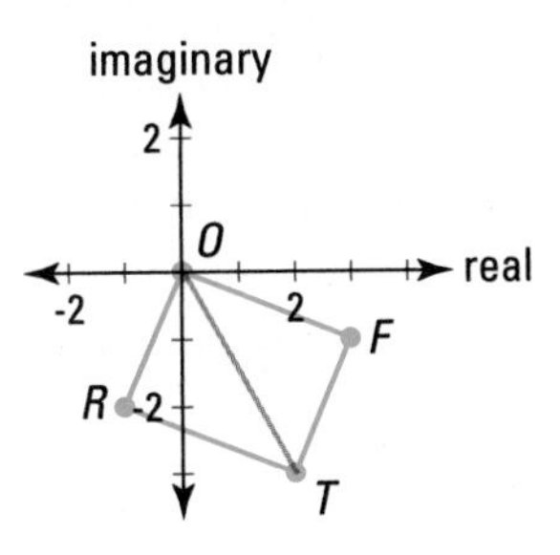

21. a. Graph $r = \csc \theta$ in rectangular coordinates.
b. Graph $r = \csc \theta$ in polar coordinates. *(Lessons 13-1, 13-5)*

22. a. Sketch a graph of $r = -\sin \theta$ in polar coordinates.
b. Prove that the graph is a circle. *(Lesson 13-5)*

23. a. Represent $\triangle ABC$ of this lesson as a 2×3 matrix.
b. Verify by matrix multiplication that $\triangle A'B'C'$ is the image of $\triangle ABC$ under a rotation of 90° and a size change of 2. *(Lesson 11-3)*

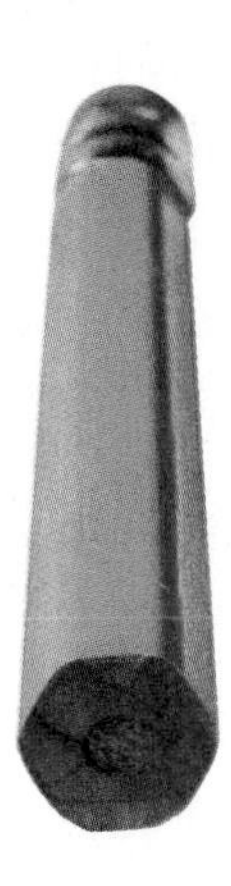

24. A coin is tossed 35 times. If the coin is hypothesized to be fair, approximate each to the nearest 0.0001.
a. The probability of getting exactly 25 heads.
b. The probability of getting fewer than 10 heads. *(Lessons 8-9, 10-6)*

In 25 and 26, expand using the Binomial Theorem. *(Lesson 8-8)*

25. $(a - b)^5$

26. $(2p + 3)^4$

27. The wooden part of a pencil is a right, regular hexagonal prism with radius 3.5 mm and length 175 mm. The "lead" is a solid cylinder with diameter 2 mm running the length of the wood. What is the volume of wood in the pencil? *(Previous course, 5-3)*

Exploration

28. Prove that $\triangle ABC$ and $\triangle A'B'C'$ in the lesson are similar triangles without using the lengths of the sides of the triangles.

LESSON

13-8

DeMoivre's Theorem

Gauss (1777–1855) was the first person to call the numbers you have been studying in the last two lessons "complex." He applied complex numbers to the study of electricity. To honor his work, a unit of electromagnetism is named after him. But during the century before Gauss, several mathematicians explored complex numbers and discovered many remarkable properties of them. This lesson presents a theorem about powers of complex numbers which is named after Abraham DeMoivre (1667–1754; his name is pronounced *de mwav'* or *dee moy'vree*).

Finding a Power of a Complex Number (Quickly)

Consider expanding $(2 + 2\sqrt{3}\,i)^4$. One way to do it is to use the Binomial Theorem.

$$\begin{aligned}(2 + 2\sqrt{3}\,i)^4 &= 2^4 + 4 \cdot 2^3(2\sqrt{3}\,i)^1 + 6 \cdot 2^2(2\sqrt{3}\,i)^2 + 4 \cdot 2^1(2\sqrt{3}\,i)^3 + (2\sqrt{3}\,i)^4 \\ &= 16 + 64\sqrt{3}\,i + 24(-12) + 8\left(24\sqrt{3}\,(-i)\right) + 16 \cdot 9 \\ &= -128 - 128\sqrt{3}\,i\end{aligned}$$

Another approach is to rewrite the number $2 + 2\sqrt{3}\,i$ in trigonometric form and use the theorems of the previous lesson. You may use the formulas or geometric inspection to find r and θ. We give all angles in degrees.

$$z = 2 + 2\sqrt{3}\,i$$
$$r = \sqrt{2^2 + (2\sqrt{3})^2} = 4$$
$$\theta = \tan^{-1}\left(\frac{2\sqrt{3}}{2}\right) = 60°$$

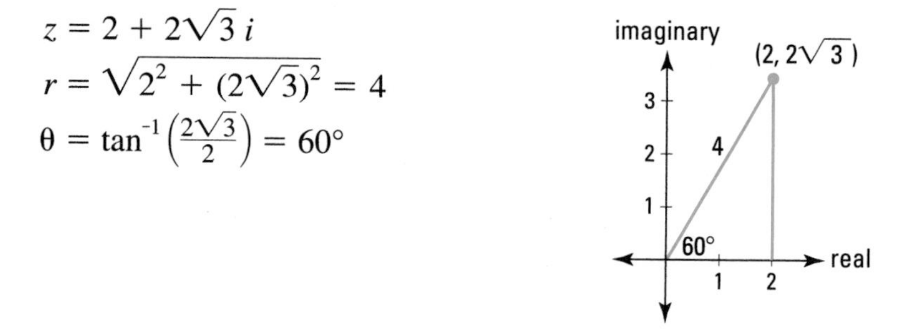

So $\quad z = 4(\cos 60° + i \sin 60°)$.

Then
$$\begin{aligned} z^2 &= 4(\cos 60° + i \sin 60°) \cdot 4(\cos 60° + i \sin 60°) \\ &= 4^2(\cos 120° + i \sin 120°), \\ z^3 &= 4^2(\cos 120° + i \sin 120°) \cdot 4(\cos 60° + i \sin 60°) \\ &= 4^3(\cos 180° + i \sin 180°),\end{aligned}$$

and
$$\begin{aligned} z^4 &= 4^3(\cos 180° + i \sin 180°) \cdot 4(\cos 60° + i \sin 60°) \\ &= 4^4(\cos 240° + i \sin 240°) \\ &= 256\left(-\frac{1}{2} - i\frac{\sqrt{3}}{2}\right) \\ &= -128 - 128\sqrt{3}\,i.\end{aligned}$$

This second approach may seem tedious, but a simple pattern is developing. Note that for each value of n, $z^n = 4^n(\cos n \cdot 60° + i \sin n \cdot 60°)$. This result, generalized, is called *DeMoivre's Theorem*.

Abraham DeMoivre

DeMoivre's Theorem

If $z = r(\cos\theta + i\sin\theta)$ and n is an integer,

then $z^n = r^n(\cos n\theta + i\sin n\theta)$.

In polar form, DeMoivre's Theorem states that if $z = [r, \theta]$, then $z^n = [r^n, n\theta]$ for all integers n. According to some historians, DeMoivre proved the theorem only for $r = 1$, but it is true for any r. The proof is beyond the scope of this course.

Graphing Powers of a Complex Number

Example 1

Let $z = 2\left(\cos\frac{\pi}{3} + i\sin\frac{\pi}{3}\right)$.

a. Find z^n for $n = 1, 2, 3, 4, 5, 6$, and 7.

b. Plot the powers in the complex plane.

Solution

a. Use DeMoivre's Theorem and convert to polar form for easy graphing.

$$z^1 = 2\left(\cos\frac{\pi}{3} + i\sin\frac{\pi}{3}\right) = \left[2, \frac{\pi}{3}\right]$$

$$z^2 = 2^2\left(\cos 2\cdot\frac{\pi}{3} + i\sin 2\cdot\frac{\pi}{3}\right) = \left[4, \frac{2\pi}{3}\right]$$

$$z^3 = 2^3\left(\cos 3\cdot\frac{\pi}{3} + i\sin 3\cdot\frac{\pi}{3}\right) = [8, \pi]$$

$$z^4 = 2^4\left(\cos 4\cdot\frac{\pi}{3} + i\sin 4\cdot\frac{\pi}{3}\right) = \left[16, \frac{4\pi}{3}\right]$$

$$z^5 = 2^5\left(\cos 5\cdot\frac{\pi}{3} + i\sin 5\cdot\frac{\pi}{3}\right) = \left[32, \frac{5\pi}{3}\right]$$

$$z^6 = 2^6\left(\cos 6\cdot\frac{\pi}{3} + i\sin 6\cdot\frac{\pi}{3}\right) = [64, 2\pi]$$

$$z^7 = 2^7\left(\cos 7\cdot\frac{\pi}{3} + i\sin 7\cdot\frac{\pi}{3}\right) = \left[128, \frac{7\pi}{3}\right]$$

b. The points are plotted at the left below. The smooth curve connecting them, shown below at the right, is called a *logarithmic spiral.*

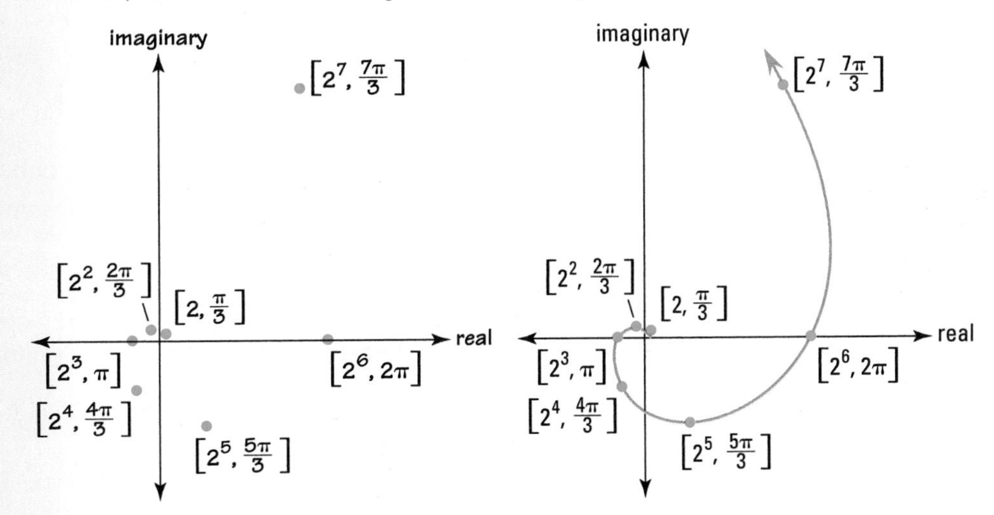

Finding the nth Roots of a Complex Number

Two complex numbers in polar and trigonometric form are equal if and only if their absolute values are equal and their arguments differ by an integral multiple of 360°. With this knowledge and DeMoivre's Theorem, you can find roots of complex numbers.

Consider, for instance, a cube root z of the complex number $8i$. By definition of cube root, $z^3 = 8i$.

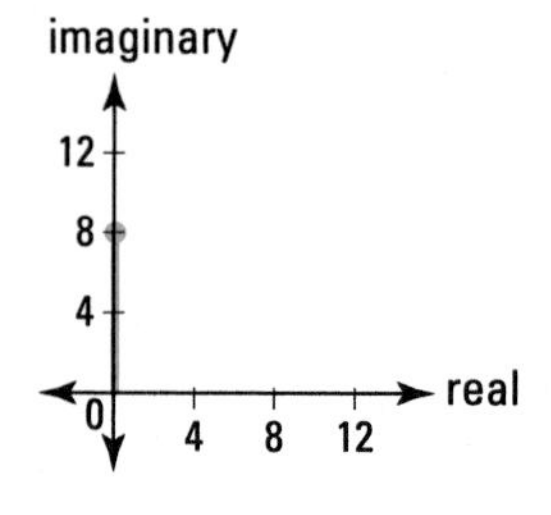

By examining the graph of $8i$ at the left, you can see that the argument of $8i$ is 90° and its absolute value is 8. So in trigonometric form, $8i = 8(\cos 90° + i \sin 90°)$. Substituting this and $z = r(\cos \theta + i \sin \theta)$ into $z^3 = 8i$ gives $(r(\cos \theta + i \sin \theta))^3 = 8(\cos 90° + i \sin 90°)$. Applying DeMoivre's Theorem, we get $r^3(\cos 3\theta + i \sin 3\theta) = 8(\cos 90° + i \sin 90°)$. For these complex numbers to be equal,

$$r^3 = 8 \quad \text{and} \quad \cos 3\theta + i \sin 3\theta = \cos 90° + i \sin 90°.$$

So $\quad r = 2 \quad$ and $\quad 3\theta = 90° + 360n°$.

Thus $\quad \theta = 30° + 120n°$, where n is an integer.

Therefore, the cube roots of $8i$ are of the form

$$z = 2(\cos (30° + 120n°) + i \sin (30° + 120n°)).$$

This solution may seem complicated, but actually there are only three distinct roots. For $n = 0, 1$, and 2, the roots are

$$2(\cos 30° + i \sin 30°) = \sqrt{3} + i,$$
$$2(\cos 150° + i \sin 150°) = -\sqrt{3} + i,$$
and
$$2(\cos 270° + i \sin 270°) = -2i.$$

For any $n > 2$, you will find that these values are repeated.

These three roots of $8i$ are plotted below. Because they all have the same absolute value 2 and are 120° apart, they lie equally spaced around a circle with center at the origin and radius 2.

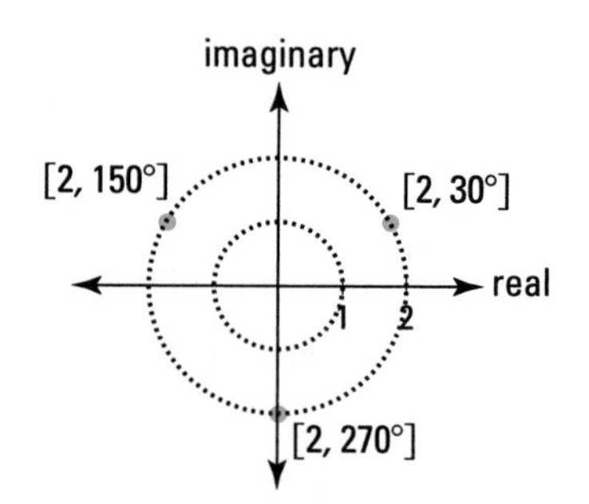

Generalizing the technique used to find the cube roots of $8i$ leads to the following theorem.

Roots of a Complex Number Theorem

Let z be any nonzero complex number and n be any positive integer. Then there are n distinct roots of $z^n = r(\cos \theta + i \sin \theta)$. They are

$$\sqrt[n]{r}\left(\cos\left(\frac{\theta}{n} + k\frac{360°}{n}\right) + i \sin\left(\frac{\theta}{n} + k\frac{360°}{n}\right)\right)$$

where $k = 0, 1, 2, \ldots, n - 1$.

Graphing the nth Roots of a Complex Number

Example 2

Find the 5th roots of $16 + 16\sqrt{3}\,i$ and graph them in the polar coordinate system.

Solution

Calculate the absolute value and an argument of $16 + 16\sqrt{3}\,i$ or examine its graph to determine that $r = 32$ and $\theta = 60°$.

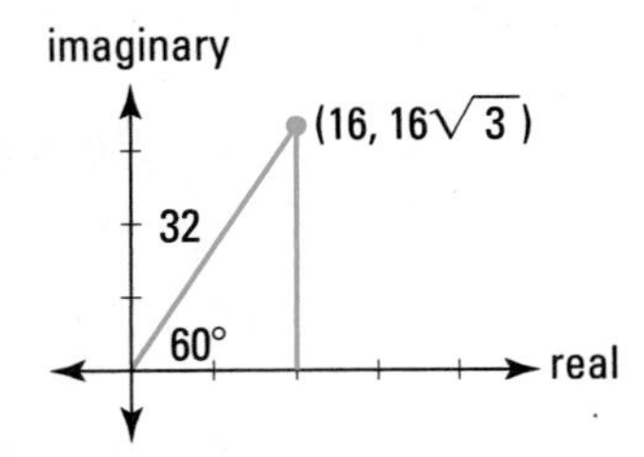

So in trigonometric form, $16 + 16\sqrt{3}\,i = 32(\cos 60° + i \sin 60°)$.
Use the theorem above. The fifth roots are

$$\sqrt[5]{32}\left(\cos\left(\frac{60°}{5} + k\frac{360°}{5}\right) + i \sin\left(\frac{60°}{5} + k\frac{360°}{5}\right)\right)$$

$$= 2(\cos(12° + 72k°) + i \sin(12° + 72k°)),$$

where $k = 0, 1, 2, 3,$ and 4.

Thus the roots are $2(\cos 12° + i \sin 12°)$, $2(\cos 84° + i \sin 84°)$, $2(\cos 156° + i \sin 156°)$, $2(\cos 228° + i \sin 228°)$, and $2(\cos 300° + i \sin 300°)$. They are graphed below. Note that the 5 fifth roots of $16 + 16\sqrt{3}\,i$ are equally spaced on a circle centered at the origin with radius $32^{1/5} = 2$.

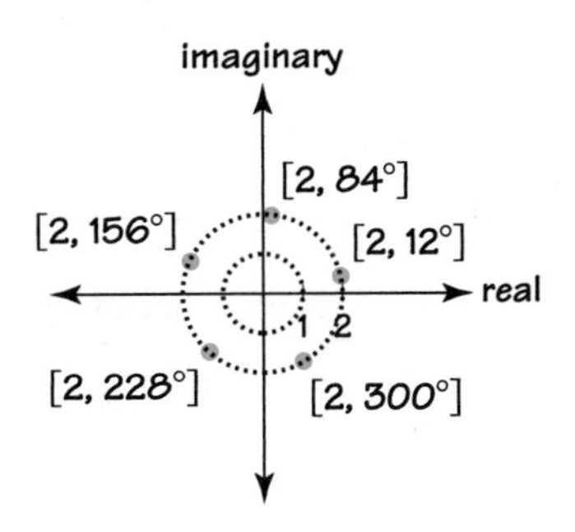

In general, for $n > 2$, the graphs of the nth roots of any nonzero complex number are vertices of a regular n-gon centered at the origin!

QUESTIONS

Covering the Reading

In 1 and 2, use DeMoivre's Theorem to find each power. Write your answer in trigonometric form.

1. $\left(3\left(\cos \frac{\pi}{5} + i \sin \frac{\pi}{5}\right)\right)^4$

2. $\left(2\left(\cos \frac{4\pi}{7} + i \sin \frac{4\pi}{7}\right)\right)^3$

3. Consider $z = 2\left(\cos \frac{\pi}{6} + i \sin \frac{\pi}{6}\right)$.
- **a.** Use DeMoivre's Theorem to calculate z^n for $n = 2$ to 6.
- **b.** Plot z^1, z^2, z^3, z^4, z^5, and z^6 in the complex plane.
- **c.** Describe the pattern in the graphs of the powers of z.

4.
- **a.** Solve the equation $z^3 = 27(\cos 150° + i \sin 150°)$.
- **b.** Plot the solutions in the complex plane.
- **c.** Describe the graph in part **b**.

5. Find the 3 cube roots of $125(\cos 30° + i \sin 30°)$.

6. Find the 4 fourth roots of $7\left(\cos \frac{4\pi}{5} + i \sin \frac{4\pi}{5}\right)$.

7. Find the square roots of -1.

Cartoonists use nth roots and other symbols to satirize advanced mathematics.

Applying the Mathematics

In 8 and 9, use DeMoivre's Theorem to find each power in $a + bi$ form.

8. $(3i)^4$

9. $\left(-\sqrt{3} + i\right)^6$

In 10 and 11, write the roots in polar form and plot them in the complex plane.

10. the fourth roots of $8 + 8\sqrt{3}\, i$

11. the sixth roots of $64i$

In 12 and 13, plot the solutions to each equation in the complex plane.

12. $z^3 = 8$

13. $z^4 = -16$

14. A ninth root of z is $2(\cos 30° + i \sin 30°)$. Find z in polar form.

Review

15. Write $7(\cos 10° + i \sin 10°)$ in $a + bi$ form. *(Lesson 13-7)*

16. If $z_1 = 8(\cos 70° + i \sin 70°)$ and $z_2 = 5(\cos 155° + i \sin 155°)$, find $z_1 \cdot z_2$. *(Lesson 13-7)*

17.
- **a.** Sketch a graph of $r = e^{\theta/3}$.
- **b.** Show that the points on the curve in part **a** satisfy the relationship $\ln r = k\theta$ for some constant k and identify k. *(Lessons 6-4, 13-5)*

18. Prove or disprove: For all α, $\sin^2 \alpha = \frac{1}{2}(1 - \cos^2 \alpha)$. *(Lesson 13-2)*

19. Determine an equation of the hyperbola with major and minor axes of lengths 4 and 1, centered around the point (3, -2), and whose major axis is rotated counterclockwise by 30° from the horizontal. *(Lesson 12-4)*

20. Find the product. $\begin{bmatrix} -1 & 0 & 1 \\ 0 & 1 & -1 \\ 1 & -1 & 0 \end{bmatrix} \cdot \begin{bmatrix} 1 & 2 & 3 \\ 2 & 3 & 1 \\ 3 & 1 & 2 \end{bmatrix}$ *(Lesson 11-1)*

21. Evaluate $\lim_{n \to \infty} \frac{n + 3}{4 - 2n}$. *(Lesson 8-2)*

Exploration

22. **a.** Graph the first ten terms of each sequence $a_n = z^n$.

i. $z = [1.25, 40°]$

ii. $z = [1, 40°]$

iii. $z = [0.9, 40°]$

b. Compare and contrast the three sets of points, and predict what happens for higher powers.

LESSON

13-9

The Mandelbrot Set

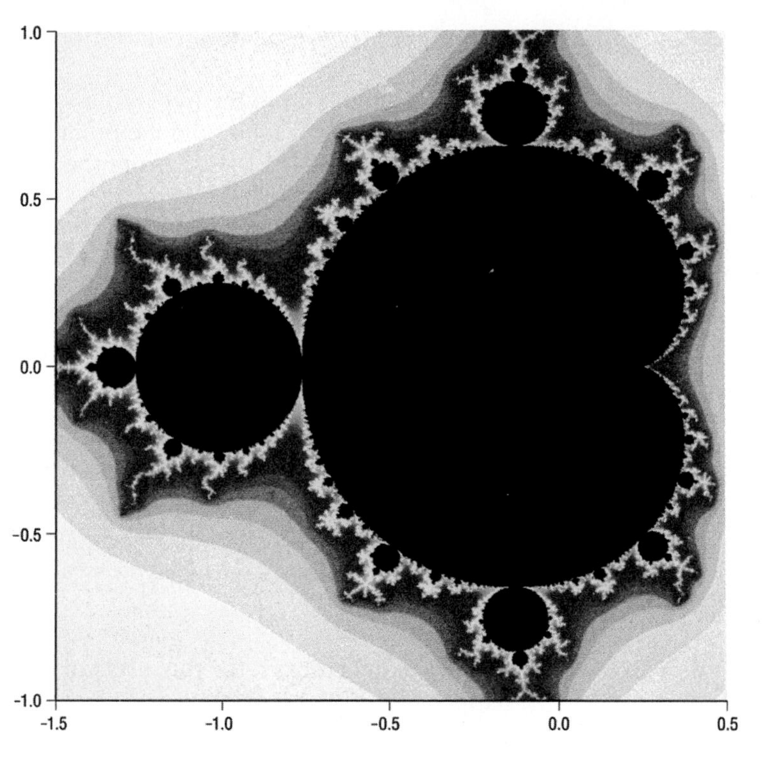

The last lesson ended with a geometrically beautiful result that has been known for about 200 years. This lesson discusses a geometric set that has been known only since 1980.

In recent years, a new field of mathematics has arisen, called *dynamical systems*, in which complex numbers play an important role. Some of the products of this field are beautiful computer-generated drawings which have won awards in art competitions. Among these are drawings involving the *Mandelbrot set* (named for Benoit Mandelbrot, a mathematician at IBM), which is a particular set of complex numbers plotted in the complex plane. Above is a graph of this set in part of the plane. Points colored black are in the Mandelbrot set. Points colored red or yellow are outside the set.

Determining Whether a Point Is in the Mandelbrot Set

Points in the Mandelbrot set are defined recursively. Let c be a fixed complex number, and consider this sequence of complex numbers starting with c.

$$\begin{cases} z_1 = c; \\ z_n = (z_{n-1})^2 + c \text{ for } n > 1. \end{cases}$$

The recursion squares the previous z value, adds c to the result, then repeats these two steps indefinitely. For many values of c, the limit of $|z_n|$ is infinity. Points in the Mandelbrot set are those values of c for which the limit of $|z_n|$ is not infinity.

For instance, let $c = -1.5 - 1.0i$. Then the sequence begins with the following values.

$$z_1 = c = -1.5 - 1.0i, \text{ so } |z_1| \approx 1.80$$
$$z_2 = (-1.5 - 1.0i)^2 + (-1.5 - 1.0i) = -0.25 + 2i, \text{ so } |z_2| \approx 2.02$$
$$z_3 = (-0.25 + 2i)^2 + (-1.5 - 1.0i) = -5.4375 - 2i, \text{ so } |z_3| \approx 5.79$$

It can be shown that $|z_n|$ will go to infinity if and only if at some stage of the iteration $|z_n| > 2$. It also turns out that for most values of c which iterate to infinity, $|z_n|$ reaches 2 rather quickly. For these reasons, $c = -1.5 - 1.0i$ is discarded as not being part of the Mandelbrot set. Note that the point (-1.5, -1.0) is not colored black in the graph on page 852.

Examining Parts of the Mandelbrot Set

By varying the initial c and the size of the window, the Mandelbrot set can be studied to virtually any degree of detail. The three graphs below show the set as you zoom in on the region around the point $-0.55 + 0.62i$. Note how the "bump" on the original graph is very similar in shape to the original graph itself. For this reason, the Mandelbrot set is sometimes called "self-similar." In fact, however, most of the parts of the graph differ in some way.

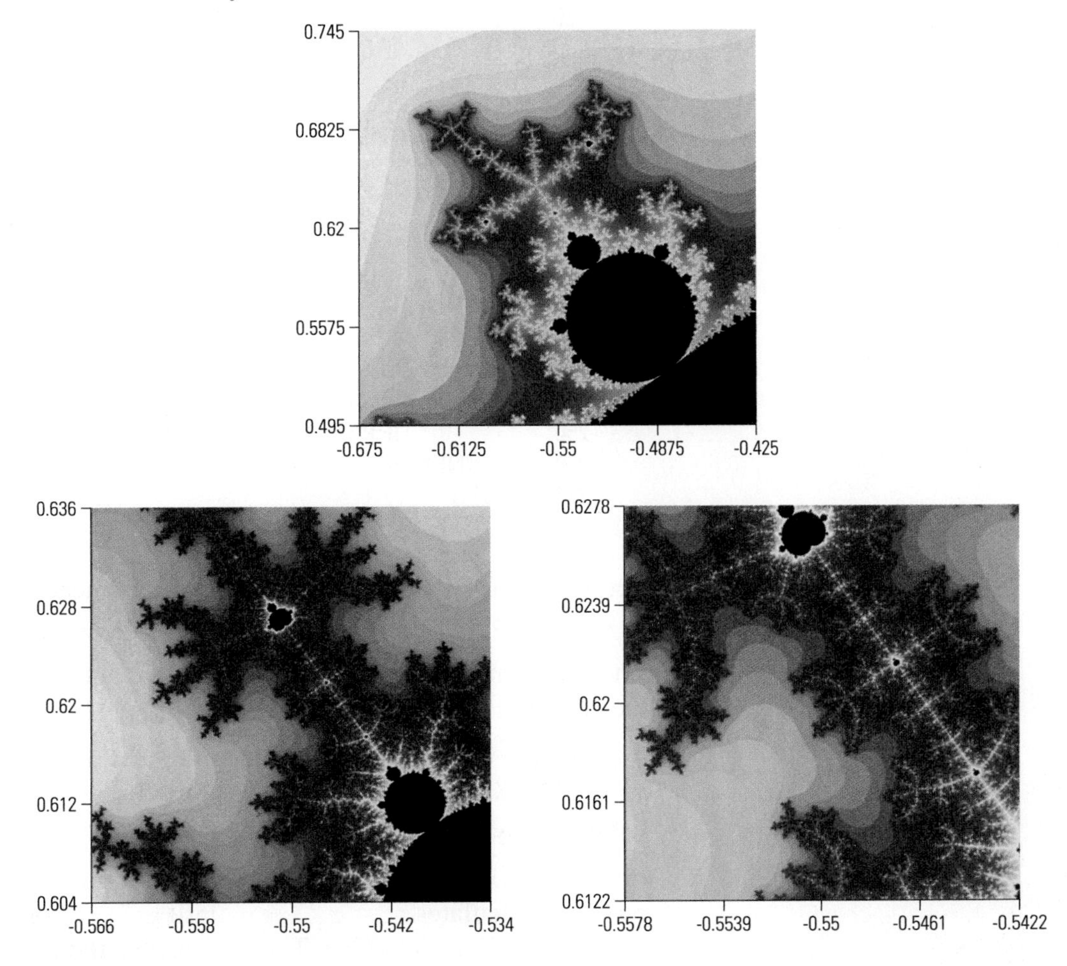

In the 1980s, John H. Hubbard, a mathematician at Cornell University, generated graphs of the Mandelbrot set using a computer. Hubbard's pioneer programs inspired many programs for drawing the Mandelbrot set. The pictures in this lesson were created with *The Beauty of Fractals Lab*, written by Thomas Eberhardt and Marc Parmet. This program makes use of sophisticated computing techniques and languages in order to increase the speed of the calculations and drawings. You can draw a small version of the set, however, using the following BASIC program.

```
10  REM MANDELZOOM
20  INPUT "ENTER THE REAL AND IMAGINARY PARTS OF C"; ACORNER,
    BCORNER
30  INPUT "ENTER THE SIZE OF THE VIEWING WINDOW"; SIZE
40  CLS
50  P = 50
60  DIM PIC(P,P)
70  GAP = SIZE / P
80  FOR J = 1 TO P
90      FOR K = 1 TO P
100         AC = ACORNER + J*GAP
110         BC = BCORNER + K*GAP
120         AZ = 0:BZ = 0: COUNT = 1
130         IF COUNT > 100 THEN 200
140             OLDAZ = AZ
150             AZ = AZ*AZ – BZ*BZ + AC
160             BZ = 2*OLDAZ*BZ + BC
170             MAGZ = SQR(AZ*AZ + BZ*BZ)
180             IF MAGZ > 2 THEN 210
190             COUNT = COUNT + 1: GO TO 130
200         PIC(J,K) = 1
210     NEXT K
220 NEXT J
230 FOR J = 1 TO P
240     FOR K = 1 TO P
250         IF PIC(J,K) = 1 THEN PSET (J,P–K)
260     NEXT K
270 NEXT J
```

The program has four major steps. (You do not need to understand every detail of the program.)

1. The program asks for the initial value of c and the size of the window in the complex plane (lines 20 and 30).

2. It scales the information from step (1) into "pixel-units" and creates an array PIC(J, K) for each pixel in the graph (lines 50–70). In this program, the rectangle is 50 pixels on a side (P = 50).

3. For every pixel with coordinates (AC, BC) in the viewing window, the program calculates $z_n = z_{n-1}^2 + c$ until $|z_n| > 2$ or $n = 100$, whichever comes first (lines 80–220). The bigger n is, the more accurate the graph, but the longer the time it takes to do the calculations. If $|z_n| \leq 2$ after

100 iterations of the squaring process, then the pixel at PIC(J, K) is set to 1 (line 200). Lines 150–170 apply the mathematics of complex numbers you learned in Lesson 13-7. For z = AZ + BZi, the real part of z^2 is $(AZ)^2 - (BZ)^2$ and the imaginary part is 2(AZ)(BZ). The variable MAGZ is the absolute value of the new iteration of z.

4. Finally the graph is drawn (lines 230–270). If PIC(J, K) = 1, the point is in the set and the pixel is turned on (line 250).

(Note: this program is written to work on Macintosh computers running MS-BASIC. For other computers and other versions of BASIC there are slight variations. Run on one particular computer with $c = -2 - 1.25i$ and size = 2.5, MANDELZOOM took 28 seconds to produce the graph at left below. When run with P = 200 (line 50) and a maximum count of 200 rather than 100 (line 130), it took 14 minutes and produced the graph at the right.)

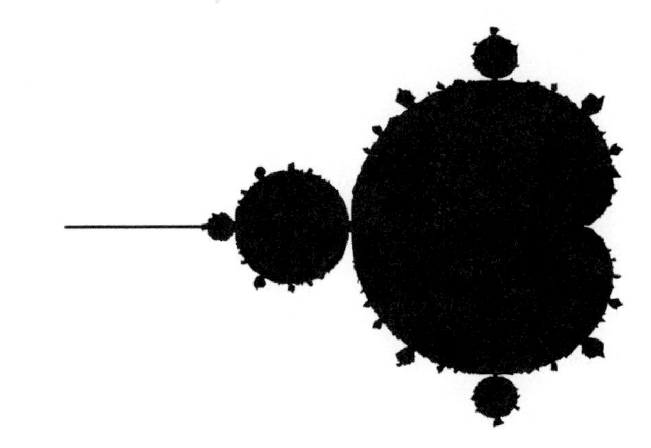

Using a BASIC program is obviously not the best way to graph the Mandelbrot set, but it shows how you can use the computing and mathematics skills you have studied in this text. With better programs and faster computers, you can apply the mathematics you know to generate gorgeous views like the ones below, centered at about $-0.76 + 0.26i$.

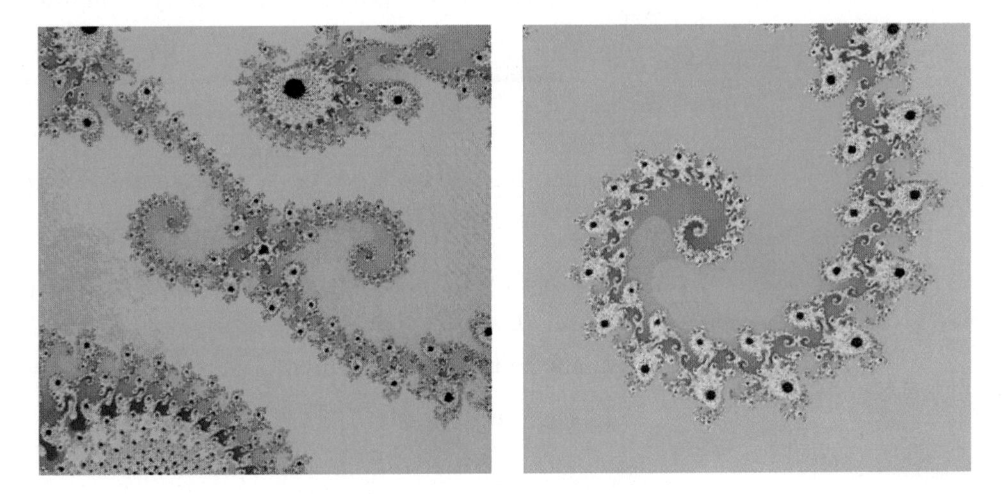

The boundary of a Mandelbrot set is an example of a *fractal*. Fractals can be generated by special functions embodying randomness. Thus, in a way, the Mandelbrot set is related to all the themes of this book—functions, statistics, and trigonometry. We hope you agree that it is a fitting subject for the last lesson of this book.

QUESTIONS

Covering the Reading

1. **a.** Calculate z_1, z_2, and z_3 in the Mandelbrot recursion for $c = 0 + 0i$.
   b. Is $c = 0 + 0i$ in the Mandelbrot set? Why or why not?

In 2–4, based on $|z_4|$, is the point in the Mandelbrot set?

2. $-1 + 0i$
3. $0 + 0.5i$
4. $1 + i$

5. Refer to the BASIC MANDELZOOM program in the lesson. Let ACORNER = 0.2, BCORNER = 0, and SIZE = 0.1 .
   a. Give the values of AC and BC the first time the computer executes lines 100 and 110.
   b. Give the values of AZ, BZ, and MAGZ the first time the computer executes lines 150–170.
   c. Will the computer turn on PIC(1, 1)?

In 6–8, run the program MANDELZOOM for complex numbers $x + yi$ in the indicated viewing window.

6. Describe the graph a computer generates for $-0.5 \le x \le -0.49$, $0 \le y \le 0.01$.

7. Draw a rough sketch of the graph a computer generates for $-1.5 \le x \le -0.9$, $-0.3 \le y \le 0.3$, $c = -1.5 - 0.3i$.

8. **a.** Use the close-up views around $c = -0.5507 + 0.6259i$ to hypothesize whether c is actually in the set.
   b. Test your hypothesis in part **a** by computing $|z_4|$ for this value of c.

Review

In 9 and 10, find each power. Write your answers in $a + bi$ form. *(Lesson 13-8)*

9. $\left(\frac{\sqrt{2}}{2} + \frac{\sqrt{2}}{2}i\right)^5$
10. $\left(1 + i\sqrt{3}\right)^6$

In 11 and 12, write each root in trigonometric form and plot it in the complex plane. *(Lesson 13-8)*

11. the 3 cube roots of $10(\cos 12° + i \sin 12°)$

12. the 5 fifth roots of i

In 13 and 14, two complex numbers z_1 and z_2 are given. **a.** Express z_1 and z_2 in trigonometric form. **b.** Evaluate $z_1 \cdot z_2$ and $\frac{z_1}{z_2}$. *(Lesson 13-7)*

13. $z_1 = 3 + \sqrt{2}\,i$, $z_2 = -3 - \sqrt{2}\,i$

14. $z_1 = \left[0, \frac{\pi}{6}\right]$, $z_2 = [2, 0]$

15. Find $|z_1 z_2|$ when $z_1 = 112 - 15i$ and $z_2 = 0.01 + 4i$. *(Lesson 13-7)*

16. The graph of $r = 2 \sin \theta \cos^2 \theta$ is called a *bifolium*.
a. Sketch the bifolium for $0 \le \theta \le \pi$.
b. Graph $r = 2$ on the same axes as the graph in part **a.** Does $2 \sin \theta \cos^2 \theta = 2$ for any θ in $0 \le \theta \le \pi$? *(Lesson 13-5)*

17. A point $[r, \theta]$ has $\theta = -180°$.
a. Where must this point be?
b. Give a rectangular equation for all such points. *(Lesson 13-4)*

In 18 and 19, a trigonometric equation is given. **a.** Use an automatic grapher to test whether the equation may be an identity. **b.** Prove your conclusion in part **a.** *(Lessons 13-2, 13-3)*

18. $\frac{1 + \cos \alpha}{\sin \alpha} = \cot \frac{\alpha}{2}$ (Hint: $\cos \alpha = \cos\left(2 \cdot \frac{\alpha}{2}\right)$ and $\sin \alpha = \sin\left(2 \cdot \frac{\alpha}{2}\right)$.)

19. $\sec \theta = \sec (\pi - \theta)$

Exploration

20. Explore the Mandelbrot set on intervals of your own choosing.

A project presents an opportunity for you to extend your knowledge of a topic related to the material of this chapter. You should allow more time for a project than you do for a typical homework question.

1 Euler's Theorem

Using calculus, it can be shown that if x is in radians,

$$\cos x = 1 - \frac{x^2}{2!} + \frac{x^4}{4!} - \frac{x^6}{6!} + \ldots$$

and $\sin x = x - \frac{x^3}{3!} + \frac{x^5}{5!} - \frac{x^7}{7!} + \ldots$.

These series are sometimes the ones used in calculators to approximate values of sine and cosine.

a. Approximate cos 0.2 using the first three terms of the appropriate series. Also, find the fourth term of the series. Show that the difference between your approximation and the calculator value of cos 0.2 is less than the absolute value of the fourth term.

b. Repeat part **a** for sin 0.2 .

c. Give an explicit definition for the nth term of each series.

d. Use the series expansion for $\sin x$ and $\cos x$ to find series expansions for $\sin 2x$ and $\cos 2x$. Check your answers with a calculator.

e. In Lesson 6-4 you studied the following series expression for e^x.

$$e^x = 1 + x + \frac{x^2}{2!} + \frac{x^3}{3!} + \frac{x^4}{4!} + \ldots$$

It can be proved that this series converges even if the exponent is a complex number. Find a series expansion for e^{ix}.

f. Use the result of part **e** to prove that

$$e^{ix} = \cos x + i \sin x.$$

g. Use the result of part **f** to show that $i = e^{i \cdot \pi/2}$.

h. Find a complex number in the form $a + bi$ for $e^{i\pi}$. (The answer to this is known as *Euler's Theorem*, and is one of the most extraordinary results in mathematics.)

i. Find i^i. (It may surprise you that i^i is a real number.)

2 Famous Polar Equations

Explore some of the following classic polar equations with an automatic grapher.

If the grapher does not have an option for entering equations in the form $r^2 = f(\theta)$, graph $r = \sqrt{f(\theta)}$ and $r = -\sqrt{f(\theta)}$ simultaneously. In all the equations, a may be any nonzero real number. Graph each equation a few times, with different values of a. Describe the patterns that you find.

a. Cardioids: $r = a(\cos \theta - 1)$

b. Cissoid of Diocles: $r = a \sin \theta \tan \theta$

c. Cochleoid (Ouija board curve): $r = \frac{a \sin \theta}{\theta}$

d. Folium of Descartes: $r = \frac{3a \sin \theta \cos \theta}{\sin^3 \theta + \cos^3 \theta}$

e. Strophoid: $r = a \cos 2\theta \sec \theta$

f. Lemniscate of Bernoulli: $r^2 = a^2 \cos 2\theta$; $r^2 = a^2 \sin 2\theta$

g. Lituus: $r^2 = \frac{a^2}{\theta}$

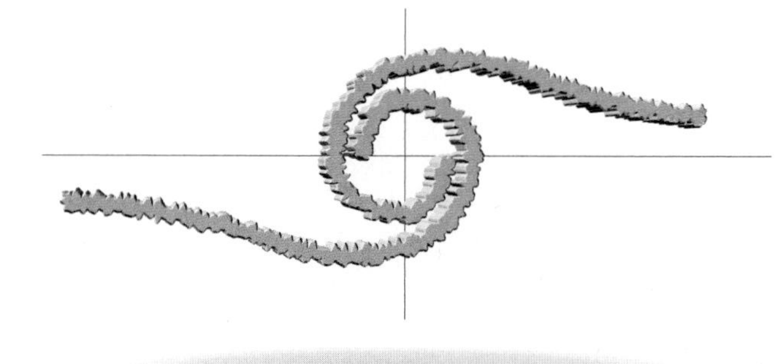

3 The Mandelbrot Set

Use the BASIC MANDELZOOM program in Lesson 13-9. Experiment with the program. Leave P = 50 and try various values of c and SIZE. Remember to be patient—the program as written takes up to 45 minutes to run. You can speed it up by changing line 130 to 130 FOR COUNT = 1 TO 50, but this decreases detail and may give you a black square as the image.

a. Reproduce the 50 × 50 pixel Mandelbrot graph in the lesson. Let $c = -2 - 1.25i$, SIZE = 2.5.

b. The image to the right has $c = 0.26 + 0i$ and SIZE = 0.01, P = 100 and COUNT = 1 to 100. It took about $1\frac{1}{2}$ hours. Try a P = 50 version if you don't have time.

c. Look around the "neck" of the set. This is the area near $-0.76 + 0i$. (Do not expect results like the fancy drawings in the lesson.)

SUMMARY

Graphs can be used to test whether an equation is an identity: check if the graphs of the functions determined by the two sides of the proposed identity coincide. While the graphs cannot prove an identity, they can help in finding a counterexample. Some of the techniques of proving identities include: start with one side and rewrite it until it equals the other side; rewrite each side independently until equal expressions are obtained on both sides; begin with a known identity and derive equivalent statements until the proposed identity appears.

Many of identities involving circular functions hold only on restricted domains, excluding points where one or more of the functions in the identity are not defined. A point where a function is undefined is called a singularity. Singularities of functions show up as vertical asymptotes or missing single points on the graphs.

In a polar coordinate system, a point is identified by $[r, \theta]$, if and only if it is the image, under a rotation θ about the pole O, of the point on the polar axis with coordinate r. Every point has infinitely many polar coordinate representations. The four relations $x = r\cos\theta$, $y = r\sin\theta$, $r = \sqrt{x^2 + y^2}$, and $\tan\theta = \frac{y}{x}$ relate polar coordinates $[r, \theta]$ and rectangular coordinates (x, y).

Graphs of sets of points which satisfy equations involving r and θ include familiar figures, such as lines and circles, and beautiful spirals, rose curves, and other curves that do not have simple descriptions in terms of rectangular coordinates.

The complex number $a + bi$ is represented in rectangular coordinates as the point (a, b). It can also be represented in polar coordinates by the point $[r, \theta]$, where $r = \sqrt{a^2 + b^2}$ and $\tan\theta = \frac{b}{a}$. The trigonometric form of this number is $r(\cos\theta + i\sin\theta)$.

If $z = a + bi$, the absolute value of z is $|z| = \sqrt{a^2 + b^2}$. Addition of complex numbers $A = a + bi$ and $B = c + di$ where A, B, and the origin are not collinear, can be represented by a parallelogram in the complex plane with vertices at the origin, point A, point B, and the point $(a + c) + (b + d)i$. For $z_1 = r_1(\cos\theta_1 + i\sin\theta_1)$ and $z_2 = r_2(\cos\theta_2 + i\sin\theta_2)$, the product z_1z_2 is equal to $|z_1z_2| \cdot (\cos(\theta_1 + \theta_2) + i\sin(\theta_1 + \theta_2))$. This product is represented graphically as the image of z_1 under the composite of a size change with magnitude $|z_2|$ and a rotation with magnitude θ_2. Similarly, $\frac{z_1}{z_2} = \frac{|z_1|}{|z_2|}(\cos(\theta_1 - \theta_2) + i\sin(\theta_1 - \theta_2))$ is the image of z_1 under the composite of a size change of magnitude $\frac{1}{|z_2|}$ and a rotation of magnitude $-\theta_2$.

Repeated multiplications of a single complex number $z = r(\cos\theta + i\sin\theta)$ lead to DeMoivre's Theorem: For all postive integers n, $z^n = r^n(\cos n\theta + i\sin n\theta)$. Working backwards leads to a theorem for finding nth roots: If $z^n = r(\cos\theta + i\sin\theta)$ with $r > 0$, then $z = \sqrt[n]{r}\left(\cos\left(\frac{\theta}{n} + k\frac{360°}{n}\right) + i\sin\left(\frac{\theta}{n} + k\frac{360°}{n}\right)\right)$ where $k = 0, 1, 2, \ldots, n - 1$.

The Mandelbrot set is a recently-discovered, important, and intriguing graph of a set of complex numbers. Each number c in the set has the property that the sequence defined by

$$\begin{cases} z_1 = c \\ z_n = (z_{n-1})^2 + c, n > 1 \end{cases}$$ is bounded.

VOCABULARY

Below are the most important terms and phrases for this chapter. You should be able to give a general description and a specific example of each and a precise definition for those marked with an asterisk (*).

Lesson 13-1
*secant, sec
*cosecant, csc
*cotangent, cot
reciprocal trigonometric functions

Lesson 13-2
corollary

Lesson 13-3
singularity
removable singularity

Lesson 13-4
polar coordinate system
pole, polar axis
polar coordinates, $[r, \theta]$
polar grid

Lesson 13-5
rose curve, petal curve
Archimedan spiral
cardioid
logarithmic spiral

Lesson 13-6
Argand diagrams
complex plane
real axis, imaginary axis
Geometric Addition Theorem
*absolute value, modulus of a complex number
*argument of a complex number
polar form of a complex number

Lesson 13-7
*trigonometric form of a complex number
Product of Complex Numbers Theorem
Division of Complex Numbers Theorem

Lesson 13-8
DeMoivre's Theorem
Roots of a Complex Number Theorem

PROGRESS SELF-TEST

Take this test as you would take a test in class. Then check the test yourself using the solutions at the back of the book.

In 1 and 2, evaluate without a calculator.

1. $\cot\left(-\frac{\pi}{6}\right)$

2. $\sec 405°$

3. Consider the function $y = \sec(x - \pi)$.

a. Sketch a graph of the function.

b. State the period of the graph.

c. State equations of two of the asymptotes.

4. Give the apparent singularities of the function whose graph is shown below.

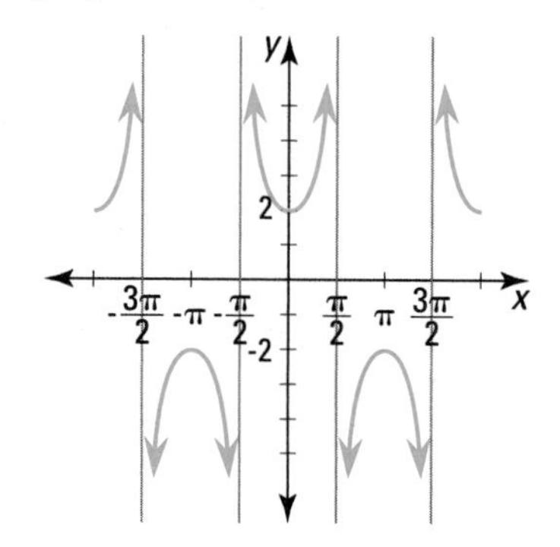

In 5 and 6, an automatic grapher shows the same graph for $f(x) = 2\cos^2 x \tan x$ and $g(x) = \sin 2x$.

5. *True or false.* This graph proves that the equation $2\cos^2 x \tan x = \sin 2x$ is an identity.

6. a. What values are not in the domain of the identity in Question 5?

b. Prove that the equation in Question 5 is an identity without using the graphs.

In 7–9, plot on an appropriate coordinate system.

7. $[r, \theta] = [4, -185°]$

8. $-4 + 3i$

9. $2\left(\cos\frac{\pi}{2} + i\sin\frac{\pi}{2}\right)$

10. The rectangular coordinates of a point are $(5, -5\sqrt{3})$. Find two pairs of polar coordinates $[r, \theta]$ that name this same point. Give θ in radians.

11. Expand $(3(\cos 20° + i\sin 20°))^4$ and write in $a + bi$ form.

12. Let $z = -\frac{1}{2} + \frac{\sqrt{3}}{2}i$. **a.** Write z in polar form.

b. Write z in trigonometric form.

13. Find the 4 fourth roots of $81(\cos 260° + i\sin 260°)$.

14. a. Give the coordinates of two points on the graph of $r = \sin 3\theta$.

b. Trace the graph below and label on your copy the points you gave in part **a**.

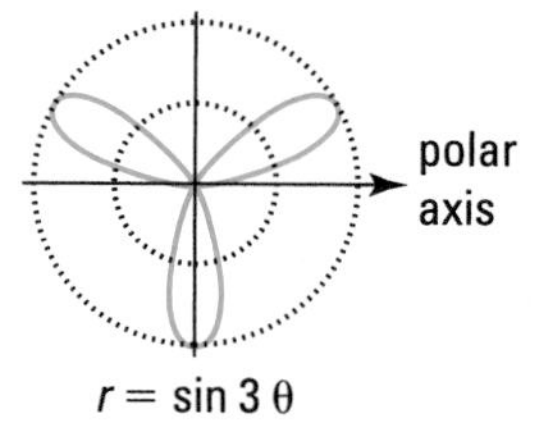

$r = \sin 3\theta$

In 15 and 16, two complex numbers z_1 and z_2 are given. **a.** Perform the indicated operation. **b.** Describe the effect of the operation on the absolute value and argument of z_1.

15. $z_1 = -3i$, $z_2 = 5\left(\cos\frac{\pi}{12} + i\sin\frac{\pi}{12}\right)$; find z_1z_2.

16. $z_1 = [6, \pi]$, $z_2 = [2, \pi]$; find $\frac{z_1}{z_2}$.

17. Prove: For all θ for which both functions are defined, $(1 - \sin^2\theta)(1 + \tan^2\theta) = 1$.

18. Graph $r = 6\cos\theta$ in the polar coordinate system.

"We did the whole room over in fractals."

CHAPTER REVIEW

Questions on SPUR Objectives

SPUR stands for **S**kills, **P**roperties, **U**ses, and **R**epresentations. The Chapter Review questions are grouped according to the SPUR Objectives for this chapter.

SKILLS DEAL WITH THE PROCEDURES USED TO GET ANSWERS.

Objective A: *Evaluate the reciprocal trigonometric functions.* *(Lesson 13-1)*

In 1–3, give exact values.

1. $\csc \frac{\pi}{2}$ **2.** $\cot\left(-\frac{\pi}{4}\right)$ **3.** $\sec 390°$

In 4–6, evaluate to the nearest hundredth.

4. $\sec 28°$ **5.** $\csc 3.7$ **6.** $\cot 237°$

Objective B: *Perform operations with complex numbers in polar or trigonometric form.* *(Lesson 13-7)*

In 7 and 8, determine z_1z_2. Leave your answer in the form of the original numbers.

7. $z_1 = 5(\cos 32° + i \sin 32°)$,
$z_2 = 3(\cos 157° + i \sin 157°)$

8. $z_1 = [7, 0]$, $z_2 = \left[1.3, \frac{\pi}{4}\right]$

In 9 and 10, given z_1 and z_1z_2, determine z_2. Leave your answer in the form of the original numbers.

9. $z_1 = 9\left(\cos \frac{\pi}{5} + i \sin \frac{\pi}{5}\right)$,
$z_1z_2 = 18\left(\cos \frac{\pi}{2} + i \sin \frac{\pi}{2}\right)$

10. $z_1 = \left[2, \frac{\pi}{6}\right]$, $z_1z_2 = \left[5, \frac{7\pi}{6}\right]$

In 11 and 12, a complex number is given. **a.** Give the absolute value. **b.** Give an argument.

11. $-10 + 12i$ **12.** $\cos \frac{\pi}{3} + i \sin \frac{\pi}{3}$

Objective C: *Represent complex numbers in different forms.* *(Lessons 13-6, 13-7)*

In 13–15, write the complex number in polar form. Use an argument θ in the interval $0° \le \theta < 360°$.

13. $-\sqrt{3} + i$ **14.** $2 + 5i$

15. $\frac{1}{8}\left(\cos \frac{\pi}{5} + i \sin \frac{\pi}{5}\right)$

In 16 and 17, write the complex number in $a + bi$ form.

16. $3(\cos(-120°) + i \sin(-120°))$ **17.** $\left[4, \frac{2\pi}{5}\right]$

18. Give two different representations of the complex number $[-2, 45°]$ in trigonometric form.

Objective D: *Find powers and roots of complex numbers.* *(Lesson 13-8)*

In 19 and 20, find z^n for the given z and n.

19. $z = \sqrt{2} + \sqrt{2}\,i$, $n = 5$

20. $z = 3(\cos 240° + i \sin 240°)$, $n = 4$

In 21 and 22, find the indicated roots.

21. the 4 fourth roots of $256(\cos 12° + i \sin 12°)$

22. the 6 sixth roots of -2

PROPERTIES DEAL WITH THE PRINCIPLES BEHIND THE MATHEMATICS.

Objective E: *Apply properties of the reciprocal trigonometric functions.* *(Lesson 13-1)*

In 23 and 24, consider the function $f(x) = \csc x$.

23. What is the period of f?

24. For what values is f undefined?

In 25 and 26, *true or false*.

25. $\sec \theta = \frac{1}{\csc \theta}$, for all θ.

26. The function $f(x) = \cot x$ is an even function.

CHAPTER THIRTEEN

Objective F: *Prove trigonometric identities.* *(Lessons 13-2, 13-3)*

27. Prove the identity $(1 - \cos^2 x)(1 + \cot^2 x) = 1$ by starting with the left-hand side and rewriting it until the other side appears.

28. Prove that $\sin\left(\theta - \frac{\pi}{4}\right) = -\cos\left(\theta + \frac{\pi}{4}\right)$ for all θ by rewriting each side of the equation independently until equal expressions are obtained.

29. Prove that $\csc^2 x - \cot^2 x = 1$ for all $x \neq n\pi$, where n is an integer, starting with the Pythagorean Identity.

30. Prove: For all θ for which the equation is defined, $\frac{\sin\theta}{\cos\theta \cdot \tan\theta} = 1$.

Objective G: *Describe singularities of functions.* *(Lesson 13-3)*

31. Explain why the restriction $x \neq n\pi$ (n an integer) is necessary for the identity in Question 29.

32. Consider the identity given in Question 30.

a. Determine all the singularities of the functions mentioned in the equation.

b. Give the biggest domain on which the identity holds.

33. a. Determine the singularities (if any) of the functions with the given equations.

i. $f(x) = \frac{x^3 - 27}{x - 3}$ **ii.** $g(x) = \frac{x^3 - 27}{x^2 + 3x + 9}$

b. *True or false.* The proposed identity is true for all real numbers x. Explain your answer.

i. $\frac{x^3 - 27}{x - 3} = x^2 + 3x + 9$

ii. $\frac{x^3 - 27}{x^2 + 3x + 9} = x - 3$

34. *True or false.* The functions $f(x) = \frac{1}{1 - \cos x}$ and $g(x) = \frac{1}{1 - \cos^2 x}$ have the same singularities. Explain your answer.

USES DEAL WITH APPLICATIONS OF MATHEMATICS IN REAL SITUATIONS.

There are no objectives relating to uses in this chapter.

REPRESENTATIONS DEAL WITH PICTURES, GRAPHS, OR OBJECTS THAT ILLUSTRATE CONCEPTS.

Objective H: *Use an automatic grapher to test a proposed identity.* *(Lessons 13-2, 13-3)*

35. *True or false.* Showing that the graphs of the functions on the two sides of a given equality in a single variable coincide when created by an automatic grapher proves that the equation is an identity.

In 36–38, an equation is given.
a. Graph the functions related to the two sides of the proposed identity. **b.** Decide if a person should attempt to prove the identity. Explain your reasoning.

36. $\frac{x^2 - 4x - 5}{x + 1} = x - 5$

37. $\sin^2 x(1 + \tan^2 x) = \tan^2 x$

38. $\frac{\csc x}{\sec x} = \tan x$

Objective I: *Given polar coordinates of a point, determine its rectangular coordinates and vice versa.* *(Lesson 13-4)*

In 39 and 40, convert from polar coordinates to rectangular coordinates.

39. $\left[4, \frac{3\pi}{2}\right]$

40. $[-3, 85°]$

In 41 and 42, give one pair of polar coordinates for each (x, y) pair.

41. $(5, 2)$

42. $(-2, -3)$

43. A point is located at $(-4\sqrt{3}, 4)$ in a rectangular coordinate system. Find three pairs of polar coordinates $[r, \theta]$ that name this same point. Assume θ is in radians.

44. When the coordinates of P are written in polar form, $\theta = \frac{\pi}{6}$. When the coordinates of P are written in rectangular form, $x = 5$. Find the polar and rectangular coordinates for P.

Objective J: *Plot points in a polar coordinate system.* *(Lesson 13-4)*

In 45 and 46, plot $[r, \theta]$, where θ is in radians.

45. $\left[3, \frac{\pi}{6}\right]$

46. $[-2, 0]$

47. *Multiple choice.* Which polar coordinate pair does not name the same point as $[4, 250°]$?

(a) $[4, -110°]$ (b) $[-4, 110°]$

(c) $[-4, 70°]$ (d) $[4, 610°]$

48. A point P has polar coordinates $\left[2, \frac{7\pi}{6}\right]$. Give two pairs of polar coordinates for P where $r = -2$.

Objective K: *Graph and interpret graphs of polar equations.* *(Lesson 13-5)*

49. Verify that $\left[2, \frac{2\pi}{3}\right]$ is on the graph of $r = 2 \cos 6\theta$.

50. Give the coordinates of two points on the graph of $r = \csc \theta$.

In 51 and 52, graph the equation in the polar coordinate system.

51. $r = 4 \sin \theta$

52. $r = 1 - \cos \theta$

In 53 and 54, a polar equation is given. **a.** Use an automatic grapher to graph the given equation. **b.** Verify the shape of the graph in part **a** by finding a rectangular coordinate equation for the relation.

53. $r = 4 \sec \theta$

54. $r = \frac{1}{3} \cos \theta$

Objective L: *Graph complex numbers.* *(Lessons 13-6, 13-7)*

In 55 and 56, graph in the complex plane.

55. $4 - 5i$

56. $8(\cos 130° + i \sin 130°)$

57. a. Graph the origin, $A = 3 + i$, $B = 1 - 3i$, and $A + B$ on one coordinate system.

b. Prove that the figure with vertices $(0, 0)$, A, B, and $A + B$ is a parallelogram.

58. Consider $z = 2(\cos 72° + i \sin 72°)$.

a. Graph z, z^2, z^3, z^4, and z^5 on one complex coordinate system.

b. Verify that z is a solution to $z^5 = 32$.

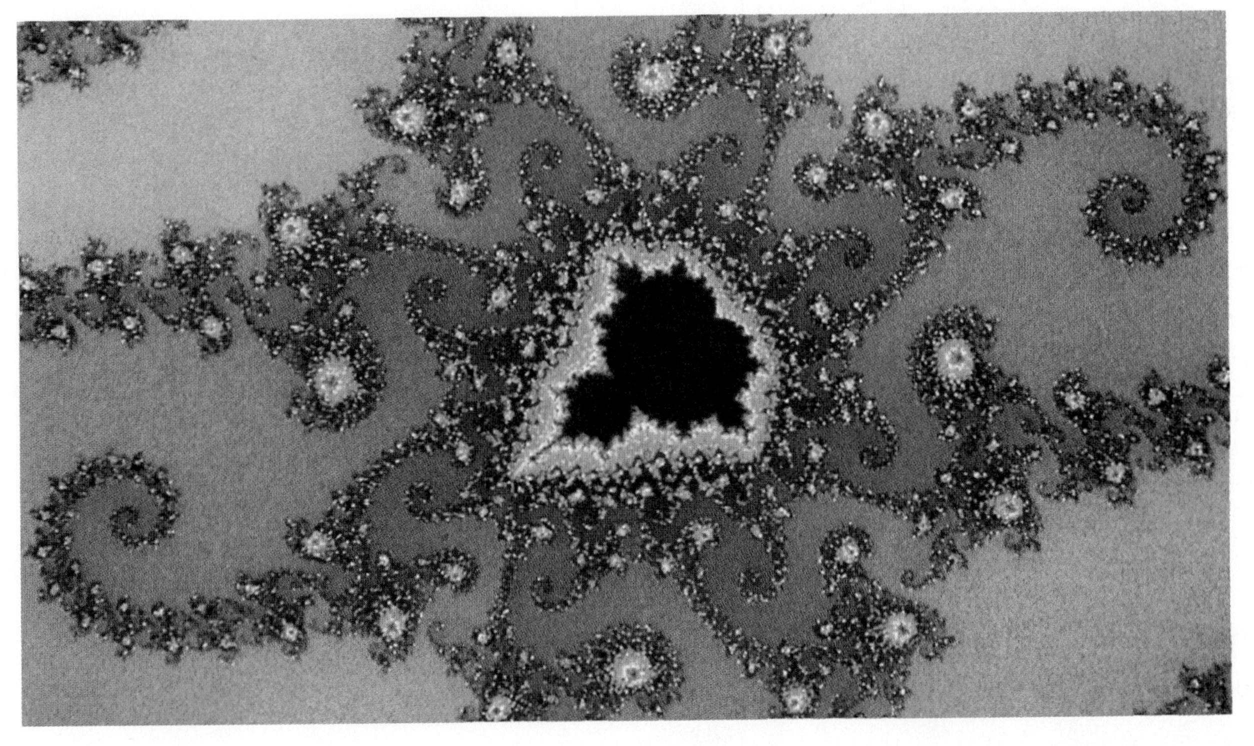

Parent Functions and Their Graphs

Type of Function	Parent Function, f *	Graph of f	Inverse Function, f^{-1} †	Graph of f^{-1}
polynomial–constant	$f(x) = k$ domain: R range: $\{k\}$	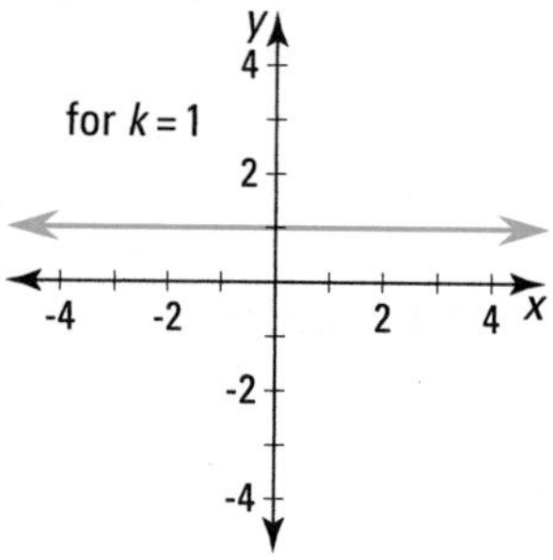 for $k=1$ y: 4, 2, -2, -4 x: -4, -2, 2, 4	none	
polynomial–linear	$f(x) = x$ domain: R range: R	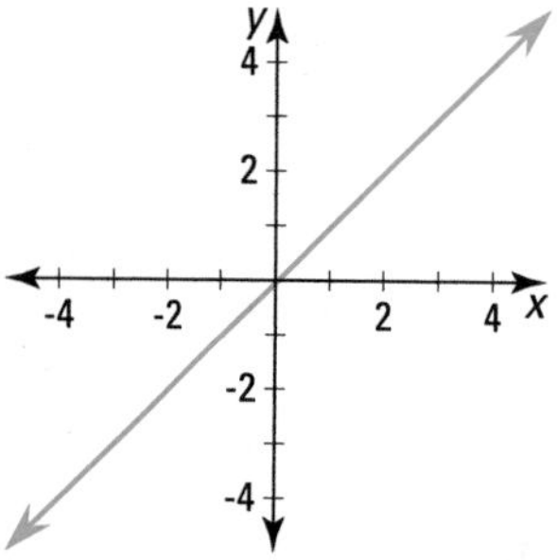 y: 4, 2, -2, -4 x: -4, -2, 2, 4	$f^{-1}(x) = x$	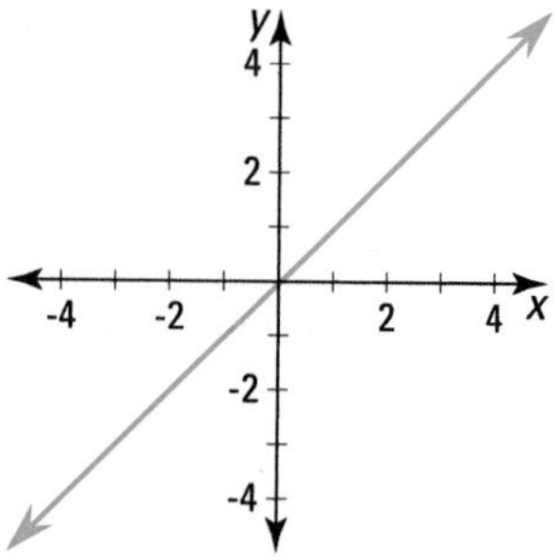 y: 4, 2, -2, -4 x: -4, -2, 2, 4
absolute value	$f(x) = \|x\|$ domain: R range: $R^+ \cup \{0\}$	y: 4, 2, -2, -4 x: -4, -2, 2, 4	none	
greatest integer	$f(x) = \lfloor x \rfloor$ domain: R range: set of integers	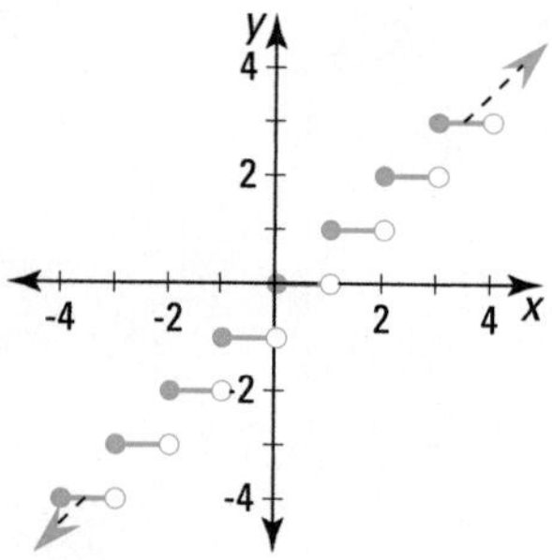 y: 4, 2, -2, -4 x: -4, -2, 2, 4	none	

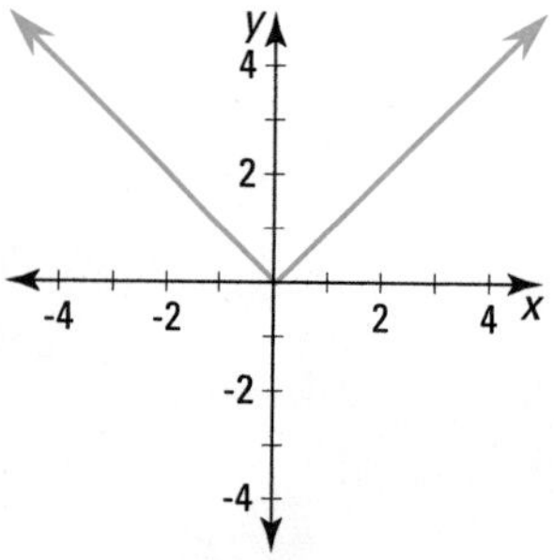

* R = set of real numbers, R^+ = set of positive real numbers.

† The domain and range of f^{-1} are the reverse of those for f except where indicated.

Type of Function	Parent Function, f *	Graph of f	Inverse Function, f^{-1} †	Graph of f^{-1}
polynomial–quadratic	$f(x) = x^2$ domain: R range: $R^+ \cup \{0\}$	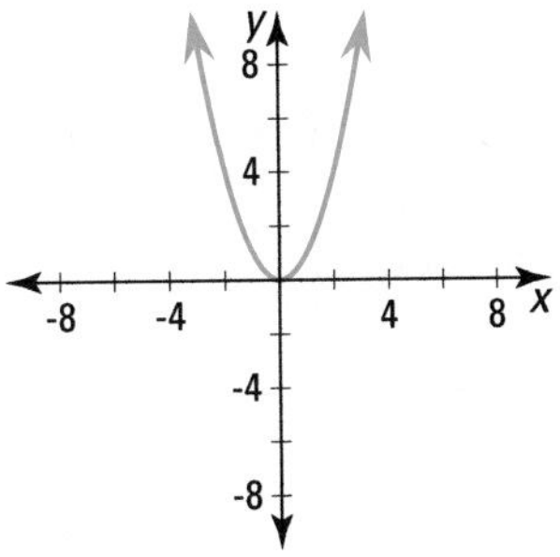	$f^{-1}(x) = \sqrt{x}$ domain: $R^+ \cup \{0\}$ range: $R^+ \cup \{0\}$	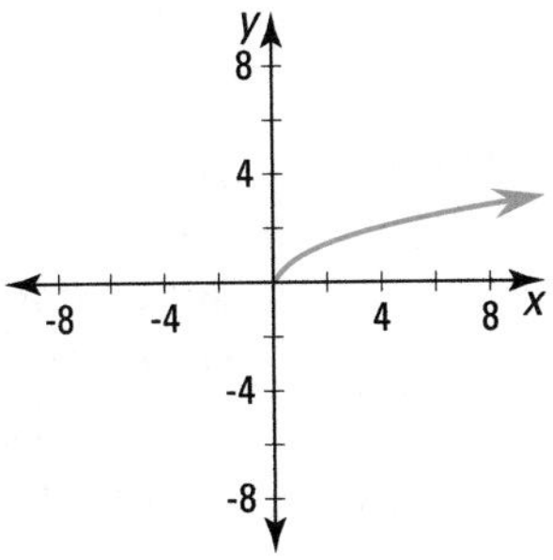
polynomial–cubic	$f(x) = x^3$ domain: R range: R	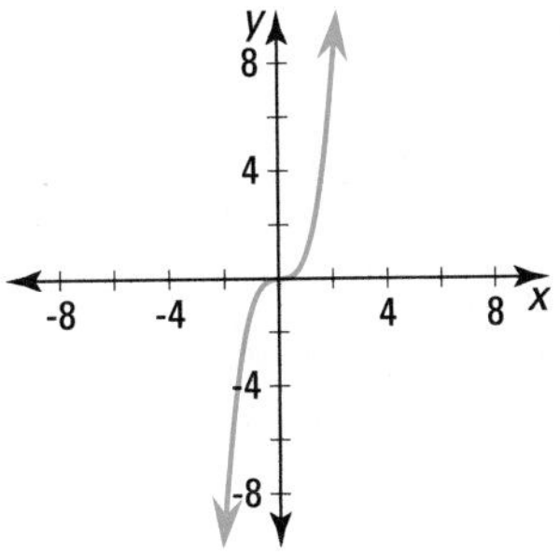	$f^{-1}(x) = \sqrt[3]{x}$	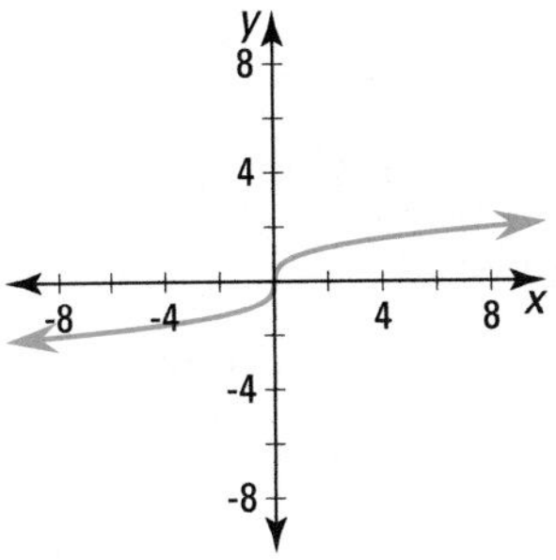
polynomial of higher degree	$f(x) = x^n$ n an odd integer domain: R range: R	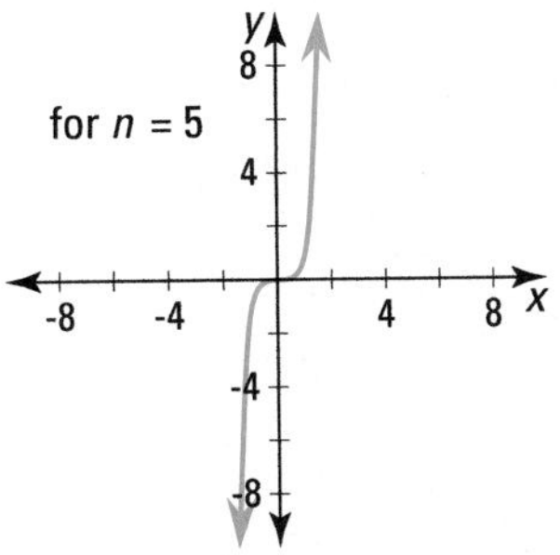 for $n = 5$	$f^{-1}(x) = \sqrt[n]{x}$	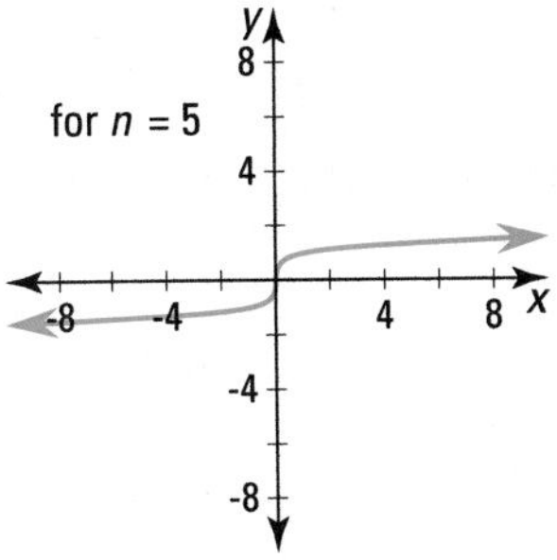 for $n = 5$
	$f(x) = x^n$ n an even integer domain: R range: $R^+ \cup \{0\}$	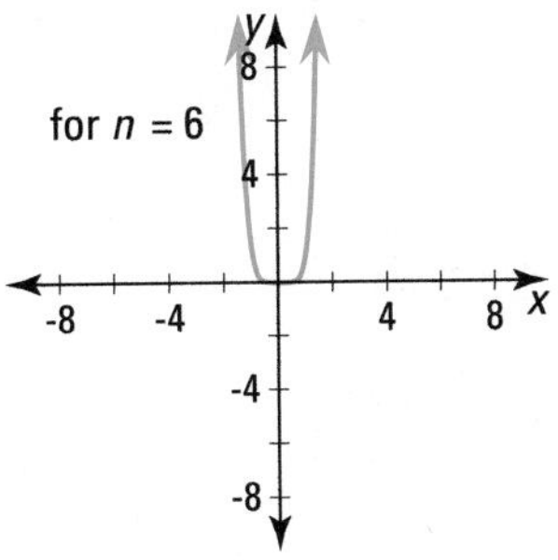 for $n = 6$	$f^{-1}(x) = \sqrt[n]{x}$ domain: $R^+ \cup \{0\}$ range: $R^+ \cup \{0\}$	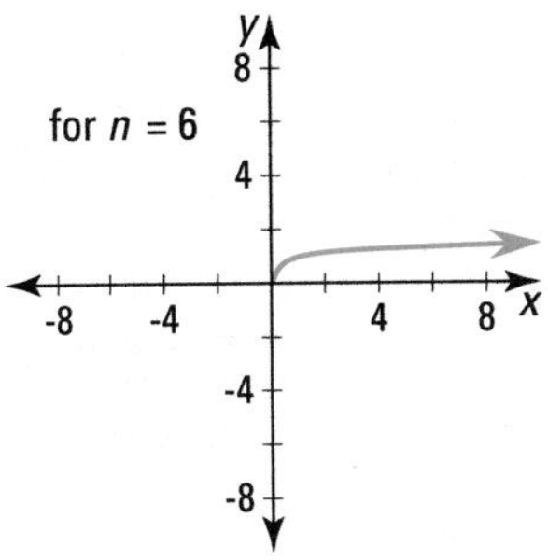 for $n = 6$

Type of Function	Parent Function, f *	Graph of f	Inverse Function, f^{-1} †	Graph of f^{-1}
hyperbola	$f(x) = \frac{1}{x}$ domain: set of nonzero reals range: set of nonzero reals	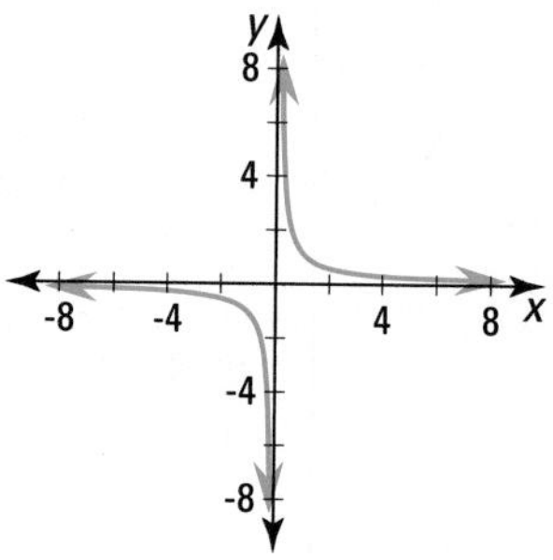	$f^{-1}(x) = \frac{1}{x}$	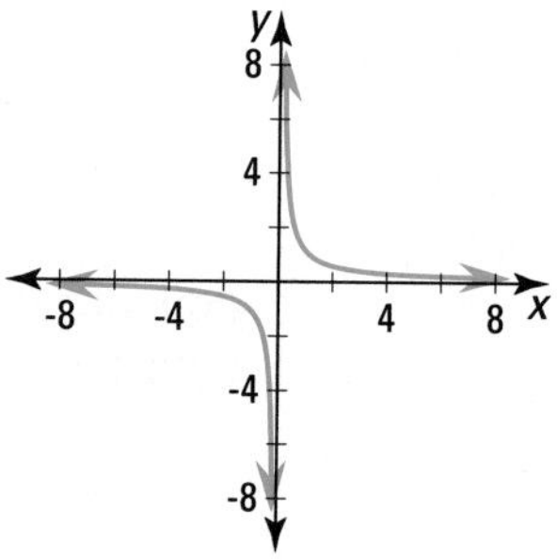
inverse-square	$f(x) = \frac{1}{x^2}$ domain: set of nonzero reals range: R^+	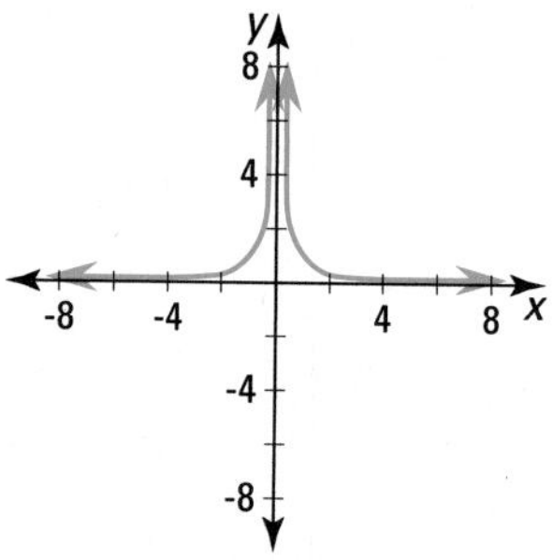	$f^{-1}(x) = \sqrt{\frac{1}{x}}$ domain: R^+ range: R^+	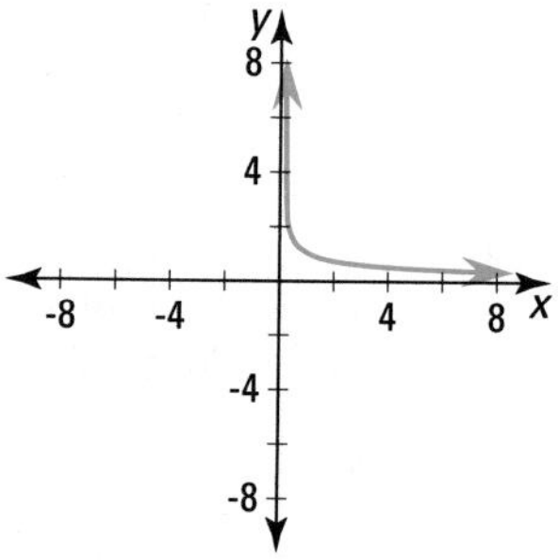
exponential any base	$f(x) = b^x$ $b > 1$ domain: R range: R^+	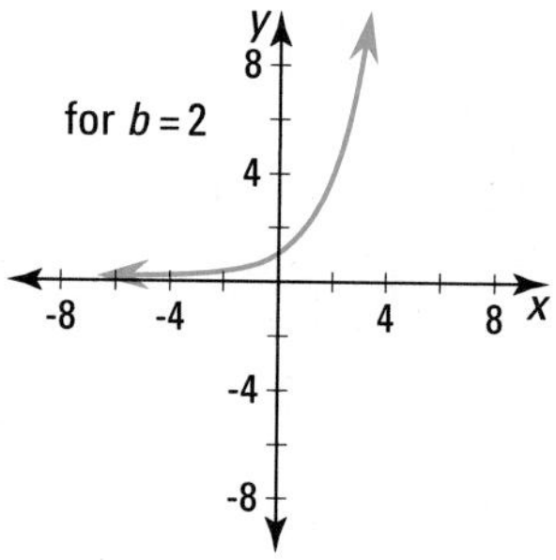 for $b = 2$	$f^{-1}(x) = \log_b x$	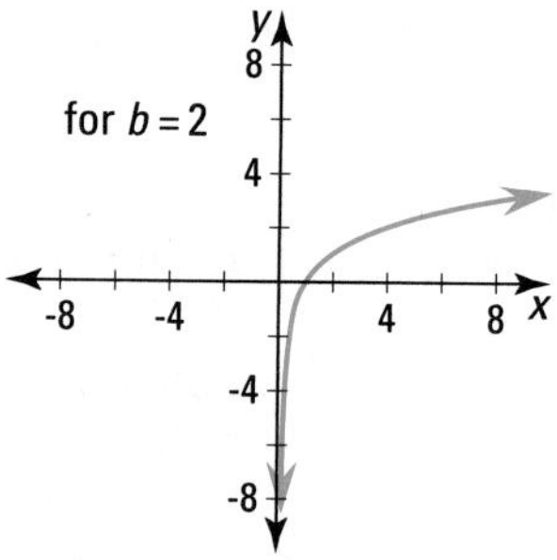 for $b = 2$
	$f(x) = b^x$ $0 < b < 1$ domain: R range: R^+	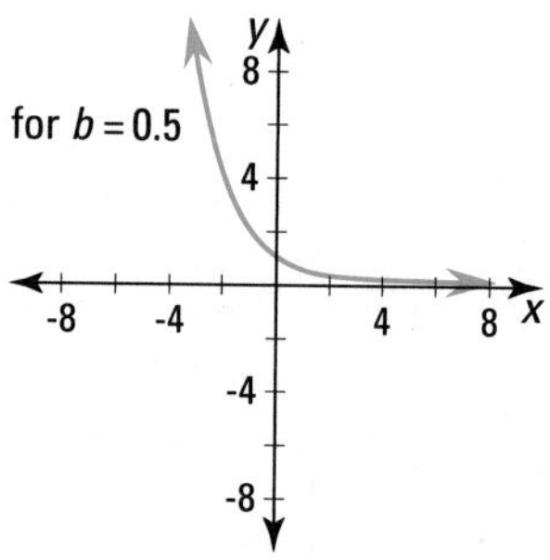 for $b = 0.5$	$f^{-1}(x) = \log_b x$	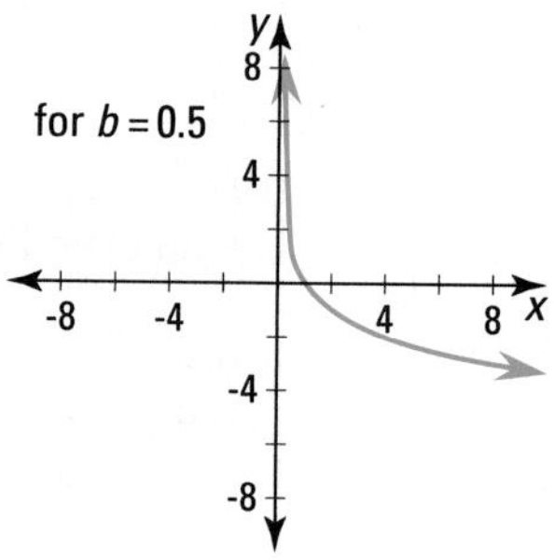 for $b = 0.5$

Type of Function	Parent Function, f *	Graph of f	Inverse Function, 1 †	Graph of f^{-1}
exponential base e	$f(x) = e^x$ domain: R range: R^+	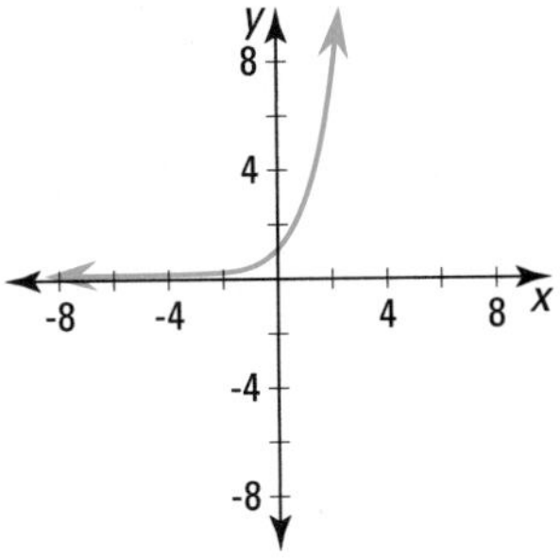 y: 8, 4, -4, -8; x: -8, -4, 4, 8	$f^{-1}(x) = \ln x$	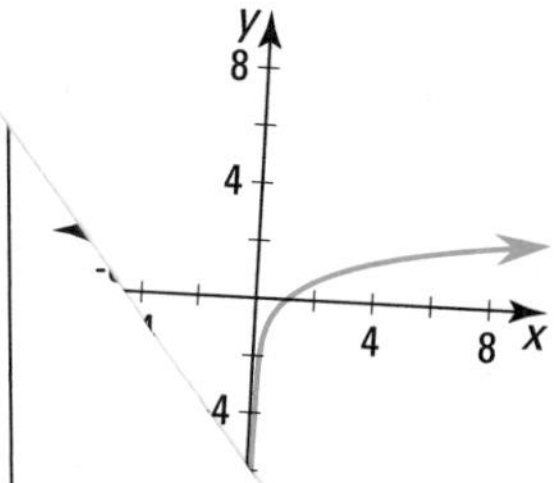 y: 8, 4, 4; x: 4, 8
circular–sine	$f(x) = \sin x$ domain: R range: $\{y: -1 \le y \le 1\}$	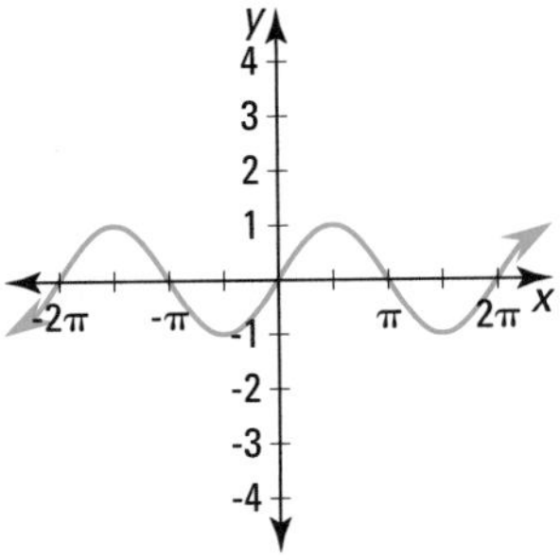 y: 4, 3, 2, 1, -1, -2, -3, -4; x: -2π, -π, π, 2π	$f^{-1}(x) = \sin^{-1} x$ domain: $\{x: -1 \le x \le 1\}$ range: $\{y: \frac{\pi}{2} \le y \le \frac{\pi}{2}\}$	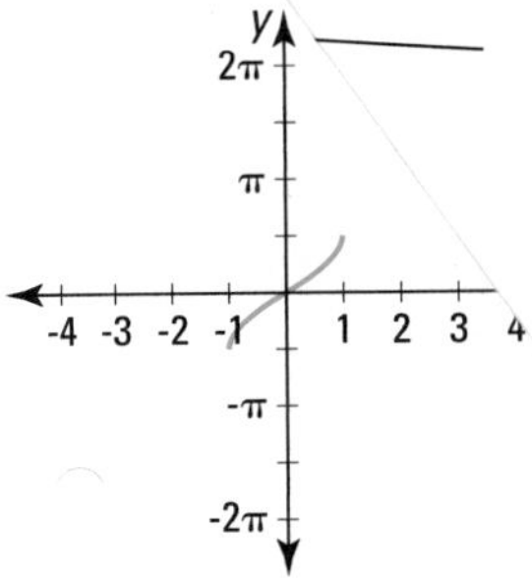 y: 2π, π, -π, -2π; x: -4, -3, -2, -1, 1, 2, 3, 4
circular–cosine	$f(x) = \cos x$ domain: R range: $\{y: -1 \le y \le 1\}$	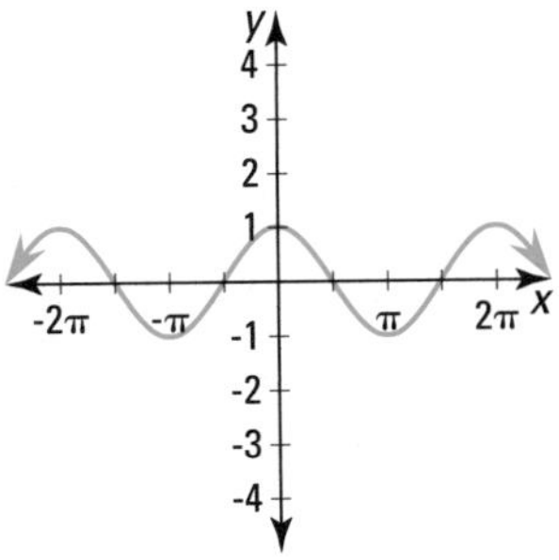 y: 4, 3, 2, 1, -1, -2, -3, -4; x: -2π, -π, π, 2π	$f^{-1}(x) = \cos^{-1} x$ domain: $\{x: -1 \le x \le 1\}$ range: $\{y: 0 \le y \le \pi\}$	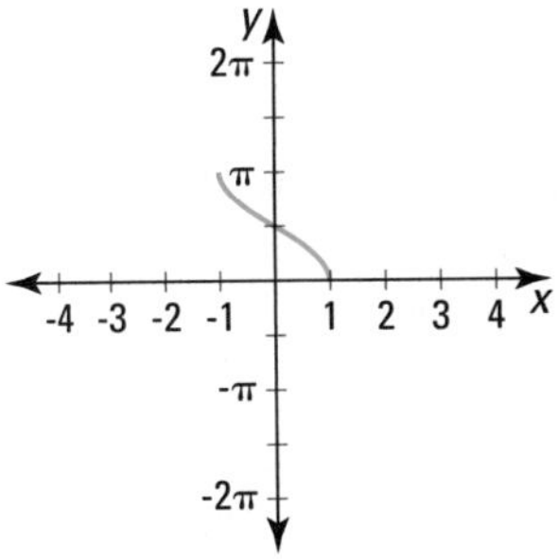 y: 2π, π, -π, -2π; x: -4, -3, -2, -1, 1, 2, 3, 4
circular–tangent	$f(x) = \tan x$ domain: R except $\frac{\pi}{2} + n\pi$, n an integer range: R	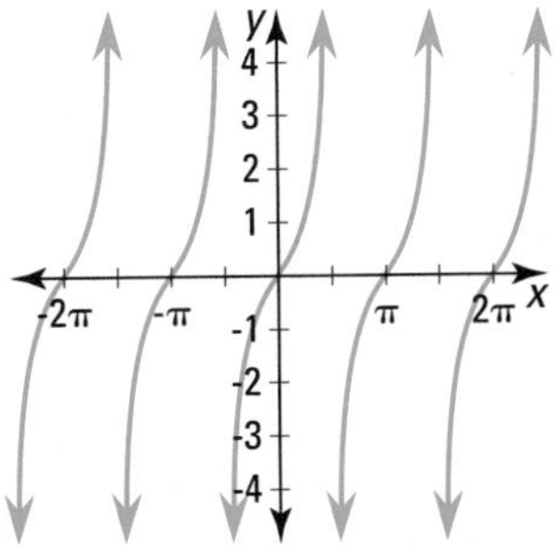 y: 4, 3, 2, 1, -1, -2, -3, -4; x: -2π, -π, π, 2π	$f^{-1}(x) = \tan^{-1} x$ domain: R range: $\{y: -\frac{\pi}{2} < y < \frac{\pi}{2}\}$	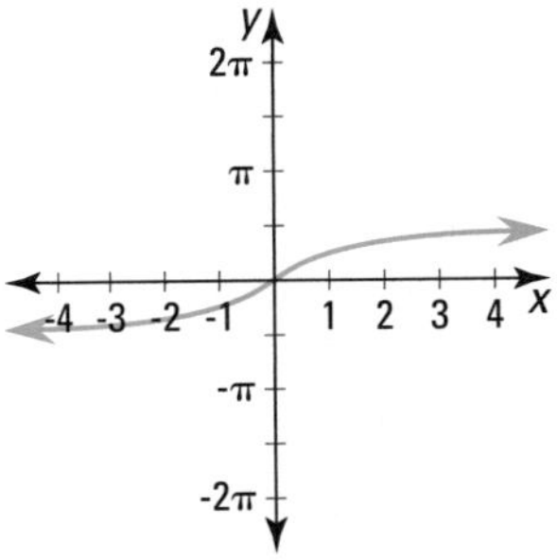 y: 2π, π, -π, -2π; x: -4, -3, -2, -1, 1, 2, 3, 4

Type of Function	Pare Function, f	Graph of f
reciprocal circular–cosecant	$x) = \csc x = \frac{1}{\sin x}$ domain: set of reals except $n\pi$, where n is an integer range: $\{y: y \geq 1 \text{ or } y \leq -1\}$	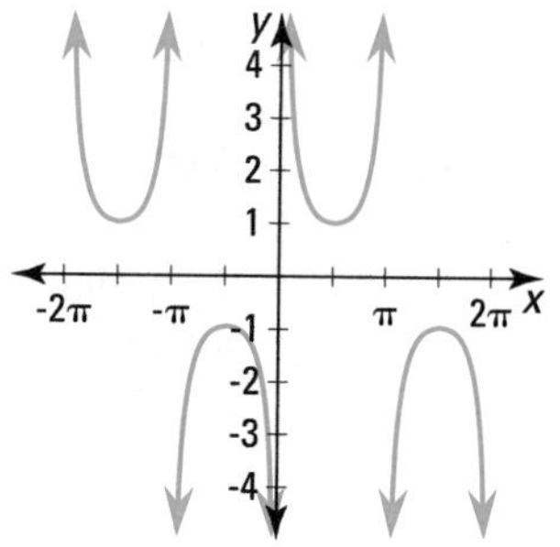
ℓ circular– re	$f(x) = \sec x = \frac{1}{\cos x}$ domain: set of reals except $\frac{\pi}{2} + n\pi$, where n is an integer range: $\{y: y \geq 1 \text{ or } y \leq -1\}$	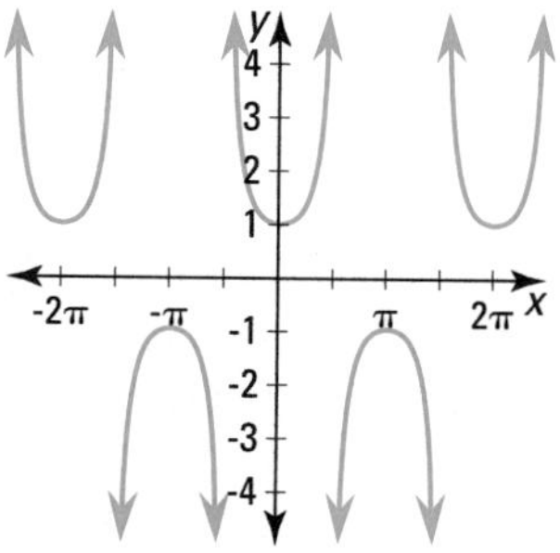
reciprocal circular–cotangent	$f(x) = \cot x = \frac{1}{\tan x}$ domain: set of reals except $n\pi$, where n is an integer range: R	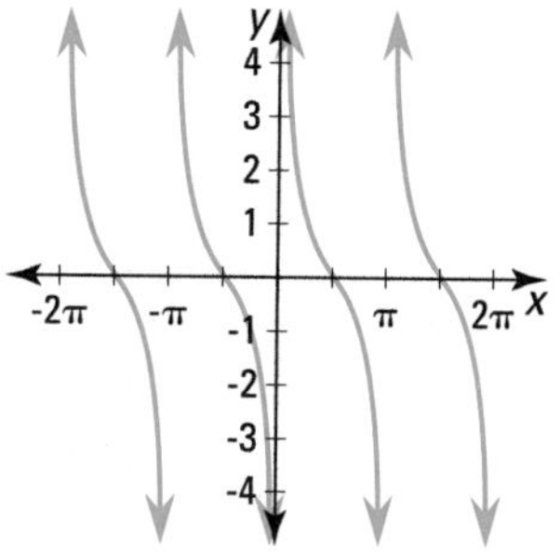
normal	$f(x) = e^{-x^2}$ domain: R range: $\{y: 0 < y \leq 1\}$	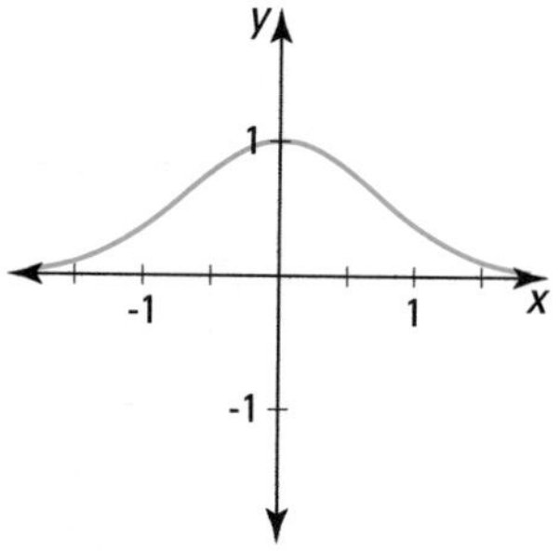

Programming Languages

COMMANDS

The BASIC commands used in this course, their translation into one calculator language, and examples of their use are given below.

LET . . . A value is assigned to a given variable. Most versions of BASIC allow you to omit the word LET in the assignment statement.

LET A = 5   5 → A

The number 5 is stored in a memory location called A.

N = N + 2   N + 2 → N

The value in the memory location called N is increased by 2 and then restored in the location called N. (N is replaced by N + 2.)

PRINT . . . The computer/calculator displays on the screen what follows the PRINT command. If what follows is a constant or variable, the value of that constant or variable is displayed. If what follows is in quotes, the quote is displayed exactly.

PRINT A   Disp A

The computer prints the number stored in memory location A.

PRINT "X = "A/B   Disp "X = ", A/B

Displayed is X = (value of A/B). Notice that the space after the equal sign in the quotes is transferred into a space after the equal sign in the displayed sentence. On some calculators, the display will place X = and the value on separate lines.

INPUT . . . The computer asks the user to give a value to the variable named, and stores that value.

INPUT X   Input X

When the program is run, the computer/calculator will prompt you to give it a value by displaying a question mark, and then will store the value you type in memory location X.

INPUT "HOW OLD"; AGE   Input "How Old", Age

The computer/calculator displays HOW OLD? and stores your response in memory location AGE.

REM . . . This command allows remarks to be inserted in a program. These may describe what the variables repesent, what the program does or how it works. REM statements are often used in long complex programs or programs others will use.

REM PYTHAGOREAN THEOREM

The statement appears when the LIST command is given, but it has no effect when the program is run. Some calculators have no corresponding command.

END This command causes a BASIC program to terminate. No BASIC program should have more than one END statement. In calculators, END statements are used to identify the ends of loops (see FOR on page 872) or conditionals (see IF . . . THEN . . . on page 872) and thus may appear more than once in a program.

END   End

▶

FOR . . .
NEXT . . .
STEP . . .

The FOR command assigns a beginning and ending value to a variable. The first time through the loop, the variable has the beginning value in the FOR command. When the program hits the line reading NEXT (or End), the value of the variable is increased by the amount indicated by STEP. The commands between FOR and NEXT (End) are then repeated.

10 FOR N = 3 TO 10 STEP 2	:For(N,3,10,2)
20 PRINT N	:Disp N
30 NEXT N	:End

The program assigns 3 to N and then displays the value of N. On reaching NEXT, the program increases N by 2 (the STEP amount), and prints 5. The next N is 7, then 9, but 11 is too large, so the program executes the command after NEXT (End). The output from both programs is given here.

3
5
7
9

IF . . . THEN . . .

The program performs the consequent (the THEN part) only if the antecedent (the IF part) is true. When the antecedent is false, the program *ignores* the consequent and goes directly to the next line of the program.

IF X <= 100 THEN PRINT X	:If X $\leq$ 100
	:Then:Disp X
	:End

If the X value is less than or equal to 100, the computer/calculator displays the value stored in X. If the value of X is greater than 100, the value will not be printed.

GOTO . . .

The program goes to whatever line of the program is indicated. GOTO statements are generally avoided because they interrupt program flow and make programs hard to interpret. Calculator programs typically do not have line numbers, and so GOTO statements are used in conjunction with a label.

10 GOTO 50	:Goto A
.	.
.	.
.	.
50 (Command)	:Lbl A
	:(Command)

The program goes to line 50 (label A) and executes that command.

FUNCTIONS

A large number of functions are built into most versions of BASIC and into all calculators. They are the same functions used outside of programming. Each function name must be followed by a variable or constant enclosed in parentheses. Here are some examples of the uses of functions in programs.

ABS

The absolute value of the number that follows is calculated.

LET A = ABS(-10)	abs(-10) → A

The program calculates $|-10| = 10$ and assigns the value 10 to memory location A.

ATN

The arctangent or inverse tangent of the number or expression that follows is calculated. In BASIC and other computer programming languages, the result is always given in radians. In calculator programs, the result can be in either radians or degrees, depending on what mode the calculator is in. (Note: Some versions of BASIC do not include built-in functions for inverse sine and inverse cosine. But these can be created, since $\cos^{-1}x = \tan$

over the domain $0 < x \le 1$ and $\sin^{-1}x = \tan^{-1}\sqrt{\frac{x^2}{1-x^2}}$ over the domain $0 \le x < 1$.)

LET P = ATN(1) $\tan^{-1}(1) \to$ P

The program calculates $\tan^{-1}1 = \frac{\pi}{4}$ and stores the value 0.785398 in the memory location P.

EXP

The number e raised to the power or expression that follows is calculated.

LET J = EXP(2) e^(2) $\to$ J

The program calculates e^2 and stores the value 7.389056 in the memory location J.

INT

The greatest integer less than or equal to the number that follows is calculated.

B = INT(N + .5) int(N + .5) $\to$ B

The program adds .5 to the value of N, calculates $\lfloor N + .5 \rfloor$, and stores the result in B.

LOG or LN

The natural logarithm (logarithm to base e) of the number that follows is calculated.

LET J = LOG(6) ln(6) $\to$ J

The program calculates ln 6 and assigns the value 1.791759469228 to memory location J. It may display only some of these decimal places.

RND(1)

A random number greater than 0 and less than 1 is generated. The argument of the RND function is always 1.

D = 2*RND(1) 2 rand $\to$ D

The program generates a random number between 0 and 1 and stores twice the value in memory location D.

SIN
COS
TAN

The sine, cosine, or tangent of the number or expression that follows is calculated. In BASIC, the argument of these functions is always in radians. On most calculators, the argument can be in either degrees or radians, depending on the mode the calculator is in.

LET R = 5*SIN(0.7) 5 sin(0.7) $\to$ R

The program finds 5 sin 0.7 and stores the value 3.221088 in the memory location R.

SQR

The square root of the number or expression that follows is calculated.

C = SQR(A*A + B*B) $\sqrt{\ }$ (A^2 + B^2) $\to$ C

The program calculates $\sqrt{A^2 + B^2}$ using the values stored in A and B and stores the result in C.

APPENDIX C

A Table of Random Numbers

row	[illegible]	2	3	4	5	6	7	8	9	10	11	12	13	14
1	10480	15011	01536	02011	81647	91646	69719	14194	62590	36207	20969	99570	91291	90700
2	22368	46573	25595	85393	30995	89198	27982	53402	93965	34095	52666	19174	39615	99505
3	24130	48360	22527	97265	76393	64809	15179	24830	49340	32081	30680	19655	63348	58629
4	42167	93093	06423	61680	17856	16376	39440	53537	71341	57004	00849	74917	97758	16379
5	37570	39975	81837	16656	06121	91782	60468	81305	49684	60672	14110	06927	01263	54613
6	77921	06907	11008	42751	27756	53498	18602	70659	90655	15053	21916	81825	44394	42880
7	99562	72905	56420	69994	98872	31016	71194	18738	44013	48840	63213	21069	10634	12952
8	96301	91977	05463	07972	18876	20922	94595	56869	69014	60045	18425	84903	42508	32307
9	89579	14342	63661	10281	17453	18103	57740	84378	25331	12566	58678	44947	05585	56941
10	85475	36857	43342	53988	53060	59533	38867	62300	08158	17983	16439	11458	18593	64952
11	28918	69578	88231	33276	70997	79936	56865	05859	90106	31595	01547	85590	91610	78188
12	63553	40961	48235	03427	49626	69445	18663	72695	52180	20847	12234	90511	33703	90322
13	09429	93969	52636	92737	88974	33488	36320	17617	30015	08272	84115	27156	30613	74952
14	10365	61129	87529	85689	48237	52267	67689	93394	01511	26358	85104	20285	29975	89868
15	07119	97336	71048	08178	77233	13916	47564	81056	97735	85977	29372	74461	28551	90707
16	51085	12765	51821	51259	77452	16308	60756	92144	49442	53900	70960	63990	75601	40719
17	02368	21382	52404	60268	89368	19885	55322	44819	01188	65255	64835	44919	05944	55157
18	01011	54092	33362	94904	31272	04146	18594	29852	71585	85030	51132	01915	92747	64951
19	52162	53916	46369	58586	23216	14513	83149	98736	23495	64350	94738	17752	35156	35749
20	07056	97628	33787	09998	42698	06691	76988	13602	51851	46104	88916	19509	25625	58104
21	48663	91245	85828	14346	09172	30168	90229	04734	59193	22178	30421	61666	99904	32812
22	54164	58492	22421	74103	47070	25306	76468	26384	58151	06646	21524	15227	96909	44592
23	32639	32363	05597	24200	13363	38005	94342	28728	35806	06912	17012	64161	18296	22851
24	29334	27001	87637	87308	58731	00256	45834	15398	46557	41135	10367	07684	36188	18510
25	02488	33062	28834	07351	19731	92420	60952	61280	50001	67658	32586	86679	50720	94953
26	81525	72295	04839	96423	24878	82651	66566	14778	76797	14780	13300	87074	79666	95725
27	29676	20591	68086	26432	46901	20849	89768	81536	86645	12659	92259	57102	80428	25280
28	00742	57392	39064	66432	84673	40027	32832	61362	98947	96067	64760	64584	96096	98253
29	05366	04213	25669	26422	44407	44048	37937	63904	45766	66134	75470	66520	34693	90449
30	91921	26418	64117	94305	26766	25940	39972	22209	71500	64568	91402	42416	07844	69618
31	00582	04711	87917	77341	42206	35126	74087	99547	81817	42607	43808	76655	62028	76630
32	00725	69884	62797	56170	86324	88072	76222	36086	84637	93161	76038	65855	77919	88006
33	69011	65797	95876	55293	18988	27354	26575	08625	40801	59920	29841	80150	12777	48501
34	25976	57948	29888	88604	67917	48708	18912	82271	65424	69774	33611	54262	85963	03547
35	09763	83473	73577	12908	30883	18317	28290	35797	05998	41688	34952	37888	38917	88050
36	91567	42595	27958	30134	04024	86385	29880	99730	55536	84855	29080	09250	79656	73211
37	17955	56349	90999	49127	20044	59931	06115	20542	18059	02008	73708	83517	36103	42791
38	46503	18584	18845	49618	02304	51038	20655	58727	28168	15475	56942	53389	20562	87338
39	92157	89634	94824	78171	84610	82834	09922	25417	44137	48413	25555	21246	35509	20468
40	14577	62765	35605	81263	39667	47358	56873	56307	61607	49518	89656	20103	77490	18062

APPENDIX D

Standard Normal Distribution Table

This table gives the area under the standard normal curve to the left of a given positive number a.

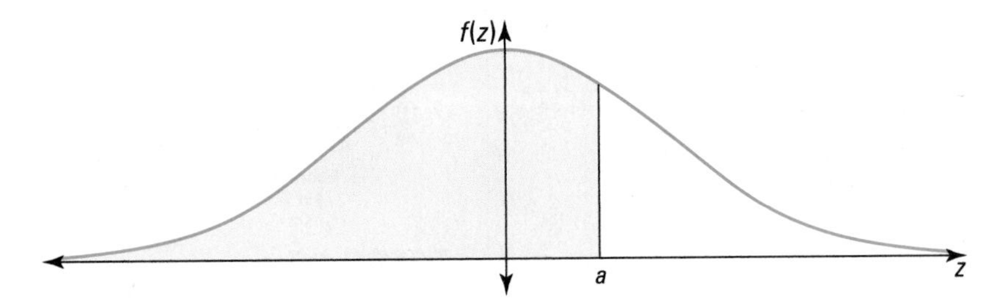

$P(z < a)$ for $a \geq 0$

a	0	1	2	3	4	5	6	7	8	9
0.0	.5000	.5040	.5080	.5120	.5160	.5199	.5239	.5279	.5319	.5359
0.1	.5398	.5438	.5478	.5517	.5557	.5596	.5636	.5675	.5714	.5753
0.2	.5793	.5832	.5871	.5910	.5948	.5987	.6026	.6064	.6103	.6141
0.3	.6179	.6217	.6255	.6293	.6331	.6368	.6406	.6443	.6480	.6517
0.4	.6554	.6591	.6628	.6664	.6700	.6736	.6772	.6808	.6844	.6879
0.5	.6915	.6950	.6985	.7019	.7054	.7088	.7123	.7157	.7190	.7224
0.6	.7257	.7291	.7324	.7357	.7389	.7422	.7454	.7486	.7517	.7549
0.7	.7580	.7611	.7642	.7673	.7704	.7734	.7764	.7794	.7823	.7852
0.8	.7881	.7910	.7939	.7967	.7995	.8023	.8051	.8078	.8106	.8133
0.9	.8159	.8186	.8212	.8238	.8264	.8289	.8315	.8340	.8365	.8389
1.0	.8413	.8438	.8461	.8485	.8508	.8531	.8554	.8577	.8599	.8621
1.1	.8643	.8665	.8686	.8708	.8729	.8749	.8770	.8790	.8810	.8830
1.2	.8849	.8869	.8888	.8907	.8925	.8944	.8962	.8980	.8997	.9015
1.3	.9032	.9049	.9066	.9082	.9099	.9115	.9131	.9147	.9162	.9177
1.4	.9192	.9207	.9222	.9236	.9251	.9265	.9279	.9292	.9306	.9319
1.5	.9332	.9345	.9357	.9370	.9382	.9394	.9406	.9418	.9429	.9441
1.6	.9452	.9463	.9474	.9484	.9495	.9505	.9515	.9525	.9535	.9545
1.7	.9554	.9564	.9573	.9582	.9591	.9599	.9608	.9616	.9625	.9633
1.8	.9641	.9649	.9656	.9664	.9671	.9678	.9686	.9693	.9699	.9706
1.9	.9713	.9719	.9726	.9732	.9738	.9744	.9750	.9756	.9761	.9767
2.0	.9772	.9778	.9783	.9788	.9793	.9798	.9803	.9808	.9812	.9817
2.1	.9821	.9826	.9830	.9834	.9838	.9842	.9846	.9850	.9854	.9857
2.2	.9861	.9864	.9868	.9871	.9875	.9878	.9881	.9884	.9887	.9890
2.3	.9893	.9896	.9898	.9901	.9904	.9906	.9909	.9911	.9913	.9916
2.4	.9918	.9920	.9922	.9925	.9927	.9929	.9931	.9932	.9934	.9936
2.5	.9938	.9940	.9941	.9943	.9945	.9946	.9948	.9949	.9951	.9952
2.6	.9953	.9955	.9956	.9957	.9959	.9960	.9961	.9962	.9963	.9964
2.7	.9965	.9966	.9967	.9968	.9969	.9970	.9971	.9971	.9973	.9974
2.8	.9974	.9975	.9976	.9977	.9977	.9978	.9979	.9979	.9980	.9981
2.9	.9981	.9982	.9982	.9983	.9984	.9984	.9985	.9985	.9986	.9986
3.0	.9987	.9987	.9987	.9988	.9988	.9989	.9989	.9989	.9990	.9990

For specific details on the use of this table, see page 655.

LESSON 1-1 (pp. 6–12)

17. 5,800 **19. a.** Sample: The number of accidental deaths is decreasing. **b.** drugs and medicines; inhalation or ingestion of objects **21. a.** $x = 20$ **b.** $x = 200$ **c.** $x = \frac{1}{20}$ **d.** $x = \frac{1}{200}$ **23. a.** Sample: (0, -4); (1, -1); (5, 11); (-2, -10); (10, 26) **b.** **See right.** **c.** 3 **d.** -4

23. b.

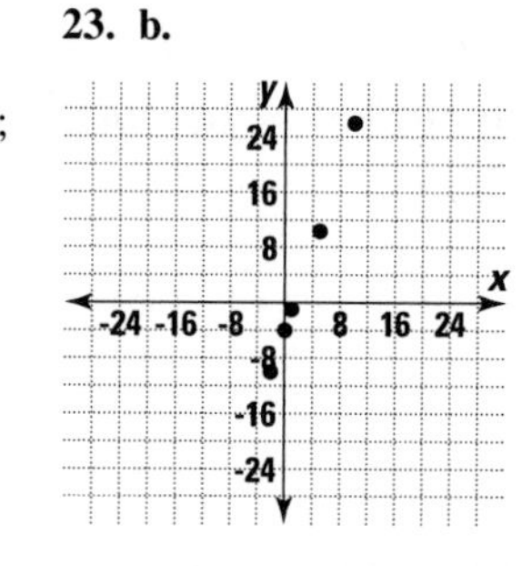

LESSON 1-2 (pp. 13–18)

15. about two times as great **17.** 9 **19. a.** the AIDS patients to whom the drug is administered **b.** all AIDS patients **c.** number of infections a patient contracts **21.** True **23. a.** $x = 128$ **b.** $x = \pm 8\sqrt{2}$ **c.** $x = 16$ or -8

LESSON 1-3 (pp. 21–28)

15. 36 **17.** Yes, for instance, for the ages {30, 40, 70, 72}, the median is 55. 0% are exactly the median age. **19.** a **21.** the difference between total U.S. imports and exports, known as the balance of trade, in 1994 **23. a.** 4 **b.** More students have 4 pairs of jeans than any other number. **25.** sample **27.** $5x - 7 = y$

LESSON 1-4 (pp. 29–37)

15. False **17. a.** **See right.** **b.** False **c.** Division C. 75% of that division's salaries are among the lowest of all salaries. **19. a.** 13 **b.** 169 **c.** 69 **21.** $31 **23. a.** $\frac{1}{2}$ **b.** Sample: $y = \frac{x}{2} + 2$

LESSON 1-5 (pp. 39–45)

13. a. 1 **b.** 52 **c.** 51 **15.** 53% **17. a.** **See right.** **b.** to the right **19.** the 23rd number **21.** about 119 cm **23. a.** 87 **b.** $\bar{x} = 54.48$ **25. a.** IV **b.** III **c.** I **d.** not pictured **e.** II

17. a. (Lesson 1-4) **17. a.** (Lesson 1-5)

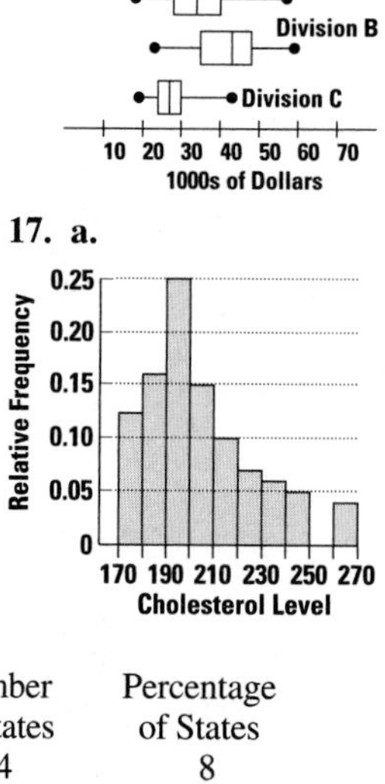

LESSON 1-6 (pp. 46–53)

13.

Number of Registered Vehicles per 1000 persons	Number of States	Percentage of States
600– 659	4	8
660– 719	8	16
720– 779	12	24
780– 839	13	26
840– 899	6	12
900– 959	1	2
960–1019	2	4
1020–1079	1	2
1080–1139	2	4
1140–1199	1	2

See below. **15.** d **17. a.** 3 **b.** 13 **c.** 100 **d.** the mean number of pairs of shoes owned **19.** 182

13.

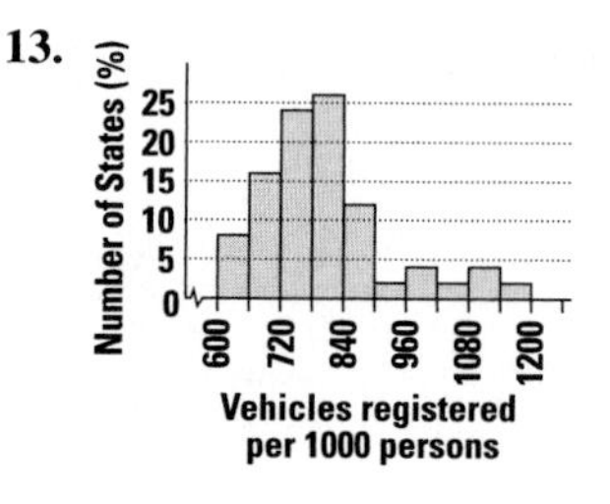

LESSON 1-7 (pp. 54–61)

11. Variance is the sum of squared deviations divided by $n - 1$, and $n > 1$, so it must be nonnegative. **13. a. i.** Group Z **ii.** Group Y **iii.** Group X **b.** Group Y's have the greatest standard deviation and Group Z's have the smallest. **c.** $s_X \approx 6.48$, $s_Y \approx 8.78$, $s_Z \approx 5.21$. Therefore $s_Z < s_X < s_Y$

15. a. i. $\sqrt{\frac{500}{n}} = 10.00$; $\sqrt{\frac{500}{n-1}} \approx 11.18$

ii. $\sqrt{\frac{500}{n}} \approx 2.236$; $\sqrt{\frac{500}{n-1}} \approx 2.247$

iii. $\sqrt{\frac{500}{n}} = 1.000$; $\sqrt{\frac{500}{n-1}} \approx 1.001$

b. Sample: As n gets larger, the values for standard deviation get closer. **17.** Sample: {70, 80, 140, 150}, s ≈ 40.8 seconds **19. a.** iv **b.** **See below.** Sample: The percent of women taking the AP exam in mathematics or computer science increased each year from 1974 to 1994. **21.** Sample: In 1994, the minimum number of immigrants received in each of 37 states was under 10,000, and the maximum number to one state was between 200,000 and 210,000. The mean is about 20,000 immigrants and the median is between 0 and 10,000. About half the total number are clustered in 43 states with an average of 10,000 to 20,000 each. The graph is skewed to the right with each of the remaining states receiving greater numbers of immigrants. There is a gap between 60,000 and 140,000 and another gap between 150,000 and 200,000. **23.** d **25. a.** Sample: Both increase as $|x|$ increases. Both have vertices at (0, 0). Both are in the 1st and 2nd quadrants except for (0, 0). **b.** Sample: One is a parabola, one is an angle; one increases at a constant rate as x increases, the other increases more quickly.

19. b.

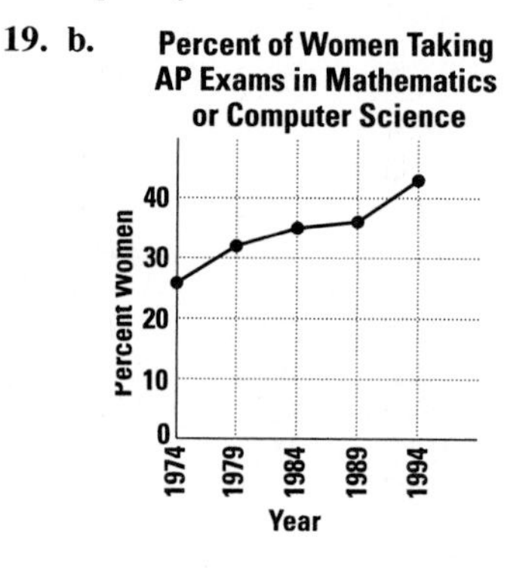

LESSON 1-8 (pp. 62–67)

11. a. lb **b.** lb **c.** lb^2 **d.** lb **13. a.** mean = 4; standard deviation ≈ 1.6 **b.** Sample: 2, 3, 4, 4, 4, 4, 5, 6 **15. a.** Jakarta: mean ≈ 6.08, standard deviation ≈ 3.34; Sydney: mean = 4, standard deviation ≈ 0.95 **b.** Sydney **c.** **See right.**

17. $\frac{1}{8}\sum_{i=1}^{8} x_i = \frac{1}{8}(x_1 + x_2 + x_3 + x_4 + x_5 + x_6 + x_7 + x_8) =$

$\frac{x_1}{8} + \frac{x_2}{8} + \frac{x_3}{8} + \frac{x_4}{8} + \frac{x_5}{8} + \frac{x_6}{8} + \frac{x_7}{8} + \frac{x_8}{8} = \sum_{i=1}^{8} \frac{x_i}{8}$

19. Sample: $y = -2x + 8$

15. c.

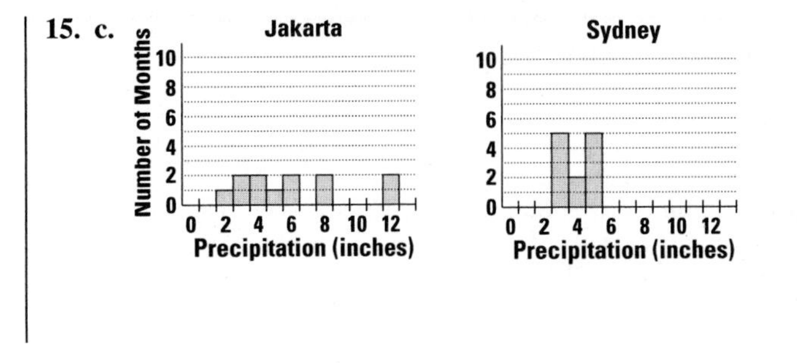

CHAPTER 1 PROGRESS SELF-TEST (pp. 71–72)

1. From the line under the table, 10.2 means that, for every 1000 women in the U.S. in 1970 who were 15 years old and over, and widowed, 10.2 of them married in 1970. **2.** In the table are the consecutive years 85–86, 86–87, 87–88. By subtracting the two values, we see that the rate decreased most between 87–88. **3.** Sample: The rate decreases from 1970 (93.4/1,000) to 1988 (58.4/1,000). This leads to the conclusion that the number of single women marrying is decreasing. **4.** The temperature at 6:00 A.M. is 21°C, while the temperature at 4:00 P.M. is 31°C. Thus, there is a 10° change. In 10 hours, $\frac{10°\text{C}}{10 \text{ hr}} = 1°\text{C}$ per hour. **5.** There are 20 observations, which means the median is the average of the 10th and 11th numbers. $\frac{4+4}{2} = 4$ heads **6.** Percentile is the amount at or below. Thus, $\frac{8}{20} = .40 =$ 40th percentile. **7.** The y-axis and frequency values would be converted to $\frac{1}{20}, \frac{2}{20}, \frac{3}{20}, \ldots$. **8. b.** because there is a greater number of numbers far from the mean. **9.** The whiskers reach from 36 to 71. 71 − 36 = 35. **10.** 51 is at the 1st quartile; this means about 75% of the presidents were older than 51. **11.** c: The median age for presidents is 55, which falls between the vice-president median age of 53 and the 3rd quartile age of 60. **12.** Sample: The ages of the vice presidents have a greater range and the values seem to have greater spread. However, both the vice presidents and the presidents have nearly 50% of their values in the 50-60 range. **13. a.** The median is the seventh value, Libya 503. The 1st quartile is the average of the 3rd and 4th value, $\frac{\text{Qatar } 150 + \text{Iraq } 183}{2} = 166.5$. The 3rd Quartile is the average of the 10th and 11th values: $\frac{\text{U.A.E. } 814 + \text{Venezuela } 885}{2} = 849.5$.
b. IQR × 1.5 = (849.5 − 166.5)(1.5) = 1024.5
849.5 + 1024.5 = 1874 which means 2,920, Saudi Arabia is an outlier. 166.5 − 1024.5 = -858, which implies no lower outliers.
c. The 5 number summary is: 111, 166.5, 503, 849.5, 2,920
See right.

14. $\sum_{i=1}^{8} x_i = x_1 + x_2 + x_3 + x_4 + x_5 + x_6 + x_7 + x_8 =$
$1 + 1 + 2 + 1 + 1 + 12 + 2 + 1 + 1 = 21$

15. a. $x = 2.625$ **b.** $\bar{x} = \frac{1}{8}\sum_{i=1}^{8} x_i$ **16. a.** The population is the entire set to be studied. A sample is a subset of the population to be studied in an experiment. **b.** Sample: Population: All U.S. voters. Sample: 800 randomly selected voters.

17. $\frac{1}{6}\sum_{i=1}^{6} x_i = \left(\frac{1}{6}\right)(449 + x_6) = 88$
$449 + x_6 = 528$
$x_6 = 79$

18. a. 16 employees **b.** $\bar{x} =$
$\frac{2(25) + 2(28) + 26 + 34 + 2(31) + 32 + 39 + 2(48) + 45 + 50 + 55 + 85}{16}$
= \$39,375

c. $s = \sqrt{\frac{1}{n-1}\sum_{i=1}^{n}(x_i - \bar{x})^2}$ where n is the number of values
x_i = the values
x = the mean
s = the standard deviation

$s \approx$ \$15,692

19. True **20.** There are clusters around 20 and 30 thousand, there is a gap between 55 and 85 thousand. **21. a.** No, a circle graph is best to compare individual data with the whole set. A total depth would not have much meaning here. **b.** **See below.**

13. c. **21. b.**

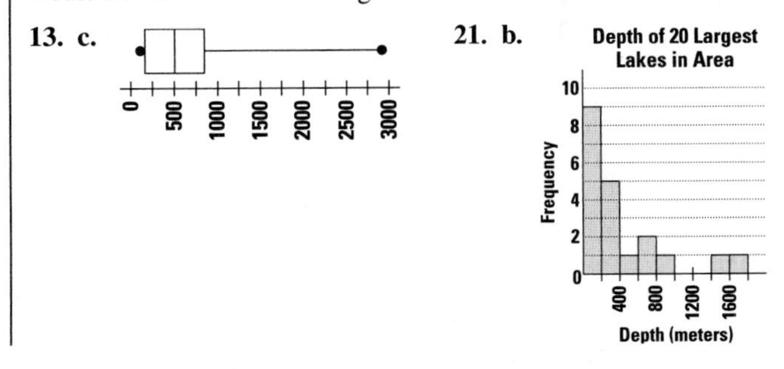

The chart below keys the questions on the **Progress Self-Test** to the objectives in the **Chapter Review** on pages 73-79 or to the **Vocabulary** (Voc.) on page 70. This will enable you to locate those **Chapter Review** questions that correspond to questions you missed on the **Progress Self-Test.** The lesson where the material is covered is also indicated on the chart.

Question	**1**	**2**	**3**	**4**	**5**	**6**	**7**	**8**	**9**	**10**
Objective	E	E	E	G	I	I	I	I	H	H
Lesson	1-1	1-1	1-1	1-6	1-2	1-2	1-5	1-5	1-4	1-4

Question	**11**	**12**	**13**	**14**	**15**	**16**	**17**	**18**	**19**	**20**	**21**
Objective	C	H	F, J	B	B	D	A	A	J	F	J
Lesson	1-3, 1-7	1-4	1-3, 1-4	1-3	1-3	1-1	1-3	1-2, 1-7	1-6	1-2	1-6

CHAPTER 1 REVIEW (pp. 73–79)

1. a. 8 **b.** 7.5 **3.** 15 **5.** 87 **7. a.** 145 **b.** 175 **9.** $\sum_{i=1}^{12} g_i$ **11.** b **13.** the mean **15.** a **17. a.** the 600 registered voters in Michigan called by the agency **b.** all registered voters in Michigan **c.** the candidate for the U.S. Senate favored by the voter **19.** Sample: Population is too large. It is too expensive to study the entire population. **21. a.** the number of people in each age category **b.** The sum of the Region numbers is 250,209. The sums are not the same because the numbers in each row were rounded to the nearest 1000 and when added resulted in a cumulative rounding error of about 1000. **23.** Seven percent of 20-24 year olds moved to a new house in a different county within the same state. **25.** about 178,000 **27. a.** mean ≈ 79.23, median = 74, s.d. ≈ 28.56 **b.** 11, 42, 174, and 176 **c.** mean ≈ 76.45, standard deviation ≈ 10.18 **d.** Sample: The members of the troop had sales averaging about 75 to 80 boxes each; the mean, median, and mode figures were 79.2, 74, and 77, respectively. Most sales were fairly close to this average range, with the exception of two scouts who sold only 42 boxes and 11 boxes, and two others who sold 174 and 176 boxes. **29. a.** Minneapolis-St.Paul **b.** Minneapolis-St. Paul **c.** Minneapolis-St. Paul Sample: The median for Minneapolis-St. Paul is about 48°, whereas Juneau's is 41°. **d.** Minneapolis-St. Paul Sample: The s.d. for Minneapolis-St. Paul is about 22.2° but Juneau's is about 11.5°.
31. a. for males: minimum = 70, lower quartile = 106, median = 119, upper quartile = 146.5, maximum = 188; for females: minimum = 90, lower quartile = 116.5, median = 138, upper quartile = 153, maximum = 200 **b.** No **c.** Sample: The primary difference between the groups is that the females scored higher; their scores were 6.5 to 20 points higher than the males' scores at each point of the five-number summary. The primary similarity is in the spread; the range and IQR for the two groups are comparable (118 and 40.5 for males, 110 and 36.5 for females) with the males' scores being only slightly more widely dispersed.

33. a. 14% **b.** 38% **35. a.** about 1.5 hours **b.** the steepness of the slope upward and the shallowness of the slope downward **c.** about midnight to 4:30 A.M. **d.** slope $= -\frac{0.15}{8} = -0.01875$ percent blood-alcohol concentration per hour **37.** 14 mpg **39.** 23 mpg **41.** 23 mpg; 27 mpg **43. a.** The 0-9 age group comprises nearly twice as great a percentage of the Mexican population as it does of the U.S. population. **b.** Sample: Wider availability and greater social acceptability of contraception might account for the fact that the 0–9 age group forms a smaller part in the U.S. than it does in Mexico. Wider access to better health care and better hygiene might account for the fact that the proportion of the population formed by each succeeding age group declines far less rapidly in the U.S. than it does in Mexico. **45.** 11 students **47.** $33\frac{1}{3}$% **49. See below. 51. See below. 53. See below.**
55. box plot **57.** line graph or scatterplot

49. **51.** **53.**

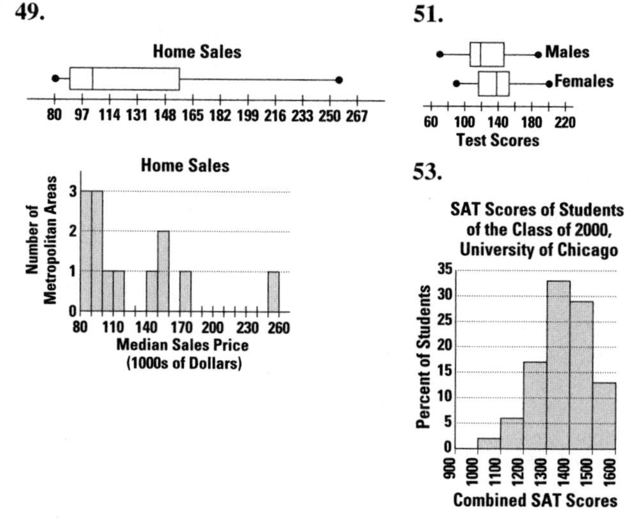

Lesson 2-1 (pp. 82–87)

15. a. See below. b. Yes; domain = the set of real numbers; range = the set of all positive real numbers **17. a. See below. b.** No **19. a.** Sample: (0, 60), (500, 180) **b.** range = $\{C: C \geq 60\}$ **c.** 0.24 **d.** the cost (in dollars) per mile driven **21.** Sample: $y = -x$; domain = the set of all positive integers **23. a.** ≈ 89.30 **b.** the mean **25.** No, because $3 \cdot 32 + 4 = 100 \neq 98$. **27. a.** II; hyperbola **b.** III; line **c.** III; line **d.** I; parabola

15. a. **17. a.**

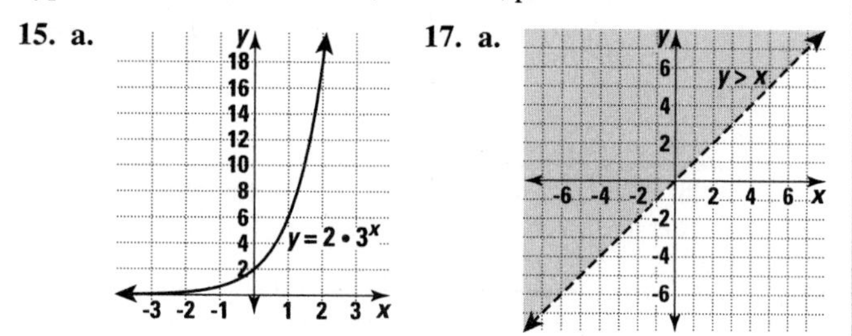

Lesson 2-2 (pp. 89–96)

15. a. ≈ 0.998 **b.** $\bar{x} = 89.111$, $s_x = 4.372$ **c.** $\bar{y} = 125.778$, $s_y = 20.897$ **d.**
$$r = \frac{1}{8}\left[\left(\frac{80-89.111}{4.372}\right)\left(\frac{82-125.778}{20.897}\right) + \left(\frac{85-89.111}{4.372}\right)\left(\frac{108-125.778}{20.897}\right) + \left(\frac{88-89.111}{4.372}\right)\left(\frac{118-125.778}{20.897}\right) + \left(\frac{89-89.111}{4.372}\right)\left(\frac{124-125.778}{20.897}\right) + \left(\frac{90-89.111}{4.372}\right)\left(\frac{131-125.778}{20.897}\right) + \left(\frac{91-89.111}{4.372}\right)\left(\frac{136-125.778}{20.897}\right) + \left(\frac{92-89.111}{4.372}\right)\left(\frac{140-125.778}{20.897}\right) + \left(\frac{93-89.111}{4.372}\right)\left(\frac{145-125.778}{20.897}\right) + \left(\frac{94-89.111}{4.372}\right)\left(\frac{148-125.778}{20.897}\right)\right]$$
≈ 0.998; to the nearest hundredth, $r = 1$. **17. a. See below. b.** $y = 1.12x - 28.48$ **c.** ≈ 63.36% **d.** ≈ 2001 **e.** ≈ 0.996 **f.** A correlation of 0.996 indicates a very strong positive relation between the variables; the line is a good model for these data.
19. a. the independent variable **b.** ≈ 20° C **c.** ≈ 80° C; it represents the difference in average temperatures between Earth and Mars at 0° latitude when it is spring in one hemisphere on each planet. **d.** $-80°C \leq M \leq -40°C$

17. a.

Percent in Labor Force; Years After 1900

Lesson 2-3 (pp. 97–104)

9. a. **See p. 879.** **b.** $y = 0.018x - 27.025$ **c.** The length of the winning long jump increases each year by about 0.018 meter, or 1.8 cm. **d.** 8.903 meters; an error of -0.403; extrapolation **e.** The center of gravity is (1945.45, 7.88), which almost lies on the regression line. (Note: There is approximation in the calculation for the regression line as well as for the center of gravity.) **f.** The outliers seem to be (1896, 6.34) and (1968, 8.90). The field of competitors may have been especially weak or strong, or the wind may have been a factor. The 1968 jump occurred in Mexico City, which was the highest altitude ever for a Summer Olympic Games. **11. a.** $y = 0.368x + 3.247$ **b.** $\approx$ 17 cm **c.** $\approx$ 19.1 cm or 7.5 in. **13. a.** 3 **b.** $\{x: x \geq -7\}$ **c.** range = the set of all nonnegative real numbers **15. a. See below.** **b.** domain = the set of all real numbers except zero; range = the set of all real numbers except zero. **17.** $a = 16$ **19.** $(10^4)^{-4}$

9. a.

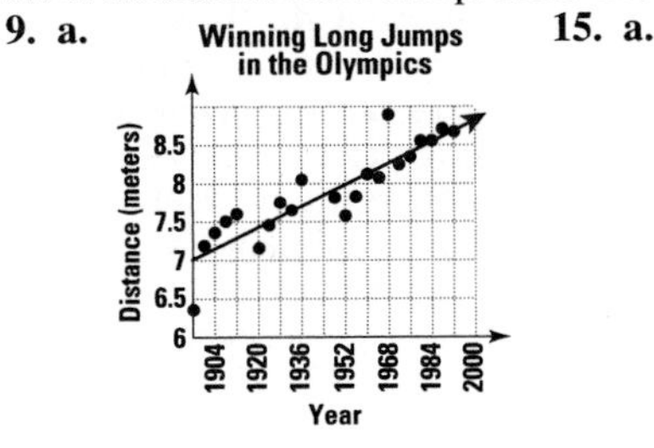

15. a.

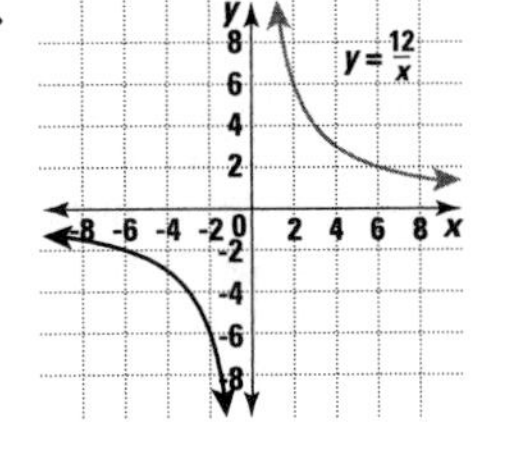

Lesson 2-4 (pp. 105–111)

13. a. See right. **b.** between 1 and 2 **c.** 1.8, 5 **15. a.** \$599.73 **b.** $\$500(1.0625)^t$

17. interpolation **19.** function

21. $a = \frac{5}{36}, b = \pm 2\sqrt{3}$

13. a.

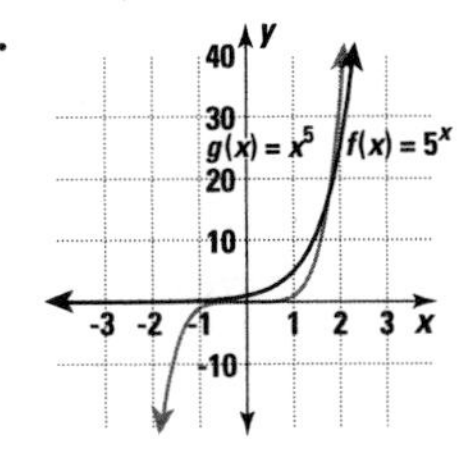

Lesson 2-5 (pp. 112–118)

9. 5700 years **11.** 2.1% **13. a., b., c. See below.** **b.** $y = 1.7083x - 3.138$ **c.** $y = 1.186(1.300)^x$ **d.** the exponential model; all of the data points are on or near the curve. **15. a.** domain = the set of all real numbers **b.** range = the set of all positive real numbers **17. a. See below.** **b.** $r = 0.6040$ **c.** $t = 0.0302d - 2.0200$ **d.** -0.047 **e.** There seems to be a moderate positive correlation between drug dosage and reaction time. **19. a.** domain = $\{x: -3 \leq x \leq 1\}$ **b.** range = $\{y: -2 \leq y \leq 0\}$ **21.** Yes; for each value of x there is exactly one value of y.

13. a., b., c. **17. a.**

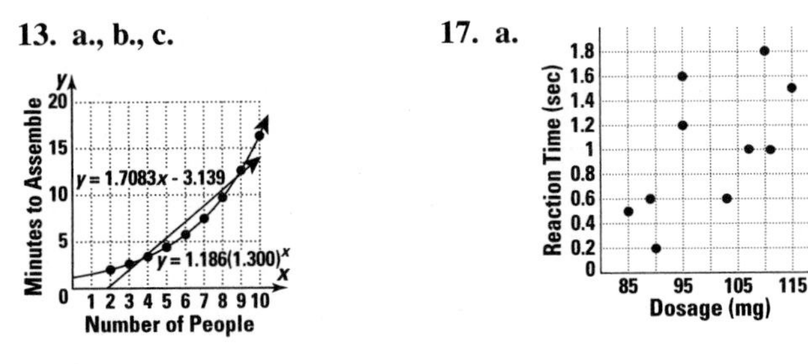

Lesson 2-6 (pp. 120–127)

13. a. See above right. **b.** $y = 0.072x^2 - 0.490x + 19.714$ **c.**

Speed (mph)	10	20	30	40	50	60	70
Stopping distance (ft)	19	42	73	116	173	248	343
Predicted stopping distance (ft)	22.014	38.714	69.814	115.314	175.214	249.514	338.214
Error	-3.014	3.286	3.186	.686	-2.214	-1.514	4.786

15. $2000(1.047)^t$
17. \$1875.91

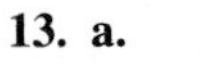

13. a.

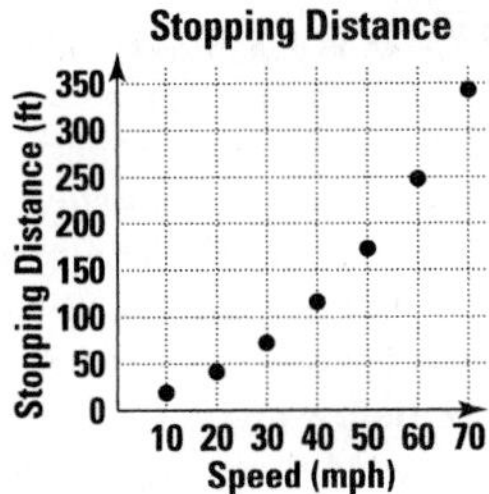

Lesson 2-7 (pp. 128–133)

15. b **17. a.** \$270 **b.** $135\left\lfloor\frac{M}{1000}\right\rfloor$ **19. a. See below.** **b.** $y = -0.79x^2 + 51.83x - 812.41$ **c.** For best mileage, the pressure in the tires should be between 32 and 33 psi. **d.** 0, because the data do not come close to any one line **e.** 0.226 **21.** d

19. a.

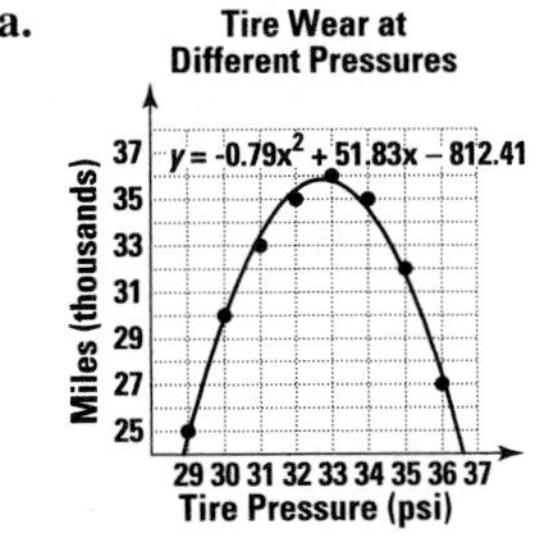

Lesson 2-8 (pp. 134–140)

11. a. Sample: $y = -9.857x^2 + 3.343x + 249.6$ **b.** -0.09, 0.14, 0.08, -0.26, 0.11 **See below.** **c.** Sample: This model's residuals tend to cluster around zero. **13. a. See below.** **b.** None of these; sample: The data seem to follow no pattern. The linear regression model has a poor correlation coefficient of 0.286. The scatterplot does not seem to follow a quadratic or exponential curve. A step function does not apply because the data change continuously. **15. a.** The function calculates the decimal portion of the positive real number. **b. See below.**

11. b. **13. a.** **15. b.**

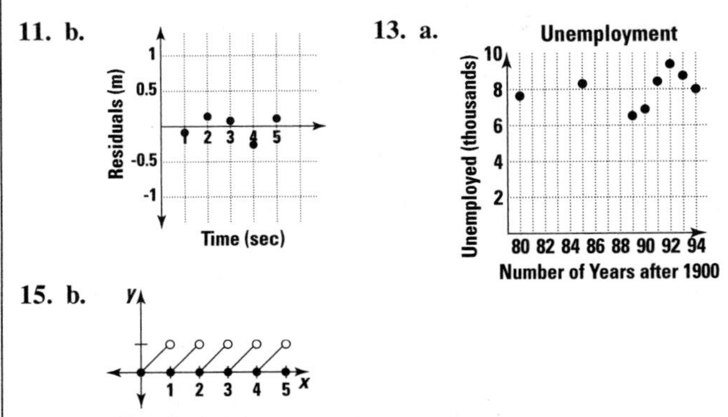

Lesson 2-9 (pp. 141–147)

11. a. 255 billion miles **b.** 1970 **13. a.** domain = the set of all real numbers **b.** range = the set of all nonnegative real numbers **15. a.** independent variable: per capita cigarette consumption in 1930; dependent variable: deaths per million men in 1950 **b.** Canada, U. S. A., Sweden, Norway, Iceland **c.** Great Britain, Finland, Switzerland, Holland, Denmark **d.** U. S. A. **e.** Sample: The lung cancer would take years to develop. **17.** Correlation has no units. **19.** c **21.** a

CHAPTER 2 PROGRESS SELF-TEST (p. 151)

1. a. It is a function. It passes the vertical line test. **b.** The domain of the function seems to be the set of all real numbers; since both of the branches stay above the x-axis, the range is the set of all nonnegative real numbers, or $\{y: y \geq 0\}$. **2. a.** The ordered pairs (4, 9) and (4, 7) both have the same first element, so the relation is not a function. **3.** $k(-3) = 2(-3)^2 - 7 = 18 - 7 = 11$ **4. a. See below right. b.** The square of any real number is nonnegative. Multiplying a nonnegative number by 2 yields a nonnegative number. Then 7 is subtracted from these values. So, the range is all real numbers greater than or equal to -7, $\{y: y \geq -7\}$. **5.** $6\pi \approx 18.85$. So $f(6\pi) = \lceil 6\pi \rceil + 1 = 19 + 1 = 20$. **6.** a; Function a models exponential decay since $0 < b < 1$, where b is the base of the exponential function. Functions b, c, and d all have bases greater than 1, so they model exponential growth. **7. a.** $304 = 7 \cdot 40 + 24$, so there will be seven full buses and an eighth bus with 24 passengers. **b.** This is a ceiling function situation since having extra places on a bus is preferred to leaving passengers behind. Hence, divide the number of passengers s by the individual bus capacity, and round fractions up to the next integer. $n = \left\lceil \frac{s}{40} \right\rceil$, where s is the total number of students **8. a.** One statistics utility gives $r \approx -0.988698$. **b.** A correlation coefficient close to -1 indicates a strong linear relation between the independent and dependent variables. The negative correlation indicates that as one variable increases, the other variable decreases. Therefore, the relationship between the year and the amount of funding available for the arts is described well by a linear model, for the years given. **c.** One statistics utility gives $y = -3.22x + 6577.86$. **d.** The slope, -3.22, represents the change in NEA funding per year. Since it is negative, funding is decreasing each year. So, funding for the arts is decreasing by about $3.22 million each year, on average. **9.** Use an exponential model $S(t) = ab^t$, where t is the time after initial inspection, a is the initial amount, and b is the rate of decay. Since the half-life is 29 years, after 29 years there will be 5 grams left of a sample initially containing 10 grams. After 58 years, there will be 2.5 grams left, after 87 years, 1.25 grams, and so on. Enter the values of t and $S(t)$ into a statistics utility, that is, (0, 10), (29, 5), (58, 2.5), (87, 1.25), and calculate an exponential regression. A statistics utility should give $a = 10$, $b \approx 0.97638$. So, $S(30) = 10 \cdot (0.97638)^{30} \approx 4.88$ g. **10. a. See below. b.** Since the data appear to fit an exponential model, use a statistic utility to do an exponential regression. One statistics utility gives $y = 53.2096 \cdot 1.2267^x$. **c.** The residuals are calculated by taking the difference between the observed y-values and the y-values predicted by the model. For the model in part **b**, these are -51.3, 5.2, 632.8, 2848.8, -942.2, -2166.7, -53,792.8 **d.** The graph passes through most of the data points, and its residuals do not seem to follow any pattern. **11. a.** Entering the data into a statistics utility and calculating a quadratic regression yields the model $h = -16t^2 + 60t + 255$. **b.** theory-based; Newton developed a theory relating the height of an object in free-fall to time. An impressionistic model is not based on any known theory. **c.** $h = -16(4)^2 + 60(4) + 255 = 239$ feet **d.** Since the point (4, 239) lies between the data points given, the prediction is an example of interpolation. **e.** When the ball hits the ground, $h = 0$. So, substitute 0 for h in the quadratic model and solve for t. $0 = -16t^2 + 60t + 255$. Using the quadratic formula $t = \frac{-60 \pm \sqrt{60^2 - 4 \cdot (-16) \cdot 255}}{2 \cdot (-16)}$ gives $t \approx 6.3$ seconds. The other value given by the quadratic formula (-2.5) must be discarded since negative values have no meaning for this problem. **12.** The correlation between x and y is given by the correlation coefficient, $r = \sqrt{r^2} = \sqrt{0.37} \approx 0.608$, which implies a moderate correlation.

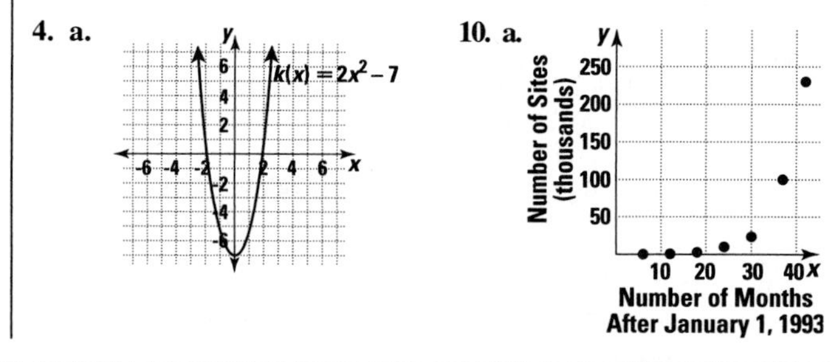

The chart below keys the questions on the **Progress Self-Test** to the objectives in the **Chapter Review** on pages 152–157 or to the **Vocabulary** (Voc.) on page 150. This will enable you to locate those **Chapter Review** questions that correspond to questions you missed on the **Progress Self-Test.** The lesson where the material is covered is also indicated on the chart.

Question	**1**	**2**	**3**	**4**	**5**	**6**	**7**	**8**	**9**	**10**
Objective	J	B	A	B, I	A	D	H	E	F	K
Lesson	2-1	2-1	2-1	2-1, 2-6	2-7	2-4	2-7	2-2, 2-3	2-5	2-8
Question	**11**	**12**								
Objective	G	C								
Lesson	2-6	2-2								

CHAPTER 2 REVIEW (pp. 152–157)

1. a. 3 **b.** $\frac{1}{3}$ **3. a.** 4 **b.** No; $(4^2 + 3) - (2^2 + 3) = 19 - 7 = 12 \neq 7$ **5. a.** 12 **b.** -5 **c.** 3 **d.** 4 **7. a.** domain = the set of all real numbers **b.** range = the set of all integers **9. a.** domain = the set of all real numbers except zero **b.** range = the set of all real numbers except zero **11. a.** domain = the set of all real numbers **b.** range = the set of all real numbers **13. a.** t **b.** A **15.** at all integer values of x **17.** A strong positive correlation means there exists a definite relation between the two variables, as overall the values of one variable increase as the values of the other variable increase. **19.** -1 **21.** $r \approx -0.894$ **23.** False **25.** True **27. a.** $b > 1$ **b.** $0 < b < 1$ **29.** (0, 1) **31.** If $a > 0$, the parabola has a minimum point. If $a < 0$, the parabola has a maximum point. **33. a.** $y = 49.487x + 72.549$ **b.** **See p. 881.** **c.** None **d.** about $1359 billion **e.** about 1999 **f.** The rate of change may not remain constant to 2010. **35. a.** $r \approx 0.946$ **b.** Yes, there is a strong positive correlation. **c.** Sample: The claim seems reasonable since high numbers of flint stones were generally found at sites with a large number of charred bones. However, there may have been an abundance of all types of fossils at these sites. There are also very few data points, making it less believable. **37.** a **39. a.** $L = A(0.5)^{h/4}$ **b.** about 29.73% **41. a.** $P = 2.876(2.019)^d$ **b. See right. c.** The exponential model is a very good fit; there is a constant percentage growth. **d.** about 53789 bacteria **e.** Yes; however, the growth rate could change due to atmospheric conditions.

43. a.

Chip	Year after 1980	MIPS	Residual
286	2	1	-0.161
386	5	5	1.082
486	9	20	0.163
Pentium	13	100	-0.424

b. The model is fairly good because the residuals are relatively small. **45. a. See right. b.** One would expect that the bass would reach a mature stage and stop growing. **c.** $L = -0.160n^2 + 3.375n + 2.896$ **d.** about 19.7 inches **e.** about 3.8 years

47. $p = \left\lfloor \frac{b}{6} \right\rfloor$ **49.** b **51. See right. 53. See right. 55.** No **57.** Yes **59.** domain = the set of all real numbers, **33. b.** range = the set of integers **61.** domain = the set of all real numbers, range = $\{y: y \leq 2\}$ **63. a.** linear **b.** negative **65. a.** linear **b.** positive **67.** b **69. a.** 80% **b.** ≈ 78% **c.** ≈ 2% **71.** the quadratic model

Total in billions ($)
Years after 1970

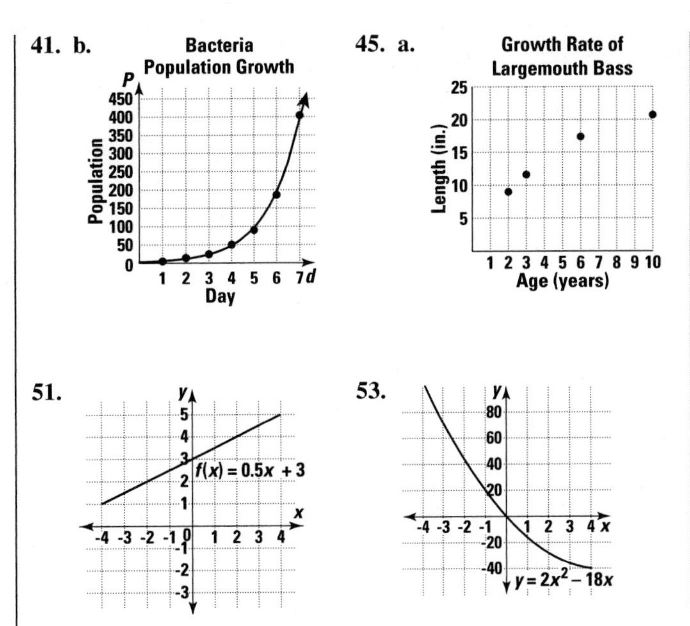

Lesson 3-1 (pp. 160–166)

13. a. See below. b. f and h are discontinuous at $x = 0$, g is discontinuous at $x = -6$. **c.** f and h have a vertical asymptote at $x = 0$, g has a vertical asymptote at $x = -6$. **d.** The graph of $g(x) = \frac{1}{x+6}$ is the image of the graph of $f(x) = \frac{1}{x}$ translated 6 units to the left. The graph of $h(x) = \frac{1}{x} + 10$ is the image of the graph of $f(x) = \frac{1}{x}$ translated 10 units up. **15. a.** 35 competitors **b.** 78 fish **c.** mean ≈ 2.23; median = 2; mode = 2 **d.** $s \approx 1.80$ **17. a., b. See below. c.** $\triangle A'B'C'$ is the image of $\triangle ABC$ under the translation 6 units to the right. **19. a.** 25 **b.** $12x$ **c.** $x + 13$ **d.** $x + a$

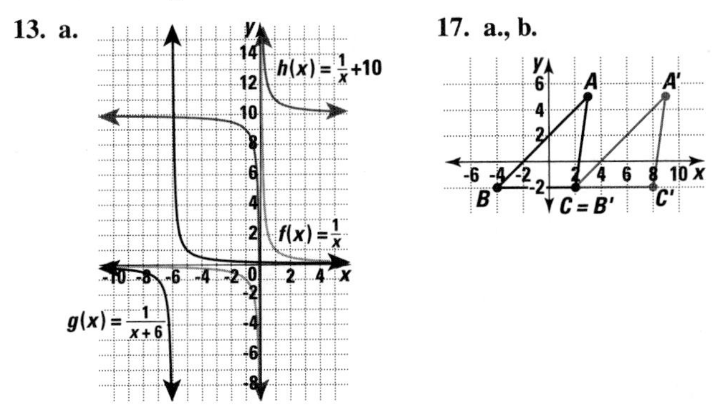

Lesson 3-2 (pp. 167–172)

15. $y = \frac{1}{x+2} - 1$ **17.** c **19. a. See above right. b.** The graphs are almost identical in the first quadrant, having the same horizontal ($y = 0$) and vertical ($x = 0$) asymptotes. **c.** The graph of $y = \frac{1}{x^2}$ is symmetric with respect to the y-axis; The graph of $y = \frac{1}{x}$ is symmetric with respect to the origin. **21.** $k = 15$ **23.** c

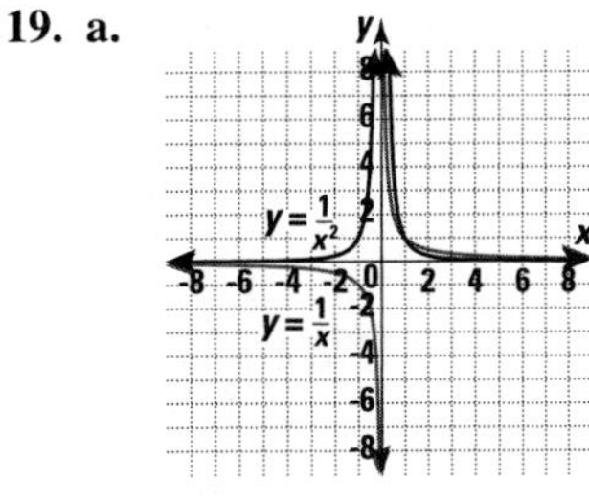

Lesson 3-3 (pp. 173–178)

9. a. See below. b. $T(x) = x + 11$ **c.** original scores: range = 16, mode = 10, mean = 13, median = 11; transformed scores: range = 16, mode = 21, mean = 24, median = 22 **11. b.** mean height = 115.5 cm, standard deviation ≈ 9.01 cm; mean weight ≈ 21.08 kg, standard deviation ≈ 3.53 kg **c. See below. d.** $w = 0.342h - 18.43$ **e.** It is translated 100 cm to the left. **See p. 882. f.** $w = 0.342h + 15.78$ **g.** mean transformed height = 15.5 cm, standard deviation of transformed heights ≈ 9.01 cm; mean transformed weight ≈ 1.08 kg, standard deviation of transformed weights ≈ 3.53 kg **h.** It is translated down 20 cm and left 100 cm. **See p. 882. i.** $w = 0.342h - 4.22$ **13. a. See p. 882 b. See p. 882. c.** $T(x, y) = (x + 7, y + 10)$ **15.** $y = |x - 9|$ **17. a.** $f(3) = 63$ **b.** $f(-3) = -45$ **c.** $-f(3) = -63$ **19. a.** (-1, 8) **b.** (-2, -6) **21. a.** $5x$ **b.** $36x$ **c.** $36x^2$

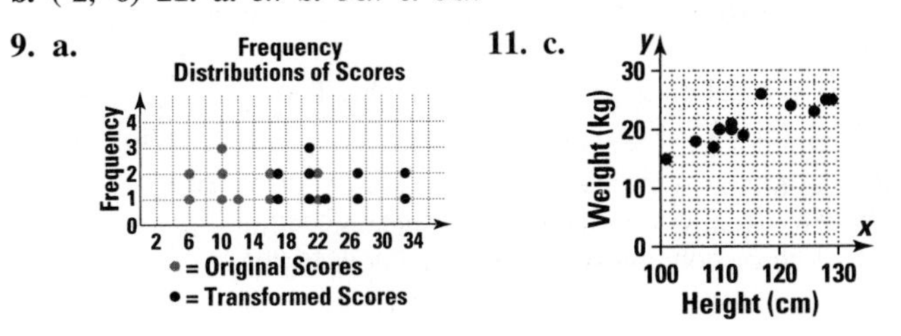

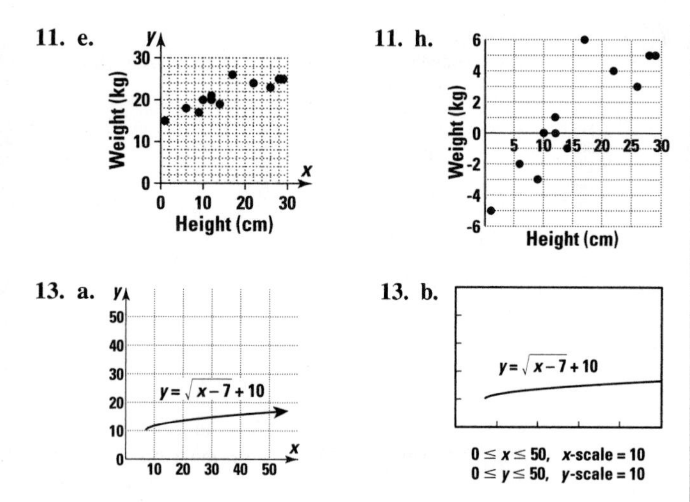

Lesson 3-4 (pp. 179–185)

13. a. See below. b. j and h are odd; g is neither. **c.** j is the parent; the graph of h is the reflection image of the graph of j over the y-axis; the graph of g is the image of the graph of j under the translation 2 units up. **d.** j and h have point symmetry about (0, 0); g has point symmetry about (0, 2) **15. a. See below. b.** r and s are even; q is neither. **c.** r is the parent; the graph of q is the image of the graph of r under the translation 5 units to the left; the graph of s is the image of the graph of r under the translation 3 units up. **d.** The axis of symmetry for the graphs of r and s is $x = 0$; the axis of symmetry for the graph of q is $x = -5$. **17. a.** 70 **b.** 65 **c.** 18 **19.** 6 **21. a.** $T(x, y) = (x + 6, y - 3)$ **b.** (18, 37) **23. a.** 200 hours **b.** 100% **25.** $S = 36L - 21.25$

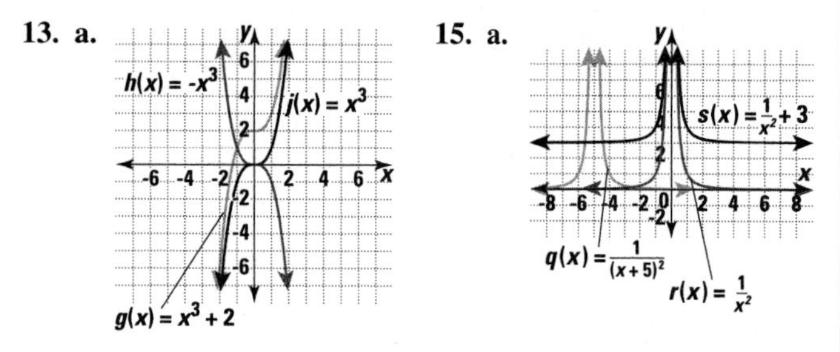

Lesson 3-5 (pp, 187–193)

11. $S(x, y) = (3x, y)$ **13. a.** Yes **b.** No **c.** Yes **d.** No **15. a.** $2\sqrt{6}$ **b.** about 25.5 mph **c.** about 126 feet **17. a.** neither **19.** The graph of g is the reflection image of the graph of f over the x-axis. **21. a.** 738 mg **b.** 6.2 mg

Lesson 3-6 (pp. 194–200)

9. a. $S: x_i \rightarrow \frac{3}{2}x_i$ **b.** original scores: range = 16, mode = 10, mean = 13, median = 11; scaled scores: range = 24, mode = 15, mean = 19.5, median = 16.5 **c. See above right.** Sample: The scaled scores are 1.5 times the original scores. **11. a. See above right. b.** $w = 0.342h - 18.43$ **c.** The scatterplot is shrunk by a factor of $\frac{1}{2.54}$ in the horizontal direction. **See above right. d.** $w = 0.869h - 18.43$ **e.** The scatterplot is shrunk by a factor of $\frac{1}{2.54}$ in the horizontal direction and stretched by a factor of $\frac{1}{0.454}$ in the vertical direction. **See above right. f.** $w = 1.914h - 40.59$ **13. a.** $S:(x, y) \rightarrow (3x, y)$ **b.** $S:(x, y) \rightarrow \left(\frac{x}{3}, y\right)$ **c. See above right.**

15. a. 60 **b.** $36k^2 + 42k$ **c.** $a^2 - a - 12$ **17.** b **19.** c **21.** Yes; each side of the larger triangle is 2.5 times the length of the corresponding side of the smaller triangle.

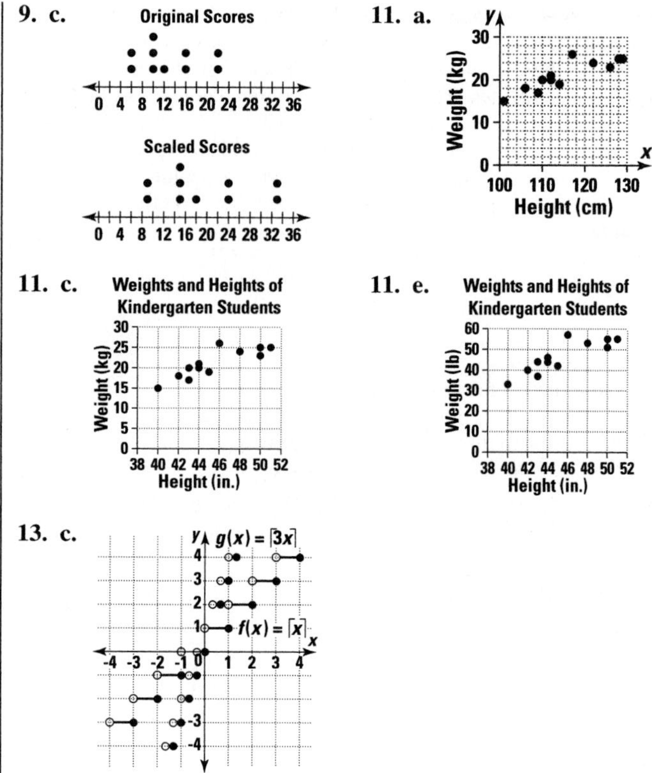

Lesson 3-7 (pp. 201–207)

11. $\sqrt{5}$ **13.** D reduces the price you pay by an amount proportional to the regular price. R reduces the price you pay by a fixed amount regardless of the price. **15.** $(D \circ R)(x) = 0.9x - 90$, $(R \circ D)(x) = 0.9x - 100$; $0.9x - 90 \neq 0.9x - 100$ **17.** No; for example, let $f(x) = 2x^2$ and $g(x) = x^2$. Then $f(g(x)) = f(x^2) = 2(x^2)^2 = 2x^4$, which is not a quadratic function. **19.** The mean will be tripled; the standard deviation will be multiplied by 3. **21.** $y = -9x^2$ **23. a. See below. b.** not a function **25.** Yes, because each element of the domain corresponds to exactly one element in the range. **27. a.–c. See below. d.** the reflection over the line $y = x$

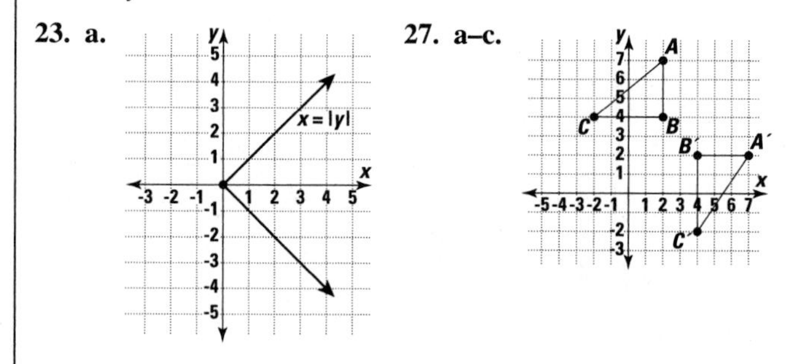

Lesson 3-8 (pp. 208–214)

13. a. $M(x) = 7.63x$, $U(x) = \frac{x}{7.63}$ **b.** \$2,621.23 **c.** Yes; $(M \circ U)(x) = M\left(\frac{x}{7.63}\right) = 7.63\left(\frac{x}{7.63}\right) = x$; $(U \circ M)(x) = U(7.63x) = \frac{7.63x}{7.63} = x$. **15. a.** **See p. 883.** **b.** No **17. a.** $f: x \rightarrow \lfloor x \rfloor$ is not one-to-one because many values in the domain go to the same value in the range, for example, $f(0) = 0$, $f(0.5) = 0$. **b.** Sample:

$y = x$ **19. a.** $y = \frac{x - b}{m}$ **b.** False; the inverse of the linear function $y = b$ for all x is $x = b$ which is not a function. **21. a.** scale change **23. a.** $p(-x) = 5 - |-x| = 5 - |x| = p(x)$. This shows that p is an even function. **b.** reflection symmetry with respect to the y-axis **25.** $\sum_{i=1}^{n} x_i y_i$ **15. a.**

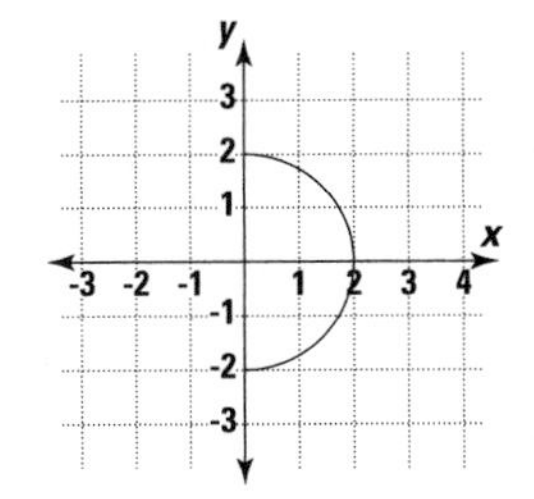

Chapter 3-9 (pp. 215–219)

11. the man who weighs 192 lb **13.** 680 **15. a.** $(T \circ S)(x) = \frac{x}{s} - \bar{x}$ **b.** mean = -56, standard deviation = 1 **c.** The mean is not the same; the standard deviation is the same. $(T \circ S)(x) \neq (S \circ T)(x)$ **17.** physics test **19.** about 29 **21. a.** True **b.** False **23.** False **25. a.** $0.945x$ **b.** It does not matter. $D(T(x)) = D(1.05x) = .9(1.05x) = 0.945x$ and $T(D(x)) = T(.9x) = 1.05(.9x) = 0.945x$ **27.** b **29. a.** 79.629 **b.** 100.33 **c.** 1411.61008

CHAPTER 3 PROGRESS SELF-TEST (p. 224)

1. To apply $S(x, y) = (x - 1, y + 5)$ to $y = 3x^2$, replace x by $x + 1$ and y by $y - 5$, $y - 5 = 3(x + 1)^2$. An equivalent form of this equation is $y = 3x^2 + 6x + 8$. **2.** The vertex of the original parabola is (0, 0), $S(0, 0) = (0 - 1,\ 0 + 5) = (-1, 5)$ **3.** The transformation $S: (x, y) \rightarrow (-x, 2y)$ is a stretch by 2 in the vertical direction and a reflection over the y-axis. **See right.** **4.** To have a vertical asymptote at $x = 0$, the function must be undefined at $x = 0$. The only parent functions which satisfy this are $y = \frac{1}{x}$ or $y = \frac{1}{x^2}$ **5. a.** The median of the translated data is changed by the amount of the translation, so the median of the original data is 7.4 + 20 = 27.4 g. **b.** Translations do not affect the range so the range of the original data is 11.8 − 3.4 = 8.4 g. **c.** Translations do not affect the variance so the variance of the original data is $1.3^2 = 1.69\text{ g}^2$. **6.** Multiply each statistic by the scale factor 0.0353: mean = $7.9 \cdot 0.0353 \approx 0.28$ oz, standard deviation = $1.3 \cdot 0.0353 \approx 0.046$ oz. **7.** $(b \circ a)(2) = b(a(2)) = b(18 - 3 \cdot 2) = b(12) = 4 \cdot 12^2 = 4 \cdot 144 = 576$ **8.** $a(b(x)) = a(4x^2) = 18 - 3 \cdot (4x^2) = 18 - 12x^2$ **9.** The domain of a is the set of all real numbers. The domain of b is the set of all real numbers. Thus the domain of $a \circ b$ is the set of all real numbers.

10. If $f(x) = y = \frac{2}{x - 3}$, then the inverse is $x = \frac{2}{y - 3}$. So $\frac{y - 3}{2} = \frac{1}{x} \Rightarrow y - 3 = \frac{2}{x} \Rightarrow y = \frac{2}{x} + 3$. **11. See right.**

12. Yes, $y = \frac{2}{x} + 3$, $x \neq 0$, is a function because each value of x yields exactly one value of y. **13.** The mean of the translated data is changed by the amount of the translation, so 12 should be subtracted from the original data. The standard deviation is affected by a scale change, so the data should be divided by 5. The composite of these transformations is $T: x \rightarrow \frac{x - 12}{5}$. **14.** Because the graph of f fails the horizontal-line test, the inverse of f is not a function. **15.** We need to show $f(-x) = f(x)$ for all x. $f(-x) = 3(-x)^2 - 2 = 3x^2 - 2 = f(x)$. Therefore, f is an even function. **16.** Sample: The point (1, 3) is the image of (1, 1), so the scale change is $(x, y) \rightarrow (x, 3y)$. This transformation changes $y = |x|$ to $\frac{y}{3} = |x|$ or $g(x) = y = 3|x|$. **17.** g is symmetric with respect to the y-axis. **18.** False; under a scale change of magnitude k, the variance of the scaled data is k^2 times the variance of the original data. **19.** True; a translation preserves distances, so the image is congruent to the preimage. **20.** Her z-scores are: biology = $\frac{72 - 60}{8} = 1.5$; psychology = $\frac{59 - 50}{4} = 2.25$. So she scored better on the psychology test compared to her peers. The z-score of 2.25 means her raw score was 2.25 standard deviations above the mean of psychology scores, while the biology raw score was only 1.5 s.d. above the biology scores mean.

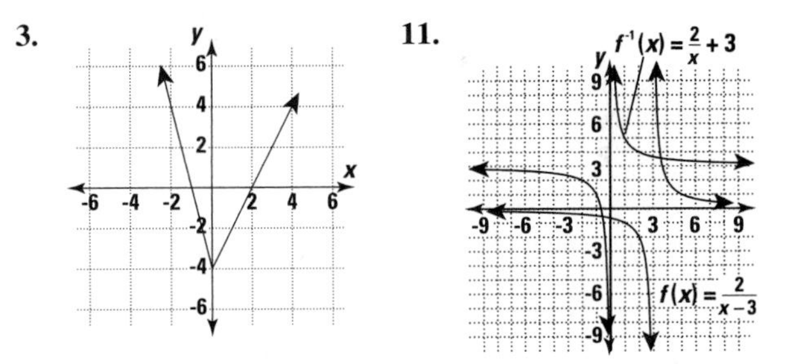

The chart below keys the questions on the **Progress Self-Test** to the objectives in the **Chapter Review** on pages 225-229 or the **Vocabulary** (Voc.) on page 223. This will enable you to locate those **Chapter Review** questions that correspond to questions you missed on the **Progress Self-Test.** The lesson where the material is covered is also indicated on the chart.

Question	**1**	**2**	**3**	**4**	**5**	**6**	**7**	**8**	**9**	**10**
Objective	C	C	K	J	I	I	A	A	G	B
Lesson	3-2	3-2	3-5	3-1	3-3	3-6	3-7	3-7	3-7	3-8
Question	**11**	**12**	**13**	**14**	**15**	**16**	**17**	**18**	**19**	**20**
Objective	M	G	H	G	F	K	L	E	D	I
Lesson	3-8	3-8	3-9	3-8	3-4	3-5	3-4	3-6	3-2	3-9

CHAPTER 3 REVIEW (pp. 225-229)

1. a. -14 **b.** -72 **3.** 13 **5. a.** -3 **b.** 4.5 **7. a.** $y = \frac{x-7}{2}$ **b.** Yes **9. a.** $y = \frac{2}{x} - 1$ **b.** Yes **11.** b **13.** $y = (x-7)^2 - 3$ **15.** $y = 5|4x|$ **17.** $T(x, y) = \left(\frac{x}{10}, y\right)$ **19.** The image is translated h units to the right and k units up. **21.** True **23.** scale change **25.** The mean increases by 10. **27.** The median is multiplied by k. **29.** The standard deviation does not change. **31.** True **33.** False **35. a.** even **b.** $s(-t) = 5(-t)^2 - (-t)^4 = 5t^2 - t^4 = s(t)$. Therefore the function is even. **37. a.** even **b.** $f(-x) = |-x| - 3 = |x| - 3 = f(x)$. Therefore the function is even. **39.** reflection over the line $y = x$ **41.** d **43.** A z-score of -1.6 corresponds to a raw score which is 1.6 standard deviations below the mean. **45.** 0 **47.** 109 **49.** mean ≈ 8 : 29.64, standard deviation ≈ 1.15 seconds; a translation of $x \rightarrow x - 8$ is appropriate because all the times are in the 8-minute range. **51.** the history test **53.** c **55.** d **57.** a **59. See right. 61. a. See right. b.** Sample: 0, 2.5, 5 **63. See right. 65.** $y = (x+2)^2 + 5$ **67.** $y = \sqrt{2x}$ **69.** even **71.** even **73.** No; fails the horizontal-line test **75.** Yes; passes the horizontal line test **77. a.** $x = y^2$ **b. See right. c.** The inverse is not a function. **78.** No **79.** Yes

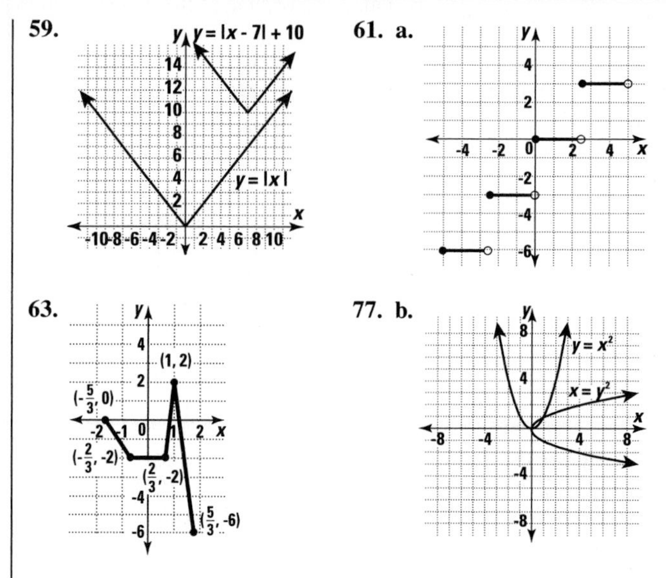

Lesson 4-1 (pp. 232–238)

17. 57 **19. a.** 2500π **b.** 1000π **21.** ≈ 10 hours **23.** $y = -\left|\frac{x}{4}\right|$ **25.** The area of circle 2 is more than twice the area of circle 1. Therefore, the amount for two portions will be more than twice the amount for one portion. **27.** $\sqrt{a^2 + b^2}$ **29.** $-b$ **31. a.** $s\sqrt{2}$ **b.** $\frac{h}{\sqrt{2}}$

Lesson 4-2 (pp. 239–243)

11. about 235.6π in^2 ≈ 740 in^2 ≈ 5.1 ft^2 **13. a.** 22π in. **b.** 3,300π in. **c.** ≈ 9.8 mph **15.** $\frac{25\pi}{8}$ units^2 **17.** Answers may vary. Samples: $\frac{5\pi}{3}, \frac{11\pi}{3}, \frac{17\pi}{3}$ **19.** $\frac{\pi}{18}$ radians **21. a.** $-0.028t^2 + 0.708t + 98.756$ **b.** ≈ 103.2°F **c.** ≈ 25.5 hours **23. a.** directly, directly, the square **b.** A is multiplied by t^2.

Lesson 4-3 (pp. 245–250)

19. $0 < \theta < \pi$ **21.**

Using the graph paper:	Using a calculator:
sin(-49°) ≈ -.8	sin(-49°) ≈ -.755
cos(-49°) ≈ .7	cos(-49°) ≈ .656
tan(-49°) ≈ $\frac{-.8}{.7}$ ≈ -1.1	tan(-49°) ≈ -1.150

See below. 23. a. $\frac{\pi}{5}$ **b.** 36° **c.** $\frac{9\pi}{5}$ units **d.** $\frac{9\pi}{10}$ units^2 **25.** π **27.** about 42 calories **29.** $(-a, b)$ **31.** $(-a, -b)$

21.

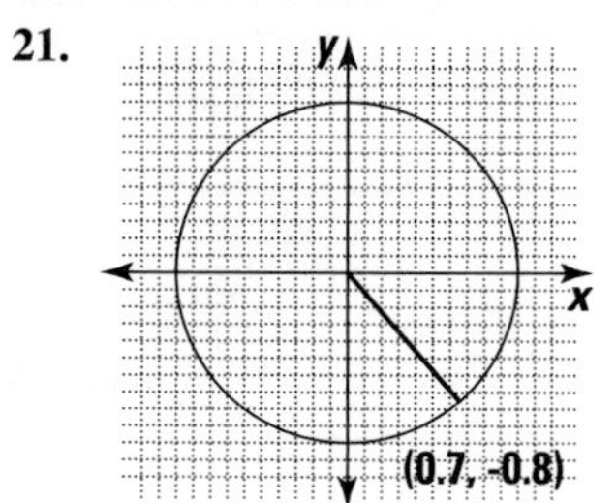

Lesson 4-4 (pp. 251–256)

17. False: **See below. 19.** Answers will vary. Sample: Let $\theta = \frac{\pi}{6}$. $\sin\left(\pi - \frac{\pi}{6}\right) = 0.5$, $\sin\pi - \sin\frac{\pi}{6} = -0.5$, so $\sin(\pi - \theta) \neq \sin\pi - \sin\theta$. **21.** From the Supplements Theorem, $\cos(\pi - \theta) = -\cos\theta$. Therefore, $\cos\theta + \cos(\pi - \theta) = \cos\theta - \cos\theta = 0$. **23.** -1 **25.** 8.5 feet **27.** $\frac{3\pi}{4}$

17.

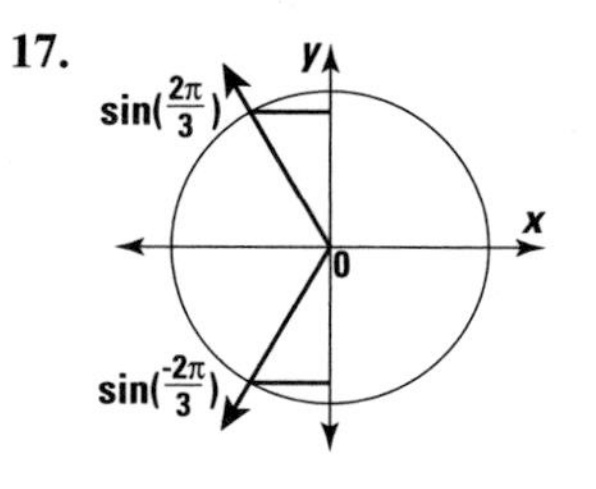

Lesson 4-5 (pp. 257–262)

11. $-\frac{\pi}{3}, \frac{\pi}{3}$ **13. a.** $-\frac{7\pi}{4}, -\frac{3\pi}{4}, \frac{\pi}{4}, \frac{5\pi}{4}$ **b.** 1 **15. a.** $\left(\cos\frac{2\pi}{7}, \sin\frac{2\pi}{7}\right)$ **b.** 0.868 **17.** False. Using the Supplements and Half-Turn theorems respectively, $\cos(\pi - \theta) + \cos(\pi + \theta) = -\cos\theta + -\cos\theta = -2\cos\theta \neq 1$ for all θ, while $\cos 2\pi = 1$. **19. a.** Since $\tan\theta = \frac{\sin\theta}{\cos\theta}$, $\cos\theta \cdot \tan\theta = \cos\theta \cdot \frac{\sin\theta}{\cos\theta} = \sin\theta$. **b.** $\tan\theta$ is not defined when $\cos\theta = 0$. **21. a.** 90π **b.** $\frac{3\pi}{2}$ **23.** (-2, 0)

Lesson 4-6 (pp. 265–271)

9. a. See p 885. b. The graphs are the same. **c.** Complements Theorem **11.** No. There is no positive real number p such that $f(x + p) = f(x)$ for all x. **13.** $\left(\frac{1}{2}, \frac{\sqrt{3}}{2}\right)$ **15.** $\frac{k\pi}{180}$ radians **17.** $y = 4\sqrt{2x} - 24$ **19.** No; all values are within 1.5 × IQR of Q_1 or Q_3.

9. a.

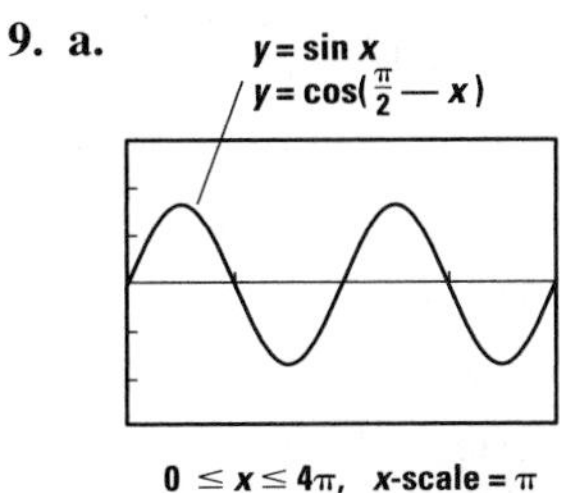

$0 \le x \le 4\pi$, x-scale = π
$1.5 \le y \le 1.5$, y-scale = 0.5

Lesson 4-7 (pp. 272–277)

13. Sample: $y = \frac{1}{8}\cos\frac{x}{12}$; zeros $(6\pi, 0)$. $(18\pi, 0)$ **See below.** **15. a.** $g(x) = \text{-}\sin\left(\frac{x}{3}\right)$ **b.** period $= 6\pi$, amplitude $= 1$ **c. See below.** **17.** Sample: $0.464 + \pi$, $0.464 - \pi$, and $0.464 + 2\pi$ **19. a. See below. b.** The graph of $y = \cos(\pi - x)$ is the image of the graph of $y = \cos x$ under a horizontal translation: $x \rightarrow x + \pi$, or under a reflection about the x-axis. **c.** Supplements Theorem **21.** $\sqrt{1 - c^2}$, when $2k\pi \le \theta \le 2k\pi + \pi$; $\text{-}\sqrt{1 - c^2}$, when $2k\pi - \pi < \theta < 2k\pi$ (k is an integer). **23. a. See below.** **b.** $f(x) = |x - 4| - 7$

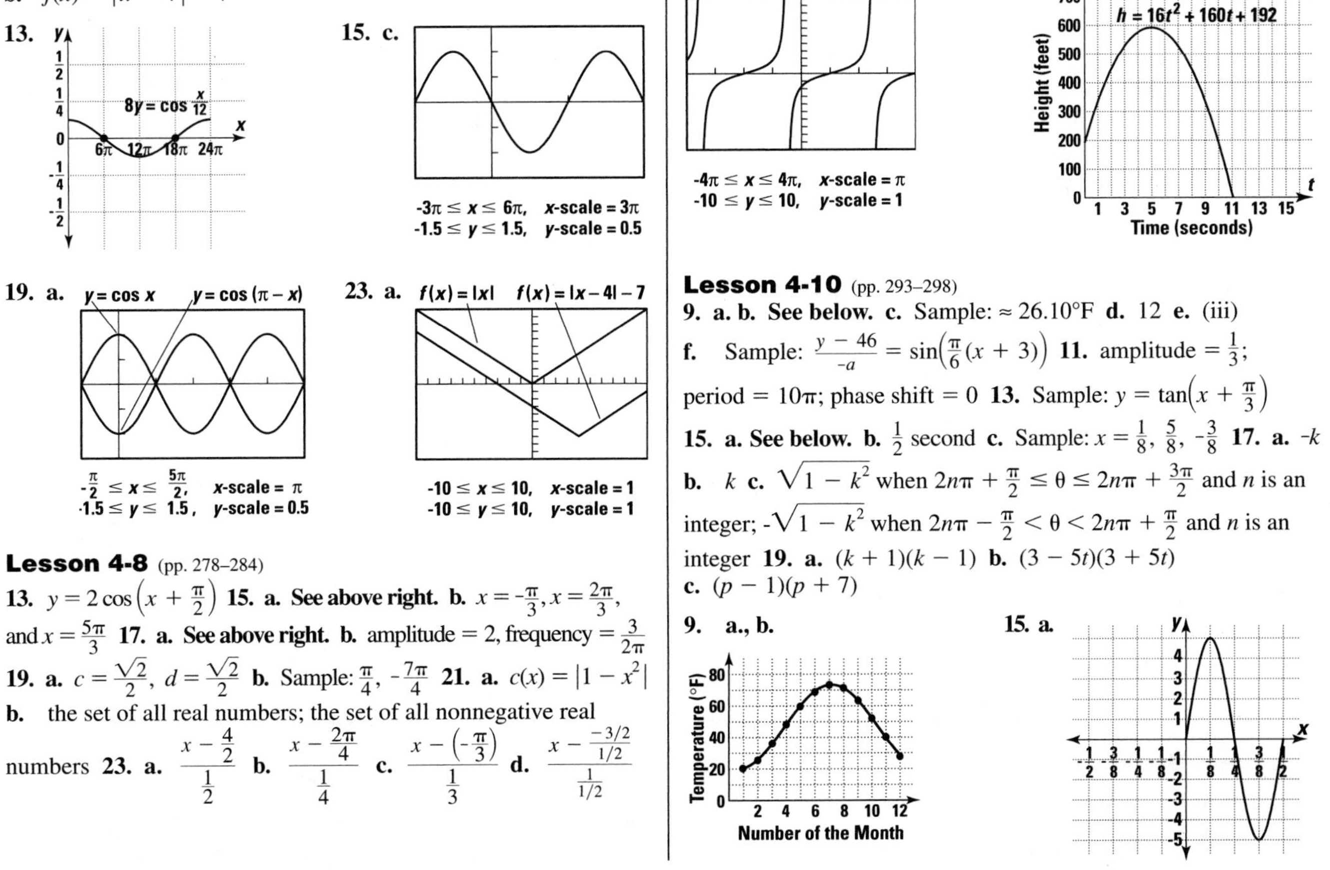

Lesson 4-8 (pp. 278–284)

13. $y = 2\cos\left(x + \frac{\pi}{2}\right)$ **15. a. See above right. b.** $x = \text{-}\frac{\pi}{3}, x = \frac{2\pi}{3}$, and $x = \frac{5\pi}{3}$ **17. a. See above right. b.** amplitude $= 2$, frequency $= \frac{3}{2\pi}$ **19. a.** $c = \frac{\sqrt{2}}{2}$, $d = \frac{\sqrt{2}}{2}$ **b.** Sample: $\frac{\pi}{4}$, $\text{-}\frac{7\pi}{4}$ **21. a.** $c(x) = |1 - x^2|$ **b.** the set of all real numbers; the set of all nonnegative real numbers **23. a.** $\dfrac{x - \frac{4}{2}}{\frac{1}{2}}$ **b.** $\dfrac{x - \frac{2\pi}{4}}{\frac{1}{4}}$ **c.** $\dfrac{x - \left(\text{-}\frac{\pi}{3}\right)}{\frac{1}{3}}$ **d.** $\dfrac{x - \frac{-3/2}{1/2}}{\frac{1}{1/2}}$

15. a.

$\text{-}\frac{\pi}{2} \le \alpha \le 2\pi$, α-scale $= \frac{\pi}{3}$
$-10 \le y \le 10$, y-scale = 1

17. a.

f(x) = 2 sin(3x)
f(x) = sin(x)

$-\pi \le x \le \pi$, x-scale $= \frac{\pi}{2}$
$-2.5 \le y \le 2.5$, y-scale = 1

Lesson 4-9 (pp. 285–291)

9. $y = 2\cos 2\left(x - \frac{\pi}{2}\right)$ **11.** $y = 10\cos(x - \pi) + 5$ or $y = 10\sin\left(x - \frac{\pi}{2}\right) + 5$ **13. a.** $(x, y) \rightarrow (3x, y)$ followed by $(x, y) \rightarrow (x + \pi, y)$ **b. See below. c.** period $= 3\pi$; phase shift $= \pi$ **15.** $y = \text{-}1 + \sin\left(x + \frac{3\pi}{4}\right)$ **17. a.** $\frac{2\pi}{|B|}$ **b.** $|A|$ **c.** all real numbers **d.** $\text{-}|A| \le h(x) \le |A|$ **19. a. See below. b.** 592 feet **c.** $t \approx 11.1$ seconds

13. b.

$-4\pi \le x \le 4\pi$, x-scale = π
$-10 \le y \le 10$, y-scale = 1

19. a.

h = 16t² + 160t + 192
Height (feet)
Time (seconds)

Lesson 4-10 (pp. 293–298)

9. a. b. See below. c. Sample: ≈ 26.10°F **d.** 12 **e.** (iii) **f.** Sample: $\frac{y - 46}{-a} = \sin\left(\frac{\pi}{6}(x + 3)\right)$ **11.** amplitude $= \frac{1}{3}$; period $= 10\pi$; phase shift $= 0$ **13.** Sample: $y = \tan\left(x + \frac{\pi}{3}\right)$ **15. a. See below. b.** $\frac{1}{2}$ second **c.** Sample: $x = \frac{1}{8}, \frac{5}{8}, \text{-}\frac{3}{8}$ **17. a.** $\text{-}k$ **b.** k **c.** $\sqrt{1 - k^2}$ when $2n\pi + \frac{\pi}{2} \le \theta \le 2n\pi + \frac{3\pi}{2}$ and n is an integer; $\text{-}\sqrt{1 - k^2}$ when $2n\pi - \frac{\pi}{2} < \theta < 2n\pi + \frac{\pi}{2}$ and n is an integer **19. a.** $(k + 1)(k - 1)$ **b.** $(3 - 5t)(3 + 5t)$ **c.** $(p - 1)(p + 7)$

9. a., b.

Temperature (°F)
Number of the Month

15. a.

Chapter 4 Progress Self-Test (p. 302)

1. $\frac{8}{9} \cdot \frac{2\pi}{1 \text{ revolution}} = \frac{16\pi}{9}$ **2.** $\text{-}\frac{3\pi}{2} \cdot \frac{180°}{\pi} = -270°$ **3.** $75° \cdot \frac{\pi}{180°} = \frac{75\pi}{180°} = \frac{5\pi}{12}$ **4.** **See p. 886.** This cross section indicates that the central angle between Adelaide and the South Pole is $90° - 34°55' = 55°05' \approx 55.08° \approx 0.96$ radians. So, the arc length $s = r\theta = 6400$ km $(0.96) \approx 6{,}150$ km **5.** $A = \frac{1}{2}\theta r^2 = \frac{1}{2}\left(\frac{5\pi}{4}\right)(12 \text{ cm})^2 = 90\pi \text{ cm}^2$ **6.** -0.969 **7.** -0.990 **8.** $\frac{\sqrt{2}}{2}$ **9.** $\sqrt{3}$ **10. a.** domain: all real numbers **b.** range: $\{y: -1 \le y \le 1\}$ **11. a.** $P(x, y) = P\left(\cos\frac{2\pi}{3}, \sin\frac{2\pi}{3}\right) = P\left(\text{-}\frac{1}{2}, \frac{\sqrt{3}}{2}\right)$ **b.** $P'(x', y') = P(x, -y) = P\left(\cos\frac{2\pi}{3}, -\sin\frac{2\pi}{3}\right) = P'\left(\text{-}\frac{1}{2}, \text{-}\frac{\sqrt{3}}{2}\right)$ **c.** **See p. 886.** Using the circle divided into 6 parts (each $\frac{\pi}{3}$ radians) it is clear that $P' = R_{4\pi/3}(1, 0)$, namely, $\theta = \frac{4\pi}{3}$. **12. a. See below right.** **b.** period $= \frac{2\pi}{|-1|} = 2\pi$ **c.** By plotting the graph of the parent function over $y = \cos(2\pi - x)$ it becomes clear that it is identical to the cosine function. **13. a.** domain: all real numbers **b.** Since the amplitude of the function is $\frac{1}{2}$ (and there is no vertical shift), the range is $\left\{y: -\frac{1}{2} \leq y \leq \frac{1}{2}\right\}$. **c.** amplitude $= \frac{1}{2}$ **d.** The function defined by $y = \sin\left(\frac{x}{a}\right)$ has period $= 2\pi|a|$. Thus, for $y = \frac{1}{2}\sin\left(\frac{x}{2}\right)$, $|a| = |2|$ and the period $= 2\pi \cdot 2 = 4\pi$ **14. a.** By the Graph Standardization Theorem, the graph of $y = \sin x$ is transformed to the graph of $y = \sin\left(x - \frac{\pi}{6}\right)$ by $(x, y) \rightarrow \left(x + \frac{\pi}{6}, y\right)$. **b.** phase shift $= \frac{\pi}{6}$ **15.** $\cos\left(\frac{\pi}{2} - \theta\right) = \sin\theta = s$ **16.** $\sin(\theta - \pi) = -\sin\theta = -s$ **17.** Because $0 < \theta < \frac{\pi}{2}$, $\cos\theta = \sqrt{1 - \sin^2\theta} = \sqrt{1 - s^2}$ **18.** Most directly, the function can be written $y = \cos x$. **19. a.** Let $y = \cos\left(\frac{x - h}{a}\right)$. Since $h = -\pi$, $y = \cos\left(\frac{x - (-\pi)}{a}\right)$. The period of $y = \cos\left(\frac{x}{a}\right)$ is $2\pi|a|$, so $\frac{\pi}{2} = 2\pi \cdot a$ and $a = \frac{1}{4}$. Thus $y = \cos\left(\frac{x + \pi}{\frac{1}{4}}\right) = \cos 4(x + \pi)$. **b. See right.** **20. a.** maximum voltage = function amplitude = 14 volts **b.** At maximum voltage $14 = 14\cos(5\pi t)$. $1 = \cos(5\pi t)$ when $5\pi t = 0, 2\pi, 4\pi, 6\pi, \ldots$ or when $t = \frac{2n}{5}$, n an integer. But $t > 0$, so at $t = 0.4$, 0.8, and 1.2 seconds, the voltage will reach maximum. **21.** Use $y = b\sin\frac{t}{a}$. The frequency is the reciprocal of the period, so $60 = \frac{1}{2\pi|a|}$, and $|a| = \frac{1}{120\pi}$. With amplitude = 0.1, $y = 0.1\sin\left(\frac{t}{\frac{1}{120\pi}}\right) = 0.1\sin(120\pi t)$. Another possible solution is $y = 0.1\cos(120\pi t)$. **22. a.** amplitude $= \frac{1}{2} \times$ vertical displacement $\approx \frac{1}{2}(71° - 22°) = \frac{1}{2}(49°) = 24.5°$; period = 12 months **b.** Note that the model indicates a phase shift (3 months for a sine wave) and a vertical shift of 46.5°. Therefore, one possible solution is $T = 46.5 + 24.5\sin\frac{\pi(n - 3)}{6}$. **c.** $46.5 + 24.5\sin\frac{\pi(1 - 3)}{6} \approx 25.3°$

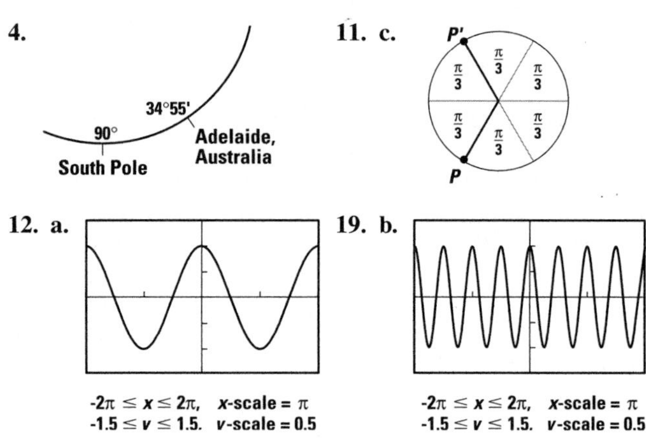

The chart below keys the questions on the **Progress Self-Test** to the objectives in the **Chapter Review** on pages 303-307 or **Vocabulary** (Voc.) on page 301. This will enable you to locate those **Chapter Review** questions that correspond to questions you missed on the **Progress Self-Test.** The lesson where the material is covered is also indicated on the chart.

Question	**1**	**2**	**3**	**4**	**5**	**6**	**7**	**8**	**9**	**10**
Objective	A	A	A	G	B	C	C	C	C	D
Lesson	4-1	4-1	4-1	4-2	4-2	4-3	4-3	4-5	4-5	4-6
Question	**11**	**12**	**13**	**14**	**15**	**16**	**17**	**18**	**19**	**20**
Objective	C, J	F, L	F	F	E	E	E	K, M	L	H
Lesson	4-3, 4-5	4-8	4-7	4-8	4-4	4-4	4-4	4-6, 4-9	4-7	4-7
Question	**21**	**22**								
Objective	I	I								
Lesson	4-10	4-10								

Chapter 4 Review (pp. 303–307)

1. a. 72° **b.** $\frac{2\pi}{5}$ **3.** -30° **5.** $\frac{3\pi}{4}$ **7.** $\frac{1}{3}$ **9.** 6π inches **11.** $\frac{25\pi}{3}$ m² **13.** $\frac{\sqrt{2}}{2}$ **15.** $\frac{\sqrt{3}}{3}$ **17.** 0.092 **19.** 0.14 **21.** -0.55 **23.** $-\frac{1}{2}$ **25.** 1 **27.** (-1, 0) **29.** $-\frac{\pi}{6}, \frac{7\pi}{6}, \frac{11\pi}{6}$ **31.** odd multiples of $\frac{\pi}{2}$ **33.** True **35.** d **37.** k **39.** $-k$

41. $-\sin\left(\frac{\pi}{2} - \theta\right) = -\cos\theta$ — Complements Theorem
$-\cos\theta = \cos(\pi - \theta)$ — Supplements Theorem
43. True: $\sin(\theta + 6\pi) = \sin\theta$ — Periodicity Theorem

45. a. $\frac{\sqrt{15}}{4}$ or $-\frac{\sqrt{15}}{4}$ **b.** $\sqrt{15}$ or $-\sqrt{15}$ **47. a.** $\frac{2}{3}$ **b.** 2 **c.** 0 **49. a.** $\frac{\pi}{2}$ **b.** undefined **c.** 0 **51. a.** 15 **b.** 5 **53. a.** $y = -2\cos 3(x - 6)$ **b.** $(x, y) \rightarrow \left(\frac{x + 18}{3}, -2y\right)$ **55.** $\frac{2604\pi}{9} \approx 909$ m² **57. a.** at about 0.0031 seconds **b.** $t = \frac{n}{30}$ seconds for any positive integer n **59. a.** $\frac{1}{2}$ radian **b.** $\frac{1}{\pi}$ **c.** $5\pi \approx 15.7$ seconds **61. a.** $y = 1.900\sin(0.017x - 1.325) + 12.126$ **b.** period $\approx 2\pi(58.82) \approx 369.58 \approx 370$ days **c.** On December 21, day 354, daylight is about

10.2 hours at 30°N latitude. **63. a.** Sample: $y = 4 \sin 240\pi t$, in t minutes; or $y = 4 \sin 4\pi t$, in t seconds **b.** 0

c. Sample: $\frac{h}{4\sqrt{2}} = \cos\left(\frac{t - \frac{1}{960}}{\frac{1}{4\pi}}\right)$, in t minutes

$\frac{h}{4\sqrt{2}} = \cos\left(\frac{t - \frac{1}{16}}{\frac{1}{4\pi}}\right)$, in t seconds

65. g **67.** f **69.** $-\frac{b}{a}$ **71. a. See below. b.** 2π **73. a.** Sample: $(x, y) \to \left(x - \frac{\pi}{2}, y\right)$ **b.** Sample: $(x, y) \to \left(x + \frac{\pi}{2}, y\right)$ **75. a. See below. b.** π **77. See right. 79. See right. 81. a.** $y = \cos\left(x + \frac{4\pi}{3}\right)$ **b. See right. 83. a. See right. b.** Period $= \frac{\pi}{2}$, max. value $= 11$ **85.** a **87.** Sample: $y = 4 \sin 2\pi x + 3$

71. a. $f(x) = \sin x$

75. a.

$-2\pi \le x \le 2\pi$, x-scale $= \pi$
$-5 \le y \le 5$, y-scale $= 1$

77. $y = 8 \cos(\pi x)$

79. $y = \sin(x + 4) - 1$

81. b. $y = \cos x$; $y = \cos\left(x + \frac{4\pi}{3}\right)$

$-2\pi \le x \le 2\pi$, x-scale $= \frac{\pi}{2}$
$-1.5 \le y \le 1.5$, y-scale $= 0.5$

83. a. $y = 6 - 5 \sin(4x + 2)$

$-\pi \le x \le \pi$, x-scale $= \frac{\pi}{2}$
$0 \le y \le 15$, y-scale $= 5$

Lesson 5-1 (pp. 310–315)

13. a. 14,600 ft **b.** maximum ≈ 17,500 ft; minimum ≈ 12,500 ft **15.** $34\frac{5}{8}''$ **17.** $\frac{\pi}{2} < \theta < \frac{3\pi}{2}$ **19. See below.**

19. a.

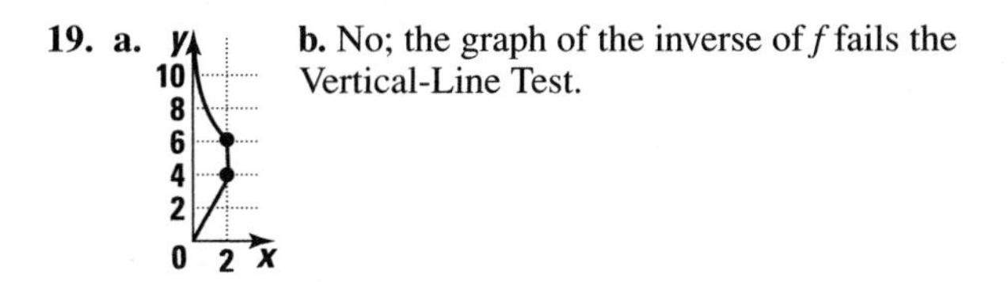

b. No; the graph of the inverse of f fails the Vertical-Line Test.

Lesson 5-2 (pp. 316–320)

11. ≈ 16.2

13. a. Let A be the largest angle. By the law of Cosines,

$15^2 = 5^2 + 9^2 - 2 \cdot 5 \cdot 9 \cdot \cos \angle A$

$119 = -90 \cdot \cos \angle A$

$\cos \angle A = -\frac{119}{90} < -1$

But $\cos \theta$ must lie between -1 and 1. So, the triangle does not exist. **b.** The Triangle Inequality states that the sum of any two sides must be greater than the third side. Since $5 + 9 \not> 15$, the triangle does not exist. **15.** ≈ 3.5° **17.** ≈ 1254.8 ft **19. a.** $f^{-1}(x) = 3x + 36$ **b.** The graph of $f^{-1}(x)$ is the reflection image of $f(x)$ over the line $y = x$. **c.** $f(f^{-1}(x)) = x$

Lesson 5-3 (pp. 321–326)

15. a. $d = \sqrt{289 - 240 \cos \theta}$ **b.** $\theta = \cos^{-1}\left(\frac{d^2 - 289}{-240}\right)$ **c.** When $d = 17$, $\theta = 90°$. When $d = 9$, $\theta \approx 29.9°$. **d. See below.** **17.** $-\frac{\sqrt{2}}{2}$ **19.** $m\angle P \approx 106.0°$, $m\angle Q \approx 14.6°$ **21. a.** $h = b \cdot \sin \angle ACB$ **b.** $A = \frac{1}{2} \cdot a \cdot b \cdot \sin \angle ACB$ **23.** ≈ 316 yd

15. d.

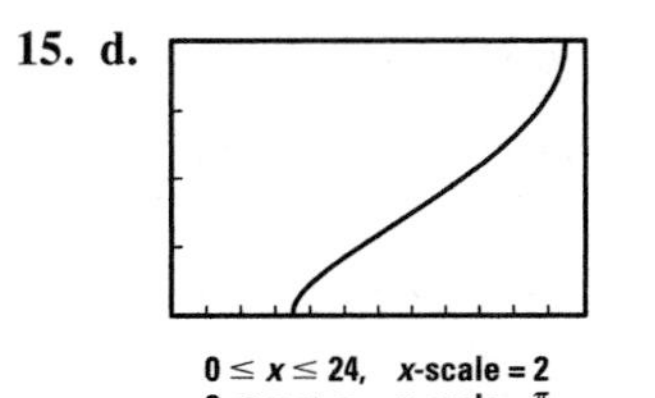

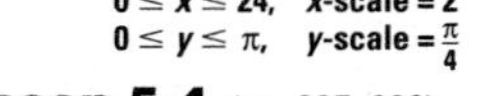

$0 \le x \le 24$, x-scale $= 2$
$0 \le y \le \pi$, y-scale $= \frac{\pi}{4}$

Lesson 5-4 (pp. 327–333)

19. ≈ 756.4 m **21. a.** domain $= \{x: -1 \le x \le 1\}$; range $= \{y: 0 \le y \le \pi\}$ **b.** The domain of $\cos^{-1}$ is the range of the cosine function. The range of $\cos^{-1}$ is the domain of the restricted cosine function. **23.** $\frac{4}{5}$ **25.** ≈ 55.3° **27.** -1

Lesson 5-5 (pp. 334–339)
21. For x between -1 and 1, let $y = \sin^{-1} x$. By the definition of $\sin^{-1} x$, $\sin y = x$. Therefore, $\sin(\sin^{-1} x) = x$ for all x such that $-1 \le x \le 1$. **23. a.** $t = \frac{1}{60\pi} \sin^{-1}\left(\frac{E}{4}\right)$ **b.** The graph of t is the image of the graph of the inverse of the parent sine function under $S: (x, y) \to \left(4x, \frac{y}{60\pi}\right)$. **25.** about 15.6 m **27.** $\approx 28.9°$ **29. a.** the set of all real numbers except $x = \frac{\pi}{4} + n\pi$ for all integers n **b.** the set of all real numbers **c.** π

Lesson 5-6 (pp. 340–344)
15. $\theta = \tan^{-1}\left(\frac{a}{2}\right)$ **17.** -19 **19. a.** $\frac{\pi}{2}$ **b.** $\tan^{-1}\left(\frac{x}{y}\right) + \tan^{-1}\left(\frac{y}{x}\right) = \frac{\pi}{2}$
c. If $\tan^{-1}\left(\frac{x}{y}\right) = A$, then $\tan A = \frac{x}{y}$. Using the Complements Theorem, $\tan\left(\frac{\pi}{2} - A\right) = \frac{\cos A}{\sin A} = \frac{1}{\tan A} = \frac{y}{x}$. So $\tan^{-1}\left(\frac{y}{x}\right) = \frac{\pi}{2} - A$, and $\tan^{-1}\left(\frac{x}{y}\right) + \tan^{-1}\left(\frac{y}{x}\right) = A + \frac{\pi}{2} - A = \frac{\pi}{2}$.
d. See below. Let x and y be legs of a right triangle.

$$m\angle A = \tan^{-1}\left(\frac{x}{y}\right)$$
$$m\angle B = \tan^{-1}\left(\frac{y}{x}\right)$$
$$m\angle A + m\angle B = \tan^{-1}\left(\frac{x}{y}\right) + \tan^{-1}\left(\frac{y}{x}\right) = 90°$$

21. 135° **23. a.** $2(y - 1) = \sin^{-1}\left(\frac{x + 2}{2}\right)$ **b. See below.**
c. domain $= \{x: -4 \le x \le 0\}$; range $= \{y: -\frac{\pi}{4} + 1 \le y \le \frac{\pi}{4} + 1\}$
25. a. See above right. b. 6 m **c.** 0, 12, and 24 hr **27.** 2

19. d. **23. b.**

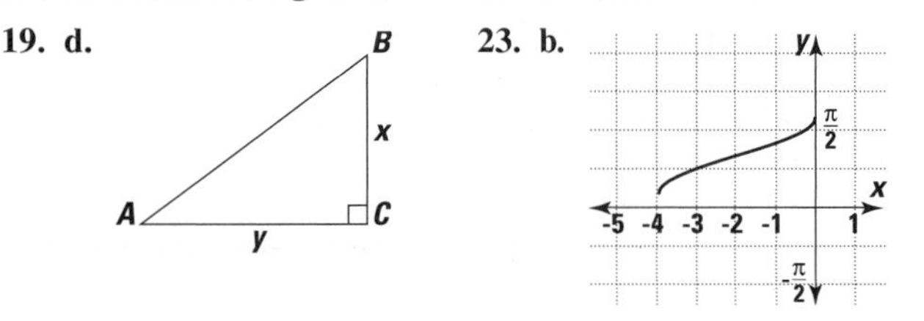

25. a.

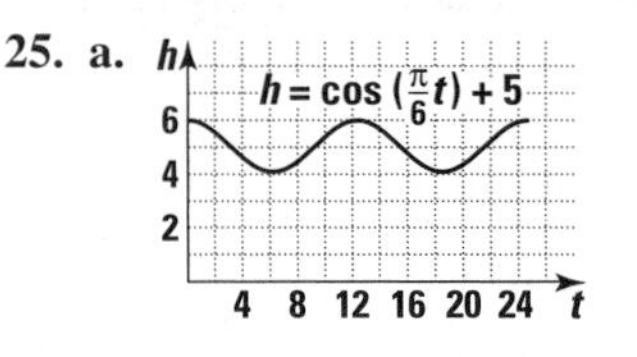

Lesson 5-7 (pp. 346–352)
11. a. 194 and 353 days **b.** October 1 and March 9 **13.** $\theta \approx 1.25$ or 4.39 **15.** $\approx 35.75°$ **17.** $\approx 4.48°$; it is within the specified range. **19.** $y = 2\sin(8x)$ **21.** even **23.** even **25.** even

Lesson 5-8 (pp. 353–359)
13. a. $x = -\frac{\pi}{4}, \frac{\pi}{4}$ **b.** $x = -\frac{7\pi}{4}, -\frac{5\pi}{4}, -\frac{3\pi}{4}, -\frac{\pi}{4}, \frac{\pi}{4}, \frac{3\pi}{4}, \frac{5\pi}{4}, \frac{7\pi}{4}$
c. $x = k\frac{\pi}{2} + \frac{\pi}{4}$ for all integers k **15. a. See below.**
b. $t = \frac{6}{\pi}\sin^{-1}\left(\frac{h - 3.5}{1.5}\right) + 4$ **c.** 7 and 19 hours after midnight
17. domain $= \{x: -1 \le x \le 1\}$; range $= \left\{y: -\frac{\pi}{2} \le y \le \frac{\pi}{2}\right\}$
19. $XZ \approx 0.59$, $YZ \approx 0.46$ **21.** ≈ 5495 ft **23. a.** $x = 81$ **b.** $x = 12$

15. a.

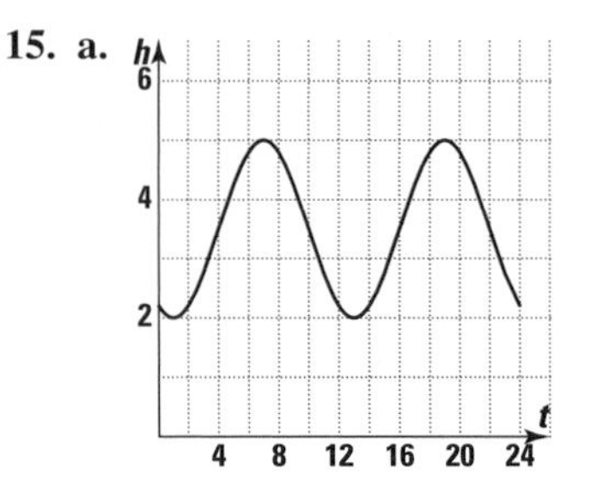

Chapter 5 Progress Self-Test (p. 363)
1. $16°35' = 16° + \frac{35°}{60} \approx 16.58°$ **2.** $\sin M = \frac{\text{opposite leg}}{\text{hypotenuse}} = \frac{15}{17}$
3. $\tan B = \frac{\text{opposite leg}}{\text{adjacent leg}} = \frac{8}{15}$ **4.** $\tan B = \frac{8}{15} \Rightarrow m\angle B = \tan^{-1}\left(\frac{8}{15}\right) \approx 28.1°$ **5.** $\cos^{-1}\left(\frac{1}{2}\right) = \theta \Rightarrow \cos\theta = \frac{1}{2}$. The only value of θ which satisfies this equation with $0 \le \theta \le \pi$ is $\frac{\pi}{3}$. **6.** $\frac{\pi}{4}$. $\tan^{-1}$ and tan are inverse operations so $\tan^{-1}(\tan x) = x$. Because $\frac{\pi}{4}$ is in the first quadrant we do not need to worry about a proper range, all inverse trigonometric functions apply to acute angles.
7. Sample: $\cos^{-1}\left(\cos\left(-\frac{\pi}{3}\right)\right) = \cos^{-1}(0.5) = \frac{\pi}{3}$, not $\frac{-\pi}{3}$.
8. a. See p. 889. b. domain $= \{x: -1 \le x \le 1\}$; range $= \left\{y: -\frac{\pi}{2} \le y \le \frac{\pi}{2}\right\}$ **9. See p. 889.** $\cos\theta = \frac{2}{12} \Rightarrow \theta = \cos^{-1}\left(\frac{2}{12}\right) \approx 80°$ **10. See p. 889.** $\theta = \cos^{-1}\left(\frac{x}{12}\right)$ **11.** Let x be the height, $\tan 41° = \frac{x}{6} \Rightarrow x = 6 \cdot \tan 41° \approx 5.2$ ft **12.** $\frac{\sin 140°}{5} = \frac{\sin 15}{x} \Rightarrow x = \frac{5 \sin 15°}{\sin 140°} \approx 2.0$ **13.** $c^2 = 200^2 + 300^2 - 2 \cdot 200 \cdot 300 \cdot \cos 55°$; $c^2 \approx 61170.83$; $c \approx 247.3$ m **14.** $\frac{\sin 35.5}{7} = \frac{\sin A}{12} \Rightarrow \sin A = \frac{12 \sin 35.5}{7}$. Because $\angle A$ is in a triangle, $m\angle A = \sin^{-1}\left(\frac{12\sin 35.5}{7}\right) \approx 84.6°$, or by the Supplements Theorem, $m\angle A = 180° - 84.6° = 95.4°$. So, $m\angle A \approx 84.6°$ or $95.4°$.
15. a. $\theta = \cos^{-1}(-0.125) \approx 1.7$ **b. See p. 889.** By symmetry of the graph, another solution is $2\pi - 1.70 \approx 4.59$. When $\cos\theta = -0.125$ and $0 \le \theta \le 2\pi$, then $\theta \approx 1.70$ or $\theta \approx 4.59$.
c. By the Periodicity Theorem, adding or subtracting 2π to the two solutions generates all solutions of $\cos\theta = -0.125$: $1.70 + 2\pi n$ or $4.59 + 2\pi n$ for all integers n. **16.** $2\sin\theta - \sqrt{2} = 0$; $\sin\theta = \frac{\sqrt{2}}{2}$. In the first quadrant, $\theta = \frac{\pi}{4}$. By the Supplements Theorem, $\pi - \frac{\pi}{4} = \frac{3\pi}{4}$ yields another solution. By the Periodicity Theorem, adding multiples of 2π generates all solutions, $\frac{\pi}{4} + 2\pi n$ or $\frac{3\pi}{4} + 2\pi n$ for all integers n. **17.** $10\cos\theta = k$; $\cos\theta = \frac{k}{10}$. The range of $\cos\theta$ is between -1 and 1. So, $-1 \le \frac{k}{10} \le 1$. Thus, $-10 \le k \le 10$. Therefore, $10\cos\theta = k$ will have no solutions for $k < -10$ and $k > 10$. **18.** The Law of Cosines applies to situations with given conditions of SSS or SAS. Both cases yield unique triangles where no other triangles could satisfy the given conditions. **19. a. See p. 889. b.** Because $V = 25\sin(3\pi t)$, the maximum output is 25 volts. **c.** According to the graph in part **a**,

there are 3 times during the first two seconds that the voltage is at maximum output. **d.** $20 = 25 \sin(3\pi t)$; $\sin(3\pi t) = \frac{20}{25}$; $3\pi t = \sin^{-1}\left(\frac{20}{25}\right) \approx 0.9273$ By the Supplements Theorem, $3\pi t \approx \pi - 0.9273 \approx 2.2143$. By the Periodicity Theorem, all solutions are $3\pi t \approx 0.9273 + 2\pi n$ or $3\pi t \approx 2.2143 + 2\pi n$, for all integers n. Thus, $t \approx 0.0984 + \frac{2}{3}n$ or $t \approx 0.2349 + \frac{2}{3}n$. Substituting $n = 0$ and $n = 1$, the first four times the voltage equals 20 are about 0.10, 0.23, 0.77, and 0.90 sec. **20.** $4 = 3 + 3\cos\left(\frac{\pi t}{5}\right)$; $\frac{1}{3} = \cos\left(\frac{\pi t}{5}\right)$; $\frac{\pi t}{5} = \cos^{-1}\left(\frac{1}{3}\right) \approx 1.2310$. From symmetry of the cosine function, another solution is $\frac{\pi t}{5} = 2\pi - 1.2310 \approx 5.0522$. $\frac{\pi t}{5} \approx 1.2310 + 2\pi n$ or $\frac{\pi t}{5} \approx 5.0522 + 2\pi n$, for all integers n. Thus, $t \approx 1.959 + 10n$ or $t \approx 8.041 + 10n$. For $n = 0$, the first two times are about 1.96 and 8.04 sec.

8. a. **9.** **10.** **15. b.** **19. a.**

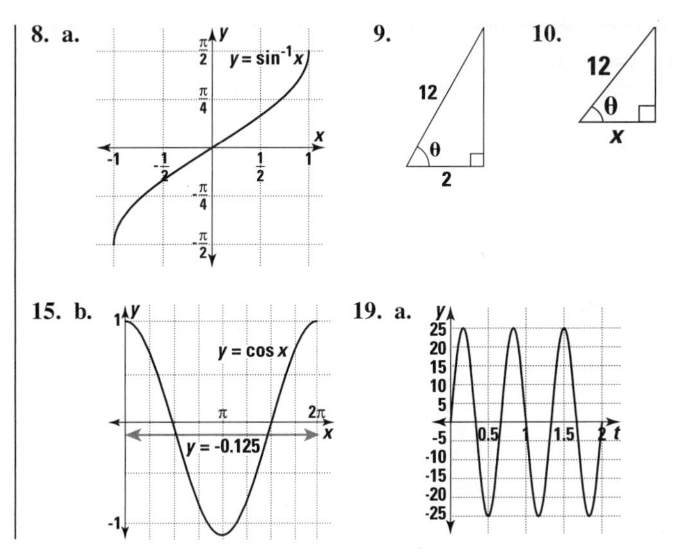

The chart below keys the **Progress Self-Test** questions to the objectives in the **Chapter Review** on pages 364-367 or to the **Vocabulary** (Voc.) on page 362. This will enable you to locate those **Chapter Review** questions that correspond to questions students missed on the **Progress Self-Test**. The lesson where the material is covered is also indicated on the chart.

Question	**1**	**2**	**3**	**4**	**5**	**6**	**7**	**8**	**9**	**10**
Objective	Voc.	A	A	C	B	B	F	J	I	I
Lesson	5-1	5-1	5-1	5-1	5-3	5-6	5-3	5-5	5-3	5-3
Question	**11**	**12**	**13**	**14**	**15**	**16**	**17**	**18**	**19**	**20**
Objective	G	C	H	C	D	D	D	E	I	I
Lesson	5-1	5-4	5-2	5-4	5-3, 5-7	5-7	5-7	5-2	5-5, 5-7	5-3, 5-7

Chapter 5 Review (pp. 364-367)

1. a. $\frac{24}{25}$ **b.** $\frac{7}{25}$ **c.** $\frac{7}{25}$ **3.** 0.287 **5.** $\frac{1}{2}$ **7.** $\frac{\sqrt{3}}{3}$ **9.** 45° **11.** 0.2 **13.** 2.6 **15.** $\frac{\pi}{4}$ **17.** $x \approx 39.4$ **19.** 82.8° **21.** $\approx 36.1°$ and $\approx 143.9°$ **23.** ≈ 179.8 ft^2 **25.** 18.66° **27.** 60° **29.** ≈ 3.489 or ≈ 5.936 **31.** ≈ 3.534 or ≈ 5.891 **33.** $\approx 1.33 + 2\pi n$ or $4.95 + 2\pi n$ for all integers n **35.** $\approx 1.03 + \pi n$ for all integers n **37.** $-0.055 + n$ or $0.56 + n$ for all integers n **39.** $A = \frac{1}{2}ab \sin C$. The lengths of the sides are the same and sin 70° = sin 110° by the Supplements Theorem. Therefore, the areas are equal. **41.** Usually, SSA does not uniquely determine a triangle. But if the side opposite the given angle is larger than the other given side, SsA, the triangle is unique. Tom is correct. **43.** $-\frac{\pi}{2} \le \theta \le \frac{\pi}{2}$ **45.** to pass the horizontal line test, so the inverse will be a function **47.** False **49.** ≈ 15.5 ft **51.** $\approx 56.4°$ **53. a.** $\approx 36.9°$, $\approx 53.1°$, and 90° **b.** $\approx 83.23°$. Answers will vary. **55.** ≈ 104.2 m **57.** ≈ 8.5 miles **59. a.** 122.1° **b.** ≈ 743.1 sq mm **61.** 1344 yd **63. a.** $t = \frac{1}{\pi}\cos^{-1}\left(\frac{d}{3}\right)$ or $t = 2n + 2 - \frac{1}{\pi}\cos^{-1}\left(\frac{d}{3}\right)$ for all nonnegative integers n. **b.** ≈ 0.27 sec **65.** 0.05, 0.45, 0.55, 0.95, and 1.05 sec **67. a.** When the paddle is in the water, the distance will be negative. **b. See right. c.** 0.13 and 0.87 minutes **69.** d **71. a.** He may have switched the domain and range so that the window was $-4 \le x \le 4$, x-scale = 1 and $-360 \le y \le 360$, y-scale = 90. **b.** Sample: **See right.**

67. b. **71. b.**

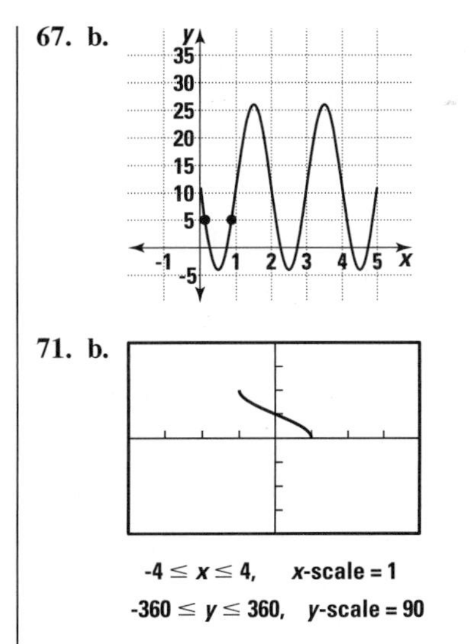

$-4 \le x \le 4$, x-scale = 1
$-360 \le y \le 360$, y-scale = 90

Lesson 6-1 (pp.370–375)

17. about 16.4 knots **19. a. See below. b.** $y^2 = x$ **21.** No. $(f \circ g)(x) = \frac{2}{\frac{x}{2}} = \frac{4}{x}$ and $(g \circ f)(x) = \frac{\frac{2}{x}}{2} = \frac{1}{x}$
23. a. $y = -0.6067x + 119.3$, $r = -0.958$ **b.** There is a high negative correlation; the line fits the data fairly well. **c.** about 58.0%
25. a. x^{16} **b.** $512x^{63}$ **c.** $\frac{1}{x^2}$

19. a.

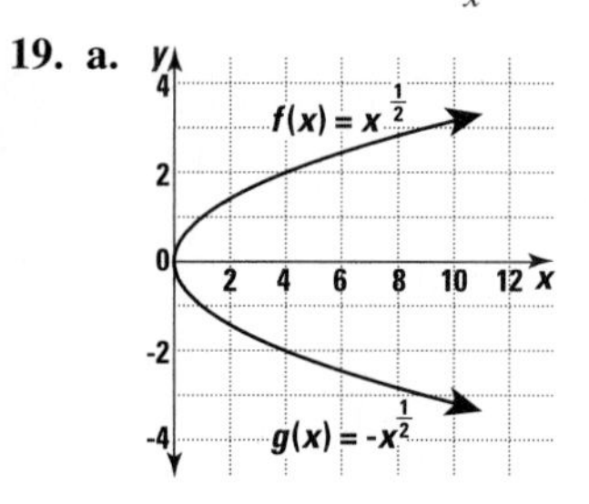

Lesson 6-2 (pp. 376–382)

15. a. 1035 g/cm^2 **b.** $\approx$ 28.70 g/cm^2 **c.** $\approx$ 2.63 g/cm^2 **17.** $x = 1.5$ to the nearest tenth **19. a. See right. b.** False **21.** $0 < x < 1$ **23.** 3^{-4}, 4^{-3}, $\frac{3}{4}$, $3^{1/4}$, 3^4 **25.** e

19. a.

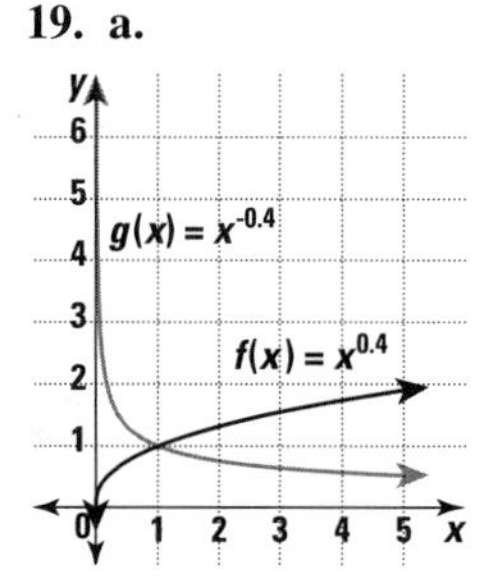

Lesson 6-3 (pp. 383–388)

17. pH $\approx$ 7.128 **19. a.** $1492 = 1.492 \times 10^3$; $149{,}200 = 1.492 \times 10^5$; $14{,}920{,}000{,}000{,}000 = 1.492 \times 10^{13}$ **b.** ≈ 3.1738, ≈ 5.1738, ≈ 13.1738 **c.** Their mathematical relations can be expressed as $\log(1.492 \times 10^n) = n + \log 1.492 = n + 0.1738$
21. $x = 2$ **23.** $\frac{1}{64}$ **25. a.** $d = \sqrt{\frac{k}{I}}$ **b.** $d = \left(\frac{k}{I}\right)^{1/2}$

Lesson 6-4 (pp. 390–396)

15. a. about 4,272,000 **b.** This answer is slightly higher; the model in Lesson 2-4 does not assume continuous growth. **17.** about 604 days **19.** $V \approx 5.76$ km/sec **21.** $f^{-1}(x) = \log_7 x$
23. $\log_{1/8}\left(\frac{1}{2}\right) = \frac{1}{3}$ **25.** <

Lesson 6-5 (pp. 398–402)

13. $\ln F = \ln G + \ln m + \ln M - 2 \ln d$ **15.** False. Sample counterexample: $\log(4 - 3) = \log 1 = 0$, and $\log 4 \neq \log 3$, so $\log 4 - \log 3 \neq 0$. Therefore $\log(4 - 3) \neq \log 4 - \log 3$.
17. $\log_b\left(\frac{1}{n}\right) = \log_b 1 - \log_b n = 0 - \log_b n = -\log_b n$ **19. a.** III **b.** II **c.** I **21.** 5 **23.** Sample: All logarithmic functions $f(x) = \log_b x$ have a domain $\{x: x > 0\}$, pass through (1, 0), and are strictly increasing. **25. a.** {20, 22, 24}
b. {10, 12, 14, 16, 18, 20, 21, 22, 23, 24, 25, 26, 27, 28, 29, 30}

Lesson 6-6 (pp. 403–408)

9. b and c **11. a.** 5 **b.** 0.2 **c.** They are reciprocals of each other. **d.** $\log_b x = \frac{\log x}{\log b}$ and $\log_x b = \frac{\log b}{\log x}$, so $\log_b x = \frac{1}{\log_x b}$. **13.** $\log N = \log A - 3 \log B$ **15. a.** 92% **b.** $\approx$ 34.4% **17.** 7 **19.** 0.03
21. a. $y = 2.216x + 5.2$ **b.** A catfish grows about 2.2 inches for each year of its life. **c.** about 31.8 inches **d.** Sample: The growth of a catfish might slow down as the fish ages. **e.** 0.997 **f.** As the age increases, the length will increase.

Lesson 6-7 (pp. 409–415)

9. a. See below. b. $y = ab^x$ **c.** $y = 73.936 \cdot 1.00186^x$ **d.** the model from part **c** **e.** Both models predict an estimated life span of over 87 years! Neither model is suitable for this age.
11. a. $\log t = \log(cx^n) = \log c + n \log x$ **b. See below.**
c. $\log t = -0.07620 \cdot \log x + 2.60503$ **d.** The logarithm of the time decreases by 0.0762 as the logarithm of the number of rowers increases by 1. **e.** $t = 402.747 \cdot x^{-0.0762}$
13. $x = \frac{\log 70}{\log 6} \approx 2.371$; $6^{2.371} \approx 69.98$ **15.** about 8916 years
17. a. $y = \frac{\log_2 x}{\log_2 3}$ **b.** $y = \log_3 x$ **19. a.** $0 < x < 1$ **b.** $x > 1$
c. For $0 < x < 1$, if $m > n$, then $x^{1/n} < x^{1/m}$. For $x > 1$, if $m > n$, then $x^{1/n} > x^{1/m}$.

9. a. **11. b.**

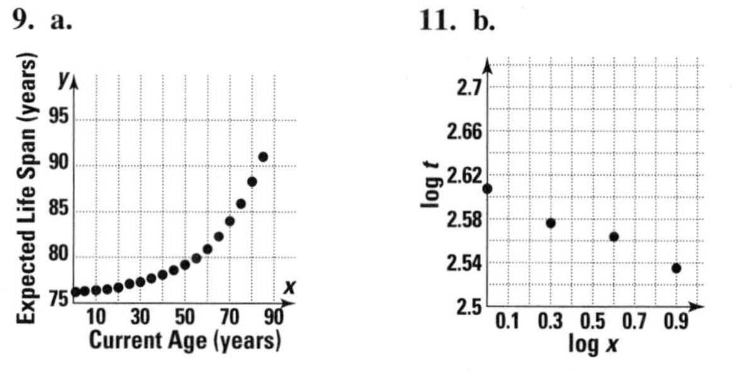

Chapter 6 Progress Self-Test (p. 419)

1. $64^{2/3} = (64^{1/3})^2 = (\sqrt[3]{64})^2 = 4^2 = 16.$ **2.** $\left(\frac{9}{25}\right)^{-1/2} = \left(\frac{25}{9}\right)^{1/2} = \left(\sqrt{\frac{25}{9}}\right) = \frac{5}{3}$ **3.** $\log_3 27 = x$; $3^x = 27$; $x = 3$ **4.** $\ln e^2 = \log_e e^2 = 2 \ln e = 2$ **5.** $f(x) = x^{4/5}$ is a rational power function. The domain and range are the set of nonnegative real numbers: [illegible]omain: $\{x: x \geq 0\}$ and range: $\{y: y \geq 0\}$. **6.** $\sqrt[5]{x^{10}y^5} =$ [illegible]$^5)^{1/5} = x^{10/5}y^{5/5} = x^2y$ **7.** $7^x = 2401 \Rightarrow \log 7^x = \log 2401 \Rightarrow$ [illegible]$7 = \log 2401 \Rightarrow x = \frac{\log 2401}{\log 7} = 4$ **8.** $5^x = 47 \Rightarrow \log 5^x =$ [illegible]$\cdot \log 5 = \log 47 \Rightarrow x = \frac{\log 47}{\log 5} \approx 2.392$ **9.** $\log_5 16 =$ [illegible] **10.** $\log_{12} 5 = \log_{12}\left(\frac{15}{3}\right) = \log_{12} 15 - \log_{12} 3 \approx$ [illegible].6479 **11.** Use $A(t) = Pe^{rt}$ as a model. $0.5 = 1 \cdot e^{r \cdot 25}$; $\ln 0.5 = 25r$; $r = \frac{\ln 0.5}{25} \approx -0.02773$. So, for Strontium-90, $A(t) \approx Pe^{-0.02773t}$. To find the amount of time for 10 grams to decay to 3 grams, substitute and solve for t. $3 \approx 10 \cdot e^{-0.02773t}$; $0.3 \approx e^{-0.02773t}$; $\ln(0.3) \approx -0.02773t$; $t \approx \frac{\ln(0.3)}{-0.02773} \approx 43.42$ years. **12. a.** **See p. 891.**
b. from the graph in Part **a**, we can see that the asymptote of g is $x = 0$. **c.** $y = b^x$ and $\log_b x = y$ are inverse functions, so $g^{-1}(t) = 3^t$. **13.** $\frac{1}{2} \log a + \log b = \frac{1}{3} \log c$; $\log a^{1/2} + \log b = \log c^{1/3}$; $\log(a^{1/2} \cdot b) = \log(c^{1/3})$; $a^{1/2} \cdot b = c^{1/3}$ **14.** True. The domains for $\log x$ and $\ln x$ are both $\{x: x > 0\}$. Let $10^{\log x} = a$. By definition, if $b^y = x$, then $y = \log_b x$; so $\log_{10} a = \log_{10} x$. Thus $a = x$, and $10^{\log x} = x$. Similarly, $e^{\ln x} = x$. So $10^{\log x} = e^{\ln x}$.
15. a. b. **See p. 891.** **c.** If $f(x) = y = x^{5/3}$, then the inverse is $x = y^{5/3}$. So $x^{3/5} = (y^{5/3})^{3/5}$; $x^{3/5} = y$. Therefore $f^{-1}(x) = x^{3/5}$

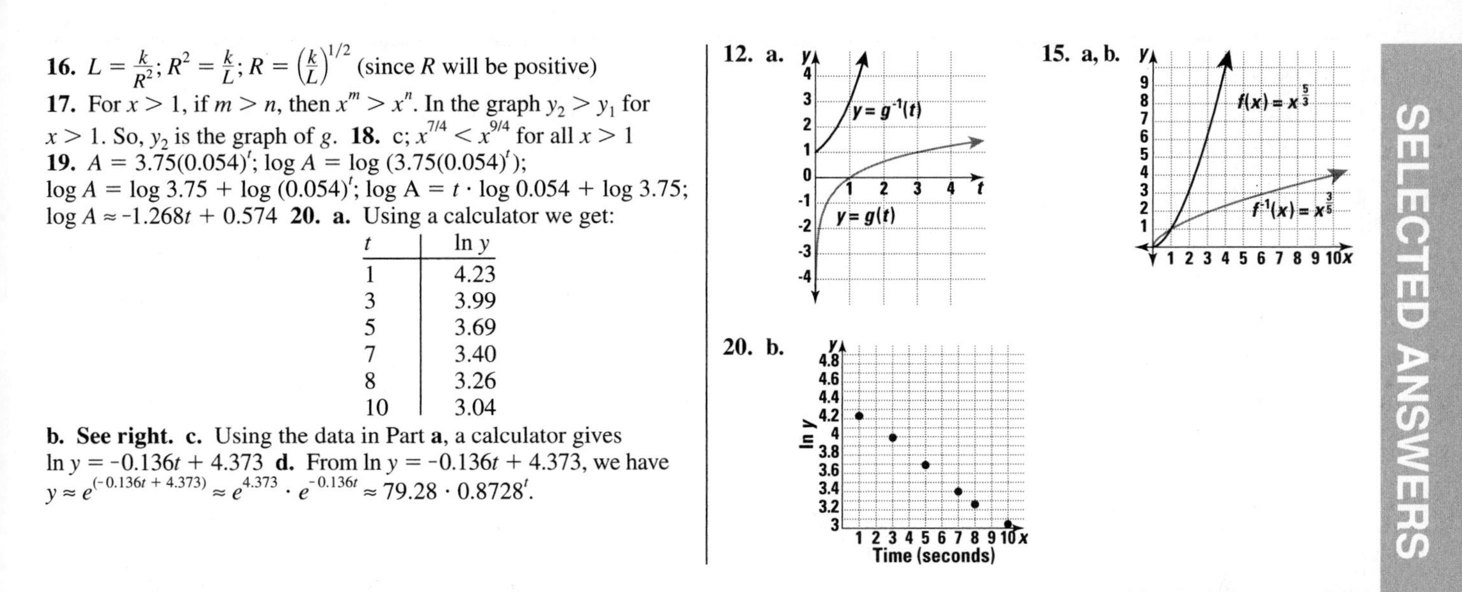

16. $L = \frac{k}{R^2}$; $R^2 = \frac{k}{L}$; $R = \left(\frac{k}{L}\right)^{1/2}$ (since R will be positive)
17. For $x > 1$, if $m > n$, then $x^m > x^n$. In the graph $y_2 > y_1$ for $x > 1$. So, y_2 is the graph of g. **18.** c; $x^{7/4} < x^{9/4}$ for all $x > 1$
19. $A = 3.75(0.054)^t$; $\log A = \log(3.75(0.054)^t)$;
$\log A = \log 3.75 + \log(0.054)^t$; $\log A = t \cdot \log 0.054 + \log 3.75$;
$\log A \approx -1.268t + 0.574$ **20. a.** Using a calculator we get:

t	$\ln y$
1	4.23
3	3.99
5	3.69
7	3.40
8	3.26
10	3.04

b. See right. **c.** Using the data in Part **a**, a calculator gives $\ln y = -0.136t + 4.373$ **d.** From $\ln y = -0.136t + 4.373$, we have $y \approx e^{(-0.136t + 4.373)} \approx e^{4.373} \cdot e^{-0.136t} \approx 79.28 \cdot 0.8728^t$.

12. a.

15. a, b.

20. b.

The chart below keys the **Progress Self-Test** questions to the objectives in the **Chapter Review** on pages 420-423 or to the **Vocabulary** (Voc.) on page 418. This will enable you to locate those **Chapter Review** questions that correspond to questions students missed on the **Progress Self-Test.** The lesson where the material is covered is also indicated on the chart.

Question	**1**	**2**	**3**	**4**	**5**	**6**	**7**	**8**	**9**	**10**
Objective	A	A	C	C	D	A	B	B	C	E
Lesson	6-2	6-2	6-3	6-3, 6-4	6-2	6-2	6-6	6-6	6-3	6-6
Question	**11**	**12**	**13**	**14**	**15**	**16**	**17**	**18**	**19**	**20**
Objective	G	I	E	E	I	F	J	D, J	E	H
Lesson	6-6	6-3	6-5	6-5	6-2	6-2	6-2	6-2	6-7	6-7

Chapter 6 Review (pp. 420–423)

1. 5 **3.** $\frac{1}{25}$ **5.** $\sqrt[3]{a^2}$ **7.** $s^{1/5}t^{7/5}$ **9.** < **11.** $8^2 = 64$ so $8^{1.96}$ is slightly less than 64. **13.** $m \approx 2.079$, $e^{2.079} \approx 7.996$ **15.** $x \approx 3.193$, $7(2.3)^{3.193} \approx 100.02$ **17.** 4 **19.** -1.73 **21.** $\frac{4}{3}$ **23.** $\log 5 = x$; $10^x = 5$ so $x < 1$. $\ln 5 = y$; $e^y = 5$ so $y > 1$. Therefore, $\ln 5 > \log 5$. **25.** 1.86 **27.** 0.46 **29.** domain: $\{x: x \geq 0\}$ range: $\{y: y \geq 0\}$
31. Sample: The definition of rational roots is that $x^{m/n} = \left(\sqrt[n]{x}\right)^m$. If this holds for negative values of x, then it holds when $x = -64$. Then, since $2/3 = 4/6$, we have $(-64)^{2/3} = (-64)^{4/6}$, which implies $(-4)^2$ equals a non-real number, because there is no real 6th root of -64. Thus the definition of rational roots cannot be extended to negative numbers without sacrificing a basic property.
33. $h^{-1}(x) = 5^x$ **35.** e is the limiting value of the sequence $a_n = \left(1 + \frac{1}{n}\right)^n$ **37.** ≈ 1.969 **39.** ≈ 0.239 **41.** $\ln\left(\frac{x^5y^2}{z}\right)$
43. $\log A = 3\log C - \log D$ **45.** True **47.** $y = 17x^3$
49. $b \approx 0.1259 \cdot 2.399^c$ **51.** $n = 189$ **53.** $N = (kT)^3$
55. a. $T(4) \approx 0.758 \cdot T_0$ **b.** about 33 days **c.** about 23.2 days
57. about 50 hours **59.** $d \approx 5.53$ **61. a.** $L = A \cdot e^{((\ln .5)/4) \cdot h} \approx A \cdot 0.841^h$ **b.** about 30% **63.** $T \approx 0.179 \cdot a^{3/2}$ **65. a.** See right. **b.** (i) and (ii) **c.** See right. **d.** $s = 16.78 \cdot \ln w + 154.9$; $r \approx 0.997$ **e.** about 221 **67. a.** See right. **b.** $x = 0, 1$ **c.** $0 < x < 1$ **d.** $x > 1$ **69.** They are reflections of each other over the line $y = x$. **71. a.** It is linear. See right. **b.** Using an automatic grapher. It checks. See right. **73.** a **75.** b

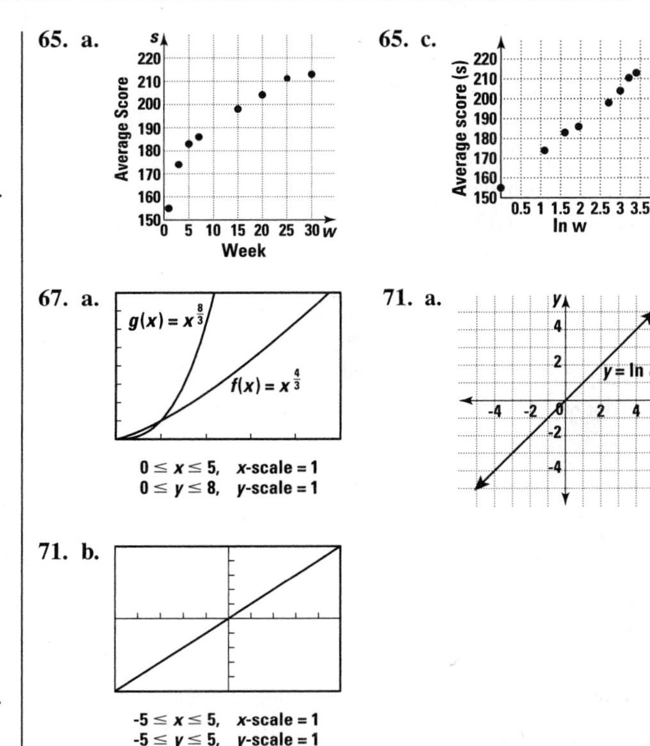

SELECTED ANSWERS

Lesson 7-1 (pp. 426-432)

13. 50 **15. a.** 1 **b.** 0 **c.** $\frac{1}{4}$ **17.** $\frac{1}{6}$ **19. a.** ≈ 0.318 **b.** 326 **21. a.** 50% **b.** $\approx 18.95\%$ **23.** 55

Lesson 7-2 (pp. 433-439)

13. Sample: The temperature is above 90°; the temperature is below 40°. **15. a.** 0.54 **b.** 0.83 **c.** 0.32 **d.** 0.44 **17. a** $\frac{25\pi}{484} \approx 0.162$ **b.** $1 - \frac{57\pi}{484} \approx 0.630$ **19. a.** 0.05 **b.** 0.45 **c.** 0.75 **d.** 0.65 **21.** 0.1 **23.** $y = -x^2 + 4x$

Lesson 7-3 (pp. 440-444)

11. $10! = 3{,}628{,}800$ **13.** 6 **15. a.** 20 **b.** $n = 9$, $r = 7$ **17.** $r + c - b$ **19. a** $\frac{1}{12} \approx 0.08$ **b** 11 to 1 **21. a.** $\frac{3\pi}{4}$

Lesson 7-4 (pp. 445-449)

13. 56 **15. a.** $10! = 3{,}628{,}800$ **b.** $2(6!\cdot 4!) = 34{,}560$ **17. a.** 16 **b. See below. 19.** 32 **21.** 61,162,590 **23.** $\frac{2}{3}$ **25 a. See below. b.** true

17. b. **25. a.**

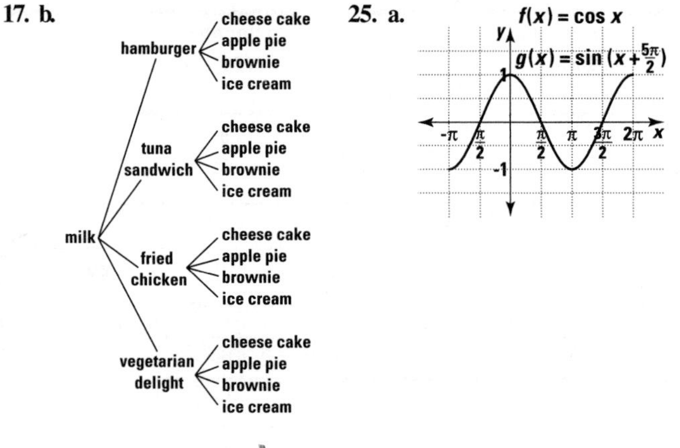

Lesson 7-5 (pp. 450-456)

9. Yes; $P(A) = \frac{1}{2}$, $P(B) = \frac{3}{4}$, $P(A \cap B) = \frac{3}{8} = \frac{1}{2} \cdot \frac{3}{4}$ **11.** Sample: We cannot answer this with certainty. If the relative frequencies represent the probabilities that the lights stop the motorist, and all the events are independent, then the probability of all happening is $\frac{20}{50} \cdot \frac{22}{50} \cdot \frac{25}{50} \cdot \frac{19}{50} \cdot \frac{24}{50}$, or about .016. This would suggest that, on the average, in 50 trips, about 0.8 times all the lights would come on. That rounds out to 1, suggesting that the lights are operating independently. **13. a.** ≈ 0.027 **b.** $\approx .0533$ **c.** $\approx .0789$ **15.** $6! = 720$ **17.** $n = 25$ and $r = 2$ or $n = 600$ and $r = 1$ **19.** 0.25 **21.** $\frac{3}{25} = 0.12$

Lesson 7-6 (pp. 457-463)

11. a. See above right. b. mean difference $= \frac{709}{360} \approx 1.97$ **13. a.** It represents a loss; it is negative because $1 must be paid for the ticket. **b.** $\frac{122}{125} = 0.976$ **c.** $-\frac{25}{125} = -$ \$0.20 or $-$ 20¢

15. a. $f(0) = -\frac{1}{4}\left|0 - \frac{3}{2}\right| + \frac{1}{2} = \frac{1}{8}$; $f(1) = -\frac{1}{4}\left|1 - \frac{3}{2}\right| + \frac{1}{2} = \frac{3}{8}$; $f(2) = -\frac{1}{4}\left|2 - \frac{3}{2}\right| + \frac{1}{2} = \frac{3}{8}$; $f(3) = -\frac{1}{4}\left|3 - \frac{3}{2}\right| + \frac{1}{2} = \frac{1}{8}$

b. Substituting $x - \frac{3}{2}$ for x and $\frac{y - \frac{1}{2}}{-\frac{1}{4}}$ for y in $y = |x|$ results in $\frac{y - \frac{1}{2}}{-\frac{1}{4}} = \left|x - \frac{3}{2}\right|$ or $y = -\frac{1}{4}\left|x - \frac{3}{2}\right| + \frac{1}{2}$. **17. a.** $\frac{31}{32} = 0.96875$ **b.** $\frac{10}{32} = 0.3125$ **c.** False **19.** $(n + 2)(n + 1) = n^2 + 3n + 2$ **21. a.** 1298 **b.** 740 **c.** Sample: median; the median is not affected by the unusually high score of 6450. **d.** about 1813 **e.** It has a great effect. If that score is removed, the standard deviation changes from about 1813 to 112.

11. a.

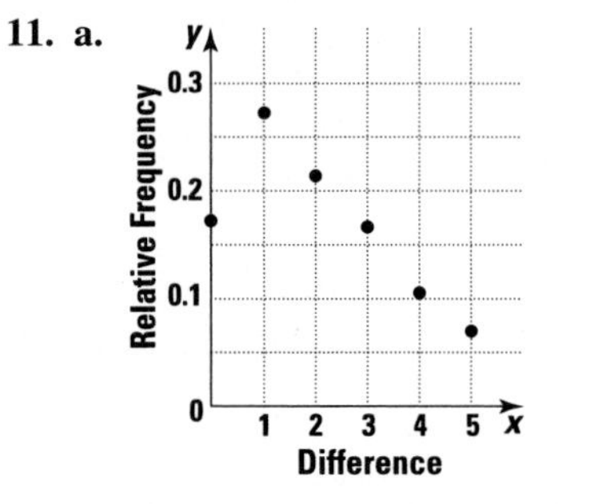

Lesson 7-7 (pp. 465-470)

9. a.–c. Designs will vary, but results should all approximate a .300 batting average. **11. a. See below. b.** The relative frequencies can be considered as the probability of randomly choosing a family of the given size from all the families in the village. **c.** $\frac{432}{87} \approx 4.97$ **13.** none of these (assumes the first student has not been replaced) **15.** mutually exclusive (assumes another possibility: "Kevin arrives exactly on time.") **17. a.** 0 **b.** $\frac{576}{27{,}907{,}200} \approx 2.1 \cdot 10^{-5}$ **19. a.** 0, 0, 1, 2 **b.** $\frac{1}{3} \le x < \frac{2}{3}$

11. a.

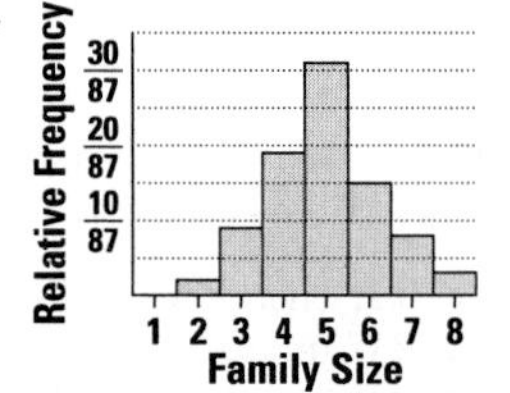

Lesson 7-8 (pp. 471–477)

15. Answers will vary. Note that the command "ROUND (RAND, 3)" will provide 3 random digits on some calculators. **17.** Answers will vary, but repeated valid simulations would reveal that 102 nails would be adequate in most cases, and 103 nails in almost all cases. **19.** $\frac{5}{144} \approx 0.035$ **21. a.** ${}_8P_5 = 8 \cdot {}_7P_4 = 8 \cdot 7 \cdot {}_6P_3 = 56 \cdot {}_6P_3$ **b.** ${}_nP_r = n \cdot {}_{n-1}P_{r-1} = n \cdot (n - 1) \cdot {}_{n-2}P_{r-2} = (n^2 - n) \cdot {}_{n-2}P_{r-2}$

Chapter 7 Progress Self-Test (p. 481)

1. a. Each outcome can be represented by a pair of numbers, one for each spinner. So $S = \{(1, 1),(1, 2), (1, 3), (2, 1), (2, 2), (2, 3), (3, 1), (3, 2), (3, 3)\}$ **b.** Of the nine possible outcomes, three have sums greater than 4. Thus $P(\text{sum} > 4) = \frac{\text{number of outcomes in the event}}{\text{number of outcomes in the sample space}} = \frac{3}{9} = \frac{1}{3} \approx 0.33$. **2.** The two dice are independent of each other, and for each one the probability of showing an odd or even number is $\frac{1}{2}$. So, P(Odd on Red *and* Even on Green) $= \frac{1}{2} \cdot \frac{1}{2} = \frac{1}{4} = 0.25$. **3.** By the Probability of a Union Theorem, $P(A \cup B) = P(A) + P(B) - P(A \cap B) = 0.6 + 0.8 - 0.5 = 0.9$. **4. a.** Since the six letters are different, by the Permutation Theorem, there are $6! = 720$ permutations. **b.** When A and T are fixed at the two ends, there are four letters (M, S, E, and R) left to permute in the middle. There are $4! = 24$ such arrangements.
5. $\frac{9!}{3!} = \frac{9 \cdot 8 \cdot \ldots \cdot 3 \cdot 2 \cdot 1}{3 \cdot 2 \cdot 1} = 9 \cdot 8 \cdot \ldots \cdot 4 = 60{,}480$
6. ${}_5P_3 = \frac{5!}{(5-3)!} = \frac{5!}{2!} = 5 \cdot 4 \cdot 3 = 60$ **7.** True, since $A = S$ (the sample space), and $P(S) = 1$. **8.** Let A be the event of scoring under 50 and B be the event of scoring between 50 and 100, inclusive. **a.** The events are mutually exclusive, and, since A and B cover all the possible scores, they are also complementary. **b.** The events are mutually exclusive, but, since $A \cup B \neq S$, they are not complementary. **9.** ${}_nP_4 = 56{}_nP_2$; $\frac{n!}{(n-4)!} = 56 \cdot \frac{n!}{(n-2)!}$; $\frac{(n-2)!}{(n-4)!} = 56$; $\frac{(n-2)(n-3)(n-4)(n-5)\ldots(1)}{(n-4)(n-5)\ldots(1)} = 56$; $(n-2)(n-3) = 56$; $n^2 - 5n + 6 = 56$; $n^2 - 5n - 50 = 0$; $(n-10)(n+5) = 0$; $n = 10$, the only positive solution.
10. a. Random selection means that the weights of the bags are independent of each other. Each has a 0.25 probability of being underweight. So, P(all three bags are underweight) $= (0.25)^3 \approx 0.016$. **b.** Each bag has a 0.75 probability of not being underweight. So, P(none of the bags is underweight) $= (0.75)^3 \approx 0.42$.
11. By the Multiplication Counting Principle, N(jeans) $\cdot$ N(sneakers) $\cdot$ N(sweatshirts) $= 3 \cdot 2 \cdot 5 = 30$. **12.** There are 15 different questions, 10 with two possible answers, 5 with four. So, by the Multiplication Counting Principle, N(answer sheets) $= 2^{10} \cdot 4^5 = 2^{20} = 1{,}048{,}576$. **13.** Designs will vary. Sample: A die thrown 100 times counting rolls of 1 and 2 as shots made, and 3, 4, 5 and 6 as shots not made. **14.** Answers will vary depending on table starting point but infections should number 2 to 4 of the 25 trials in most cases. **15.** Answers will vary, but random coordinates should be generated with the range 0 to $\frac{\pi}{2}$ for x, and 0 to 1 for y, and the area should be estimated by multiplying the resulting proportion of points below the line by $\frac{\pi}{2}$. The actual area is 1. **16. a.** Each value of $P(x)$ satisfies $0 \leq P(x) \leq 1$ and their sum is 1. **b.** See right. **c.** $\mu = \sum_{i=1}^{5}(x_i \cdot P(x_i)) = 1(.03) + 2(.47) + 3(.22) + 4(.05) + 5(.23) = 2.98$.

16. b.

The chart below keys the **Progress Self-Test** questions to the objectives in the **Chapter Review** on pages 482-485 or to the **Vocabulary** (Voc.) on page 480. This will enable you to locate those **Chapter Review** questions that correspond to questions students missed on the **Progress Self-Test.** The lesson where the material is covered is also indicated on the chart.

Question	**1**	**2**	**3**	**4**	**5**	**6**	**7**	**8**	**9**	**10**
Objective	A, B	B	B	C	D	D	E	F	G	H
Lesson	7-1	7-1	7-2	7-4	7-3	7-4	7-1	7-2	7-4	7-5
Question	**11**	**12**	**13**	**14**	**15**	**16**				
Objective	I	I	J	J	K	L				
Lesson	7-3	7-3	7-7	7-7	7-8	7-6				

Chapter 7 Review (pp. 482-485)

1. {HHH, HHT, HTH, HTT, THH, THT, TTH, TTT} **3.** True **5.** $\varnothing$ **7.** $\frac{1}{4} = 0.25$ **9.** $\frac{5}{12} \approx 0.417$ **11.** $\frac{2}{10} = 0.2$ **13.** 128 **15. a.** 720 **b.** 6 **17.** 5040 **19.** 21 **21.** 197,149,680 **23.** 5040 **25.** 0.77 **27.** False **29.** False **31.** mutually exclusive **33.** False **35.** c **37.** a, b **39.** $x = 8$ **41.** $n = 16$ **43.** $\frac{26}{257} \approx 0.1012$ **45.** 0.28 **47.** $4^{20} \approx 1.1 \times 10^{12}$ **49.** 120 **51.** $26^2 \cdot 10^4 = 6{,}760{,}000$
53. Answers may vary. Sample: Use 100 small pieces of paper numbered from 1 to 100. If a piece of paper is numbered less than 26, call it damaged; otherwise, call it undamaged. Randomly choose 16 pieces of paper from the 100, and record the number of pieces of paper numbered less than 26. Repeat that 5 times and get 5 samples. Our result shows the percentage of corn damaged in each sample as follows: .25, .375, .5625, .12, and .3125.
55. Answers may vary. Sample: Choose a triple of digits from 000 to 999, and if it is from 000 to 324, John gets a hit; if it is from 325 to 999, he does not get a hit. Run it 10 times and record the number of times with 4 or more hits. Repeat the above procedure a certain number of times (e.g., 10 times). Our result shows the estimated probability is .4. (The actual probability is .418.) **57.** Answers will vary, but should approximate 0.06.
59. Estimate should be close to $\frac{10}{3}$. **61. a.** $P(0) = \frac{1}{6}$, $P(1) = \frac{1}{3}$, $P(2) = \frac{1}{3}$, $P(4) = \frac{1}{6}$ **b.** See below. **c.** $\frac{5}{3}$ **63.** See right.
65. $\frac{381}{85} \approx 4\frac{1}{2}$ years

61. b.

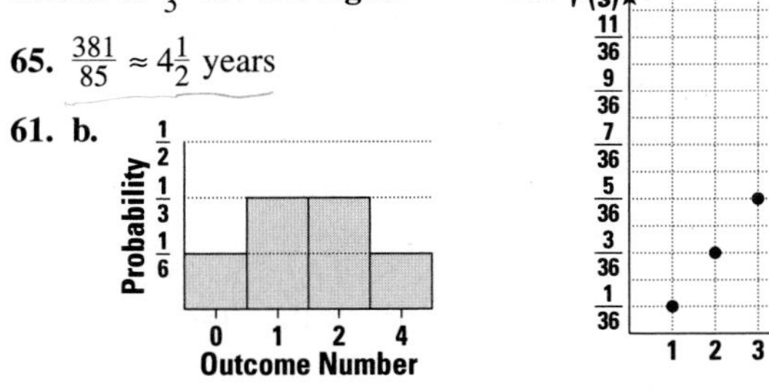

63.

Lesson 8-1 (pp. 488-495)

13. a. $U_n = (2 \div 3) * U_{n-1}$ or $U_n = 36\left(\frac{2}{3}\right)^{n-1}$; U_nStart = 36; $_n$Start = 1 **b.** 36, 24, 16, 10.67, 7.11, 4.74, 3.16, 2.11, 1.40, 0.936, 0.624, 0.416, 0.277, 0.185, 0.123, 0.082, 0.055, 0.037, 0.024, 0.016 **15.** $3 \cdot (1.10)^5 \approx 4.8$ miles **17. a.** $O_n = n(n + 2)$ **b.** $O_{100} = 10{,}200$ **19. a.** -97, -93, -89, -85, -81, -77, -73, -69, -65, -61, -57, -53, -49, -45, -41, -37, -33, -29, -25, -21 **b.** the 25th **21.** $x \approx 19.7$ **23. a.** Sample: $y = \frac{3x}{x+1}$ **See below.** **b.** Sample: $y = 3$

23. a.

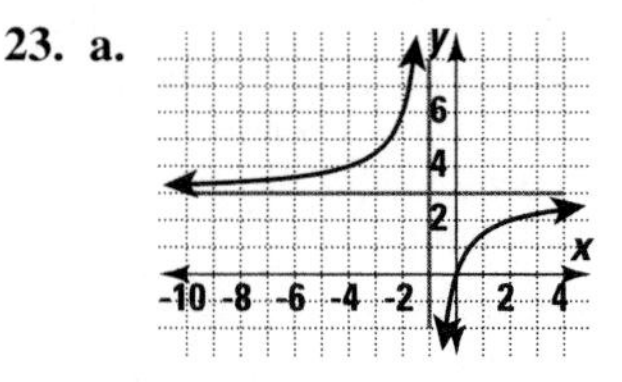

Lesson 8-2 (pp. 496-502)

15. a. exists; 0 **b.** does not exist **c.** does not exist **d.** exists; 0 **e.** If $|r| < 1$, $\lim_{n\to\infty} r^n = 0$. If $|r| > 1$, $\lim_{n\to\infty} r^n$ does not exist. **17.** Step 2: Limit Property 4 Step 3: Limit Property 6 Step 4: Algebraic Definition of Division **19. a.** $x - y$ **b.** $52x - 47y$ **21. a.** $t_n = 5(3)^{n-1}$ **b.** $\log 5 \approx .70$, $\log 15 = 1.18$, $\log 45 \approx 1.65$, $\log 135 \approx 2.13$, $\log 405 \approx 2.61$ **c.** $t_n = 5 \cdot (3)^{n-1}$, so $\log t_n = \log(5 \cdot 3^{n-1}) = \log 5 + \log 3^{n-1} = \log 5 + (n-1)\log 3$. Therefore, the terms of $\log t_n$ form an arithmetic sequence with first term log 5 and constant difference log 3. **23. a.** $\sum_{i=1}^{4} a_i$ **b.** $\sum_{n=2}^{10} b_n$ **c.** $\sum_{j=1}^{n} m_j$

Lesson 8-3 (pp. 503-508)

11. 873,612 **13.** 78 **15.** 21 **17.** convergent; $\frac{1}{4}$ **19. a.** $\frac{\sqrt{3}}{2}, \frac{1}{2}, 0, -\frac{1}{2}, -\frac{\sqrt{3}}{2}$ **b.** neither **c.** $\lim_{n\to\infty} t_n$ does not exist

21. a. $\begin{cases} a_{1996} = 206.6 \\ a_n = 1.015a_{n-1} \text{ for } n > 1996 \end{cases}$ **b.** $206.6(1.015)^{14} \approx$ 254.5 million **c.** Samples: Immigration may increase. The birth rate may change.

Lesson 8-4 (pp. 509-514)

13. 4265.625 **15. a.** Samples: 1, 1, 1, 1, ... 1; $c, c, c, \ldots, c$ **b.** Sample: $\frac{1(1 - 1^n)}{1 - 1}$ is not equal to the sum since the denominator is zero. **c.** Samples: n; cn **17.** about 62 ft **19. a.** \$25,250 **b.** \$218,750 **21.** 12 **23. a.** $(x, y) \to (x - 8, y + 5)$ **b.** $x = -8$, $y = 5$

Lesson 8-5 (pp. 516-522)

11. a. $1 + \frac{1}{2} + \frac{1}{3} + \frac{1}{4} + \frac{1}{5}$ **b.** i. 11 ii. 83 **c.** True **13. a.** $|b| < 4$ **b.** $\frac{4b}{4 - b}$ **15.** 420 ft **17. a.** ≈ 19.7 ft **b.** ≈ 268 ft **c.** about 9 minutes **19.** 1092 **21.** 3 **23.** True

Lesson 8-6 (pp. 523-528)

13. n **15.** $_nP_r$ is larger. Sample: $\frac{_nP_r}{_nC_r} = \frac{\frac{n!}{(n-r)!}}{\frac{n!}{r!(n-r)!}} = r! > 1$, so $_nP_r > {_nC_r}$. **17. a.** 20 **b.** $_nC_3 = \frac{n!}{3!(n-3)!}$ **19. a.** $_{52}C_5 =$ 2,598,960 hands **b.** $_{13}C_5 = 1287$ hands **c.** $\frac{1287}{2{,}598{,}960} \approx .0004952 \approx 0.0005 \approx \frac{1}{2000}$ **21. a.** 0.8 **b.** $0.8b$ **23.** $x = 23$

Lesson 8-7 (pp. 529-534)

11. 27, 1 **13.** Sample: the "hockey stick" pattern. In any shape as shown below, with any number of terms in the "handle" but only one in the "blade," the sum of the terms in the handle is equal to the term in the blade. For example, 1 + 3 + 6 + 10 = 20. **See below.** **15.** $_{22}C_{11} = 705{,}432$ **17. a.** $\frac{27}{64}$ **b.** i. ≈ 2421.19 cm^3 ii. ≈ 2421.62 cm^3 **19.** 15 **21. a.** 96 units^3 **b.** 24π units^3 **c.** 8π units^3

13.

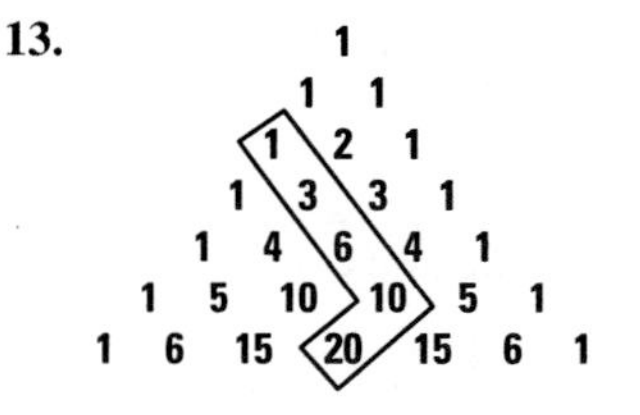

Lesson 8-8 (pp. 535-539)

11. True **13.** True **15.** $\frac{11}{16} = 68.75\%$ **17.** $2^n = (1 + 1)^n$

$$= \sum_{k=0}^{n} {_nC_k}(1)^{n-k}1^k$$

$$= \sum_{k=0}^{n} {_nC_k}$$

19. 210 **21. a.** permutation **b.** 94,109,400 **23.** $\frac{98}{161700} \approx$ 0.000606 **25.** 128

Lesson 8-9 (pp. 540-545)

11. a. 4 **b.** 3.5 **13. a.** $\frac{1}{3}$

b.

x	0	1	2	3	4
$P(x)$	0.198	0.395	0.296	0.099	0.012

c. See below. **d.** 0.111 **e.** 0.802 **15. a.** $(1 - a)$ **b.** $(35)a^3(1 - a)^4$ **17.** $a^6 + 12a^5b + 60a^4b^2 + 160a^3b^3 + 240a^2b^4 + 192ab^5 + 64b^6$ **19.** $\frac{1}{_{55}C_6} = \frac{1}{28989675} \approx 3.4 \times 10^{-8}$ **21.** 0.220 **23.** 4475

13. c.

P(x)
0.4
0.3
0.2
0.1
0
1 2 3 4 x

Chapter 8 Progress Self-Test (p. 550)

1. The sequence is neither geometric nor arithmetic. **2.** $g_1 = 0$; $g_2 = g_1 + 2^2 = 0 + 4 = 4$; $g_3 = g_2 + 3^2 = 4 + 9 = 13$; $g_4 = g_3 + 4^2 = 29$ **3.** $a_{15} = a_1 + (15 - 1)(d) = -12 + 14d$ **4.** $g_n = 9 \cdot \left(\frac{1}{3}\right)^{n-1}$, so $g_7 = 9 \cdot \left(\frac{1}{3}\right)^6 = \frac{1}{81}$ **5. a.** The employee's salary is (19,000)(1.05) during the second year, $(19{,}000)(1.05)^2$ during the third year, and $(19{,}000)(1.05)^3 \approx \$21{,}994.88$ during the fourth year. **b.** This is a geometric sequence, so the salary during the nth year is $S_n = \$19{,}000(1.05)^{n-1}$. **6. a.** **See p. 895.** Some initial values are: $a_1 = 3$, $a_2 = 3 - \frac{1}{2}(2) = 2$, $a_3 = 2 - \frac{1}{2}(3) =$

$\frac{1}{2}, a_4 = \frac{1}{2} - \frac{1}{2}(4) = -\frac{3}{2}, \ldots$ **b.** As n grows large, the a_ns become larger negative numbers. So the sequence does not converge. **7.** This is a geometric series with $g_1 = 75$ and $r = 0.70$. Then $S = \frac{g_1}{1-r} = \frac{75}{1-0.70} = 250$ cm. **8.** Using the sequence mode on a calculator, $\sum_{i=1}^{\infty} \frac{3}{i^3} = 3.606$ when rounded to three decimal places. **9.** This is an arithmetic series with $a_1 = 100$, $d = 1$, so $S_n = n \cdot \frac{(a_1 + a_n)}{2}$. Then $100 + 101 + \ldots 200 = S_{101} = \frac{101}{2}(100 + 200) = 15{,}150$. **10.** This is a geometric series with $g_1 = 7 \cdot \frac{3}{4} = \frac{21}{4}$, $r = \frac{3}{4}$, and $n = 10$. Then, $S_{10} = \frac{g_1(1 - r^{10})}{1 - r} = \frac{\frac{21}{4}\left(1 - \left(\frac{3}{4}\right)^{10}\right)}{1 - \frac{3}{4}} \approx 19.8174$. **11.** The distances Lillian runs each day are given by an arithmetic sequence with $a_1 = 0.5$ and $a_{12} = 3.25$. For the twelfth partial sum, $S_{12} = \frac{12}{2}(0.5 + 3.25) = 22.5$ miles.

12. ${}_nC_2 = \frac{n!}{(n-2)!2!} = \frac{n(n-1)(n-2)!}{(n-2)!2} = \frac{n(n-1)}{2}$;

${}_nC_{n-2} = \frac{n!}{(n-n+2)!(n-2)!} = \frac{n!}{2!(n-2)!} = \frac{n(n-1)}{2}$.

So ${}_nC_2 = {}_nC_{n-2} = \frac{n(n-1)}{2}$ **13. a.** $(x + y)^3 = x^3 + 3x^2y + 3xy^2 + y^3$ **b.** The coefficients are the terms in row 3 of Pascal's Triangle. **14.** By the Binomial Theorem, the 4th term is ${}_{10}C_3(2c)^{10-3}(-b)^3 = \frac{10!}{3!7!}(2c)^7(-b)^3 = \frac{10 \cdot 9 \cdot 8}{3!}(2c)^7(-b)^3$, or choice d. **15.** Three out of 50 are chosen without respect to order. So ${}_{50}C_3 = \frac{50!}{3!47!} = \frac{50 \cdot 49 \cdot 48}{3!}$, or choice d. **16.** This is a binomial experiment with $p = 0.86$ and $n = 5$. Then $P(\text{at least 4 successes}) = P(\text{4 successes}) + P(\text{5 successes}) = {}_5C_4(0.86)^4(0.14) + {}_5C_5(0.86)^5 \approx 0.85$.

17. Sample:

In row 1, ${}_1C_0 = {}_1C_1 = 1$.

In row 3, ${}_3C_0 + {}_3C_2 = 1 + 3 = 3 + 1 = {}_3C_1 + {}_3C_3$.

In row 4, ${}_4C_0 + {}_4C_2 + {}_4C_4 = 1 + 6 + 1 = 4 + 4 = {}_4C_1 + {}_4C_3$.

6. a.

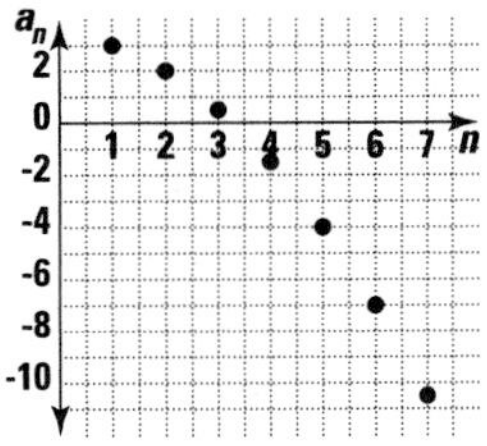

The chart below keys the **Progress Self-Test** questions to the objectives in the **Chapter Review** on pages 551-553 or to the **Vocabulary** (Voc.) on page 549. This will enable you to locate those **Chapter Review** questions that correspond to questions students missed on the **Progress Self-Test.** The lesson where the material is covered is also indicated on the chart.

Question	**1**	**2**	**3**	**4**	**5**	**6**	**7**	**8**	**9**	**10**
Objective	E	A	B	B	I	F	I	G	C	C
Lesson	8-1	8-1	8-1	8-1	8-1	8-2	8-5	8-5	8-3	8-4
Question	**11**	**12**	**13**	**14**	**15**	**16**	**17**			
Objective	I	H	D	D	J	K	L			
Lesson	8-3	8-7	8-8	8-8	8-6	8-9	8-7			

Chapter 8 Review (pp. 551-553)

1. a. 0, 2, 6, 12, 20 **b.** 132 **3. a.** 3, 6, 12, 24, 48 **b.** 6144 **5. a.** -749 **b.** $a_n = 84 - 17(n - 1)$ **7.** $k_n = 22{,}000(0.8)^{n-1}$ **9.** 2358 **11.** 7,174,453 **13.** 18,900 **15.** $a^3 + 3a^2b + 3ab^2 + b^3$ **17.** $16x^4 - 160x^3 + 600x^2 - 1000x + 625$ **19.** $-12x^{11}y$ **21.** possibly arithmetic **23.** possibly arithmetic **25.** definitely geometric **27.** yes; 0 **29.** yes; 0 **31. a.** yes **b.** $\frac{3}{2}$ **33.** not convergent **35.** convergent; $\frac{5}{6}a$ **37. a.** when $b^2 < 1$ **b.** $\frac{a^3b^2}{1 - b^2}$ **39.** ${}_nC_1 = \frac{n!}{1!(n-1)!} = \frac{n(n-1)!}{(n-1)!} = n$; ${}_nC_{n-1} = \frac{n!}{(n-1)!(n-n+1)!} = \frac{n(n-1)!}{(n-1)!} = n$ **41.** False **43. a.** 8 **b.** 50 **45. a.** \$ 692.67 **b.** about \$ 96,113 **47.** 286 **49. a.** 201,376 **b.** 4368 **51.** 1,058,400 **53.** $\approx .67232 \approx 67\%$ **55.** $\approx .73582 \approx 74\%$ **57.** True of every row; each is symmetric **59.** True in every row except row 1

Lesson 9-1 (pp. 556-562)

13. Sample: $x^3yz + xyz$ **15.** leading coefficient: c_n; degree: n. **17.** True

19. $t(n) + t(n + 1) = \frac{1}{2}n(n + 1) + \frac{1}{2}(n + 1)(n + 2)$

$= \frac{1}{2}(n + 1)[n + (n + 2)]$

$= \frac{1}{2}(n + 1)(2n + 2)$

$= \frac{1}{2}(n + 1) \cdot 2(n + 1)$

$= (n + 1)^2 = s(n + 1)$

21. a. Yearbook **b.** Sample: In general, drama clubs have a higher ineligibility rate than other activities. Half of the schools declared at least 30% of drama-club members ineligible, and at least one school declared all drama-club members ineligible. On the other hand, yearbook enjoys the lowest median ineligibility rate, with baseball a close second. Band and track are in the middle with median ineligibility rates of about 22% and 25%, respectively. Yearbook displays the widest diversity among many schools with $\frac{3}{4}$ of the schools declaring from 0% to 38% of the yearbook staff ineligible. In contrast, baseball has the least diversity among schools while having a median ineligibility rate only slightly higher than yearbook. Half of the schools declared from 10% to 20% of baseball players ineligible. **23.** $3x^2 + 14x + 15$ **25. a.** **See p.896.** **b.** **See p.896.**

25. a. **25. b.**

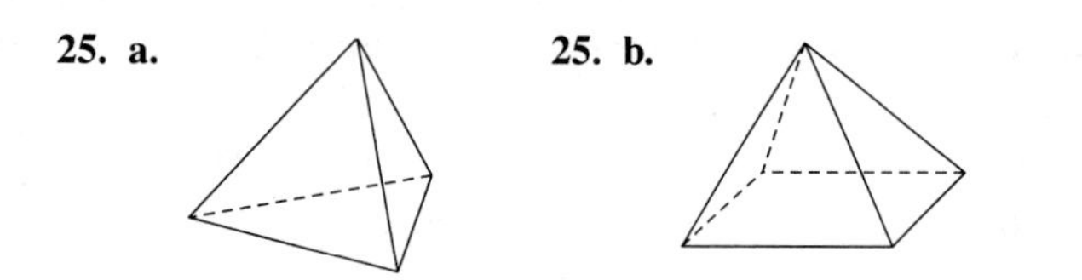

Lesson 9-2 (pp. 564-569)

9. a. $V = 4x^3 - 340x^2 + 7000x$ **b. See below.**
c. $x < 0$ or $35 < x < 50$; the side length of the square cannot be within these intervals because the volume must be positive.
d. $\approx (13.5, 42{,}377)$ **e.** ≈ 13.5 cm **f.** $\approx 42{,}377$ cm^3 **11. a.** ≈ 8 sec and ≈ 23 sec **b.** ≈ 3916 ft **c.** ≈ 31 sec **13. See below.** 1 relative minimum **15. See below.** 1 relative minimum **17. a.** r
b. $n - 1$ **19. a.** $A = (x + h)(y + h)$ **b.** $A = xy + xh + yh + h^2$
c. See below. **21.** 6 **23.** $x = \frac{-b \pm \sqrt{b^2 - 4ac}}{2a}$ **25.** $(x - 6)(x - 5)$

9. b.

$-10 \le x \le 60$, x-scale = 10
$-20000 \le y \le 50000$, y-scale = 10000

13.

15.

19. c.

h^2	xh	h
yh	xy	y
h	x	

Lesson 9-3 (pp. 570-576)

11. a.

1	2	3	4	5	6
340	320	290	250	200	140

b. 2 **c.** $y = -5x^2 - 5x + 350$

d. $\begin{cases} t_0 = 350 \\ t_n = t_{n-1} - 10n, \text{ for integers } n > 0 \end{cases}$

13. a. $f(1) = a + b + c + d$
$f(2) = 8a + 4b + 2c + d$
$f(3) = 27a + 9b + 3c + d$
$f(4) = 64a + 16b + 4c + d$
$f(5) = 125a + 25b + 5c + d$
$f(6) = 216a + 36b + 6c + d$

b. 1st differences: $7a + 3b + c$, $19a + 5b + c$, $37a + 7b + c$, $61a + 9b + c$, $91a + 11b + c$
2nd differences: $12a + 2b$, $18a + 2b$, $24a + 2b$, $30a + 2b$
3rd differences: $6a$, $6a$, $6a$

15. No **17. a.** $750(1 + r)^2 + 750(1 + r) + 750$ **b.** \$2359.73
19. a. $P = 62.5e^{0.017n}$ **b.** ≈ 66.9 million **c.** in the year 2024
21. a. $x = 0, x = 7$ **b.** $y = -9, y = \frac{7}{3}$ **c.** $z = -15, z = -8, z = 5$

Lesson 9-4 (pp. 577-583)

11. a. $q(a) = a + 5$, $r(a) = 5a + 15$ **b.** degree of remainder = 1, degree of divisor = 2 **c.** $(a^2 - 5)(a + 5) + (5a + 15) = (a^3 + 5a^2 - 5a - 25) + (5a + 15) = a^3 + 5a^2 - 10$

13. $x^2 + 3xy + y^2$ **15. a. See below.** **b.** The graphs of f and h are the same because $\frac{2x^4 - 8x^3 + 12}{x^2 - 2} = 2x^2 - 8x + 4 + \frac{-16x + 20}{x^2 - 2}$. g is very close to h for sufficiently large values of x because the remainder will become negligible (as x approaches positive or negative infinity, the denominator will become much larger than the numerator so the fraction will approach zero). f and h have asymptotes because both functions are undefined at $x = \sqrt{2}$ and $x = -\sqrt{2}$. g does not have these discontinuities. **17. a. See below.**
b. increasing: $-3.7 < x < -0.1$ or $x > 1.6$
decreasing: $x < -3.7$ or $-0.1 < x < 1.6$
c. positive: $x < -5$ or $-1 < x < 1$ or $x > 2$
negative: $-5 < x < -1$ or $1 < x < 2$
19. a. 7 **b.** $128a^7$ **c.** $-2187b^7$

15. a.

$h(x)$ $g(x)$ $f(x)$

$-10 \le x \le 10$, x-scale = 1
$-50 \le y \le 100$, y-scale = 10

17. a.

$-6 \le x \le 4$, x-scale = 1
$-100 \le y \le 20$, y-scale = 10

Lesson 9-5 (pp. 584-589)

9. $(x + 2)$ and $(x - 1)$ **11.** $p = -2$ or $p = -5$
13. $f(x) = -(x + 8)(x)(x - 5)(x - 10) = -(x^4 - 7x^3 - 70x^2 + 400x)$
15. -972 **17.** $x^4 - 3x^3 + 9x^2 - 27x + 81$
19. a. 1st differences: 4 7 10
2nd differences: 3 3
b. $p(n) = \frac{3}{2}n^2 - \frac{1}{2}n$ **c.** $p(5) = 35$, $p(6) = 51$ **See right.** **21. a.** 0.54 **b.** ≈ 0.45 **c.** 0.46 **d.** ≈ 0.19 **e.** ≈ 0.28

19. c.

Lesson 9-6 (pp. 590-595)

23. a. $(x - b)$ is a factor of $g(x)$ **b.** Yes **25. a.** $f(2 + i) = 0$ **b.** $f(2 - i) = 0$ **c.** $x^2 - 4x + 5 = (x - (2 + i))(x - (2 - i)) = (x - 2 - i)(x - 2 + i)$ **27. a.** $-1 + 0i$ **b.** $w = \frac{1}{2} - \frac{\sqrt{3}}{2}i$; $w^3 = -1 + 0i$ **c.** -1 **d.** -1 **29.** Samples:
$f(x) = (x - 2)(x - 4)\left(x + \frac{6}{5}\right) = x^3 - \frac{24}{5}x^2 + \frac{4}{5}x + \frac{48}{5}$
$g(x) = 10(x - 2)(x - 4)\left(x + \frac{6}{5}\right) = 10x^3 - 48x^2 + 8x + 96$
$h(x) = x^2(x - 2)(x - 4)\left(x + \frac{6}{5}\right) = x^5 - \frac{24}{5}x^4 + \frac{4}{5}x^3 + \frac{48}{5}x^2$
31. a. $0 \le P(x_i) \le 1$ for all x_i and $\sum_{i=1}^{8} P(x_i) = 1$ **b. See right.**
c. $\frac{109}{24} \approx 4.54$ **d.** Over a long period of time, the mean of the numbers the spinner lands on will approach $\frac{109}{24}$.

31. b.

$P(x)$: $\frac{1}{4}$, $\frac{5}{24}$, $\frac{1}{6}$, $\frac{1}{8}$, $\frac{1}{12}$, $\frac{1}{24}$
x: 1 2 3 4 5 6 7 8

Lesson 9-7 (pp. 596-602)
15. $1, -1, i, -i$ **17.** $p(x) = (x - 3)(x - (1 - 2i))(x - (1 + 2i)) = x^3 - 5x^2 + 11x - 15$ **19. a.** Yes; a horizontal line crosses the graph at most 2 times, so the degree is greater than or equal to 2. **b.** Yes; a horizontal line crosses the graph at most 4 times, so the degree is greater than or equal to 4. **c.** No; the graph crosses the x-axis 6 times, so the degree is at least 6. **21. a.** $w = 3 + 8i$ **b.** $6 + 0i$ **c.** $0 + 16i$ **d.** $73 + 0i$ **e.** $-\frac{55}{73} + \frac{48}{73}i$ **23.** $(2p + 3)(2p - 3)$ **25.** Multiply the quotient and divisor, then add the remainder. The result should equal the dividend. **27. a.** $V(r) = 17\pi r^2 + \frac{2}{3}\pi r^3$ **b.** 3 **c.** $\frac{2}{3}\pi$ **d.** maximum ≈ 1597 m^3, minimum ≈ 537 m^3 **29. a, b.** Both will increase by 5%. **31.** True

Lesson 9-8 (pp. 603-607)
15. $7x^2(2y + x)(2y - x)$ **17.** $(2xy + 7z)(4x^2y^2 - 14xyz + 49z^2)$ **19. a.** $p(x) = x(x + 2)(x - 2)(x + 1)(x - 1)$, so the zeros are $-2, -1, 0, 1$, and 2 **b.** See below. **21.** True **23. a.** True **b.** False **c.** True **d.** True **e.** True **25. a.** ${}_{12}C_3 \cdot (0.36)^3(0.64)^9 \approx 0.18$ **b.** ≈ 0.32

19. b.

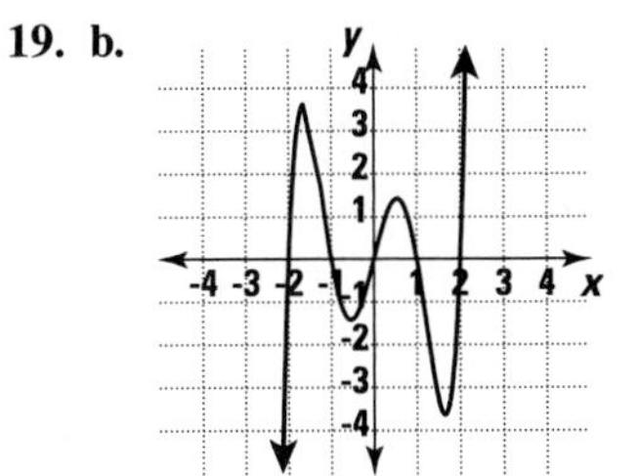

Lesson 9-9 (pp. 608-611)
7. a. $f(x) = x^2(2x - 5) + 3(2x - 5) = (x^2 + 3)(2x - 5) = (x + i\sqrt{3})(x - i\sqrt{3})(2x - 5)$ The zeros of f are $\frac{5}{2}, i\sqrt{3}$, and $-i\sqrt{3}$. **b.** See below. **9.** $(x - z)(2x + y)$ **11.** Sample: $x^3 - x^2y^2 - xy + y^3 = 0$ **13.** $(x - 2)(x^2 + 2x + 4)$ **15.** $(6x^3 - yz^2)(6x^3 + yz^2)$ **17.** $\sqrt[3]{10}, -\frac{\sqrt[3]{10}}{2} + \frac{\sqrt{3}\sqrt[3]{10}}{2}i, -\frac{\sqrt[3]{10}}{2} - \frac{\sqrt{3}\sqrt[3]{10}}{2}i$ **19. a.** $x = 0, \frac{1}{2}$ **b.** $x = -1, \frac{1}{2}, 1$ **c.** $\theta = \frac{\pi}{6} + 2\pi n, \frac{5\pi}{6} + 2\pi n, \frac{\pi}{2} + \pi n$ for n an integer **21. a.** 10 **b.** r **c.** $\frac{8}{9}$ **23. a.** 3024 **b.** 336

7. b.

Lesson 9-10 (pp. 612-616)
9. $p(x) = (x + 1)^2(x^2 - x + 1)(x - 1)$; zeros are -1 (multiplicity 2), $1, \frac{1}{2} + \frac{\sqrt{3}}{2}i, \frac{1}{2} - \frac{\sqrt{3}}{2}i$ **11.** $\theta = \frac{\pi}{4}, \frac{3\pi}{4}, \frac{5\pi}{4}$, and $\frac{7\pi}{4}$ **13. a.** $2i$ **b.** $-24i, 48$ **c.** $3 \cdot 2^{100}$ **15. a.** $ax^3 - ax^2 - 2ax = f(x)$ **b.** $\frac{1}{2}x^3 - \frac{1}{2}x^2 - x = g(x)$ **c.** $\frac{1}{2}x^3 - \frac{1}{2}x^2 - x = g(x)$ is the specific case of $ax^3 - ax^2 - 2ax = f(x)$ for $a = \frac{1}{2}$. **17. a.** $V(x) = x^3 - 2x^2 - 15x$ **b.** $S(x) = 6x^2 - 8x - 30$ **c.** $V(x)$: cubic centimeters; $S(x)$: square centimeters **19.** mean = 16.5 oz; standard deviation = 0.45 oz

Chapter 9 Progress Self-Test (p. 621)
1.

1st differences	1	7	13	19	25	31
2nd differences	6	6	6	6	6	

Therefore, the function is a polynomial function of degree 2. Let $f(x) = ax^2 + bx + c$.
$f(1)$: $-4 = a + b + c$
$f(2)$: $-3 = 4a + 2b + c$
$f(3)$: $4 = 9a + 3b + c$
Solving this system yields $a = 3$, $b = -8$, $c = 1$. So the equation is $y = 3x^2 - 8x + 1$.
2. See below right. $x \approx 1.42$
3.

$$\begin{array}{r|l} & 3x^3 - 13x^2 + 34x - 82 \\ \hline x + 2 & 3x^4 - 7x^3 + 8x^2 - 14x - 10 \\ & 3x^4 + 6x^3 \\ \hline & -13x^3 + 8x^2 \\ & -13x^3 - 26x^2 \\ \hline & 34x^2 - 14x \\ & 34x^2 + 68x \\ \hline & -82x - 10 \\ & -82x - 164 \\ \hline & 154 \end{array}$$

Therefore, $q(x) = 3x^3 - 13x^2 + 34x - 82$; $r(x) = 154$
4. $9x^2 - 3x - 2 = 9x^2 - 6x + 3x - 2 = 3x(3x - 2) + (3x - 2) = (3x - 2)(3x + 1)$ **5.** $t^6 + 1000y^3 = (t^2)^3 + (10y)^3 = (t^2 + 10y)(t^4 - 10t^2y + 100y^2)$ **6.** By the Factor Theorem, if $f(1) = 0$, then $x - 1$ is a factor of f. The choice is a. **7. a.** $2z + w = 2(2 + 5i) + (3 - i) = (4 + 3) + (2 \cdot 5 - 1)i = 7 + 9i$ **b.** $\frac{z}{w} = \frac{2 + 5i}{3 - i} = \frac{(2 + 5i)(3 + i)}{(3 - i)(3 + i)} = \frac{1}{10}(6 + 15i + 2i + 5 \cdot i^2) = \frac{1}{10} + \frac{17}{10}i$ **8.** $-\frac{3}{2}$ **9.** 6 **10.** 3 **11.** It must have 7 zeros (counting multiplicities). Since complex zeros come in conjugate pairs, and the polynomial has an odd number of zeros, at least one of the roots must be real. **12.** Because i is a solution, $-i$ is also a solution. Divide $x^4 + 11x^2 + 10$ by $x^2 + 1$. From this, $x^4 + 11x^2 + 10 = (x^2 + 1)(x^2 + 10)$. So the solutions are $x = i, -i, \sqrt{10}i, -\sqrt{10}i$ **13.** From the data, we can get the equation of the quadratic function $y = .06875x^2 - 1.0125x + 9.2$. Substitute $x = 16$ into the equation. We get the price \$10.60. **14.** From $x^2 + (x^2)^2 = (x^3)^2$, we have $x^6 - x^4 - x^2 = 0$ $x^2(x^4 - x^2 - 1) = 0$ Solve the equation. We get $x = 0$, or $x \approx 1.27$. As $x > 0$, $x \approx 1.27$. **15. a.** Observing the intersections of the part of the graph shown with the x-axis, there seems to be one real zero of multiplicity two and another real zero for a total of at least 3 real zeros. **b.** The graph crosses a horizontal line $y = d$ $(0 < d < t(0))$ three times. So the degree of $t(x)$ must be at least 3. **16.** $V = \pi r^2 \cdot 25 - \pi(r - .35)^2 \cdot 25 = 17.5\pi r - 3.0625\pi$ cubic meters

2.

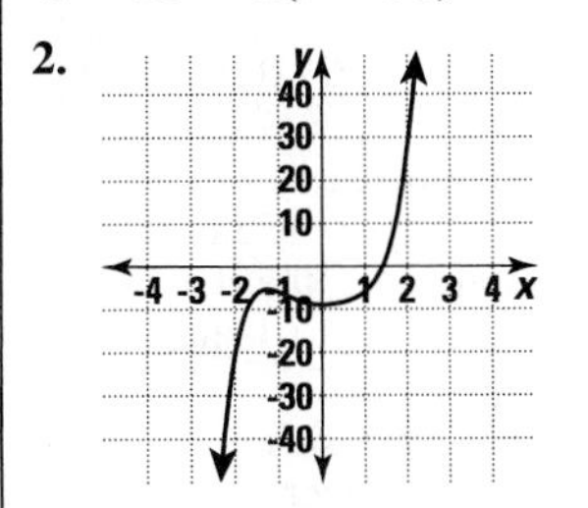

SELECTED ANSWERS

The chart below keys the **Progress Self-Test** questions to the objectives in the **Chapter Review** on pages 622-655 or to the **Vocabulary** (Voc.) on page 620. This will enable you to locate those **Chapter Review** questions that correspond to questions students missed on the **Progress Self-Test.** The lesson where the material is covered is also indicated on the chart.

Question	**1**	**2**	**3**	**4**	**5**	**6**	**7**	**8**	**9**	**10**
Objective	A	B	C	D	D	G	E	F	F	G
Lesson	9-3	9-2	9-4	9-9	9-8	9-5	9-6	9-7	9-1	9-5
Question	**11**	**12**	**13**	**14**	**15**	**16**				
Objective	H	H	I	J	K	J				
Lesson	9-7	9-7	9-3	9-1	9-7	9-1				

Chapter 9 Review (pp. 622-625)
1. a. 4 **b.** 5 **3. a.** No **5.** -1.62 **7.** Because $g(3) = 0$, by the Factor-Solution-Intercept Equivalence Theorem, 3 must be a t-intercept of the graph of g. **9.** $q(t) = 2t^3 - 9t + 1$; $r(t) = 27t + 8$ **11.** $q(x) = x^3 - 2x^2 + x - 1$; $r(x) = 0$ **13.** True **15.** $(3t - u)(81t^4 + 27t^3u + 9t^2u^2 + 3tu^3 + u^4)$ **17.** $(z - 2)(z + 1 - \sqrt{3}i)(z + 1 + \sqrt{3}i)$ **19.** $(2x - 1)(10x + 1)$ **21. a.** $20 + 6i$ **b.** $-2 + 6i$ **c.** $107 - 102i$ **d.** $\frac{3}{4} + \frac{1}{2}i$ **23.** $\frac{14}{25} + \frac{27}{25}i$ **25.** 0 **27. a.** 7 **b.** 3 **c.** 0 **d.** -127 **e.** 7 **29.** False **31.** False **33.** True **35.** For all real a, $a = a + 0i$. The complex conjugate of $a + 0i$ is $a - 0i = a$. Thus every real number is equal to its complex conjugate. **37.** All four zeros must not be real. **39.** True. If $2 + i$ is a zero, then $2 - i$ must also be a zero because non-real zeros occur as conjugate pairs. If $1 + i$ were a zero, then $1 - i$ would also have to be a zero. But, since the polynomial is a cubic polynomial, it only has three zeros. The zeros must be $2 + i$, $2 - i$, and another zero which must be real. **41. a.** $l = 510 - w$; $A(w) = w(510 - w)$ **b. i.** 41,000 ft^2 ii. 65,000 ft^2 iii. 63,000 ft^2 **c.** $l = 255$ ft, $w = 255$ ft

43. $V = \frac{1}{3}\pi r^2h + \frac{2}{3}\pi r^3$ **45. a.** $V = \frac{1}{3}\pi(25 - x^2)(x + 5) = -\frac{1}{3}\pi x^3 - \frac{5}{3}\pi x^2 + \frac{25}{3}\pi x + \frac{125}{3}\pi$ **b.** 3 **c.** 4 inches **47.** 24 cm^2 **49. a. See below. b.** relative maximum: (-2.6, 0.4); relative minimum: (-1.4, -0.4) **c.** -3, -2, -1 **51. a. See below. b.** relative maximum: (-1, 0); relative minimum: (0, -1) **c.** -1 (multiplicity 2); 1 **53.** False; the equation $0.1x^5 - 2x^3 + x^2 - 27 = 0$ has exactly three real solutions.

49. a. **51. a.**

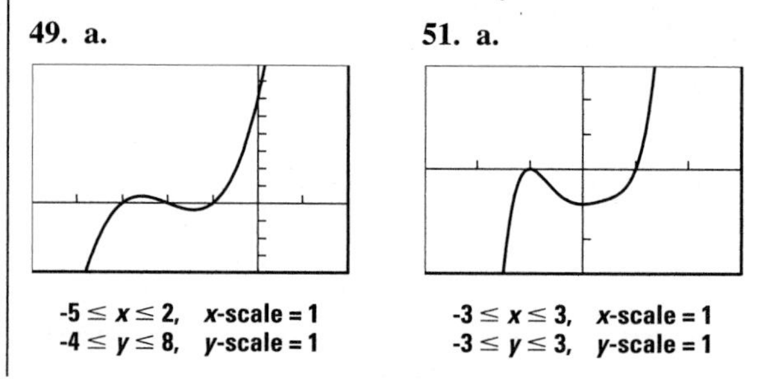

$-5 \le x \le 2$, x-scale = 1
$-4 \le y \le 8$, y-scale = 1

$-3 \le x \le 3$, x-scale = 1
$-3 \le y \le 3$, y-scale = 1

Lesson 10-1 (pp. 628–633)
9. a. 0.939 **b.** 0.103 **c.** 0.061 **11.** binomial
13. Sample: Use the command rand on a TI-83 to generate 20 random numbers x between 0 and 1. If $0 \le x \le 0.15$, the watermelon is large, if $0.15 < x \le 0.5$, then the watermelon is small, if $0.5 < x \le 1$, then the watermelon is medium. In our simulation, we obtained 3 large, 7 small, and 10 medium watermelons. **15.** $\approx 117.5°$

Lesson 10-2 (pp. 634–640)
7. a.

x	0	1	2	3	4
$P(x)$	0.316	0.422	0.211	0.047	0.004

b. See right. c. 1 **d.** $\frac{\sqrt{3}}{2} \approx .866$ **9.** 24 **11. a.** True **b.** False
13. a.

x	0	1	2	3	4	5	6	7	8	9	10
$P(x) \approx$	0.555	0.337	0.092	0.015	0.002	0	0	0	0	0	0

See right.
b. about 0.984 **c.** Sample: The mode would increase, the standard deviation decrease, and the graph become closer to bell-shaped. **d.** Sample: The mode would increase, the standard deviation increase, and the graph become closer to bell-shaped. **15. a. See right. b.** $T(x, y) \rightarrow (-x, y)$ **c.** 0 **d.** 0 **17.** $\pm 3\sqrt{110}$ **19. a.** 540° **b.** Assume 4 angles are acute. Then their sum is less than 360° which implies the remaining angle is larger than 180°. This implies the pentagon is not convex, which contradicts our assumption. Therefore, a pentagon cannot have 4 acute angles.

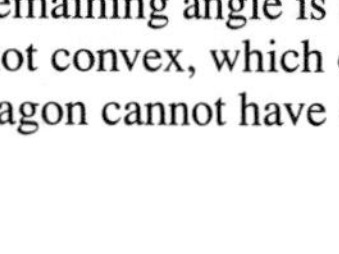

7. b.

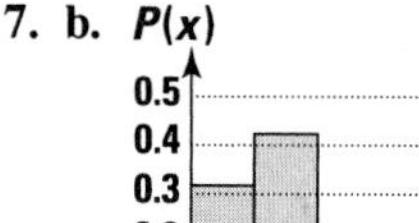

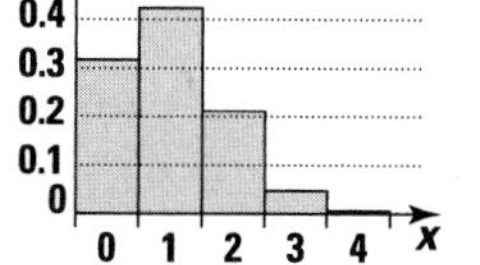

13. a.

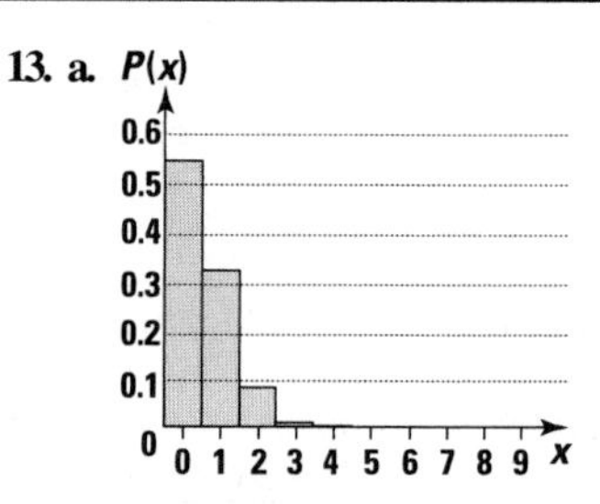

15. a.

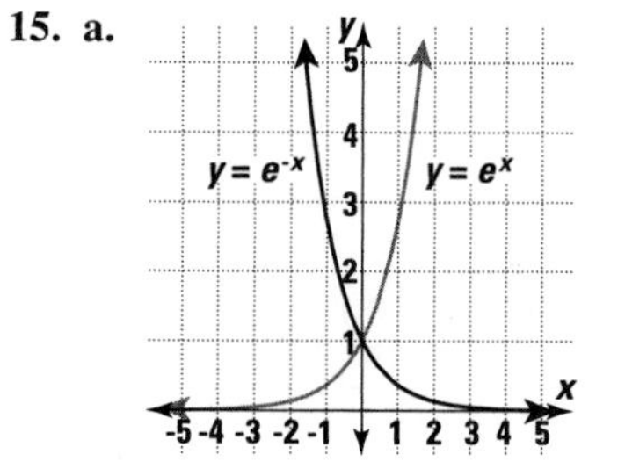

Lesson 10-3 (pp. 641–647)

7. $P\left(5 \text{ or more heads given the probability of heads is } \frac{1}{3}\right) \approx 0.213 > 0.05$. Thus, we cannot reject the null-hypothesis at the 0.05 level. **9.** mean $= 3\frac{1}{3}$; $\sigma = \frac{\sqrt{20}}{3}$ **11.** True **13.** $2a^5(1 + 3bc^2)(1 - 3bc^2 + 9b^2c^4 - 27b^3c^6 + 81b^4c^8)$ **15. a., c. See below. b.** 0.258 **17. a.** 0.01 **b.** 0.64 **c.** 0.11

15. a., c.

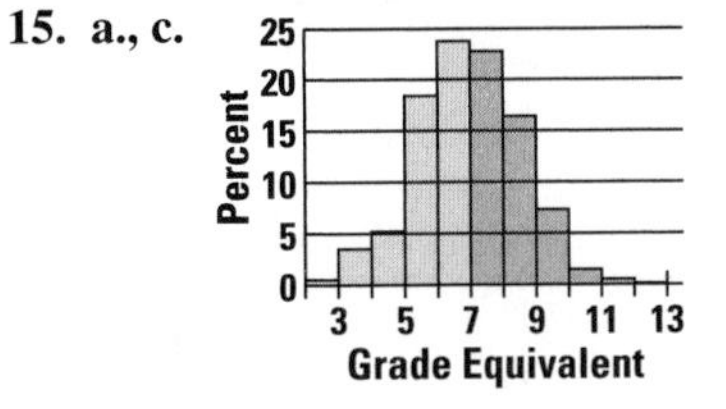

Lesson 10-4 (pp. 649–653)

15. ≈ 0.96 **17.** Let x = number of tails. $P(x \geq 8 \text{ or } x \leq 3) \approx .2266$ which is greater than 0.01, so the hypothesis cannot be rejected. **19.** $x^4 + 2x^3 + 4x^2 + 8x + 16$ **21. a.** False, A and B might not be mutually exclusive. **b.** True, by the definition of complementary

Lesson 10-5 (pp. 654–661)

13. ≈ 1.96 **15.** ≈ -0.67 **17.** The area under $y = e^{-x^2}$ is $\sqrt{\pi}$, while the area under the standard normal curve is 1. **19.** $2x + 3 + 2h$ **21. a.** $0, \frac{3 \pm \sqrt{5}}{2}$ **b. See above right.** From the graph, zeros are $0, \approx 2.62, \approx 0.38$. **23.** ≈ 0.166 **25. a.** $g(x) = -9x^2 - 12x + 5$ **b.** The axis of symmetry for the graph of g is $\frac{2}{3}$ units to the left of the axis of symmetry for the graph of f. **c. see above right.**

21. b.

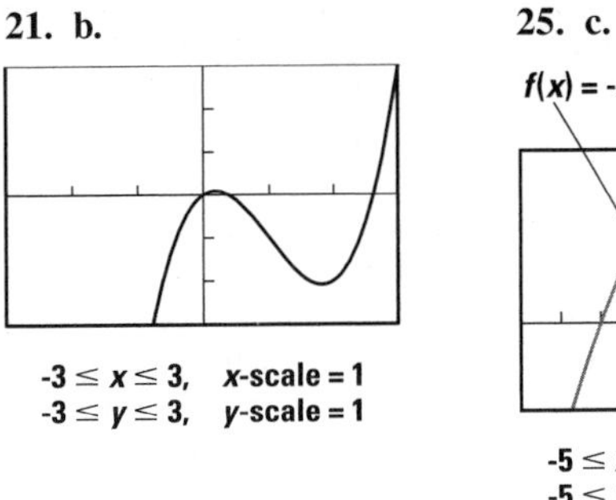

25. c.

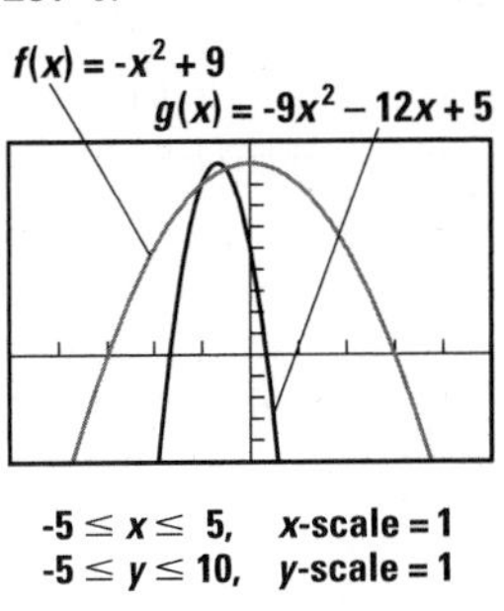

Lesson 10-6 (pp. 662-669)

11. a. $z = \frac{t - 100}{4}$ **b.** $\mu = 0, \sigma = 1$ **13.** almost 0 **15.** Sample: **a.** 500 **b.** 0.05 **c.** between 228 and 272 **17.** ≈ 0.0038 **19.** ${}_{20}C_5 \cdot {}_{300}C_2 = 695{,}354{,}400$ **21.** ≈ 0.998

Lesson 10-7 (pp. 671-679)

15. No, the distribution for the small samples is skewed. **17. a.** They are the same. **b.** The scores of the 45 games; these scores are the population with a standard deviation σ. While the 15 weekly averages are a subset consisting of 15 samples of size 3 with a standard deviation $\sigma_{\bar{x}} = \frac{\sigma}{\sqrt{3}}$. **19. a.** ≈ 0 **b.** H_0: The students at Acme scored the same as the nation. H_1: The students at Acme scored higher than the nation. Since the $P\{z \geq 3.9\} \approx 0$, we reject the null hypothesis in favor of the alternative. **21.** $\approx .901$ **23.** Sample: **a.** H_0: The baby has no color preference between red and green. H_1: The baby prefers red to green. **b.** (3 red, 1 green) and (4 red, 0 green) **c.** We should accept the null hypothesis at the .05 level. **25. a.** $\approx 20°8'$ **b.** At that time the shadow will be near its shortest length and thus its lowest price. **27.** $x = zs + m$

Lesson 10-8 (pp. 680-686)

9. a. $25\% \leq \mu \leq 31\%$ **b.** No **11. a.** $170 \leq \mu \leq 190$ **b.** No **13.** False **15. a.** uniform distribution **b.** 54.5 **17.** about 14 **19.** b **21.** a **23.** d **25. a.** 112 **b.** geometric **27. a.** ≈ 0.028 **b.** ≈ 0.972

Chapter 10 Progress Self-Test (p. 691)

1. By the Binomial Probability Theorem, for each value of x, $P(x \text{ of 10 survive}) = {}_{10}C_x(0.89)^x(0.11)^{10-x}$. Evaluating this expression for each possible value of x gives the following table:

x	$P(x$ of 10 survive$)$
0	2.6×10^{-10}
1	2.1×10^{-8}
2	7.6×10^{-7}
3	1.6×10^{-5}
4	2.3×10^{-4}
5	0.0023
6	0.015
7	0.071
8	0.214
9	0.385
10	0.312

These data are graphed in the histogram. **See p 900.**
2. The domain would increase; the range would "flatten" or decrease; and the shape would approach a normal distribution.

3. $\mu = np = .2 \cdot 60 = 12$; $\sigma = \sqrt{npq} = \sqrt{60 \cdot .2 \cdot .8} = \sqrt{9.6} \approx 3.1$ **4.** The mean resistance is 1500 ohms, because it is the center of the distribution. The 99% confidence interval is reported as 1500 ohms $\pm 5\%$, which gives a margin of error of $\pm 5\% \times 1500 = \pm 75$ oms. From the table of the Standard Normal Distribution, in order for the confidence level to be 99%, z, which equals $\frac{\bar{x} - \mu_{\bar{x}}}{\sigma}$, must equal 2.5. Therefore, $\sigma = \frac{75}{2.57} \approx 29$ ohms. **5.** Yes, $x = 0$, because $f(-x) = \frac{1}{2}e^{-(-x)^2} = \frac{1}{2}e^{-x^2} = f(x)$. **6.** False; the standard normal curve has the equation $f(x) = \frac{1}{\sqrt{2\pi}} e^{\frac{-x^2}{2}}$.

7. Using the Standard Normal Distribution Table we get $P(z < 1.3) = .9032$. **8.** $P(-1.5 < z < 1.5) = 1 - 2P(z < -1.5) = 1 - 2(1 - P(z < 1.5)) = 0.8664$, using the Standard Normal Distribution Table. **9. a.** H_0: Average "normal" body temperature is 98.6°F. H_1: Average "normal" body temperature is not 98.6°F. **b.** $z = \frac{98.2 - 98.6}{\frac{.7}{\sqrt{130}}} \approx -6.52$, $P(z < -6.52) = 0 < 0.01$ Thus, we reject the null hypothesis H_0 in favor of the alternative H_1 that average "normal" body temperature is not 98.6°F. **10.** Using the Central Limit Theorem, we would expect a sample of 40 girls from this high school to have a mean height of about 170 cm with a standard deviation of about $\frac{7.2}{\sqrt{40}}$ cm, or 1.14 cm. A sample mean of 180 cm is about 6 standard deviations from the population mean. A Standard Normal Distribution Table shows even 3.09 standard deviations from the mean to have a probability of less than 0.001. So the event is quite unusual. **11.** 1.96. We must find a value $a > 0$ such that $P(-a < z < a) = 0.95$. Since $P(-a < z < a) = P(z < a) - (1 - P(z < a)) = 2P(z < a) - 1 < 0.95 \Rightarrow 2P(z < a) < 1.95 \Rightarrow P(z < a) < = 0.975$. Using the Standard Normal Distribution Table, we see that the probability value 0.975 corresponds to the z-value $a = 1.96$. **12.** standard normal **13.** 0.0091. Let x be the number of miles a student travels to school. Then, because x is normally distributed with a mean of 2.15 miles and a standard deviation of 0.36, the variable $z = \frac{x - 2.15}{0.36}$ has a standard normal distribution. So $P(x > 3) = 1 - P(x < 3) = 1 - P\left(z < \frac{3 - 2.15}{0.36} \approx 2.36\right) \approx 1 - 0.9909 = 0.0091$. **14.** 0.6424. $P(|z| < 0.92) = P(-0.92 < z < 0.92) = P(z < 0.92) - (1 - P(z < 0.92)) = -1 + 2P(z < 0.92) = -1 + 2(0.8212) = -1 + 1.6424 = 0.6424$.

1.

The chart below keys the **Progress Self-Test** questions to the objectives in the **Chapter Review** on pages 692-695 or to the **Vocabulary** (Voc.) on page 690. This will enable you to locate those **Chapter Review** questions that correspond to questions students missed on the **Progress Self-Test**. The lesson where the material is covered is also indicated on the chart.

Question	**1**	**2**	**3**	**4**	**5**	**6**	**7**	**8**	**9**	**10**
Objective	I	C	A	H	D	D	B	B	F	G
Lesson	10-1	10-1	10-2	10-8	10-4	10-4	10-5	10-5	10-3,10-7	10-7
Question	**11**	**12**	**13**	**14**						
Objective	D	D	E	J						
Lesson	10-5	10-6	10-6	10-5						

Chapter 10 Review (pp. 692-695)

1. mean = 36, $\sigma = \sqrt{14.4} \approx 3.8$ **3.** $\mu = 10$, $\sigma = \sqrt{5} \approx 2.24$ **5.** 100 **7. a.** 0.7994 **b.** 0.7994 units^2 **9.** ≈ 0.1359 **11.** ≈ 0.0013 **13.** False **15.** True **17. a.** $f(-x) = e^{-(-x)^2} = e^{-x^2} = f(x)$ **b.** reflection symmetry over the y-axis **19.** False **21.** ≈ 0.35

23.

highly extroverted	score ≥ 49
extroverted	$42 \leq$ score ≤ 48
average	$29 \leq$ score ≤ 41
introverted	$22 \leq$ score ≤ 28
highly introverted	score < 22

25. c **27.** $P(\text{weight} > 27.8) \approx 0.0708 \geq 0.01$; the null hypothesis cannot be rejected at the 0.01 significance level. **29.** True **31.** very close to zero **33.** 0.025 **35. a.** $0.624 \leq$ radius ≤ 0.626 **b.** about 864

37. a.

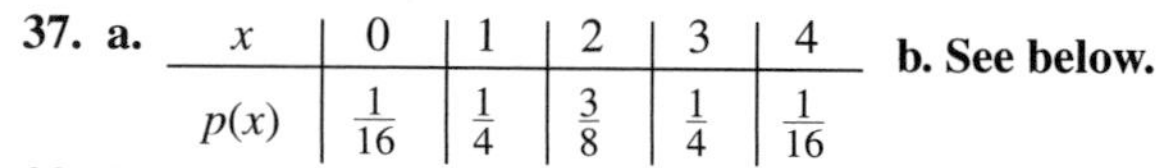

x	0	1	2	3	4
$p(x)$	$\frac{1}{16}$	$\frac{1}{4}$	$\frac{3}{8}$	$\frac{1}{4}$	$\frac{1}{16}$

b. See below. **39.** See below. **41.** Samples: It is continuous; $p(x) > 0$ for arbitrarily large values of x. **43.** ≈ 0.9772 **45.** ≈ 0.9544 **47.** $\frac{r}{2}$

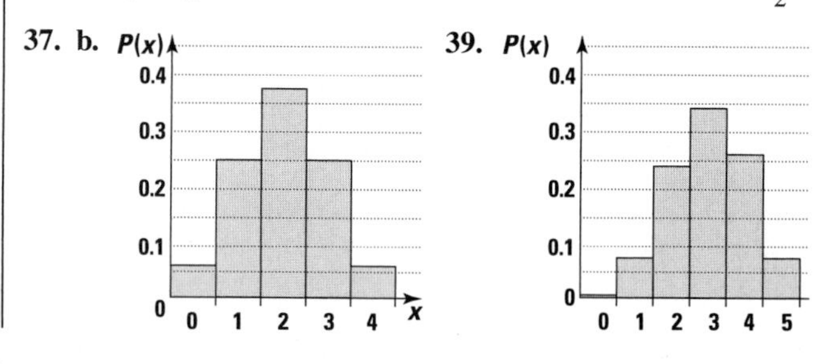

Lesson 11-1: (pp. 698–703)

15. $x = -2$ **17. a.** $\begin{bmatrix} 4 & 0 \\ 0 & 4 \end{bmatrix}$ **b.** $\begin{bmatrix} 0 & -8 \\ -8 & 0 \end{bmatrix}$ **19. a.** $\begin{bmatrix} 2860 \\ 2918 \\ 2640 \end{bmatrix}$ **b.** \$2860

21. a. {0, 1, 2, 3, 4}

b.

b	0	1	2	3	4
$P(b)$	0.3164	0.4219	0.2109	0.0469	0.0039

c. See right.

23. $f(g(x)) = 9x^2 - 6x + 3$ **25. a.** v **b.** i **c.** ii **d.** iv **e.** iii

21. c.

Lesson 11-2 (pp. 704–709)

9. a. $\begin{bmatrix} 0 & 1 \\ 1 & 0 \end{bmatrix}$ **b.** $\begin{bmatrix} 1 & 0 \\ 0 & 1 \end{bmatrix}$ **c.** the identity transformation

11. $\begin{bmatrix} 0 & 1 & 2 & 3 & 4 & 5 & 5 & 4 & 1 & 0 \\ 4 & 6 & 4 & 4 & 6 & 4 & -3 & -4 & -4 & -3 \end{bmatrix}$

13. a. $A' = \begin{bmatrix} 30 \\ -17 \end{bmatrix}$, $B' = \begin{bmatrix} 14 \\ -8 \end{bmatrix}$, $C' = \begin{bmatrix} -18 \\ 10 \end{bmatrix}$ **b.** Yes **c.** No

15. a. 3×4 **b.** 12 **17.** Product does not exist.

19. a. $\begin{bmatrix} -7 & -1 \\ -14 & -10 \end{bmatrix}$ **b.** $\begin{bmatrix} -7 & -1 \\ -14 & -10 \end{bmatrix}$ **c.** the Associative Property

21. $\theta = k\pi$ for all integers k

Lesson 11-3 (pp. 710–715)

13. See below. $u \circ t(\triangle ABC) = \begin{bmatrix} 28 & 30 & -110 \\ 0 & 3 & -18 \end{bmatrix}$

15. a. $r_x \circ r_{y=x} = \begin{bmatrix} 1 & 0 \\ 0 & -1 \end{bmatrix}\begin{bmatrix} 0 & 1 \\ 1 & 0 \end{bmatrix} = \begin{bmatrix} 0 & 1 \\ -1 & 0 \end{bmatrix}$ **b.** R_{270}

17. $\begin{bmatrix} 3 & -1 \\ 1 & 1 \end{bmatrix}$ **19.** $x = -2, y = 7$ **21.** d **23. a. b. See below.**

c. $S:(x, y) \rightarrow \left(\frac{x}{2}, \frac{y}{2}\right)$ **25.** $\frac{5\sqrt{3}}{4}$

13.

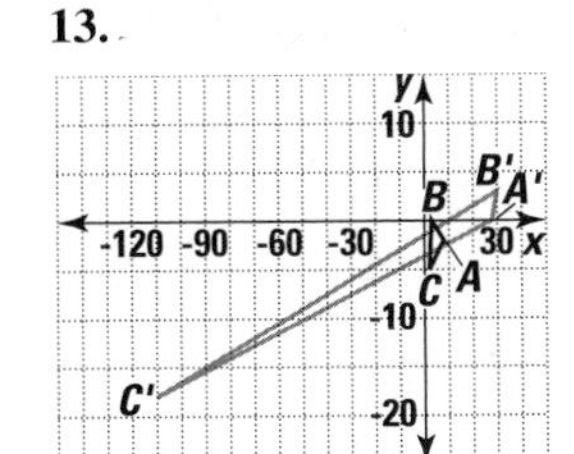

23 a,b.

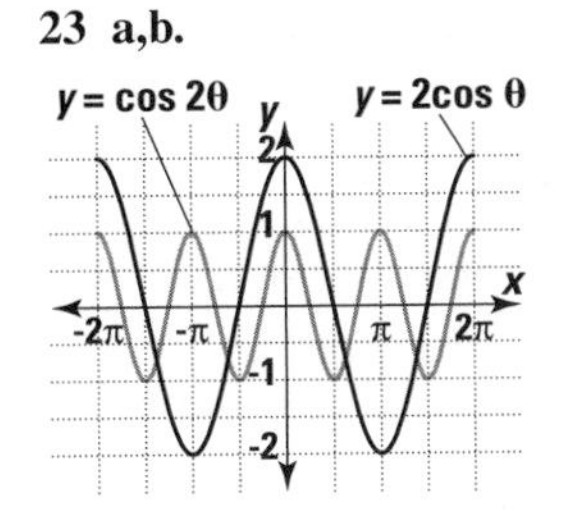

Lesson 11-4 (pp. 716–720)

11. a. $\begin{bmatrix} 0 & -4\sqrt{3} & -2\sqrt{3} \\ 0 & -4 & -6 \end{bmatrix}$ **b. See below. 13. a.** A clockwise rotation of θ is equivalent to a counterclockwise rotation of -θ. So $R_{-\theta} = \begin{bmatrix} \cos(-\theta) & -\sin(-\theta) \\ \sin(-\theta) & \cos(-\theta) \end{bmatrix} = \begin{bmatrix} \cos\theta & \sin\theta \\ -\sin\theta & \cos\theta \end{bmatrix}$.

b. $\begin{bmatrix} \cos 90° & \sin 90° \\ -\sin 90° & \cos 90° \end{bmatrix} = \begin{bmatrix} 0 & 1 \\ -1 & 0 \end{bmatrix}$ **15. a.** Yes **b.** No **c.** Yes **d.** No **17. a.** $y = x^2 - 2x + 1$ **b.** There is not a unique cubic function through three points. Sample: Using (0, 0) as a fourth point, the function containing these four points is $y = \frac{1}{3}x^3 + 2x^2 - \frac{7}{3}x$. **19.** False **21.** False **23.** a **25. a.** $c = 0.12n + 5$ **b.** $245

11. b.

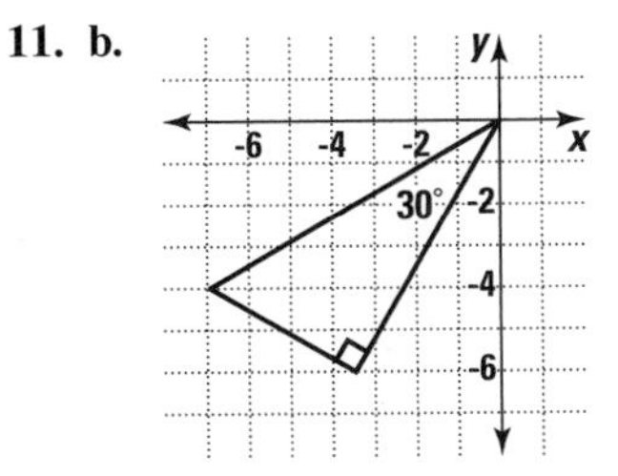

Lesson 11-5 (pp. 721-725)

11. $\frac{-\sqrt{2} - \sqrt{6}}{4}$ **13.** $\begin{bmatrix} \frac{\sqrt{6} - \sqrt{2}}{4} & -\frac{\sqrt{6} + \sqrt{2}}{4} \\ \frac{\sqrt{6} + \sqrt{2}}{4} & \frac{\sqrt{6} - \sqrt{2}}{4} \end{bmatrix}$

15. a. $g(x)$ **b. See below. c.** $f(x) = 2\sin\left(x + \frac{\pi}{6}\right) = 2\left(\sin x \cos\frac{\pi}{6} + \cos x \sin\frac{\pi}{6}\right) = 2\left(\frac{\sqrt{3}}{2}\sin x + \frac{1}{2}\cos x\right) = \sqrt{3}\sin x + \cos x = h(x)$ **17.** $\sin\left(x - \frac{\pi}{2}\right) = \sin\left(x + \left(-\frac{\pi}{2}\right)\right) = \sin x \cos\left(-\frac{\pi}{2}\right) + \cos x \sin\left(-\frac{\pi}{2}\right) = \sin x \cdot 0 + \cos x \cdot -1 = -\cos x$

19. a. $\frac{1 - 2\sqrt{6}}{6}$ **b.** $\frac{2\sqrt{6} - 1}{6}$ **c.** Sample: **See below.**

21. a. $P' = \begin{bmatrix} 2 & 12 & 16 & 6 \\ -1 & -1 & -4 & -4 \end{bmatrix}$ **b.** It is a scale change: $(x, y) \rightarrow (2x, -y)$ **23. a.** 15 **b.** Friday **c.** HR **d.** $52.80

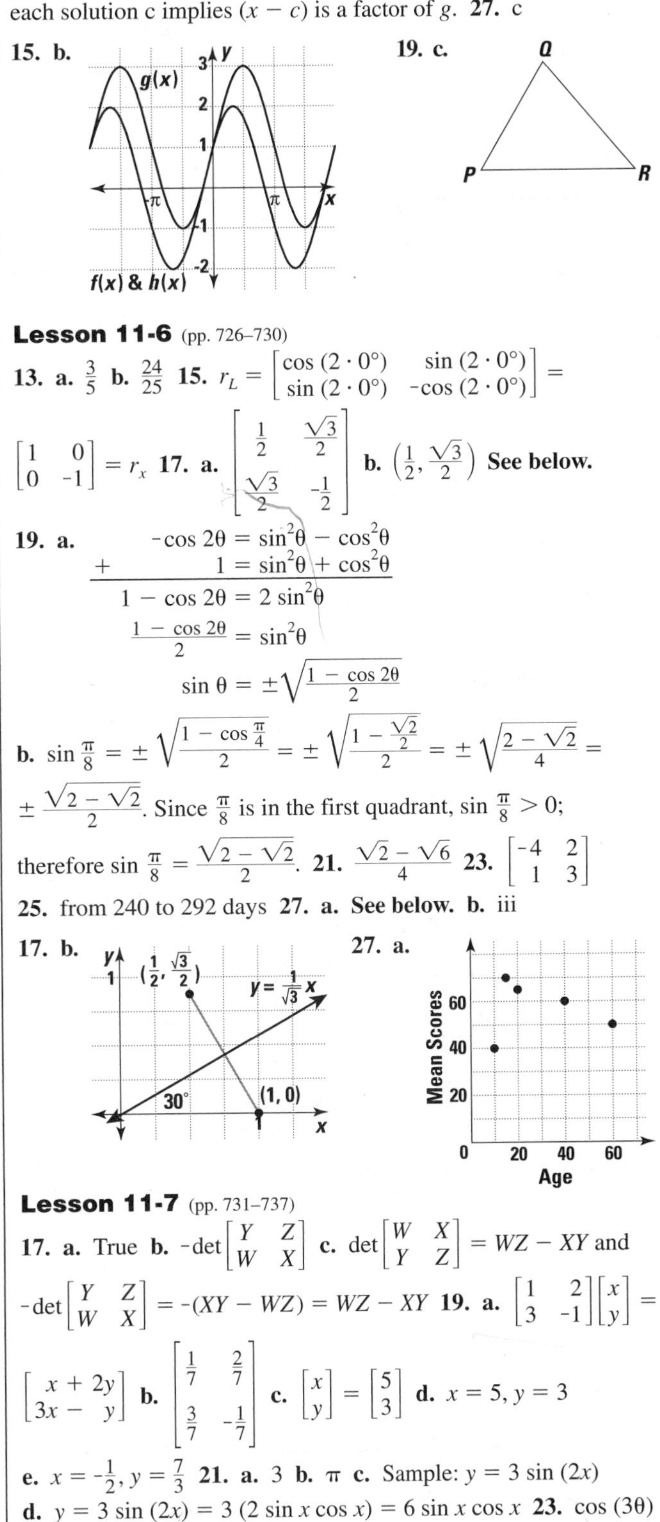

25. a. 3 **b.** 4 **c.** True. There are four observable solutions to $g(x) = 0$, counting the double root twice. By the Factor Theorem, each solution c implies $(x - c)$ is a factor of g. **27.** c

15. b.

19. c.

Lesson 11-6 (pp. 726–730)

13. a. $\frac{3}{5}$ **b.** $\frac{24}{25}$ **15.** $r_L = \begin{bmatrix} \cos(2 \cdot 0°) & \sin(2 \cdot 0°) \\ \sin(2 \cdot 0°) & -\cos(2 \cdot 0°) \end{bmatrix} = \begin{bmatrix} 1 & 0 \\ 0 & -1 \end{bmatrix} = r_x$ **17. a.** $\begin{bmatrix} \frac{1}{2} & \frac{\sqrt{3}}{2} \\ \frac{\sqrt{3}}{2} & -\frac{1}{2} \end{bmatrix}$ **b.** $\left(\frac{1}{2}, \frac{\sqrt{3}}{2}\right)$ **See below.**

19. a.

$$\begin{aligned} -\cos 2\theta &= \sin^2\theta - \cos^2\theta \\ + \quad 1 &= \sin^2\theta + \cos^2\theta \\ \hline 1 - \cos 2\theta &= 2\sin^2\theta \\ \frac{1 - \cos 2\theta}{2} &= \sin^2\theta \\ \sin\theta &= \pm\sqrt{\frac{1 - \cos 2\theta}{2}} \end{aligned}$$

b. $\sin\frac{\pi}{8} = \pm\sqrt{\frac{1 - \cos\frac{\pi}{4}}{2}} = \pm\sqrt{\frac{1 - \frac{\sqrt{2}}{2}}{2}} = \pm\sqrt{\frac{2 - \sqrt{2}}{4}} = \pm\frac{\sqrt{2 - \sqrt{2}}}{2}$. Since $\frac{\pi}{8}$ is in the first quadrant, $\sin\frac{\pi}{8} > 0$; therefore $\sin\frac{\pi}{8} = \frac{\sqrt{2 - \sqrt{2}}}{2}$. **21.** $\frac{\sqrt{2} - \sqrt{6}}{4}$ **23.** $\begin{bmatrix} -4 & 2 \\ 1 & 3 \end{bmatrix}$

25. from 240 to 292 days **27. a. See below. b.** iii

17. b.

27. a.

Lesson 11-7 (pp. 731–737)

17. a. True **b.** $-\det\begin{bmatrix} Y & Z \\ W & X \end{bmatrix}$ **c.** $\det\begin{bmatrix} W & X \\ Y & Z \end{bmatrix} = WZ - XY$ and $-\det\begin{bmatrix} Y & Z \\ W & X \end{bmatrix} = -(XY - WZ) = WZ - XY$ **19. a.** $\begin{bmatrix} 1 & 2 \\ 3 & -1 \end{bmatrix}\begin{bmatrix} x \\ y \end{bmatrix} = \begin{bmatrix} x + 2y \\ 3x - y \end{bmatrix}$ **b.** $\begin{bmatrix} \frac{1}{7} & \frac{2}{7} \\ \frac{3}{7} & -\frac{1}{7} \end{bmatrix}$ **c.** $\begin{bmatrix} x \\ y \end{bmatrix} = \begin{bmatrix} 5 \\ 3 \end{bmatrix}$ **d.** $x = 5, y = 3$

e. $x = -\frac{1}{2}, y = \frac{7}{3}$ **21. a.** 3 **b.** π **c.** Sample: $y = 3\sin(2x)$ **d.** $y = 3\sin(2x) = 3(2\sin x\cos x) = 6\sin x\cos x$ **23.** $\cos(3\theta)$

25. a. R_a **b.** r_x. **27. a.** $M = \begin{bmatrix} 2 & 5 & 5 \\ -1 & -1 & -5 \end{bmatrix}$ **b.** See p.902.

c. $M' = \begin{bmatrix} 1 & 1 & 5 \\ -2 & -5 & -5 \end{bmatrix}$ **d.** See p.902. **e.** $\begin{bmatrix} -1 & -1 \\ 2 & \end{bmatrix}$

29. a. $x = 729$ **b.** $x = 729.00$

27. b. **27. d.**

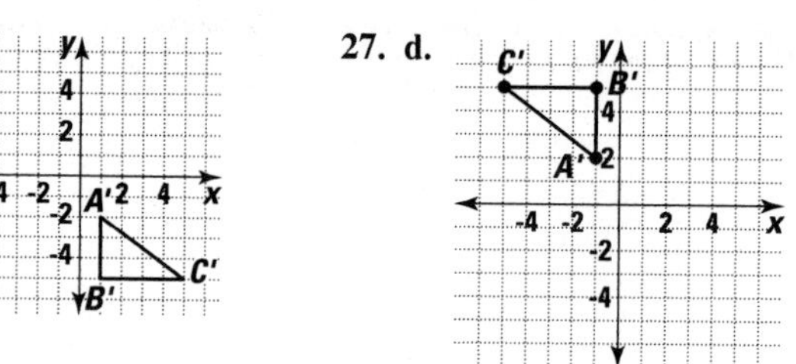

Lesson 11-8 (pp. 738–744)

13. a. r_x **b.** $\begin{bmatrix} 1 & 0 \\ 0 & -1 \end{bmatrix}$ **c.** r_x **15.** If T_1 and T_2 are scale changes with T_1: $(x, y) \rightarrow \left(3x, \frac{1}{2}y\right)$ and T_2: $(x, y) \rightarrow \left(\frac{1}{3}x, 2y\right)$, then $T_1 \circ T_2 = I$, where I is the identity transformation. **17.** $\sin 3\theta = 3 \sin \theta - 4\sin^3\theta$ **19. a.** $\frac{\sqrt{2} - \sqrt{6}}{4}$ **b.** 1 **21. a.** $\begin{bmatrix} 3 & 5 \\ -1 & 4 \end{bmatrix}$ **b.** (0, 0) **c.** (8, 3)

Chapter 11 Progress Self-Test (p. 748)

1. Multiply the number of voters in each region by the percentage of people expected to vote Republican in that region and then add the three results; for example, .29(3.4) + .41(0.6) + .58(2.1) = 2.45 million **2.** $VP = \begin{bmatrix} 0.50 & 0.47 & 0.29 \\ 0.29 & 0.41 & 0.58 \\ 0.21 & 0.12 & 0.13 \end{bmatrix} \begin{bmatrix} 3.4 \\ 0.6 \\ 2.1 \end{bmatrix} =$

$$\begin{bmatrix} 0.5 \cdot 3.4 + 0.47 \cdot 0.6 + 0.29 \cdot 2.1 \\ 0.29 \cdot 3.4 + 0.41 \cdot 0.6 + 0.58 \cdot 2.1 \\ 0.21 \cdot 3.4 + 0.12 \cdot 0.6 + 0.13 \cdot 2.1 \end{bmatrix} = \begin{bmatrix} 2.591 \\ 2.45 \\ 1.059 \end{bmatrix}$$

3. To obtain the first row of VP, we multiplied the percentage of urban voters that are expected to vote Democrat by the total number of registered urban voters, added the percentage of rural voters that are expected to vote Democrat times the total number of rural voters, and then added the percentage of suburban voters that are expected to vote Democrat times the total number of suburban voters. Thus the entry in the first row is the total number of registered voters expected to vote Democrat. Similarly, the second and third rows represent the total number of voters expected to vote Republican and Independent, respectively.

4. $\begin{bmatrix} 5 & -1 \\ 2 & 0 \end{bmatrix} \begin{bmatrix} 3 & 8 \\ -1 & 1 \end{bmatrix} = \begin{bmatrix} 5 \cdot 3 + -1 \cdot -1 & 5 \cdot 8 + -1 \cdot 1 \\ 2 \cdot 3 + 0 \cdot -1 & 2 \cdot 8 + 0 \cdot 1 \end{bmatrix} = \begin{bmatrix} 16 & 39 \\ 6 & 16 \end{bmatrix}$

5. Since M is a 3 × 4 matrix and N is a 4 × t matrix, MN is a 3 × t matrix (the number of rows of M by the number of columns of N). Since Z = 3 × 5 and $MN = Z$, then $t = 5$. **6.** $A = (0, 2)$, $B = (-3, 0)$, and $C = (4, -1)$ so the point matrix for $\triangle ABC$ is $\begin{bmatrix} 0 & -3 & -4 \\ 2 & 0 & -1 \end{bmatrix}$. **7.** $XM = \begin{bmatrix} -1 & 0 \\ 0 & 2 \end{bmatrix} \begin{bmatrix} 0 & -3 & -4 \\ 2 & 0 & -1 \end{bmatrix} =$

$$\begin{bmatrix} -1 \cdot 0 + 0 \cdot 2 & -1 \cdot -3 + 0 \cdot 0 & -1 \cdot -4 + 0 \cdot -1 \\ 0 \cdot 0 + 2 \cdot 2 & 0 \cdot -3 + 2 \cdot 0 & 0 \cdot -4 + 2 \cdot -1 \end{bmatrix} = \begin{bmatrix} 0 & 3 & 4 \\ 4 & 0 & -2 \end{bmatrix}$$

8. See below right. 9. a. The reflection $r_{y=x}$: $(x, y) \rightarrow (y, x)$ maps (1, 0) to (0, 1) and (0, 1) to (1, 0). Therefore, the matrix representing $r_{y=x}$ is $\begin{bmatrix} 0 & 1 \\ 1 & 0 \end{bmatrix}$. **b.** $\begin{bmatrix} 0 & 1 \\ 1 & 0 \end{bmatrix} \begin{bmatrix} 0 & 1 \\ 1 & 0 \end{bmatrix} = \begin{bmatrix} 1 & 0 \\ 0 & 1 \end{bmatrix}$, which is the identity matrix. So $r_{y=x} \circ r_{y=x} = I$. **10.** $R_{30°} =$

$$\begin{bmatrix} \cos 30° & -\sin 30° \\ \sin 30° & \cos 30° \end{bmatrix} = \begin{bmatrix} \frac{\sqrt{3}}{2} & -\frac{1}{2} \\ \frac{1}{2} & \frac{\sqrt{3}}{2} \end{bmatrix}$$, which is choice b.

11. a. r_x **b.** The matrix representing r_x is $\begin{bmatrix} 1 & 0 \\ 0 & -1 \end{bmatrix}$, and the matrix representing R_{180} is $\begin{bmatrix} -1 & 0 \\ 0 & -1 \end{bmatrix}$. So the matrix representing $R_{180} \circ r_x$ is $\begin{bmatrix} -1 & 0 \\ 0 & -1 \end{bmatrix} \begin{bmatrix} 1 & 0 \\ 0 & -1 \end{bmatrix} = \begin{bmatrix} -1 & 0 \\ 0 & 1 \end{bmatrix}$. **12.** $\triangle PQR$ is represented by the matrix $\begin{bmatrix} 0 & 1 & 0 \\ 0 & 0 & 1 \end{bmatrix}$, and the rotation R_θ is represented by the matrix $\begin{bmatrix} \cos\theta & -\sin\theta \\ \sin\theta & \cos\theta \end{bmatrix}$. So the image of $\triangle PQR$ is represented by the point matrix $\begin{bmatrix} \cos\theta & -\sin\theta \\ \sin\theta & \cos\theta \end{bmatrix} \begin{bmatrix} 0 & 1 & 0 \\ 0 & 0 & 1 \end{bmatrix} = \begin{bmatrix} 0 & \cos\theta & -\sin\theta \\ 0 & \sin\theta & \cos\theta \end{bmatrix}$

13. By the Subtraction Formula for Sine, $\sin(\alpha - \beta) = \sin\alpha\cos\beta - \cos\alpha\sin\beta$. So, $\sin 83° \cos 42° - \cos 83° \sin 42° = \sin(83° - 42°) = \sin 41°$. **14.** $\cos(\alpha + \beta) = \cos\alpha\cos\beta - \sin\alpha\sin\beta$. So, $\cos(\pi + \theta) = \cos\pi\cos\theta - \sin\pi\sin\theta = -1 \cdot \cos\theta - 0 \cdot \sin\theta = -\cos\theta$. **15.** Because A is acute, $\cos A = \sqrt{1 - \sin^2 A}$. $\sin 2A = 2 \sin A \cos A = 2 \sin A\left(\sqrt{1 - \sin^2 A}\right) = 2 \cdot 0.40 \cdot \sqrt{1 - (0.40)^2} \approx 0.733$. **16.** If $A = \begin{bmatrix} a & b \\ c & d \end{bmatrix}$, then $A^{-1} =$ $\begin{bmatrix} \frac{d}{\det A} & -\frac{b}{\det A} \\ -\frac{c}{\det A} & \frac{a}{\det A} \end{bmatrix}$. For C, $\det C = 1 \cdot 5 - 3 \cdot -1 = 8$. So $C^{-1} =$ $\begin{bmatrix} \frac{5}{8} & \frac{1}{8} \\ -\frac{3}{8} & \frac{1}{8} \end{bmatrix}$. **17.** $\det G = 3x \cdot 10 - 6 \cdot 5x = 30x - 30x = 0$. A matrix with a zero determinant has no inverse.

18. a. $\begin{bmatrix} 3 & -1 \\ 5 & -2 \end{bmatrix} \begin{bmatrix} x \\ y \end{bmatrix} = \begin{bmatrix} 6 \\ 11 \end{bmatrix}$

b. $\det\begin{bmatrix} 3 & -1 \\ 5 & -2 \end{bmatrix} = -1$, so $\begin{bmatrix} 3 & -1 \\ 5 & -2 \end{bmatrix}^{-1} = \begin{bmatrix} \frac{-2}{-1} & \frac{1}{-1} \\ \frac{-5}{-1} & \frac{3}{-1} \end{bmatrix} = \begin{bmatrix} 2 & -1 \\ 5 & -3 \end{bmatrix}$.

Multiplying both sides of the equation in part **a** on the left by the inverse gives

$\begin{bmatrix} 2 & -1 \\ 5 & -3 \end{bmatrix} \begin{bmatrix} 3 & -1 \\ 5 & -2 \end{bmatrix} \begin{bmatrix} x \\ y \end{bmatrix} = \begin{bmatrix} 2 & -1 \\ 5 & -3 \end{bmatrix} \begin{bmatrix} 6 \\ 11 \end{bmatrix}$;

$\begin{bmatrix} 1 & 0 \\ 0 & 1 \end{bmatrix} \begin{bmatrix} x \\ y \end{bmatrix} = \begin{bmatrix} 12 + -11 \\ 30 + -33 \end{bmatrix}$; $\begin{bmatrix} x \\ y \end{bmatrix} = \begin{bmatrix} 1 \\ -3 \end{bmatrix}$.

8.

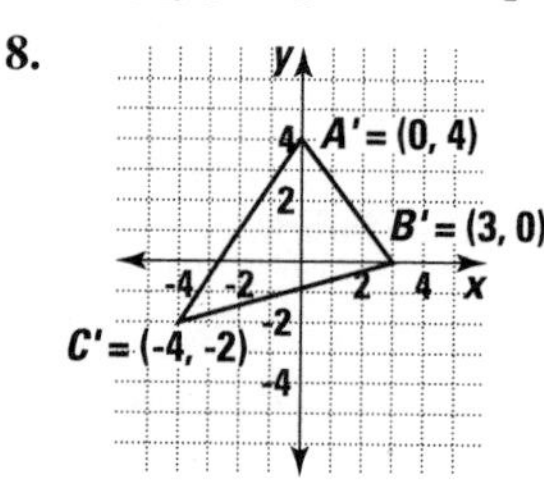

The chart below keys the **Progress Self-Test** questions to the objectives in the **Chapter Review** on pages 749-751 or to the **Vocabulary** (Voc.) on page 747. This will enable you to locate those **Chapter Review** questions that correspond to questions students missed on the **Progress Self-Test.** The lesson where the material is covered is also indicated on the chart.

Question	**1**	**2**	**3**	**4**	**5**	**6**	**7**	**8**	**9**	**10**
Objective	F	A	F	A	D	I	I	I	C, G	G
Lesson	11-1	11-1	11-1	11-1	11-1	11-2	11-2	11-2	11-2,11-7	11-4
Question	**11**	**12**	**13**	**14**	**15**	**16**	**17**	**18**		
Objective	H	I	E	E	E	C	C	B		
Lesson	11-3	11-4	11-5, 11-6	11-5	11-6	11-7	11-7	11-7		

Chapter 11 Review (pp. 749–751)

1. c **3.** $[x - 21]$ **5.** $x = 5$ **7.** $x = \frac{3}{5}, y = \frac{3}{2}$ **9.** $x = 3, y = 2, z = 1$ **11.** $\begin{bmatrix} \cos 40° & \sin 40° \\ -\sin 40° & \cos 40° \end{bmatrix}$ **13.** a, e **15.** 5×2 **17.** Sample: a rotation about the origin, a reflection over a line containing the origin, and the identity transformation. **19.** $\frac{\sqrt{6} - \sqrt{2}}{4}$ **21.** 0.96 **23.** $-\cos\theta$ **25.** $\sin 2A$ **27.** $\cos 50°$ **29.** By the derivation in **28.**, $\cos(\alpha + \beta) = \cos\alpha\cos\beta - \sin\alpha\sin\beta$. So, if $\alpha = \theta$ and $\beta = \theta$, $\cos(\theta + \theta) = \cos\theta\cos\theta - \sin\theta\sin\theta$; $\cos 2\theta = \cos^2\theta - \sin^2\theta$. Also, from the identity $\sin^2\theta + \cos^2\theta = 1$, $\sin^2\theta = 1 - \cos^2\theta$ and $\cos^2\theta = 1 - \sin^2\theta$. So, by substitution, $\cos^2\theta = 1 - 2\sin^2\theta$, and $\cos 2\theta = 2\cos^2\theta - 1$. **31.** \$10,900 **33. a.** \$491.76 **b.** True **35.** $\begin{bmatrix} 1 & 0 \\ 0 & \frac{1}{3} \end{bmatrix}$ **37.** a size change of magnitude 11 **39.** R_{180} **41.** $\begin{bmatrix} -\frac{1}{2} & -\frac{\sqrt{3}}{2} \\ \frac{\sqrt{3}}{2} & -\frac{1}{2} \end{bmatrix}$ **43. a.** $\begin{bmatrix} 5 & 0 \\ 0 & -1 \end{bmatrix}$ **b.** (5, -1) **45.** a counterclockwise rotation of 90°, followed by a reflection over the line $y = x$, followed by a counterclockwise rotation of 32°. **47. a.** $\begin{bmatrix} -1 & 0 \\ 0 & 1 \end{bmatrix}$ **b.** r_y **49. a.** Sample: $\begin{bmatrix} 0 & 7 & 7 & 0 \\ 0 & -1 & 0 & 1 \end{bmatrix}$ **b. See below.** **51.** $R_{-75} = \begin{bmatrix} \cos(-75°) & -\sin(-75°) \\ \sin(-75°) & \cos(-75°) \end{bmatrix} = \begin{bmatrix} \cos 75° & \sin 75° \\ -\sin 75° & \cos 75° \end{bmatrix}$

49. b.

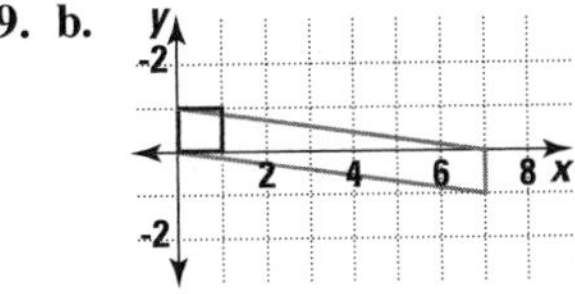

Lesson 12-1 (pp. 754–759)

11. True. The center of the circle is the location of both foci. The focal constant is twice the radius of the circle. **13. a.** There is no smallest focal constant, but it must be larger than 1 meter. **b.** As the focal constant gets larger, the ellipse looks more and more like a circle. **c.** There is no largest focal constant; it can be arbitrarily large as long as it is larger than 1 meter. **15.** $\{x: B < x < D\}$, $\{x: x > F\}$ **17.** No **19.** False. Counterexample: $g(f(-2)) = ((-2)^6)^{\frac{1}{6}} = 2$, but $f(g(-2))$ is undefined. **21.** $4ab$ **23.** $\sqrt{(a - x)^2 + (b - y)^2}$

Lesson 12-2 (pp. 760–767)

13. Dividing both sides of the equation $2x^2 + 3y^2 = 12$ by 12 gives the equation $\frac{x^2}{6} + \frac{y^2}{4} = 1$, which is an equation of an ellipse in standard form. **15. a.** $\frac{x^2}{100} + \frac{y^2}{49} = 1$ **b.** $\frac{(x - 3)^2}{100} + \frac{(y + 6)^2}{49} = 1$ **17. a.** Eccentricity $= \frac{c}{a}$, where $c^2 = a^2 - b^2$ **b.** greater **19.** ≈ 0.25 **21.** hyperbola **23.** $\approx 125°$ **25. a.** about 3971 megabytes **b.** 5000 megabytes

Lesson 12-3 (pp. 768–775)

11. Let $F_1 = (\sqrt{2}, 0)$, $F_2 = (-\sqrt{2}, 0)$, the focal constant $k = 2$, and $P = (1, 0)$. We have to show $|PF_1 - PF_2| = 2$, or, equivalently, $(PF_1 - PF_2)^2 = 4$. $(PF_1 - PF_2)^2 = \left(\sqrt{(1 - \sqrt{2})^2 + (0 - 0)^2} - \sqrt{(1 + \sqrt{2})^2 + (0 - 0)^2}\right)^2 = \left(\sqrt{(3 - 2\sqrt{2})} - \sqrt{(3 + 2\sqrt{2})}\right)^2 = 3 - 2\sqrt{2} - 2\sqrt{(3 - 2\sqrt{2})(3 + 2\sqrt{2})} + 3 + 2\sqrt{2} = 6 - 2\sqrt{9 - 8} = 4$ **13. a.** Dividing both sides of the equation $x^2 - 2y^2 = 2$ by 2 gives the equivalent equation $\frac{x^2}{2} - y^2 = 1$, which is the equation for a hyperbola in standard form, with $a = \sqrt{2}$ and $b = 1$. **b.** foci: $(\sqrt{3}, 0)$, $(-\sqrt{3}, 0)$; focal constant: $2\sqrt{2}$ **15. a.** (h, k) **b.** $(a + h, k)$, $(-a + h, k)$ **c.** $(\sqrt{a^2 + b^2} + h, k)$, $(-\sqrt{a^2 + b^2} + h, k)$ **d.** $\frac{y - k}{b} = \frac{x - h}{a}$, $\frac{y - k}{b} = -\frac{(x - h)}{a}$ **17. a.** center: (-2, 5) foci: $(\sqrt{21} - 2, 5)$, $(-\sqrt{21} - 2, 5)$ **b.** major axis: 10 minor axis: 4 **c. See below.** **19.** about 8 **21.** $4a^2 + 2b^2$

17. c.

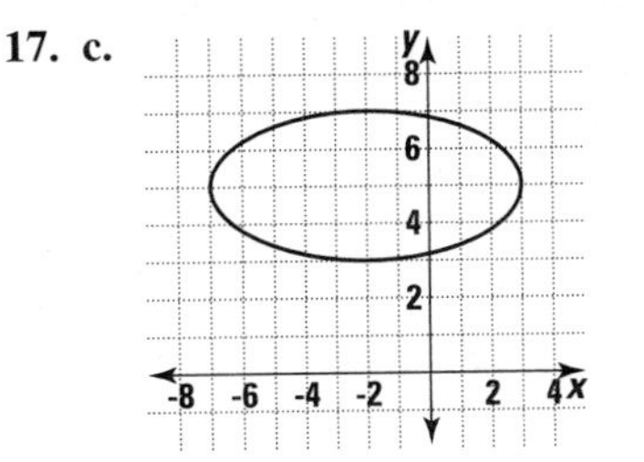

Lesson 12-4 (pp. 776-783)

9. a. Sample: $y^2 - x^2 = 2k$ **b.** True **11.** An equation for the x-axis is $y = 0$. By the Graph Rotation Theorem, the image of the x-axis under R_θ has equation $-x \sin\theta + y\cos\theta = 0$. Solving for y yields $y = x\tan\theta$.

13. a. **See below.** **b.** $y = \frac{1}{6}x, y = -\frac{1}{6}x$

c. $\frac{y^2}{36} - x^2 = 1$

15. a. an equation which is true for all values in the domain of the variables **b.** Sample: $\cos^2\theta + \sin^2\theta = 1$ **c.** Sample: $\cos\theta + \sin\theta = 1$ **17.** a **19.** d

13. a.

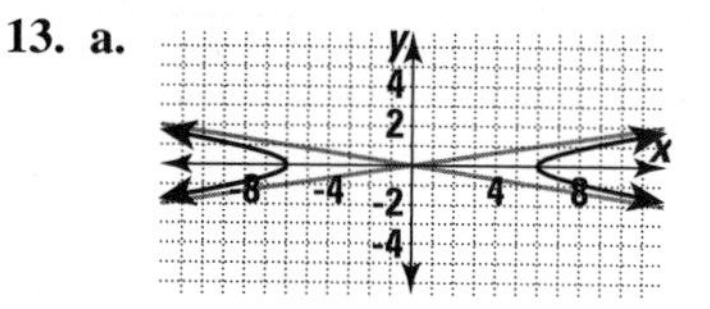

Lesson 12-5 (pp. 784-791)

15. Let $s = \sin\theta$ and $t = \cos\theta$.

$B'^2 - 4A'C' = (2(A - C)ts + B(t^2 - s^2))^2 - 4(At^2 - Bts + Cs^2)(As^2 + Bts + Ct^2) = 4(A - C)^2t^2s^2 + 4(A - C)B(t^2 - s^2)ts + B^2(t^2 - s^2)^2 - 4(A^2s^2t^2 - B^2s^2t^2 + C^2s^2t^2 + AB(st^3 - s^3t) + AC(s^4 + t^4) + BC(s^3t - st^3)) = 4A^2t^2s^2 - 8ACt^2s^2 + 4AB(t^3s - ts^3) - 4BC(t^3s - ts^3) + B^2t^4 - 2B^2t^2s^2 + B^2s^4 - 4A^2s^2t^2 + 4B^2s^2t^2 - 4C^2s^2t^2 - 4AB(st^3 - s^3t) - 4AC(s^4 + t^4) - 4BC(s^3t - st^3) = B^2(t^2 + s^2)^2 - 4AC(t^2 + s^2)^2 = B^2(t^4 + 2t^2s^2 + s^4) - 4AC(t^4 + 2t^2s^2 + s^4) = B^2 - 4AC$

17. $x^2 - 2\sqrt{3}xy - y^2 = 2$ **19. a.** **See below.** **b.** $\frac{x^2}{25} + \frac{y^2}{4} = 1$

21. $-\cos\theta$

23. False; if $x = 0$, then $\sin\left(\frac{\pi}{2} - x\right) = \sin\left(\frac{\pi}{2}\right) = 1$, but $\sin\left(x - \frac{\pi}{2}\right) = \sin\left(0 - \frac{\pi}{2}\right) = \sin\left(-\frac{\pi}{2}\right) = -1$.

19. a.

Lesson 12-6 (pp. 792-796)

11. hyperbola **13. a.** $y^2 - x^2 = -12$ **b.** True **15. a.** **See below.** **b.** $(-\sqrt{33}, 0), (\sqrt{33}, 0)$ **c.** 10 **17.** 32,000 miles

15. a.

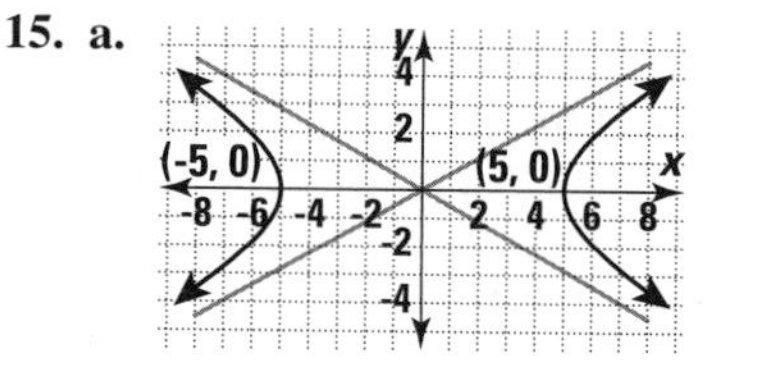

Chapter 12 Progress Self-Test (p. 801)

1. a. By taking the intersection of the cone with a plane while the angle formed by the cone's axis and the plane is greater than the angle between the axis and the rotating line. **b.** **See p. 905.** **2.** The graph is an ellipse, the image of the unit circle under the stretch $(x, y) \rightarrow (5x, 9y)$. So the endpoints of its axes are (5, 0), (-5, 0), (0, 9), and (0, -9). **See p. 905.** **3.** Dividing each side of the equation by 9 converts the equation into standard form $\frac{x^2}{9} - y^2 = 1$ The graph is a hyperbola with vertices (3, 0) and (-3, 0) and asymptotes $y = \pm\frac{1}{3}x$. **See p. 905.** **4.** The graph is the translation image of the ellipse $\frac{x^2}{36} + \frac{y^2}{20}$ under the translation $(x, y) \rightarrow (x + 2, y - 1)$. The endpoints of the axes of the parent ellipse are (6, 0), (-6, 0), $(0, \sqrt{20}$, and $(0, -\sqrt{20})$. So the endpoints of the axes of this ellipse are (8, -1), (-4, -1), $(2, \sqrt{20} - 1)$, and $(2, -\sqrt{20} - 1)$. **See p. 905.** **5.** The hyperbola with foci $(c, 0)$ and $(-c, 0)$ and focal constant $2a$ has equation $\frac{x^2}{a^2} - \frac{y^2}{b^2} = 1$, where $b^2 = c^2 - a^2$. Here $c = 7$ and $2a = 10$ $\Rightarrow a = 5$. Thus $b^2 = 7^2 - 5^2 = 24$, so an equation for the hyperbola is $\frac{x^2}{25} - \frac{y^2}{24} = 1$. **6.** The ellipse should have the shape of the ellipse below, where the distance between the foci is 8 cm and the minor axis is 6 cm. **See p. 905.** **7. a.** A hyperbola of the form $\frac{x^2}{a^2} - \frac{y^2}{b^2} = 1$ has asymptotes with equations $y = \frac{b}{a}x$ and $y = \frac{-b}{a}x$. Thus the hyperbola $\frac{x^2}{81} - \frac{y^2}{100} = 1$ has asymptotes $y = \frac{10}{9}x$ and $y = \frac{-10}{9}x$. **b.** The symmetry lines of a hyperbola are the axes of the hyperbola. One axis is the line through the foci, $x = 0$. The other is the perpendicular bisector of the segment joining the foci, $y = 0$. **8.** By the Graph Rotation Theorem, find the image of $y = x^2 - 3x - 4$ under $R_{\pi/3}$ by replacing x with $x\cos\frac{\pi}{3} + y\sin\frac{\pi}{3} = \frac{1}{2}x + \frac{\sqrt{3}}{2}y$ and y with $-x\sin\frac{\pi}{3} + y\cos\frac{\pi}{3} = \frac{-\sqrt{3}}{2}x + \frac{1}{2}y$. This gives $\frac{-\sqrt{3}}{2}x + \frac{1}{2}y = \left(\frac{1}{2}x + \frac{\sqrt{3}}{2}y\right)^2 - 3\left(\frac{1}{2}x + \frac{\sqrt{3}}{2}y\right) - 4 = \frac{1}{4}x^2 + \frac{\sqrt{3}}{2}xy + \frac{3}{4}y^2 - \frac{3}{2}x - \frac{3\sqrt{3}}{2}y - 4$. Simplifying, $\frac{1}{4}x^2 + \frac{\sqrt{3}}{2}xy + \frac{3}{4}y^2 + \frac{-3 + \sqrt{3}}{2}x + \frac{-1 - 3\sqrt{3}}{2}y - 4 = 0$. **9.** No; the asymptotes $y = \frac{\sqrt{30}}{2}x$ and $y = -\frac{\sqrt{30}}{2}x$ are not perpendicular, thus the hyperbola is not rectangular. **10.** $64x^2 - 9y^2 - 576 = 0$ $A = 64, B = 0, C = -9, D = 0, E = 0, F = -576$ **11.** $B^2 - 4AC = (-6)^2 - 4 \cdot 2 \cdot 18 = 36 - 144 < 0$, so the graph of this equation is either an ellipse, a single point, or the null set. Substituting 0 for x we get $18y^2 + 6y - 110 = 0$. Solving using the quadtratic formula gives $y = \frac{-1 \pm \sqrt{21}}{6}$. Since the points $\left(0, \frac{-1 + \sqrt{21}}{6}\right)$ and $\left(0, \frac{-1 - \sqrt{21}}{6}\right)$ are on the graph it cannot be a single point or the null set. Thus, the graph is an ellipse. **12.** $B^2 - 4AC = (-2)2 - 4 \cdot 9 \cdot 1 = 4 - 36 < 0$, so the graph of this equation is either an ellipse, a single point, or the null set. Substitute a value, call it a, for x to get the quadratic equation $y^2 - 2ay + (9a^2 - 4a + 22) = 0$. This equation has solution $\frac{2a \pm \sqrt{4a^2 - 4(9a^2 - 4a + 22)}}{2} = a \pm\sqrt{a^2 - 9a^2 + 4a - 22} = a \pm\sqrt{-8a^2 + 4a - 22}$. The value under the radical sign is always negative (this can be seen by graphing the parabola $y = -8x^2 + 4x - 22$), thus $9x^2 - 2xy + y^2 - 4x + 22 = 0$ is not defined for any value of x so its graph must be the null set.

13. The situation is illustrated at the right. The center of the orbit is the origin and the sun is at $(c, 0)$ where the unit is one million miles. The maximum and minimum distances from the sun will be achieved when Jupiter intersects the x-axis. From the given information $a - c = 460$ and $c - (-a) = 508$. Adding these equations gives $2a = 968$, so $a = 484$. Thus $c = 24$. So the second focus is $(-24, 0)$ and is 48 million miles from the sun. **See right.**

1. b.

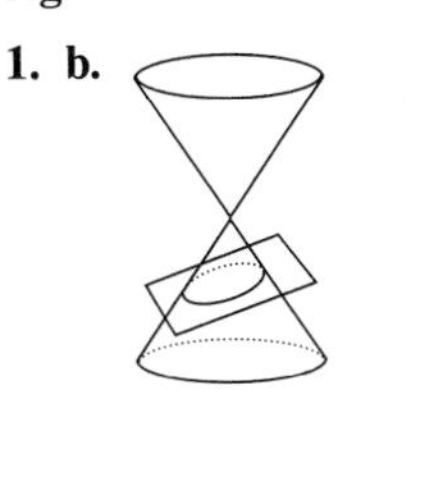

2.

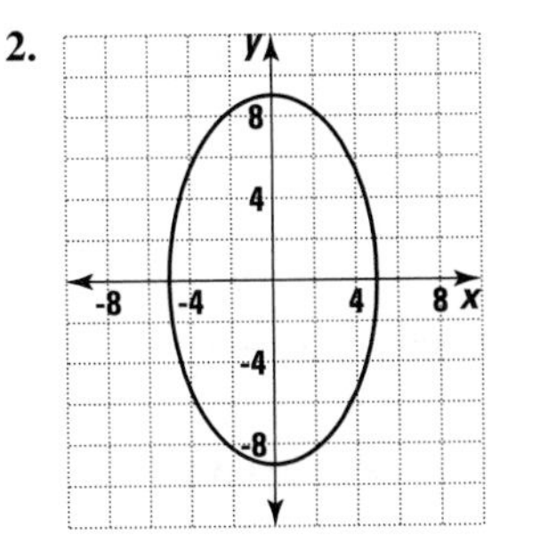

3. **4.** **6.** **13.**

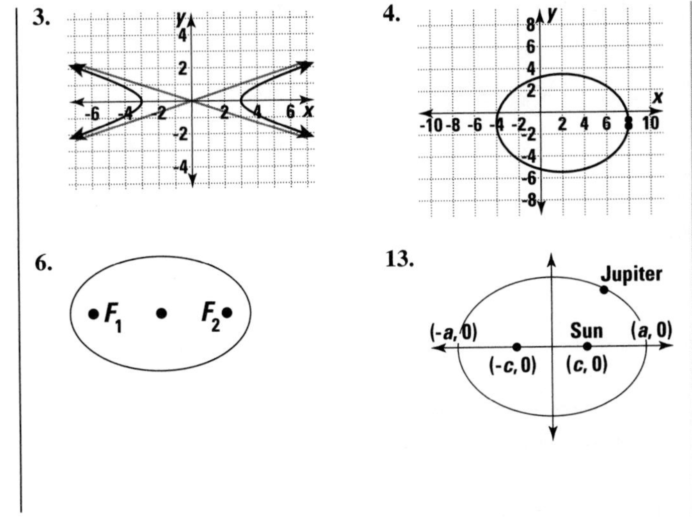

The chart below keys the **Progress Self-Test** questions to the objectives in the **Chapter Review** on pages 802-803 or to the **Vocabulary** (Voc.) on page 800. This will enable you to locate those **Chapter Review** questions that correspond to questions students missed on the **Progress Self-Test**. The lesson where the material is covered is also indicated on the chart.

Question	**1**	**2**	**3**	**4**	**5**	**6**	**7**	**8**	**9**	**10**
Objective	E	G	G	H	A	D	D	B	D	C
Lesson	12-1	12-2	12-3	12-2	12-3	12-1	12-3	12-4	12-4	12-5

Question	**11**	**12**	**13**
Objective	I	I	F
Lesson	12-5	12-5	12-2

Chapter 12 Review (pp. 802–803)

1. $\frac{x^2}{64} + \frac{y^2}{289} = 1$ **3.** $\frac{x^2}{81} + \frac{4y^2}{49} = 1$ **5.** Sample: $5x^2 + 6xy + 5y^2 = 72$ **7.** Sample: $3x^2 + 2\sqrt{3}\,xy + y^2 + 2x - 2\sqrt{3}\,y - 32 = 0$ **9.** Sample: $y^2 - x^2 = 240$ **11.** $49x^2 + 25y^2 - 1225 = 0$ $A = 49$, $B = 0$, $C = 25$, $D = 0$, $E = 0$, $F = -1225$ **13.** $7xy - 8 = 0$ $A = 0$, $B = 7$, $C = 0$, $D = 0$, $E = 0$, $F = -8$ **15.** The ellipse should have the shape of the ellipse below with 6 cm between the foci and a minor axis of $2\sqrt{7} \approx 5.3$ cm. **See right.** **17.** 2 **19.** No, because the asymptotes $y = \sqrt{2}x$ and $y = -\sqrt{2}x$ are not perpendicular. **21.** The cone is formed by rotating one of two intersecting, non-perpendicular lines about the other. **23. See right.** **25.** 15,120,000 miles **27.** The endpoints of the axes of the ellipse are (1, 0), (-1, 0), (0, 4), and (0, -4). **See right.** **29.** The vertices of the hyperbola are $\left(0, \pm\sqrt{40}\right)$ and its asymptotes have equations $y = \pm\frac{\sqrt{40}}{3}x$. **See p. 906.** **31.** The hyperbola has vertices $(0, \pm 1)$ and the equations of its asymptotes are $y = \pm x$. **See p. 906.** **33.** $\frac{x^2}{64} + \frac{y^2}{16} = 1$ **35.** The ellipse has center (4, -2) and the endpoints of its axes are (-1, -2), (9, -2), (4, 0), and (4, -4). **See p. 906.** **37.** The hyperbola has vertices $\left(\sqrt{20}, \sqrt{20}\right)$ and $\left(-\sqrt{20}, -\sqrt{20}\right)$. Its asymptotes are the x-axis and the y-axis. **See p. 906.** **39.** the null set **41.** parabola

15. **23.** **27.**

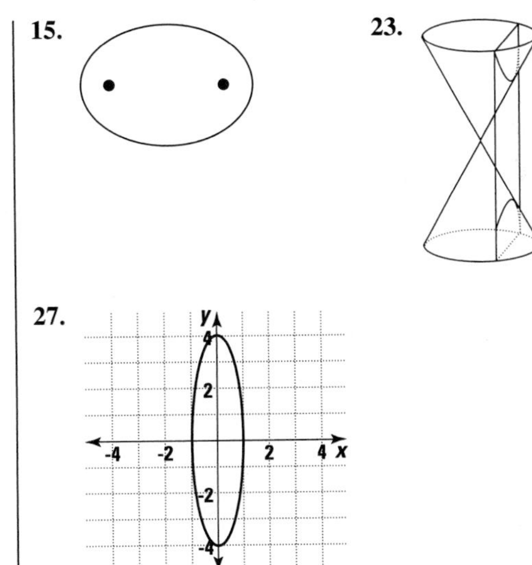

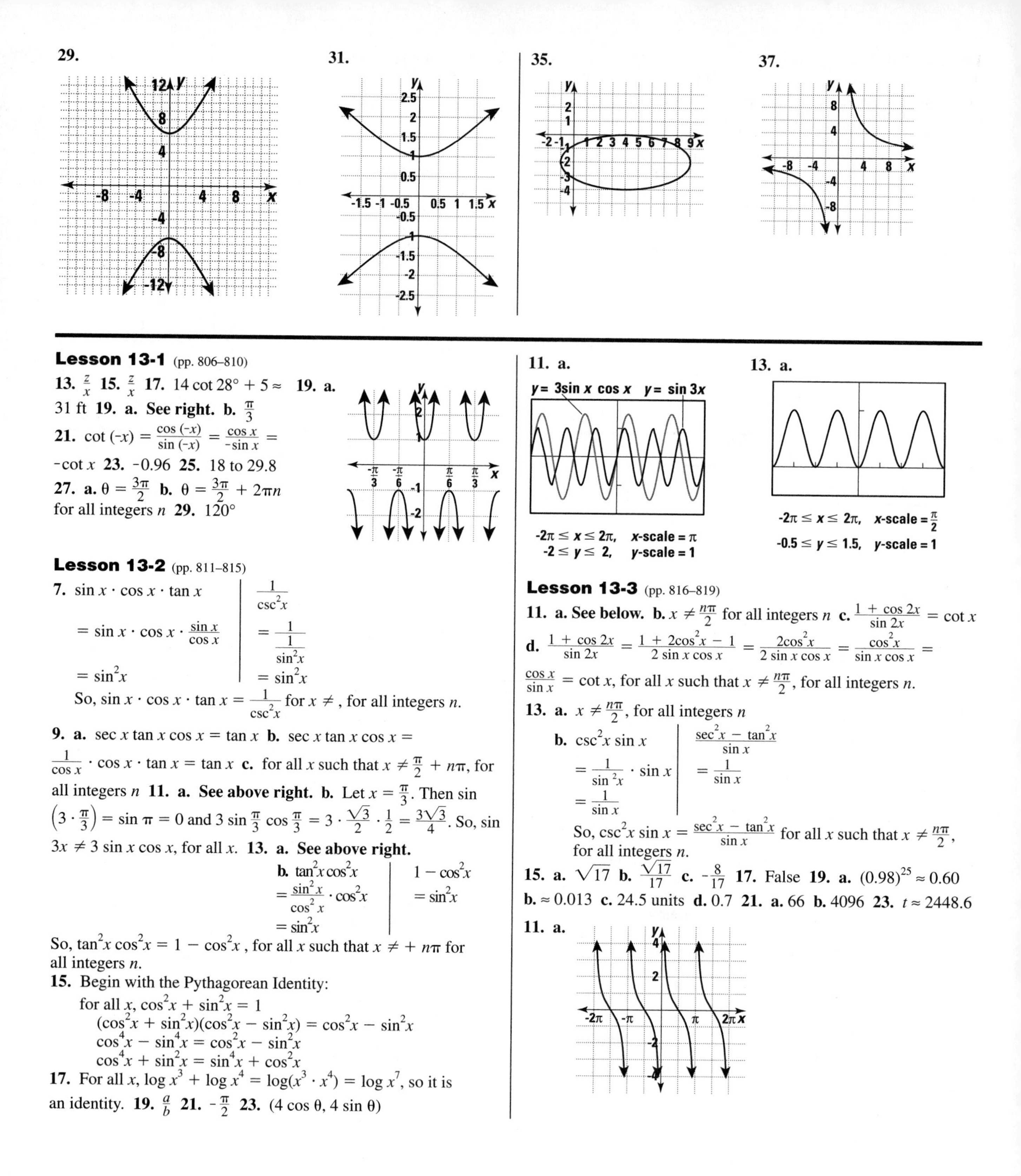

29.

31.

35.

37.

Lesson 13-1 (pp. 806–810)

13. $\frac{z}{x}$ **15.** $\frac{z}{x}$ **17.** $14 \cot 28° + 5 \approx 31$ ft **19. a.** **See right. b.** $\frac{\pi}{3}$
21. $\cot(-x) = \frac{\cos(-x)}{\sin(-x)} = \frac{\cos x}{-\sin x} = -\cot x$ **23.** -0.96 **25.** 18 to 29.8
27. a. $\theta = \frac{3\pi}{2}$ **b.** $\theta = \frac{3\pi}{2} + 2\pi n$ for all integers n **29.** $120°$

19. a.

Lesson 13-2 (pp. 811–815)

7.

$\sin x \cdot \cos x \cdot \tan x$	$\frac{1}{\csc^2 x}$
$= \sin x \cdot \cos x \cdot \frac{\sin x}{\cos x}$	$= \frac{1}{\frac{1}{\sin^2 x}}$
$= \sin^2 x$	$= \sin^2 x$

So, $\sin x \cdot \cos x \cdot \tan x = \frac{1}{\csc^2 x}$ for $x \neq$, for all integers n.

9. a. $\sec x \tan x \cos x = \tan x$ **b.** $\sec x \tan x \cos x = \frac{1}{\cos x} \cdot \cos x \cdot \tan x = \tan x$ **c.** for all x such that $x \neq \frac{\pi}{2} + n\pi$, for all integers n **11. a. See above right. b.** Let $x = \frac{\pi}{3}$. Then $\sin\left(3 \cdot \frac{\pi}{3}\right) = \sin \pi = 0$ and $3 \sin \frac{\pi}{3} \cos \frac{\pi}{3} = 3 \cdot \frac{\sqrt{3}}{2} \cdot \frac{1}{2} = \frac{3\sqrt{3}}{4}$. So, $\sin 3x \neq 3 \sin x \cos x$, for all x. **13. a. See above right.**

b.

$\tan^2 x \cos^2 x$	$1 - \cos^2 x$
$= \frac{\sin^2 x}{\cos^2 x} \cdot \cos^2 x$	$= \sin^2 x$
$= \sin^2 x$	

So, $\tan^2 x \cos^2 x = 1 - \cos^2 x$, for all x such that $x \neq + n\pi$ for all integers n.

15. Begin with the Pythagorean Identity:
for all x, $\cos^2 x + \sin^2 x = 1$
$(\cos^2 x + \sin^2 x)(\cos^2 x - \sin^2 x) = \cos^2 x - \sin^2 x$
$\cos^4 x - \sin^4 x = \cos^2 x - \sin^2 x$
$\cos^4 x + \sin^2 x = \sin^4 x + \cos^2 x$

17. For all x, $\log x^3 + \log x^4 = \log(x^3 \cdot x^4) = \log x^7$, so it is an identity. **19.** $\frac{a}{b}$ **21.** $-\frac{\pi}{2}$ **23.** $(4 \cos \theta, 4 \sin \theta)$

11. a.

$y = 3\sin x \cos x$ $y = \sin 3x$

$-2\pi \le x \le 2\pi$, x-scale = π
$-2 \le y \le 2$, y-scale = 1

13. a.

$-2\pi \le x \le 2\pi$, x-scale = $\frac{\pi}{2}$
$-0.5 \le y \le 1.5$, y-scale = 1

Lesson 13-3 (pp. 816–819)

11. a. See below. b. $x \neq \frac{n\pi}{2}$ for all integers n **c.** $\frac{1 + \cos 2x}{\sin 2x} = \cot x$
d. $\frac{1 + \cos 2x}{\sin 2x} = \frac{1 + 2\cos^2 x - 1}{2 \sin x \cos x} = \frac{2\cos^2 x}{2 \sin x \cos x} = \frac{\cos^2 x}{\sin x \cos x} = \frac{\cos x}{\sin x} = \cot x$, for all x such that $x \neq \frac{n\pi}{2}$, for all integers n.

13. a. $x \neq \frac{n\pi}{2}$, for all integers n

b.

$\csc^2 x \sin x$	$\frac{\sec^2 x - \tan^2 x}{\sin x}$
$= \frac{1}{\sin^2 x} \cdot \sin x$	$= \frac{1}{\sin x}$
$= \frac{1}{\sin x}$	

So, $\csc^2 x \sin x = \frac{\sec^2 x - \tan^2 x}{\sin x}$ for all x such that $x \neq \frac{n\pi}{2}$, for all integers n.

15. a. $\sqrt{17}$ **b.** $\frac{\sqrt{17}}{17}$ **c.** $-\frac{8}{17}$ **17.** False **19. a.** $(0.98)^{25} \approx 0.60$ **b.** ≈ 0.013 **c.** 24.5 units **d.** 0.7 **21. a.** 66 **b.** 4096 **23.** $t \approx 2448.6$

11. a.

Lesson 13-4 (pp. 820–826)
15. a circle with radius 8 and center at the pole **17.** Samples: $\left[6, -\frac{\pi}{3}\right], \left[-6, \frac{2\pi}{3}\right]$ **19. a.** south **b.** 10° W of N **c.** 40° E of S **d.** 20° W of S **21.** $\sin\left(\frac{\pi}{2} + x\right) = \sin\frac{\pi}{2}\cos x + \cos\frac{\pi}{2}\sin x = 1 \cdot \cos x + 0 \cdot \sin x = \cos x$ for all x **23. a.** 1 **b.** 25 **25.** center: (-1, -4), radius: 5 **27. a. b. See below.**

27. a, b.

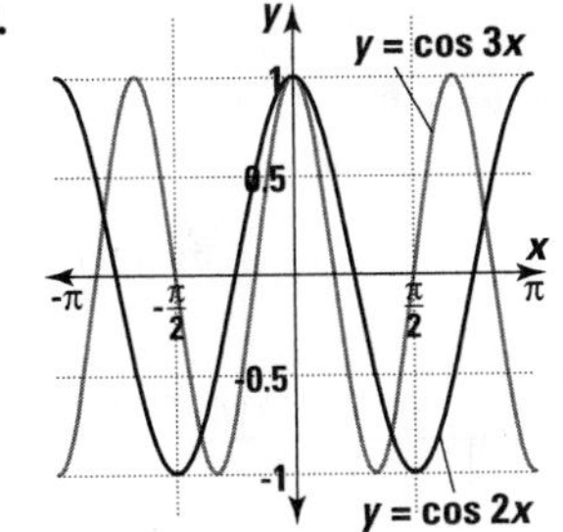

Lesson 13-5 (pp. 827–832)
9. See below. 11. See below. 13. a. $[1, 0], \left[1.72, \frac{\pi}{4}\right], \left[2.97, \frac{\pi}{2}\right], \left[5.12, \frac{3\pi}{4}\right], [8.82, \pi], \left[15.21, \frac{5\pi}{4}\right], \left[26.22, \frac{3\pi}{2}\right], \left[45.19, \frac{7\pi}{4}\right]$ **b. See below. 15.** a, b, and c **17. a.** Not an identity. **See below. b.** When $x = 30°$, $\tan 2x = \tan 60° = \sqrt{3}$ and $2\tan x = 2\tan 30° = 2 \cdot \frac{1}{\sqrt{3}} = \frac{2\sqrt{3}}{3}$. So $\tan 2x = 2\tan x$ is not an identity. **19.** $9, -\frac{9}{2} + \frac{9\sqrt{3}}{2}i, -\frac{9}{2} - \frac{9\sqrt{3}}{2}i$

9.

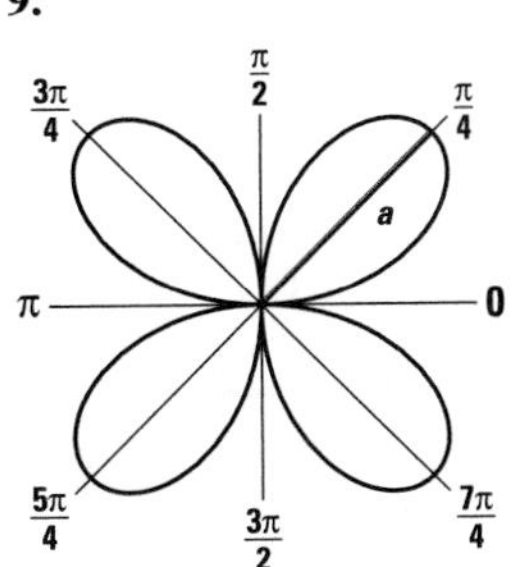

11.

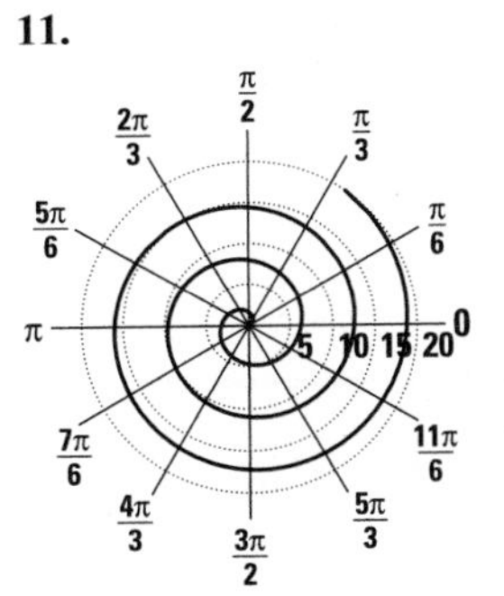

13. b.

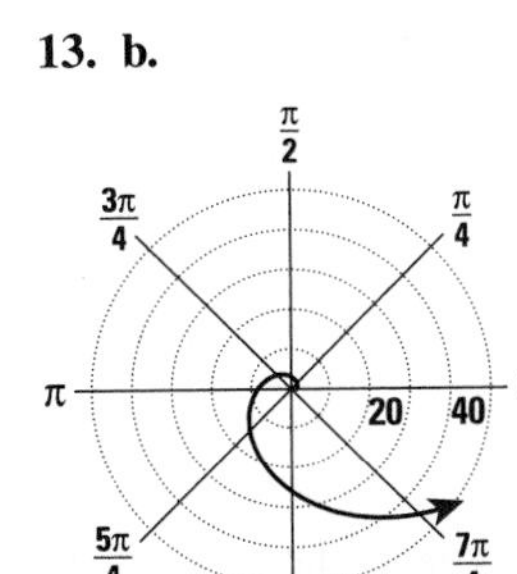

17. a.

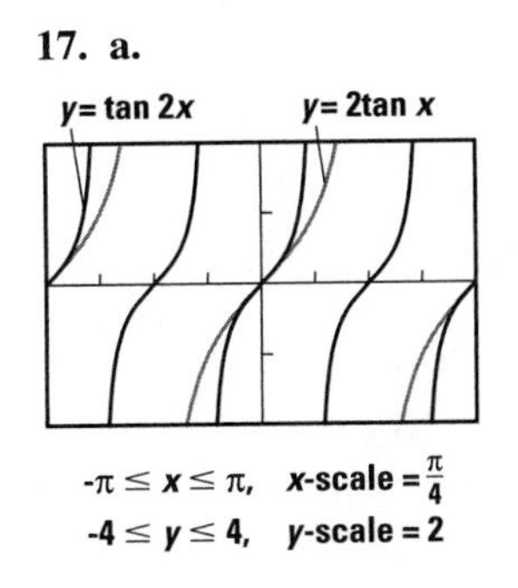

Lesson 13-6 (pp. 833–837)
13. a. Let $A = z - w$, $B = z + w$, $C = w - z$, and $D = -(z + w)$. Then, the slope of $AB = \frac{2 - 10}{10 - 6} = -2$; the slope of $BC = \frac{-10 - 2}{-6 - 10} = \frac{3}{4}$; the slope of $CD = \frac{-2 - -10}{-10 - -6} = -2$; the slope of $DA = \frac{-10 - -2}{-6 - -10} = \frac{3}{4}$. Because the slopes of the opposite sides of $ABCD$ are equal, the opposite sides are parallel, and the quadrilateral is a parallelogram. **b.** 8 **15.** Yes, the distance from $u = a + bi$ to $v = c + di$ in the complex plane is $|u - v|$. Proof: $u - v = (a - c) + (b - d)i$, and $|u - v| = \sqrt{(a - c)^2 + (b - d)^2}$, which is the distance between the points (a, b) and (c, d). **17. See below. 19. See below. 21.** $x^2 + (y - 1)^2 = 1$ **23.** $(11\cos\theta - 6\sin\theta, 11\sin\theta + 6\cos\theta)$ **25. a.** $-1 - 5i$ **b.** $-5i$ **c.** -1 **27.** about 36 miles

17. **19.**

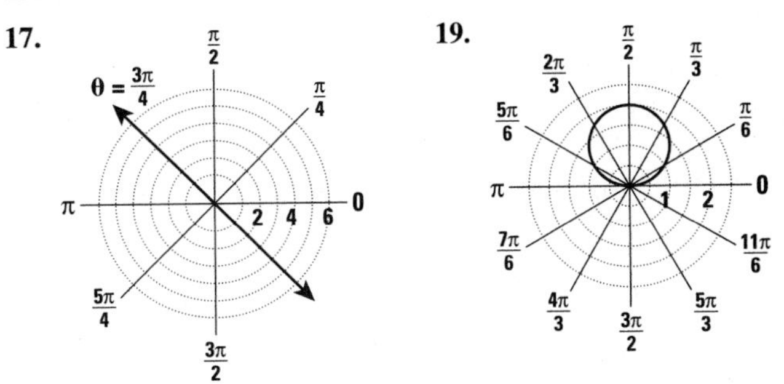

Lesson 13-7 (pp. 839–845)
17. $\frac{z_1}{z_2} = \frac{r_1(\cos\theta_1 + i\sin\theta_1)}{r_2(\cos\theta_2 + i\sin\theta_2)} = \frac{r_1(\cos\theta_1 + i\sin\theta_1)(\cos\theta_2 - i\sin\theta_2)}{r_2(\cos\theta_2 + i\sin\theta_2)(\cos\theta_2 - i\sin\theta_2)}$
$= \frac{r_1}{r_2}\frac{(\cos\theta_1 + i\sin\theta_1)(\cos(-\theta_2) + i\sin(-\theta_2))}{(\cos^2\theta_2 + \sin^2\theta_2)}$
$= \frac{r_1}{r_2}\frac{(\cos\theta_1\cos(-\theta_2) - \sin\theta_1\sin(-\theta_2) + i\cos\theta_1\sin(-\theta_2) + i\sin\theta_1\cos(-\theta_2))}{1}$
$= \frac{r_1}{r_2}(\cos(\theta_1 - \theta_2) + i\sin(\theta_1 - \theta_2))$
19. a. $z^2 = 4(\cos 30° + i\sin 30°)$, $z^3 = 8(\cos 45° + i\sin 45°)$, $z^4 = 16(\cos 60° + i\sin 60°)$, $z^5 = 32(\cos 75° + i\sin 75°)$ **b.** $z^n = 2^n(\cos(n \cdot 15°) + i\sin(n \cdot 15°))$. $z^{10} = 2^{10}(\cos 150° + i\sin 150°)$ **21. a. See below. b. See below. 23. a.** $\begin{bmatrix} 0 & 4 & 5 \\ 3 & -3 & 0 \end{bmatrix}$ **b.** $R_{90} = \begin{bmatrix} 0 & -1 \\ 1 & 0 \end{bmatrix}$ and $S_2 = \begin{bmatrix} 2 & 0 \\ 0 & 2 \end{bmatrix}$ So, $(S_2 \circ R_{90})(\triangle ABC) = \begin{bmatrix} 2 & 0 \\ 0 & 2 \end{bmatrix} \cdot \begin{bmatrix} 0 & -1 \\ 1 & 0 \end{bmatrix}\begin{bmatrix} 0 & 4 & 5 \\ 3 & -3 & 0 \end{bmatrix} = \begin{bmatrix} -6 & 6 & 0 \\ 0 & 8 & 10 \end{bmatrix}$, which is the matrix for $\triangle A'B'C'$. **25.** $a^5 - 5a^4b + 10a^3b^2 - 10a^2b^3 + 5ab^4 - b^5$ **27.** about 5019.8 mm^3

21. a. **b.**

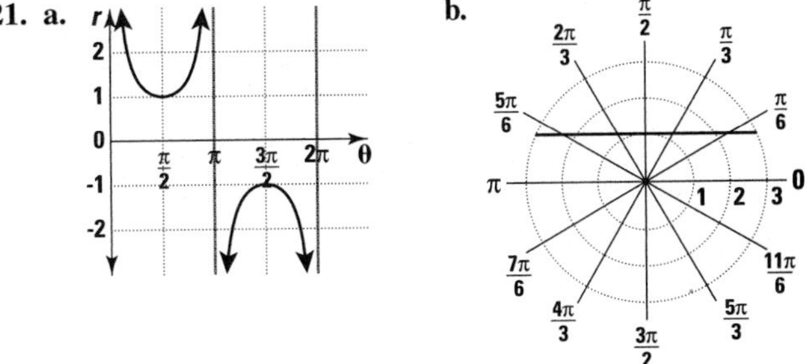

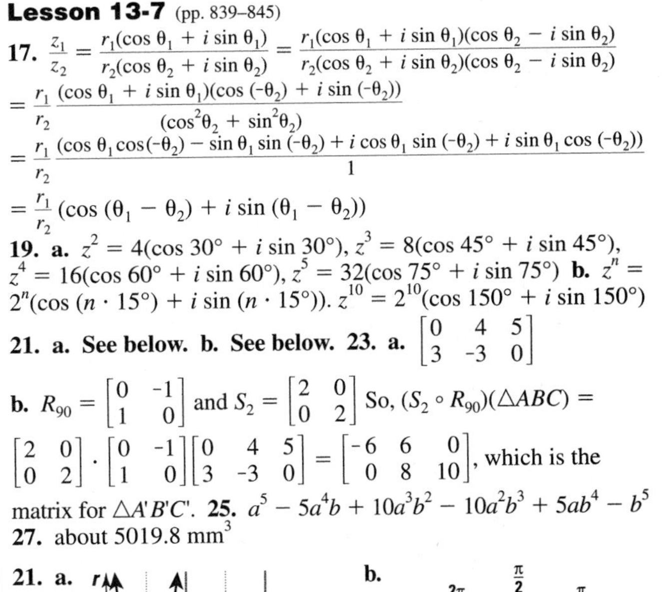

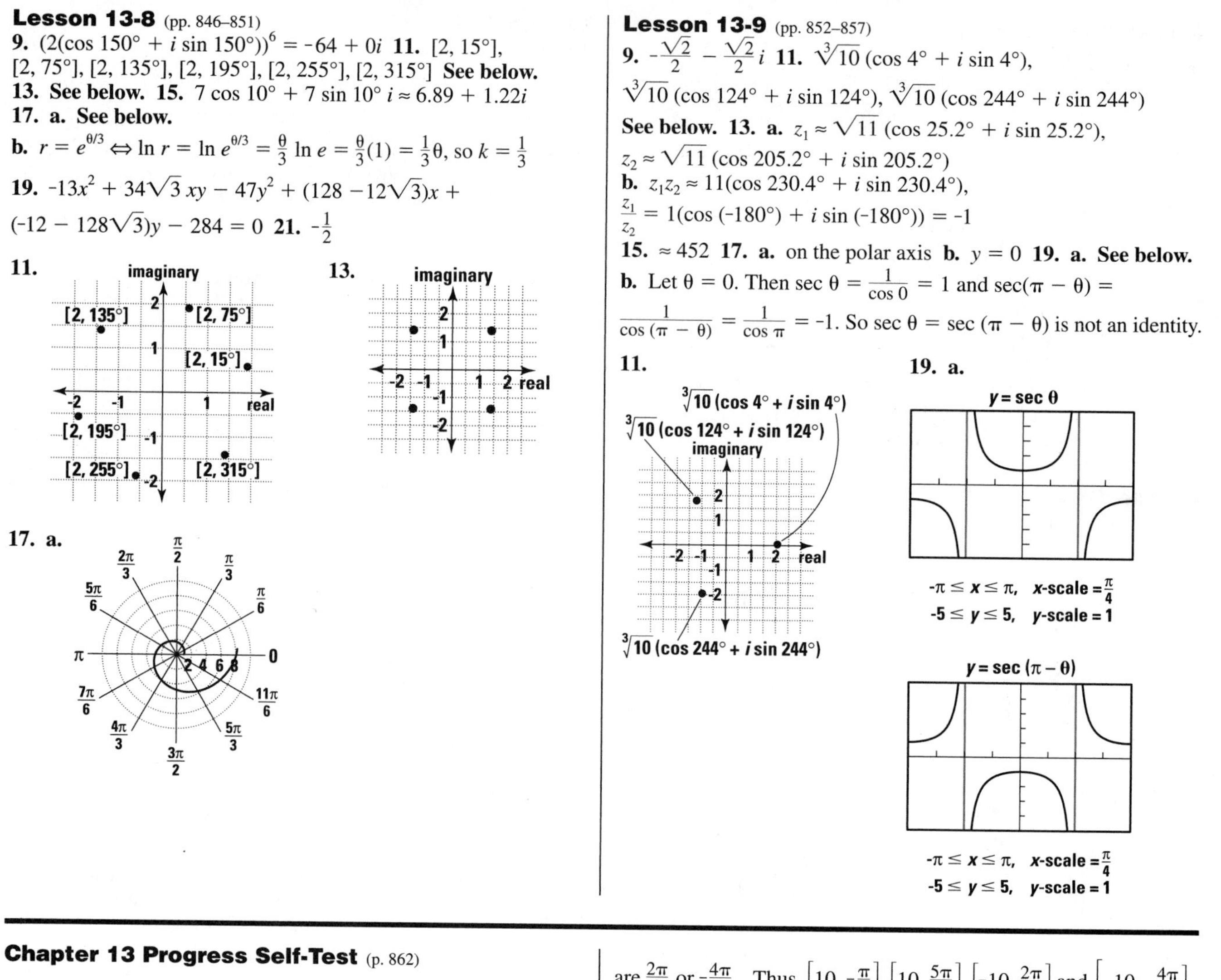

Lesson 13-8 (pp. 846–851)
9. $(2(\cos 150° + i \sin 150°))^6 = -64 + 0i$ **11.** [2, 15°], [2, 75°], [2, 135°], [2, 195°], [2, 255°], [2, 315°] **See below.**
13. See below. **15.** $7 \cos 10° + 7 \sin 10°\, i \approx 6.89 + 1.22i$
17. a. See below.
b. $r = e^{\theta/3} \Leftrightarrow \ln r = \ln e^{\theta/3} = \frac{\theta}{3} \ln e = \frac{\theta}{3}(1) = \frac{1}{3}\theta$, so $k = \frac{1}{3}$
19. $-13x^2 + 34\sqrt{3}\,xy - 47y^2 + (128 - 12\sqrt{3})x + (-12 - 128\sqrt{3})y - 284 = 0$ **21.** $-\frac{1}{2}$

Lesson 13-9 (pp. 852–857)
9. $-\frac{\sqrt{2}}{2} - \frac{\sqrt{2}}{2}i$ **11.** $\sqrt[3]{10}(\cos 4° + i \sin 4°)$, $\sqrt[3]{10}(\cos 124° + i \sin 124°)$, $\sqrt[3]{10}(\cos 244° + i \sin 244°)$
See below. **13. a.** $z_1 \approx \sqrt{11}(\cos 25.2° + i \sin 25.2°)$, $z_2 \approx \sqrt{11}(\cos 205.2° + i \sin 205.2°)$
b. $z_1 z_2 \approx 11(\cos 230.4° + i \sin 230.4°)$, $\frac{z_1}{z_2} = 1(\cos(-180°) + i \sin(-180°)) = -1$
15. ≈ 452 **17. a.** on the polar axis **b.** $y = 0$ **19. a. See below.**
b. Let $\theta = 0$. Then $\sec \theta = \frac{1}{\cos 0} = 1$ and $\sec(\pi - \theta) = \frac{1}{\cos(\pi - \theta)} = \frac{1}{\cos \pi} = -1$. So $\sec \theta = \sec(\pi - \theta)$ is not an identity.

Chapter 13 Progress Self-Test (p. 862)

1. $\cot\left(-\frac{\pi}{6}\right) = \frac{\cos\left(-\frac{\pi}{6}\right)}{\sin\left(-\frac{\pi}{6}\right)} = \frac{\frac{\sqrt{3}}{2}}{-\frac{1}{2}} = -\sqrt{3}$ **2.** $\sec 405° = \frac{1}{\cos 405°} = \frac{1}{\cos(405° - 360°)} = \frac{1}{\cos 45°} = \frac{1}{\frac{\sqrt{2}}{2}} = \frac{2}{\sqrt{2}} = \sqrt{2}$ **3. a.** **See p. 909.**
b. 2π **c.** Sample: $x = -\frac{\pi}{2}, x = \frac{\pi}{2}$ **4.** $x \neq \frac{\pi}{2} + n\pi$ for all integers n, as signaled by each vertical asymptote. **5.** False, a graph can only show the functions on a finite domain; a proof must show that the equation is an identity for all values for which the functions are defined. **6. a.** Singularities occur where $\tan x$ is not defined, that is, at $\frac{\pi}{2} + n\pi$, for all integers n.
b. $2\cos^2 x \tan x = 2\cos^2 x \cdot \frac{\sin x}{\cos x} = 2 \cos x \sin x = \sin 2x$
7. See p. 909. **8. See p. 909.** **9. See p. 909.**
10. $r^2 = x^2 + y^2 = 5^2 + (-5\sqrt{3})^2 = 25 + 75 = 100 \Rightarrow r = \pm 10$. $\tan \theta = \frac{y}{x} = \frac{-5\sqrt{3}}{5} = -\sqrt{3} \Rightarrow \theta = -\frac{\pi}{3} \pm n\pi$. The choice of values of θ and r depend on matching the angle to the quadrant. If we choose $r = 10$ then to match $(5, -5\sqrt{3})$ in the fourth quadrant $\theta = -\frac{\pi}{3}$ or $\theta = \frac{5\pi}{3}$. If we choose $r = -10$, possible choices for θ are $\frac{2\pi}{3}$ or $-\frac{4\pi}{3}$. Thus, $\left[10, -\frac{\pi}{3}\right]$, $\left[10, \frac{5\pi}{3}\right]$, $\left[-10, \frac{2\pi}{3}\right]$ and $\left[-10, -\frac{4\pi}{3}\right]$ are polar coordinate representations of $(5, -5\sqrt{3})$.
11. By DeMoivre's Theorem, $(3(\cos 20° + i \sin 20°))^4 = 3^4(\cos 4 \cdot 20° + i \sin 4 \cdot 20°) = 81(\cos 80° + i \sin 80°) = 81 \cos 80° + 81\, i \sin 80° \approx 14.07 + 79.77i$.
12. a. $r^2 = a^2 + b^2 = \left(-\frac{1}{2}\right)^2 + \left(\frac{\sqrt{3}}{2}\right)^2 = \frac{1}{4} + \frac{3}{4} = 1 \Rightarrow r = \pm 1$. $\tan \theta = \frac{b}{a} = \frac{\frac{\sqrt{3}}{2}}{-\frac{1}{2}} = -\sqrt{3}$. Since $\left(-\frac{1}{2}, \frac{\sqrt{3}}{2}\right)$ is in the second quadrant, we can choose $r = 1$ and $\theta = 120°$ giving the polar form [1, 120°].
b. $-\frac{1}{2} + \frac{\sqrt{3}}{2}i = r\cos\theta + i \sin\theta = \cos 120° + i \sin 120°$.
13. By the Roots of a Complex Number Theorem, the fourth roots of $81(\cos 260° + i \sin 260°) = \sqrt[4]{81}\left(\cos\left(\frac{260°}{4} + k \cdot \frac{360°}{4}\right)\right) = 3(\cos(65° + 90°k) + i \sin(65° + 90°k))$ where $k = 0, 1, 2, 3$. Thus, the fourth roots are $3(\cos 65° + i \sin 65°)$, $3(\cos 155° + i \sin 155°)$, $3(\cos 245° + i \sin 245°)$, and $3(\cos 335° + i \sin 335°)$.
14. a. Sample: When $\theta = \frac{\pi}{6}$, $r = \sin\left(3 \cdot \frac{\pi}{6}\right) = \sin\left(\frac{\pi}{2}\right) = 1$. When $\theta = -\frac{\pi}{6}$, $r = \sin\left(3 \cdot -\frac{\pi}{6}\right) = \sin\left(-\frac{\pi}{2}\right) = -1$. So two points

on the graph of $r = \sin 3\theta$ are $\left[1, \frac{\pi}{6}\right]$ and $\left[-1, -\frac{\pi}{6}\right]$. **b.** Sample: **See right. 15. a.** Converting $z = -3i$ to trigonometric form gives $z_1 = 3\left(\cos\left(-\frac{\pi}{2}\right) + i \sin\left(-\frac{\pi}{2}\right)\right)$. By the Product of Complex Numbers Theorem, $z_1 z_2 = 3 \cdot 5\left(\cos\left(-\frac{\pi}{2} + \frac{\pi}{12}\right) + i \sin\left(-\frac{\pi}{2} + \frac{\pi}{12}\right)\right)$ $= 15\left(\cos\left(-\frac{5\pi}{12}\right) + i \sin\left(-\frac{5\pi}{12}\right)\right)$. **b.** The absolute value of z_1 is multiplied by 5, which is a scale change of magnitude 5. $\frac{\pi}{12}$ is added to the argument, which is a rotation around the origin by an angle $\frac{\pi}{12}$. **16. a.** By the Division of Complex Numbers Theorem, $\frac{z_1}{z_2} = \left[\frac{6}{2}, \pi - \pi\right] = [3, 0]$. **b.** Sample: The absolute value of z_1 is divided by 2, which is a size change of magnitude $\frac{1}{2}$. Then π is subtracted from the argument, which is a rotation about the origin by an angle of $-\pi$. **17.** For all θ except where $\tan\theta$ is not defined, that is $\theta \neq \frac{\pi}{2} + n\pi$ for all integers n, $(1 - \sin^2\theta)(1 + \tan^2\theta) = (\cos^2\theta)\left(1 + \frac{\sin^2\theta}{\cos^2\theta}\right) = \cos^2\theta + \sin^2\theta = 1$.
18. See right.

3. a.

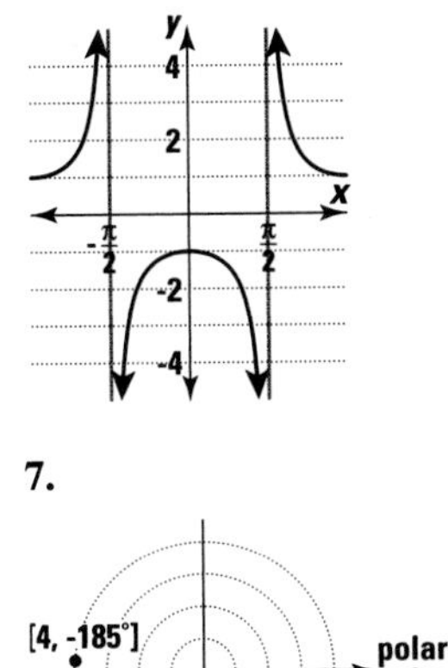

7.

[4, -185°] polar axis

8.

9.

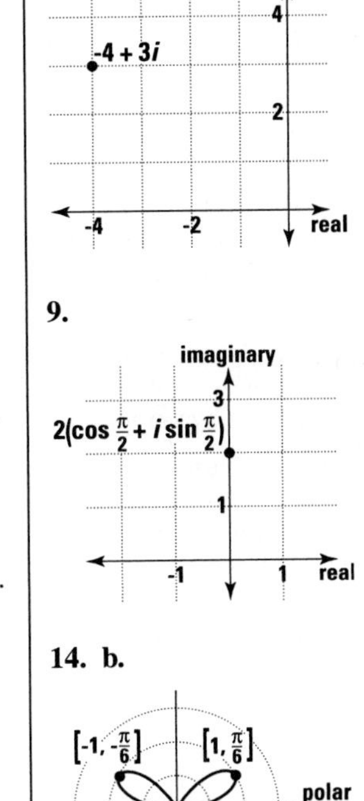

14. b.

18.

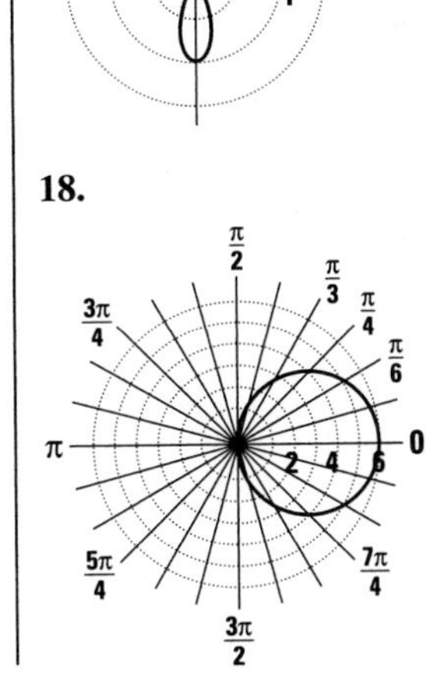

The chart below keys the **Progress Self-Test** questions to the objectives in the **Chapter Review** on pages 863-865 or to the **Vocabulary** (Voc.) on page 861. This will enable you to locate those **Chapter Review** questions that correspond to questions students missed on the **Progress Self-Test**. The lesson where the material is covered is also indicated on the chart.

Question	**1**	**2**	**3**	**4**	**5**	**6**	**7**	**8**	**9**	**10**
Objective	A	A	E	G	H	F, G	J	L	L	I
Lesson	13-1	13-1	13-1	13-3	13-2	13-2, 13-3	13-4	13-6	13-7	13-4

Question	**11**	**12**	**13**	**14**	**15**	**16**	**17**	**18**
Objective	C	D	D	K	B	B	F	K
Lesson	13-6, 13-7	13-8	13-8	13-5	13-7	13-7	13-2	13-5

Chapter 13 Review (pp. 863–865)

1. 1 **3.** $\frac{2\sqrt{3}}{3}$ **5.** -1.89 **7.** $15(\cos 189° + i \sin 189°)$

9. $2\left(\cos \frac{3\pi}{10} + i \sin \frac{3\pi}{10}\right)$ **11. a.** $2\sqrt{61} \approx 15.62$ **b.** Sample: 129.8°

13. [2, 150°] **15.** $\left[\frac{1}{8}, 36°\right]$ **17.** $4 \cos\left(\frac{2\pi}{5}\right) + 4i \sin\left(\frac{2\pi}{5}\right) \approx 1.24 + 3.80i$ **19.** $z^5 = 32(\cos 225° + i \sin 225°) = -16\sqrt{2} - 16\sqrt{2}i$

21. $4(\cos 3° + i \sin 3°)$, $4(\cos 93° + i \sin 93°)$, $4(\cos 183° + i \sin 183°)$, $4(\cos 273° + i \sin 273°)$ **23.** 2π **25.** False

27. $(1 - \cos^2 x)(1 + \cot^2 x) = (\sin^2 x)\left(1 + \frac{\cos^2 x}{\sin^2 x}\right) = \sin^2 x + \cos^2 x = 1$ for all $x \neq n\pi$ for all integers n.

29. $\sin^2 x + \cos^2 x = 1 \Rightarrow 1 - \cos^2 x = \sin^2 x \Rightarrow \frac{1}{\sin^2 x} - \frac{\cos^2 x}{\sin^2 x} = \frac{\sin^2 x}{\sin^2 x} \Rightarrow \csc^2 x - \cot^2 x = 1$ **31.** Because of division by $\sin x$, the values for which $\sin x = 0$ must be excluded. These are $x = n\pi$ for all integers n. **33. a.** i. $x = 3$ ii. none **b.** i. False, it is not true for $x = 3$. ii. True, the denominator is not zero for any real value of x. **35.** False **37. a. See below. b.** Yes, the graphs seem to coincide. **39.** (0, -4) **41.** Sample: $\approx$ [5.39, 21.8°]

43. Samples: $\left[8, \frac{5\pi}{6}\right], \left[8, -\frac{7\pi}{6}\right], \left[-8, -\frac{\pi}{6}\right]$ **45. See below. 47.** b

49. For $\theta = \frac{2\pi}{3}$, $r = 2 \cos 6\theta = 2 \cos\left(6 \cdot \frac{2\pi}{3}\right) = 2 \cos(4\pi) = 2$

51. See right. 53. a. See right. b. For $\theta \neq \frac{\pi}{2} + n\pi$, where n is an integer, $r = 4 \sec \theta = \frac{4}{\cos \theta} \Leftrightarrow r \cos \theta = 4 \Leftrightarrow x = 4$, which is a line. **55. See right. 57. a. See right.**

b. Let $C = A + B = 4 - 2i$. The slope of $OA = \frac{1 - 0}{3 - 0} = \frac{1}{3}$; the slope of $BC = \frac{-2 - -3}{4 - 1} = \frac{1}{3}$; the slope of $OB = \frac{-3 - 0}{1 - 0} = -3$; and the slope of $AC = \frac{-2 - 1}{4 - 3} = -3$. Because the slopes of both pairs of opposite sides of $OACB$ are equal, the opposite sides are parallel and $OACB$ is a parallelogram.

37. a.

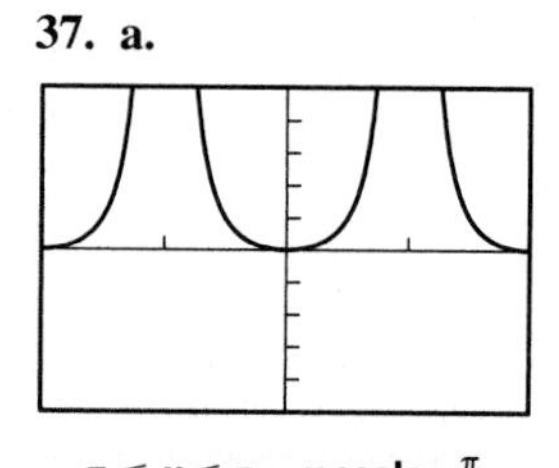

$-\pi \leq x \leq \pi$, x-scale $= \frac{\pi}{2}$
$-5 \leq y \leq 5$, y-scale = 1

45.

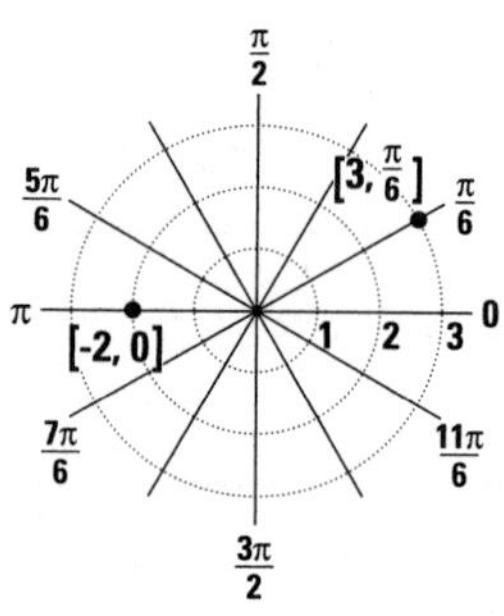

51.

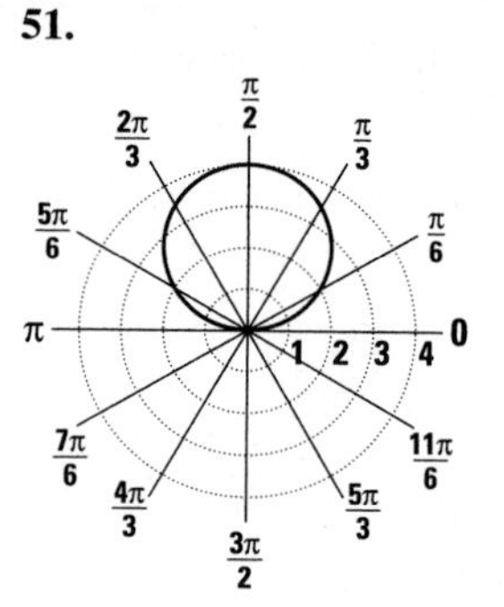

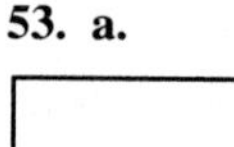
53. a.

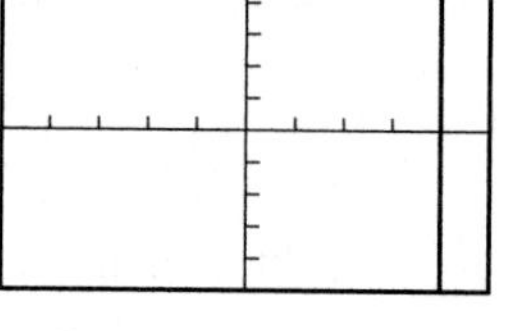

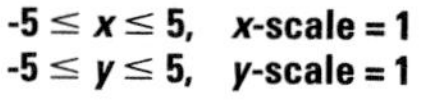
$-5 \leq x \leq 5$, x-scale = 1
$-5 \leq y \leq 5$, y-scale = 1

55.

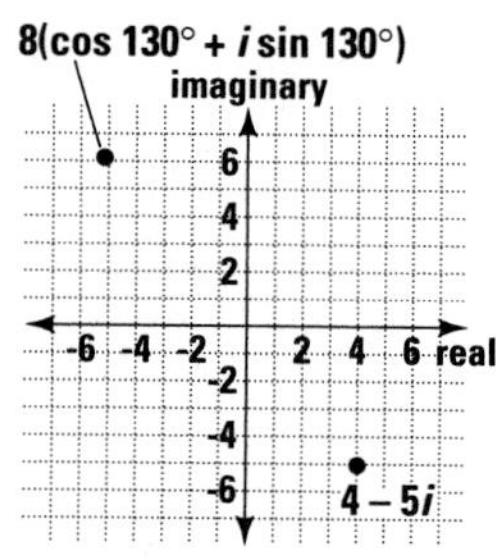

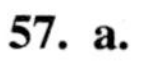
57. a.

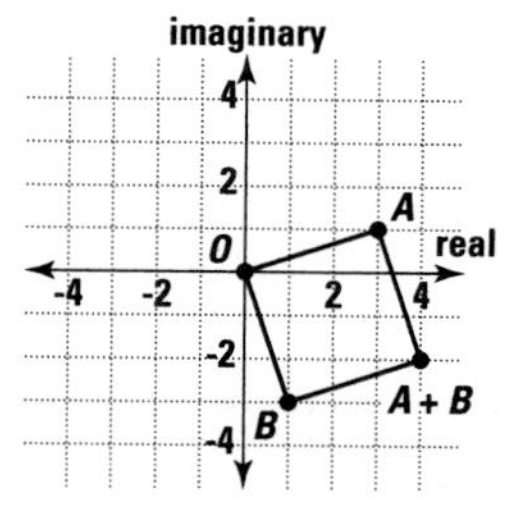

absolute value of a complex number, $|z|$ The distance of the graph of a complex number from the origin or pole. Also called *modulus*. (835)

acceleration due to gravity The acceleration of a free-falling object toward another object caused by gravitational forces; on the surface of Earth equal to approximately 32 feet or 9.8 meters per second per second. (122)

Addition Counting Principle (General Form) For any finite sets A and B, $N(A \cup B) = N(A) + N(B) - N(A \cap B)$. (435)

Addition Counting Principle (Mutually Exclusive Form) If two finite sets A and B are mutually exclusive, then $N(A \cup B) = N(A) + N(B)$. (433)

Addition Formulas for the Cosine and Sine For all real numbers α and β, $\cos(\alpha + \beta) = \cos\alpha\cos\beta - \sin\alpha\sin\beta$, and $\sin(\alpha + \beta) = \sin\alpha\cos\beta + \cos\alpha\sin\beta$. (722)

Alternate Formula for ${}_nP_r$ Theorem The number of permutations of n objects taken r at a time is ${}_nP_r = \frac{n!}{(n-r)!}$. (446)

alternating harmonic sequence The sequence $-1, \frac{1}{2}, -\frac{1}{3}, \frac{1}{4}, \ldots$ in which $c_n = \frac{(-1)^n}{n}$. (498)

alternative hypothesis, H_1 A hypothesis usually contrasted with the null hypothesis in an experiment. (643)

ambiguous case The situation in which two noncongruent triangles each satisfy a given SSA condition. (329)

amplitude One-half the difference between the maximum and minimum values of a sine wave. (272)

angle The union of two rays (its **sides**) with the same endpoint (its **vertex**). (232)

angle of depression An angle measured downward from a horizontal line. (311)

angle of elevation An angle measured upward from a horizontal line. (312)

angle of incidence The angle formed by the path of an object hitting a surface, and the ray perpendicular to the surface at the point of contact. (792)

angle of reflection The angle of the path of a ray formed by the path of an object reflecting off a surface, and the ray perpendicular to the surface at the point of contact. (792)

Arccos function See *inverse cosine function*.

Archimedean spiral The graph of $r = k\theta$, for $\theta > 0$, in the polar plane. (832)

Arcsin function See *inverse sine function*.

Arctan function See *inverse tangent function*.

area under a curve The area between the curve and the x-axis. (651)

Argand diagram A graphical representation of the complex number $a + bi$ as (a, b) in the coordinate plane. (833)

argument of a complex number For the complex number $[r, \theta]$, θ. (835)

argument of a function The variable x of a function $f(x)$. (85)

arithmetic sequence A sequence in which the difference between consecutive terms is constant. (490)

arithmetic series An indicated sum of the terms of an arithmetic sequence. (503)

ascending order Rank-ordered from lowest to highest value. (29)

astronomical unit (a.u.) A unit of distance equal to the radius of Earth's orbit, with a value of approximately 93 million miles or 150 million kilometers. (758)

asymptote A line that the graph of a function $y = f(x)$ approaches as the variable x approaches a fixed value or increases or decreases without bound. (108, 163)

asymptotes of a hyperbola Lines to which the hyperbola's branches approach as they are farther and farther from its center. (771)

at random See *randomly*.

automatic grapher A calculator or computer software that can draw and display the graph of a relation. (160)

average See *mean*.

average rate of change (between two points) The slope of the line segment joining the points. (47)

axes of a hyperbola The lines of symmetry for a hyperbola. (772)

axis of a cone The fixed line in the procedure for generating a cone. (754)

axis of symmetry In a plane, a reflecting line ℓ over which a figure can be mapped onto itself; in three-dimensional space, a line around which a figure can be rotated onto itself. Also called *line of symmetry*. (179)

back-to-back stemplot A stemplot in which the stem is written in the center of the graph, with one set of leaves to the right of the stem and another set of leaves to the left. (14)

bar graph A two-dimensional display of data in which one axis labels categories or variables and the other is a numerical scale typically with counts or percentages. (9)

base (of an exponential function) The number b in the exponential function $f(x) = ab^x$. (106)

base (of a logarithmic function) The number b in the logarithmic function $f(x) = \log_b x$. (383)

Basic Properties of Probability Theorem Let S be the sample space associated with an experiment, and let $P(E)$ be the probability of E. Then $0 \le P(E) \le 1$; if $E = S$, then $P(E) = 1$; and if $E = \varnothing$, then $P(E) = 0$. (430)

bearing An angle measured clockwise from due north. (315)

bell-shaped curve See *normal curve*.

binomial A polynomial with two terms. (558)

binomial coefficients The coefficients in the series expansion of $(x + y)^n$; the combinations ${}_nC_k$. (536)

binomial distribution function The function $B(k) = {}_nC_k\, p^k(1-p)^{n-k}$, giving the probability of getting exactly k successes in n binomial trials, each of which has a probability p of success. (629)

binomial experiment An experiment with a fixed number of independent trials, each with only two possible outcomes, often called *success* and *failure*, and each with the same probability of success. (540)

binomial probability distribution The probability distribution generated from the probability of x successes in a binomial experiment. (542)

Binomial Probability Theorem Suppose that in a binomial experiment with n trials the probability of success is p in each trial, and the probability of failure is q, where $q = 1 - p$. Then P(exactly k successes) $= {}_nC_k \cdot p^k q^{n-k}$. (541)

Binomial Theorem For any nonnegative integer n, $(x+y)^n = {}_nC_0x^n + {}_nC_1x^{n-1}y + {}_nC_2x^{n-2}y^2 + \ldots + {}_nC_kx^{n-k}y^k + \ldots + {}_nC_ny^n = \sum_{k=0}^{n} {}_nC_kx^{n-k}y^k$. (536)

birthday problem The problem of determining the probability that n people have n different birthdays. (478)

bivariate data Data involving two variables. (81)

box plot A visual representation of the five-number summary of a data set in which a box represents the part of the data from the first to the third quartile, with another line segment crossing the box at the set's median, and two segments protruding from the box (called **whiskers**) to represent the rest of the data. (31)

box-and-whiskers plot See *box plot*.

cardioid The graph of $r = a(\cos\theta - 1)$ or $r = a(\sin\theta - 1)$ in the polar plane. (832)

ceiling function See *rounding-up function*.

census A survey of an entire population; in the U.S., a survey, conducted every ten years, of the entire population of the United States. (6)

center of a hyperbola The intersection of the hyperbola's axes, the midpoint of the segment joining its foci. (772)

center of an ellipse The intersection of the ellipse's axes, the midpoint of the segment joining its foci. (762)

center of gravity of a data set The point whose coordinates are the means of the corresponding coordinates of the points in the data set. (99)

center of symmetry for a figure The center of a rotation under which the figure is mapped onto itself. (179)

central angle of a circle An angle whose vertex is the center of the circle. (239)

Central Limit Theorem Suppose random samples of size n are selected from a population with mean μ and standard deviation σ. Then, as n increases the following occur: The mean $\mu_{\bar{x}}$ of the distribution of sample means approaches μ; the standard deviation $\sigma_{\bar{x}}$ of the distribution of sample means approaches $\frac{\sigma}{\sqrt{n}}$; and the distribution of sample means approaches a normal curve with mean μ and standard deviation $\frac{\sigma}{\sqrt{n}}$. (673)

Change of Base Theorem For all values of a, b, and c for which the logarithms exist, $\log_b a = \frac{\log_c a}{\log_c b}$. (406)

circle graph A display of numerical data in which the total is represented by the entire circle and sectors of a circle represent parts of the total in proportion to their contribution to the total. Also called *pie chart.* (9)

circular functions The trigonometric functions, when defined in terms of the unit circle. (267)

circular motion Movement of a point around a circle. (288)

Circular Arc Length Formula If s is the length of the arc of a central angle of θ radians in a circle of radius r, then $s = r\theta$. (240)

Circular Sector Area Formula If A is the area of the sector formed by a central angle of θ radians in a circle of radius r, then $A = \frac{1}{2}\theta r^2$. (240)

cliometrics The discipline of applying mathematics to history. (64)

cluster In a frequency distribution of a set of data, a place where a relatively large number of data are near each other. (14)

coefficient The numbers a_n, $a_{n-1}, \ldots a_0$ of the polynomial $a_nx^n + a_{n-1}x^{n-1} + \ldots a_1x + a_0$; more generally, a constant factor of a variable term. (557)

column matrix A matrix consisting of a single column. (699)

combination A collection of objects in which the order of objects does not matter. (524)

combination of n things taken r at a time, ${}_nC_r$, $\binom{n}{r}$ A subset of r objects from a set of n objects. (525)

common logarithm A logarithm with a base equal to 10. (384)

complementary events Events that are mutually exclusive and whose union is the entire sample space. (437)

Complements Theorem For all θ in radians, $\sin\left(\frac{\pi}{2} - \theta\right) = \cos\theta$ and $\cos\left(\frac{\pi}{2} - \theta\right) = \sin\theta$. (254)

complex conjugates A pair of complex numbers in the form $a + bi$ and $a - bi$. (592)

complex number The number of the form $a + bi$, where a and b are real numbers and $i = \sqrt{-1}$. (591)

complex plane A coordinate plane for representing complex numbers. Also called *Argand diagram.* (833)

composite The function $g \circ f$ defined by $(g \circ f)(x) = g(f(x))$, whose domain is the set of values of x in the domain of f for which $f(x)$ is in the domain of g. (202)

composition of functions The binary operation that maps two functions g and f onto their composite $g \circ f$. (202)

compounded continuously The limit of compounding interest as the number of compoundings grows larger and larger in a given time period. (392)

concave down Said of an interval that is curving downwards, that is, its slope is continuously decreasing. (648)

concave up Said of an interval that is curving upwards, that is, its slope is continuously increasing. (648)

confidence interval An interval within which a certain specified percentage (usually 90%, 95%, or 99%) of outcomes from an experiment is expected to occur. (681)

conic section The intersection of a two-napped cone with a plane not containing the vertex of the cone: an ellipse, a parabola, or a hyperbola. (754)

Conjugate Zeros Theorem Let $p(x) = a_n x^n + a_{n-1}x^{n-1} + \ldots + a_1 x + a_0$ where $a_n, a_{n-1}, \ldots, a_1, a_0$ are all real numbers, and $a_n \neq 0$. If $z = a + bi$ is a zero of $p(x)$, then the complex conjugate of z, $a - bi$, is also a zero of $p(x)$. (599)

constant A variable whose values do not change in the course of a problem. (Previous course)

constant function Any function with an equation $f(x) = k$, where k is a fixed value. (Previous course)

continuous function A function that has no points of discontinuity in its domain. Informally, a function whose graph can be drawn without lifting the pencil off the paper. (129)

Continuous Change Model If a quantity p grows or decays continuously at an annual rate r, the amount $A(t)$ after t years is given by $A(t) = Pe^{rt}$. (392)

convergent sequence (to *L*) A sequence which has a finite limiting value L. If this value exists, the sequence is said to be *convergent to L*. (497)

convergent series A series in which the limit of the sequence of partial sums exists. (516)

corollary A theorem that can be quickly deduced from another theorem. (814)

correlation coefficient, *r* A measure of the strength of the linear relation between two variables. (91)

cosecant (csc) of a real number *x* For a real number x, $\csc x = \frac{1}{\sin x}$, when $\sin x \neq 0$. (806)

cosine (cos) of an acute angle θ in a right triangle $\frac{\text{leg adjacent to } \theta}{\text{hypotenuse}}$ (310)

cosine (cos) of a real number *x* The first coordinate of the image of the point (1, 0) under a rotation of magnitude x about the origin. (245)

cosine function The function that maps x onto $\cos x$ for all x in its domain. (266)

cotangent (cot) of a real number *x* For a real number x, $\cot x = \frac{\cos x}{\sin x}$, when $\sin x \neq 0$. (806)

cross section of a three-dimensional figure The intersection of a plane with the figure. Also called *section*. (754)

cube root For a number k, a number x that satisfies $x^3 = k$. (370)

cumulative binomial probability table A table that gives, for fixed n (number of trials) and p (probability of success), the probabilities for k or fewer successes. (633)

cumulative percentage curve See *percentile curve*.

cycle One period of a periodic function, such as a sine wave. (265)

data The plural of *datum*, the Latin word for fact; a piece of information. (6)

decreasing A function is decreasing on an interval if the segment connecting any two points on the graph of the function over that interval has negative slope. (47, 566)

deductive reasoning Reasoning adhering to strict principles of logic. (64)

default window The viewing window which is present in an automatic grapher until changed by the user. (160)

degenerate conic section The intersection of a cone and a plane containing the vertex of the cone; the graph of a quadratic relation that is not a conic section. (786)

degree A unit for measuring angles or rotations. (232)

degree of a polynomial In a polynomial with a single variable, the number n in the polynomial $a_n x^n + a_{n-1}x^{n-1} + \ldots + a_1 x + a_0$; in a polynomial in more than one variable, the largest sum of the exponents of the variables in any term. (557, 559)

DeMoivre's Theorem If $z = r(\cos\theta + i\sin\theta)$ and n is an integer, then $z^n = r^n(\cos n\theta + i\sin n\theta)$. (847)

dependent events Events A and B in which $P(A \cap B) \neq P(A) \cdot P(B)$. (452)

dependent variable The second variable in a relation. (82)

determinant, det A number associated with a matrix used to determine whether the matrix has an inverse. For the 2×2 matrix $\begin{bmatrix} a & b \\ c & d \end{bmatrix}$, $ad - bc$. (720)

deviation The difference of a value in a set from the set's mean. Also, see *error*. (54, 97)

dimensions of a matrix The numbers of rows and columns of the matrix. (698)

discontinuous function A function that has one or more points of discontinuity in its domain. (129)

discriminant of a quadratic equation For the equation $ax^2 + bx + c = 0$, the number $b^2 - 4ac$. (593)

discriminant of a quadratic relation For the relation $Ax^2 + Bxy + Cy^2 + Dx + Ey + F = 0$, the value of $B^2 - 4AC$. If the discriminant is less than zero, then the figure is an ellipse, a single point, or the null set. If greater, the figure is a hyperbola or a pair of lines. If it is equal to zero, the figure is a parabola, two parallel lines, a line, or the null set. (789)

disjoint The sets with no elements in common. Also called *mutually exclusive*. (433)

disk The union of a circle and its interior. (240)

divergent sequence A sequence with no finite limit. (497)

divergent series A series in which the sequence of partial sums does not have a finite limit. (516)

dividend The number or expression a when a is divided by b. (577)

Division of Complex Numbers Theorem If $z_1 = r_1(\cos\theta_1 + i\sin\theta_1)$ and $z_2 = r_2(\cos\theta_2 + i\sin\theta_2)$, then $\frac{z_1}{z_2} = \frac{r_1}{r_2}(\cos(\theta_1 - \theta_2) + i\sin(\theta_1 - \theta_2))$. (842)

divisor The number or expression b when a is divided by b. (577)

domain The set of first elements of ordered pairs of a function; more generally, the set of replacement values for a variable. (82)

dotplot A graph of a frequency distribution in which the number of dots over each individual value is the frequency of that value. Also called *dot frequency diagram.* (15)

Double Angle Formulas For all real numbers θ, $\sin 2\theta = 2\sin\theta\cos\theta$ and $\cos 2\theta = \cos^2\theta - \sin^2\theta = 2\cos^2\theta - 1 = 1 - 2\sin^2\theta$. (726)

doubling time The time it takes a quantity to grow to double its original amount, usually applied to exponential growth situations. (114)

e $\lim_{n\to\infty}\left(1 + \frac{1}{n}\right)^n \approx 2.718$; the base of natural logarithms. (390)

eccentricity of a conic The ratio $\frac{c}{a}$ for a conic section, where c is the distance from the center of the conic to a focus, and a is one-half the focal constant. (798)

element An object in an array. A member of a set. (698)

ellipse The set of all points P such that $PF_1 + PF_2 = k$ and $k > F_1F_2$, where F_1 and F_2 are points (the **foci,** singular **focus**) and k is the **focal constant.** (756)

ellipsoid The three-dimensional surface formed by rotating an ellipse about one of its axes. (793)

elliptic paraboloid The quadric surface formed by the equation $z = \frac{x^2}{a^2} + \frac{y^2}{b^2}$. (798)

end behavior of a sequence The description of what happens to the values t_n of a sequence as n gets very large. (497)

error (in a prediction) The difference between the observed and the expected value of a variable. Also called *deviation.* (97)

even function A function f such that for all x in its domain, $f(-x) = f(x)$. (181)

event Any subset of the sample space of an experiment. (427)

expected value A value predicted by a mathematical model. Also called *predicted value.* (97)

expected value of a probability distribution See *mean of a probability distribution.*

experiment A situation that has several possible outcomes. (426)

explicit formula for a sequence A formula which gives the nth term of the sequence in terms of n. (488)

exponent The number n in the expression r^n. (Previous course)

exponential decay A situation that can be modeled by $f(x) = ab^x$ with base $0 < b < 1$. (108)

exponential decay curve The graph of an exponential decay function. (108)

exponential decay function An exponential function $f(x) = ab^x$ with $a > 0$ and $0 < b < 1$. (108).

exponential equation An equation to be solved for a variable in an exponent. (403)

exponential function The exponential function with base b is a function with a formula of the form $f(x) = ab^x$, where $a \neq 0$, $b > 0$, and $b \neq 1$. (106)

exponential growth curve The graph of an exponential growth function. (106)

exponential growth function An exponential function with a base greater than one and a leading coefficient greater than zero. (106)

exponential model A mathematical model of a situation in the form of an exponential function. (112)

exponential regression The method of fitting an exponential function to a set of data. (114)

extrapolation Estimating a value beyond known values of data. (100)

extrema of functions The extreme values for a function, classified as either *maxima* or *minima.* (564)

f^{-1} See *inverse function.*

Factor Theorem For any polynomial $f(x)$, a number c is a solution to $f(x) = 0$ if and only if $(x - c)$ is a factor of $f(x)$. (585)

Factor-Solution-Intercept Equivalence Theorem For any polynomial f, the following are logically equivalent statements: $(x - c)$ is a factor of f; $f(c) = 0$; c is an x-intercept of the graph of $y = f(x)$; c is a zero of f; the remainder when $f(x)$ is divided by $(x - c)$ is 0. (585)

failure (binomial) See *binomial experiment.*

fair experiment An experiment in which all outcomes of the sample space are equally likely. Also called *unbiased experiment.* (428)

Federalist, The Essays written between 1787 and 1788 by James Madison, Alexander Hamilton, and John Jay under the collective pen name "Publius" to persuade the citizens of the state of New York to ratify the U.S. Constitution. (62)

finite series A series where the number of terms added is finite. (503)

first (lower) quartile In a data set, the median of the numbers less than the set's median. (30)

five-number summary The three quartiles, the maximum, and the minimum of a data set. (30)

floor function See *greatest integer function.*

focal constant of a hyperbola See *hyperbola.*

focal constant of an ellipse See *ellipse.*

focus (foci) of a hyperbola See *hyperbola.*

focus (foci) of an ellipse See *ellipse.*

Formula for $_nC_r$ Theorem For all whole numbers n and r, with $r \leq n$, $_nC_r = \frac{n!}{(n-r)!r!}$. (525)

Formula for $_nP_r$ Theorem The number of permutations of n objects taken r at a time is $_nP_r = n(n-1)(n-2) \cdot \ldots \cdot (n-r+1)$. (446)

frequency The number of times an item of an event occurs. The number of cycles in a period of a periodic function. (15, 275)

frequency distribution A function that maps events onto their frequencies. (15)

frequency histogram A histogram that displays the number of values that fall into each interval of the histogram. (39)

function A set of ordered pairs (x, y) in which each value of x is paired with exactly one value of y. A correspondence between two sets A and B in which each element of A corresponds to exactly one element of B. (82, 83)

function notation The notation $f(x)$ for the value of a function f when the value of the independent variable is x. (85)

Fundamental Theorem of Algebra If $p(x)$ is any polynomial of degree $n \geq 1$ with complex coefficients, then $p(x) = 0$ has at least one complex zero. (597)

Galton board See *quincunx*.

general form of a quadratic relation in two variables The form $Ax^2 + Bxy + Cy^2 + Dx + Ey + F = 0$ where at least one of A, B, and C is not zero. (784)

general solution to a trigonometric equation A solution to an equation for all real numbers for which the variable is defined. (346)

geometric sequence A sequence in which the ratio of consecutive terms is constant. (491)

geometric series An indicated sum of the terms of a geometric sequence. (510)

Geometric Addition Theorem If the complex numbers $a + bi$ and $c + di$ are not collinear with the origin in the complex plane, then their sum $(a + c) + (b + d)i$ is the fourth vertex of a parallelogram with consecutive vertices $a + bi$, 0, and $c + di$. (834)

gradient (grad) A unit for measuring angles. 100 grads = 90 degrees. (237)

Graph Rotation Theorem In a relation described by a sentence in x and y, replacing x by $x \cos \theta + y \sin \theta$ and y by $-x \sin \theta + y \cos \theta$ yields the same graph as applying the rotation of magnitude θ about the origin to the graph of the original equation. (778)

Graph Scale-Change Theorem In a relation described by a sentence in x and y, replacing x by $\frac{x}{a}$ and y by $\frac{y}{b}$ in the sentence yields the same graph as applying the scale change $(x, y) \to (ax, by)$ to the graph of the original relation. (188)

Graph-Standardization Theorem In a relation described by a sentence in x and y, replacing x by $\frac{x-h}{a}$ and y by $\frac{y-k}{b}$ in the sentence yields the same graph as applying the scale change $(x, y) \to (ax, by)$, where $a \neq 0$ and $b \neq 0$, followed by applying the translation $(x, y) \to (x + h, y + k)$ to the graph of the original relation. (286)

Graph Translation Theorem In a relation described by a sentence in x and y, replacing x by $x - h$ and y by $y - k$ in the sentence yields the same graph as applying the translation $(x, y) \to (x + h, y + k)$ to the graph of the original relation. (169)

great circle A circle on a sphere that has the same center as the sphere. (353)

greatest integer function, $\lfloor \ \rfloor$ The function f such that $f(x)$ is the greatest integer less than or equal to x. Also called the *rounding-down function* or the *floor function*. (129)

Greenwich meridian See *prime meridian*.

grouping A technique used to factor polynomials which contain groups of terms with common factors. (608)

growth factor In an exponential growth situation, the base of the exponential function. (112)

growth rate The factor by which a quantity changes during a given time period. (106)

Half Angle Formulas For all θ, $\cos \theta = \pm \sqrt{\frac{1 + \cos 2\theta}{2}}$ and $\sin \theta = \pm \sqrt{\frac{1 - \cos 2\theta}{2}}$. The sign is determined by the quadrant in which θ lies. (729)

half-life The time it takes a quantity to decay to half its original amount, usually applied to exponential decay situations. (114)

Half-Turn Theorem For all θ in radians, $\cos(\pi + \theta) = -\cos \theta$, $\sin(\pi + \theta) = -\sin \theta$, and $\tan(\pi + \theta) = \tan \theta$. (255)

harmonic sequence The sequence of the reciprocals of the positive integers. (497)

histogram A bar graph in which the range of values of a numerical variable are broken into non-overlapping intervals of equal width, and side-by-side bars display the number of values that fall into each interval. (39)

homogeneous form The increasing of the dimension of a point or matrix in order for it to be treated. For the point (x, y) the homogenous form is $(x, y, 1)$. For the 2×2 transformation matrix $\begin{bmatrix} a & b \\ c & d \end{bmatrix}$ the homogenous form is $\begin{bmatrix} a & b & 0 \\ c & d & 0 \\ 0 & 0 & 1 \end{bmatrix}$. (739)

homogeneous population A population in which members are very similar on some measure. (60)

horizontal scale change A transformation that maps (x, y) to (ax, y) for all (x, y), where $a \neq 0$. (188)

horizontal scale factor The number a in the transformation that maps (x, y) to (ax, by). (188)

hyperbola The set of all points P such that $|PF_1 - PF_2| = k$ and $k < F_1F_2$ where F_1 and F_2 are points (the **foci,** singular **focus**) and k is the **focal constant.** (769)

hypothesis In statistics, a statement to be tested. (642)

hypothesis testing The process of using statistics to find if a given hypothesis fits a situation within a given significance level. (643)

identity An equation that is true for all values of the variable(s) for which the expressions are defined. (251)

identity function, I A function that maps each element in its domain onto itself, that is, $I(x) = x$ for all x. (211)

identity transformation The transformation I with $I(P) = P$ for all points P. (731)

GLOSSARY

image The result of a transformation. (167, 173)

imaginary axis The vertical axis (axis of second coordinates) in a complex plane. (833)

imaginary numbers The number $i = \sqrt{-1}$ and its nonzero real-number multiples. (590)

imaginary part of a complex number The real number b in the complex number $a + bi$. (591)

impressionistic model A model where no theory exists that explains why the model fits the data. Also called *non-theory based model.* (125)

in-phase circuit An alternating current circuit in which the voltage and current flow coincide. (280)

increasing function A function is increasing on an interval if the segment connecting any two points on the graph of the function over that interval has positive slope. (47, 566)

independent events Events A and B such that $P(A \cap B) = P(A) \bullet P(B)$. (451)

independent variable The first variable in a relation. (82)

index A variable indicating the position of a number in an ordered list or sequence. (21)

inductance Property of an alternating current circuit created when the current flow lags behind the voltage. (280)

inferential reasoning Reasoning based on principles of probability. (64)

infinite series An indicated sum of the terms of an infinite sequence. (503, 516)

infinity, ∞ The limit of a sequence whose terms after a given point become larger than any fixed number one might choose; greater than any given number. (497)

inflection point A point on a graph where the graph changes concavity. (648)

initial side (of an angle) The side of an angle from which the angle is considered to have been generated, and from which the angle is measured. (232)

initial value In a function f modeling a situation, the value $f(0)$. (112)

interest rate In an investment, the percent by which the principal is multiplied to obtain the interest paid to the investor. (391)

International Date Line The meridian which is 180° W (and 180° E) of the prime meridian. (354)

interpolation Estimating a value between known values of data. (100)

interquartile range (IQR) The difference between the third quartile and the first quartile. (30)

intersection, $A \cap B$ The set of elements that are in both set A and set B. (433)

invariant Unchanged by a particular transformation. (176)

inverse cosine function, $\cos^{-1}$, Arccos The function $y = \cos^{-1} x =$ Arccos x, if and only if $x = \cos y$ and $0 \le y \le \pi$. (322)

inverse function, f^{-1} The function which is the inverse of the function f. (210)

inverse matrices Two matrices whose product is the identity matrix for matrix multiplication. (732)

inverse of a function The relation formed by switching the coordinates of the ordered pairs of a given function. (208)

inverse sine function, $\sin^{-1}$, Arcsin The function $y = \sin^{-1} x =$ Arcsin x if and only if $x = \sin y$ and $-\frac{\pi}{2} \le y \le \frac{\pi}{2}$. (335)

inverse tangent function, $\tan^{-1}$, Arctan The function $y = \tan^{-1} x =$ Arctan x if and only if $x = \tan y$ and $-\pi < y < \pi$. (340)

inverse transformation If P is a point and $T(P) = Q$, then the inverse transformation T^{-1} is such that $T^{-1}(Q) = P$. (731)

Inverse Function Theorem Two functions f and g are inverse functions if and only if $f(g(x)) = x$ for all x in the domain of g, and $g(f(x)) = x$ for all x in the domain of f. (211)

Inverse of a 2 × 2 Matrix Theorem If $ad - bc \ne 0$, then $\begin{bmatrix} a & b \\ c & d \end{bmatrix}^{-1} = \begin{bmatrix} \frac{d}{ad - bc} & \frac{-b}{ad - bc} \\ \frac{-c}{ad - bc} & \frac{a}{ad - bc} \end{bmatrix}$. (734)

isometry A composite of translations, rotations, and reflections; a distance-preserving transformation. (780)

latitude A measure of the extent to which a point is north of south of the equator determined by the angle subtended at the center of the earth by an arc on a line of longitude. (354)

Law of Cosines In any triangle ABC, $c^2 = a^2 + b^2 - 2ab \cos C$. (316)

Law of Sines In any triangle ABC, $\frac{\sin A}{a} = \frac{\sin B}{b} = \frac{\sin C}{c}$. (328)

leading coefficient (of a polynomial) The coefficient of the term of the highest degree a polynomial. (557)

leaf The digits with lower place value in a stemplot, typically listed in a row originating from their respective stems. (13)

limit of a sequence, $\lim_{n \to \infty} s_n$ A number to which the terms of a sequence approach as their position increases (or decreases). Also called a *limiting value.* (496)

line graph The graph of a set of ordered pairs (x, y) connected by segments in order of the values of x. (46)

line of best fit The line that fits a set of data points with the smallest value for the sum of the squares of the deviations (vertical distances) from the data points to the line. Also called *regression line* or *least-squares line.* (97)

line of symmetry See *axis of symmetry.*

linear function A function with an equation of the form $y = mx + b$, where m and b are constants. (89)

linear regression The method of finding a line of best fit to a set of points. (88, 90)

linearity A relation's degree of correlation to a linear model. (93)

ln See *natural logarithm.*

logarithm (log) Let $b > 0$ and $b \ne 1$. Then y is the logarithm of x to the base b, written $y = \log_b x$, if and only if $b^y = x$. (383)

logarithm function (with base b) The function which maps x onto $\log_b x$. (385)

logarithmic transformation A transformation under which a variable x is replaced by $\log_b x$. (412)

Logarithm of 1 Theorem For any base b, $\log_b 1 = 0$. (398)

Logarithm of a Power Theorem For any base b, and for any positive real number x, and any real number p, $\log_b x^p = p \log_b x$. (399)

Logarithm of a Product Theorem For any base b, and for any positive real numbers x and y, $\log_b(xy) = \log_b x + \log_b y$. (398)

Logarithm of a Quotient Theorem For any base b and for any positive real numbers x and y, $\log_b \frac{x}{y} = \log_b x - \log_b y$. (399)

logarithmic spiral The polar graph of $r = ka^{\theta}$, where $a > 0$. (832)

longitude The number of degrees that a meridian is E or W of the prime meridian, used as a coordinate of a location on Earth. (354)

lower quartile See *first quartile*.

major axis of an ellipse The longer of the two axes of a noncircular ellipse, the axis containing the foci. (762)

Mandelbrot set The set of complex numbers c for which the limit of the sequence defined by

$$\begin{cases} z_1 = c \\ z_n = (z_{n-1})^2 + c \text{ for } n > 1 \end{cases}$$

is not infinity. (852)

MANDELZOOM A computer program for generating graphs of the Mandelbrot set. (854)

margin of error Half the length of a confidence interval. (681)

mathematical model A mathematical description of a real situation, often involving some simplifications and assumptions about that situation. (81)

Matrices for Reflections Theorem The matrix for r_x, reflection over the x-axis, is $\begin{bmatrix} 1 & 0 \\ 0 & -1 \end{bmatrix}$. The matrix for r_y, reflection over the y-axis, is $\begin{bmatrix} -1 & 0 \\ 0 & 1 \end{bmatrix}$. The matrix for $r_{y=x}$, reflection over the line $y = x$, is $\begin{bmatrix} 0 & 1 \\ 1 & 0 \end{bmatrix}$. (705)

Matrices for Rotations Theorem The matrix for R_{90}, the rotation of 90° around the origin, is $\begin{bmatrix} 0 & -1 \\ 1 & 0 \end{bmatrix}$. The matrix for R_{180}, the rotation of 180° around the origin, is $\begin{bmatrix} -1 & 0 \\ 0 & -1 \end{bmatrix}$. The matrix for R_{270}, the rotation of 270° around the origin, is $\begin{bmatrix} 0 & 1 \\ -1 & 0 \end{bmatrix}$. (712)

matrix A rectangular arrangement of objects into m rows and n columns. (698)

Matrix Basis Theorem Suppose T is a transformation represented by a 2×2 matrix. If $T(1, 0) = (x_1, y_1)$ and $T(0, 1) = (x_2, y_2)$ then T has the matrix $\begin{bmatrix} x_1 & x_2 \\ y_1 & y_2 \end{bmatrix}$. (713)

matrix multiplication An operation on an $m \times n$ matrix A and an $n \times p$ matrix B whose result is the product matrix $A \cdot B$, an $m \times p$ matrix whose element in row i and column j is the sum of the products of elements in row i of A and corresponding elements in column j of B. (700)

matrix representing a transformation A matrix M such that whenever F, a matrix for a geometric figure, is multiplied by M, the product is a matrix for the image of F under the transformation T. (705)

maximum The largest value in a set. (14)

maximum value of a function The largest value in a function's range. (120, 564)

mean The sum of the elements of a numerical data set divided by the number of items in the data set. Also called *average*. (19, 22)

Mean of a Binomial Distribution Theorem The mean μ of a binomial distribution with n trials and probability p of success on each trial is given by $\mu = np$. (636)

mean of a probability distribution For the probability distribution $\{(x_1, P(x_1)), (x_2, P(x_2)), \dots, (x_n, P(x_n))\}$, the number $\mu = \sum_{i=1}^{n} (x_i \cdot P(x_i))$. Also called *expected value of a probability distribution*. (459)

measure of an angle A number that represents the size and direction of rotation used to generate an angle. (232)

measure of center A statistic describing a typical value of a numerical data set. Measures of center include the *mean* and *median*, and sometimes the *mode*. Also called *measure of central tendency*. (24)

measure of central tendency See *measure of center*.

measure of spread A statistic that describes how far data are from a center of a distribution. (54)

median The middle value of a set of data placed in ascending or descending order. The median of a set with an even number of elements is the mean of the two middle values. (19, 22)

meridian A semicircle of a great circle on the surface of Earth from the north pole to the south pole. Also called *line of longitude*. (354)

method of least squares The process of finding the line of best fit. (97)

middle quartile See *second quartile*.

minimum The smallest value in a set. (14)

minimum value of a function The smallest value in a function's range. (120, 544)

minor axis of an ellipse The shorter of the two axes of a non-circular ellipse. (762)

minute (of a degree) A unit for measuring angles. 60 minutes = 1 degree. (312)

mode The item(s) with the greatest frequency in a data set. (19, 24)

modulus See *absolute value of a complex number*.

monomial A polynomial with one term. (558)

Monte Carlo method The method of using random numbers and related probabilities to simulate events for the purpose of solving a problem. (465)

Multiplication Counting Principle Let A and B be any finite sets. The number of ways to choose one element from A and then one element from B is $N(A) \cdot N(B)$. (440)

multiplicity of a zero For a zero r of a polynomial, the highest power of $(x - r)$ that appears as a factor of that polynomial. (597)

mutually exclusive See *disjoint.*

***n* factorial, *n*!** For a positive integer n, the product of the positive integers from 1 to n. In symbols, $n! = n \cdot (n-1) \cdot (n-2) \cdot (n-3) \cdot \ldots \cdot 3 \cdot 2 \cdot 1$. $0! = 1$. (442)

nappe One of the two halves of a generated cone, consisting of the points that lie on one side of the cone's vertex. (754)

natural logarithm, ln The logarithm to the base e, written $\ln x$. (394)

natural logarithm function The function that maps x to $\ln x$. (394)

$_nC_r$ See *Formula for $_nC_r$ Theorem.*

Negative Exponent Theorem For all $x \neq 0$ and n for which x^n is defined, $x^{-n} = \frac{1}{x^n}$. (378)

negative relation A relation between two variables where the larger values of the one variable are associated with smaller values of the other. (91)

non-theory-based model See *impressionistic model.*

normal curve The graph of a normal distribution. (649)

normal distribution The continuous function that the binomial distribution approaches as n, the number of trials, increases without bound. (649)

not *A* The complement of an event A, that is, the set of outcomes of the sample space that are not in A. (437)

***n*th partial sum** The sum of the first n terms of a sequence. (510)

***n*th root,** $\sqrt[n]{x} = k$ if and only if $k^n = x$ where n is an integer ≥ 2. If $x \geq 0$, $\sqrt[n]{x} = x^{\frac{1}{n}}$. (372)

***n*th root function** A function with an equation of the form $y = x^{1/n}$, where n is an integer with $n \geq 2$. (372)

***n*th roots of unity** The zeros of $x^n - 1$. (601)

null hypothesis, H_0 The main hypothesis used in hypothesis testing of a situation. (643)

Number of Zeros of a Polynomial Theorem A polynomial of degree $n \geq 1$ with complex coefficients has exactly n complex zeros, if multiplicities are counted. (598)

oblate spheroid See *spheroid.*

observed values Data collected from sources such as experiments or surveys. (97)

odd function A function f such that for all x in its domain, $f(-x) = -f(x)$. (181)

1.5 X IQR criterion A criterion under which those elements of a data set greater than 1.5 X IQR plus the third quartile or less than the first quartile minus 1.5 X IQR are considered to be outliers. (33)

ogive See *percentile curve.*

one-to-one function A function in which no two domain values correspond to the same range value. (213)

Opposites Theorem For all θ, $\cos(-\theta) = \cos\theta$, $\sin(-\theta) = -\sin\theta$, and $\tan(-\theta) = -\tan\theta$. (252)

oscilloscope An instrument for representing the oscillations of varying voltage or current on the fluorescent screen of a cathode-ray tube. (231)

out-of-phase circuit An alternating current circuit in which the current flow lags behind the voltage. (280)

outcome A possible result of an experiment. (426)

outlier An element of a set of numbers which is very different from most or all of the other elements. (14)

overlapping sets Two sets that are not disjoint. (433)

parabola The graph of a quadratic function. The intersection of a plane and a cone, where the plane is parallel to an edge of the cone, but does not intersect the cone's vertex. (120, 754)

paraboloid The three-dimensional surface formed by rotating a parabola about its axis. (794)

parameters of the binomial distribution The numbers n (number of trials) and p (probability of success) in the binomial distribution function $B(k) = {_nC_x}p^k(1 - p)^{n-k}$. (629)

parent function A simple form or the simplest form of a class of functions, from which other members of the class can be derived by transformations. (162, Appendix A)

partial sum See *nth partial sum.*

Pascal's Triangle The values of $_nC_r$ arranged in an array in the form of a triangle; the $(r + 1)$st term in row n of Pascal's Triangle is $_nC_r$. (529)

pentagonal numbers The sequence of numbers 1, 5, 12, 22, ..., each of which represents the number of dots in pentagonal arrays and sharing a single vertex. (589)

percentile The pth percentile of a set of numbers is the value in the set such that p percent of the numbers are less than or equal to that value. (31)

percentile curve A curve in which each ordered pair (x, y) represents the percent y of the data in the set that are less than x. Also called a *cumulative percentage curve* or *ogive.* (687)

perfect correlation A correlation coefficient of 1 or -1; a situation in which all data points lie on the same line. (91)

periodic function A function f in which there is a positive real number p such that $f(x + p) = f(x)$ for all x. The smallest positive value of p is the **period** of the function. (268)

Periodicity Theorem For all θ, and for every integer n, $\sin(\theta + 2\pi n) = \sin\theta$, $\cos(\theta + 2\pi n) = \cos\theta$, and $\tan(\theta + \pi n) = \tan\theta$. (268)

permutation Each different arrangement of a set of objects. (445)

permutation of n objects taken r at a time, ${}_nP_r$ An arrangement of r objects from a set of n objects. (446)

Permutation Theorem The are $n!$ permutations of n different elements. (445)

petal curve See *rose curve.*

phase shift The least positive or the greatest negative horizontal translation that maps the graph of a circular function onto a given sine wave. (278)

pie chart See *circle graph.*

point matrix The matrix $\begin{bmatrix} a \\ b \end{bmatrix}$, when it represents the point (a, b). (704)

point of discontinuity A value of x for which a function is not continuous. (129, 163)

point-symmetric figure A figure that has 180° rotation-symmetry. (179)

polar axis A ray, usually horizontal and drawn to the right, through the pole of a polar coordinate system, from which magnitudes of rotations are measured. (820)

polar coordinate system A coordinate system in which a point is identified by a pair of numbers $[r, \theta]$, where $|r|$ is the distance of the point from a fixed point (the pole), and θ is a magnitude of rotation from the polar axis. (820)

polar coordinates, $[r, \theta]$ The description of a point in a polar coordinate system. (820)

polar form of a complex number The description of a complex number using polar coordinates. (835)

polar grid A grid of rays and concentric circles radiating from a central point, used for plotting points and sketching curves in the polar plane. (822)

pole See *polar coordinate system.*

polynomial A sum of multiples of nonnegative integer powers of a variable or variables. (555)

polynomial function A function whose rule can be written as a polynomial. (557)

polynomial in x An expression of the form $a_nx^n + a_{n-1}x^{n-1} + a_{n-2}x^{n-2} + \ldots + a_1x + a_0$ where n is a nonnegative integer and $a_n \neq 0$. Also called *the general form of a polynomial in one variable.* (557)

Polynomial Difference Theorem The function $y = f(x)$ is a polynomial function of degree n if and only if, for any set of x-values that form an arithmetic sequence, the nth differences of corresponding y-values are equal and nonzero. (571)

population The set of all individuals or objects to be studied. (6)

population standard deviation, σ See *standard deviation.*

population variance, σ^2 See *variance.*

position of a term in a sequence The domain value of a term in the sequence. (488)

positive relation A relation between two variables where larger values of one variable are associated with larger values of the other. (91)

power function A function f with an equation of the form $y = ax^n$, where n is an integer greater than 1. (181)

predicted values See *expected value.*

preimage The domain or set of domain values of a transformation. (167)

prime meridian The meridian through Greenwich, England, from which all other meridians are measured. (354)

probability A number which indicates the measure of certainty of an event. (425)

probability distribution A function which maps each value of a random variable onto its probability. (457)

probability of an event, $P(E)$ If E is an event in a finite sample space S, and each outcome in S is equally likely, then the probability that E occurs, denoted $P(E)$, is given by $P(E) = \dfrac{\text{number of outcomes in the event}}{\text{number of outcomes in the sample space}}$. (428)

probability theory The branch of mathematics that studies chance. (426)

Probability of the Union of Mutually Exclusive Events Theorem If A and B are mutually exclusive events in the same finite sample space, then $P(A \cup B) = P(A) + P(B)$. (433)

Probability of a Union of Events Theorem (General Form) If A and B are any events in the same finite sample space, then $P(A \text{ or } B) = P(A \cup B) = P(A) + P(B) - P(A \cap B)$. (435)

Probability of Complements Theorem If A is any event, then $P(\text{not } A) = 1 - P(A)$. (437)

product matrix See *matrix multiplication.*

Product of Complex Numbers Theorem (Trigonometric Form) If $z_1 = r_1(\cos\theta_1 + i\sin\theta_1)$ and $z_2(\cos\theta_2 + i\sin\theta_2)$, then $z_1z_2 = r_1r_2(\cos(\theta_1 + \theta_2) + i\sin(\theta_1 + \theta_2))$. (841)

prolate spheroid See *spheroid.*

pseudo-random numbers Numbers generated by an algorithm (such as a computer program) that are very nearly, but not quite, random. (471)

Pythagorean identity For every θ, $\cos^2\theta + \sin^2\theta = 1$. (251)

quadratic function A function of the form $f(x) = ax^2 + bx + c$ where $a \neq 0$. (565)

quadratic models A quadratic function used to estimate data in a set. (120)

quadratic regression A method of finding an equation for the best-fitting parabola through a set of points. (123)

quadratic relation The set of ordered pairs (x, y) satisfying an equation of the form $Ax^2 + Bxy + Cy^2 + Dx + Ey + F = 0$, where at least one of A, B, and C is not zero. (753)

quadric surfaces Three-dimensional surfaces formed by the revolution of conics, all of which satisfy the general equation $Ax^2 + By^2 + Cz^2 + Dxy + Exz + Fyz + Gx + Hy + Iz + J = 0$. (798)

quartiles The three values which divide an ordered set into four subsets of approximately the same size. See *first (lower) quartile, second (middle) quartile*, and *third (lower) quartile.* (30)

GLOSSARY

quincunx A device, invented by Sir Francis Galton, used to illustrate binomial experiments, consisting of a box in which balls striking an array of pins form, at the bottom of the box, a normal distribution. Also called *Galton board.* (687)

quotient The answer to a division problem. For polynomials, the polynomial $q(x)$ when $f(x)$ is divided by $d(x)$, where $f(x) = q(x)d(x) + r(x)$, and either $r(x) = 0$ or the degree of $r(x)$ is less than the degree of $d(x)$. (579)

radian A unit for measuring an angle or the magnitude of a rotation. 2π radians = 360°. (233)

radical The symbol $\sqrt{}$ used to denote square roots or nth roots. (372)

rand A function on some calculators that automatically generates pseudo-random numbers. (472)

random numbers A set of numbers such that each number has the same probability of occurring, each pair of numbers has the same probability of occurring, each trio of numbers has the same probability of occurring, and so on. (466)

random variable A variable whose values are numbers determined by the outcome of an experiment. (457)

randomly A property of sampling a population so that every member of the population has an equal chance of being chosen. Also referred to as *at random.* (7)

range The difference between the highest and lowest values in a set. The set of values of the dependent variable in a function. (14, 82)

rank ordered Sequenced in order on some scale. (29)

Rational Exponent Theorem For all positive integers m and n, and all real numbers $x \geq 0$, $x^{m/n} = (x^{1/n})^m = (\sqrt[n]{x})^m$ and $x^{m/n} = (x^m)^{1/n} = \sqrt[n]{x^m}$. (377)

rational power function A function f with an equation of the form $f(x) = ax^{m/n}$, where m and n are nonzero integers and $a \neq 0$. (379)

raw data Data that has not been transformed or statistically manipulated. (216)

real axis The horizontal axis (axis of first coordinates) in a complex plane. (833)

real part of a complex number The real number a in the complex number $a + bi$. (591)

reciprocal trigonometric functions The secant, cosecant, and cotangent functions. (806)

rectangular hyperbola A hyperbola whose asymptotes are perpendicular to one another. (780)

recursive formula A formula for a sequence in which the first term or the first few terms are given, and then the nth term is expressed using the preceding term(s). (489)

Reflecting Property of an Ellipse Theorem If P is a point on an ellipse with foci F_1 and F_2, then $\overrightarrow{PF_1}$ and $\overrightarrow{PF_2}$ form equal angles with the line tangent to the ellipse at P. (794)

reflection-symmetric figure A figure that can be mapped onto itself by a reflection over some line ℓ. (179)

regression line See *line of best fit.*

relation A set of ordered pairs. (82)

relative extrema Relative maxima or relative minima. (564)

relative frequency The ratio of the number of times an event occurred to the number of times it could have occurred. (39, 430)

relative frequency distribution A function mapping events onto their relative frequencies. (39)

relative frequency histogram A histogram that displays the percent of values that fall into each interval of the histogram. (39)

relative maximum A point or value at which a function has a maximum on a specified interval. (564)

relative minimum A point or value at which a function has a minimum on a specified interval. (565)

remainder (in polynomial division) The polynomial $r(x)$ when $f(x)$ is divided by $d(x)$ and $f(x) = q(x)d(x) + r(x)$. Either $r(x) = 0$ or the degree of $r(x)$ is less than the degree of $d(x)$. (579)

Remainder Theorem If a polynomial $f(x)$ is divided by $x - c$, then the remainder is $f(c)$. (580)

removable singularity A point of discontinuity of a function that can be "removed" by adding a single point to the function. (817)

rescaling See *scaling.*

residual The difference between the observed value and a value predicted by a model. (134)

revolution A unit for measuring rotations. 1 revolution (counterclockwise) = 360°. (232)

root function A function that maps x onto some root of x, such as its square root. (370)

root of a polynomial function For the polynomial function $f(x) = a_nx^n + a_{n-1}x^{n-1} + \ldots + a_1x + a_0$, any value of x such that $f(x) = 0$. Also called *zero* of the function. (565)

Roots and Coefficients of Polynomials Theorem For the polynomial equation $x^n + a_1x^{n-1} + a_2x^{n-2} + \ldots + a_{n-1}x + a_n = 0$, the sum of the roots is $-a_1$, the sum of the products of the roots two at a time is a_2, the sum of the roots three at a time is $-a_3$, . . ., and the product of all of the roots is $\begin{cases} a_n, & \text{if } n \text{ is even,} \\ -a_n, & \text{if } n \text{ is odd} \end{cases}$. (614)

Roots of a Complex Number Theorem For any positive integer n, the n distinct roots of $z^n = r(\cos\theta + i\sin\theta)$, $r > 0$, are

$$z = \sqrt[n]{r}\left[\cos\left(\frac{\theta}{n} + k\frac{360°}{n}\right) + i\sin\left(\frac{\theta}{n} + k\frac{360°}{n}\right)\right]$$

where $k = 0, 1, 2, \ldots, n - 1$. (848)

rose curve The graph of the polar equation $r = a\sin b\theta$ or $r = a\cos b\theta$, where b is a positive integer and $a \neq 0$. Also called *petal curve.* (829)

Rotation Matrix Theorem The matrix for R_θ, the rotation of magnitude θ about the origin, is $\begin{bmatrix} \cos\theta & -\sin\theta \\ \sin\theta & \cos\theta \end{bmatrix}$. (716)

rotation-symmetric figure A figure that can be mapped onto itself under a nonzero rotation. (179)

rounding-down function See *greatest integer function.*

rounding-up function, ⌈ ⌉ The function which pairs each number x with the smallest integer greater than or equal to x. Also called *ceiling function.* (130)

row matrix A matrix consisting of a single row. (699)

rubberband transformation A transformation that is the composite of scale changes and translations. (286)

Rule of 72 The formula $t = \frac{72}{r}$, used to estimate the length of time t it takes to double an investment at an interest rate of r%. (408)

sample The subset of a population that is studied in an experiment. (6)

sample space The set of all possible outcomes of an experiment. (426)

sample standard deviation, s See *standard deviation.*

sample variance, s^2 See *variance.*

sampling distribution A distribution of the means of samples from the same population. (671)

SAS Area Formula for a Triangle The area of any triangle is one-half the product of the lengths of any two sides and the sine of their included angle. (328)

scale change (of data) A transformation that maps each data value x_i in a set of data $\{x_1, x_2, \ldots, x_n\}$ to ax_i, where a is a nonzero constant. (194)

scale change (in the plane) The transformation that maps (x, y) to (ax, by), where $a \neq 0$ and $b \neq 0$ are constants. (188)

scale factor The nonzero constant by which each data value is multiplied in a scale change. (194)

scale image The result of a scale change, or the point it represents. (194)

scaling Applying a scale change to a data set. Also called *rescaling.* (194)

scatterplot A graph of a finite set of ordered pairs in the coordinate plane. (46)

secant (sec) of a real number For any real number x, $\sec x = \frac{1}{\cos x}$, for $\cos x \neq 0$. (806)

second (middle) quartile The median of a set of data. (30)

second (of a degree) A unit for measuring angles. 60 seconds = 1 minute, and 3600 seconds = 1 degree. (312)

section See *cross section.*

sector (of a circle) A part of the circle's disk that is on or in the interior of a given central angle. (240)

Selections with Replacement Theorem Let S be a set with n elements. Then there are n^k possible arrangements of k elements from S with replacement. (441)

Selections without Replacement Theorem Let S be a set with n elements. Then there are $n!$ possible arrangements of the n elements without replacement. (442)

sequence A function whose domain is a set of consecutive integers greater than or equal to a fixed integer k. (488)

sequence of partial sums The sequence whose nth term is the sum of the first n terms of a given sequence. (516)

series An indicated sum of the terms of a sequence. (503)

sides (of an angle) See *angle.*

Σ (sigma) A symbol for sum. (21)

Σ (sigma-notation) See *summation notation.* (21)

significance level The level of probability (often 0.05 or 0.01) that is chosen to test a hypothesis. (643)

similar figures Figures in which one is the image of the other under a composite of reflections, rotations, translations, and/or size changes. (221)

simulation An experimental model of a situation that attempts to capture all aspects of the situation that affect the outcomes. (465)

sine function The function that maps x onto $\sin x$ for all x in its domain. (265)

sine (sin) of an acute angle θ in a right triangle $\frac{\text{leg opposite } \theta}{\text{hypotenuse}}$. (310)

sine (sin) of a real number x The second coordinate of the image of the point (1, 0) under a rotation of magnitude x about the origin. (245)

sine wave The graph of the image of the sine or cosine function, under a composite of translations and scale changes. (231, 272)

singularity An isolated value for which a function is undefined. (816)

sinusoidal Varying in the manner of a sine wave of the sine function. (231)

size change A scale change in which the scale factors are equal; a transformation that maps (x, y) to (kx, ky), where k is a nonzero constant. (188)

slope For the segment joining (x_1, y_1) and (x_2, y_2), the number $(y_2 - y_1)/(x_2 - x_1)$. (47)

spherical triangle A triangle on a sphere whose sides are arcs of great circles of that sphere. (356)

Spherical Law of Cosines If ABC is a spherical triangle with sides a, b, and c, then $\cos c = \cos a \cos b + \sin a \sin b \cos c$. (356)

spheroid A three-dimensional figure formed by the equation $\frac{x^2}{a^2} + \frac{y^2}{b^2} + \frac{z^2}{c^2} = 1$, where at least two of a, b and c are equal. A **prolate spheroid** is formed by rotating an ellipse about its major axis. An **oblate spheroid** is created by rotating an ellipse about its minor exis. (798)

spread An indication of how the value of data in a set vary. (29)

square matrix A matrix with the same number of rows as columns. (735)

square numbers The values of the function $s(n) = n^2$, where n is an integer. (561)

square root A solution to an equation of the form $x^2 = k$. (370)

standard deviation The square root of the sample variance (s) or the population variance (σ). (54, 57)

GLOSSARY

standard form equation for a hyperbola The hyperbola with foci $(c, 0)$ and $(-c, 0)$ and focal constant $2a$ has equation $\frac{x^2}{a^2} - \frac{y^2}{b^2} = 1$, where $b^2 = c^2 - a^2$. (770)

standard form equation for an ellipse The ellipse with foci $(c, 0)$ and $(-c, 0)$ and focal constant $2a$ has equation $\frac{x^2}{a^2} + \frac{y^2}{b^2} = 1$, where $b^2 = a^2 - c^2$. (761)

standard normal curve The graph of the function $f(x) = \frac{1}{\sqrt{2\pi}}e^{-x^2/2}$. (651)

standard normal distribution The probability distribution represented by the standard normal curve. (651)

standard score See *z-score*.

Standard Normal Distribution Table A table that gives the area under the standard normal curve to the left of a given positive number a. (655, 875)

standardized data Data that has been transformed into z-scores. (216)

standardizing a variable The process of transforming a variable's data values into z-scores. (216)

statistical inference Judgments using probabilities derived from statistical tests. (683)

statistics The branch of mathematics dealing with the collection, organization, analysis, and interpretation of information, usually numerical information. (6)

statistics utility A graphics calculator with statistics capability or statistics software for use on a computer. (19)

stemplot A display of numerical data in which digits with higher place values are listed in a column as **stems** while digits with lower place values, called **leaves**, are listed in rows originating from their respective stems. Also called *stem-and-leaf diagram*. (13)

step function A function whose graph resembles a series of steps. (128)

stretch A vertical or horizontal scale change with magnitude > 1. (187, 188)

strictly decreasing Said of a function that decreases across an interval, or across its entire domain. (108)

strictly increasing Said of a function that increases across an interval, or across its entire domain. (108)

strong relation A relation for which the data in a data set falls close to a line (or another specified curve). (91)

success (binomial) See *binomial experiment*.

sum of an infinite series, S_∞, $\sum_{i=1}^{\infty} a_i$ The limit of the sequence of partial sums $S_n = \sum_{i=1}^{n} a_i$ of the series, provided the limit exists and is finite. (516)

summation notation The use of the symbol Σ to represent a summation. Also called *sigma-notation* or *Σ-notation*. (21)

Sums and Differences of Cubes Theorem For all x and y, $x^3 + y^3 = (x + y)(x^2 - xy + y^2)$ and $x^3 - y^3 = (x - y)(x^2 + xy + y^2)$. (604)

Sums and Difference of Odd Powers Theorem For all x and y and for all odd positive integers n, $x^n + y^n = (x + y)(x^{n-1} - x^{n-2}y + x^{n-3}y^2 - \ldots - xy^{n-2} + y^{n-1})$ and $x^n - y^n = (x - y)(x^{n-1} + x^{n-2}y + x^{n-3}y^2 + \ldots + xy^{n-2} + y^{n-1})$. (605)

Supplements Theorem For all θ in radians, $\sin(\pi - \theta) = \sin\theta$, $\cos(\pi - \theta) = -\cos\theta$, and $\tan(\pi - \theta) = -\tan\theta$. (253)

survey A gathering of facts or opinions through an interview or questionnaire; to gather such facts. (6)

symmetric to the origin A relation such that if (x, y) is on its graph then so is $(-x, -y)$. (180)

symmetric with respect to the *y*-axis A relation such that, for each point (x, y) on its graph, the point $(-x, y)$ is on the graph. (179)

symmetric with respect to the *x*-axis A relation such that, for each point (x, y) on its graph, the point $(x, -y)$ is on the graph. (180)

symmetry to a point P See *point symmetry*.

table of random numbers A listing of (pseudo-)random numbers used to simulate random situations. (466, Appendix C)

tangent function The function that maps x onto $\tan x$ for all x in its domain. (267)

tangent (tan) of a real number x For all real numbers x, $\frac{\sin x}{\cos x}$, if $\cos x \neq 0$. (246)

tangent (tan) of an acute angle in a right triangle $\frac{\text{leg opposite the angle}}{\text{leg adjacent to the angle}}$ (310)

term An element in the range of a sequence. (488)

tessellation A covering of the plane with congruent regions that overlap only on their boundaries. Also spelled *tesselation*. (546)

tetrahedral array A three-dimensional array made up of layers of points arranged in triangular arrays. (570)

tetrahedral numbers The values $T(n)$ of the sequence defined by

$$\begin{cases} T(1) = 1; \\ T(n) = T(n-1) + t(n), \text{ for all} \end{cases}$$

integers $n > 1$, where $t(n)$ is the nth triangular number. (570)

theory-based model A model based on a concrete theory that explains why the model should fit the data. (120)

third (upper) quartile In a data set, the median of the numbers greater than the set's median. (30)

time-series data A function with a finite domain in which the independent variable is time. (46)

transformation A one-to-one correspondence between sets of points. (159)

translation (in the plane) A transformation that maps each point (x, y) to $(x + h, y + k)$, where h and k are constants. (168)

translation (of data) A transformation that maps each x_i of a data set to $x_i + h$, where h is some constant. (173)

translation image The result of a translation. (167, 173)

tree diagram A method of graphically presenting the possible outcomes of a sample space by using a network of branches, resembling a tree. (440)

trial One of the instances of an experiment. (465, 540)

triangular numbers The values of the sequence $t(n) = \frac{n(n+1)}{2}$. (561)

trigonometric equation An equation in which the variable to be found is in an argument of a trigonometric function. (346)

trigonometric form of a complex number The form $r(\cos\theta + i\sin\theta)$ of the complex number $a + bi$. (840)

trigonometric functions The sine, cosine, tangent, cotangent, secant, and cosecant functions and their offspring. Also called *circular functions.* (309)

trigonometry The branch of mathematics that deals with the study of the circular functions, and the relations between sides and angles of triangles using these functions. (309)

trinomial A polynomial with three terms. (558)

2 × 2 Identity Matrix The matrix $\begin{bmatrix} 1 & 0 \\ 0 & 1 \end{bmatrix}$, which maps any point (x, y) to itself. (705)

unbiased See *fair.*

union, $A \cup B$ The set of all elements that are either in set A or set B, or in both. (433)

unit circle The circle with center at the origin and radius 1. (245)

univariate data Data involving a single variable. (81)

upper quartile See *third quartile.*

variable (in statistics) A characteristic of a person or thing which can be classified, counted, ordered, or measured. (6)

variance, s^2, σ^2 In a data set, the sum of the squared deviations of the data from the mean divided by one less than the number of elements in the set (sample variance s^2) or by the number of elements in the set (population variance σ^2). (56, 57)

variance of a probability distribution For a probability distribution $\{(x_i, P(x_i)\}$ with n outcomes and mean μ, $\sigma^2 = \sum_{i=1}^{n} x_i^2 \cdot P(x_i)) - \mu^2$. (636)

Variance and Standard Deviation of a Binomial Distribution Theorem In a binomial distribution with n trials, probability p of success and probability q of failure on each trial, the variance $\sigma^2 = npq$, and the standard deviation $\sigma = \sqrt{npq}$. (637)

Venn diagram A method of displaying unions and intersections of sets, using circles. (433)

vertex (of a cone) The point of intersection of the two lines used in the generation of a cone. (754)

vertex (of an angle) See *angle.*

vertical line test A test to determine whether a set of ordered pairs in the coordinate plane is a function; if there exists a vertical line that intersects the set in more that one point, then the set is not a function. (84)

vertical scale change A transformation that maps (x, y) to (x, by), where $b \neq 0$ is a constant. (187)

vertical scale factor The number b in the transformation that maps (x, y) to (ax, by). (188)

vertices of a hyperbola The points where a hyperbola intersects the axis that contains the foci. (772)

vector processor A high-speed computer processor designed to multiply a matrix row and a matrix column in one step. (741)

viewing window The subset of the coordinate plane that appears on the screen of an automatic grapher. Also called *viewing rectangle.* (160)

weak relation A relation for which, although a linear trend can be seen, many points are not very close to the line (or another specified curve). (92)

whispering gallery An ellipsoidal room where whispers from one focus can be heard at the other focus even though the two foci are quite far apart. (793)

window See *viewing window.*

world coordinates Coordinate systems which are used for representing three-dimensional objects. (741)

yield The actual percentage accrued to the principal in an investment annually, given by $\left(1 + \frac{r}{n}\right)^n$, where r is the annual interest rate and n is the number of compoundings per year. (391)

z-score The value $z = \frac{x - \bar{x}}{s}$ for a member x of a data set with mean $\bar{x}$ and standard deviation s. (216)

Zero Exponent Theorem If b is an nonzero real number, $b^0 = 1$. (378)

zero of a function For a function f, a value of x such that $f(x) = 0$. (565)

INDEX

 MATHEMATICAL SYMBOLS

Algebra

$\approx$	is approximately equal to
$\pm$	positive or negative
e	the base of the natural logarithms $\approx 2.71828...$
π	pi
∞	infinity
$!$	factorial
$\lvert x \rvert$	absolute value of x
$\sqrt{x}$	positive square root of x
$\sqrt[n]{x}$	nth root of x
$a + bi$	complex number
(a, b)	rectangular coordinates; rectangular form of a complex number
$[r, \theta]$	polar coordinates; polar form of a complex number
$r(\cos\theta + i\sin\theta)$	trigonometric form of a complex number
$\overline{z}$	complex conjugate of a complex number
$\lvert z \rvert$	modulus of a complex number
i	imaginary unit, $\sqrt{-1}$
$\begin{bmatrix} a & b \\ c & d \end{bmatrix}$	2×2 matrix

Functions and Sequences

$\lim\limits_{n\to\infty} a_n$	limit of sequence a as n approaches infinity
a_n	nth term of sequence a
$\sum\limits_{i=1}^{n} x_i$	summation notation; the sum $x_1 + x_2 + \ldots + x_n$
S_∞	sum of the infinite series S
$\log x$	common logarithm of x
$\log_b x$	logarithm of x to the base b
$\ln x$	natural logarithm of x
$\lfloor x \rfloor$	greatest integer function of x, or floor function of x
$\lceil x \rceil$	ceiling function of x
f^{-1}	inverse function of f
$f \circ g$	composite of functions f and g
$x \to \infty$	x approaches infinity

Geometry

$\overleftrightarrow{AB}$	line through A and B
$\overrightarrow{AB}$	ray from A passing through B
$\overline{AB}$	segment with endpoints A and B
AB	distance from A to B
$\angle ABC$	angle ABC
$m\angle ABC$	measure of angle ABC
$\triangle ABC$	triangle with vertices A, B, and C
$ABCD$	polygon with vertices A, B, C, and D
$//$	is parallel to
$\cong$	is congruent to
$\sim$	is similar to
$T_{h,k}$	translation of h units horizontally and k units vertically
$S_{a,b}$	scale change with horizontal magnitude a and vertical magnitude b
S_a	size change of magnitude a
R_θ	rotation of magnitude θ
r_x	reflection over the x-axis
r_y	reflection over the y-axis
$r_{y=x}$	reflection over the line $y = x$
r_ℓ	reflection over line ℓ

Probability

${}_nP_r$	number of permutations of n elements taken r at a time
${}_nC_r$ or $\binom{n}{r}$	number of combinations of n elements taken r at a time
$A \cup B$	union of sets A and B
$A \cap B$	intersection of sets A and B
$N(A)$	number of elements of set A
$P(E)$	probability of event E

Statistics

$\overline{x}$	mean of a data set or of a sample
s	standard deviation of a data set or of a sample
s^2	variance of a data set or of a sample
μ	Greek letter mu, mean of a population, or expected value of a probability distribution
σ	Greek letter sigma, standard deviation of a population or of a probability distribution
σ^2	variance of a population or of a probability distribution
$\mu_{\overline{x}}$	mean of the distribution of sample means
$\sigma_{\overline{x}}$	standard deviation of the distribution of sample means
r	correlation coefficient
$B(k)$	binomial distribution function
H_0	null hypothesis
H_1	alternative hypothesis

Acknowledgments

Unless otherwise acknowledged, all photographs are the property of Addison Wesley Educational Publishers, Inc. Page abbreviations are as follows: (t) top, (c) center, (b) bottom, (l) left, (r) right.

ix Randy Faris/Westlight **vi(r)** Superstock, Inc. **vi(l)** Superstock, Inc. **vii(r)** Japack/Westlight **vii(l)** Superstock, Inc. **viii** Curtis Martin/Photographic Resources **x** Japack/Westlight **4-5(b)** Paolo Koch/Photo Researchers **4(t&bl)** Superstock, Inc. **4-5(c)** Superstock, Inc. **5(tr)** Centers for Disease Control **5(tl)** Superstock, Inc. **6** John Olson/Stock Market **7** Stephen Frisch/Stock Boston **11** Christopher Brown/Stock Boston **15** King Features Syndicate **21** Richard Laird/FPG International Corp. **26** United Feature Syndicate **30** David Young-Wolff/PhotoEdit **35** James Porto/FPG International Corp. **39** Bob Daemmrich/Image Works **42** Tom Stewart/Stock Market **46** Miro Vintoniv/Stock Boston **54** Tom Strattman/AP/Wide World **61(t)** The Byron Collection/Museum of the City of New York **62** Signing of the Constitution, National Historical Park Collections, Eastern National Parks & Monuments Association **64** Erich Lessing/Art Resource **65(b)** James Monroe Memorial Library **65(c)** Rare Book Room/New York Public Library, Astor, Lenox & Tilden Foundations **65(t)** Independence Historic Park Collection/Eastern National Parks & Monuments Association **66** Joel Sartore/Grant Heilman Photography **67(all)** Superstock, Inc. **68(all)** Superstock, Inc. **69(tr&b)** Superstock, Inc. **80-81(all)** Superstock, Inc. **82** Richard Ellis/Sygma **89** Superstock, Inc. **95** Joseph Thorn **96** NASA **97** Zoom/Allsport **102** Mike Powell/Allsport **105** Superstock, Inc. **106** Bachmann/Stock Boston **109** Ted Wood/Tony Stone Images **112** Phil Degginger/Tony Stone Images **113** Dr. Jeremy Burgess/SPL/Photo Researchers **114** Corbis/Bettmann **121** John Moore **124** Robert Maier/Animals Animals **127(b)** D. R. Specker/Animals Animals **130(b)** Cameramann International, Ltd. **130(t)** George Hunter/Tony Stone Images **132** John Livzey/Tony Stone Images **134** Superstock, Inc. **140** Peter Correz/Tony Stone Images **141** UPI/Corbis-Bettmann **148** Warren Morgan/Westlight **149(l)** Orion Press/Westlight **149(tr, tc, br)** Superstock, Inc. **158-159(t)** Superstock, Inc. **158-159(c)** Carol Barrington/TexStock Photo Inc. **158(b, tl), 159(b)** Superstock, Inc. **160** State Road Commission of Utah **163** Fletcher/Bhylis/Photo Researchers **165** Harvey Lloyd/Stock Market **167** Pal Hermansen/Tony Stone Images **172** Ken Biggs/Tony Stone Images **173** Tony Duffy/Allsport **174** Bachmann/Stock Boston **180** N. Corraro/Sygma **187** Superstock, Inc. **193** Joe Cornish/Tony Stone Images **197** AP/Wide World **201(tl, tr, tcr, tcl, b)** John Fitzgerald Kennedy Library **201(cr)** AP/Wide World **201(cl)** Frank J. Scherschel **207** James King-Holmes/SPL/Photo Researchers **213** Sidney Harris **214** AP/Wide World **215** Jack Manning/New York Times **219** Superstock, Inc. **221(b)** Randy Faris/Westlight **221(t)** Daniel J. Cox/Tony Stone Images **224** Superstock, Inc. **227** Steve Curtis **230(b)** Japack/Westlight **230-231(t&c)** Superstock, Inc. **230(cl)** Leo de Wys, Inc. **231(b)** Superstock, Inc. **231(r&cc)** Cameramann International, Ltd. **234** Steve Elmore/Stock Market **236** Raj Kamal/Earth Scenes **237** NASA **239** Vandystadt/Allsport **241** Mike Andrews/Earth Scenes **249** Superstock, Inc. **251** Scala/Art Resource **257, 262, 271** Superstock, Inc. **272** Cameramann International, Ltd. **275, 276** Richard Megna/Fundamental Photographs **278** Joe Sohm/Stock Market **280** Cameramann International, Ltd. **284** Nancy Sefton/Photo Researchers **292** Chuck Pefley/Tony Stone Images **295** NASA **297** Chris Arend/AlaskaStock **299** Superstock, Inc. **300(b)** Aaron Jones Studios/Tony Stone Images **300(t)** Joerg Hardtke/Tony Stone Images **305** Cameramann International, Ltd. **308-309(br), 308(bl&c)** Superstock, Inc. **308(t)** R. Ian Loyd/Westlight **309(t)** Curtis Martin/Photographic Resources **310** Gary Braasch/Tony Stone Images **313** Carolyn A. McKeone/Photo Researchers **316** Stephen Dunn/Allsport **327** Tom Bean/Tony Stone Images **334** NASA **339** Tom Stewart/Stock Market **341** Joe Towers/Check Six **343** Joseph Nettis/Stock Boston **344** Larry Ulrich/Tony Stone Images **346** Kevin Horan/Tony Stone Images **351** Chad Slattery/Tony Stone Images **353** Robert Llewellyn **358** Anthony Cassidy/Tony Stone Images **360(b)** Charles D. Winters/Photo Researchers **360(tr)** Scott Camazine/Photo Researchers **360(tl), 361(b)** Superstock, Inc. **361(t)** Westlight **368-369(t), 368(tl), 369(b)** Superstock, Inc. **368-369(c)** Ralph Clevenger/Westlight **368(b)** Dennis Degnan/Westlight **374** Mel Lindstrom/Tony Stone Images **381** Mark C. Burnett/Photo Researchers **383** Courtesy, IBM Corporation **388** Everett Collection, Inc. **393** Mark Petersen/Tony Stone Images **394, 395** NASA **399** AP/Wide World **402** Russell D. Curtis/Photo Researchers **405** P. Plailly/Eurelios/SPL/Photo Researchers **408** Private Collection **409** Renee Lynn/Photo Researchers **411** J. H. Robinson/Photo Researchers **415** F. Stuart Westmorland/Photo Researchers **416, 417** Superstock, Inc. **424(c&br), 425(c)** Superstock, Inc. **424(bl)** Robert Landau/Westlight **424(t)** Myron Taplin/Tony Stone Images **426** Michael Orton/Tony Stone Images **427** Bob Shaw/Stock Market **434** Peter Kiar/University of Chicago **439** Jonathan Daniel/Allsport **441** ©1968 United Feature Syndicate, Inc. Reprinted by permission of UFS, Inc. **441** United Feature Syndicate **443** John Margolies/Esto Photographics Inc. **444** Thomas Sennett/Magnum Photos **447** Everett Collection, Inc. **453** Joe Towers/Check Six **455** Hamman/Heldring/Animals Animals **457** Penny Gentieu/Tony Stone Images **461** Sygma **464** Gerard LACZ/Animals Animals **466** Lawrence Migdale/Tony Stone Images **469** Art Wolfe/Tony Stone Images **470** Bob Daemmrich/Stock Boston **478(all)** Superstock, Inc. **483** Richard During/Tony Stone Images **485** David Lissman/Image Works **486-487(all)** Superstock, Inc. **488** Bruce Iverson **492** Courtesy, Ford Motor Company **494** Lori Adamski Peek/Tony Stone Images **496** Lucia Eames dba Eames Office, ©1961, 1997, www.eamesoffice.com **504** Walter Sanders, Courtesy Stadtisches Museum, Brunswick, Germany **512** Kunsthistorisches Museum, Art History Museum, Burgring 5 A-101, Vienna, Austria **513** Jon Feingersh/Stock Boston **520** Cameramann International, Ltd. **521** Tom Carroll/FPG International Corp. **522** J. Sneesby/B. Wilkins/Tony Stone Images **524** Ulrike Welsch/PhotoEdit **525** Lawrence Migdale/Stock Boston **528** Reprinted with permission, The Chicago Sun-Times ©1996 **530** Hand-colored by Cheryl Kucharzak **534(b)** Kathi Lamm/Tony Stone Images **536** Corbis-Bettmann Archive **539** John Lawrence/Tony Stone Images **540** Hank Morgan/SS/Photo Researchers **540(inset)** Dr. Gopal Murti/SPL/Photo Researchers **543** Robert Mizono **544** Cameramann International, Ltd. **546** Courtesy, Bausch & Lomb, Hand-colored by Cheryl Kucharzak **554-555(all)** Superstock, Inc. **556** Comstock Inc. **558, 562** Superstock, Inc. **569** Walter Chandoha **576(t)** Superstock, Inc. **589** Andrea Renault/Globe Photos, Inc. **602** Larry Lefever/Grant Heilman Photography **607** Charles Gupton/Stock Boston **611** Mark Gamba/Stock Market **616** Walter Chandoha **626(b)** Bill Ross/Westlight **626(tl)** Superstock, Inc. **626-627(c)** Doug Wilson/Westlight **626-627(tr)** Randy Faris/Westlight **627(b)** Walter Hodges/Westlight **631** Doug Pensinger/Allsport **634** Jose More/©1996 Copyrighted, The Chicago Tribune. All Rights Reserved. **637** Kevin R. Morris/Tony Stone Images **639** Globe Photos, Inc. **645** Robert Maier/Animals Animals/Earth Scenes **646** Focus on Sports, Inc. **647** Superstock, Inc. **648** David McGlynn/FPG International Corp. **651** Eastern National Park and Monument Association/Independence National Historical Park Collection **666** Brent Jones **678** Laura Dwight **679** By permission of Johnny Hart and Creators Syndicate, Inc. **681** University of California, Berkeley **686** Superstock, Inc. **688** Jim Richardson/Westlight **694** Superstock, Inc. **696-697(b), 696(tl)** Superstock, Inc. **696-697(tr)** Photri, Inc. **696(b)** W. Cody/Westlight **697(b)** Ron Watts/Westlight **701** Stephen Crowley/New York Times **703(t)** Dawn Murray **706** Superstock, Inc. **714** Paul Griffin/Stock Boston **720** Everett Collection, Inc. **721** Berenguier/Jerrican/Photo Researchers **725** Bob Daemmrich/Stock Boston **729** Focus on Sports, Inc. **730** David M. Grossman/Photo Researchers **738** Courtesy Evans and Sutherland **742** STAR WARS ™ © Lucasfilm Ltd. 1997. All Rights Reserved. **745** Focus on Sports, Inc. **752-753(c)** Superstock, Inc. **752-753(br)** Michael Busselle/Tony Stone Images **752(bl)** Branson Reynolds/Index Stock Photography, Inc. **752(tl), 753(t)** Superstock, Inc. **757** Corbis-Bettmann **759** Ronald Sheridan/Ancient Art & Architecture Collection **763** Sidney Harris **764** Vivian Hoette **765** Lawrence Sromovsky, University of Wisconsin-Madison, NASA **766** Galleria Borghese, Rome, Italy/Art Resource **767** NASA **782** National Portrait Gallery, London **792** Ralph Cowan/FPG International Corp. **793** Museum of Science and Industry, Chicago **795** Eduardo Garcia/FPG International Corp. **796** NASA **801(b)** Erich Lessing/Art Resource **801(t)** HST Comet Team/NASA **804-805(tr)** Bill Ross/Westlight **804(b)** Stock Connection **804-805(c)** Allen Prier/Panoramic Images **804(tl)** The Dickmans/Westlight **805(b)** Orion Press/Westlight **807** Michael Newman/PhotoEdit **809** A. Ramey/PhotoEdit **817** L. Ferrarese, Johns Hopkins University/NASA **819** Bob Daemmrich/Tony Stone Images **826** Joe Towers/Hall, George/Check Six **829(all)** Walter Chandoha **830, 832** Superstock, Inc. **837** Everett Collection, Inc. **859** From THE BEAUTY OF FRACTALS by Peitgen & Richter, ©1986, Springer-Verlag, Berlin, Heidelberg **862** Sidney Harris **865** From THE BEAUTY OF FRACTALS by Peitgen & Richter, ©1986 Springer-Verlag, Berlin, Heidelberg